Hotels and Bed & Breakfast 2003

Front & rear cover photographs
Charlotte Street Hotel, London W1T 1RJ

Guide to inspected properties
Great Britain & Ireland

First published 2002
Copyright © RAC 2002

Published by BBC Worldwide Limited
Woodlands, 80 Wood Lane, London W12 0TT
Telephone: 020 8433 2000
Fax: 020 8433 3752

ISBN 0-563-48877-8

Publisher: Adam Waddell
Advertising Sales Manager: Rob Wicker
Advertising Sales Executive: Paul Bentley
                              Jeff Crudgington

Editorial, production and repro: Thalamus Publishing
    Oliver Frey, Charlotte Taylor, Warren Lapworth
    Neil Williams, Joanne Dovey, Franco Frey, Roger Kean

Cartographic production: Mapworld, David Fryer
                        Pixel Cartography, Hilary Austin

This book includes mapping data licensed from Ordnance Survey® with the permission
of the Controller of Her Majesty's Stationery Office.
© Crown copyright 2002. All rights reserved. Licence number *PU100020482*

Set in 8pt Helvetica Neue 55
Printed and bound in Spain by Cayfossa-Quebecor, Barcelona

RAC Motoring Services
1 Forest Road
Feltham
Middlesex
TW13 7RR
RAC Hotel Services
Telephone: 020 8917 2840
Fax: 020 8917 2813
Email: hotelservices@rac.co.uk

Contents

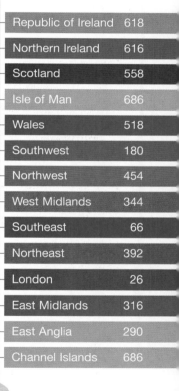

Welcome

to RAC Hotels and Bed & Breakfast 2003

What's your idea of the perfect getaway?
A romantic hideaway in Cornwall…
a penthouse suite overlooking the Thames…
a cosy bed & breakfast in Cork…
or a castle in the Highlands of Scotland?
Whatever you're after, you'll find it listed here.

RAC Hotels and Bed & Breakfast 2003 offers
you a simple way to find the accommodation
you're looking for. Whether you want gourmet
cuisine, a homely atmosphere or sophisticated
style, we have just the place for you. And you
can stay for a week, a weekend, or just
overnight…. it's up to you.

All our accommodation has been visited by an
RAC inspector, providing you with complete
reassurance. And they've also been classified
according to our ratings and awards scheme,
which is designed to bring you the information
you need to make the right choice.

The guide is easy to use too. Overleaf,
you'll find an outline of the symbols and
abbreviations used throughout. And all the
accommodation is ordered by region, so you
can go straight to the pages you need. If you're
looking for somewhere really special, you'll
find our award-winning properties listed at the
beginning of each regional section.

At the back of the book you'll find useful
Ordnance Survey maps which pinpoint where
RAC inspected properties are located.

We hope you'll enjoy all that the guide has
to offer… making your stay special wherever
you go.

How to use this guide

Town and county
The guide is broken down into 12 regional sections. Within each region, towns are listed alphabetically.

Dartford, Kent

Rowhill Grange Hotel

Blue Ribbon Winner

★★★★★ ☕ ☕ ☕

Wilmington, Dartford, Kent, DA2 7QH
Tel: 01322 615136 Fax: 01322 615137
Email: admin@rowhillgrange.com
Web: www.rowhillgrange.com

With 9 acres of mature gardens and the finest health spa in the south, Rowhill Grange is ideal for business or pleasure – just 2 miles from the M25.

Rooms: 38 all ensuite ☕ ☒
Pricing: Sgl £134 Dbl £165
Dinner from £29.95
CC: Accepted
Room facilities: ☐ ☎ ☒
Access: ⥮ ⚬
Conference: 7 meeting rooms (Thtr 160 max), 24hr-delegate from £165, day-delegate rate from £55
Children: Welcome 5yrs min age ☒
Licences: ⚬ ⚬⚬⚬
Leisure: Indoor pool, Gym, Health spa, Beauty salon
Parking: Off-street and monitored
Directions: Leave M20 junction 1 / M25 Junction 3 to Swanley. Follow B2175 through 3 roundabouts to Hextable on B258. Hotel is 1½ miles on left opposite garage.
See advert on this page

Property name

Classification and relevant awards
For information on RAC ratings, please turn to page 9. For more information on RAC awards, please turn to page 13.

Address and contact details
Please note, for properties in the Republic of Ireland, telephone and fax numbers are shown with the international dialling code. To dial from the UK, drop the (0). To dial from within the Republic, drop the +353 from the number.

Description of the property and picture
Not all properties listed have opted for these two items.

Number of ensuite rooms and room prices
For further details see page 7.

Meal prices
For further details see page 7.

Credit Cards accepted

Meeting and Conference Information
For further details see page 7.

Other information
These symbols (explained opposite) give you further information on the property, bedrooms and general facilities.

How to find the property

Advertisement nearby
This indicates that there is an advertisement for the property nearby with more detail.

What the symbols mean

Classifications

★ Hotel classification (from 1 to 5 Stars) or Townhouse classification (from 4 to 5 Stars).

♦ Guest Accommodation classification (from 1 to 5 Diamonds).

Travel Accommodation is denoted by the name only and does not carry a Star or Diamond rating.

Restaurant with Rooms is denoted by the name only and does not carry a Star or Diamond rating.

❖ A small number of properties joined the scheme just before the guide went to print so we have been unable to confirm their classification. This symbol indicates that a property is awaiting inspection.

Awards

For further information on RAC's awards, please see page 13.

Gold Ribbon Award

Blue Ribbon Award

Little Gem   Little Gem Award

Dining Award (from 1 to 5 quality grades)

Sparkling Diamond Award

Warm Welcome Award

Room Facilities

Family bedrooms sleeping four or more persons

Four-poster beds available

Non-smoking rooms available. Some properties may be 100% non-smoking, so smokers are advised to enquire in advance whether smoking rooms are available

TV in all rooms

Telephone in all rooms

Tea/coffee-making facilities in all rooms

Computer connection available

Air conditioning in all rooms

Meetings and Conferences

Rates are shown exclusive of VAT. Please note that prices shown are a guide only. Please check with the property for full pricing information.

Access

Lift

Bedrooms with wheelchair access. For a full list of properties inspected for accessibility for guests with disabilities, please contact:

Holiday Care Service
2nd Floor
Imperial Buildings
Victoria Road
Horley
RH6 7PZ
Tel. information: 01293 774535
Tel. reservations: 01293 773716
www.holidaycare.org.uk

Children

Supervised creche facility

Baby listening service

Children's meal menu

Licensing information

Property is licensed for the sale of alcohol

Licensed for the performance of wedding ceremonies

Pricing information

Sgl   Rate for single room with breakfast

Dbl   Rate for double/twin room with breakfast (based on double occupancy)

Note: All room prices quoted in this guide are approximate and include VAT and service where applicable. Prices are shown as a range and may vary according to season and are based on what hoteliers have told us they expect to charge for 2003. Please check before booking.

Cancellation policies, terms & conditions may apply. Meal prices are also approximate and show the minimum price for a meal on the menu. We advise that you check with the Hotel or Guest Accommodation prior to booking a table.

Payment methods

Major Credit cards accepted where indicated.

If credit cards are not accepted at the property, cash is normally accepted or cheques to a given amount with a cheque guarantee card. Please check at the time of booking.

RAC Ratings

From simplicity to luxury, it's your choice

The RAC Hotel and Guest Accommodation Scheme is designed to provide you with an objective, comprehensive guide to accommodation in the UK and Ireland. It enables you to choose exactly the type of property that suits you, your style and your budget.

Hotels and Guest Accommodation are graded annually following a visit from an RAC inspector (see page 19), who follows strict guidelines to ensure that standards of quality are maintained.

Star Ratings for Hotels – What to expect

★ Hotel

One Star Hotels have everything you need for a pleasant stay, including polite, courteous staff, informal service, and at least one dining area serving simple, tasty meals (although lunch may not always be served), as well as a small range of wines. Most of the bedrooms will have an ensuite bath or shower room, as well as a television, and should be well-maintained, clean and comfortable.
Last orders for dinner no earlier than 6.30pm

★★ Hotel

Two Star Hotels are usually small to medium sized, with smart, well-presented staff offering informal service. You can expect to enjoy a wider range of food and drink, with at least one restaurant or dining room open to residents for breakfast and dinner. Rooms should be comfortable and well-equipped with an ensuite bath or shower room and with a television in-room.
Last orders for dinner no earlier than 7.00pm

★★★ Hotel

At this level, you should find the reception and lounges more spacious, with a receptionist on duty. Staff should be professionally presented and may wear uniforms, responding to your requests promptly and efficiently. You can also expect a restaurant which serves residents and non-residents, as well as a wide selection of drinks served throughout the day and evening in the bar or lounge. All bedrooms should have ensuite bath or shower rooms and offer good standards of comfort, with extra touches like remote-control television, hairdryer, direct-dial telephone, toiletries in the bathroom and room service. There is also some provision for business travellers, like fax or email services.
Last orders for dinner no earlier than 8.00pm

Langshott Manor, Horley

RAC Ratings

★★★★ Hotel

At this level, you'll find the reception and lounge areas have good quality furnishings and décor, with smartly dressed, uniformed staff and a 24-hour reception. These Hotels pride themselves on offering top quality food and drink, taking a more serious approach to cuisine. You can expect at least one restaurant open to both residents and non-residents, with meals served seven days a week, an extensive choice of dishes and a comprehensive wine list. Drinks should also be available throughout the day and evening. Extra services like porterage, express checkout facilities (where appropriate), newspapers delivered to rooms, 24-hour room service and dry cleaning should also be available. Your room should be spacious and well-designed, with an ensuite bathroom including a fixed shower, remote control television, direct-dial telephone and a range of high quality toiletries.

Last orders for dinner no earlier than 9.00pm

★★★★★ Hotel

The whole Hotel should be spacious and luxurious, with impressive interior design, immaculate furnishings and attention to the very smallest detail. You should enjoy flawless service which, while it meets your every need, is never intrusive. The staff should be multilingual, professional and attentive, escorting you to your room on arrival, and there should be an efficient luggage handling system in place to ensure minimum delay. A doorman should greet you as you arrive, and there should be a full concierge service. You should also have access to at least one restaurant, with a high quality menu and a wine list which complements the style of cooking. Staff should show a real enthusiasm for and commitment to food and wine, and there should be a range of drinks and cocktails served in the bar or lounge, with table service also available.

You can expect an elegant, spacious room, with remote-control television, direct-dial telephone at the bedside and desk, a range of luxury toiletries, bath sheets and robes, as well as an ensuite bathroom with fixed shower.

Last orders for dinner no earlier than 10.00pm

Townhouse Accommodation

If you want to stay in a town or city but would prefer a more personal level of service, a Townhouse is ideal. These properties can offer you a greater level of privacy than an Hotel, while still providing luxuriously furnished bedrooms and suites. High quality room service is usually offered rather than public rooms or formal dining rooms usually associated with Hotels. They are usually in areas well-served by restaurants, and fall broadly into the four and five Star classification.

Restaurant with Rooms

Restaurant with Rooms is usually a local (or national) destination for eating out which also offers accommodation, albeit on a smaller scale. Most have 12 bedrooms or less, and public areas may be limited to the restaurant itself. No star rating is given to Restaurant with Rooms but bedrooms reflect at least the level of quality normally associated with a 2 Star Hotel.

Culloden Hotel, Holywood, Co. Down

Diamond ratings for Guest Accommodation – What to expect

If you're looking for accommodation where service is on a personal level, you might like to choose a property in this classification. It includes guest houses, farmhouses, inns, restaurants with rooms and bed and breakfasts.

In the UK and Ireland, our bed and breakfasts in particular are known for offering a style and warmth envied around the world.

These properties are graded according to the Guest Accommodation Scheme, which assesses the accommodation at five levels of quality, or 'Diamonds'. One Diamond represents the simplest type of accommodation, while five Diamonds is the most luxurious.

The Diamond rating takes into account the level of general comfort, the style and quality of the furnishings and décor, the service shown by the staff, the friendliness of the atmosphere and the quality of the meals.

At all Diamond levels, cleanliness, good housekeeping, guest care and quality are of the highest importance. You can expect to find the following minimum standards at a Guest Accommodation property:

- A comfortable, modern room with fittings in good condition, and adequate storage and seating

- Sufficient hot water

- Bedding and towels changed at least once a week during your stay, with extra pillows and blankets available

- Wholesome, tasty, well-presented meals, including a full cooked breakfast (unless otherwise advertised)

- A professional welcome and departure with a properly prepared bill

Travel Accommodation

Ideal for an overnight stay, properties in this category usually provide budget or lodge accommodation in purpose-built units. They are becoming increasingly popular in major cities, but are usually conveniently located close to main roads, airports and motorways. They may be sited within motorway service areas. Many of the lodges now also provide meeting facilities and are geared up to meet the needs of business travellers. Your room should be well-fitted, ensuite and provide consistent standards which meet your expectations regardless of the location.

Awaiting inspection

If a property joined the scheme just before the deadline for entries to this guide closed, they will carry this symbol.

Ivyleigh House, Portlaoise

RAC Awards

Our guide to Britain and Ireland's best Hotels and Guest Accommodation

If you're looking for somewhere really special, choose one of our award-winning Hotels, Townhouses or Guest Accommodation properties.

These exceptional establishments are committed to delivering top quality service, with those little touches that make all the difference.

RAC Dining Award

The RAC Dining Award is particularly sought after. At properties displaying the Dining Award symbol below, you can expect a commendable dining experience and quality food.

This Award was introduced in 2000 after lengthy market research, and focuses not just on good food but the entire dining experience... from the quality and presentation of the food on the plate to the ambience and the knowledge of those serving you. It is awarded to Hotels, Townhouses and Guest Accommodation properties that serve meals, as well as Restaurants with Rooms.

The Awards are given following an incognito visit by one of our RAC inspectors, who are all professionally qualified with wide experience in the industry and trained to high RAC standards. Dinner, breakfast and room service (where appropriate) are taken into account when considering this Award.

There are no set criteria for a Dining Award, as each establishment is different, but the emphasis is on the quality of cooking. Our inspectors consider the whole dining experience, including the surroundings, the warmth of welcome, table appointments and the quality of the wine list.

The Dining Award is given starting at grade one, a high achievement in itself, through to grade five, representing superlative standards.

This grade of Award recognises establishments that produce above average meals, with tasty, carefully prepared food. The menu should be created with care and enthusiasm, and only fresh ingredients should be used. You can expect to enjoy warm, friendly service in simple, comfortable surroundings.

At this grade, you should expect a more serious approach to cooking, with a higher degree of technical skill and a combination of good quality ingredients enhancing the natural flavour of the food. The menu should have a selection of imaginative dishes as well as more traditional combinations, presented in comfortable surroundings by knowledgeable staff. Properties with two ar more Dining Awards should be licenced (residential and restaurant) to serve alcohol.

At this grade you should enjoy cooking of the highest national standard, with well developed technical skill, an imaginative menu and first class ingredients. Dishes should have balance, depth of flavour and flair, and the chef will probably choose to make their own bread, pasta and so on. The surroundings may be more sophisticated, and you should enjoy more professional service.

SWALLOW HOTELS

Drive in to a warm welcome at Swallow Hotels:

3 or 4 star hotels with a high standard of facilities and en-suite accommodation

FREE access to leisure club and indoor heated pool at every hotel

Superb dining with many hotels holding RAC dining awards

Ideal for a great value relaxing break

A.	**Glasgow Swallow**	0141 427 3146
B.	**Dundee Swallow**	01382 631 200
C.	**Carlisle Swallow Hilltop**	01228 529 255
D.	**Preston Swallow**	01772 877 351
E.	**Newcastle Swallow Imperial**	0191 281 5511
F.	**Newcastle Gateshead Swallow**	0191 477 1105
G.	**Rushyford** nr. Durham **Swallow Eden Arms**	01388 720 541
H.	**Chollerford** nr. Hexham **Swallow George**	01434 681 611
I.	**Durham Swallow Three Tuns**	0191 386 4326
J.	**Stockton on Tees Swallow**	01642 679 721
K.	**Harrogate Swallow St. George**	01423 561 431
L.	**Old Harlow Swallow Churchgate**	01279 420 246
M.	**Ipswich Swallow Belstead Brook**	01473 684 241

RAC Awards

At this grade, you can indulge in innovative and exciting cuisine prepared by a highly accomplished chef, with a menu distinguished by flair and imagination. Dishes should be faultlessly presented, resulting in a memorable and noteworthy meal. Surroundings may be luxurious, with a depth of quality, comfort and style.

Only establishments offering superlative standards of cuisine are given a grade five Dining Award, offering the very highest level of quality in all areas. Flavours will be intense, daring and exciting with ingredients cooked to perfection and a harmonious combination of flavours. Menus may be innovative or classic, but will always be created using luxury ingredients, and served by immaculately uniformed and exceptionally competent staff. Chefs who receive this award are likely to be at the cutting edge of gastronomy and at the top of their profession, making for a truly memorable dining experience.

Hotel Awards

Only Hotels and Townhouses that truly exceed the standards required by RAC are awarded our Gold and Blue Ribbons. At these properties, you can expect a commitment to getting it right first time… every time.

Our Gold and Blue Ribbon Awards are given annually following an overnight, incognito inspection and can be achieved at all Star levels.

Gold Ribbon Award

Hotels and Townhouses that achieve this accolade are at the very pinnacle within their Star rating, and in many cases represent the 'cutting edge' of excellence in hotel keeping. They offer superlative standards of comfort, hospitality, food, service, customer care and guest awareness, and have that 'special something' that really makes them stand out from the crowd.

Blue Ribbon Award

The familiar RAC Blue Ribbon is given to those Hotels and Townhouses that continue to promote very high quality standards. The majority are personally owned and managed with professionalism, individual attention and boundless dedication. At any one of these properties, you will enjoy superior standards in comfort, service, hospitality and food.

Award winners for 2002-2003 can be found at the beginning of each regional section.

Sheen Falls Lodge, Kenmare

RAC Awards

Guest Accommodation Awards

The following awards are made specifically to Guest Accommodation properties and recognise those which put comfort and hospitality first. Guest Accommodation includes small hotels, bed and breakfasts, guest houses, farmhouses and inns.

Little Gem Award

Little Gem

This prestigious award is given to those properties that achieve the very height of excellence within the Guest Accommodation scheme. They will invariably be personally owned and managed with great dedication and enthusiasm, and really 'hit the spot' when it comes to hospitality.

At these properties, you can expect all-round quality in décor and furnishings, a warm welcome, genuine customer care and attention to detail, as well as high quality home cooked breakfasts and dinners (if served), all adding up to a memorable stay. Little Gem Award winners are listed at the beginning of each regional section.

Sparkling Diamond Award

This Award is made to those properties which achieve excellent standards when it comes to guest comfort, focusing on cleanliness and hygiene.

Warm Welcome Award

As the name implies, this Award is made to those properties that achieve the very highest levels of hospitality, making you feel at home from the moment you arrive to the time you depart.

Kirkton House, Cardross

Credit to the Industry Award

Back by popular demand. This award is given to the small independent group of hotels which has set new standards of excellence, going the extra mile to give their customers an unbeatable stay.

This year's winner, Marston Hotels, can be very proud of their achievements.

In a difficult year for hoteliers everywhere, they have not only added several new hotels to their group, but have also improved the quality of their customers' stay at every one. Thanks to their outstanding service, delicious food and relaxed atmosphere, Marston Hotels are the perfect choice for business and leisure guests alike.

MARSTON HOTELS

Stade Court Hotel, Hythe	122
Hythe Imperial Hotel, Hythe	122
Oxford Belfry, Oxford	145
Lansdown Grove Hotel, Bath	188
Chester Crabwall Manor, Chester	472
Bridgewood Manor, Rochester	154
Hogarth, London	50
Coulsdon Manor, Croydon	93
Hampshire Centre Court, Basingstoke	75
Stratford Victoria, Stratford-upon-Avon	381
Aldwark Manor Hotel, York	446
Hellidon Lakes Hotel, Golf & Country Club, Daventry	326
Winchester Royal, Winchester	174
Eastwell Manor, Ashford	72
Stratford Manor, Stratford-upon-Avon	381
Tankersley Manor, Barnsley	398

Chester Crabwall Manor, Chester

Hotel Group of the Year Award

This is awarded to the large hotel group that has consistently given its customers all over the world the same outstanding facilities and exceptional service.

Competition for this award was particularly fierce, but this year's undoubted winners are Millennium & Copthorne Hotels. The group boasts seventeen 4 Star Hotels across the UK, offering the discerning traveller luxury facilities and high standards of service within a delightful environment.

MILLENNIUM HOTELS AND RESORTS

Millennium Gloucester Hotel, London	44
Copthorne Hotel London, Gatwick Airport	108
Millennium Hotel London, Mayfair	45
Copthorne Hotel Plymouth, Plymouth	245
Copthorne Hotel Birmingham, Birmingham	348
Copthorne Hotel Manchester, Manchester	494
Copthorne Hotel Aberdeen, Aberdeen	565
Copthorne Tara Hotel, London	42
Copthorne Hotel Effingham Park, Gatwick Airport	108
Copthorne Hotel Newcastle, Newcastle-upon-Tyne	424
Copthorne Hotel Cardiff, Cardiff	529
Copthorne Hotel Merry Hill, Dudley	364
Millennium Hotel Glasgow, Glasgow	590
Millennium Bailey's Hotel, London	44
Millennium Hotel Knightsbridge, London	45
Copthorne Hotel Slough-Windsor, Slough	161
Millennium Madejski Hotel, Reading	152

Millennium Bailey's Hotel, London

Relax and Unwind

Take the stress out of finding an hotel with RAC Hotel Reservations

On the move and looking for an hotel or a cosy B&B? Look no further than RAC Hotel Reservations.

With just one phone call, RAC Hotel Reservations gives you unique access to over 3000 quality hotels and B&Bs throughout the UK & Ireland. Each one is inspected, rated and the best ones awarded on your behalf by our team of discerning inspectors for quality and service.

We'll not only source the perfect hotel or B&B to suit your pocket and your needs, we'll also source the latest deals and make the booking for you, completely free of charge*.

So if you are looking for somewhere to relax and unwind, whether on business or leisure, call us now.

Call 0870 603 9109 and quote RAC 05
or visit www.rac.co.uk/hotels

*Calls will be charged at National rates

A to B - we RAC to it

rac

How we grade our hotels

When you see an RAC sign outside an Hotel or any of the other type of accommodation featured in this guide, it doesn't just mean they belong to the RAC scheme.

It also means that one of our team of inspectors has actually slept in one of their beds and eaten their breakfast... testing it out on your behalf. So we have first-hand experience of what it is like to stay in the accommodation you are about to enjoy.

RAC inspectors are trained professionals who visit each property on a regular basis, checking up on every detail of the service... from the first impression formed at booking, right up until they leave. They also observe the service received by others, to ensure they form a well-rounded opinion.

What does it take to be an RAC inspector?

RAC inspectors are special people. They have a strong background in the hospitality industry, an eye for detail and a knack for getting on with others. They try to place themselves in the shoes of a whole variety of guests, to ensure that everyone's needs are taken into account.

They also need to keep up to date with the latest developments in the industry... so they can advise on everything from menu selection to improvements in technology.

How an inspection works

All properties are inspected on an annual basis. RAC inspectors arrive unannounced as 'mystery guests', to ensure that they receive no special treatment. This helps them form a completely objective opinion of the accommodation.

Working to strict standards, the inspectors carry out an assessment of the establishment, deciding which rating should be given... and whether or not it is worthy of an award.

The inspection process is carefully controlled to ensure consistency, and a uniform approach is used in all inspections. Once completed, the inspector provides the owner or manager with a full and detailed report in person... so they will know exactly where they are doing well, and where there is room for improvement.

Our promise to you

When you choose an RAC Hotel or Guest Accommodation, you can rest assured that the property has been inspected and graded according to our ratings and awards scheme, providing you with an objective, reliable assessment.

Making the most of RAC services

RAC offers you a range of services to help ensure your holiday arrangements run smoothly. From our Hotel booking service to traffic news, insurance to route planning, we've got it covered.

Booking an Hotel or B&B

If you can't decide where to stay, why not ask the experts? In one phone call, RAC Hotel Reservations can help you find a place to stay that meets your needs. We have over 3,000 RAC inspected Hotels and Guest Accommodation properties, so if your first choice doesn't have availability, we can recommend the next best alternative. And we can also source the latest special offers, ensuring you get a great deal. Plus, we can help you with bookings abroad, although obviously these properties won't be RAC inspected. To make a booking, simply call 0870 603 9109 quoting RAC 05.

If you prefer to book online, visit RAC HotelFinder at www.rac.co.uk/hotels

Here, you can check availability, make a booking, view the latest special offers and find out more about thousands of RAC Hotels and Guest Accommodation throughout the UK and Ireland.

Travelling to your accommodation

RAC offers you a range of motoring services to help you get safely to your destination... with the least amount of hassle.

RAC Traffic Alert 1740 brings you up to the minute traffic information over the phone for motorways and major A roads. Simply dial 1740 from any mobile phone.

There's also online assistance at www.rac.co.uk, where you can access our free pan-European route planner, with live UK traffic updates.

Booking tips:

- Book as early as possible, especially for peak periods (June – September) and public holidays

- If booking via RAC Hotel Reservations (see left), please have your credit card handy as this may be required to guarantee your booking

- Always check what the property's cancellation policy is. If you do have to cancel your booking, ensure you give as much notice as possible to avoid cancellation charges. If you wish to be protected against a booking cancellation outside the cancellation terms, you might like to consider taking out RAC Travel Insurance. Call 0800 55 00 55 to find out more and quote GUI3

RAC Hotel Reservations: 0870 603 9109
www.rac.co.uk/hotels

Wake up to Travelodge

Making the most of RAC services

Travelling to Ireland and abroad

Going abroad? The help you need is just a click away at the RAC website. You can apply online for competitively-priced travel insurance. There's even advice on driving in Europe, European Motoring Assistance (should you break down at the side of the road) and much, much more.

Please visit www.rac.co.uk or call RAC Travel Sales on 0800 55 00 55 and quote GUI3

Queries or complaints?

If you have any queries or feel dissatisfied with the level of service you have received at any RAC inspected properties, please first speak to the manager or owner directly at the time of your complaint so they have an opportunity to put things right straight away. If this approach doesn't work, please write to us, and we will take up the issue the next time we inspect the property. We value your feedback and will do everything we can to ensure your comments are taken seriously.

Please write to us, including all details and any relevant correspondence, at the following address:

RAC Hotel Services
1 Forest Road
Feltham
TW13 7RR

Please note: RAC will not obtain compensation for complaints or enter into any correspondence.

Luxury
British Hotels

A warm welcome awaits you at Paramount. Choose from 13 great locations and enjoy fabulous service and value for money at every one. From exciting city breaks to peaceful country settings, Paramount Group of Hotels has all you need.

LOCATION	HOTEL	DESCRIPTION	RAC RATING
Scotland			
Edinburgh	☼ The Carlton	One of Edinburgh's finest	★★★★
Stirling	☼ The Stirling Highland	Historic hotel in Stirling's Old Town	★★★★
Troon	☼ The Marine	Coastal location, views of Isle of Arran	★★★★
England			
Harrogate	☼ The Majestic	Elegant, historic hotel in Spa town	★★★★
County Durham	☼ Redworth Hall	Stunning country manor	★★★★
Blackpool	☼ The Imperial	Blackpool's Hotel of the Year 2002	★★★★
Nr. Manchester	☼ Shrigley Hall	18 hole golf course on-site	★★★★
Buxton	☼ The Palace	Famous Victorian hotel	★★★★
Cheltenham	☼ The Cheltenham Park	Georgian hotel in Cotswolds	★★★★
Oxford	☼ The Oxford	£11million refurbishment	★★★★
Brighton	The Old Ship	Stylish hotel on sea front	★★★★
Torquay	☼ The Imperial	Area's only five star venue	★★★★★
Wales			
Cardiff	The Angel Hotel	Centrally located for attractions	★★★★

☼ Leisure facilities available

Map of the United Kingdom showing locations: Stirling, Edinburgh, Troon, Co. Durham, Harrogate, Blackpool, Cheshire, Buxton, Cheltenham, Oxford, Cardiff, Torquay, Brighton

130 locations in the UK alone - including most of the major airports, naturally - and at major holiday and business destinations across Europe and around the Mediterranean.

Going further afield? No problem, altogether we have nearly 3,000 locations worldwide and a global fleet of more than a quarter of a million vehicles!

And everywhere you travel, you'll

Rent a car with National and take advantage of our great rates. Whether for business or leisure we've got the vehicle to suit your needs.

Business or leisure
for great deals and a l

More locations

And you'll have the reassurance and convenience of renting from the UK's leading car rental specialist.

We're at over

benefit from our friendly, award-winning customer care.

Greater choice

You'll find we offer a really wide choice of vehicles, too. From family saloons and four-wheel drives to spacious vans and mini-buses, we have all the latest models and specifications.

So whether you're looking for a suitcase-swallowing

hatchback or a multi-seat people carrier, a local runabout or a long-distance tourer, we're sure to come up with the right car for your holiday or business needs.

And don't forget our luxury self-drive service, Guy Salmon, where you can enjoy the performance and prestige of a top vehicle without the cost of owning one. Call **0870 600 7006** for more information.

branch for details of our latest offers.

Simpler booking

For more information on National Car Rental, and for easy online booking with

ent with National
ge choice of wheels!

Better deals

National's rates are always competitive, and our weekend and weekly rental rates are especially keen. Also, our exclusive One Rate tariff operates throughout Europe: if you're travelling from the UK, you can pre-book a National car in over 30 countries at a single guaranteed Euro rate. We even hold valuable money-saving promotions from time to time. So be sure to call your nearest

a £5 discount, just visit our website at **www.nationalcar.co.uk**

Alternatively you can call our Central Reservations team on **0870 400 4582.**

London

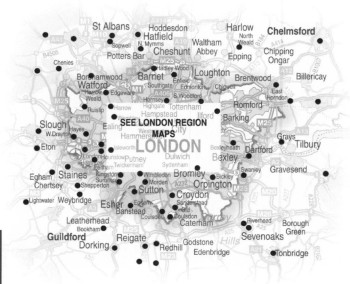

Note:
Dark blue dots represent the location of RAC-inspected accommodation

map blue marker number
map reference:
   OL = Greater London (map pages 28-29)
   IL = Central London (map pages 30-31)
map grid reference

82 OL C1 ⬅

Index of London Accommodation

London

Greater London Map

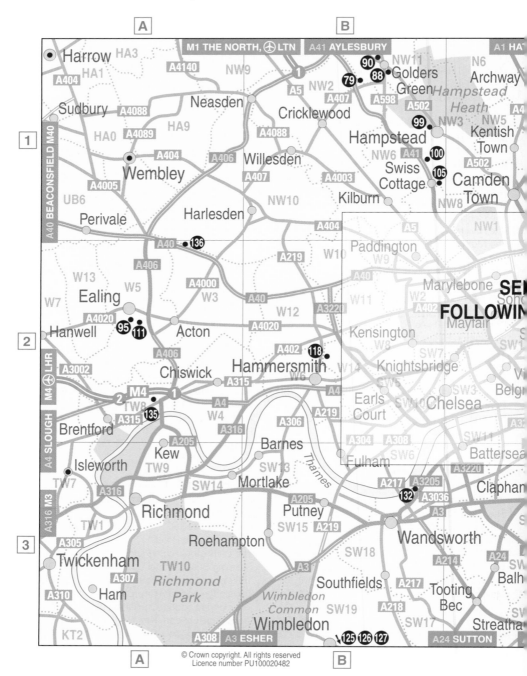

For accommodation name index see pages 26-27

Note: Dark blue numbered dots represent the location of RAC-inspected accommodation

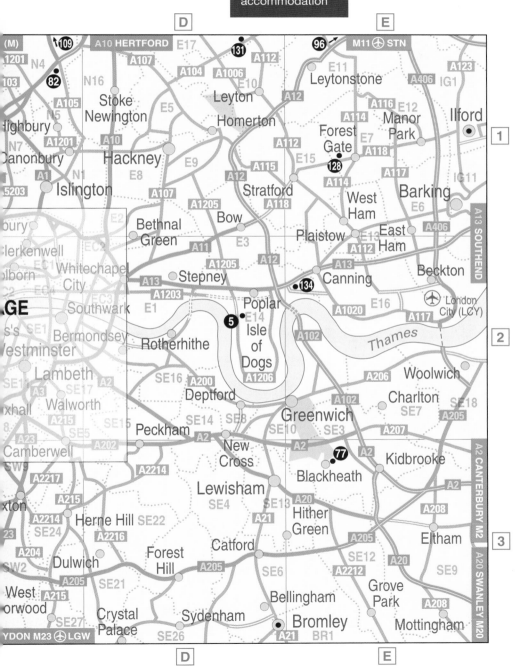

Central London Map

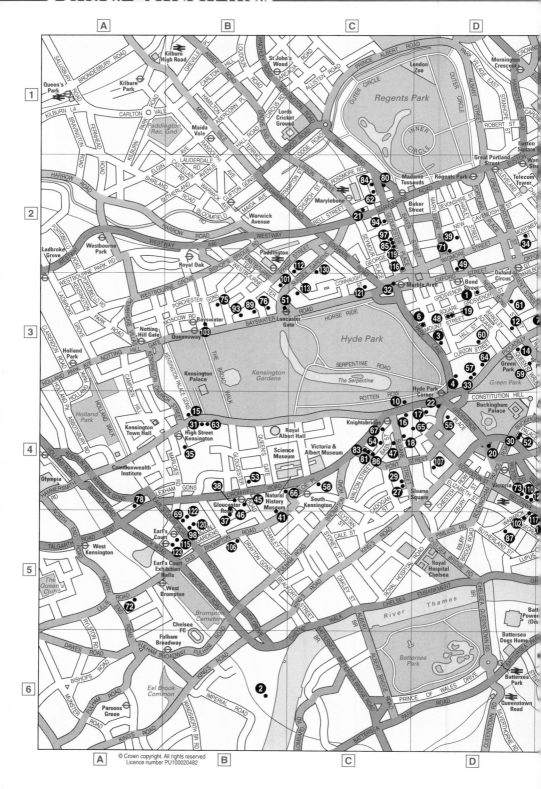

Note: Dark blue numbered dots represent the location of RAC-inspected accommodation

London

Gold Ribbon Award

Athenaeum Hotel	★★★★	41
Berkeley	★★★★★	36
Claridge's	★★★★★	33
Four Seasons Hotel	★★★★★	33
Mandarin Oriental Hyde Park	★★★★★	35
The Capital Hotel	★★★★	46
The Connaught	★★★★★	37
The Dorchester Hotel	★★★★★	33
The Halkin Hotel	★★★★	47
The Landmark Hotel	★★★★★	37
The Lanesborough Hotel	★★★★★	38
The Ritz Hotel	★★★★★	35
The Savoy	★★★★★	38

Gold Ribbon Award Townhouses

"41"	★★★★★	40
51, Buckingham Gate Luxury Suites & Apartments	★★★★★	39
Charlotte Street Hotel	★★★★★	39
The Covent Garden Hotel	★★★★★	40
The Milestone Hotel	★★★★★	41

Blue Ribbon Award

Four Seasons Hotel Canary Wharf	★★★★★	34
One Aldwych	★★★★★	35
The Stafford	★★★★	48
Renaissance Chancery Court Hotel	★★★★★	35
Royal Garden Hotel	★★★★★	36

Blue Ribbon Award Townhouses

22 Jermyn Street	★★★★★	38
Dorset Square Hotel	★★★★	48
Durley House	★★★★★	40
Kensington House Hotel	★★★★	49
The Cliveden Town House	★★★★★	40
The Pelham Hotel	★★★★	49

London

Claridge's

Gold Ribbon Winner

★★★★★

Brook Street, Mayfair, London, W1A 2JQ
Tel: 020 7950 5491 Fax: 020 7950 5481
Email: info@claridges.co.uk
Web: www.claridges.co.uk

Claridge's marries 1930s glamour with up-to-the-minute technology. Claridge's bar is one of Mayfair's hottest meeting places, the foyer offers luxurious all day dining, whilst Gordon Ramsay at Claridge's is London's finest culinary experience.
Rooms: 203 all ensuite
Pricing: Sgl £295–429 Dbl £295–482
Dinner from £29.50 CC: Accepted
Room facilities: Access:
Conference: 8 meeting rooms (Thtr 260 max), day-delegate rate from £84 Children: Welcome
Licences:
Leisure: Gym, Health spa, Beauty salon,
Directions: Between Hyde Park and Bond Street, closest underground Bond Street or Green Park.

Conrad London

★★★★★

Chelsea Harbour, London, SW10 0XG
Tel: 020 7823 3000 Fax: 020 7351 6525
Email: lonch_gm@hilton.com
Spacious and elegant, the Conrad London is the only 5-star all-suite property in the capital. Situated in exclusive Chelsea harbour, we offer our guests views of the marina and River Thames.
Rooms: 160 all ensuite
Pricing: Dinner from £21 CC: Accepted
Room facilities: Access:
Conference: 14 meeting rooms (Thtr 250 max), 24hr-delegate from £350, day-delegate rate from £78
Children: Welcome Dogs: Welcome Licences:
Leisure: Indoor pool, Gym, Health spa, Beauty salon
Parking: Off-street and monitored
Directions: A4; then Earl's Court Road going south. Right into King's Road, left down Lot's Road and hotel is straight ahead over roundabout.

Dorchester

Gold Ribbon Winner

★★★★★

Park Lane, London, W1A 2HJ
Tel: 020 7629 8888 Fax: 020 7409 0114
Email: reservations@dorchesterhotel.com
Web: www.dorchesterhotel.com
Rooms: 250 all ensuite
Pricing: Sgl £367–390 Dbl £426.75–492
Dinner from £39.50 CC: Accepted
Room facilities:
Access:
Conference: 9 meeting rooms (Thtr 500 max), day-delegate rate from £85
Children: Welcome
Dogs: Guide dogs only
Licences:
Leisure: Gym, Health spa, Beauty salon
Parking: Off-street and monitored
Directions: The Dorchester is located on Park Lane, opposite Hyde Park, approximately halfway between Marble Arch and Hyde Park Corner.

Four Seasons Hotel

Gold Ribbon Winner

★★★★★

Hamilton Place, Park Lane, London, W1A 1AZ
Tel: 020 7499 0888 Fax: 020 7493 1895/6629
Email: fsh.london@fourseasons.com
Web: www.fourseasons.com
Rooms: 220 all ensuite CC: Accepted
Room facilities:
Access:
Conference: 6 meeting rooms (Thtr 400 max), day-delegate rate from £81.50
Children: Welcome
Dogs: Welcome
Licences:
Leisure: Gym
Parking: Off-street and monitored (cost £26)
Directions: Set back from Park Lane in Hamilton Place. Closest tubes are Hyde Park Corner and Green Park. Well-situated for Victoria and Paddington stations.

Ask the experts

To book a Hotel or Guest Accommodation, or for help and advice, call RAC Hotel Reservations on 0870 603 9109 and quote 'Guide 2003'

Mobile traffic information

Just dial 1740* from any mobile phone to get up-to-the-minute RAC traffic information on motorways and major A roads. Try it now! *Calls to 1740 cost up to 59p per minute. Check with your network.

Four Seasons Hotel Canary Wharf

Blue Ribbon Winner

★ ★ ★ ★ ★ ☗ ☗

Westferry Circus, Canary Wharf, London, E14 8RS
Tel: 020 7510 1999 Fax: 020 7510 1998
Web: www.fourseasons.com

Four Seasons Hotel Canary Wharf is situated at
Westferry Circus, and within the Canary Riverside
development, in this vibrant, fast-growing area of
London. The hotel offers 142 rooms including 14
suites, a Northern Italian restaurant, a fitness centre (as
well as access to Holmes Place at Canary Riverside
Health Club and Spa) and a wide range of meeting
facilities. The Hotel is located a convenient 10 minute
drive from London City Airport linking it to key
European destinations. With the recent extension of
the Jubilee underground line, it is also conveniently
located for London's West End.
Rooms: 142 all ensuite ✤ ⊛ CC: Accepted
Room facilities: ☐ ☎ ☏ ❅ Access: ⎄ ♿
Conference: 4 meeting rooms (Thtr 210 max),
day-delegate rate from £73 Children: Welcome �🍴 ☕
Dogs: Welcome Licences: ◮ ♟
Leisure: Indoor pool, Gym, Health spa, Beauty salon,
Tennis
Parking: Off-street and monitored (cost £24)

Le Méridien Grosvenor House

★ ★ ★ ★ ★ ☗ ☗

86–90 Park Lane, London, W1K 7TN
Tel: 0800 028 2840 Fax: 020 7493 3341
Email: grosvenor.reservations@lemeridien.com
Web: www.lemeridien-grosvenorhouse.com
Rooms: 587 all ensuite ✤ ⊛
Pricing: Dinner from £35 CC: Accepted
Room facilities: ☐ ☎ ☏ ❅ Access: ⎄ ♿
Conference: 21 meeting rooms (Thtr 110 max),
24hr-delegate from £265, day-delegate rate from £72
Children: Welcome ☕ Dogs: Guide dogs only
Licences: ◮ ♟
Leisure: Indoor pool, Gym, Health spa, Beauty salon
Parking: Off-street and monitored
Directions: Situated on Park Lane, in the heart of
Mayfair, overlooking Hyde Park.

Le Méridien Piccadilly

★ ★ ★ ★ ★ ☗ ☗ ☗

21 Piccadilly, London, W1V 0BH
Tel: 0800 028 2840 Fax: 020 7437 3574
Email: lmpicrcs@lemeridien.com
Web: www.lemeridien-piccadilly.com
Rooms: 266 all ensuite ☗ ⊛
Pricing: Dinner from £18.50 CC: Accepted
Room facilities: ☐ ☎ ☏ ❅ Access: ⎄ ♿
Conference: 10 meeting rooms (Thtr 250 max),
day-delegate rate from £77.50 Children: Welcome
Dogs: Guide dogs only Licences: ◮ ♟
Leisure: Indoor pool, Gym, Beauty salon
Directions: From M4, directly to Cromwell Road,
through Knightsbridge and on to Piccadilly.
Underground — Piccadilly Circus (Piccadilly &
Bakerloo Lines), 2 mins walk.

Le Méridien Waldorf

★ ★ ★ ★ ★

Aldwych, London, WC2B 4DD
Tel: 0800 028 2840 Fax: 020 7836 7244
Email: reception.waldorf@lemeridien.com
Web: www.lemeridien-waldorf.com
Rooms: 292 all ensuite ☗ ⊛
Room facilities: ☐ ☎ ☏ ❅ Access: ⎄
Conference: 13 meeting rooms (Thtr 250 max),
24hr-delegate from £400, day-delegate rate from £85
Children: Welcome ☕ Dogs: Guide dogs only
Licences: ◮ ♟ Leisure: Indoor pool, Gym
Directions: Nearest underground stations are Covent
Garden and Holborn. Charing Cross railway is 1/2 mile.
Waterloo and Eurostar 3/4 mile.

London Marriott Hotel, County Hall

★ ★ ★ ★ ★ ☗ ☗

County Hall, London, SE1 7PB
Tel: 020 7591 1599 Fax: 020 7591 1128
Web: www.marriott.com/marriott/lonch
Rooms: 200 all ensuite ✤ ☗ ⊛
Pricing: Dbl £280.82–346.62 Dinner from £30
CC: Accepted Room facilities: ☐ ☎ ☏ ☏ ❅
Access: ⎄ ♿ Conference: 8 meeting rooms (Thtr 72
max), day-delegate rate from £72
Children: Welcome ⍾ ☕ Dogs: Guide dogs only
Licences: ◮ ♟ Leisure: Indoor pool, Gym, Health
spa, Beauty salon
Parking: Off-street and monitored
Directions: The hotel entrance is on the south side of
Westminster Bridge; nearest underground stations are
Westminster and Waterloo, both 5 minutes' walk.

Mandarin Oriental Hyde Park
Gold Ribbon Winner

★★★★★ 🎀🎀🎀

66 Knightsbridge, London, SW1X 7LA
Tel: 020 7235 2000 Fax: 020 7235 2001
Email: molon-reservations@mohg.com
Web: www.mandarinoriental.com

Situated in the heart of Knightsbridge and having completed a £50 million restoration, this award-winning hotel offers sumptuous rooms, a Michelin star restaurant, a buzzing bar, exclusive spa and Mandarin Oriental's legendary service.
Rooms: 200 all ensuite 🛏️ 🖥️ ⊗
Room facilities: 📺 ☎️ 🔌 ❄️ Access: ↕️ ♿
Conference: 5 meeting rooms (Thtr 250 max), day-delegate rate from £85 Children: Welcome 🍴
Dogs: Guide dogs only Licences: 🔷 ♟️
Leisure: Gym, Health spa
Parking: Off-street and monitored
Directions: Just off the A4, the hotel is located directly opposite Harvey Nichols, in the heart of Knightsbridge.

One Aldwych
Blue Ribbon Winner

★★★★★ 🎀🎀

1 Aldwych, London, WC2B 4RH
Tel: 020 7300 1000 Fax: 020 7300 1001
Email: reservations@onealdwych.com
Web: www.onealdwych.com

This award-winning, privately owned luxury hotel incorporates sleek contemporary design, cutting-edge technology, a fabulous location in Covent Garden and thoughtful, friendly service.

Rooms: 105 all ensuite ⊗
Pricing: Sgl £220–370 Dbl £240–490
Dinner from £32.50 CC: Accepted
Room facilities: 📺 ☎️ 🔌 ❄️ Access: ↕️ ♿
Conference: 6 meeting rooms (Thtr 60 max), day-delegate rate from £79 Children: Welcome 🍴
Dogs: Guide dogs only Licences: 🔷 ♟️
Leisure: Indoor pool, Gym, Health spa, Beauty salon
Directions: At the point where The Aldwych meets The Strand, opposite Waterloo Bridge and close to Covent Garden.

Raffles Brown's Hotel

★★★★★ 🎀🎀🎀

Albemarle Street, Mayfair, London, W1S 4BP
Tel: 020 7518 4140 Fax: 020 7518 4141
Email: reservations.browns@raffles.com
Web: www.raffles-brownshotel.com
Rooms: 118 all ensuite 🛏️ 🖥️
Pricing: Sgl £371.75 Dbl £407 Dinner from £38
CC: Accepted Room facilities: 📺 ☎️ 🔌 ❄️ Access: ↕️
Conference: 7 meeting rooms (Thtr 70 max), day-delegate rate from £75 Children: Welcome ⊷
Dogs: Guide dogs only Licences: 🔷 ♟️ Leisure: Gym
Directions: From Hyde Park Corner into Piccadilly, then left into Dover Street.

Renaissance London Chancery Court Hotel
Blue Ribbon Winner

★★★★★ 🎀🎀

252 High Holborn, London, WC1V 7EN
Tel: 020 7829 9888 Fax: 020 7829 9889
Email: sales.chancerycourt@renaissancehotels.com
Web: www.renaissancehotels.com/loncc
Rooms: 356 all ensuite 🛏️ ⊗
Pricing: Sgl £175–285 Dbl £175–285 Dinner from £35
CC: Accepted Room facilities: 📺 ☎️ 🖥️ 🔌 ❄️
Access: ↕️ ♿ Conference: 14 meeting rooms (Thtr 400 max), day-delegate rate from £82
Children: Welcome 🍴 Dogs: Guide dogs only
Licences: 🔷 ♟️
Leisure: Gym, Health spa, Beauty salon
Directions: By Holborn tube station, which runs through both the West End and The City.

Ritz Hotel
Gold Ribbon Winner

★★★★★ 🎀🎀🎀

150 Piccadilly, London, W1J 9BR
Tel: 020 7300 2308/9 Fax: 020 7493 2687
Email: enquire@theritzlondon.com
Web: www.theritzlondon.com
Rooms: 133 all ensuite ⊗
Pricing: Sgl £390–2315 Dbl £475–2340 Dinner from £52
CC: Accepted Room facilities: 📺 ☎️ 🔌 ❄️
Access: ↕️ ♿ Conference: 2 meeting rooms (Thtr 60 max) Children: Welcome 🍴 ⊷ Dogs: Guide dogs only
Licences: 🔷 ♟️ Leisure: Gym, Beauty salon
Parking: Off-street and monitored
Directions: Located on Piccadilly, next to Green Park, a few steps from Bond Street. From Victoria station, north on Victoria Line to Green Park. Ritz 100 yards away.

Royal Garden Hotel

Blue Ribbon Winner

★ ★ ★ ★ ★ ★ RAC RAC RAC

2-24 Kensington High Street, London, W8 4PT
Tel: 020 7937 8000 Fax: 020 7361 1991
Email: sales@royalgardenhotel.co.uk
Web: www.royalgardenhotel.co.uk

Situated in the heart of Kensington, overlooking Hyde
Park and Kensington Gardens, The Royal Garden Hotel
offers contemporary accommodation, three bars, two
restaurants, health club and 24-hour business centre.
Rooms: 396 all ensuite 🏊 Ⓢ
Pricing: Sgl £305–305 Dbl £395–395 Dinner from £25
CC: Accepted Room facilities: 🖵 ☎ 📞 ❄
Access: |↓↑ ♿
Conference: 10 meeting rooms (Thtr 600 max),
day-delegate rate from £68 Children: Welcome ♯ ☕
Dogs: Guide dogs only Licences: ◁ ♀♀♀
Leisure: Gym, Beauty salon
Parking: Off-street and monitored
Directions: On Kensington High Street (A315), between
Kensington Church Street and Kensington Palace
Gardens.

Sheraton Park Tower

★ ★ ★ ★ ★ RAC RAC RAC

101 Knightsbridge, London, SW1X 7RN
Tel: 020 7235 8050 Fax: 020 7235 8231
Email: central.london.reservations@sheraton.com
Web: www.sheraton.com/parktower
Rooms: 280 all ensuite Ⓢ
Pricing: Dbl £289–497 Dinner from £18 CC: Accepted
Room facilities: 🖵 ☎ 📞 ❄ Access: |↓↑
Conference: 4 meeting rooms (Thtr 60 max),
day-delegate rate from £80
Children: Welcome ♯
Dogs: Guide dogs only Licences: ♀♀♀
Leisure: Gym
Parking: Off-street and monitored
Directions: Located in the heart of Knightsbirdge, next
to the Harvey Nichols store. The nearest underground
station is Knightsbridge.

Plan your route

Visit www.rac.co.uk for RAC's
interactive route planner, including
up to the minute traffic reports.

The Berkeley

Gold Ribbon Winner

★ ★ ★ ★ ★ RAC RAC RAC RAC RAC

Wilton Place, London, SW1X 7RL
Tel: 020 7950 5490 Fax: 020 7950 5480
Email: info@the-berkeley.co.uk
Web: www.the-berkeley.com

Perfectly placed for shopping in Knightsbridge, The
Berkeley is a showcase for some of England's leading
interior designers. Facilities include the popular new
Blue Bar and roof-top swimming pool.
Rooms: 214 all ensuite 🖨 Ⓢ
Pricing: Sgl £398 Dbl £484
Dinner from £25 CC: Accepted
Room facilities: 🖵 ☎ 📞 ❄
Conference: 6 meeting rooms (Thtr 250 max),
day-delegate rate from £79
Access: |↓↑ Children: Welcome ☕
Dogs: Guide dogs only Licences: ◁ ♀♀♀
Leisure: Indoor pool, Gym, Health spa,
Beauty salon
Parking: Off-street and monitored
Directions: 200 yards down Knightsbridge from Hyde
Park Corner, on left-hand side.

The Carlton Tower

★ ★ ★ ★ ★ RAC RAC

On Cadogan Place, London, SW1X 9PY
Tel: 020 7235 1234
Email: contact@carltontower.com
Web: www.carltontower.com
Rooms: 220 all ensuite 🖨 Ⓢ
Pricing: Sgl £325–475 Dinner from £21 CC: Accepted
Room facilities: 🖵 ☎ 📞 ❄ Access: |↓↑
Conference: 6 meeting rooms (Thtr 420 max),
day-delegate rate from £78
Children: Welcome ♯ ☕
Dogs: Guide dogs only
Licences: ◁ ♀♀♀
Leisure: Indoor pool, Gym, Health spa,
Beauty salon, Tennis
Parking: Off-street and monitored
Directions: Follow M4 to London then take A4 to
Knightsbridge, turn right at Sloane Street intersection,
hotel situated on Cadogan Place.

The Connaught

★ ★ ★ ★ ★ ᴿ ᴿ ᴿ

Carlos Place, Mayfair, London, W1K 2AL
Tel: 020 7950 5493 Fax: 020 7950 5483
Email: info@the-connaught.co.uk
Web: www.the-connaught.com

The Connaught's rooms and suites are plush comfort zones with high-tech facilities. The drawing rooms and red room are perfect for light dining. The fitness studio allows guests to pursue their fitness regimes.
Rooms: 92 all ensuite Pricing: Sgl £376 Dbl £504
CC: Accepted Room facilities: ▢ ☎ 📞 ❄ Access: ♿
Conference: 2 meeting rooms Children: Welcome
Licences: ⛉ Leisure: Gym
Directions: Between Berkeley and Grosvenor Squares. Nearest underground stations Bond St and Green Park.

The Goring

★ ★ ★ ★ ★ ᴿ ᴿ

Beeston Place, Grosvenor Gardens,
London, SW1W 0JW
Tel: 020 7396 9000 Fax: 020 7834 4393
Email: reception@goringhotel.co.uk
Web: www.goringhotel.co.uk

Operated by four generations of the Goring Family since it opened in 1910, The Goring remains a bastion of elegance and sophistication yet exemplifies all the best and most advanced advantages of modern technology and comfort.
Rooms: 74 all ensuite 🚭
Pricing: Sgl £245–245 Dbl £310–360 Dinner from £39
CC: Accepted Room facilities: ▢ ☎ 📞 ❄ Access: ♿
Conference: 3 meeting rooms (Thtr 80 max),
day-delegate rate from £60 Children: Welcome ⊓ ☯
Licences: ⛉ Parking: Off-street, monitored (£21)

The Landmark London

★ ★ ★ ★ ★ ᴿ ᴿ ᴿ

222 Marylebone Road, London, NW1 6JQ
Tel: 020 7631 8000 Fax: 020 7631 8080
Email: reservations@thelandmark.co.uk
Web: www.landmarklondon.co.uk

Set in fashionable Marylebone, The Landmark is a Victorian era masterpiece. Offering some of the largest guest rooms in London, all with marble ensuites, your stay at The Landmark will be spectacular.
Rooms: 299 all ensuite 🚭 ⬛ 🚭
Pricing: Sgl £202–1786 Dbl £219–1815
Dinner from £32 CC: Accepted
Room facilities: ▢ ☎ 📞 ❄
Access: ♿ ♿
Conference: 11 meeting rooms (Thtr 380 max),
day-delegate rate from £85
Children: Welcome ⊓
Licences: ⛷ ⛉
Leisure: Indoor pool, Gym, Health spa,
Beauty salon
Parking: Off-street and monitored
Directions: In front of Marylebone main line station and underground, also fronting Marylebone Road near Madame Tussaud's. Easy access to M40 and M4.

The Lanesborough · Gold Ribbon Winner

★ ★ ★ ★ ★ ♔ ♔ ♔ ♔

Hyde Park Corner, London, SW1X 7TA
Tel: 020 7259 5599 Fax: 020 7259 5606
Email: info@lanesborough.com
Web: www.lanesborough.com

One of London's pre-eminent hotels,
The Lanesborough represents a revival of traditional
hospitality. Originally a country retreat, the hotel
captures the style and elegance of a private 19th
century residence.
Rooms: 95 all ensuite 🛗 ⓢ
Pricing: Sgl £323.13–381.88 Dbl £452.38–528.75
CC: Accepted Room facilities: 🖵 ☎ 📞 ❄
Access: 𝍖 ♿
Conference: 6 meeting rooms (Thtr 120 max),
24hr-delegate from £80, day-delegate rate from £80
Children: Welcome 🍴 Dogs: Welcome
Licences: ◊ ♟ Leisure: Fitness studio
Parking: Off-street and monitored
Directions: Follow signs to Hyde Park Corner.

The Savoy · Gold Ribbon Winner

★ ★ ★ ★ ★ ♔ ♔ ♔ ♔

The Strand, London, WC2R 0EU
Tel: 020 7950 5492 Fax: 020 7950 5482
Email: info@the-savoy.co.uk
Web: www.the-savoy.com

The most famous of super-famous hotels, The Savoy
now boasts 263 rooms, many with outstanding river
views. Dine in the Savoy Grill, river restaurant or
"upstairs". Swim, relax or work out in the Fitness
Gallery.
Rooms: 263 all ensuite 🛗
Pricing: Sgl £401 Dbl £490 Dinner from £17
CC: Accepted
Room facilities: 🖵 ☎ 📞 ❄ Access: 𝍖 ♿
Conference: 10 meeting rooms (Thtr 500 max),
day-delegate rate from 82.50
Children: Welcome 🍴 Licences: ◊ ♟
Leisure: Indoor pool, Gym, Health spa,
Beauty salon
Parking: Off-street and monitored
Directions: Between Aldwych and Trafalgar Square on
The Strand. Nearest underground stations Charing
Cross and Covent Garden.

22 Jermyn Street · Blue Ribbon Winner

★ ★ ★ ★ ★ Townhouse

22 Jermyn Street, St James's, London, SW1Y 6HL
Tel: 020 7734 2353 Fax: 020 7734 0750
Email: office@22jermyn.com
Web: www.22.jermyn.com

22 Jermyn Street has a superb location, an enviable
reputation for first class service, wide-ranging facilities
for business and leisure travellers and is the winner of
many prestigious hotel awards.
Rooms: 18 all ensuite 🛗
Pricing: Sgl £259.40 Dbl £272.05 CC: Accepted
Room facilities: 🖵 ☎ 📞 ❄ Access: 𝍖 ♿
Conference: 4 meeting rooms (Thtr 8 max)
Children: Welcome 🍴 Dogs: Welcome Licences: ♟
Leisure: Indoor pool, Gym, Health spa,
Beauty salon
Parking: Off-street and monitored
Directions: From Hyde Park Corner take the underpass
leading to Piccadilly. Turn right onto Duke Street, left
into King Street onto St James' Square. Take left again
at Charles II Street. Left into Lower Regent Street and
left again on Jermyn Street.

51 Buckingham Gate
Townhouse   Gold Ribbon Winner

★ ★ ★ ★ ★   ❦ ❦

51 Buckingham Gate, London, SW1E 6AF
Tel: 020 7769 7766 Fax: 020 7233 5014
Email: info@51-buckinghamgate.co.uk
Web: www.51-buckinghamgate.co.uk
Rooms: 82 all ensuite ❧
Pricing: Dbl £390–398 Dinner from £15
CC: Accepted
Room facilities: ▢ ☎ ☕ ✆ ❄
Access: ⋔ ♿
Children: Welcome ⋔ Dogs: Guide dogs only
Licences: ◁ ♦♦♦
Leisure: Gym, Health spa, Beauty salon
Parking: Off-street and monitored
Directions: Walk down Victoria Sreet and turn left into
Buckingham Gate. A short walk from Buckingham
Palace and St James' Station.
See advert on this page

Charlotte Street Hotel
Townhouse   Gold Ribbon Winner

★ ★ ★ ★ ★ ★   ❦ ❦

15-17 Charlotte Street, London, W1T 1RJ
Tel: 020 7806 2000 Fax: 020 7806 2002
Email: charlotte@firmdale.com
Web: www.firmdale.com

Situated north of Soho, this luxurious boutique hotel is
decorated in a fresh modern English style, and is
perfectly appointed with the modern traveller in mind:
even the bathrooms have mini colour televisions.
Rooms: 52 all ensuite ❧ ▤ ⊗
Pricing: Sgl £234.88–234.55 Dbl £281.75–281.75
Dinner from £25 CC: Accepted
Room facilities: ▢ ☎ ✆ ❄ Access: ⋔
Conference: 4 meeting rooms (Thtr 25 max)
Children: Welcome ⋔ 🎠
Licences: ♦♦♦
Leisure: Gym
Directions: From Oxford Street, turn into Rathbone
Place, which leads onto Charlotte Street. Hotel is on left.

Cliveden Town House
Townhouse   Blue Ribbon Winner

★★★★★★ ⓡ ⓡ ⓡ

26 Cadogan Gardens, London, SW3 2RP
Tel: 020 7730 6466 Fax: 020 7730 0236
Email: reservations@clivedentownhouse.co.uk
Web: www.clivedentownhouse.co.uk

A perfect balance of luxury, service, privacy and location. At the very centre of fashionable London. Combining the grandeur of the past with the luxuries and conveniences of today.
Rooms: 35 all ensuite
Pricing: Sgl £214.26 Dbl £369.75 CC: Accepted
Room facilities: Access:
Conference: 1 meeting room (Thtr 12 max)
Children: Welcome Dogs: Welcome Licences:
Directions: From M4, follow signs to Central London. After Natural History Museum, road veers left, becoming Brompton Road. Take fourth right turn at lights into Beauchamp Place. Turn right into Cadogan Square and fifth left into Gardens.

Covent Garden Hotel
Townhouse   Gold Ribbon Winner

★★★★★ ⓡ ⓡ

10 Monmouth Street, London, WC2H 9HB
Tel: 020 7806 1000 Fax: 020 7806 1100
Email: covent@firmdale.com
Web: www.firmdale.com

Located in the heart of theatreland, this luxurious boutique hotel combines dramatically-designed interiors, superb service and the best that modern design and technology can offer.
Rooms: 58 all ensuite
Pricing: Sgl £245.63–245.63 Dbl £309.13–379.63
Dinner from £25 CC: Accepted
Room facilities: Access: Conference: 4
meeting rooms (Thtr 30 max) Children: Welcome
Licences: Leisure: Gym, Beauty salon
Directions: Nearest tube is Covent Garden. Walk to the end of Neal Street (opposite tube) and turn left onto Monmouth Street. Hotel is on right.

Durley House
   Blue Ribbon Winner

★★★★★ Townhouse
115 Sloane Street, London, SW1X 9PJ
Tel: 020 7235 5537 Fax: 020 7259 6977
Email: info@durleyhouse.com
Web: www.durleyhouse.com
Situated in Sloane Street, this all-suite hotel comprises 11 elegantly-furnished apartments. Perfect for Knightsbridge shopping, playing tennis in the private garden or entertaining in the privacy of your own suite.
Rooms: 11 all ensuite
Pricing: Sgl £275–436 Dbl £350–640
Dinner from £8 CC: Accepted
Room facilities: Access:
Children: Welcome Dogs: Guide dogs only Licences:
Leisure: Tennis
Directions: From Knightsbridge turn down Sloane Street, away from Hyde Park and Durley House is on right 100 yards before Sloane Square.

No. 41
Townhouse   Gold Ribbon Winner

★★★★★ ⓡ ⓡ

41 Buckingham Palace Road, London, SW1W 0PS
Tel: 020 7300 0041 Fax: 020 7300 0141
Email: book41@rchmail.com
Web: www.redcarnationhotels.com
Rooms: 20 all ensuite

Small, intimate and providing outstanding, affordable 5 star service, 41 is quietly situated, overlooking the Royal Mews and Buckingham Palace Gardens. The hotel reflects a remarkable attention to detail and the 16 deluxe bedrooms and 4 split-level suites are furnished with traditional mahogany and black leather decor.
Pricing: Sgl £212–360 Dbl £222–270 Dinner from £25
CC: Accepted Room facilities:
Access: Conference: 1 meeting rooms (Thtr 10 max)
24hr-delegate from £300, day-delegate rate from £60
Children: Welcome Dogs: Welcome Licences:
Directions: Just 5 minutes walk from Victoria train station. Situated on Buckingham Palace Road opposite The Royal Mews, Buckingham Palace.

The Milestone Hotel & Apartments
Townhouse   Gold Ribbon Winner

★ ★ ★ ★ ★ ® ® ®

1 Kensington Court, London, W8 5DL
Tel: 020 7917 1234 Fax: 020 7917 1133
Email: guestservicesms@rchmail.com
Web: www.redcarnationhotels.com

The Milestone, a Victorian architectural showpiece built in the 1880s, is a five-star intimate boutique hotel and offers a history rich in tradition, style and unparalleled attention to detail and service.
Rooms: 57 all ensuite 🍽 ⌨ 🚫
Pricing: Sgl £305.25–951.50 Dbl £340.25–963
Dinner from £36.50 CC: Accepted
Room facilities: ▢ ☎ 🖥 🔌 ❄ Access: ⬆ ♿
Conference: 3 meeting rooms (Thtr 30 max), day-delegate rate from £65
Children: Welcome ⍭ ☕
Dogs: Welcome Licences: ◈ ⛊
Leisure: Gym
Directions: Directly opposite Kensington Palace, The Milestone is about 400 yards from High Street Kensington underground station.

Art + Tech by Le Meridien, London, Hyde Park

★ ★ ★ ★

1A Great Cumberland Place, Marble Arch, London, W1A 4RF
Tel: 0800 028 2840 Fax: 020 7724 4621
Email: reservations.cumberland@lemeridien.com
Web: www.lemeridien.com
Rooms: 894 all ensuite 🚫
Room facilities: ▢ ☎ 🖥 🔌 Access: ⬆ ♿
Conference: meeting rooms (Thtr 400 max)
Children: Welcome ⍭
Dogs: Guide dogs only
Licences: ⛊
Directions: Situated on Oxford Street overlooking Marble Arch and Hyde Park. Underground: Central Line, Marble Arch Station.

One click does it all

Book RAC inspected hotels and B&Bs at www.rac.co.uk/hotels

Athenaeum Hotel & Apartments
         Gold Ribbon Winner

★ ★ ★ ★ ® ® ®

116 Piccadilly, London, W1J 7BJ
Tel: 020 7499 3464 Fax: 020 7493 1860
Email: info@athenaeumhotel.com
Web: www.athenaeumhotel.com

A luxurious family-owned hotel in the heart of Mayfair, the Athenaeum offers traditional warmth and hospitality. In addition to the well-appointed rooms, the Edwardian-style apartments adjacent to the hotel offer an ideal home away from home.
Rooms: 157 all ensuite 🍽 🚫
Pricing: Sgl £195–700 Dbl £195–700
Dinner from £14 CC: Accepted
Room facilities: ▢ ☎ 🖥 🔌 Access: ⬆
Conference: 4 meeting rooms (Thtr 70 max), 24hr-delegate from £265, day-delegate rate from £65
Children: Welcome ⍭ ☕
Licences: ◈ ⛊
Leisure: Gym, Health spa, Beauty salon
Directions: Located on Piccadilly in the heart of Mayfair overlooking Green Park. Nearest tube is Green Park or Hyde Park corner.

Berners Hotel

★ ★ ★ ★ ★ ® ®

Berners Street, London, W1A 3BE
Tel: 020 7666 2002 Fax: 020 7666 2010
Email: berners@berners.co.uk
Web: www.thebernershotel.co.uk
Rooms: 216 all ensuite 🍽 🚫
Pricing: Sgl £205.95–220 Dbl £247–300
Dinner from £16.95 CC: Accepted
Room facilities: ▢ ☎ 🖥 🔌
Access: ⬆ ♿
Conference: 4 meeting rooms (Thtr 150 max), day-delegate rate from £65
Children: Welcome ⍭ ☕
Dogs: Guide dogs only
Licences: ◈ ⛊
Directions: Located just off Oxford Street opposite Wardour Street and between Oxford Circus and Tottenham Court Road underground stations.

Copthorne Tara Hotel London Kensington

★★★★

Scarsdale Place, Wrights Lane, Kensington,
London, W8 5SR
Tel: 020 7872 2000 Fax: 020 7937 7100
Email: sales.tara@mill-cop.com
Web: www.millenniumhotels.com

Set just off Kensington High Street, this hotel offers access to some of the best shops and attractions in London. A short walk to Kensington Palace. Weekend rates available.
Rooms: 834 all ensuite ⊛
Pricing: Sgl £230 Dbl £245 Dinner from £19
CC: Accepted
Room facilities: ⬜ ☎ ⊙ ⬟ ❄ Access: |⌊↑ ⅏
Conference: 10 meeting rooms (Thtr 380 max),
24hr-delegate from £205, day-delegate rate from £65
Children: Welcome ⅊ Dogs: Guide dogs only
Licences: ⅏⅏⅏ Parking: Off-street and monitored
Directions: From M25, take exit 15 towards Earls Court. Scarsdale Place is just off Kensington High Street.

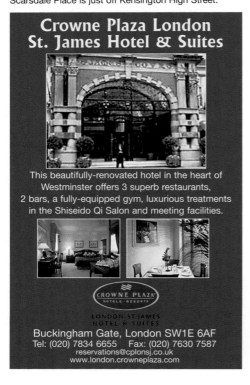
Crowne Plaza London St James Hotel & Suites

★★★★★ ℝℝ

41-54 Buckingham Gate, London, SW1E 6AF
Tel: 020 7834 6655 Fax: 020 7630 7587
Email: reservations@cplonsj.co.uk
Web: www.london.crowneplaza.com
Rooms: 342 all ensuite ⊛
Pricing: Dbl £320–328 Dinner from £15 CC: Accepted
Room facilities: ⬜ ☎ ⊙ ⬟ ❄ Access: |⌊↑ ⅏
Conference: 19 meeting rooms (Thtr 180 max),
24hr-delegate from £290, day-delegate rate from £79
Children: Welcome ⅊ Dogs: Guide dogs only
Licences: ◁▷ ⅏⅏⅏ Leisure: Gym, Health spa, Beauty salon
Parking: Off-street and monitored
Directions: Walk down Victoria Street and turn left into Buckingham Gate. A short walk from Buckingham Palace and St James' Station.
See advert on this page

Harrington Hall

★★★★★ ℝℝ

5-25 Harrington Gardens, London, SW7 4JW
Tel: 020 7396 9696 Fax: 020 7396 9090
Email: harringtonsales@compuserve.com
Web: www.harringtonhall.co.uk
Rooms: 200 all ensuite ⊛
Pricing: Sgl £195.50–200 Dbl £216–230
Dinner from £22.95 CC: Accepted
Room facilities: ⬜ ☎ ⊙ ⬟ ❄ Access: |⌊↑
Conference: 9 meeting rooms (Thtr 200 max),
24hr-delegate from £215, day-delegate rate from £69
Children: Welcome ⅊ Dogs: Guide dogs only
Licences: ⅏⅏⅏ Leisure: Gym
Directions: 100 yards from Gloucester Road underground station (Piccadilly, Circle and District lines). One mile from M4 and A4.

Holiday Inn London — Kensington South

★★★★

97 Cromwell Road, London, SW7 4DN
Tel: 020 7370 5757 Fax: 020 7373 1448
Email: hikensingtonsouth@6c.com
Web: www.london-kensingtonsouth.holiday-inn.com
Rooms: 910 all ensuite ⊛
Pricing: Dinner from £25 (2002 rate) CC: Accepted
Room facilities: ⬜ ☎ ⊙ ⬟ ❄ Access: |⌊↑ ⅏
Children: Welcome ⅊ ⅌ Dogs: Guide dogs only
Licences: ⅏⅏⅏ Leisure: Gym
Parking: Off-street and monitored

Jurys Clifton Ford Hotel
★★★★
Welbeck Street, London, W1M 8DN
Tel: +353(0)1 6070000 Fax: +353(0)1 6316999
Email: bookings@jurysdoyle.com
Web: www.jurysdoyle.com

Rooms: 255 all ensuite
Pricing: Sgl £162–217 Dbl £179–234 Dinner from £27
CC: Accepted
Room facilities: ▢ ☎ ☺ ☕ ❄
Access: ⬆ ♿
Children: Welcome ⴕ
Dogs: Welcome Licences: ⟡ ⵜ
Leisure: Indoor pool, Gym, Health spa,
Beauty salon
Parking: Off-street
Directions: Located 18 miles from London Heathrow.
Paddington Station 2 miles and Bond St tube ¼ mile.
Just five minute walk from Bond and Oxford Streets.

Jurys Great Russell Street
★★★★ ⵎ
16-22 Great Russell Street, London, WC1B 3NN
Tel: +353(0)1 6070000 Fax: +353(0)1 6316999
Email: bookings@jurysdoyle.com
Web: www.jurysdoyle.com

JURYS DOYLE
HOTELS

Rooms: 169 all ensuite ⊛
Pricing: Sgl £173–238 Dbl £191–256 Dinner from £25
CC: Accepted
Room facilities: ▢ ☎ ☺ ☕ ❄
Access: ⬆ ♿
Children: Welcome ⴕ
Dogs: Guide dogs only
Directions: Take the Piccadilly line (Blue Line) to
Holborn. Walk from Holborn: turn left outside station,
walk up New Oxford Street, turn right at Dominion
Theatre. Hotel is 2nd on right-hand side.

Jurys Kensington Hotel
★★★★
109-113 Queen's Gate, South Kensington,
London, SW7 5LR,
Tel: +353(0)1 6070000 Fax: +353(0)1 6316999
Email: bookings@jurysdoyle.com
Web: www.jurysdoyle.com

JURYS DOYLE
HOTELS

Rooms: 173 all ensuite ⊛
Pricing: Sgl £147–217 Dbl £164–234
Dinner from £20 CC: Accepted
Room facilities: ▢ ☎ ☺ ☕ ❄
Access: ⬆ ♿ Children: Welcome ⴕ
Licences: ⵜ
Parking: Off-street and monitored
Directions: Located 13 miles/21 km from London
Heathrow. South Kensington tube 5 minutes walk.
Victoria station 1½ miles/2 km.

Kingsway Hall
★★★★★ ⵎ ⵎ ⵎ
Great Queen Street, Covent Garden,
London, WC2B 5BX
Tel: 020 7309 0909 Fax: 020 7309 9696
Email: kingswayhall@compuserve.com
Web: www.kingswayhall.co.uk
Rooms: 170 all ensuite ⊛
Pricing: Sgl £241.25–245.25 Dbl £262.50–270.50
Dinner from £22.50 CC: Accepted
Room facilities: ▢ ☎ ☺ ☕ ❄
Access: ⬆ ♿
Conference: 11 meeting rooms (Thtr 150 max),
24hr-delegate from £285, day-delegate rate from £68
Children: Welcome
Dogs: Guide dogs only
Licences: ⵜ Leisure: Gym
Directions: Turn left onto Kingsway from Holborn
underground then right onto Great Queen Street. Hotel
is adjacent to New Connaught rooms.

Le Meridien Russell
★★★★
Russell Square, London, WC1B 5BE
Tel: 0800 028 2840 Fax: 020 7837 2857
Web: www.lemeridien.com
Rooms: 371 all ensuite ⵣ ⊛
Room facilities: ▢ ☎ ☺ ☕ ❄
Access: ⬆
Conference: 15 meeting rooms (Thtr 450 max)
Children: Welcome ⵛ
Dogs: Guide dogs only
Licences: ⟡ ⵜ
Directions: 2 minute walk from Russell Square tube
station, within 1 mile of Euston, King's Cross and St
Pancras main line rail stations.

London

London Bridge Hotel

★★★★★ ♖ ♖ ♖

8-18 London Bridge Street, London, SE1 9SG
Tel: 020 7855 2200 Fax: 020 7855 2233
Email: sales@london-bridge-hotel.co.uk
Web: www.london-bridge-hotel.co.uk

Elegant four-star hotel. 138 air-conditioned bedrooms
and suites with excellent facilities. Meeting rooms,
French restaurant, wine bar, gymnasium and three
luxury serviced apartments. Close to many exciting
tourist attractions.
Rooms: 138 all ensuite 🍴 Ⓢ
Pricing: Sgl £201–205 Dbl £212–220 Dinner from £25
CC: Accepted Room facilities: ▢ ☎ ☺ ☎ ❋
Access: |↕ Conference: 5 meeting rooms (Thtr 100 max)
Children: Welcome Licences: ♦♦♦ Leisure: Gym
Directions: Directly opposite London Bridge station.
Rail and underground links — Jubilee and Northern
lines, nearest motorway M11.

Millennium Bailey's Hotel
London Kensington

★★★★★ ♖ ♖

140 Gloucester Road, Kensington, London, SW7 4QH
Tel: 020 7373 6000 Fax: 020 7370 3760
Email: sales.baileys@mill-cop.com
Web: www.millenniumhotels.com

A magnificently restored Victorian town house hotel in
the heart of Kensington, dating back to 1876; the
Millennium Bailey's is central yet intimate in size and
ambience. Weekend rates available.

Rooms: 212 all ensuite Ⓢ
Pricing: Sgl £263 Dbl £276 CC: Accepted
Room facilities: ▢ ☎ ☺ ☎ ❋
Access: |↕
Conference: 21 meeting rooms (Thtr 500 max),
day-delegate rate from £85
Children: Welcome ♴ ☕
Dogs: Guide dogs only Licences: ♦♦♦
Parking: Off-street and monitored
Directions: Opposite Gloucester Road underground
station serviced by Piccadilly, Circle and District lines.
40 mins to London Heathrow and Gatwick airports.

Millennium Gloucester Hotel
London Kensington

★★★★ ♖

4-18 Harrington Gardens, London, SW7 4LH
Tel: 020 7373 6030 Fax: 020 7373 0409
Email: sales.gloucester@mill-cop.com
Web: www.millenniumhotels.com

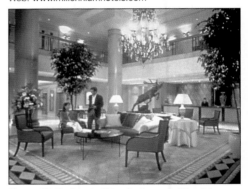

Situated in the heart of Kensington, a fashionable area
of West London. Close to Hyde Park, Earls Court and
some of London's most famous museums. Weekend
rates are also available.
Rooms: 610 all ensuite 🍴 Ⓢ
Pricing: Sgl £265 Dbl £280 CC: Accepted
Room facilities: ▢ ☎ ☺ ☎ ❋ Access: |↕
Conference: 21 meeting rooms (Thtr 500 max),
day-delegate rate from £85
Children: Welcome
Dogs: Guide dogs only Licences: ♴ ♦♦♦
Leisure: Gym
Parking: Off-street and monitored
Directions: Next to Gloucester Road underground
station served by Piccadilly, Circle and District lines. 40
minutes to London Heathrow airport.

Millennium Hotel London Knightsbridge

★★★★★ 🛎 🛎 🛎

17 Sloane Street, Knightsbridge, London, SW1X 9NU
Tel: 020 7838 9650 Fax: 020 7235 7125
Email: knightsbridge.reservations@mill-cop.com
Web: www.millenniumhotels.com

Situated on Sloane Street, surrounded by elegant shops including Harrods and Harvey Nichols. The new restaurant, Mju, offers the chance to experience a quite unique dining experience. Weekend rates available.
Rooms: 222 all ensuite 🐾 🚭
Pricing: Sgl £116–529 Dbl £116–529
Dinner from £25 CC: Accepted
Room facilities: 🖥 ☎ 🍵 📞 ❄
Access: ⬆
Conference: 4 meeting rooms (Thtr 120 max), 24hr-delegate from £265, day-delegate rate from £75
Children: Welcome 🍴 🍼
Dogs: Guide dogs only
Licences: 👫
Parking: Monitored
Directions: Knightsbridge tube station is a two-minute walk from the Millennium Knightsbridge or follow the A4 signs to Knightsbridge.

Millennium Hotel London Mayfair

★★★★★ 🛎 🛎

Grosvenor Square, Mayfair, London, W1K 2HP
Tel: 020 7629 9400 Fax: 020 7629 7736
Email: reservations@mill-cop.com
Web: www.millenniumhotels.com

The elegant and luxurious Millennium Mayfair is situated in London's prestigious Grosvenor Square. The hotel is just 5 minutes walk from Oxford Street and Hyde Park.

Rooms: 348 all ensuite 🚭
Pricing: Sgl £218–400 Dbl £335–400 Dinner from £20
CC: Accepted Room facilities: 🖥 ☎ 🍵 📞 ❄
Access: ⬆ ♿
Conference: 14 meeting rooms, 24hr-delegate from £255, day-delegate rate from £85
Children: Welcome Licences: 🍷 👫 Leisure: Gym
Directions: Situated on Grosvenor Square, which can be reached via Park Lane or Berkeley Square.

Radisson Edwardian Berkshire Hotel

★★★★★ 🛎 🛎 🛎

350 Oxford Street, London, W1N 0BY
Tel: 020 7514 3403 Fax: 020 7514 3427
Email: resberk@radisson.com
Web: radissonedwardian.com
Rooms: 148 all ensuite 🚭
Pricing: Sgl £120–305 Dbl £150–400 CC: Accepted
Room facilities: 🖥 ☎ 🍵 📞 ❄ Access: ⬆
Conference: 2 meeting rooms (Thtr 24 max)
Children: Welcome 🍼
Dogs: Guide dogs only
Licences: 👫
Directions: London underground: Bond Street station. By car: onto Wigmore Street, turn into Welbeck Street, turn right into Maryleborne Lane, turn left.

Royal Horseguards

★★★★ 🛎 🛎 🛎

Whitehall Court, London, SW1A 2EL
Tel: 020 7839 3400 Fax: 020 7930 4010
Email: royal.horseguards@thistle.co.uk
Web: www.thistlehotels.com
Rooms: 280 all ensuite 🚭
Room facilities: 🖥 ☎ 🍵 📞 ❄ Access: ⬆
Children: Welcome 🍴 Licences: 🍷 👫
Leisure: Gym
Directions: Two minutes from Charing Cross and 10 minutes from Victoria and Waterloo stations. Nearest underground station is Embankment.

Royal Lancaster Hotel

★★★★★ 🛎 🛎 🛎

Lancaster Terrace, London, W2 2TY
Tel: 020 7262 6737 Fax: 020 7724 3191
Email: book@royallancaster.com
Web: www.royallancaster.com
Rooms: 416 all ensuite 🚭
Pricing: Sgl £305.23–393.35 Dbl £320.23–408.35
Dinner from £15 CC: Accepted
Room facilities: 🖥 ☎ 📞 ❄ Access: ⬆
Conference: 3 meeting rooms (Thtr 1400 max), day-delegate rate from £72
Children: Welcome 🍴
Dogs: Guide dogs only Licences: 👫
Leisure: Beauty salon Parking: Off-street and monitored
Directions: Adjacent to Lancaster Gate underground, Paddington main line station (Heathrow express terminus) and underground 5 minutes' walk. A40 1 mile.

Rubens at The Palace

★★★★★

39 Buckingham Palace Road, London, SW1W 0PS
Tel: 020 7834 6600 Fax: 020 7828 5401
Email: jraggett@rubens.redcarnationhotels.com
Web: www.redcarnationhotels.com
Rooms: 173 all ensuite
Room facilities: ⬜ ☎ ⬛ ✆ ❋ Access: ⬆
Children: Welcome ♈ ℭ Dogs: Welcome Licences: ⚏
Directions: 3 minutes walk from Victoria tube station.
From Gatwick Airport, take Gatwick Rail Express to
Victoria and then a short walk to the hotel.

Rydges Kensington Plaza

★★★★ ❣

61 Gloucester Road, Kensington, London, SW7 4PE
Tel: 020 7584 8100 Fax: 020 7823 9175
Email: rydges_kensington@rydges.com
Web: www.rydges.com
Rooms: 89 all ensuite
Pricing: Sgl £75–130 Dbl £108–170
Dinner from £12.50 CC: Accepted
Room facilities: ⬜ ☎ ⬛ ✆ Access: ⬆
Conference: 2 meeting rooms (Thtr 35 max),
24hr-delegate from £165, day-delegate rate from £40
Children: Welcome ♈
Licences: ⬥ ⚏
Directions: Two minutes walk from Gloucester Road
underground station, near the corner of Gloucester
Road and Cromwell Road.
See advert on this page

The Capital Hotel

★★★★ ❣ ❣ ❣ ❣

22 Basil Street, Knightsbridge, London, SW3 1AT
Tel: 020 7589 5171 Fax: 020 7225 0011
Email: reservations@capitalhotel.co.uk
Web: www.capitalhotel.co.uk

The Capital is unique, a jewel set in the heart of
Knightsbridge, each of its 48 air-conditioned suites and
bedrooms is individually designed, subtle luxuries and
supremely comfortable.
Rooms: 48 all ensuite
Pricing: Sgl £190 Dbl £245–375 Dinner from £54
CC: Accepted Room facilities: ⬜ ☎ ❋ Access: ⬆
Conference: 3 meeting rooms (Thtr 26 max),
24hr-delegate from £150, day-delegate rate from £77.50
Children: Welcome ℭ Dogs: Welcome Licences: ⚏
Parking: Off-street and monitored
Directions: Heading west along A4 turn left after
Harrods, into Brompton Place then left again and
straight on into Basil Street.

The Halkin

★★★★★ ℝ ℝ ℝ

Halkin Street, Belgravia, London, SW1X 7DJ
Tel: 020 7333 1000 Fax: 020 7333 1100
Email: res@halkin.co.uk
Web: www.halkin.co.uk

The Halkin continues to set the standard in contemporary luxury hotels. Great emphasis is placed upon guest comfort and the highest levels of personal yet unobtrusive service and cuisine are legendary.
Rooms: 41 all ensuite
Pricing: Sgl £346–528 Dbl £346–528 Dinner from £47
CC: Accepted Room facilities: 🖵 ☎ ✆ ❄
Access: ⑂
Children: Welcome ⃝
Dogs: Guide dogs only
Licences: ⦀
Directions: Located between Belgrave Square and Grosvenor Place. Access via Chapel Street into Headfort Place and left into Halkin Street.

The Montague

★★★★ ℝ

15 Montague Street, London, WC1B 5BJ
Tel: 020 7637 1001
Email: bookmt@rchmail.com
Web: www.redcarnationhotels.com

Intimate boutique townhouse hotel engendering feeling of fine country hotel. Regular live jazz entertainment and summer BBQs overlooking secluded private garden for an oasis of tranquility in central London.

Rooms: 104 all ensuite ♨ ✎ ⊘
Pricing: Sgl £175–228 Dbl £209–279
Dinner from £15.50 CC: Accepted
Room facilities: 🖵 ☎ ☕ ✆ ❄
Access: ⑂ ♿
Conference: 7 meeting rooms (Thtr 120 max), day-delegate rate from £65
Children: Welcome ⅄
Dogs: Welcome Licences: ◁ ⦀
Leisure: Gym
Directions: Located in Montague Street just off Russell Square, close to British Museum. 5 minutes' walk from Russell Square underground.

The Park Lane Hotel

★★★★ ℝ ℝ

Piccadilly, London, W1Y 8BX
Tel: 020 7499 6321 Fax: 020 7499 1965
Email: central.london.reservations@sheraton.com
Web: www.sheraton.com/parklane
Rooms: 307 all ensuite ✎ ⊘
Pricing: Dbl £220–396 Dinner from £19
CC: Accepted
Room facilities: 🖵 ☎ ✆ Access: ⑂ ♿
Conference: 11 meeting rooms (Thtr 500 max), day-delegate rate from £84
Children: Welcome ⅄
Dogs: Guide dogs only
Licences: ◁ ⦀
Parking: Monitored
Directions: Located on Piccadilly Avenue opposite Green Park, just one block from the Hard Rock Cafe. Nearest underground station, Green Park.

The Rembrandt

★★★★

11 Thurloe Place, Knightsbridge, London, SW7 2RS
Tel: 020 7589 8100 Fax: 020 7225 3476
Email: rembrandt@sarova.co.uk
Web: www.sarova.com
Rooms: 195 all ensuite ⊘
Pricing: Sgl £250 Dbl £250 Dinner from £17.95
CC: Accepted
Room facilities: 🖵 ☎ ☕ ✆
Access: ⑂
Conference: 14 meeting rooms (Thtr 200 max), 24hr-delegate from £230, day-delegate rate from £76
Children: Welcome ⅄ ⃝
Dogs: Guide dogs only
Licences: ◁ ⦀
Leisure: Indoor pool, Gym, Health spa, Beauty salon
Directions: Follow A4 (Cromwell Road) into Central London. The Rembrandt is opposite Victoria & Albert Museum. Nearest tube South Kensington.

Making a booking?

Don't forget to mention RAC Hotels and Bed & Breakfast 2003.

London

The Stafford

★★★★★ ☆ ☆ **Blue Ribbon Winner**

St James's Place, London, SW1A 1NJ
Tel: 020 7493 0111 Fax: 020 7493 7121
Email: info@thestaffordhotel.co.uk
Web: www.thestaffordhotel.co.uk

Charming, small, luxurious hotel with exquisite private dining rooms, including 350-year-old working cellars. Individually furnished rooms include the world-famous carriage house rooms. Offers outstanding service and traditional elegance.
Rooms: 81 all ensuite 🖥 Pricing: Sgl £275
CC: Accepted Room facilities: ☐ ☎ 📞 ❄ Access: ↕
Conference: 4 meeting rooms (Thtr 30 max)
Children: Welcome
Dogs: Guide dogs only
Licences: ◁ ♦♦♦

The Washington — Mayfair

★★★★

5 Curzon Street, London, W1J 5HE
Tel: 020 7499 7000 Fax: 020 7499 7030
Email: sales@washington-mayfair.co.uk
Web: www.washington-mayfair.co.uk.
Rooms: 171 all ensuite 🚭
Pricing: Sgl £247.95 Dbl £260.90 Dinner from £19.95
CC: Accepted
Room facilities: ☐ ☎ 📞 ❄
Access: ↕ ♿
Conference: 3 meeting rooms (Thtr 110 max),
24hr-delegate from £250, day-delegate rate from £57
Children: Welcome Dogs: Welcome
Licences: ♦♦♦
Leisure: Gym
Directions: Five minutes' walk from Green Park station. West along Piccadilly, right into Clarges Street; Curzon Street is at the end.

Ask the experts

To book a Hotel or Guest Accommodation, or for help and advice, call RAC Hotel Reservations on 0870 603 9109 and quote 'Guide 2003'

Westbury

★★★★★ ☆ ☆ ☆

Bond Street, Mayfair, London, W1S 2YF
Tel: 020 7629 7755 Fax: 020 7495 1163
Email: paul.liazbinski@westburymayfair.com
Web: www.westbury-london.co.uk
Rooms: 254 all ensuite 🚭
Pricing: Sgl £282 Dbl £310.50 Dinner from £19.50
CC: Accepted Room facilities: ☐ ☎ 📞 ❄
Access: ↕ ♿
Conference: 4 meeting rooms (Thtr 100 max),
day-delegate rate from £65
Children: Welcome ♖
Dogs: Welcome Licences: ♦♦♦
Leisure: Gym
Parking: Off-street and monitored
Directions: On Bond Street, Mayfair. Underground: Bond Street, Green Park, Oxford Circus, Piccadilly Circus.

Dorset Square Hotel

★★★★ Townhouse ☆ **Blue Ribbon Winner**

39 Dorset Square, London, NW1 6QN
Tel: 020 7723 7874 Fax: 020 7724 3328
Email: dorset@firmdale.com
Web: www.firmdale.com

Just like a grand country house in town. Located in Marylebone. Bond Street, Regent's Park. West End theatres and the City's business centre are all within easy reach.
Rooms: 38 all ensuite 🛏 🖥 🚭
Pricing: Sgl £129.15 Dbl £192.50–257.13
Dinner from £25 CC: Accepted
Room facilities: ☐ ☎ 📞 ❄ Access: ↕
Children: Welcome ♖ 🐴
Licences: ♦♦♦
Parking: Monitored
Directions: Nearest underground station is Baker Street, or proceed from M40 onto A40 (Euston Road). Take left-hand lane off flyover. Turn left on Gloucester Place. Dorset Square Hotel is 1st left.

Kensington House Hotel

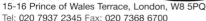

★★★★ Townhouse
15-16 Prince of Wales Terrace, London, W8 5PQ
Tel: 020 7937 2345 Fax: 020 7368 6700
Email: reservations@kenhouse.com
Web: www.kenhouse.com

Contemporary town house restored to its original 19th century elegance. Stylish, modern interiors. Rooms are light and airy with good facilities. The Tiger Bar offers anything from coffee to a three-course meal.
Rooms: 41 all ensuite ⊗ Pricing: Sgl £150–155
Dbl £175–195 Dinner from £8.95 CC: Accepted
Room facilities: ▢ ☎ ☐ ☍ Access: |↓↑
Children: Welcome ⍭ Dogs: Guide dogs only
Licences: ⵈ
Directions: Just off Kensington High Street, corner of Prince of Wales Terrace and Victoria Road, which is opposite Kensington Palace.

The Fox Club

★★★★ Townhouse
46 Clarges Street, Mayfair, London, W1Y 7PJ
Tel: 020 7495 3656 Fax: 020 7495 3656
Email: foxclub@clubhaus.com
Web: www.clubhaus.com
Rooms: 9 all ensuite Room facilities: ▢ ☎ ☍ ✳
Children: Welcome Dogs: Welcome Licences: ⵈ
Directions: From Green Park underground station, turn right towards Hyde Park. Take third street on right.

Mobile traffic information

Just dial 1740* from any mobile phone to get up-to-the-minute RAC traffic information on motorways and major A roads. Try it now! *Calls to 1740 cost up to 59p per minute. Check with your network.

The Lowndes Hotel

★★★★ Townhouse ⏣
21 Lowndes Street, London, SW1X 9ES
Tel: 020 7823 1234 Fax: 020 7235 1154
Email: contact@lowndeshotel.com
Web: www.lowndeshotel.com

The four-star deluxe Lowndes Hotel is located in the heart of Belgravia, home to many of the world's most exclusive shops. The hotel offers a total of 78 deluxe guestrooms and suites.
Rooms: 78 all ensuite ⊗
Pricing: Dinner from £27 CC: Accepted
Room facilities: ▢ ☎ ☍ ✳ Access: |↓↑
Children: Welcome ⍭ ⅋ Dogs: Guide dogs only
Licences: ⵈ Leisure: Outdoor swimming
Parking: Off-street and monitored
Directions: Nearest underground: Knightsbridge 5 minutes walk down Sloane street, turn left, enter Cadogan Place and left again onto Lowndes Street.

The Pelham Hotel

★★★★ Townhouse ⏣ ⏣
15 Cromwell Place, London, SW7 2LA
Tel: 020 7589 8288 Fax: 020 7584 8444
Email: pelham@firmdale.com
Web: www.firmdale.com

Steps away from South Kensington museums and underground, this luxury townhouse is managed in a traditional manner, offering the highest standards of comfort and service.
Rooms: 51 all ensuite ⅋ ⊗
Pricing: Sgl £193.75 Dbl £246.50–328.75
Dinner from £25 CC: Accepted
Room facilities: ▢ ☎ ☍ ✳ Access: |↓↑
Children: Welcome ⍭ ⍩ Licences: ⵈ
Directions: Opposite South Kensington tube station.

Basil Street Hotel

Situated in Knightsbridge – a few steps from Harrods, this 80-bedroom hotel offers a traditional style and service that draws people back time after time. Restaurant open every day.

Knightsbridge, London, SW3 1AH
Tel: 020 7581 3311 Fax: 020 7581 3693
Email: info@thebasil.com
Web: www.thebasil.com

Basil Street Hotel

★★★
Knightsbridge, London, SW3 1AH
Tel: 020 7581 3311 Fax: 020 7581 3693
Email: info@thebasil.com
Web: www.thebasil.com
Rooms: 80 all ensuite ♨ ⊛
Pricing: Sgl £177 Dbl £263 Dinner from £25
CC: Accepted Room facilities: ▢ ☎ ☏ Access: ⊥↑
Conference: 4 meeting rooms (Thtr 30 max),
24hr-delegate from £231, day-delegate rate from £55
Children: Welcome ⊼ Dogs: Welcome Licences: ♦♦♦
Parking: Monitored (cost £26)
Directions: One-minute walk from Knightsbridge
Underground Station. The hotel is located between
Harrods and Sloane Street.
See advert on this page

Bonnington in Bloomsbury

★★★
92 Southampton Row, London, WC1B 4BH
Tel: 020 7242 2828 Fax: 020 7831 9170
Email: sales@bonnington.com
Web: www.bonnington.com

Recently refurbished, independent hotel, ideally situated for London's major attractions. Offers a warm welcome to all guests. 'Waterfalls' restaurant. 'Malt' bar and extensive conference facilities.
Rooms: 243 all ensuite ♨ ⊛
Pricing: Sgl £82–180 Dbl £99–180 Dinner from £20.75
CC: Accepted Room facilities: ▢ ☎ ☏ ☏ ❄
Access: ⊥↑ ♿
Conference: 11 meeting rooms (Thtr 250 max),
24hr-delegate from £140, day-delegate rate from £36
Children: Welcome ⊼ Dogs: Guide dogs only
Licences: ♦♦♦
Directions: M40 Euston Road, opposite station. Turn south into Upper Woburn Place, past Russell Square into Southampton Row. Bonnington on left.

Hogarth

★★★
Hogarth Road, Kensington, London, SW5 0QQ
Tel: 020 7370 6831 Fax: 020 7373 6179
Email: hogarth@marstonhotels.com
Web: www.marstonhotels.com

Located in residential road within Royal Borough of Kensington, air-conditioned executive rooms available. The terrace bistro/bar offering full all-day service, conveniently located for Earls Court and Olympia exhibition centres.
Rooms: 86 all ensuite ♨ ⊛
Pricing: Sgl £115 Dbl £149 Dinner from £20
CC: Accepted Room facilities: ▢ ☎ ☏ ☏ Access: ⊥↑
Conference: 5 meeting rooms (Thtr 50 max),
24hr-delegate from £140, day-delegate rate from £54.50
Children: Welcome ⊼ ☕ Dogs: Guide dogs only
Licences: ♦♦♦ Parking: Off-street and monitored
Directions: Two-minute walk from Earl's Court Underground Station.

Jurys Inn London
★★★
60 Pentonville Road, Islington, London, N1 9LA
Tel: +353(0)1 6070000 Fax: +353(0)1 6316999
Email: bookings@jurysdoyle.com
Web: www.jurysdoyle.com

JURYS DOYLE
HOTELS

Rooms: 229 all ensuite 🍴 🕾
Pricing: Sgl £99 Dbl £99 Dinner from £17
CC: Accepted Room facilities: 🖵 🕾 🗇 📞 ❄
Access: |↓↑ ᕕ Children: Welcome 🍴
Dogs: Guide dogs only Licences: 👫
Directions: Located 25 miles from London Heathrow
Airport. London City 15 miles. Euston Mainline 15 mins
walk and Angel tube 3 mins walk.

Mandeville Hotel
★★★
Mandeville Place, London, W1H 2BE
Tel: 020 7935 5599 Fax: 020 7935 9588
Email: info@mandeville.co.uk
Web: www.mandeville.co.uk
Rooms: 166 all ensuite 🕾
Pricing: Sgl £137–160 Dbl £180–200 Dinner from £19
CC: Accepted Room facilities: 🖵 🕾 🗇 📞 Access: |↓↑
Conference: Meeting rooms (Thtr 35 max)
Children: Welcome Dogs: Guide dogs only
Licences: 👫

Paragon Hotel
★★★
47 Lillie Road, London, SW6 1UD
Tel: 020 7610 0880 Fax: 020 7381 4450
Email: sales.london@paragonhotel.net
Web: www.paragonhotel.net

Ideal for Earls Court events, convenient for Olympia,
quick transport to the West End, with bright, well-
equipped bedrooms, many offering panoramic views,
two restaurants, extensive conference facilities and
secure underground car parking.
Rooms: 502 all ensuite 🕾
Pricing: Sgl £149.95–152.95 Dbl £164.95–167.95
Dinner from £14.50 CC: Accepted
Room facilities: 🖵 🕾 🗇 📞 Access: |↓↑ ᕕ
Conference: 6 meeting rooms (Thtr 1500 max),

24hr-delegate from £160, day-delegate rate from £60
Children: Welcome 🍴 Dogs: Guide dogs only
Licences: ◁ 👫 Parking: Off-street and monitored
Directions: Opposite Earl's Court Exhibition Centre
between Warwick Road and North End Road, close to
West Brompton and Earl's Court tube stations.

Quality Hotel Westminster
★★★
82-83 Eccleston Square, London, SW1V 1PS
Tel: 020 7834 8042 Fax: 020 7630 8942
Email: admin@gb614.u-net.com
Web: www.choicehotels.com
Rooms: 107 all ensuite 🍴 🗃 🕾
Pricing: Dinner from £14.95
CC: Accepted
Room facilities: 🖵 🕾 🗇 📞
Access: |↓↑
Conference: 5 meeting rooms (Thtr 120 max),
24hr-delegate from £145, day-delegate rate from £43
Children: Welcome 🍴 ⚡ Dogs: Welcome
Licences: 👫
Directions: Situated close to Victoria rail, coach and
tube stations.

Strand Palace Hotel
★★★
372 The Strand, London, WC2R 0JJ
Tel: 0870 400 8702 Fax: 020 7936 2077
Email: reservations@strandpalacehotel.co.uk
Web: www.strandpalacehotel.co.uk
Rooms: 785 all ensuite 🕾
Pricing: Sgl £69–160
Dbl £138–200 Dinner from £10.95
CC: Accepted
Room facilities: 🖵 🕾 🗇 📞
Access: |↓↑
Conference: 7 meeting rooms (Thtr 200 max),
24hr-delegate from £195, day-delegate rate from £63
Children: Welcome 🍴
Licences: 👫
Directions: Situated on the Strand in the heart of
theatreland. 5 minutes walk from Charing Cross or
Covent Garden stations.

The Blakemore Hotel
★★★
30 Leinster Gardens, London, W2 3AN
Tel: 020 7262 4591 Fax: 020 7724 1472

The Gresham Hyde Park

★★★

66 Lancaster Gate, London, W2 3NZ
Tel: 020 726 25090 Fax: 020 772 31244
Email: info@gresham-hydeparkhotel.com
Web: www.gresham-hotels.com

GRESHAM HOTELS

Recently refurbished hotel with restaurant, bar and fitness suite.
Rooms: 188 all ensuite ⊗ Pricing: Sgl £85 Dbl £85
Dinner from £17.25 CC: Accepted
Room facilities: ▢ ☎ ⊗ ✆ ❄ Access: |↓↑
Conference: 1 meeting rooms (Thtr 35 max), 24hr-delegate from £170, day-delegate rate from £40
Children: Welcome Dogs: Guide dogs only Licences: ♦♦♦
Leisure: Gym
Directions: Located on Lancaster Gate off Bayswater Road, 1 mile from Marble Arch in between Lancaster Gate Station and Queensway Station (Central line).

Clarendon Hotel

★★

8-16 Montpelier Row, Blackheath, London, SE3 0RW
Tel: 020 8318 4321 Fax: 020 8318 4378
Email: relax@clarendonhotel.com
Web: www.clarendonhotel.com
Rooms: 183 all ensuite ✍ ✇ ⊗
Pricing: Dinner from £17.50 CC: Accepted
Room facilities: ▢ ☎ ⊗ Access: |↓↑ ⟺
Children: Welcome ♌ Dogs: Welcome
Licences: ◇ ♦♦♦ Leisure: Games room
Parking: Off-street and monitored
Directions: Situated just off the A2 on Blackheath. Close to major motorways (M2/M25/A20) — M25 junctions 2 and 3.
See advert on facing page

Comfort Inn Kensington

★★

22/32 West Cromwell Road, Kensington, London, SW5 9QJ
Tel: 020 7373 3300 Fax: 020 7835 2040
Email: admin@gb043.u-net.com
Web: www.choicehotels.com
Rooms: 125 all ensuite ⊗ Pricing:
Dinner from £14.95 CC: Accepted
Room facilities: ▢ ☎ ⊗ ✆ ❄ Access: |↓↑
Conference: 1 meeting rooms (Thtr 70 max), 24hr-delegate from £139.50, day-delegate rate from £40
Children: Welcome ♌ Licences: ♦♦♦
Directions: Located on West Cromwell Road. Continuation of A4(M) main arterial road into London from West.

Garth Hotel

★★

64-76 Hendon Way, Cricklewood, London, NW2 2NL
Tel: 020 8209 1511 Fax: 020 8455 4744
Email: enquiry@garthhotel.co.uk
Web: www.garth-hotel.co.uk
Rooms: 57 all ensuite ✍ ⊗
Pricing: Sgl £55–75 Dbl £70–90 Dinner from £13.50
CC: Accepted Room facilities: ▢ ☎ ⊗
Conference: 2 meeting rooms (Thtr 350 max)
Children: Welcome ♌ Licences: ♦♦♦ Parking: Off-street
Directions: Hotel is located on southbound carriageway of the A41 Hendon way, between Vale and Cricklewood junctions.

Regents Park Hotel

★★

154-156 Gloucester Place, Marylebone, London, NW1 6DT
Tel: 020 7258 1911 Fax: 020 7258 0288
Email: rph-reservation@usa.net
Web: www.regentsparkhotel.com
Rooms: 29 all ensuite ✍ Pricing: Dinner from £10
CC: Accepted Room facilities: ▢ ☎ ⊗ ✆ Children:
Welcome Dogs: Guide dogs only Licences: ♦♦♦
Directions: Out of Baker Street undergound main exit turn right, right again at petrol station, straight down past Dorset Square.

Knightsbridge Hotel

✦

10 Beaufort Gardens, London, SW3 1PT
Tel: 020 7584 6300 Fax: 020 7584 6355
Email: knightsbridge@firmdale.com
Web: www.firmdalehotels.com
Rooms: 44 all ensuite Pricing: Sgl £158.63–170.37
Dbl £182.13–287.88 CC: Accepted
Room facilities: ▢ ☎ ✆ ❄ Access: |↓↑
Children: Welcome Dogs: Guide dogs only Licences: ♦♦♦
Directions: Beaufort Gardens is just off Brompton Road, in between Harrods and Beauchamp Place.

The CLARENDON HOTEL

BLACKHEATH, LONDON

Conference & Banqueting

Restaurant

Honeymoon Suite

Parkes Hotel Limited

41 Beaufort Gardens, Knightsbridge, London, SW3 1PW
Tel: 020 7581 9944 Fax: 020 7581 1999
Email: info@parkeshotel.com
Web: www.parkeshotel.com

Fully refurbished and situated in a quiet tree lined cul-de-sac 100 metres from Harrods. Parkes Hotel provides modern business facilities including wireless ADSL with luxurious, comfortable surroundings and marble bathrooms.
Rooms: 33 all ensuite
Pricing: Sgl £235 Dbl £294
CC: Accepted
Room facilities: ☐ ☎ 🔌 ❄ Access: ↓↑
Children: Welcome Dogs: Guide dogs only
Licences: ♦♦♦
Directions: Off Brompton Road, Knightsbridge, 100 metres from Harrods.

Four Seasons Hotel

173 Gloucester Place, Regent's Park,
London, NW1 6DX
Tel: 020 7724 3461 Fax: 020 7402 5594
Email: fourseasons@dial.pipex.com
Web: www.4seasonshotel.co.uk
Rooms: 28 all ensuite ♨ ⊗
Pricing: Sgl £95–105 Dbl £115–125 CC: Accepted
Room facilities: ☐ ☎ 🔌 Children: Welcome

St George Hotel

49 Gloucester Place, London, W1U 8JE
Tel: 020 7486 8586 Fax: 020 7486 6567
Email: reservations@stgeorge-hotel.net
Web: www.stgeorge-hotel.net
Rooms: 19 all ensuite ♨ ⊗
Pricing: Sgl £85–95 Dbl £125–140 CC: Accepted
Room facilities: ☐ ☎ ⊙
Children: Welcome, 4yrs min age Dogs: Guide dogs only
Directions: A short walk from Oxford Street and Baker Street. Nearest tube is Marble Arch.

The Claverley Hotel

13-14 Beaufort Gardens, Knightsbridge, London, SW3 1PS
Tel: 020 7589 8541 Fax: 020 7584 3410
Email: reservations@claverleyhotel.co.uk
Web: www.claverleyhotel.co.uk

An intimate, elegant designer-hotel located on a quiet tree-lined cul-de-sac in prestigious Knightsbridge, a two-minute stroll from Harrods. All room rates include full English breakfast and VAT.
Rooms: 30 (27 ensuite) 🛏 ⊗ Pricing: Sgl £85–120 Dbl £120–200 CC: Accepted Room facilities: ☐ ☎
Access: ↓↑ ♿ Children: Welcome Dogs: Guide dogs only
Directions: Exit Knightsbridge tube at Brompton Road. Third street on the left past Harrods.

Windermere Hotel

142-144 Warwick Way, Victoria, London, SW1V 4JE
Tel: 020 7834 5163 Fax: 020 7630 8831
Email: windermere@compuserve.com
Web: www.windermere-hotel.co.uk

An intimate, boutique hotel renowned for its friendly and personalised service. Well-equipped and individually-designed bedrooms. English breakfast and dinner are served in the elegant licensed restaurant. Parking available.
Rooms: 22 (20 ensuite) ♨ ⊗ Pricing: Sgl £69–96 Dbl £89–139 CC: Accepted
Room facilities: ☐ ☎ ⊙ 🔌 Children: Welcome ⊼
Licences: ♦♦♦ Parking: Monitored
Directions: Turn left opposite Victoria coach station, take first right into Hugh Street. Proceed along to Alderney Street. Hotel is directly opposite on corner of Alderney Street and Warwick Way.

Anchor Hotel

◆ ◆ ◆

10 West Heath Drive, London, NW11 7QH
Tel: 020 8458 8764 Fax: 020 8455 3204
Email: res@anchor-hotel.co.uk
Web: www.anchor-hotel.co.uk
Rooms: 11 (8 ensuite) 🐾 ⊗
Pricing: Sgl £39–57 Dbl £49–76 CC: Accepted
Room facilities: ▯ ☎ ⊗ 🔌 Access: ♿
Children: Welcome Parking: Off-street
Directions: One-minute walk from Golders Green tube
station, or by car take North Circular Road (A406)
onto A598 Finchley Road. At tube turn left, then take
first right.

Averard Hotel

◆ ◆ ◆

10 Lancaster Gate, Hyde Park, London, W2 3LH
Tel: 020 7723 8877 Fax: 020 7706 0860
Email: sales@averard.com
Web: www.averard.com

Rooms: 52 all ensuite
Pricing: Sgl £55–70 Dbl £75–95 CC: Accepted
Room facilities: ▯ ☎ Access: ⌊↑ Children: Welcome
Dogs: Welcome Licences: ▮▮▮
Directions: From Lancaster Gate underground station,
turn right onto Bayswater Road, cross main traffic
lights. After Swan Pub, turn right to Lancaster Gate.

Central Hotel

◆ ◆ ◆

35 Hoop Lane, Golders Green, London, NW11 8BS
Tel: 020 8458 5636 Fax: 020 8455 4792
Rooms: 30 all ensuite Pricing: Sgl £50–60 Dbl £70–80
CC: Accepted Room facilities: ▯ ☎ Access: ♿
Children: Welcome Parking: Off-street
Directions: From M1, take North Circular Road East,
turn right onto A598. After 1 mile, turn into Hoop Lane
at Golders Green.

Comfort Inn Kings Cross

◆ ◆ ◆

2-5 St Chad's Street, London, WC1H 8BD
Tel: 020 7837 1940 Fax: 020 7278 5033
Email: annie@midhot.demon.co.uk
Web: www.comfortinnkingscross.co.uk
Rooms: 53 all ensuite ⊗ Pricing: Sgl £80–90
Dbl £90–93 CC: Accepted Room facilities: ▯ ☎ ⊗ 🔌
Access: ⌊↑ Children: Welcome Dogs: Guide dogs only
Directions: Kings Cross Station go to street level,
McDonalds on right, walk up Grays Inn Road, take 3rd
turning on right into St Chad's Street.

Comfort Inn Vauxhall

◆ ◆ ◆

87 South Lambeth, Vauxhall, London, SW8 1RN
Tel: 020 7735 9494 Fax: 020 7735 1001
See advert on next page

Craven Gardens Hotel

◆ ◆ ◆

16 Leinster Terrace, London, W2 3ES
Tel: 020 7262 3167 Fax: 020 7262 2083
Email: craven@dircon.co.uk
Rooms: 43 all ensuite 🐾 Pricing: Sgl £50–70
Dbl £75–85 CC: Accepted Room facilities: ▯ ☎ ⊗
Access: ⌊↑ ♿ Children: Welcome, 13yrs min age
Licences: ▮▮▮
Directions: Underground, Lancaster Gate/Queensway
(Central Line), Bayswater (Circle/District Line). British
Rail: Paddington, Heathrow Express from Heathrow to
Paddington.
See advert on next page

Georgian Hotel

◆ ◆ ◆

87 Gloucester Place, London, W1U 6JF
Tel: 020 7486 3151 Fax: 020 7486 7535
Email: info@georgian-hotel.demon.co.uk
Web: www.londoncentralhotel.com
Rooms: 19 all ensuite 🐾
Pricing: Sgl £70–75 Dbl £85–90
CC: Accepted
Room facilities: ▯ ☎ ⊗
Access: ⌊↑
Children: Welcome, 5yrs min age
Directions: Close to Baker Street Tube and Paddington
Station.

London

Grove Hill Hotel

◆ ◆ ◆

38 Grove Hill, South Woodford, London, E18 2JG
Tel: 020 8989 3344 Fax: 020 8530 5286
Rooms: 23 (12 ensuite) 🍵
Pricing: Sgl £33–45 Dbl £53–61 CC: Accepted
Room facilities: 🖵 ☕ Access: ♿
Children: Welcome 🍴 Dogs: Welcome
Licences: ♙♙♙
Parking: Off-street and monitored
Directions: Off A11 London Road. By tube, to South
Woodford, walk up George Lane, turn left at George
Pub, second right. London City Airport, 7 miles,
London 30 min by tube.

Hart House Hotel

◆ ◆ ◆

51 Gloucester Place, London, W1H 3PE
Tel: 020 7935 2288 Fax: 020 7935 8516
Email: reservations@harthouse.co.uk
Web: www.harthouse.co.uk

A highly recommended, clean and comfortable hotel
run by the Bowden family for the last 32 years. It is in
the heart of London's West End just off Oxford Street.
Ideal for all tourist attractions.
Rooms: 15 all ensuite 🍵
Pricing: Dbl £105 CC: Accepted
Room facilities: 🖵 ☎ ☕ Children: Welcome ☕
Directions: Just off Oxford Street, behind Selfridges.
Close to Marble Arch and Baker Street underground
stations.

Henley House

◆ ◆ ◆

30 Barkston Gardens, Earls Court, London, SW5 0EN
Tel: 020 7370 4111 Fax: 020 7370 0026
Email: reservations@henleyhousehotel.com
Web: www.henleyhousehotel.com

Henley House is a small but very charming
boutique-style hotel. The cosy and comfortable
rooms are rich in decor and style with much
attention paid to detail.
Rooms: 20 all ensuite
Pricing: Sgl £60–73 Dbl £75–92
CC: Accepted
Room facilities: 🖵 ☎ ☕ Access: ↕️
Children: Welcome
Dogs: Guide dogs only Parking: Off-street
Directions: From A4 turn down Earl's Court Road
(A3220). Barkston Gardens is 2nd left after tube station.

La Gaffe

◆ ◆ ◆

107-111 Heath Street, Hampstead, London, NW3 6SS
Tel: 020 7435 8965 Fax: 020 7794 7592
Email: la-gaffe@msn.com
Web: www.lagaffe.co.uk
Rooms: 18 all ensuite 🍵 ⊘ ⊘
Pricing: Sgl £65–100 Dbl £90–125
Dinner from £10
CC: Accepted Room facilities: 🖵 ☎ ☕
Children: Welcome
Licences: ♙♙♙
Directions: Hotel 3 minutes from Hampstead
underground, three miles from Kings Cross and 18
miles from Heathrow.
See advert on previous page

Langorf Hotel and Apartments

◆ ◆ ◆

20 Frognal, Hampstead, London, NW3 6AG
Tel: 020 7794 4483 Fax: 020 7435 9055
Email: langorf@aol.com
Web: www.langorfhotel.com

Rooms: 36 all ensuite 🍵
Pricing: Sgl £82–90 Dbl £98–110 CC: Accepted
Room facilities: 🖵 ☎ ☕ ⚿ Access: ↕️
Children: Welcome
Directions: 3 miles north of Oxford Street. 3 miles
south of M1 Junction 1. Off the A41 Finchley Road.

London

Mitre House Hotel

◆ ◆ ◆

178-184 Sussex Gardens, Hyde Park, London, W2 1TU
Tel: 020 7723 8040 Fax: 020 7402 0990
Email: reservations@mitrehousehotel.com
Web: www.mitrehousehotel.com

Rooms: 70 all ensuite ♨ Ⓢ
Pricing: Sgl £70 Dbl £80 CC: Accepted
Room facilities: ☐ ☎ Access: ⌊↥ ♿
Children: Welcome ⁛ Licences: ♦♦♦
Parking: Off-street and monitored
Directions: One block north of Hyde Park, Paddington Station and buses to major sights. Heathrow Express to airport in 15 mins is also one block away.
See advert on previous page

New England Hotel

◆ ◆ ◆

20 St George's Drive, Victoria, London, SW1V 4BN
Tel: 020 7834 1595 Fax: 020 7834 9000
Email: racstay@newenglandhotel.com
Web: www.newenglandhotel.com

Privately owned hotel renowned for its blend of warm, friendly hospitality and high standards in a fantastic London location. It boasts an enviably high level of repeat business and pleasure clientele. Close to all major attractions.
Rooms: 25 all ensuite ♨ Ⓢ
Pricing: Sgl £55–65 Dbl £69–89 CC: Accepted
Room facilities: ☐ ☎ ⌕ Access: ⌊↥ Children: Welcome
Directions: From Victoria Station go onto Wilton Road and turn right at the Warwick Way junction. Straight then second left onto St George's Drive and the New England is on your left. See map on website.
See advert on this page

London

Sidney Hotel
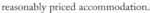
LONDON-VICTORIA

68/76 Belgrave Road • Victoria • London • SW1V 2BP • Website: www.sidneyhotel.com
Telephone: +44 (020) 7834 2738   Facsimile:+44 (020) 7630 0973
Electronic Mail: reservations@sidneyhotel.com

Formed from the amalgamation of five, six storey townhouses, an Elegant Georgian structure is a favourite haunt of tourists from both home & abroad & a preferred base for business men & women with reasonably priced accommodation.

LONDON

Within a small radius of the Hotel, historical landmarks such as Big Ben & The Houses of Parliament jostle with modern day celebrated attractions whilst the theatre district of the 'West End' is just a short distance.

For those who wish to enjoy a diverse range of shops, the renowned districts of Oxford Circus, Bond Street & Kensington with their fashionable store, and boutiques are only minutes away. And Victoria Coach, Rail/Underground Station(s) a short walk from the hotel, getting around the capital couldn't be easier

82 comfortable ensuite bedrooms with modern amenities.
Complimentary hospitality tray.
Satellite television.
Two passenger lifts.
Safe deposit facilities.
A hearty English buffet breakfast.
Enticing array of restaurants in nearby streets.

Park Lodge Hotel

◆ ◆ ◆

73 Queensborough Terrace, Bayswater, London, W2 3SU
Tel: 020 7229 6424 Fax: 020 7221 4772
Email: info@hotelparklodge.com
Web: www.hotelparklodge.com
Rooms: 29 all ensuite
Pricing: Sgl £50–70 Dbl £65–85 CC: Accepted
Room facilities: Access: |↓↑

Sidney Hotel

◆ ◆ ◆

68/76 Belgrave Road, Victoria, London, SW1V 2BP
Tel: 020 7834 2738 Fax: 020 7630 0973
Email: reservations@sidneyhotel.com
Web: www.sidneyhotel.com
Rooms: 82 all ensuite 🛏 ⓢ
Pricing: Sgl £76 Dbl £97 CC: Accepted
Room facilities: Access: |↓↑ ♿
Children: Welcome Licences: ♦♦♦
Directions: Centrally situated near Victoria Station, from station take Wilton Road, go straight to third traffic lights, turn left, hotel situated on your right.
See advert on this page

Swiss Cottage Hotel

◆ ◆ ◆

4 Adamson Road, Swiss Cottage, London, NW3 3HP
Tel: 020 7722 2281 Fax: 020 7483 4588
Email: reservations@swisscottagehotel.co.uk
Web: www.swisscottagehotel.co.uk

Our Victorian townhouse is one minute from the tube station and ten minutes from the West End. Each bedroom is individual and most are furnished with period paintings and antiques. All have modern amenities, room service available 24 hours.
Rooms: 59 all ensuite 🛏 ⓢ Pricing: Sgl £65–95
Dbl £65–115 CC: Accepted Room facilities:
Access: |↓↑ Conference: 4 meeting rooms (Thtr 35 max), 24hr-delegate from £150, day-delegate rate from £45
Children: Welcome Dogs: Guide dogs only
Licences: ♦♦♦ Parking: Off-street
Directions: From Swiss Cottage underground leave at exit 2 and walk straight ahead; hotel is one minute's walk.

Swiss House Hotel

◆ ◆ ◆

171 Old Brompton Road, South Kensington,
London, SW5 0AN
Tel: 020 7373 2769 Fax: 020 7373 4983
Email: recep@swiss-hh.demon.co.uk
Web: www.swiss-hh.demon.co.uk

"Excellent value for money" has always been our
motto. This hotel knows guests' priorities and aims to
meet them all. Clean and friendly atmosphere.
Rooms: 15 (14 ensuite) ☕ ⊛
Pricing: Sgl £53–74 Dbl £93–109 CC: Accepted
Room facilities: ☐ ☎ ⒮ Children: Welcome ⟦
Directions: From M4 turn right into Earls Court Road.
Down the road, turn left onto Old Brompton Road and
hotel is situated after the first set of lights on the right
hand side.

The Diplomat Hotel

◆ ◆ ◆

2 Chesham Street, Belgravia, London, SW1X 8DT
Tel: 020 7235 1544 Fax: 020 7259 6153
Email: diplomat.hotel@btinternet.com
Web: www.btinternet.com/~diplomat.hotel

The Diplomat is situated in Belgravia, the most
exclusive and sought-after neighbourhood in London.
It is within easy walking distance of Harrods and the
fashionable Knightsbridge and Chelsea shops.

Rooms: 26 all ensuite ☕
Pricing: Sgl £95–98 Dbl £130–175 Dinner from £6
CC: Accepted Room facilities: ☐ ☎ ⒮
Access: ⼪ ⛮
Children: Welcome ⼬ ⟦ Licences: ⼀
Parking: Monitored
Directions: Victoria, Knightsbridge and Sloane Square
underground stations all within 10 minutes walk.

The Victoria Inn

◆ ◆ ◆

65-67 Belgrave Road, Victoria, London, SW1V 2BG
Tel: 020 7834 0182 Fax: 020 7931 0201
Email: info@victoriainn.co.uk
Web: www.victoriainn.co.uk
Rooms: 43 all ensuite ☕ Room facilities: ☐ ☎ ⒮
Access: ⼪ Children: Welcome
Directions: From Victoria Station, take Wilton Road, turn
left into Belgrave Road; hotel is on the left after 500m.

White Lodge Hotel

◆ ◆ ◆

1 Church Lane, Hornsey, London, N8 7BU
Tel: 020 8348 9765 Fax: 020 8340 7851
Rooms: 16 (8 ensuite) ☕
Pricing: Sgl £30–32 Dbl £40–48 CC: Accepted
Room facilities: ☐ ⒮ Children: Welcome ⟦
Dogs: Guide dogs only
Directions: A406 follow sign to Bounds Green then
Hornsey Hish Road and Church Lane off Tottenham
Lane, N8.

Winchester Hotel

◆ ◆ ◆

17 Belgrave Road, London, SW1V 1RB
Tel: 020 7828 2972 Fax: 020 7828 5191
Web: www.winchester-hotel.net
Rooms: 18 all ensuite ☕ ⊛ Pricing:8585
Room facilities: ☐ Children: Welcome, 4yrs min age
Dogs: Guide dogs only
Directions: Victoria Street, a few mins walk Gatwick
Airport to Victoria Street.

Abbey Lodge Hotel

◆ ◆

51 Grange Park, Ealing, London, W5 3PR
Tel: 020 8567 7914 Fax: 020 8579 5350
Email: enquiries@londonlodgehotels.com
Web: www.londonlodgehotels.com
Seasonclosure: Christmas/New Year
Rooms: 16 all ensuite ☕
Pricing: Sgl £45–49 Dbl £57–62 CC: Accepted
Room facilities: ☐ ⒮ Access: ⛮
Children: Welcome ⟦ Dogs: Welcome
Directions: From M4 junction 2, A406 to second set of
lights. Turn left into A4020, following Ealing Common
to end, turn left, third right into Grange Park.

Ashley Hotel

◆ ◆

15 Norfolk Square, Paddington, London, W2 1RU
Tel: 020 7723 3375 Fax: 020 7723 0173
Email: ashhot@btinternet.com
Web: www.ashleyhotels.com
Rooms: 53 (43 ensuite) 🍴
Pricing: Sgl £36.50–50 Dbl £75–77 CC: Accepted
Room facilities: 🖵 ☎ 🍵 Children: Welcome
Dogs: Guide dogs only
Directions: Use Paddington Station as your landmark: hotel is a 2-minute walk away.

Barry House Hotel

◆ ◆

12 Sussex Place, Hyde Park, London, W2 2TP
Tel: 020 7723 7340 Fax: 020 7723 9775
Email: hotel@barryhouse.co.uk
Web: www.barryhouse.co.uk

Providing family-like care. Friendly, comfortable B&B with ensuite bedrooms. English breakfast included in competitive rates. Central location close to Paddington Station.
Rooms: 18 (15 ensuite) 🍴 ⊗
Pricing: Sgl £38–45 Dbl £75–85 CC: Accepted
Room facilities: 🖵 ☎ 🍵 🔌 Children: Welcome
Directions: Come out of Paddington Station, walk into London Street to the traffic lights. Cross over into Sussex Place.

Carlton Hotel

◆ ◆

90 Belgrave Road, Victoria, London, SW1V 2BJ
Tel: 020 7976 6634 Fax: 020 7821 8020
Email: info@cityhotelcarlton.co.uk
Web: www.cityhotelcarlton.co.uk
Rooms: 18 all ensuite 🍴 📺 ⊗
Pricing: Sgl £49–59 Dbl £59–69 CC: Accepted
Room facilities: 🖵 ☎ 🍵 🔌 Children: Welcome
Parking: Off-street and monitored
Directions: From Victoria Station take Wilton Road, turn left into Belgrave Road; hotel is about 500m on the right, 8 minutes walk from Victoria Station.

Comfort Inn Earls Court

◆ ◆

11-13 Penywern Road, London, SW5 9TT
Tel: 020 7373 6514 Fax: 020 7370 3639
Email: info@comfortinnearlscourt.co.uk
Web: www.comfortinnearlscourt.co.uk
Rooms: 53 all ensuite ⊗
Pricing: Sgl £69–69 Dbl £95–95 CC: Accepted
Room facilities: 🖵 ☎ 🍵
Children: Welcome, 16yrs min age Dogs: Welcome

Edward Lear Hotel

◆ ◆

30 Seymour Street, Marble Arch, London, W1H 5WD
Tel: 020 7402 5401 Fax: 020 7706 3766
Email: edwardlear@aol.com
Web: www.edlear.com
Rooms: 34 (4 ensuite) 🍴 ⊗
Pricing: Sgl £49–65 Dbl £69.50–93 CC: Accepted
Access: ♿ Children: Welcome

Hamilton House Hotel

◆ ◆

60 Warwick Way, Victoria, London, SW1V 1SA
Tel: 020 7821 7113 Fax: 020 7630 0806
Email: info@hamiltonhousehotel.com
Web: www.hamiltonhousehotel.com
Rooms: 40 (32 ensuite)
Pricing: Sgl £40–69 Dbl £55–85 CC: Accepted
Room facilities: 🖵 ☎ 🍵 🔌
Children: Welcome Dogs: Guide dogs only
Directions: The hotel is situated about five minutes walk, at the back of Victoria Station, around the corner from Belgrave Road.

Hotel Orlando

◆ ◆

83 Shepherds Bush Road, London, W6 7LR
Tel: 020 7603 4890 Fax: 020 7603 4890
Email: hotelorlando@btconnect.com
Web: www.hotelorlando.co.uk

A family-run business of 22 years, this privately-owned 14-room hotel in a Victorian terrace is within easy walking distance of Hammersmith Underground Station, ideal for easy connection to central London and Heathrow Airport.
Rooms: 14 all ensuite
Pricing: Sgl £40–45 Dbl £52–58 CC: Accepted
Room facilities: Children: Welcome
Directions: Situated between Hammersmith Underground Station and Shepherds Bush Underground Station. 5 minutes walk either way.

Lincoln House Hotel
◆ ◆

33 Gloucester Place, Marble Arch, London, W1U 8HY
Tel: 020 7486 7630/0500 007 208 Fax: 020 7486 0166
Email: reservations@lincoln-house-hotel.co.uk
Web: www.lincoln-house-hotel.co.uk

Georgian B&B hotel in London, with modern comforts and ensuite rooms. Close to Oxford Street shopping, theatreland and nightlife. Recommended by famous guide books.
Freephone (UK only) 0500 007 208
Rooms: 23 all ensuite
Pricing: Sgl £59–75 Dbl £69–79 CC: Accepted
Room facilities: Access:
Children: Welcome Dogs: Guide dogs only
Directions: Out of Marble Arch Station, turn left, then second turning on the left into Portman Street. The continuation is Gloucester Place.

Need help booking?

RAC Hotel Reservations will find the accommodation that's right for you – and book it too. Call today on 0870 603 9109 and quote 'Guide 2003'

Ask the experts
To book a Hotel or Guest Accommodation, or for help and advice, call RAC Hotel Reservations on 0870 603 9109 and quote 'Guide 2003'

Merlyn Court Hotel
◆ ◆

2 Barkston Gardens, London, SW5 0EN
Tel: 020 7370 1640 Fax: 020 7370 4986
Email: london@merlyncourt.demon.co.uk
Web: www.merlyncourthotel.com

Comfortable, good value, family-run hotel in a central location off a quiet Edwardian square in Kensington. Bright and airy rooms, some with 3 or 4 beds. Easy access to Olympia and Earl's Court exhibition halls, train stations and motorways. Non-smoking environment.
Rooms: 17 (11 ensuite)
Pricing: Sgl £30–45 Dbl £55–75 CC: Accepted
Room facilities: Children: Welcome Dogs: Welcome
Directions: In Kensington, central London, links to airport, M4, M40, M1, M3 and nearest tube is Earl's Court.

Parkwood Hotel
◆ ◆

4 Stanhope Place, London, W2 2HB
Tel: 020 7402 2241 Fax: 020 7402 1574
Email: prkwd@aol.com
Web: www.parkwoodhotel.com
Rooms: 14 (12 ensuite)
Room facilities: Children: Welcome
Directions: Marble Arch nearest tube station.

Ramsees Hotel
◆ ◆

32-36 Hogarth Road, Earl's Court, London, SW5 0PU
Tel: 020 7370 1445 Fax: 020 7244 6835
Email: ramsees@rasool.demon.co.uk
Web: www.ramseeshotel.com
A family-run hotel with 67 bedrooms, ideally located in fashionable Kensington area. Only a minute's walk from Earl's Court and just a few minutes from all tourist attractions by underground.
Rooms: 67 (56 ensuite) Pricing: Sgl £35–45 Dbl £48–55
CC: Accepted Room facilities: Access:
Children: Welcome
Directions: From A4, turn down Earl's Court Road. At Lloyd's Bank on left, turn down Hogarth Road.

Rasool Court Hotel

 ◆◆

19/21 Penywern Road, Earls Court, London, SW5 9TT
Tel: 020 7373 8900 Fax: 020 7244 6835
Email: rasool@rasool.demon.co.uk
Web: www.rasoolcourthotel.com
A family-run hotel with 57 bedrooms, ideally located in
fashionable Kensington area. Only a minute's walk
from Earl's Court and just a few minutes from all tourist
attractions by underground.
Rooms: 57 (47 ensuite)
Pricing: Sgl £35–45 Dbl £48–55 CC: Accepted
Room facilities: 🖵 ☎ 🖲 Access: |↕|
Children: Welcome
Directions: A4 towards central London; then turn onto
Earls Court Road. Underground station on right, take
next right onto Penywern Road.

Stanley House Hotel

 ◆◆

19-21, Belgrave Road, Victoria, London, SW1V 1RB
Tel: 020 7834 5042/7292 Fax: 020 7834 8439
Email: cmahotel@aol.com
Web: www.londonbudgethotels.co.uk

Located in the City of Westminster, off Buckingham
Palace Road. Railways: Victoria Station, easy
connection to Gatwick, Heathrow, Luton and
Stanstead airports. Buses: Victoria bus terminal.
Underground: Victoria Coach Station, coaches to all
cities in UK/Europe. Facilities: Colour TV, D/D
telephones, hairdryers, tea & coffee, drinks available 24
hours from vending machine. Rates: Triple room from
£75 (inc. ensuite), Quad from £25 per person (inc.
ensuite), shower & WC supplement £10/room. Excellent
location, clean & comfortable accommodation,
affordable budget rates.
Rooms: 44 (38 ensuite)
Pricing: Sgl £40–45 Dbl £50–55 CC: Accepted
Room facilities: 🖵 ☎ Children: Welcome 5yrs min age
Directions: 4/5 minutes walk behind Victoria train/tube
station.

Trochee Hotel

 ◆◆

52 Ridgeway Place, Wimbledon, London, SW19 4SW
Tel: 020 8946 9425 Fax: 020 8946 1579
Web: www.trocheehotel.co.uk
Rooms: 15 (9 ensuite) 🍴
Room facilities: 🖵 🖲 Children: Welcome
Dogs: Guide dogs only Parking: Off-street
Directions: From Wimbledon Station, turn right and
take second left into Worple Road. Take third right into
Ridgway Place.
See advert on next page

Trochee Hotel

 ◆◆

21 Malcolm Road, Wimbledon, London, SW19 4AS
Tel: 020 8946 1579 Fax: 020 8946 1579
Email: info@trocheehotel.co.uk
Web: www.trocheehotel.co.uk
Rooms: 17🍴
Pricing: Sgl £43–46 Dbl £59–59 CC: Accepted
Room facilities: 🖵 🖲 Children: Welcome
Dogs: Guide dogs only Parking: Off-street
Directions: From train station right up hill, second lights
turn left, then second turning right and hotel is top of
Malcolm Road.
See advert on next page

Wimbledon Hotel

 ◆◆

78 Worple Road, Wimbledon, London, SW19 4HZ
Tel: 020 8946 9265 Fax: 020 8946 9265
Email: www.wimbledonhotel.co.uk
Rooms: 14 (11 ensuite)
Pricing: Sgl £50–55 Dbl £65–75 CC: Accepted
Room facilities: 🖵 ☎ 🖲 Access: ♿
Children: Welcome Dogs: Guide dogs only
Parking: Off-street
Directions: From M25, take A3 to London, Kingston.
Take Merton exit, turn left at next traffic lights, keep to
right in U-turn.

Forest View Hotel

 ◆

227 Romford Road, Forest Gate, London, E7 9HL
Tel: 020 8534 4844 Fax: 020 8534 8959
Rooms: 28 (15 ensuite) 🍴
Pricing: Sgl £39.50 Dbl £58.50–70.50
Dinner from £12.80 CC: Accepted
Room facilities: 🖵 ☎ 🖲 🕯
Children: Welcome, 2yrs min age 🍼
Dogs: Guide dogs only Licences: ♟
Leisure: Games room, Snooker/billiards,
Parking: Off-street and monitored
Directions: From North Circular Road, turn off at Ilford
and turn left into Romford Road (A118). Follow road to
Forest Gate.

Guilford House Hotel

Russell Square, 6 Guilford Street, London, WC1N 1DR
Tel: 020 7430 2504 Fax: 020 7430 0697
Email: guilford-hotel@lineone.net
Web: guilfordhotel.co.uk
Rooms: 14 all ensuite 🛏 🖥 ⊗
Pricing: Sgl £45–49 Dbl £54–59 CC: Accepted
Room facilities: ▢ ☎ ☕
Access: ♿ Children: Welcome ⋔
Directions: Come out of Russell Square Underground Station walk right and turn right into Grenville Street. Turn left into Guilford Street and walk for 5 minutes, hotel is just before the traffic lights.

The Darlington, Hyde Park

111-117 Sussex Gardens, London, W2 2RU
Tel: 020 7460 8800 Fax: 020 7460 8828
Email: darlinghp@aol.com
Web: www.darlingtonhotel.co.uk
Rooms: 39 all ensuite ⊗
Pricing: Sgl £90–130 Dbl £130–150 CC: Accepted
Room facilities: ▢ ☎ ☕ 📞
Access: ⏫ Children: Welcome Dogs: Guide dogs only
Licences: ⚏
Directions: In the centre of Sussex Gardens halfway between Edgware Road and Lancaster Gate, five minutes walk from Paddington Station.

Sleeping Beauty Motel

Travel Accommodation
543 Lea Bridge Road, Leyton, London, E10 7EB
Tel: 020 8556 8080 Fax: 020 8556 8080
Rooms: 84 all ensuite 🛏
Pricing: Sgl £50–60 Dbl £50–60 CC: Accepted
Room facilities: ▢ ☎ ☕ Access: ⏫ ♿
Children: Welcome, 4yrs min age Licences: ⚏
Leisure: Gym Parking: Off-street and monitored
Directions: Ten minutes' walking distance from Walthamstow Central Underground Station.

Travelodge London, Battersea (SA)

Travel Accommodation
A3205, Southampton House, 200 York Road, Battersea, London, SW11 3SA
Web: www.travelodge.co.uk
Room facilities: ▢ ☕

Travelodge London City (SA)

Travel Accommodation
1 Harrow Place, London, E1 7DB
Web: www.travelodge.co.uk
Room facilities: ▢ ☕

Travelodge London, Docklands (SA)

Travel Accommodation
A13, Coriander Avenue, Off East India Dock Road, Docklands, London, E14 2AA
Web: www.travelodge.co.uk
Rooms: (232 ensuite) ⊗
Pricing: Sgl £74.40 Dbl £78.85
CC: Accepted Room facilities: ▢ ☕ Access: ♿

Travelodge London Kew Bridge

Travel Accommodation
North Road, High Street, Brentford, London, TW8 OBO
Web: www.travelodge.co.uk
Pricing: Sgl £84.40 Dbl £88.85
CC: Accepted
Room facilities: ▢ ☕

Travelodge London, Park Royal (SA)

Travel Accommodation
A40, 614 Western Avenue, Acton, London, W3 0TE
Web: www.travelodge.co.uk
Room facilities: ▢ ☕

London

Southeast

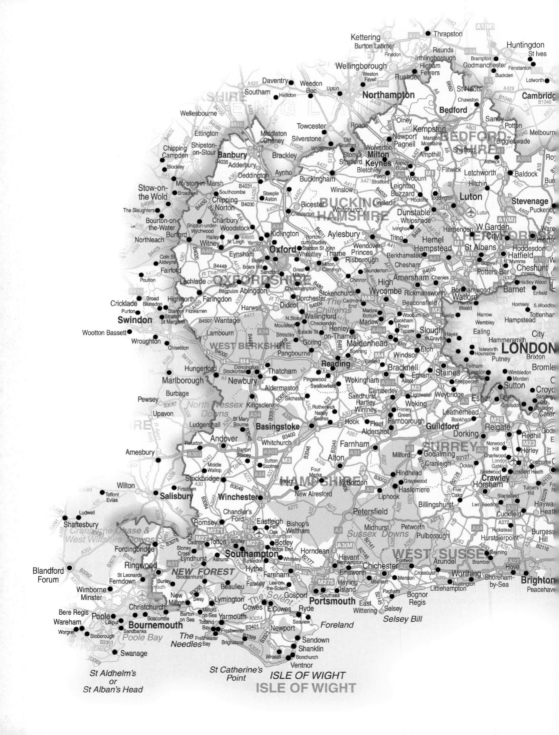

Southeast

Southeast

Gold Ribbon Award

Alexander House Hotel, Turners Hill	★★★	109
Ashdown Park, Forest Row	★★★★	107
Chewton Glen Hotel, New Milton	★★★★★	142
Cliveden House, Taplow	★★★★★	168
Gravetye Manor Hotel, East Grinstead	★★★	98
Hartwell House Hotel & Spa, Aylesbury	★★★★	73
Langshott Manor, Horley	★★★	110
Le Manoir aux Quat'Saisons, Great Milton	★★★★	111
South Lodge, Lower Beeding	★★★★	109
The George Hotel, Yarmouth	★★★	96
Tylney Hall Hotel, Basingstoke	★★★★	120

Blue Ribbon Award

Beetle & Wedge Hotel, Moulsford-on-Thames	★★	141
Danesfield House Hotel, Marlow	★★★★	138
Donnington Valley Hotel & Golf Course, Newbury	★★★★	142
Eastwell Manor, Ashford	★★★★	72
Grand Hotel, Eastbourne	★★★★★	99
Horsted Place Hotel, Uckfield	★★★	135
Maison Talbooth Hotel, Dedham	★★★	92
Rowhill Grange Hotel & Spa, Dartford	★★★★	95
St Michael's Manor, St. Albans	★★★	164

The Feathers, Woodstock	★★★	177
Westover Hall, Milford-on-Sea	★★★	139
Vineyard at Stockcross, Newbury	★★★★★	142

Little Gem

Burberry House - Tudor Lodgings, Brighton	◆◆◆◆◆	81
May Cottage, Nr. Andover	◆◆◆◆	70
Pinnacle Point, Eastbourne	◆◆◆◆◆	102
The Nurse's Cottage, Lymington	◆◆◆◆◆	168
The Penfold Gallery Guest House, Steyning	◆◆◆◆◆	166

Abingdon, Oxfordshire

Abingdon Four Pillars

★★★

Marcham Road, Abingdon, Oxfordshire, OX14 1TZ
Tel: 01235 553456 Fax: 01235 554117
Email: abingdon@four-pillars.co.uk
Web: www.four-pillars.co.uk
Rooms: 62 all ensuite
Pricing: Sgl £65–101.25 Dbl £79–123.50
Dinner from £15.95 CC: Accepted
Room facilities:
Conference: 7 meeting rooms (Thtr 140 max), 24hr-
delegate from £130, day-delegate rate from £32
Children: Welcome Dogs: Welcome
Licences: Parking: Off-street and monitored
Directions: From A34 take junction for A415 towards
Abingdon. At Abingdon, hotel is on right of roundabout.

The Upper Reaches

★★★

High Street Abingdon, Thames Street, Abingdon,
Oxfordshire, OX14 3JA
Tel: 0870 400 8101 Fax: 01235 555182
Email: upperreaches@heritage-hotels.co.uk
Web: www.macdonaldhotels.co.uk
Rooms: 31 all ensuite
Pricing: Sgl £65 Dbl £130 CC: Accepted
Room facilities:
Conference: 1 meeting room (Thtr 25 max)
Children: Welcome Dogs: Welcome
Licences: Parking: Off-street and monitored
Directions: Upon reaching Abingdon town centre, turn
from Stratton Way into Stert Street (A415). Follow road
towards Dorchester. Stop just before bridge and turn left.

Aldershot, Hampshire

Potters International Hotel

★★★

1 Fleet Road, Aldershot, Hampshire, GU11 2ET
Tel: 01252 344000 Fax: 01252 311611
Web: www.lakesidecomplex.co.uk
Rooms: 97 all ensuite
Pricing: Sgl £105–£120 Dbl £140 Dinner from £17.50
CC: Accepted Room facilities: Access:
Conference: 11 meeting rooms (Thtr 400 max), 24hr-
delegate from £165, day-delegate rate from £45
Children: Welcome Dogs: Guide dogs only
Licences: Leisure: Indoor pool, Gym, Health spa,
Beauty salon, Snooker/billiards
Parking: Off-street and monitored
Directions: Leave the M3 motorway at Junction 4,
follow the signs for Farnborough, at the 4th
roundabout, called the Queen's roundabout go straight
across on to the dual carriageway towards Farnham on
the A325. Take the first slip road signposted 'Malta
Barracks", turn right at the bottom of the slip road
going under the dual carriage way – you are now on
Fleet Road. About 500 yards down the road turn sharp
left just before the bend, Potter's International Hotel is
at the end of the road on the left hand side.

Alfriston, East Sussex

The Star Inn

★★★

High Street, Alfriston, East Sussex, BN26 5TA
Tel: 0870 400 8102 Fax: 01323 870922
Email: starinn@heritage-hotels.co.uk
Web: www.macdonaldhotels.co.uk
Rooms: 37 all ensuite
Pricing: Sgl £69 Dbl £138 Dinner from £19
CC: Accepted
Room facilities:
Conference: 1 meeting room (Thtr 30 max)
Children: Welcome
Dogs: Welcome
Licences:
Parking: Off-street
Directions: Located in the centre of Alfriston, which is
accessed via the A27 between Brighton and
Eastbourne.

White Lodge Country House Hotel

★★★

Sloe Lane, Alfriston, East Sussex, BN26 5UR
Tel: 01323 870265 Fax: 01323 870284
Email: sales@whitelodge-hotel.com
Web: www.whitelodge-hotel.com
Rooms: 19 all ensuite
Pricing: Dinner from £21.50 (2002 rate)
CC: Accepted
Room facilities:
Access:
Children: Welcome
Dogs: Welcome
Licences:
Leisure: Snooker/billiards
Parking: Monitored

Alton, Hampshire

Alton Grange Hotel

★★★★

London Road, Alton, Hampshire, GU34 4EG
Tel: 01420 86565 Fax: 01420 541346
Email: info@altongrange.co.uk
Web: www.altongrange.co.uk
Seasonal closure: December 23 to January 3
Rooms: 31 all ensuite
Pricing: Sgl £82–99 Dbl £99–160 Dinner from £30
CC: Accepted
Room facilities:
Access:
Conference: 5 meeting rooms (Thtr 80 max), 24hr-
delegate from £146, day-delegate rate from £39
Children: Welcome 5yrs min age
Dogs: Welcome
Licences:
Parking: Off-street
Directions: Leave M3 at J-4. Take A331 then A31 in
Farnham/Winchester direction. Turn right after 7 miles
at roundabout (signed B3004 to Alton/Bordon). Hotel is
350 yards on left.

Travelodge Alton (Fourmarks)

Travel Accommodation
A31 Northbound, Winchester Road, Four Marks, Alton,
Hampshire, GU34 5HZ
Web: www.travelodge.co.uk
Rooms: 31 all ensuite
Pricing: Sgl £49.40–54.40 Dbl £53.85–58.85
CC: Accepted Room facilities: ▢ 🖥 Access: ♿

Amersham, Buckinghamshire

The Crown

★ ★ ★

16 High Street, Amersham, Buckinghamshire, HP7 0DH
Tel: 0870 400 8103 Fax: 01494 431 283
Email: crown@heritage-hotels.co.uk
Web: www.macdonaldhotels.co.uk
Rooms: 37 all ensuite
Pricing: Sgl £59 Dbl £118 Dinner from £22.95
CC: Accepted Room facilities: ▢ ☎ 🖥 🐾 Access: ♿
Conference: 1 meeting room (Thtr 15 max)
Children: Welcome Dogs: Welcome
Licences: ♟ Parking: Off-street and monitored
Directions: From M25 Junction 18, take A404. Follow
signs for Old Amersham. At Tesco roundabout, go
straight ahead, past pelican crossing. The Crown is
on left.

Andover, Hampshire

Fifehead Manor Hotel

★ ★ ★ ★ ℝ ℝ

Middle Wallop, Stockbridge, Hampshire, SO20 8EG
Tel: 01264 781565 Fax: 01264 781400
Email: fifeheadmanor@ukonline.co.uk
Web: www.johansens.com
Rooms: 17 all ensuite
Pricing: Sgl £70–80 Dbl £110–130 CC: Accepted
Room facilities: ▢ ☎ 🖥
Conference: 2 meeting rooms (Thtr 25 max)
Children: Welcome ♀ ❄ Dogs: Welcome
Licences: ⚘ ♟ Parking: Off-street
Directions: Located on A343, 6 miles from Andover
and 12 miles from Salisbury.
See advert on next page

White Hart Hotel

★ ★ ★

12 Bridge Street, Andover, Hampshire, SP10 1BH
Tel: 01264 352266 Fax: 01264 323767
Rooms: 27 (29 ensuite) ❦ ✂ ⊗
Pricing: Sgl £50 Dbl £55–70
Room facilities: ▢ ☎ 🖥
Conference: 1 meeting room (Thtr 140 max)
Children: Welcome
Dogs: Guide dogs only Licences: ⚘
Parking: Off-street
Directions: From A303, A34, A343: follow signs for the
town centre, take directional signs for London street,
Bridge street and High street. The hotel is situated on
the left hand side, halfway along Bridge street.

May Cottage

Little Gem

◆ ◆ ◆ ◆ ✻ ✿ ☂

Thruxton, near Andover, Hampshire, SP11 8LZ
Tel: 01264 771241 Fax: 01264 771770
Rooms: 3 all ensuite
Pricing: Sgl £40–50 Dbl £60–70
Room facilities: ▢ 🖥 Children: Welcome 5yrs min age
Leisure: Snooker/billiards
Parking: Off-street and monitored
Directions: From A303, take turning marked 'Thruxton
(village only)'. May Cottage is located almost opposite
The George Inn.
See advert on next page

Bourne Valley Inn

◆ ◆ ◆

St Mary Bourne, Nr. Andover, Hampshire, SP11 6BT
Tel: 01264 738361 Fax: 01264 738126
Email: bournevalley@wessexinns.fsnet.co.uk
Rooms: 9 all ensuite
Pricing: £50–60 Dinner from £7 CC: Accepted
Room facilities: ▢ ☎ 🖥
Conference: 1 meeting room (Thtr 100 max)
Children: Welcome ♀ Dogs: Guide dogs only
Licences: ♟ Leisure: Games room Parking: Off-street
Directions: Off the A343 Newbury to Andover road in
main village.

Travelodge Barton Stacey

Travel Accommodation
A303, Barton Stacey, Nr. Andover,
Hampshire, SO21 3NP
Web: www.travelodge.co.uk
Rooms: 20 all ensuite ⊗
Pricing: Sgl £57.40 Dbl £61.85
CC: Accepted Room facilities: ▢ 🖥 Access: ♿

Arundel, West Sussex

Comfort Inn Arundel

★ ★

Junction A27/A284, Crossbush, Arundel,
West Sussex, BN17 7QQ
Tel: 01903 840840 Fax: 01903 849849
Email: admin@gb642.u-net.com
Web: www.choicehotels.com
Situated 20 minutes from Portsmouth and Brighton we
make the ideal venue for you whether you're on
business or pleasure. Located in the heart of the
West Sussex countryside our comfortable, modern
hotel awaits you. All rooms are ensuite with TV and
refreshment facilities.
Rooms: 53 all ensuite ⊗
Pricing: Dinner from £12.75 CC: Accepted
Room facilities: ▢ ☎ 🖥 Access: ♿
Conference: 2 meeting rooms, 24hr-delegate from
£61.50, day-delegate rate from £27.50
Children: Welcome ♀ Dogs: Welcome
Licences: ♟ Parking: Off-street
Directions: Follow the signs to the services at Vunchen
A27/A284.

Travelodge Bognor Regis, Fontwell

Travel Accommodation
A27/A29, Fontwell, Nr. Arundel, West Sussex, BN18 0SB
Web: www.travelodge.co.uk
Rooms: 62 all ensuite ⊗
Pricing: Sgl £54.40 Dbl £58.85
CC: Accepted Room facilities: ▢ ☕ Access: ♿

Ascot, Berkshire

The Berystede
★★★★ ⓡ
Bagshot Road, Ascot, Berkshire, SL5 9JH
Tel: 01344 623311 Fax: 01344 872301
Email: sales.berystede@heritage-hotels.co.uk
Web: www.macdonaldhotels.co.uk
Rooms: 90 all ensuite ⊛ ▦ ⊗
Pricing: Sgl £54 Dbl £108
Dinner from £25
CC: Accepted
Room facilities: ▢ ☎ ☕ ☏
Access: ⬍ ♿
Conference: 14 meeting rooms (Thtr 125 max)
Children: Welcome ☰ ⓒ
Dogs: Welcome
Licences: ⬥ ⅲ
Leisure: Outdoor pool,
Parking: Off-street and monitored
Directions: From Ascot, take A330 for Brockenhurst.

Southeast

Ashford, Kent

Eastwell Manor

★★★★ ♛ ♛ ♛ ♛

Blue Ribbon Winner

Eastwell Park, Boughton Lees, Ashford, Kent, TN25 4HR
Tel: 01233 213000 Fax: 01233 635530
Email: eastwell@btinternet.com
Web: www.eastwellmanor.co.uk

MARSTON HOTELS

Enjoy luxury combined with history at this magnificent manor house in Kent set within beautiful grounds. Award winning restaurant, excellent leisure facilities including indoor and outdoor pools and beauty salon.
Rooms: 62 all ensuite
Pricing: Sgl £170–325 Dbl £200–355 Dinner from £32
CC: Accepted
Room facilities: Access:
Conference: 7 meeting rooms (Thtr 180 max), 24hr-delegate from £195, day-delegate rate from £65
Children: Welcome
Dogs: Welcome Licences:
Leisure: Indoor pool, Outdoor pool, Gym, Health spa, Beauty salon, Tennis,
Parking: Off-street
Directions: Take left hand road at roundabout J9/M20 into Trinity Road, follow over 4 roundabouts turn left at lights onto A251.

London Beach Hotel and Golf Club

★★★

Ashford Road, St Michaels, Tenterden, Ashford, Kent, TN20 6SP
Tel: 01580 766279 Fax: 01580 763884
Email: enquiries@londonbeach.com
Web: www.londonbeach.com
Rooms: 27 all ensuite
Room facilities:
Access:
Children: Welcome Licences:
Leisure: Golf, Fishing, Games room, Snooker/billiards,
Parking: Off-street and monitored
Directions: Leave M20 at J9, follow signs for Tenterden; hotel 1/2 mile before Tenterden.
See advert on this page

Croft Hotel

◆ ◆ ◆

Canterbury Road, Kennington, Ashford, Kent, TN25 4DU
Tel: 01233 622140 Fax: 01233 635271
Email: crofthotel@btconnect.com

Small family-run hotel set in 2 acres of grounds near to Canterbury, Leeds Castle, Ashford International and Channel Tunnel. Dover 20 minutes.
Rooms: 27 (54 ensuite)
Pricing: Sgl £50–65 Dbl £68–78 Dinner from £11
CC: Accepted
Room facilities:
Access:
Conference: meeting rooms, 24hr-delegate from £85, day-delegate rate from £25
Children: Welcome Dogs: Welcome
Licences:
Parking: Off-street and monitored
Directions: From M20 Junction 9 or 10, follow A28 signs to Canterbury. Croft Hotel is on right.

Travelodge Ashford

Travel Accommodation
M20, Eureka Leisure Park, Rutherford Road, Ashford, Kent, TN25 4BN
Web: www.travelodge.co.uk
Rooms: 67 all ensuite
Pricing: Sgl £64.40 Dbl £68.85
CC: Accepted Room facilities: Access:

Ashurst, Hampshire

Busketts Lawn Hotel

174 Woodlands Road, Woodlands, Nr. Southampton,
Ashurst, Hampshire, SO40 7GL
Tel: 02380 292272 Fax: 02380 292487
Email: enquiries@buskettslawnhotel.co.uk
Web: www.buskettslawnhotel.co.uk

A delightful family-run country house hotel in a two-acre garden set in a quiet forest location. Facilities include a Victorian four-poster suite and a seasonal outdoor pool, with golf and riding nearby.
Rooms: 14 all ensuite
Pricing: Sgl £42–45 Dbl £80–85 Dinner from £18.50
CC: Accepted
Room facilities:
Conference: 2 meeting rooms (Thtr 120 max), 24hr-delegate from £97.50, day-delegate rate from £29.50
Children: Welcome
Dogs: Welcome
Licences:
Leisure: Outdoor pool,
Parking: Off-street
Directions: Accessible from J2 M27. Woodlands is a mile from the A35 Ashurst and a mile from A336 Netley Marsh.

Aylesbury, Buckinghamshire

Hartwell House   Gold Ribbon Winner
★★★★
Oxford Road, near Aylesbury,
Buckinghamshire, HP17 8NL
Tel: 01296 747444 Fax: 01296 747450
Email: info@hartwell-house.com
Web: www.hartwell-house.com

With its tradition of courtesy and service, its elegant drawing-rooms and excellent dining-rooms. Hartwell House is one of the most beautiful places in which you could wish to stay.
Rooms: 46 all ensuite
Pricing: Sgl £158–162 Dbl £262–272 Dinner from £46
CC: Accepted
Room facilities: Access:
Conference: 4 meeting rooms (Thtr 60 max)
Children: Welcome 8yrs min age
Licences:
Leisure: Indoor pool, Gym, Health spa, Beauty salon, Tennis, Fishing
Parking: Off-street and monitored
Directions: In Aylesbury, take A418 towards Oxford. Hartwell House is 2 miles along this road on the right-hand side.

Baldock, Bedfordshire

Travelodge Baldock, Beds
Travel Accommodation
A1, Great North Road, Hindlex, Nr.Baldock,
Bedfordshire, SG7 5EX
Web: www.travelodge.co.uk
Pricing: Sgl £54.40 Dbl £58.85
CC: Accepted Room facilities: Access:

Banbury, Oxfordshire

Whately Hall
★★★★
Banbury Cross, Banbury, Oxfordshire, OX16 0AN
Tel: 0870 400 8104 Fax: 01295 271736
Email: whatelyhall@heritage-hotels.co.uk
Web: www.macdonald-hotels.co.uk
Rooms: 69 all ensuite
Pricing: Sgl £57 Dbl £114 Dinner from £23.50
CC: Accepted
Room facilities:
Access:
Conference: 6 meeting rooms (Thtr 100 max)
Children: Welcome Dogs: Welcome
Licences:
Parking: Off-street and monitored
Directions: M40 take junction 11. Follow A422 to Chipping Norton till Banbury Cross. Hotel is just before on the right.

Southeast

Lismore Hotel

★★

61 Oxford Road, Banbury, Oxfordshire, OX16 9AJ
Tel: 01295 267661 Fax: 01295 269010
Rooms: 23 all ensuite
Pricing: Sgl £58–65 Dbl £78–85 Dinner from £19.95
CC: Accepted
Room facilities:
Conference: 1 meeting room (Thtr 18 max), 24hr-delegate from £85, day-delegate rate from £25
Children: Welcome
Dogs: Welcome
Licences:
Parking: Off-street and monitored
Directions: From Banbury Cross in town centre, follow road south. Take fourth turning left into Old Parr Road, then first right into car park.

La Madonette Country Guest House

◆◆◆◆

North Newington Road, Banbury, Oxfordshire, OX15 6AA
Tel: 01295 730212 Fax: 01295 730363
Email: lamadonette@aol.com
Web: www.lamadonette.co.uk

17th-century millhouse, peacefully situated in rural surroundings on outskirts of Banbury. Well located for Cotswolds, Stratford-upon-Avon, Oxford and Silverstone. Licenced. Gardens, outdoor pool.
Rooms: 6 all ensuite
Pricing: Sgl £45–50 Dbl £67–95 CC: Accepted
Room facilities:
Conference: 1 meeting room (Thtr 25 max), day-delegate rate from £32
Children: Welcome
Licences:
Leisure: Outdoor pool
Parking: Off-street and monitored
Directions: From M40 Junction 11, follow signs to Banbury Cross. Take B4035 for approximately 2 miles, turn right for North Newington, then ¼ mile on right before village.

Need help booking?

RAC Hotel Reservations will find the accommodation that's right for you – and book it too. Call today on 0870 603 9109 and quote 'Guide 2003'

Easington House Hotel

◆◆◆

50 Oxford Road, Banbury, Oxfordshire, OX16 9AN
Tel: 01295 270181 Fax: 01295 269527

15th Century farmhouse all rooms ensuite, tour the nearby Cotswolds, visit Oxford, Blenheim Palace at Woodstock, Stratford and Warwick convenient for shopping in Banbury or walk along the canal banks.
Rooms: 13 all ensuite
Pricing: Sgl £55 Dbl £65 CC: Accepted
Room facilities:
Children: Welcome
Dogs: Welcome
Parking: Off-street
Directions: Five minutes up the hill from the Banbury Cross on your right.

The Unicorn Inn

◆◆◆

Market Place, Deddington, Banbury, Oxfordshire, OX15 0SE
Tel: 01869 338838 Fax: 01869 338592
Email: unicorn@traditionalfreehouses.com
Rooms: 6 all ensuite
Pricing: Sgl £50 Dbl £60 Dinner from £6 CC: Accepted
Room facilities:
Conference: 1 meeting room (Thtr 20 max)
Children: Welcome
Dogs: Guide dogs only
Licences:
Leisure: Games room

Barton-on-Sea, Hampshire

Cliff House Hotel

★★★

Marine Drive West, New Milton, Barton-on-Sea, Hampshire, BH25 7QL
Tel: 01425 619333 Fax: 01425 612462
Rooms: 9 all ensuite
Room facilities:
Children: Welcome 10yrs min age
Licences:
Parking: Off-street and monitored
Directions: Turn off A35 on B3058 to New Milton. Turn right at roundabout on A337, then left onto Sea Road at Barton-on-Sea. Hotel is at end of Sea Road on cliff top.

Basildon, Essex

Chichester Hotel

★★★

Old London Road, Wickford, Basildon, Essex, SS11 8UE
Tel: 01268 560555 Fax: 01268 560580
Web: www.chichester-essex.co.uk
Rooms: 33 all ensuite
Pricing: Sgl £66–81 Dbl £82–90 Dinner from £10.75
CC: Accepted Room facilities: ☐ ☎ ☕ ☏ Access: ♿
Licences: ♦♦♦ Parking: Off-street
Directions: Exit M25 at Junction 29. Turn east on A127
(signposted Southend on Sea). After 13 miles, turn
north on the A130, after 1 mile turn west on the A129,
after ¼ mile turn right at hotel sign.

Campanile Hotel

Travel Accommodation
A127 Southern Arterial road, Pipps Hill, Burches,
Basildon, Essex, SS14 3AE
Tel: 01268 530810 Fax: 01268 286710
Web: www.campanile.fr

Campanile hotels offer comfortable and convenient
budget accommodation and a traditional French style
Bistro providing freshly-cooked food for breakfast, lunch
and dinner. All rooms ensuite with tea/coffee making
facilities, DDT and TV with pay-per-view channels.
Rooms: 97 all ensuite ⊗
Pricing: Sgl £40.95–49.90 Dbl £46.90–55.85
Dinner from £5.95 CC: Accepted
Room facilities: ☐ ☎ ☕ ☏ Access: ♿
Conference: 1 meeting room (Thtr 35 max), 24hr-
delegate from £68, day-delegate rate from £19.50
Children: Welcome ♿ Dogs: Welcome
Licences: ♦♦♦
Parking: Off-street and monitored
Directions: Exit J29 M25, follow A127 then A176
towards Basildon and Billericay. Left at first
roundabout and also at second, then first left.

Travelodge Basildon (SA)

Travel Accommodation
Festival Leisure Park, Festival Way, Basildon,
Essex, SS14 3WB
Web: www.travelodge.co.uk
Rooms: 60 all ensuite ⊗
Pricing: Sgl £64.40 Dbl £68.85
CC: Accepted Room facilities: ☐ ☕ Access: ♿

Basingstoke, Hampshire

Hampshire Centre Court

★★★★ ⓡ

Centre Drive, Basingstoke, Hampshire, RG24 8FY
Tel: 01256 816664 Fax: 01256 816727
Email: hampshirec@marstonhotels.com
Web: www.marstonhotels.com

MARSTON HOTELS

Modern hotel on outskirts of Basingstoke, unique
leisure facilities comprising 5 indoor and 5 outdoor
tennis courts, full coaching facilities, indoor pool, large
gymnasium, spa, sauna, steam and beauty treatments.
Rooms: 50 all ensuite ⊕ ⊗
Pricing: Sgl £129 Dbl £149 Dinner from £25
CC: Accepted
Room facilities: ☐ ☎ ☕ ☏ Access: ⋔
Conference: 10 meeting rooms (Thtr 100 max), 24hr-
delegate from £160, day-delegate rate from £54.50
Children: Welcome ♿ ☕ Dogs: Guide dogs only
Licences: ♦♦♦ Leisure: Indoor pool, Gym, Health spa,
Beauty salon, Tennis
Parking: Off-street and monitored
Directions: Leave M3 at Junction 6. Follow A33 for
Reading. Turn right at Chineham Centre roundabout.
Hotel ¼ mile on left.

Romans Country House Hotel

★★★★ ⓡ ⓡ

Little London Road, Silchester, Basingstoke,
Hampshire, RG7 2PN
Tel: 0118 970 0421 Fax: 0118 970 0691
Email: romanshotel@hotmail.com
Web: romanshotel.co.uk
Rooms: 25 all ensuite ⊕ ⊞ ⊗
Pricing: Sgl £70–95 Dbl £98.50–140 Dinner from £25
CC: Accepted Room facilities: ☐ ☎ ☕ ☏ Access: ♿
Conference: 5 meeting rooms (Thtr 60 max), 24hr-
delegate from £130, day-delegate rate from £40
Children: Welcome ♿ ☕
Dogs: Welcome Licences: ⚘ ♦♦♦
Leisure: Outdoor pool, Gym, Health spa, Tennis
Parking: Off-street
Directions: Leave M3 at Junction 6 and follow signs on
A340 to Tadley/Aldermarston. At Pamber end, follow
hotel signs to Silchester.
See advert on following page

See advert on following page

Southeast

Romans
Country House Hotel

RAC ★★★
RAC Dining Award RAC RAC

Country House set in the tranquil village of Silchester, ideal for conferences and short break holidays. Gourmet restaurant. Real log fire in the oak panelled lounge. Leisure centre with Tennis, Gymnasium, Sauna and unique outdoor pool heated to a steaming 30° C year round.

Little London Road, Silchester, Basingstoke, Hampshire RG7 2PN
Tel: 01189 700421   Fax: 01189 700691
Email: romanhotel@hotmail.com
Website:www.romanshotel.co.uk

Hanover International Hotel & Club Basingstoke

✤

Nately Scures, Hook, Hampshire, RG27 9JS
Tel: 0870 2417103 Fax: 01256 768341
Email: crso@hanover-international.com
Web: www.hanover-international.com

HANOVER INTERNATIONAL
HOTELS & CLUBS

Surrounded by mature woodland, this elegant hotel with superb leisure club is conveniently located within a mile of the M3.
Rooms: 100 all ensuite 🐾 📺 ⊗
Room facilities: 🖥 ☎ ☕ 🔌 Access: ↕ ♿
Conference: 12 meeting rooms (Thtr 240 max), 24hr-delegate from £165, day-delegate rate from £60

Children: Welcome ♀ Dogs: Guide dogs only
Licences: 🔔 ♦♦♦
Leisure: Indoor pool, Gym, Health spa, Beauty salon, Games room
Parking: Off-street and monitored
Directions: From M3 junction 5 take A30 towards Basingstoke, the hotel is situated on the right hand side after one mile.

Travelodge Basingstoke (SA)

Travel Accommodation
A303, Stag & Hounds, Winchester Road, Basingstoke, Hampshire, RG22 6HN
Web: www.travelodge.co.uk
Rooms: 44 all ensuite ⊗
Pricing: Sgl £54.40–64.40 Dbl £58.85–68.85
CC: Accepted Room facilities: 🖥 ☕ Access: ♿

Battle, East Sussex

Powder Mills

★★★★ ℞ ℞

Powdermill Lane, Battle, East Sussex, TN33 0SP
Tel: 01424 775511 Fax: 01424 774540
Email: powdc@aol.com
Web: www.powdermills.co.uk
Rooms: 40 all ensuite 📺
Pricing: Sgl £80–110 Dbl £105–145 Dinner from £27.50
CC: Accepted
Room facilities: 🖥 ☎ ☕
Access: ♿
Conference: 5 meeting rooms (Thtr 200 max), 24hr-delegate from £140, day-delegate rate from £35
Children: Welcome ♀
Dogs: Welcome
Licences: 🔔 ♦♦♦
Leisure: Outdoor pool, Fishing
Parking: Off-street and monitored
Directions: Through the town of Battle, towards Hastings. Take first turning right after Battle Abbey, Powder Mills 1 mile down lane.

Little Hemingfold Hotel

◆◆◆ ℞

Telham, Battle, East Sussex, TN33 0TT
Tel: 01424 774338 Fax: 01424 775351
Seasonal closure: 2 January to 11 February
Rooms: 12 all ensuite 🐾 📺
Pricing: Sgl £54–82.50 Dbl £88–95 Dinner from £24.50
CC: Accepted
Room facilities: 🖥 ☎ ☕
Children: Welcome 7yrs min age ♀
Dogs: Welcome
Licences: ♦♦♦
Leisure: Outdoor pool, Tennis, Fishing
Parking: Off-street
Directions: 1½ miles south of Battle on A2100 towards Hastings. Look out for blue hotel sign adjacent to sign depicting sharp bend. Turn down track to left of road for ½ mile.

Beaconsfield, Buckinghamshire

Chequers Inn

★★

Kiln Lane, Wooburn Common, Beaconsfield,
Buckinghamshire, HP10 0JQ
Tel: 01628 529575 Fax: 01628 850124
Email: info@chequers-inn.com
Web: www.chequers-inn.com
Rooms: 17 all ensuite
Pricing: Sgl £92.50–99.50 Dbl £97.50–107.50
Dinner from £21.95 CC: Accepted
Room facilities:
Conference: 1 meeting room (Thtr 30 max), 24hr-delegate from £150, day-delegate rate from £40
Children: Welcome
Licences:
Parking: Off-street and monitored
Directions: Leave M40 at Junction 2. Follow signs to Beaconsfield. Take A40 towards High Wycombe, left into Broad Lane, stay on road. Hotel on left.
See advert on this page

Beaulieu, Hampshire

Beaulieu Hotel

★★★

Beaulieu Road, Lyndhurst, Hampshire, SO42 7YQ
Tel: 0238 029 3344 Fax: 0238 029 2729
Email: beaulieu@carehotels.co.uk
Web: www.carehotels.co.uk
Rooms: 18 all ensuite
Pricing: Sgl £52.50–65 Dbl £105–130
Dinner from £21.50 CC: Accepted
Room facilities:
Access:
Children: Welcome
Dogs: Welcome Licences:
Leisure: Indoor pool
Parking: Off-street and monitored
Directions: From M27, follow signs to Lyndhurst, then Beaulieu on B3056. Beaulieu Hotel is approximately 3 miles along the road.
See advert on this page

Master Builders House Hotel

★★★★

Bucklers Hard, Beaulieu, Hampshire, SO42 7XB
Tel: 01590 616253 Fax: 01590 616297
Email: res@themasterbuilders.co.uk
Web: www.themasterbuilders.co.uk
Rooms: 25 all ensuite
Pricing: Sgl £125–220 Dbl £170–220 Dinner from £35
CC: Accepted
Room facilities:
Conference: 2 meeting rooms (Thtr 50 max), 24hr-delegate from £185, day-delegate rate from £65
Children: Welcome
Dogs: Guide dogs only
Licences:
Parking: Off-street and monitored

Berkhamsted, Hertfordshire

Kings Arms Hotel

147, High Street, Berkhamsted, Hertfordshire, HP4 3HL
Tel: 01442 866595 Fax: 01442 877782
Email: kingsarmshotel@ccn.go-free.co.uk
Web: www.kingsarmshotel.com
Rooms: 21 all ensuite
Pricing: Sgl £63.95–83.95 Dbl £82.90–102.90
Dinner from £19 CC: Accepted
Room facilities: Access:
Conference: 1 meeting room, 24hr-delegate from £175,
day-delegate rate from £30
Dogs: Welcome
Licences: Parking:
Directions: Junction 20 off M25, A41 towards
Aylesbury 2nd exit Berkhamsted, follow road into town,
we are opposite Tesco.

Bexhill-on-Sea, East Sussex

Park Lodge Hotel

16 Egerton Road, Bexhill-on-Sea,
East Sussex, TN39 3HH
Tel: 01424 216547 Fax: 01424 217460
Rooms: 10 (8 ensuite)
Pricing: Sgl £21–33 Dbl £44–50 Dinner from £10
CC: Accepted
Room facilities:
Children: Welcome Dogs: Welcome
Licences: Parking: Off-street
Directions: From the A259 follow directions to the De
La Warr Pavilion, the hotel is situated 100 yards to
west over the roundabout.

Bexleyheath, Kent

Bexleyheath Marriott Hotel

1 Broadway, Bexleyheath, Kent, DA6 7JZ
Tel: 020 8298 1000 Fax: 020 8298 1234
Email: bexleyheath@marriotthotels.co.uk
Rooms: 142 all ensuite
Pricing: Dinner from £19.75 (2002 rate) CC: Accepted
Room facilities:
Access: Children: Welcome
Dogs: Guide dogs only Licences:
Leisure: Indoor pool, Gym
Parking: Off-street and monitored
Directions: The Bexleyheath Marriott is located just off
the A2 and only minutes from Junction 2 of the M25.

Bicester, Oxfordshire

Bignell Park Hotel

Chesterton, Nr Bicester, Oxon, OX26 1UE
Tel: 01869 326550 Fax: 01869 322729

Westfield Farm

The Fenway, Steeple Aston, Bicester, Oxfordshire,
OX25 4SS
Tel: 01869 340591 Fax: 01869 347594
Email: info@westfieldmotel.u-net.com
Web: www.oxlink.co.uk/accom/westfield-farm/
Rooms: 9 all ensuite
Pricing: Sgl £50–55 Dbl £65–75 Dinner from £7.50
CC: Accepted
Room facilities:
Access:
Children: Welcome Dogs: Welcome
Licences: Parking: Off-street
Directions: 8 miles south of Banbury on A4260, turn
first left into Steeple Aston. Hotel ½ mile, entrance on
right.

Travelodge Bicester Cherwell Valley (MOTO)

Travel Accommodation
M40 Moto Service Area, Northampton Road, Ardley,
Cherwell Valley, Nr. Bicester, Oxfordshire, OX6 9RD
Web: www.travelodge.co.uk
Rooms: 98 all ensuite
Pricing: Sgl £54.40–57.40 Dbl £58.85–61.85
CC: Accepted Room facilities: Access:

Bickley, Kent

Glendevon House Hotel

80 Southborough Road, Bickley, Kent, BR1 2EN
Tel: 020 8467 2183 Fax: 020 8295 0701
Web: www.avishotel.com
Rooms: 12 all ensuite
Pricing: Sgl £35–45 Dbl £53.50–65 CC: Accepted
Room facilities:
Children: Welcome 2yrs min age

Billingshurst, West Sussex

Travelodge Billingshurst, Five Oaks

Travel Accommodation
A29 Northbound, Stane Street , Five Oaks,
Billingshurst, West Sussex, RH14 9AE
Web: www.travelodge.co.uk
Rooms: 26 all ensuite
Pricing: Sgl £54.40 Dbl £58.85
CC: Accepted Room facilities: Access:

Bishop's Stortford, Hertfordshire

Down Hall Country House Hotel

★★★★

Hatfield Heath, near Bishop's Stortford,
Hertfordshire, CM22 7AS
Tel: 01279 731441 Fax: 01279 730416
Email: reservations@downhall.co.uk
Web: www.downhall.co.uk

Victorian mansion of notable historic interest. Set in
110 acres of woodland, park and landscaped gardens.
100 ensuite bedrooms, plenty of parking and
conference facilities for up to 240 people.
Rooms: 100 all ensuite
Pricing: Sgl £144–184 Dbl £180–220 Dinner from £28
CC: Accepted
Room facilities: ▢ ☎ ⌂ ⌕
Access: ⊞ ⌯
Conference: 26 meeting rooms (Thtr 240 max), 24hr-
delegate from £180, day-delegate rate from £60
Children: Welcome ⚜
Licences: ◈ ⅲ
Leisure: Indoor pool, Tennis, Snooker/billiards
Parking: Off-street and monitored
Directions: Exit M11 at Junction 8. Take A1250 through
Bishop's Stortford then A1060 to Hatfield Heath.
Follow signs to Down Hall.

The Cottage

◆ ◆ ◆ ◆

71 Birchanger Lane, Birchanger, Bishop's Stortford,
Hertfordshire, CM23 5QA
Tel: 01279 812349 Fax: 01279 815045
Web: www.thecottagebirchanger.co.uk
Seasonal closure: Christmas to New Year
Rooms: 16 (13 ensuite) ⊛
Pricing: Sgl £45–54 Dbl £68–70 CC: Accepted
Room facilities: ▢ ⌂
Children: Welcome
Dogs: Guide dogs only
Licences: ⅲ
Parking: Off-street
Directions: Leave M11 at Junction 8. Take A120 west
for 1 mile. Take B1383 north towards Newport and
Saffron Waldon, then first right into Birchanger Lane.

George Hotel

◆ ◆ ◆

1 North Street, Bishop's Stortford, Herts, CM23 2LQ
Tel: 01279 504128 Fax: 01279 655135
Email: enquiries@stanstedhotels.net
Web: www.stanstedhotels.net
Rooms: 30 (17 ensuite) ⊛
Room facilities: ▢ ⌂ Children: Welcome
Licences: ⅲ Parking: Off-street

The Old Post Office B&B

◆ ◆ ◆

Church End, Broxted, Great Dunmow, Essex, CM6 2BU
Tel: 01279 850050 Fax: 01279 850050
Rooms: 3 all ensuite ⊛ ⊛
Room facilities: ▢ ⌂ Children: Welcome
Dogs: Guide dogs only Parking: Off-street
Directions: Exit M11 at Stansted Airport junction.

Botley, Hampshire

MacDonald Botley Park

★★★★

Winchester Road, Boorley Green, Botley,
Hampshire, SO32 2UA
Tel: 01489 780888 Fax: 01489 789242
Email: info@botleypark.macdonald-hotels.co.uk
Web: www.macdonald-hotels.co.uk/botleypark-hotels
Rooms: 100 all ensuite ⊛
Pricing: Dinner from £20 (2002 rate) CC: Accepted
Room facilities: ▢ ☎ ⌂ ⌕ Access: ⌯
Children: Welcome ⚜ Dogs: Guide dogs only
Licences: ◈ ⅲ
Leisure: Indoor pool, Gym, Beauty salon, Tennis, Golf
Parking: Off-street and monitored
Directions: From J11 of M3, 15 minutes: from J7 of
M27, 5 minutes.

Bracknell, Berkshire

Coppid Beech Hotel

★★★★

John Nike Way, Bracknell, Berkshire, RG12 8TF
Tel: 01344 303333 Fax: 01344 301200
Email: welcome@coppid-beech-hotel.co.uk
Web: www.coppidbeech.com
Rooms: 205 all ensuite ⊛ ⊛
Pricing: Sgl £145–165 Dbl £165–180
Dinner from £24.95 CC: Accepted
Room facilities: ▢ ☎ ⌂ ⌕
Access: ⊞ ⌯
Conference: 11 meeting rooms (Thtr 320 max), 24hr-
delegate from £180, day-delegate rate from £60
Children: Welcome ⚜ ⌇
Dogs: Welcome Licences: ◈ ⅲ
Leisure: Indoor pool, Gym, Beauty salon
Parking: Off-street and monitored
Directions: Leave M4 at Junction 10. Take A329(M) to
Wokingham. After 3 miles take first exit to Coppid
Beech roundabout. Take first exit and in 300 yards the
hotel is on the right.

Southeast

Travelodge Bracknell (SA)

Travel Accommodation
B3408, London Road, Binfiel, Nr. Bracknell,
Berkshire, RG12 4AA
Web: www.travelodge.co.uk
Rooms: 35 all ensuite ⊛
Pricing: Sgl £74.40 Dbl £78.85
CC: Accepted Room facilities: ⌨ ☕ Access: ♿

Brentford, Essex

Primrose House

56 Boston Gardens, Brentford, London, TW8 9LP
Tel: 020 85685573
Email: information@primrosehouse.com
Web: www.primrosehouse.com
Rooms: 2 (1 ensuite) 🛏 ⊛
Pricing: Sgl £35–45 Dbl £50–60 CC: Accepted
Room facilities: ⌨ Dogs: Guide dogs only
Parking: Off-street
Directions: A4 to Boston Manor road (A3002), north to
Boston Gardens – turn left. Underground Piccadilly line
– right from Boston Manor station.

Brentwood, Essex

Marygreen Manor Hotel

★★★★★ 🍷🍷

London Road, Brentwood, Essex, CM14 4NR
Tel: 01277 225252 Fax: 01277 262809
Email: info@marygreenmanor.co.uk
Web: www.marygreenmanor.co.uk
Rooms: 45 all ensuite 🛏 ⊛
Pricing: Sgl £141–203 Dbl £170–252 Dinner from £30
CC: Accepted
Room facilities: ⌨ ☎ ☕ 🔌 ❄ Access: ♿
Conference: 7 meeting rooms (Thtr 50 max)
Children: Welcome 🍼 🎠
Dogs: Guide dogs only Licences: ⚜ 👯
Parking: Off-street
Directions: Exit the M25 at Junction 28. Take A1023,
after two minutes the hotel is on right.
See advert on next page

Heybridge Hotel

★★★ 🍷

Roman Road, Ingatestone, Essex, CM4 9AB
Tel: 01277 353288 Fax: 01277 353288
Rooms: 22 all ensuite ⊛
Pricing: Sgl £92–129 Dbl £102–149 Dinner from £16
CC: Accepted
Room facilities: ⌨ ☎ ☕ 🔌 Access: ♿
Conference: 4 meeting rooms (Thtr 550 max), 24hr-
delegate from £136, day-delegate rate from £33.50
Children: Welcome
Licences: ⚜ 👯
Parking: Off-street
Directions: M25-Junction 28 – A12 towards
Chelmsford. Take B1002 to Mountnessing/Ingatestone.
After 2 miles bridge A12 turn right, 200 yards on left.

Travelodge Brentwood, East Horndon

Travel Accommodation
A127, Halfway House, East Hornden, Brentwood,
Essex, CM13 3LL
Web: www.travelodge.co.uk Rooms: 45 all ensuite ⊛
Pricing: Sgl £64.40 Dbl £68.85
CC: Accepted Room facilities: ⌨ ☕ Access: ♿

Brighton, East Sussex

Old Ship Hotel

★★★★
Kings Road, Brighton, East Sussex, BN1 1NR
Tel: 01273 329001 Fax: 01273 820718
Email: oldship@paramount-hotels.co.uk
Web: www.paramount-hotels.co.uk

PARAMOUNT
GROUP OF HOTELS

Rooms: 152 all ensuite 🍴
Pricing: Sgl £132.50–192.50 Dbl £170–220
Dinner from £18.50 CC: Accepted
Room facilities: ⌨ ☎ ☕ Access: 🛗
Conference: 11 meeting rooms (Thtr 300 max), 24hr-
delegate from £178, day-delegate rate from £59
Children: Welcome 🍴 Dogs: Welcome
Licences: ⚜ 👯 Parking: Off-street and monitored
Directions: From M25 take M23 to Brighton, follow signs
for seafront, hotel is located on seafront (Kings) road.

Kings Hotel

★★★
139–141 Kings Road, Brighton, East Sussex, BN1 2NA
Tel: 01273 820854 Fax: 01273 828309
Email: kingshotel@vienna-group.co.uk
Web: www.viennagroup.co.uk
Rooms: 84 all ensuite 🍴 🛏
Pricing: Sgl £25–80 Dbl £50–150 Dinner from £12
CC: Accepted Room facilities: ⌨ ☎ ☕ 🔌 Access: 🛗
Conference: 4 meeting rooms (Thtr 80 max), 24hr-
delegate from £145, day-delegate rate from £40
Children: Welcome 🍴 Dogs: Guide dogs only
Licences: 👯 Parking: Off-street and monitored
Directions: From London or M25, take M23/A23 to
Brighton. Follow signs for the seafront. On reaching
Brighton Pier roundabout take third exit and drive
west. Hotel is opposite West Pier.

Quality Hotel Brighton

★★★

West Street, Brighton, East Sussex, BN1 2RQ
Tel: 01273 220033 Fax: 01273 778000
Email: admin@gb057.u-net.com
Web: www.choicehotels.com
Rooms: 138 all ensuite
Pricing: Sgl £89.75 Dbl £116.50 Dinner from £8.75
CC: Accepted
Room facilities: Access:
Conference: 8 meeting rooms (Thtr 200 max), 24hr-delegate from £110, day-delegate rate from £32
Children: Welcome Dogs: Welcome
Licences:
Directions: Follow A23 into Brighton until seafront, turn right at roundabout, 2nd set of lights turn right into West street.

It's easier online

For all your motoring and travel needs, www.rac.co.uk

Plan your route

Visit www.rac.co.uk for RAC's interactive route planner, including up to the minute traffic reports.

Burberry House – Tudor Lodgings

Little Gem

◆ ◆ ◆ ◆ ◆

Burberry House, 32A Dyke Road Avenue, Brighton, East Sussex, BN1 5LB
Tel: 01273 564634
Email: burberryhouse@fsmail.net

Tudor Lodge nestled in Brighton's wealthy suburbia offering an abundance of fine furnishings within its two bedroomed suite. Pedestal bathtub, robes, crisp linens and champagne offered, indulging and relaxing times.
Rooms: 2
Pricing: Sgl £95–175 Dbl £95–175 CC: Accepted
Room facilities:
Children: Welcome Dogs: Guide dogs only
Parking: Off-street and monitored
Directions: Right at roundabout at end of A23 onto Mill lane. Next roundabout 1st exit, Burberry house 3/4 mile on left.

Marygreen Manor Hotel

Pantheon Hotels & Leisure

This historic 16th-century Tudor House Hotel hosts an elegant Baronial Hall Restaurant, which offers creative international cuisine from a superior A La Carte or Fixed Price Menu accompanied by an award-winning wine list. An all day snack menu and afternoon teas are also available. Guests will enjoy a warm, friendly and highly professional service accompanied by traditional comforts such as our oak-panelled lounge with log fire, four-poster bedrooms and tranquil courtyard garden.

London Road, Brentwood,
Essex CM14 4NR
Tel: 01277 225252   Fax: 01277 262809

Southeast

Adelaide Hotel

51 Regency Square, Brighton, East Sussex, BN1 2FF
Tel: 01273 205286 Fax: 01273 220904
Email: adelaide@pavilion.co.uk
Rooms: 12 all ensuite ☕ Room facilities: ▢ ☎ ☕
Licences: ⚲

Arlanda Hotel

◆◆◆◆

20 New Steine, Brighton, East Sussex, BN2 1PD
Tel: 01273 699300 Fax: 01273 600930
Email: arlanda@brighton.co.uk
Seasonal closure: Christmas
Rooms: 16 all ensuite ☕ ⊛ Pricing: Sgl £28–48
Dbl £40–120 CC: Accepted Room facilities: ▢ ☕
Children: Welcome ⚲ Dogs: Guide dogs only
Licences: ⚲
Directions: From the Palace Pier, Brighton, travel 400
yards east on Marine Parade. Hotel is in New Steine
on left.

Ascott House Hotel

21 New Steine, Marine Parade, Brighton,
East Sussex, BN2 1PD
Tel: 01273 688085 Fax: 01273 623733
Email: welcome@ascotthousehotel.com
Web: www.ascotthousehotel.com
Rooms: 15 (14 ensuite) ☕ ☕ ⊛ Pricing: Sgl £30–42
Dbl £65–120 CC: Accepted Room facilities: ▢ ☎ ☕
Children: Welcome 2yrs min age ⚲ Licences: ⚲
Directions: Follow A23 to the seafront. Turn left at the
roundabout in front of Palace Pier. Take ninth turning
on left off Marine Parade.

Fyfield House

26 New Steine, Brighton, East Sussex, BN2 1PD
Tel: 01273 602770 Fax: 01273 602770
Email: fyfield@aol.com
Web: www.brighton.co.uk/hotels/fyfield
Seasonal closure: Christmas
Rooms: 9 (7 ensuite) ☕ ☕ ⊛ Pricing: Sgl £25–45
Dbl £60–90 CC: Accepted Room facilities: ▢ ☕
Children: Welcome ⚲ Dogs: Welcome
Directions: Town centre, at the Palace Pier, take A259
east. Eighth turning into the square, which has a one-
way system.

Hotel Twenty One

21 Charlotte Street, Marine Parade, Brighton,
East Sussex, BN2 1AG
Tel: 01273 686450 Fax: 01273 695560
Email: the21@pavilion.co.uk
Web: www.smoothhound.co.uk/hotels/21.html
Rooms: 8 all ensuite ☕
Pricing: Sgl £25–40 Dbl £60–105 CC: Accepted
Room facilities: ▢ ☎ ☕

Directions: From Palace Pier turn left onto A259. After
³/₄ mile, turn left onto Charlotte Street. Hotel Twenty
One is on left-hand side.

Paskins Hotel

18/19 Charlotte Street, Brighton, East Sussex, BN2 1AG
Tel: 01273 601203 Fax: 01273 621973
Email: welcome@paskins.co.uk
Web: www.paskins.co.uk

Paskins has resolutely cast aside ordinariness in favour
of its own values. Stylish and genuinely green in outlook.
Just yards from the beach and close to the centre of
things. Nineteen attractive rooms, with the odd four-
poster, all are impeccably clean and snug. Breakfast,
taken in a memorable art deco room includes a varied
menu of organic traditional and inspired vegetarian food.
Rooms: 19 (16 ensuite) ☕ ☕
Pricing: Sgl £25–45 Dbl £55–115 CC: Accepted
Room facilities: ▢ ☎ ☕ ☏ Children: Welcome ⚲ ☕
Dogs: Welcome Licences: ⚲
Directions: At Brighton pier, turn left. Paskins Hotel is
on 11th road on right.

Regency Hotel

28 Regency Square, Brighton, East Sussex, BN1 2FH
Tel: 01273 202690 Fax: 01273 220438
Email: enquiries@regencybrighton.co.uk
Web: www.regencybrighton.co.uk
Rooms: 13 (10 ensuite) ☕ ☕ ⊛
Pricing: Sgl £55–70 Dbl £85–100 CC: Accepted
Room facilities: ▢ ☎ ☕
Conference: 2 meeting rooms (Thtr 15 max)
Children: Welcome 6yrs min age ⚲ Licences: ⚲
Parking: Off-street and monitored
Directions: Regency Square is off the coastal road
(Kings Road) directly opposite the West Pier.
See advert on next page

Trouville

11 New Steine, Marine Parade, Brighton,
East Sussex, BN2 1PB
Tel: 01273 697384
Seasonal closure: Christmas and January
Rooms: 8 (6 ensuite) 🔲
Pricing: Sgl £29–45 Dbl £59–65 CC: Accepted
Room facilities: 🔲 ♨
Children: Welcome Licences: 🔱
Directions: Take A23 to Palace Pier. Turn left onto
A259. New Steine is the first square on left, after
approx 300 yards.

Allendale Hotel

3 New Steine, Brighton, East Sussex, BN2 1PB
Tel: 01273 675436 Fax: 01273 602603
Email: allendalehotel@tinyworld.co.uk
Seasonal closure: closed during Christmas
Rooms: 12 (10 ensuite) 🔲 ♨
Pricing: Sgl £25–35 Dbl £60–80 CC: Accepted
Room facilities: 🔲 ☎ ♨
Children: Welcome Dogs: Guide dogs only
Licences: 🔱
Directions: Take A23 to Palace pier, turn left at the
roundabout, New Steine is the ninth turning on the left.

Brighton Marina House Hotel

8 Charlotte Street, Brighton, East Sussex, BN2 1AG
Tel: 01273 605349 Fax: 01273 679484
Email: rooms@jungs.co.uk
Web: www.brighton-mh-hotel.co.uk
Rooms: 10 (7 ensuite) 🔲
Pricing: Dinner from £19.50 CC: Accepted
Room facilities: 🔲 ☎ ♨
Children: Welcome Parking: Off-street
Directions: At Brighton pier turn up Marine Parade
(A259). After second traffic lights, take fifth left
(Charlotte Street).
See advert on following page

Cavalaire House

34 Upper Rock Gardens, Brighton,
East Sussex, BN2 1QF
Tel: 01273 696899 Fax: 01273 600504
Email: welcome@cavalaire.co.uk
Web: www.cavalaire.co.uk
Seasonal closure: mid-January to mid-February
Rooms: 10 all ensuite ♨ 🔲 ♨
Pricing: Sgl £29–55 Dbl £49–80 CC: Accepted
Room facilities: 🔲 ♨ ⚲
Children: Welcome 5yrs min age
Dogs: Guide dogs only Licences: 🔱
Parking: Off-street
Directions: Follow signposts to town centre/seafront.
At Brighton Pier roundabout, take A259 Rottingdean.
At second set of lights, turn left into Lower Rock
Gardens. Hotel up hill.

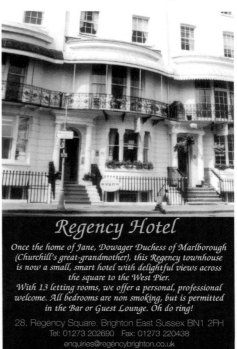

Genevieve Hotel

18 Maderia Place, Brighton, East Sussex, BN2 1TN
Tel: 01273 681653 Fax: 01273 681653
Email: rac@genevievehotel.co.uk
Web: www.genevievehotel.co.uk
Rooms: 11 (6 ensuite) 🔲 ♨
Pricing: Sgl £40–50 Dbl £50–90 CC: Accepted
Room facilities: 🔲 ♨
Directions: From Brighton Pier go east along Seafront
Road A259 (Marine Parade). Madeira Place is the 5th
turning on the left.

The Lanes Hotel

70-72 Marine Parade, Brighton, East Sussex, BN2 1AE
Tel: 01273 674231

The Garth

28 Cornwall Gardens, Brighton, East Sussex, BN1 6RJ
Tel: 01273 561515 Fax: 01273 561515
Email: mike-edwards@mistral.co.uk
Rooms: 3 ♨
Pricing: Sgl £25–35 Dbl £50–65
Room facilities: 🔲 ♨
Children: Welcome 5yrs min age
Directions: A23 into Brighton becomes London Road;
after 1 mile turn left into Varndean Road; Cornwall
Gardens is first right.

Southeast

Marina House Hotel

8 Charlotte Street, Brighton BN2 1AG

Tel: 0044 (0) 1273 605349   Fax: 0044 (0) 1273 679484

Email: rooms@jungs.co.uk

Web: www.brighton-mh-hotel.co.uk

Location

Located off the sea front within 3 minutes walk to the beach. Our exquisitely appointed rooms offer a unique and innovative experience in today's Bed & Breakfast.

We offer

For your special pleasure and comfort we offer en-suite facility with the required modern comforts.

Most rooms non- smoking

Rooms available without breakfast.

Free Internet access and e-mail facility.

Special Sunday - Friday offer.

0800 local cab number

Eastern Style Room

You will love our "Sexy beds"

Yummy Breakfast

After sleeping in our Sexy beds, you will love our yummy breakfast. We cater for Vegan, Vegetarian, Continental and the full English.

Please call us for more information or take a look at our web site for a new and unique experience in today's Bed and Breakfast.

French 4-poster Room

Tariff: £25.00 to £50.00 per person per night.

Tudor Style Room

Tudor Room - balcony

Malvern Hotel

33 Regency Square, Brighton , East Sussex, BN1 2GG
Tel: 01273 324302 Fax: 01273 324285

Enjoy the comfort of a luxury house, rooms with sea views, en-suite, designed by oriental artist with her personal touch.
Rooms: 10 all en-suite ⚓ ⊛
Pricing: Sgl £45 Dbl £75 CC: accepted
Room facilities: ▢ ☎ ☕ Children: Welcome ⴕ ⁑℃
Dogs: Welcome Parking: Monitored
Directions: Opposite West pier in Regency square.

Travelodge Brighton Central (SA)

Travel Accommodation
A23, 165-167 Preston Road, Brighton, BN1 6AU
Web: www.travelodge.co.uk
Rooms: 94 all ensuite ⊛
Pricing: Sgl £64.40–74.40 Dbl £68.85–78.85
CC: Accepted Room facilities: ▢ ☕ Access: ♿

Broadstairs, Kent

Fayreness Hotel

Marine Drive, Kingsgate, Broadstairs, Kent, CT10 3LG
Tel: 01843 868641

Bay Tree Hotel

12 Eastern Esplanade, Broadstairs, Kent, CT10 1DR
Tel: 01843 862502 Fax: 01843 860589
Rooms: 11 all ensuite ⊛
Pricing: Sgl £30–34 Dbl £60–68 Dinner from £15
CC: Accepted Room facilities: ▢ ☕
Children: Welcome 10yrs min age
Licences: ⁙ Parking: Off-street and monitored
Directions: Situated on clifftop Eastern Esplanade. Follow main road through town, turning right into Rectory Road on leaving Broadstairs.

Devonhurst Hotel

Eastern Esplanade, Broadstairs, Kent, CT10 1DR
Tel: 01843 863010 Fax: 01843 868940
Email: info@devonhurst.co.uk
Web: www.devonhurst.co.uk
Rooms: 9 all ensuite ⊛
Pricing: Sgl £36 Dbl £58–66 Dinner from £14.50
CC: Accepted Room facilities: ▢ ☕

Children: Welcome 5yrs min age ⴕ Licences: ⁙
Directions: Follow main high street to the bottom, bearing left into Albion Street. Take third right into Dickens Road, then Eastern Esplanade.

Oakfield Private Hotel

11 The Vale, Broadstairs, Kent, CT10 1RB
Tel: 01843 862506 Fax: 01843 600659
Email: info@oakfield-hotel.com
Web: www.oakfield-hotel.com
Rooms: 10 all ensuite ⊛
Pricing: Sgl £32–35 Dbl £56–64 Dinner from £14
CC: Accepted Room facilities: ▢ ☎ ☕
Dogs: Guide dogs only Licences: ⁙
Leisure: Games room Parking: Off-street
Directions: Halfway down High Street, turn right into Queens Road, then take the third right. Hotel is 25 yards on right.

Brockenhurst, Hampshire

New Park Manor Hotel

Brockenhurst, Hampshire, SO42 7QH
Tel: 01590 623467 Fax: 01590 622268
Email: enquiries@newparkmanorhotel.co.uk
Web: www.newparkmanorhotel.co.uk
Rooms: 24 all ensuite 🛏 ⊛
Pricing: Sgl £85 Dbl £110 Dinner from £27.50
CC: Accepted
Room facilities: ▢ ☎ ☕
Conference: 5 meeting rooms (Thtr 120 max), 24hr-delegate from £135, day-delegate rate from £45
Children: Welcome ⴕ Dogs: Welcome
Licences: ⬥ ⁙ Leisure: Outdoor pool, Tennis, Riding
Parking: Off-street and monitored
Directions: Leave M27 at Junction 1. Follow A337 to Lyndhurst and Brockenhurst. Hotel sign and private drive on right midway between Lyndhurst and Brockenhurst.

Rhinefield House

Rhinefield Road, Brockenhurst, Hampshire, SO42 7QB
Tel: 01590 622922 Fax: 01590 622800
Email: rhinefield-house@arcadianhotels.co.uk
Web: www.rhinefieldhousehotel.co.uk
Rooms: 34 all ensuite 🛏 ⊛
Pricing: Sgl £110–130 Dbl £125–170
Dinner from £29.50 CC: Accepted
Room facilities: ▢ ☎ ☕
Conference: 6 meeting rooms (Thtr 150 max), 24hr-delegate from £165, day-delegate rate from £55
Children: Welcome ⴕ ⁑℃ Dogs: Guide dogs only
Licences: ⬥ ⁙
Leisure: Indoor pool, Outdoor pool, Gym, Tennis, Games room Parking: Off-street and monitored
Directions: J1 M27 A337 to Lyndhurst; then A35 west to Christchurch. Turn left after 2¹/₂ miles into Ornamental Drive, signposted Rhinefield House.

Watersplash Hotel

★★

The Rise, Brockenhurst, Hampshire, SO42 7ZP
Tel: 01590 622344 Fax: 01590 624047
Email: bookings@watersplash.co.uk
Web: www.watersplash.co.uk
Rooms: 23 (19 ensuite) 🍽️ 🖨️
Pricing: Sgl £56–77 Dbl £78–106 Dinner from £22
CC: Accepted
Room facilities: 🖵 ☎ 🍵
Access: ♿
Children: Welcome 🍴 ℃
Dogs: Welcome
Licences: ♦♦♦
Leisure: Outdoor pool, Snooker/billiards
Parking: Off-street

The Rose and Crown

◆ ◆ ◆

Lyndhurst Road, Brockenhurst, Hampshire, SO42 7RH
Tel: 01590 622225 Fax: 01590 623056
Email: roseandcrown.brockenhurst@eldridge-pope.co.uk
Web: www.eldridge-pope-inns.co.uk
Rooms: 14 all ensuite 🍽️ 🖨️ ⊗
Pricing: Sgl £55 Dbl £55 Dinner from £7
CC: Accepted
Room facilities: 🖵 ☎ 🍵 ☏
Access: ♿
Children: Welcome 🍴
Dogs: Welcome
Licences: ♦♦♦
Leisure: Games room
Parking: Off-street
Directions: From M27 take A337 through Lyndhurst towards Lymington. Rose and Crown is on the left when entering Brockenhurst.

Bromley, Kent

Bromley Court

★★★

Bromley Hill, Bromley, Kent, BR1 4JD
Tel: 020 8464 5011 Fax: 020 8460 0899
Email: bromleyhotel@btinternet.com
Web: www.bromley-hotel.co.uk
Rooms: 115 all ensuite 🍽️ ⊗
Pricing: Sgl £98–105 Dbl £100–120 Dinner from £15
CC: Accepted
Room facilities: 🖵 ☎ 🍵 ☏ ❄
Access: ⬆ ♿
Conference: 9 meeting rooms (Thtr 150 max), 24hr-delegate from £39, day-delegate rate from £140
Children: Welcome 🍴
Dogs: Guide dogs only
Licences: ⚓ ♦♦♦
Leisure: Gym, Health spa
Parking: Off-street and monitored
Directions: Exit J4 M25, A21 to Bromley use Kentish Way to London Road A21 Private Drive off Bromley Hill opposite Mercedes showroom.

Buckingham, Buckinghamshire

Villiers Hotel

★★★★ 🍴 🍴 🍴

3 Castle Street, Buckingham,
Buckinghamshire, MK18 1BS
Tel: 01280 822444 Fax: 01280 822113
Email: villiers@villiershotel.demon.co.uk
Rooms: 46 all ensuite 🍽️ 🖨️
Pricing: Sgl £85–140 Dbl £110–195 Dinner from £25
CC: Accepted
Room facilities: 🖵 ☎ 🍵 ☏
Access: ⬆ ♿
Conference: 7 meeting rooms (Thtr 250 max), 24hr-delegate from £165, day-delegate rate from £45
Children: Welcome 🍴 ℃
Licences: ⚓ ♦♦♦
Parking: Off-street
Directions: From Junction 9 on M40 or Junction 13 on M1, take A421 to Buckingham. Hotel is situated in Castle Street.

Burford, Oxfordshire

Travelodge Burford, Cotswolds

Travel Accommodation
A40, Bury Barn, Burford, Oxfordshire, OX8 4JF
Web: www.travelodge.co.uk
Rooms: 40 all ensuite ⊗
Pricing: Sgl £57.40 Dbl £61.85
CC: Accepted Room facilities: 🖵 🍵 Access: ♿

Burley, Hampshire

Moorhill House Hotel

★★★

Burley, near Ringwood, Hampshire, BH24 4AG
Tel: 01425 403285 Fax: 01425 403715
Email: moorhill@carehotels.co.uk
Web: www.carehotels.co.uk
Rooms: 24 all ensuite 🍽️
Pricing: Dinner from £21.50 CC: Accepted
Room facilities: 🖵 ☎ 🍵
Children: Welcome 🍴 ℃
Dogs: Welcome
Licences: ♦♦♦
Leisure: Indoor pool, Gym
Parking: Off-street and monitored
Directions: From M27, take A31 and follow signs to Burley. Bear left at War Memorial and right past Queens Head. Moorhill House is signposted on right.
See advert on next page

Cadnam, Hampshire

Bartley Lodge Hotel

★★★

Lyndhurst Road, Cadnam, Hampshire, SO40 2NR
Tel: 02380 812248 Fax: 02380 812075
Email: bartley@carehotels.co.uk
Web: www.carehotels.co.uk
Rooms: 31 all ensuite
Pricing: Dinner from £21.50 CC: Accepted
Room facilities:
Children: Welcome
Dogs: Welcome
Licences:
Leisure: Indoor pool, Gym, Health spa, Tennis
Parking: Off-street
Directions: From M27 exit at junction one, left at first roundabout, right at second Bartley Lodge is on the left.
See advert on this page

Camberley, Surrey

Frimley Hall

★★★

Lime Avenue, off Portsmouth Road, Camberley, Surrey, GU15 2BG
Tel: 0870 4008224 Fax: 01276 691253
Email: frimleyhall@heritage-hotels.co.uk
Web: www.macdonaldhotels.co.uk
Rooms: 86 all ensuite
Pricing: Sgl £49 Dbl £98 CC: Accepted
Room facilities:
Access: &
Conference: 4 meeting rooms (Thtr 60 max)
Children: Welcome
Dogs: Welcome
Licences:
Parking: Off-street
Directions: From M3 Junction 3, pick up A30 towards Camberley for 1 mile, then A325 towards Farnham. Conifer Drive 1 mile on right.

Camberley Guest House

◆◆◆

116 London Road, Camberley, Surrey, GU15 3TJ
Tel: 01276 24410 Fax: 01276 65409
Seasonal closure: Christmas
Rooms: 5 all ensuite
Pricing: Sgl £55 Dbl £70 CC: Accepted
Room facilities:
Children: Welcome
Parking: Off-street and monitored
Directions: Situated on main A30, running parallel to M3. From London, take exit 3, from south coast take exit 4. Hotel in town centre of Camberley.

Making a booking?

 Don't forget to mention RAC Hotels and Bed & Breakfast 2003.

Moorhill House Hotel

Situated in the beautiful new forest village of Burley, this comfortable hotel lies in 2 acres of grounds. Leisure facilities include an indoor pool, mini-gym and sauna. The lounges overlook the lawns on which guests can play croquet and mini golf.

Burley, near Ringwood,
Hampshire BH24 4AG
Tel: 01425 403285 fax: 01425 403715
email: moorhill@carehotels.co.uk
www.carehotels.co.uk

Bartley Lodge Hotel

Grade II listed country house hotel set in 8 acres of grounds and gardens directly adjoining the New Forest.

31 delightfully furnished bedrooms, excellent cuisine, indoor leisure centre with pool, sauna, fitness room and two hard-surface tennis courts.

Cadnam, New Forest SO40 2NR

Tel: 023 80812 248   Fax: 023 80812 075
Email: bartley@carehotels.co.uk
Website: www.carehotels.co.uk

Canterbury, Kent

The Chaucer

★★★

Ivy Lane, Canterbury, Kent, CT1 1TU
Tel: 0870 400 8106 Fax: 01227 450397
Email: chaucer@heritage-hotels.co.uk
Web: www.macdonaldhotels.co.uk
Rooms: 42 all ensuite
Pricing: Sgl £69 Dbl £138 Dinner from £18
CC: Accepted
Room facilities: Access:
Conference: 2 meeting rooms (Thtr 140 max)
Children: Welcome Dogs: Welcome
Licences: Parking: Off-street and monitored
Directions: Leave M2 at Junction 7. Follow signs to Canterbury. At fifth roundabout turn right. Hotel is on left.

Canterbury Hotel

★★

71 New Dover Road, Canterbury, Kent, CT1 3DZ
Tel: 01227 450551 Fax: 01227 780145
Email: canterbury.hotel@btinternet.com
Web: www.canterbury-hotel-apartments.co.uk
Rooms: 23 all ensuite
Pricing: Sgl £55–82 Dbl £78–115 Dinner from £16.50
CC: Accepted
Room facilities:
Access:
Children: Welcome 6yrs min age
Dogs: Welcome
Licences:
Parking: Off-street and monitored
Directions: On A2 – New Dover Road.

Thanington Hotel

140 Wincheap, Canterbury, Kent, CT1 3RY
Tel: 01227 453227 Fax: 01227 453225
Email: thanington@lineone.net
Web: www.thanington-hotel.co.uk
Seasonal closure: Christmas

Family owned listed Georgian manor house with modern 10 bedroom extension and within walking distance of cathedral & city centre. Superb accommodation, private bar, heated indoor pool, secure parking & games room.
Rooms: 15 all ensuite
Pricing: Sgl £55–68 Dbl £73–110 CC: Accepted
Room facilities:
Access:
Children: Welcome Dogs: Welcome
Licences:
Leisure: Indoor pool, Games room, Snooker/billiards
Parking: Off-street and monitored
Directions: Located on Canterbury-to-Ashford A28 outside city walls, ten minutes' walk from city centre

Travelodge Canterbury West

Travel Accommodation
A2 Northbound Trunk Road, Gate Services, Dunkirk, Nr. Canterbury, Kent, ME13 9LN
Web: www.travelodge.co.uk
Rooms: 40 all ensuite
Pricing: Sgl £54.40 Dbl £58.85
CC: Accepted Room facilities: Access:

Chawston, Bedfordshire

Travelodge Bedford East

Travel Accommodation
A1 North, Black Cat Roundabout, Nr. Chawston, Bedfordshire, MK44 3OT
Web: www.travelodge.co.uk
Rooms: 40 all ensuite
Pricing: Sgl £47.40–54.40 Dbl £51.85–58.85
CC: Accepted Room facilities: Access:

Checkendon, Berkshire

The Highwayman

♦ ♦ ♦ ♦

Exlade Street, Checkendon, Berkshire, RG8 0UA
Tel: 01491 682020 Fax: 01491 682229
Rooms: 4 all ensuite
Pricing: £60–70 Dinner from £9 CC: Accepted
Room facilities:
Children: Welcome 5yrs min age
Dogs: Guide dogs only
Licences:
Parking: Off-street
Directions: Situated just off the A4074 Wallingford to Reading Road.

Plan your route

Visit www.rac.co.uk for RAC's interactive route planner, including up to the minute traffic reports.

Chelmsford, Essex

Atlantic Hotel
★★★
New Street, Chelmsford, Essex, CM1 1PP
Tel: 01245 268168 Fax: 01245 268169
Email: book@atlantichotel.co.uk
Web: www.atlantichotel.co.uk

Rooms: 59 all ensuite ⊛
Pricing: Sgl £59–79 Dbl £69–125 Dinner from £20
CC: Accepted
Room facilities: ❑ ☎ ⊙ ☍ ❄ Access: ☍
Conference: 3 meeting rooms (Thtr 15 max)
Children: Welcome
Licences: ♦♦♦ Leisure: Gym
Parking: Off-street and monitored
Directions: A1016 to Chelmsford and signs to station.
Over two mini-roundabouts, turn left then right. At
traffic lights left into New Street.

County Hotel
★★★★ ®
29 Rainsford Road, Chelmsford, Essex, CM1 2QA
Tel: 01245 455700 Fax: 01245 492762
Email: sales@countyhotel-essex.co.uk
Web: www.countyhotel-essex.co.uk
Rooms: 36 all ensuite
Room facilities: ❑ ☎ ⊙ ☍ Access: ☍
Children: Welcome ♦ Licences: ⟁ ♦♦♦
Parking: Off-street
Directions: From M25 Junction 28, take A12 to
Chelmsford. From town centre, take road to rail
station. Pass station, under bridge, hotel on left after
traffic lights.

Ivy Hill Hotel
★★★
Writtle Road, Margaretting, Essex, CM4 0EH
Tel: 01277 353040 Fax: 01277 355038
Email: sales@ivyhillhotel.co.uk
Web: www.ivyhillhotel.co.uk
Rooms: 33 all ensuite ⊛ ▱
Pricing: Sgl £80 Dbl £95 Dinner from £20.95
CC: Accepted Room facilities: ❑ ☎ ⊙ Access: ☍
Conference: 6 meeting rooms (Thtr 110 max), 24hr-
delegate from £140, day-delegate rate from £35
Children: Welcome ♦ Licences: ⟁ ♦♦♦
Leisure: Outdoor pool, Tennis
Parking: Off-street and monitored
Directions: 8 miles east of the M25 on the A12. Take
the second exit on the B1002 for Margaretting.

Beechcroft Hotel
♦♦♦
211 New London Road, Chelmsford, Essex, CM2 0AJ
Tel: 01245 352462 Fax: 01245 347833
Email: enquiries@beechcrofthotel.com
Web: www.beechcrofthotel.com
Rooms: 19 (13 ensuite) ⊛ ⊛
Room facilities: ❑ ⊙ Children: Welcome
Dogs: Welcome Parking: Off-street
Directions: Exit J28 M25 onto A12; then A414. Cross
three mini-roundabouts, then first left at next one.
Hotel is on right after first traffic lights.

Tanunda Hotel
♦♦♦
217-219 New London Road, Chelmsford,
Essex, CM2 0AJ
Tel: 01245 354295 Fax: 01245 345503
Rooms: 20 (11 ensuite)
Pricing: Sgl £36–62 Dbl £54–63 CC: Accepted
Room facilities: ❑ ☎ ⊙ Access: ☍
Children: Welcome Licences: ♦♦♦

Chenies, Hertfordshire

Bedford Arms Hotel
★★★★ ®
Chenies, near Rickmansworth, Hertfordshire, WD3 6EQ
Tel: 01923 283301 Fax: 01923 284825
Email: contact@bedfordarms.co.uk
Web: www.bedfordarms.co.uk
Rooms: 10 all ensuite ▱ ⊛
Pricing: Sgl £60–130 Dbl £95–140 Dinner from £25
CC: Accepted Room facilities: ❑ ☎ ⊙ ☍
Conference: 2 meeting rooms (Thtr 18 max), 24hr-
delegate from £142.50, day-delegate rate from £42.50
Children: Welcome ♦ ⊙ Dogs: Guide dogs only
Licences: ♦♦♦ Parking: Off-street
Directions: 2 miles from M25 Junction 18 on A404,
Amersham direction. Signposted Chenies, on right.
See advert on following page

Southeast

Bedford Arms Hotel

Tranquil Country House Hotel dating back in part to 1841 set in an acre garden with an oak panelled restaurant serving award winning food by Simon Whitley and his talented young brigade. Daily chef's specials. Real ale and quality wines from around the world. Wonderful walks and River Chess nearby.

Chenies, near Rickmansworth, Hertfordshire, WD3 6EQ
Tel: 01923 283301   Fax: 01923 284825
Email:contact@bedfordarms.co.uk
Website:www.bedfordarms.co.uk

Chichester, West Sussex

Millstream Hotel
★★★★ 🅐🅑🅒 🅡

Bosham Lane, Bosham, Chichester, West Sussex, PO18 8HL
Tel: 01243 573234 Fax: 01243 573459
Email: info@millstream-hotel.co.uk
Web: www.millstream-hotel.co.uk

Beautifully-appointed country house dating from 1701, set in a picturesque sailing village. Bar, sitting-room, restaurant and a bedroom designed for wheelchair access, all on ground floor. Locally renowned award-winning restaurant.
Rooms: 35 all ensuite 🐕 📺 ⊗
Pricing: Sgl £79–85 Dbl £125–135 Dinner from £25
CC: Accepted
Room facilities: 🖥 ☎ 🍵 🔌 Access: ♿

Conference: 1 meeting room (Thtr 40 max), 24hr-delegate from £120, day-delegate rate from £30
Children: Welcome ⍓ ⋇🄲
Dogs: Welcome Licences: 🐚 ♟
Parking: Off-street and monitored
Directions: From Chichester or Havant take the A259 to Bosham. From Swan roundabout follow brown signs south to hotel.

Ship Hotel
❖

North Street, Chichester, West Sussex, PO19 1NH
Tel: 01243 778000 Fax: 01243 788000
Email: www.ship.chichester@eldridge-pope.co.uk
Rooms: 36 all ensuite 📺 ⊗
Pricing: Sgl £79 Dbl £99 Dinner from £10
CC: Accepted Room facilities: 🖥 ☎ 🍵 🔌 Access: ⊥
Conference: 2 meeting rooms (Thtr 70 max)
Children: Welcome ⍓ ⋇🄲 Dogs: Welcome
Licences: ♟ Parking: Off-street
Directions: From the A27 follow signs for Chichester, in Chichester follow signs for city centre hotel, at Northgate roundabout the Ship Hotel is signposted.

Aberlands House Hotel
◆◆◆◆

Merston, Chichester, West Sussex, PO20 6DY
Tel: 01243 532675 Fax: 01243 788884
Rooms: 7 all ensuite 🐕 📺
Room facilities: 🖥 🍵 Access: ♿
Children: Welcome ⍓ ⋇🄲 Licences: ♟
Parking: Off-street and monitored

The Vestry
◆◆◆◆

23 Southgate, Chichester, West Sussex, PO19 1ES
Tel: 01243 773358 Fax: 01243 530633
Email: vestry.chichester@eldridge-pope.co.uk
Rooms: 11 all ensuite 📺 ⊗
Pricing: Sgl £60–70 Dbl £70–80 Dinner from £8.50
CC: Accepted
Room facilities: 🖥 ☎ 🍵 🔌
Children: Welcome ⍓ Dogs: Guide dogs only
Licences: ♟
Parking: Off-street and monitored
Directions: From the A27 join the Chichester ring road and follow signs for Southgate. The Vestry is on South Street.

Chinnor, Oxfordshire

The Peacock Hotel
★★ 🅡

Henton, Chinnor, Oxfordshire, OX9 4AH
Tel: 01844 353519 Fax: 01844 353891
Email: brat22@villagepubs.co.uk
Web: www.villagepubs.co.uk
Rooms: 26 all ensuite 📺
Room facilities: 🖥 ☎ 🍵 Dogs: Welcome
Parking: Off-street and monitored

Chipping Norton, Oxfordshire

Southcombe Lodge

◆ ◆ ◆

Southcombe, Chipping Norton, Oxfordshire, OX7 5QH
Tel: 01608 643068 Fax: 01608 642948
Email: georgefindlysouthcombelodge@tinyworld.co.uk
Rooms: 6 (4 ensuite) ⊛
Pricing: Sgl £35 (2002 rate) Dbl £54 (2002 rate)
Room facilities: ▢ ⊛ Children: Welcome ⼞
Licences: ∰ Parking: Off-street and monitored
Directions: On A44 from Oxford to Chipping Norton,
next to Chipping Norton Golf Course.

Clacton-on-Sea, Essex

Le Vere Private Hotel

◆ ◆ ◆

15 Agate Road, Marine Parade West, Clacton-on-Sea,
Essex, CO15 1RA
Tel: 01255 423044 Fax: 01255 423044
Rooms: 6 all ensuite ⊛ ⊟ ⊛
Pricing: Dinner from £12 CC: Accepted
Room facilities: ▢ ⊛
Children: Welcome ⼞
Dogs: Welcome Licences: ∰
Parking: Off-street and monitored
Directions: Go to seafront. From London Road, turn
right. Cross the lights. Agate Road is next turn on right;
hotel is halfway up on left, a pink and white building.

The Sandrock Hotel

◆ ◆ ◆

1 Penfold Road, Marine Parade West, Clacton-on-Sea,
Essex, CO15 1JN
Tel: 01255 428215 Fax: 01255 428215

Rooms: 9 all ensuite ⊛ ⊛
Pricing: Sgl £35.50–36 Dbl £53 Dinner from £12.95
CC: Accepted Room facilities: ▢ ⊛ Access: ♿
Children: Welcome ⼞ Dogs: Welcome Licences: ∰
Parking: Off-street
Directions: Take A120 to Clacton. Turn right at the
seafront. The Sandrock Hotel is in the second turning
on the right, past pier.

Colchester, Essex

Five Lakes Hotel, Golf, Country Club & Spa

★ ★ ★ ★ ⊛ ⊛

Colchester Road, Tolleshunt Knights, Maldon,
Essex, CM9 8HX
Tel: 01621 868888 Fax: 01621 869696
Email: enquiries@fivelakes.co.uk
Web: www.fivelakes.co.uk

Set in 320 acres including two golf courses. Extensive
leisure, health, beauty and sporting facilities plus a
choice of restaurants and bars. Spacious bedrooms,
four posters and suites. Children welcome.
Rooms: 114 all ensuite ⊛ ⊟ ⊛
Pricing: £117.95–173.90 Dinner from £18.50
CC: Accepted, Room facilities: ▢ ☎ ⊛ ⬧
Access: ⬆ ♿
Conference: 21 meeting rooms (Thtr 2000 max), 24hr-
delegate from £174.50, day-delegate rate from £49
Children: Welcome ⼞ ⬧
Dogs: Guide dogs only
Licences: ⬧ ∰
Leisure: Indoor pool, Gym, Health spa, Beauty salon,
Tennis, Golf, Games room, Snooker/billiards
Parking: Off-street and monitored
Directions: Take the A12 in the direction of Kelvedon,
then follow the brown and white 'Five Lakes' tourist
board signage.

Butterfly Hotel

★ ★ ★

A12/A120 Junction, Old Ipswich Road,
Colchester, Essex, CO7 7QY
Tel: 01206 230900 Fax: 01206 231095
Email: colbutterfly@lineone.net
Web: www.butterflyhotels.co.uk
Rooms: 50 all ensuite ⊛
Pricing: Sgl £63.50–88 Dbl £72–96.50
Dinner from £17.50 CC: Accepted
Room facilities: ▢ ☎ ⊛ ⬧
Access: ♿
Conference: 4 meeting rooms (Thtr 80 max)
Children: Welcome ⼞
Dogs: Guide dogs only Licences: ∰
Parking: Off-street
Directions: Situated north of Colchester by the
A12/A120 Ardleigh junction.

George

★★★ ℞

116 High Street, Colchester, Essex, CO1 1TD
Tel: 01206 578494 Fax: 01206 761732
Email: colcgeorge@aol.com
Rooms: 47 all ensuite
Room facilities:
Children: Welcome Dogs: Welcome
Licences: Parking: Off-street and monitored
Directions: Follow signs for Colchester Town Centre.
Once on the High Street, the hotel is 1/2 mile down on
the left-hand side.

Maison Talbooth

★★★★ ℞℞℞

Stratford Road, Dedham, Colchester, Essex, CO7 6HN
Tel: 01206 322367 Fax: 01206 322752
Email: maison@talbooth.co.uk
Web: www.talbooth.com

Tranquility is the essence of this Victorian house with
its imposing views over the Stow Valley. Its restaurant
is the renowned Le Talbooth, a short distance away
along the riverbank.
Rooms: 10 all ensuite
Pricing: Sgl £120–150 Dbl £155–210 Dinner from £46
CC: Accepted
Room facilities: Access:
Conference: 2 meeting rooms (Thtr 32 max), 24hr-
delegate from £140, day-delegate rate from £35
Children: Welcome Dogs: Guide dogs only
Licences: Parking: Off-street and monitored

The Rose & Crown Hotel

★★★

East Street, Colchester, Essex, CO1 2TZ
Tel: 01206 866677 Fax: 01206 866616
Email: info@rose-and-crown.com
Web: www.rose-and-crown.com
Rooms: 29 all ensuite
Pricing: Sgl £59–110 Dbl £69–135 Dinner from £17.95
CC: AcceptedRoom facilities:
Access:
Conference: 2 meeting rooms (Thtr 100 max)
Children: Welcome Dogs: Guide dogs only
Licences:
Parking: Off-street and monitored
Directions: From M25 exit at J28(A12), take Colchester
exit (A134), follow Roller World signs – hotel opposite.

Travelodge Feering, Colchester

Travel Accommodation
A12, London Road Northbound, Feering, Nr.
Colchester, Essex, CO5 9EL
Web: www.travelodge.co.uk
Rooms: 39 all ensuite
Pricing: Sgl £47.40–54.40 Dbl £51.85–58.85
CC: Accepted Room facilities: Access:

Copthorne, Sussex

Hedgehog Inn

♦♦♦

Effingham Road, Copthorne, Nr Crawley,
Sussex, RH10 2HY
Tel: 01342 716 202 Fax: 01342 716 245
Email: www.hedgehog.copthorne@eldridge-pope.co.uk
Rooms: 12 all ensuite
Pricing: Dbl £55 Dinner from £7 CC: Accepted
Room facilities: Access:
Children: Welcome Dogs: Guide dogs only
Licences: Parking: Off-street
Directions: Junction 10 of A23 taking the A264 to East
Grinstead. At Dukes Head Pub roundabout take road to
Horley, left at staggered crossroads, 400 yds on left.

Coulsdon, Surrey

Aries Guest House

♦♦♦♦

38 Brighton Road, Coulsdon, Surrey, CR5 2BA
Tel: 020 8668 5744 Fax: 020 8668 5744
Email: enquiries@arieshouse.co.uk
Web: www.arieshouse.co.uk
Rooms: 5 (2 ensuite)
Pricing: Sgl £26–30 Dbl £35–42 CC: Accepted
Room facilities:
Children: Welcome 7yrs min age
Dogs: Guide dogs only
Parking: Off-street and monitored
Directions: Situated on the A23 between Purley and
Coulsdon – 400 yards north of Coulsdon Shopping
Centre and Smitham Rail Station.

Crawley, West Sussex

Little Foxes Hotel

♦♦♦♦

Charlwood Road, Ifield Wood, Crawley,
West Sussex, RH11 0YJ
Tel: 01293 529206 Fax: 01293 551434

Need help booking?

RAC Hotel Reservations will find
the accommodation that's right
for you – and book it too.
Call today on 0870 603 9109
and quote 'Guide 2003'

Waterhall Country House

Prestwood Lane, Ifield Wood, near Crawley,
West Sussex, RH11 0LA
Tel: 01293 520002 Fax: 01293 539905
Email: waterhallcountryhouse@lineone.net
Web: www.smoothhound.co.uk/hotels/waterhall
Rooms: 11 all ensuite ⚥ 🚭 Room facilities: ▢ ☕
Access: ♿ Children: Welcome Dogs: Welcome
Licences: ♟ Parking: Off-street and monitored
Directions: Exit J10 M23, A2011 Crawley Avenue. Right
at third roundabout into Ifield Avenue. Continue for 2
miles, Prestwood Lane on left.

Travelodge Gatwick Airport (SA)

Travel Accommodation
A23, Church Road, Lowfield Heath, Crawley,
West Sussex, RH11 0PQ
Web: www.travelodge.co.uk Rooms: 186 all ensuite 🚭
Pricing: Sgl £49.40–54.40 Dbl £53.85–58.85
CC: Accepted Room facilities: ▢ ☕ Access: ♿

Crowborough, East Sussex

Plough and Horses

Walshes Road, Crowborough, East Sussex, TN6 3RE
Tel: 01892 652614 Fax: 01892 652614
Rooms: 15 all ensuite ⚥ 🚭
Pricing: Sgl £28–37 Dbl £48–52 CC: Accepted
Room facilities: ▢ ☕
Conference: 2 meeting rooms (Thtr 70 max)
Children: Welcome ♟ Dogs: Welcome
Licences: ♟ Parking: Off-street and monitored
Directions: A26 Tunbridge Wells to Crowborough. First
left at Boars Head roundabout. Cross junction with
Crowborough Hill to the end of Tollwood Road.

Croydon, Surrey

Coulsdon Manor

★★★★ 🚗🚗🚗

Coulsdon Court Road, Old Coulsdon, Croydon,
Surrey, CR5 2LL
Tel: 020 8668 0414 Fax: 020 8668 3118
Email: coulsdonmanor@marstonhotels.com
Web: www.marstonhotels.com

Manor house in 140 acres of parkland with 18 hole golf
course, convenient for Central London, 2AA rosette

restaurant. Leisure facilities include: squash, tennis,
gym, sunbed and aerobic studio.
Rooms: 35 all ensuite ⚥ 🚭
Pricing: Sgl £115 Dbl £149 Dinner from £28
CC: Accepted Room facilities: ▢ ☎ ☕ ✆ Access: ♿
Conference: 14 meeting rooms (Thtr 180 max), 24hr-
delegate from £160, day-delegate rate from £54.50
Children: Welcome ♟ ☕ Dogs: Guide dogs only
Licences: ⚜ ♟ Leisure: Gym, Tennis, Golf
Parking: Off-street and monitored
Directions: Follow M2 towards Croydon. Drive through
Coulsdon on A23. Take turning right into Stoats Nest
Road. Hotel is 1 mile on right.

Croydon Park Hotel

★★★★

7 Altyre Road, Croydon, Surrey, CR9 5AA
Tel: 020 8401 0900 Fax: 020 8286 7676
Email: reservations@croydonparkhotel.co.uk
Web: www.croydonparkhotel.co.uk
The hotel has an excellent reputation as a 4-star leisure
destination, offering extensive facilities and a prime
location, with easy access by train to London Victoria
and Gatwick Airport.
Rooms: 212 all ensuite 🚭
Pricing: Dinner from £18.95 CC: Accepted
Room facilities: ▢ ☎ ☕ ✆ ❄ Access: ♿ ♿
Conference: 9 meeting rooms (Thtr 300 max), 24hr-
delegate from £160, day-delegate rate from £55
Children: Welcome ♟ ☕ Dogs: Welcome
Licences: ⚜ ♟ Leisure: Indoor pool, Gym,
Health spa Parking: Off-street and monitored
Directions: Enter Croydon on A235 Brighton Road.
Follow signs to Fairfield Halls. At major roundabout
system, take first left exit into Fairfield Road. Take first
left into Altyre Road.
See advert on following page

South Park Hotel

★★

3-5 South Park Hill, Croydon, Surrey, CR2 7DY
Tel: 020 8688 5644 Fax: 020 8760 0861

Jurys Inn Croydon

Wesselsey Road, Croydon, Surrey, CR0 9XY
Tel: +353(0)1 6070000 Fax: +353(0)1 6316999
Email: bookings@jurysdoyle.com
Web: www.jurydoyle.com
Rooms: 240 all ensuite ⚥ 🚭
Pricing: Sgl £73 Dbl £73 CC: Accepted
Room facilities: ▢ ☎ ☕ ❄ Access: ♿ ♿

JURYSDOYLE
HOTELS

Conference: 16 meeting rooms (Thtr 120 max)
Children: Welcome ♟ Dogs: Guide dogs only
Licences: ♟
Directions: Five minute walk to hotel from East
Croydon station.

Southeast

The Croydon Park Hotel ★★★★

An excellent centrally located property. The ideal venue for business or pleasure, offering free car-parking, exclusive leisure club and a gourmet restaurant. Easy access by train to London Victoria & Gatwick Airport.

- 212 Individually Air-Conditioned Ensuite Bedrooms.
- Gourmet Restaurant – Offering International & Traditional Cuisine.
- Health & Leisure Club with Indoor Heated Swimming Pool.
- 15 Minutes by Train to Central London & Gatwick Airport.
- Perfect Venue for Weddings. Dinner Dance and Conferences.
- Direct Tram Link to Hotel from Wimbledon.

7 Altyre Road, Croydon, Surrey. CR9 5AA
Tel: 020 86809200   Fax: 020 82867676
Email: reservations@croydonparkhotel.co.uk
Website: www.croydonparkhotel.co.uk

Kirkdale Hotel

◆◆◆◆

22 St Peters Road, Croydon, Surrey, CR0 1HD
Tel: 020 8688 5898 Fax: 020 8680 6001
Email: info@kirkdalehotel.co.uk
Web: www.kirkdalehotel.co.uk
Seasonal closure: Christmas to New Year
Rooms: 19 all ensuite
Pricing: Sgl £50–75 Dbl £60–85 CC: Accepted
Room facilities:
Conference: 1 meeting room Children: Welcome
Licences: Parking: Off-street
Directions: M25 at Junction 7 and follow signs for Croydon (9 miles). A few minutes from East Croydon and South Croydon stations.

Woodstock Hotel

◆◆◆

30 Woodstock Road, Croydon, Surrey, CR0 1JR
Tel: 020 8680 1489 Fax: 020 8667 1229
Email: woodstockhotel@croydon-surrey.fsworld.co.uk
Web: www.woodstockhotel.co.uk
Seasonal closure: Christmas day

Located in a quiet residential area. Five minutes' walk to town centre. Rail and tram network and major roads. Spacious comfortable rooms. High standards of housekeeping. Awarded RAC Sparkling Diamond.
Rooms: 8 (6 ensuite)
Pricing: Sgl £40.99–45.99 Dbl £70.99
CC: Accepted
Room facilities:
Children: Welcome 4yrs min age
Parking: Off-street and monitored
Directions: From A232 or A212 at Park Lane roundabout exit towards South Croydon. Third road off Park Lane is Woodstock Road.

Cuckfield, Sussex

Wheatsheaf

♦ ♦ ♦

Broad Street, Cuckfield, Sussex, RH17 5DW
Tel: 01444 454078
Email: www.wheatsheaf.cuckfield@eldridge-pope.co.uk
Rooms: 10 all ensuite 🚭
Pricing: Sgl £55 Dbl £65 Dinner from £10
CC: Accepted
Room facilities: 🖵 ☎ 🍵
Children: Welcome 12yrs min age ╅
Dogs: Guide dogs only
Licences: ◁ ┆┆┆
Leisure: Games room
Parking: Off-street and monitored
Directions: M23 motorway to junction of A272
Haywards Heath, follow to large roundabout, turn left
to Cuckfield, at mini roundabout turn right, we are ³/₄
mile along on Broad Street.

Dartford, Kent

Rowhill Grange Hotel   Blue Ribbon Winner

★★★★★ 🍵 🍵 🍵
Wilmington, Dartford, Kent, DA2 7QH
Tel: 01322 615136 Fax: 01322 615137
Email: admin@rowhillgrange.com
Web: www.rowhillgrange.com

With 9 acres of mature gardens and the finest health
spa in the south, Rowhill Grange is ideal for business
or pleasure – just 2 miles from the M25.
Rooms: 38 all ensuite 🗐 🚭
Pricing: Sgl £134 Dbl £165 Dinner from £29.95
CC: Accepted
Room facilities: 🖵 ☎ 🕾
Access: ┃┃┃ ♿
Conference: 7 meeting rooms (Thtr 160 max), 24hr-
delegate from £165, day-delegate rate from £55
Children: Welcome 5yrs min age ╅
Licences: ◁ ┆┆┆
Leisure: Indoor pool, Gym, Health spa,
Beauty salon
Parking: Off-street and monitored
Directions: Leave M20 junction 1 / M25 Junction 3 to
Swanley. Follow B2175 through 3 roundabouts to
Hextable on B258. Hotel is 1¹/₂ miles on left opposite
garage.

Campanile Hotel

1 Clipper Boulevard West, Crossways Business Park,
Dartford, Kent, DA2 6QN
Tel: 01322 278925 Fax: 01322 278948
Email: dartford@envergure.co.uk
Web: www.envergure.fr

Typical Campanile bistro

Rooms: 127 all ensuite 🐾 🚭
Pricing: Sgl £44.90–50.90 Dbl £50.85–56.85
Dinner from £6.25 CC: Accepted
Room facilities: 🖵 ☎ 🕾 🕾
Access: ♿
Conference: 2 meeting rooms (Thtr 30 max), 24hr-
delegate from £68, day-delegate rate from £19.50
Children: Welcome ╅
Dogs: Welcome
Licences: ┆┆┆
Parking: Off-street and monitored
Directions: From M25 south junction 1A until the ferry
terminal, or from Dartford Bridge follow signs for ferry
terminal.

Travelodge Dartford (SA)

Travel Accommodation
A206, Charles Street, Off Crossways Boulevard,
Dartford, Kent, DA2 6QQ
Web: www.travelodge.co.uk
Rooms: 65 all ensuite 🚭
Pricing: Sgl £64.40 Dbl £68.85
CC: Accepted Room facilities: 🖵 🕾 Access: ♿

Deal, Kent

Kilgour House

♦ ♦ ♦ ♦ 🕸
22 Gilford Road, Deal, Kent, CT14 7DJ
Tel: 01304 368311
Email: kilgourhouse@hotmail.com
Web: kilgourhousebed&breakfast
Rooms: 4 (3 ensuite) 🐾 🗐
Pricing: Dbl £40
Room facilities: 🖵 🕾
Children: Welcome ╅
Dogs: Welcome
Parking: Off-street

Dorchester-on-Thames, Oxfordshire

The George Hotel

★★★★

High Street, Dorchester-on-Thames,
Oxfordshire, OX10 7HH
Tel: 01865 340404 Fax: 01865 341620
Rooms: 17 all ensuite
Pricing: Dinner from £25 CC: Accepted
Room facilities:
Access:
Conference: 2 meeting rooms (Thtr 40 max), 24hr-delegate from £120, day-delegate rate from £45
Children: Welcome
Dogs: Welcome
Licences:
Parking: Off-street and monitored
Directions: Leave M40, junction 6 onto B4009 through Watlington & Benson; take A4074 at BP petrol station, follow sign posts to Dorchester, hotel on left.

White Hart

★★★

High Street, Dorchester-on-Thames,
Oxfordshire, OX10 7HN
Tel: 01865 340074 Fax: 01865 341082
Email: whitehartdorches@aol.com
Web: oxford-restaurants-hotels.co.uk
Rooms: 23 all ensuite
Pricing: Sgl £70 (2002 rate) Dbl £80 (2002 rate)
Dinner from £20 (2002 rate) CC: Accepted
Room facilities:
Access:
Children: Welcome
Dogs: Welcome
Licences:
Parking: Off-street
Directions: Just off A415/A4074 (from M40 Junction 6).
Nearest rail station: Didcot.

Dorking, Surrey

The Burford Bridge

★★★★

At the foot of Boxhill, Dorking, Surrey, RH5 6BX
Tel: 0870 4008283 Fax: 01306 880386
Email: burfordbridge@heritage-hotels
Web: www.macdonaldhotels.co.uk
Rooms: 57 all ensuite
Pricing: Sgl £64 Dbl £128 Dinner from £25
CC: Accepted
Room facilities:
Conference: 7 meeting rooms (Thtr 200 max)
Children: Welcome
Dogs: Welcome
Licences:
Leisure: Outdoor pool
Parking: Off-street and monitored
Directions: Junction 9 of M25, four miles south on A24.
Two miles north of Dorking.

Gatton Manor Hotel Golf & Country Club

★★★

Standon Lane, Ockley, Dorking, Surrey, RH5 5PQ
Tel: 01306 627555 Fax: 01306 627713
Email: gattonmanor@enterprise.net
Web: www.gattonmanor.co.uk
Rooms: 18 all ensuite
Pricing: Sgl £69.50 Dbl £105
Dinner from £12.50 CC: Accepted
Room facilities:
Conference: 3 meeting rooms (Thtr 50 max), 24hr-delegate from £120, day-delegate rate from £38.50
Children: Welcome
Dogs: Guide dogs only Licences:
Leisure: Gym, Health spa, Beauty salon, Tennis, Golf, Fishing Parking: Off-street
Directions: Situated off A24/A29 between Horsham and Dorking.

The White Horse

★★★

High Street, Dorking, Surrey, RH4 1BE
Tel: 0870 400 8282 Fax: 01306 887241
Email: whitehorsedorking@heritage-hotels.co.uk
Web: www.macdonaldhotels.co.uk
Rooms: 78 all ensuite
Pricing: Sgl £49 Dbl £98 CC: Accepted
Room facilities: Access:
Conference: 4 meeting rooms (Thtr 40 max)
Children: Welcome Dogs: Welcome
Licences: Parking: Off-street and monitored
Directions: Take Junction 9 off M25 – 6 miles south on A24, located on the High Street in Dorking.

Travelodge Dorking

Travel Accommodation
A25, Reigate Road, Dorking, Surrey, RH4 1QB
Web: www.travelodge.co.uk
Rooms: 55 all ensuite
Pricing: Sgl £59.40–64.40 Dbl £63.85–68.85
CC: Accepted Room facilities: Access:

Dover, Kent

Churchill

★★★

Dover Waterfront, Dover, Kent, CT17 9BP
Tel: 01304 203633 Fax: 01304 216320
Email: enquiries@churchill-hotel.com
Web: www.churchill-hotel.com
Rooms: 66 all ensuite
Pricing: Sgl £59–68 Dbl £68–97 CC: Accepted
Room facilities:
Access:
Children: Welcome
Dogs: Guide dogs only
Licences:
Leisure: Gym, Beauty salon
Parking: Off-street and monitored
Directions: From A20 follow signs for Hoverport, turn left onto seafront, hotel is 800 yards along.

Wallett's Court Country House

★★★★

Westcliffe, St Margaret's Bay, Dover, Kent, CT15 6EW
Tel: 01304 852424 Fax: 01304 853430
Email: wc@wallettscourt.com
Web: www.wallettscourt.com

Set in the heart of White Cliffs Country, this 17th-Century hotel with highly acclaimed restaurant and spa is simply beautiful. Relaxed and secluded, yet only 3 miles from Dover.
Rooms: 16 all ensuite
Pricing: Sgl £75–95 Dbl £90–130 Dinner from £27.50
CC: Accepted Room facilities: 🖵 ☎ ⛾ 🔌
Conference: 3 meeting rooms (Thtr 30 max), 24hr-delegate from £127.50, day-delegate rate from £27.50
Children: Welcome 🍴 ⅛℃ Licences: ⅲ
Leisure: Indoor pool, Gym, Health spa, Tennis
Parking: Off-street
Directions: From M2/A2 or M20/A20, signs A258 Deal. On A258, first right for Westcliffe, St Margaret's-at-Cliffe. Hotel 1 mile on right.

East Lee Guest House

◆◆◆◆ ⚹

108 Maison Dieu Road, Dover, Kent, CT16 1RT
Tel: 01304 210176 Fax: 01304 206705
Email: eastlee@eclipse.co.uk
Web: www.eastlee.co.uk
Rooms: 4 all ensuite ⊗ Pricing: Dbl £23–26
CC: Accepted Room facilities: 🖵 ☎ ⛾
Children: Welcome 🍴 Parking: Off-street and monitored
Directions: Approaching from M20/A20, at York Street Roundabout, turn left and proceed straight over next Roundabout. Turn right at Dover town hall. At end of street, turn right into Maison Dieu Road.

Number One Guest House

◆◆◆◆ ⚹

1 Castle Street, Dover, Kent, CT16 1QH
Tel: 01304 202007 Fax: 01304 214078
Email: res@number1guesthouse.co.uk
Web: www.number1guesthouse.co.uk
Rooms: 3 all ensuite ⬟
Pricing: Dbl £46–52 CC: Accepted
Room facilities: 🖵 ⛾ Children: Welcome 🍴
Parking: Off-street and monitored
Directions: Just off A20 turn right to castle on corner before Castle Hill. A2 1 mile, 2 minutes from port, 10 minutes from tunnel

Tower House

◆◆◆◆ ⚹ ⚲

Priory Hill, Dover, Kent, CT17 0AE
Tel: 01304 208212 Fax: 01304 208212
Email: enquiries@towerhouse.net
Web: www.towerhouse.net
Rooms: 2 all ensuite ⊗
Pricing: Dbl £42–54
Room facilities: 🖵 ⛾
Children: Welcome
Parking: Off-street
Directions: M20 – B2011 to Dover; turn left at roundabout, then third turning left at main traffic lights to top of Priory Hill.

Ardmore Private Hotel

◆◆◆

18 Castle Hill Road, Dover, Kent, CT16 1QW
Tel: 01304 205895 Fax: 01304 208229
Email: res@ardmoreph.co.uk
Web: www.ardmoreph.co.uk
Seasonal closure: Christmas
Rooms: 4 all ensuite ⊗
Pricing: Dbl £40–50 CC: Accepted
Room facilities: 🖵 ⛾
Children: Welcome
Directions: On A258 next to Dover Castle. Follow signs for castle from all roads to Dover. 10 minutes to Channel Tunnel, close to ports.

Gateway Hovertel

◆◆◆

Snargate Street, Dover, Kent, CT17 9BZ
Tel: 01304 205479 Fax: 01304 211504
Email: dspeters@hovertel.fsnet.co.uk
Seasonal closure: closed Christmas & New Year
Rooms: 27 all ensuite ⬟
Pricing: Sgl £40–45 Dbl £52–58 CC: Accepted
Room facilities: 🖵 ⛾
Children: Welcome
Dogs: Guide dogs only
Licences: ⅲ
Parking: Off-street and monitored
Directions: Follow M20/A20 into Dover over Hoverport roundabout on the left overlooking marine, close to ferry and cruise terminals.

Hubert House Guest House

◆◆◆ ⚲

9 Castle Hill Road, Dover, Kent, CT16 1QW
Tel: 01304 202253 Fax: 01304 210142
Email: huberthouse@btinternet.com
Web: www.huberthouse.co.uk
Seasonal closure: October
Rooms: 6 all ensuite
Pricing: Sgl £32–38 Dbl £44–50 CC: Accepted
Room facilities: 🖵 ⛾
Children: Welcome
Parking: Off-street and monitored
Directions: Situated on the A258 Deal Road at the bottom of Castle Hill, close to Dover town centre.

Pennyfarthing

◆ ◆ ◆

109 Maison Dieu Road, Dover, Kent, CT16 1RT
Tel: 01304 205563 Fax: 01304 204439
Email: pennyfarthing.dover@btinternet.com
Web: www.pennyfarthingdover.com
Rooms: 6 (5 ensuite) 🛁 ⊛
Pricing: Sgl £24–26 Dbl £44–48 Room facilities: ▢ ☕
Children: Welcome ♇ Parking: Off-street

St Martins Guest House

◆ ◆ ◆

17 Castle Hill Road, Dover, Kent, CT16 1QW
Tel: 01304 205938 Fax: 01304 208229
Email: res@stmartinsgh.co.uk
Web: www.stmartinsgh.co.uk
Seasonal closure: Christmas
Rooms: 6 all ensuite 🛁 ⊛
Pricing: Sgl £30–35 Dbl £38–48 CC: Accepted
Room facilities: ▢ ☕ Children: Welcome
Directions: On the A258. Follow signs to Dover Castle
from all roads to Dover. 10 minutes from Channel
Tunnel, minutes from ports.

Dunstable, Bedfordshire

Hanover International Hotel Dunstable

★ ★ ★

Church Street, Dunstable, Bedfordshire, LU5 4RT
Tel: 0870 241 7079 Fax: 01582 696422
Email: crso@hanover-international.com
Web: www.hanover-international.com

HANOVER INTERNATIONAL
HOTELS & CLUBS

An original hotel with many exquisite features offering
old English charm. Close to Whipsnade, Woburn and
other local attractions.
Rooms: 68 all ensuite 🖃 ⊛
Pricing: Sgl £60–117 Dbl £80–143 Dinner from £17.50
CC: Accepted Room facilities: ▢ ☎ ☕ 🐾 Access: ↕↑
Conference: 2 meeting rooms (Thtr 50 max), 24hr-
delegate from £135, day-delegate rate from £39
Children: Welcome Licences: ◁◇ ♦♦♦
Parking: Off-street and monitored
Directions: Off Junction 11 of the M1. Follow signs to
Dunstable town centre. Pass under bridge, hotel 200m
further, opposite the Priory church on the right.

Dymchurch, Kent

Waterside Guest House

◆ ◆ ◆ ◆

15 Hythe Road, Dymchurch, Kent, TN29 0LN
Tel: 01303 872253 Fax: 01303 872253
Email: info@watersideguesthouse.co.uk
Web: www.watersideguesthouse.co.uk
Rooms: 5 all ensuite 🛁 ⊛
Pricing: Sgl £25–30 Dbl £40–45 Dinner from £4.50
CC: Accepted
Room facilities: ▢ ☕
Children: Welcome 🕯
Licences: ♦♦♦
Parking: Off-street and monitored
Directions: From M20 take Junction 11. Follow signs to
Hythe. Turn right onto A259. Guest House
approximately 7 miles on right-hand side.

East Grinstead, West Sussex

Gravetye Manor Hotel  Gold Ribbon Winner

★ ★ ★ ♛ ♛ ♛ ♛

Vowels Lane, near East Grinstead,
West Sussex, RH19 4LJ
Tel: 01342 810567 Fax: 01342 810080
Email: info@gravetyemanor.co.uk
Web: www.gravetyemanor.co.uk
Rooms: 18 all ensuite 🖃
Pricing: Sgl £106–166 Dbl £182–360 Dinner from £56
CC: Accepted
Room facilities: ▢ ☎
Conference: 1 meeting room (Thtr 12 max), 24hr-
delegate from £235, day-delegate rate from £60
Children: Welcome 7yrs min age 🕯
Licences: ◁◇ ♦♦♦
Parking: Off-street and monitored
Directions: Leave M23 at Exit 10, and take A264
towards East Grinstead. After 2 miles, at roundabout,
take third exit (B2028) towards Turners Hill.

Eastbourne, East Sussex

Grand Hotel

★ ★ ★ ★ ★ 🏨 🏨 🏨 Blue Ribbon Winner

King Edward's Parade, Eastbourne,
East Sussex, BN21 4EQ
Tel: 01323 412345 Fax: 01323 412233
Email: reservations@grandeastbourne.co.uk
Web: www.grandeastbourne.co.uk

England's finest resort hotel, The Grand Hotel in
Eastbourne reflects the glories of Victorian architecture.
Recently restored, this magnificent hotel offers award-
winning cuisine, health club and conscientious, friendly
service.
Rooms: 152 all ensuite 🛏 🎯 ⊗
Pricing: Sgl £125–385 Dbl £159–410 Dinner from £35
CC: Accepted
Room facilities: ▢ ☎ ☕ 📞
Access: ♿ 🦽
Conference: 17 meeting rooms (Thtr 300 max), 24hr-
delegate from £250, day-delegate rate from £80
Children: Welcome 🍴 🐴 🍼
Dogs: Welcome Licences: 🔷 🍴
Leisure: Indoor pool, Outdoor pool, Gym, Health spa,
Beauty salon, Snooker/billiards
Parking: Off-street and monitored
Directions: Located at west end of Eastbourne seafront.

Chatsworth

★ ★ ★

Grand Parade, Eastbourne, East Sussex, BN21 3YR
Tel: 01323 411016 Fax: 01323 643270
Email: stay@chatsworth-hotel.com
Web: www.chatsworth-hotel.com
Rooms: 47 all ensuite 🛏 ⊗
Pricing: Sgl £52–67 Dbl £82–107 Dinner from £19.50
CC: Accepted
Room facilities: ▢ ☎ ☕ 📞
Access: ♿
Conference: 3 meeting rooms (Thtr 100 max), 24hr-
delegate from £110, day-delegate rate from £25
Children: Welcome 🍴 🍼
Dogs: Welcome Licences: 🔷 🍴
Parking: Monitored
Directions: M23 towards Brighton; then A27 to
Polegate; then A22 to Eastbourne. Follow seafront
signs. Hotel between pier and bandstand.

Hydro Hotel

★ ★ ★

Mount Road, Eastbourne, East Sussex, BN20 7HZ
Tel: 01323 720643 Fax: 01323 641167
Email: sales@hydrohotel.com
Web: www.hydrohotel.com

An elegant traditional hotel offering the highest
standards of cuisine and service. Situated in a unique
clifftop garden setting with panoramic sea views.
Rooms: 84 (82 ensuite) 🛏 ⊗
Pricing: Sgl £41–68 Dbl £76–130 Dinner from £19.50
CC: Accepted
Room facilities: ▢ ☎ ☕ 📞
Access: ♿ 🦽
Children: Welcome 🍴 🍼
Dogs: Welcome
Licences: 🔷 🍴
Leisure: Outdoor pool, Gym, Beauty salon
Parking: Off-street
Directions: Proceed along King Edwards Parade to the
Grand Hotel. Note sign Hydro Hotel. Proceed up South
Cliff and the Hydro Hotel signs are visible.

Lansdowne Hotel

★ ★ ★

King Edward's Parade, Eastbourne,
East Sussex, BN21 4EE
Tel: 01323 725174 Fax: 01323 739721
Email: reception@lansdowne-hotel.co.uk
Web: www.lansdowne-hotel.co.uk
Seasonal closure: 1–16 January inc
Rooms: 110 all ensuite 🛏 ⊗
Pricing: Sgl £48–67 Dbl £82–122 Dinner from £18.50
CC: Accepted
Room facilities: ▢ ☎ ☕ 📞
Access: ♿ 🦽
Conference: 12 meeting rooms (Thtr 120 max), 24hr-
delegate from £90, day-delegate rate from £30
Children: Welcome 🍴 🍼
Dogs: Welcome
Licences: 🔷 🍴
Leisure: Games room, Snooker/billiards
Parking: Off-street and monitored
Directions: M23, A23, A27, A22 or A259 to
Eastbourne. Hotel at west end of seafront (B2103)
facing Western Lawns.
See advert on following page

Lansdowne Hotel

Traditional, privately owned seafront hotel close to theatres, shops and Conference Centre. Established since 1912. Attractive Regency Bar. Elegant lounges and foyer facing sea. 22 lock-up garages. English cuisine. 110 ensuite bedrooms. Leisure Breaks November–mid-May. Duplicate/Social Bridge Weekends. Golfing holidays all year. Murder Mystery weekends. A warm welcome awaits you!

King Edward's Parade, Eastbourne, East Sussex BN21 4EE

Tel: 01323 725174   Fax: 01323 739721
Email: reception@lansdowne-hotel.co.uk
Web: www.lansdowne-hotel.co.uk

Mansion Hotel

★★★
Grand Parade, Eastbourne, East Sussex, BN21 3YS
Tel: 01323 727411 Fax: 01323 720665
Rooms: 95 all ensuite
Pricing: Sgl £45–80 Dbl £48–90 Dinner from £12.95
CC: Accepted
Room facilities: 🖵 ☎ 🍵 ⌇
Access: ⬆
Children: Welcome ⼑ Dogs: Welcome
Licences: ⅲ
Directions: M25 leave at junction 7 to Gatwick – Via M23 join A27 – Lewes heading to Eastbourne. Follow signs to seafront. We are between the pier and bandstand.

Wish Tower Hotel

★★★
King Edward's Parade, Eastbourne, East Sussex, BN21 4EB
Tel: 01323 722676 Fax: 01323 721474
Email: wishtower@british-trust-hotels.com
Web: www.british-trust-hotels.com

Sea front location. Friendly and welcoming hotel. Close to town centre. Easy walking distance of the famous Prom and Victorian Pier. Traditional seaside conference and leisure break hotel overlooking the Promenade and 'Carpet Gardens'.
Rooms: 61 all ensuite
Pricing: Sgl £30 Dbl £60 Dinner from £18
CC: Accepted
Room facilities: 🖵 ☎ ⌇
Children: Welcome ⼑
Dogs: Welcome Licences: ⅲ
Parking: Off-street

York House Hotel

★★★
Royal Parade, Eastbourne, East Sussex, BN22 7AP
Tel: 01323 412918 Fax: 01323 646238
Email: frontdesk@yorkhousehotel.co.uk
Web: www.yorkhousehotel.co.uk
Rooms: 87 all ensuite
Pricing: Sgl £55–65 Dbl £90–120 Dinner from £16
CC: Accepted
Room facilities: 🖵 ☎ 🍵 ⌇
Access: ⬆ ♿
Conference: 3 meeting rooms (Thtr 100 max), 24hr-delegate from £25, day-delegate rate from £80
Children: Welcome ⼑ ⼋
Dogs: Welcome
Licences: ⚑ ⅲ
Leisure: Indoor pool, Games room
Directions: Seafront position, 1/4 mile east of the pier, 2 miles west of Sovereign Harbour.

Congress Hotel

31–37 Carlisle Road, Eastbourne, East Sussex, BN21 4JS
Tel: 01323 732118 Fax: 01323 720016
Seasonal closure: January to February

Located by main theatres in a level area. Ramped entrance, so accessible for wheelchair users. Family owned and managed – 'Service our aim'.
Rooms: 62 all ensuite
Pricing: Sgl £29–39 Dbl £58–78 Dinner from £10
CC: Accepted Room facilities: ☐ ☕ Access: ↟ ♿
Children: Welcome ♀ ☽ Dogs: Welcome
Licences: ♙♙♙ Leisure: Games room, Snooker/billiards
Parking: Off-street and monitored
Directions: Opposite Congress Theatre, approx 150 yards from the seafront. Follow signs for 'Theatres'.

New Wilmington Hotel

25 Compton Street, Eastbourne, East Sussex, BN21 4DU
Tel: 01323 721219 Fax: 01323 745255
Email: info@new-wilmington-hotel.co.uk
Web: www.new-wilmington-hotel.co.uk

This friendly family run hotel will make you feel welcome from the time you arrive. Close to theatres, conference facilities, sea front and town centre, excellent variety of home-cooked food.
Rooms: 40 all ensuite
Pricing: Sgl £36.50–42.50 Dbl £36–75 Dinner from £14
CC: Accepted Room facilities: ☐ ☎ ☕ Access: ↟
Children: Welcome ♀ Dogs: Guide dogs only
Licences: ♙♙♙ Parking: Off-street and monitored
Directions: Follow signs to sea front, keeping sea on left. At Wilmington Gardens turn right. At end of road turn left.

Oban

King Edward's Parade, Eastbourne,
East Sussex, BN21 4DS
Tel: 01323 731581 Fax: 01323 721994
Seasonal closure: December to March
Rooms: 31 all ensuite ☽
Pricing: Sgl £21–40 Dbl £42–80 Dinner from £15
CC: Accepted
Room facilities: ☐ ☎ ☕
Access: ↟
Children: Welcome ☽
Dogs: Welcome
Licences: ♙♙♙
Parking: Monitored
Directions: The Oban is on the seafront, facing the Wish Tower, minutes from the Winter Garden, theatres, tennis and bandstand.

Princes Hotel

Lascelles Terrace, Eastbourne, East Sussex, BN21 4BL
Tel: 01323 722056 Fax: 01323 727469
Email: princes-hotel@btconnect.com
Web: www.princes-hotel.co.uk
Seasonal closure: January
Rooms: 45 all ensuite ☕ ☽
Pricing: Dinner from £14.50 (2002 rate) CC: Accepted
Room facilities: ☐ ☎ ☕
Access: ↟
Children: Welcome
Dogs: Welcome
Licences: ⟨⟩ ♙♙♙

Quality Hotel Langham

Royal Parade, Eastbourne, East Sussex, BN22 7AH
Tel: 01323 731451 Fax: 01323 646623
Email: info@langhamhotel.co.uk
Web: www.langhamhotel.co.uk
Rooms: 85 all ensuite ☕ ☽
Pricing: Sgl £39–52 Dbl £63–119 Dinner from £13.95
CC: Accepted
Room facilities: ☐ ☎ ☕ ☏
Access: ↟ ♿
Conference: 3 meeting rooms (Thtr 80 max), 24hr-delegate from £60, day-delegate rate from £25
Children: Welcome ♀ ☽
Dogs: Welcome
Licences: ♙♙♙
Leisure: Games room
Parking: Off-street and monitored
Directions: Follow Eastbourne seafront signs from A27, A22 and A259. Hotel is ³/₄ of a mile east of the pier near Redoubt Gardens.

Southeast

West Rocks Hotel

★ ★

Grand Parade, Eastbourne, East Sussex, BN21 4DL
Tel: 01323 725217 Fax: 01323 720421
Seasonal closure: mid-November to 1 March

Private seafront hotel with real comfort and renowned
personal attention. English cuisine with leisure breaks
through all seasons. Open Christmas with traditional style
family Christmas celebrations, a special hotel indeed!
Rooms: 47 (45 ensuite) ➿ ⊗
Pricing: Sgl £31–67 Dbl £50–136 Dinner from £14.25
CC: Accepted
Room facilities: ☐ ☎ � ⌨ Access: ↥ ⅁
Conference: 1 meeting room (Thtr 36 max), 24hr-
delegate from £90, day-delegate rate from £32
Children: Welcome 3yrs min age ⒣ ⅀
Dogs: Guide dogs only Licences: ⅙
Directions: On seafront between the bandstand and
the Wish Tower, 600 yards west from the pier.

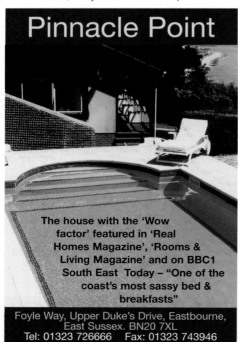

Pinnacle Point   Little Gem

◆ ◆ ◆ ◆ ◆ ⚲ ℘

Foyle Way, Upper Duke's Drive, Eastbourne,
East Sussex, BN20 7XL
Tel: 01323 726666 Fax: 01323 743946
Email: info@pinnacle-point.co.uk
Web: www.pinnaclepoint.co.uk
Seasonal closure: Christmas and New Year
Rooms: 3 all ensuite ⊞ ⊗
Pricing: Sgl £50–60 Dbl £80–100
Room facilities: ☐ � ❄
Children: Welcome 12yrs min age
Dogs: Guide dogs only Leisure: Outdoor pool
Parking: Off-street and monitored
Directions: From centre of Eastbourne take seafront
road west of pier, after one mile turn left after St
Bede's School. House straight ahead.
See advert on this page

Brayscroft Hotel

◆ ◆ ◆ ◆

13 South Cliff Avenue, Eastbourne,
East Sussex, BN20 7AH
Tel: 01323 647005 Fax: 01323 720705
Email: brayscroft@hotmail.com
Web: www.brayscrofthotel.co.uk
Rooms: 5 all ensuite ⊗
Pricing: Sgl £29–31.50 Dbl £58–63 Dinner from £13
CC: Accepted Room facilities: ☐ ☐
Children: Welcome 14yrs min age Dogs: Welcome
Licences: ⅙
Directions: B2103 (Grand Parade) from pier towards
Beachy Head. Past Grand Hotel, take right incline up
South Cliff, then first right.

Bay Lodge Hotel

◆ ◆ ◆

61–62 Royal Parade, Eastbourne,
East Sussex, BN22 7AQ
Tel: 01323 732515 Fax: 01323 735009
Email: beryl@mnewson.freeserve.co.uk
Rooms: 12 (9 ensuite) ➿
Pricing: Sgl £25–30 Dbl £50–60 Dinner from £9
CC: Accepted Room facilities: ☐ ☐
Children: Welcome ⒣
Licences: ⅙

Sheldon Hotel

◆ ◆ ◆

9–11 Burlington Place, Eastbourne,
East Sussex, BN21 4AS
Tel: 01323 724120 Fax: 01323 430406
Rooms: 24 all ensuite ➿ ⊗
Pricing: Sgl £26–33 Dbl £52–66 Dinner from £8
CC: Accepted Room facilities: ☐ ☎ ☐
Access: ↥ Children: Welcome ⒣
Dogs: Welcome Licences: ⅙
Parking: Off-street
Directions: From pier, travel west towards bandstand.
Turn right by side of Cavendish Hotel. Sheldon Hotel is
150m on left.

Sherwood Hotel

◆ ◆ ◆

7 Lascelles Terrace, Eastbourne, East Sussex, BN21 4BJ
Tel: 01323 724002 Fax: 01323 439989
Email: sherwood-hotel@supanet.com
Web: www.sherwood-hotel-eastbourne.co.uk

Cosy Victorian townhouse, 100yds seafront, 100yds
Devonshire/Congress Theatres. All rooms ensuite. Four
Poster Room. Licenced bar. Small functions catered
for. Home-cooked meals. Nicely appointed. Friendly,
courteous service.
Rooms: 14 all ensuite 🛏
Pricing: Sgl £25–35 Dbl £50–80 Dinner from £8
CC: Accepted
Room facilities: 🖵 ☕
Children: Welcome
Dogs: Guide dogs only
Licences: ♟
Directions: From A22 follow directions to town west
and theatres. Lascelles Terrace runs between
Devonshire Park and seafront.

Eastleigh, Hampshire

13 Camelia Grove

◆

Fair Oak, near Eastleigh, Hampshire, SO50 7GZ
Tel: 02380 692822
Rooms: 2🅿
Pricing: Sgl £17–17 Dbl £34–34
Room facilities: 🖵 ☕
Children: Welcome
Dogs: Guide dogs only
Parking: Off-street
Directions: M3 J11. Left onto B3354, through Twyford
to Fair Oak. Up Mortimer Lane on left, fourth turning
on left.

Travelodge Southampton, Eastleigh (SA)

Travel Accommodation
A335, Ham Farm, A335 Tywford Road, Eastleigh,
Hampshire, SO50 4LF
Web: www.travelodge.co.uk
Rooms: 32 all ensuite 🅿
Pricing: Sgl £59.40 Dbl £63.85
CC: Accepted Room facilities: 🖵 ☕ Access: ♿

Egham, Surrey

Runnymede Hotel & Spa

★ ★ ★ ★ ⓐⓑⓒ ⓡ ⓡ

Windsor Road, Egham, Surrey, TW20 0AG
Tel: 01784 436171 Fax: 01784 436340
Email: info@runnymedehotel.com
Web: www.runnymedehotel.com

There's much more to life at the Runnymede: renowned
friendly service, private spa, tennis, two restaurants,
award-winning cuisine, river terrace; Windsor, Eton,
Savill Gardens, the Thames — and much more.
Rooms: 180 all ensuite 🅿
Pricing: Sgl £88–172 Dbl £136–210 Dinner from £28.50
CC: Accepted Room facilities: 🖵 📺 ☎ ☕ 📞 ❄
Access: 🛗 ♿ Conference: 12 meeting rooms (Thtr
170 max), 24hr-delegate from £245, day-delegate rate
from £75 Children: Welcome ♟ Dogs: Guide dogs only
Licences: ⚓ ♟
Leisure: Indoor pool, Gym, Health spa, Beauty salon,
Tennis, Snooker/billiards
Parking: Off-street and monitored
Directions: Leave M25 at Junction 13. Take A308 to
Egham/Windsor. The Runnymede is on the right at the
entrance to Runnymede Meadows.

Emsworth, Hampshire

Jingles Hotel

◆ ◆ ◆

77 Horndean Road, Emsworth, Hampshire, PO10 7PU
Tel: 01243 373755 Fax: 01243 373755
Rooms: 14 (8 ensuite) 🍽 🛏 🅿
Pricing: Sgl £28–39.50 Dbl £50–65 Dinner from £14
CC: Accepted Room facilities: 🖵 ☕
Children: Welcome ♟ 🎨 Dogs: Welcome
Licences: ♟ Leisure: Outdoor pool
Parking: Off-street
Directions: From A259 in Emsworth, head north on the
B2148 towards Rowlands Castle for approximately 1 mile.

Southeast

Enfield, Middlesex

West Lodge Park Hotel

★★★★

Cockfosters Road, Hadley Wood, Hertfordshire, EN4 0PY
Tel: 020 8216 3900 Fax: 020 8216 3937
Email: info@westlodgepark.com
Web: www.westlodgepark.com
Rooms: 59 all ensuite
Pricing: Dinner from £35 CC: Accepted
Room facilities:
Access:
Children: Welcome
Dogs: Guide dogs only
Licences:
Leisure: Beauty salon
Parking: Off-street and monitored
Directions: Exit J24 M25. Follow A111 towards
Cockfosters. After one mile hotel is on left-hand side.

Royal Chace Hotel

★★★★

The Ridgeway, Enfield, Middlesex, EN2 8AR
Tel: 020 8884 8181 Fax: 020 8884 8150
Web: www.royal-chace.com
Rooms: 92 all ensuite
Pricing: Sgl £99–110 Dbl £115–125 Dinner from £19.95
CC: Accepted
Room facilities:
Access:
Conference: 10 meeting rooms (Thtr 250 max), day-
delegate rate from £40
Children: Welcome
Licences:
Leisure: Outdoor pool
Parking: Off-street and monitored
Directions: Leave M25 at Junction 24. Take A1005
towards Enfield. The Royal Chace Hotel is situated 3
miles along on right-hand side.

Oak Lodge Hotel

★★

80 Village Road, Enfield, Middlesex, EN1 2EU
Tel: 020 8360 7082
Email: oaklodge@fs.mail.net
Web: www.oaklodgehotel.co.uk
Rooms: 7 all ensuite
Pricing: Sgl £79.50–89.50 Dbl £89.50–110
Dinner from £15 CC: Accepted
Room facilities:
Access:
Conference: 1 meeting room (Thtr 16 max), 24hr-
delegate from £150, day-delegate rate from £35
Children: Welcome
Dogs: Welcome
Licences:
Parking: Off-street and monitored
Directions: Leave M25 at junction 25. Turn right at 11th
set of lights south along A10. Turn right at next lights
onto A105. Hotel ¼ mile on right.

The Enfield Hotel

★★

52 Rowan Tree Road, Enfield, Middlesex, EN2 8PW
Tel: 020 8366 3511 Fax: 020 8366 2432
Email: enfield@meridianleisure.com
Web: www.meridianleisure.com
Rooms: 34 all ensuite
Pricing: Sgl £60–85 Dbl £70–95 Dinner from £3.25
CC: Accepted Room facilities:
Conference: 3 meeting rooms (Thtr 45 max), 24hr-
delegate from £85, day-delegate rate from £27
Children: Welcome
Dogs: Guide dogs only Licences:
Parking: Off-street and monitored
Directions: M25 J24, A1005 pass hospital on left. Take
right fork at mini-roundabout. Third left into Bycullar
road 2nd left.

Epping, Essex

Travelodge Harlow East, Stanstead

Travel Accommodation
A414, Epping Road, Tylers Green, North Weald,
Epping, Essex, CM16 6BJ
Web: www.travelodge.co.uk Rooms: 60 all ensuite
Pricing: Sgl £64.40 Dbl £68.85
CC: Accepted Room facilities: Access:

Epsom, Surrey

Epsom Downs Hotel

◆◆◆

9 Longdown Road, Epsom, Surrey, KT17 3PT
Tel: 01372 740643 Fax: 01372 723259
Seasonal closure: 20 Dec-4 Jan
Rooms: 11 all ensuite
Pricing: Sgl £65–85 Dbl £75–95 CC: Accepted
Room facilities:
Dogs: Guide dogs only Licences:
Parking: Off-street
Directions: 1 mile from town centre.

Fareham, Hampshire

Solent Hotel

★★★★

Solent Business Park, Whiteley, Fareham,
Hampshire, PO15 7AJ
Tel: 01489 880000 Fax: 01489 880007
Email: solent@shirehotels.co.uk
Web: www.shirehotels.co.uk
Rooms: 111 all ensuite
Pricing: Sgl £129 Dbl £126 Dinner from £28.50
CC: Accepted Room facilities:
Access:
Conference: 13 meeting rooms (Thtr 200 max)
Children: Welcome Licences:
Leisure: Indoor pool, Gym, Tennis
Parking: Off-street and monitored
Directions: Leave M27 at Junction 9 to Whiteley. Turn
left at first roundabout. Hotel on your right.

Avenue House Hotel

◆ ◆ ◆

22 The Avenue, Fareham, Hampshire, PO14 1NS
Tel: 01329 232175 Fax: 01329 232196
Rooms: 19 all ensuite
Pricing: Sgl £55–60 Dbl £60–65 CC: Accepted
Room facilities: 📺 ☎ ☕
Access: ♿
Conference: 2 meeting rooms (Thtr 40 max), 24hr-delegate from £90, day-delegate rate from £25
Children: Welcome
Dogs: Guide dogs only
Parking: Off-street
Directions: M27 Junction 9 (signposted Fareham West), A27 to Fareham. After five minutes, Fareham College on right, hotel 300 yards further on left.

Faringdon, Oxfordshire

Faringdon Hotel

★ ★

1 Market Place, Faringdon, Oxfordshire, SN7 7HL
Tel: 01367 240536 Fax: 01367 243250

Within easy reach of Oxford, Swindon and White Horse hill, authentic Thai restaurant within the hotel.
Nearest bus/railway stations Swindon 12 miles, Oxford 18 miles, M40 20 miles, M4 14 miles and Faringdon is on A420.
Rooms: 20 all ensuite 🖥
Pricing: Sgl £50–60 Dbl £65–95 Dinner from £10
CC: Accepted
Room facilities: 📺 ☎ ☕
Conference: 1 meeting room (Thtr 26 max), 24hr-delegate from £110, day-delegate rate from £25
Children: Welcome ♭ ❄
Dogs: Welcome
Licences: ♦♦♦
Parking: Off-street

Farnborough, Hampshire

Falcon Hotel

★ ★ ★

68 Farnborough Road, Farnborough, Hampshire, GU14 6TH
Tel: 01252 545378 Fax: 01252 522539
Email: falcon@meridianleisure.com
Web: www.meridianleisure.com
Rooms: 30 all ensuite 🖥 ❄
Pricing: Sgl £55–90 Dbl £65–105 Dinner from £19.95
CC: Accepted
Room facilities: 📺 ☎ ☕ 🔌
Access: ♿
Children: Welcome ♭ ❄
Dogs: Guide dogs only
Licences: ♦ ♦♦♦
Parking: Off-street

Farnham, Surrey

Bishop's Table Hotel

★ ★ ★ ★ ❀ ❀ ❀

27 West Street, Farnham, Surrey, GU9 7DR
Tel: 01252 710222 Fax: 01252 733494
Email: welcome@bishopstable.com
Web: www.bishopstable.com
Seasonal closure: 23 December to 6 January
Rooms: 17 all ensuite 🖥 ❄
Pricing: Sgl £100–190 Dbl £140–190 Dinner from £35
CC: Accepted
Room facilities: 📺 ☎ ☕
Conference: 2 meeting rooms (Thtr 20 max), 24hr-delegate from £165, day-delegate rate from £37
Children: Welcome 16yrs min age
Dogs: Guide dogs only
Licences: ♦♦♦
Directions: Take M3 Junction 4, follow 'Birdworld' signs and Farnham town centre signs. Located nextdoor to library.

The Bush Hotel

★ ★ ★

The Borough, Farnham, Surrey, GU9 7NN
Tel: 0870 400 8225 Fax: 01252 733530
Email: bush@heritage-hotels.co.uk
Web: www.macdonaldhotels.co.uk
Rooms: 83 all ensuite 🖥 ❄
Pricing: Sgl £54 Dbl £108 CC: Accepted
Room facilities: 📺 ☕ 🔌
Access: ♿
Children: Welcome ♭ ❄
Dogs: Welcome
Licences: ♦ ♦♦♦
Parking: Off-street and monitored
Directions: Follow signs to town centre. At lights turn left and immediate right into hotel car park on South Street.

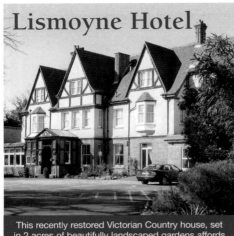

Lismoyne Hotel

This recently restored Victorian Country house, set in 2 acres of beautifully landscaped gardens affords all the luxury and comfort you would expect of an executive three star hotel. We can guarantee you, excellent food, professionally served, in a relaxing environment. Nearby attractions, include Windsor Castle, Legoland and Chessington, with the sights of London within easy reach.

Church Road, Fleet, Hampshire GU51 4NE
Tel:01252 628555   Fax:01252 811761
Email: info@lismoynehotel.com
Website: www.lismoynehotel.com

Clifton Hotel

Folkestone's premier hotel occupies a cliff-top position on the Leas, with views over the English Channel and minutes from the town centre. Dating back to 1864, the hotel is tastefully decorated in the Victorian style. Five well-equipped conference rooms, seating from 5-80. Bar and restaurant. Channel Tunnel terminus 4 miles. Dover ferry and Hoverspeed terminals 7 miles. Folkestone Hoverspeed ½ mile.

For further details call or email us.

The Leas, Folkestone, Kent CT20 2EB
Tel: 01303 851231   Fax; 01303 223949
Email: reservations@thecliftonhotel.com
Website: www.thecliftonhotel.com

Faversham, Kent

Travelodge Canterbury North

Travel Accommodation
A299, Thanet Way, Faversham, Kent, ME13 9EL
Web: www.travelodge.co.uk
Rooms: 40 all ensuite 🚭
Pricing: Sgl £54.40 Dbl £58.85
CC: Accepted Room facilities: ▢ 🍵 Access: ♿

Fleet, Hampshire

Lismoyne Hotel
★★★
Church Road, Fleet, Hampshire, GU13 4NA
Tel: 01252 628555 Fax: 01252 811761
Email: info@lismoynehotel.com
Web: www.lismoynehotel.com
Rooms: 64 (62 ensuite) 🐾 ▦ 🚭
Pricing: Sgl £50–100 Dbl £70–150 Dinner from £18.95
CC: Accepted
Room facilities: ▢ ☎ 🍵 📠
Access: ♿
Conference: 4 meeting rooms (Thtr 170 max), 24hr-delegate from £148, day-delegate rate from £49
Children: Welcome ⅋ ⅌
Dogs: Guide dogs only
Licences: ⬦ ⅏
Leisure: Gym, Riding
Parking: Off-street and monitored
Directions: Approach town on B3013. Cross over railway bridge and continue towards town centre. Pass through traffic lights and take fourth right. Hotel ¼ of a mile on left.
See advert on this page

Folkestone, Kent

Clifton Hotel
★★★
The Leas, Clifton Gardens, Folkestone, Kent, CT20 2EB
Tel: 01303 851231 Fax: 01303 223949
Email: reservations@thecliftonhotel.com
Web: www.thecliftonhotel.com
Rooms: 80 all ensuite 🐾 🚭
Pricing: Sgl £59–98 Dbl £79–102 Dinner from £18.50
CC: Accepted
Room facilities: ▢ ☎ 🍵 📠
Access: ⅃⅂ ♿
Children: Welcome ⅋ ⅌
Dogs: Welcome
Licences: ⅏
Leisure: Games room
Directions: From M20 Junction 13, The Clifton Hotel is ¼ mile west of town centre on A259.
See advert on this page

Lighthouse Inn & Restaurant

◆ ◆ ◆ ◆

111 Old Dover Road, Capel le Ferne, near Folkestone, Kent, CT18 7HT
Tel: 01303 223300 Fax: 01303 256501
Email: info@lighthouse-inn.co.uk
Web: www.lighthouse-inn.co.uk

Set on a cliff top with stunning panoramic sea views. Ideal for a relaxing break or a stop over before setting off to France with Dover being only 3 miles away.
Rooms: 4 all ensuite ⊗
Pricing: Sgl £35–48 Dbl £50–70 CC: Accepted
Room facilities: ▢ ☕
Children: Welcome ♀
Dogs: Guide dogs only
Licences: ♦♦♦
Parking: Off-street
Directions: M20/A20 leave B2011 Capel le Ferne, Old Dover Road (cliff top road, overlooking the sea).

Langhorne Garden Hotel

◆ ◆ ◆

10-12 Langhorne Gardens, Folkestone, Kent, CT20 2EA
Tel: 01303 257233
Email: info@langhorne.co.uk
Web: www.langhorne.co.uk
Rooms: 29 all ensuite ⚓
Pricing: Sgl £30 Dbl £57 Dinner from £10
CC: Accepted
Room facilities: ▢ ☎ ☕
Access: ↕↑
Conference: 1 meeting room (Thtr 20 max)
Children: Welcome ♀ ☾ℂ
Dogs: Welcome
Licences: ♦♦♦
Leisure: Games room
Directions: Exit M20 junct 13, follow brown tourist signs for 'Leas'. Two miles from motorway to hotel through town.

Fordingbridge, Hampshire

Ashburn Hotel & Restaurant

★ ★

Station Road, Fordingbridge, Hampshire, SP16 1JP
Tel: 01425 652060 Fax: 01425 652150
Email: ashburn@mistral.co.uk
Web: www.ashburn.mistral.co.uk

Rooms: 20 all ensuite ⚓ ☐ ⊗
Pricing: Sgl £41.50 Dbl £78–105
Dinner from £17.50 CC: Accepted
Room facilities: ▢ ☎ ☕
Conference: 3 meeting rooms (Thtr 120 max), 24hr-delegate from £75, day-delegate rate from £20
Children: Welcome ♀ ☾ℂ
Dogs: Welcome
Licences: ◁◈ ♦♦♦
Leisure: Outdoor pool
Parking: Off-street
Directions: From Fordingbridge high street, follow road signposted Damerham, pass police and fire station, hotel is 400 yds on left hand side.

Forest Row, East Sussex

Ashdown Park Hotel & Country Club
Gold Ribbon Winner

★ ★ ★ ★ ☖ ☖ ☖

Wych Cross, Forest Row, East Sussex, RH18 5JR
Tel: 01342 824988 Fax: 01342 826206
Email: reservations@ashdownpark.com
Web: www.ashdownpark.com

A stunning 186-acre country house hotel, Ashdown Park offers log fires, gourmet cuisine, fine wines, panoramic views, golf, beautiful bedrooms and a luxurious country club. Ideal for relaxation and indulgence.
Rooms: 107 all ensuite ☐
Pricing: Sgl £125–315 Dbl £159–340 Dinner from £35
CC: Accepted
Room facilities: ▢ ☎ ☙
Access: ↕↑ ♿
Conference: 16 meeting rooms (Thtr 160 max), 24hr-delegate from £190, day-delegate rate from £72
Children: Welcome ♀ ☾ℂ
Dogs: Guide dogs only
Licences: ◁◈ ♦♦♦
Leisure: Indoor pool, Gym, Health spa, Beauty salon, Tennis, Golf, Snooker/billiards
Parking: Off-street and monitored
Directions: M23 J10. Take A264 to East Grinstead. Take A22 to Eastbourne through Forest Row. Continue through Forest Row on A22 for 2 miles. At Wych Cross turn left to Hartfield. Ashdown Park is ³/₄ of a mile on the right.

Frimley Green, Surrey

Lakeside International Hotel

★★★

Wharf Road, Frimley Green, Surrey, GU16 6JR
Tel: 01252 838000 Fax: 01252 837857

Gatwick Airport

Copthorne Hotel Effingham Park Gatwick

★★★★

West Park Road, Copthorne,
West Sussex, RH10 3EU
Tel: 0870 8900 214/ 237 Fax: 0870 8900 215
Email: sales.effingham@mill-cop.com
Web: www.millenniumhotels.com

Former stately home set in 40 acres of peaceful
parkland. Superb leisure facilities including a nine-hole
golf course. Close to many local attractions. Weekend
break rates also available.
Rooms: 122 all ensuite 🏌 🛏 🚭
Pricing: Sgl £135 Dbl £135 Dinner from £20 CC:
Accepted Room facilities: ▢ ☎ 🍵 🔌
Access: ↕ 🚹
Conference: 12 meeting rooms (Thtr 550 max), 24hr-
delegate from £169, day-delegate rate from £49.50
Children: Welcome Ħ 🐎 Dogs: Guide dogs only
Licences: ⟁ 🚹
Leisure: Indoor pool, Gym, Beauty salon, Tennis, Golf
Parking: Off-street and monitored
Directions: Leave M23 at Junction 10, taking A264
towards East Grinstead. At second roundabout, turn
left onto B2028. Hotel is on the right.

Copthorne Hotel London Gatwick

★★★★ 🔴 🔴

Copthorne Road, Copthorne, West Sussex, RH10 3PG
Tel: 01342 348800 Fax: 01342 348833
Email: coplgw@mill-cop.com
Web: www.millennium-hotels.com

Traditional, welcoming country house hotel built around
a 16th century farmhouse in 100 acres of gardens.
Ideal for many local attractions. Weekend break rates
also available.
Rooms: 227 all ensuite 🛏 🚭
Room facilities: ▢ ☎ 🍵 🔌
Access: 🚹
Conference: 15 meeting rooms (Thtr 150 max), 24hr-
delegate from £169, day-delegate rate from £49.50
Children: Welcome Ħ 🐎
Dogs: Welcome
Licences: ⟁ 🚹
Leisure: Indoor pool, Gym, Health spa,
Beauty salon
Parking: Off-street and monitored
Directions: Leave M23 at Junction 10, taking A264
towards East Grinstead. At first roundabout, take third
exit which is the hotel entrance.

Le Méridien London Gatwick

★★★★ 🔴

North Terminal, Gatwick Airport, West Sussex, RH6 0PH
Tel: 0800 028 2840 Fax: 01293 567739
Email: reservations.gatwick@lemeridien.com
Web: www.lemeridien-gatwick.com
Rooms: 494 all ensuite 🛏 🚭
Pricing: Dinner from £23.95 CC: Accepted
Room facilities: ▢ ☎ 🍵 🔌 ❄
Access: ↕ 🚹
Conference: 19 meeting rooms (Thtr 220 max), 24hr-
delegate from £180, day-delegate rate from £60
Children: Welcome Ħ 🐎
Dogs: Guide dogs only
Licences: ⟁ 🚹
Leisure: Indoor pool, Gym, Health spa, Beauty salon,
Snooker/billiards
Parking: Off-street and monitored
Directions: M23 exit 9 towards Gatwick. At roundabout
proceed straight across. Next roundabout second exit.
Hotel entrance on right.

Renaissance London Gatwick Hotel

★★★★

Povey Cross Road, Horley, Surrey, RH6 0BE
Tel: 01293 820169 Fax: 01293 820259
Email:rhi.lgwbr.reservations.mgr@renaissancehotels.com
Web: www.renaissancehotels.com
Rooms: 254 all ensuite 🐟 🗐 🚫
Pricing: Dinner from £18.50 (2002 rate) CC: Accepted
Room facilities: 🖵 ☎ 🍵 ☎ Access: ⊞ ♿
Children: Welcome ⴘ Dogs: Welcome
Licences: ⛨⛨⛨
Leisure: Indoor pool, Gym, Health spa, Beauty salon, Games room, Snooker/billiards
Parking: Off-street and monitored
Directions: M23 J9, follow signs for North Terminal. At roundabout, take last exit, turn left at next one and hotel is 500 yards on the left.

South Lodge Hotel   Gold Ribbon Winner

★★★★🎗🎗🎗

Brighton Road, Lower Beeding, West Sussex, RH13 6PS
Tel: 01403 891711 Fax: 01403 891766
Email: enquiries@southlodgehotel.co.uk
Web: www.exclusivehotels.co.uk
Rooms: 40 all ensuite 🐟 🗐
Pricing: Sgl £99–125 Dbl £145–380
Dinner from £40 CC: Accepted
Room facilities: 🖵 ☎ ☎ Access: ♿
Children: Welcome ⴘ 🎠 Dogs: Welcome
Licences: ⚓ ⛨⛨⛨
Leisure: Gym, Tennis, Fishing, Snooker/billiards
Parking: Off-street and monitored
Directions: From Gatwick, take M23 southbound. Turn off onto B2110 to Handcross. Follow road to Leonardslee Gardens. Turn left and the hotel is on right.
See advert on this page

Alexander House Hotel   Gold Ribbon Winner

★★★★🎗🎗🎗

Turners Hill, West Sussex, RH10 4QD
Tel: 01342 714914 Fax: 01342 717328
Email: info@alexanderhouse.co.uk
Web: www.alexanderhouse.co.uk
Rooms: 15 all ensuite 🗐
Pricing: Dinner from £34 (2002 rate) CC: Accepted
Room facilities: 🖵 ☎ ☎
Access: ⊞ ♿
Licences: ⚓ ⛨⛨⛨
Parking: Off-street

Southeast

Langshott Manor

★★★★ ⓡ ⓡ ⓡ Gold Ribbon Winner

Langshott, Horley, near Gatwick, Surrey, RH6 9LN
Tel: 01293 786680 Fax: 01293 783905
Email: admin@langshottmanor.com
Web: www.langshottmanor.com

'Europe's most civilised airport hotel' 2 miles and 400 years from Gatwick Airport. An Elizabethan manor house providing the best in hospitality and cuisine, yet with the most modern services.
Rooms: 22 all ensuite 🖾 ⊗
Pricing: Sgl £170 Dbl £220 Dinner from £37.50
CC: Accepted Room facilities: ☐ ☎ ⬰ Access: ♿
Conference: 3 meeting rooms (Thtr 30 max), 24hr-delegate from £60, day-delegate rate from £200
Children: Welcome ⁇ Licences: ⬩ ♦♦♦
Parking: Off-street and monitored
Directions: From Horley, take A23 towards Redhill. At roundabout with Shell petrol station, take third exit into Ladbroke Road. Langshott is ³/₄ mile on right.

Stanhill Court Hotel

★★★★ ⓡ

Stan Hill, Charlwood, Surrey, RH6 0EP
Tel: 01293 862166 Fax: 01293 862773
Email: enquiries@stanhillcourthotel.co.uk
Web: www.stanhillcourthotel.co.uk

The Victorians excelled at building baronial mansions and Stanhill Court Hotel is a fine example of their skills. 35 acres of glorious countryside. Restaurant 1881 for fine dining.
Rooms: 14 all ensuite 🖾 ⊗
Pricing: Dinner from £32.50 (2002 rate) CC: Accepted
Room facilities: ☐ ☎ ⊿ Children: Welcome ♠
Licences: ⬩ ♦♦♦ Parking: Off-street and monitored
Directions: On leaving Charlwood village, pass the Rising Sun Pub on your right, pass TH Gorringe on left. Take next right (NOT Gatwick Zoo). Pass 40mph sign. Stanhill Court signposted.

The Lawn Guest House

♦ ♦ ♦ ♦ ⹂

30 Massets Road, Gatwick, Horley, Surrey, RH6 7DF
Tel: 01293 775751 Fax: 01293 821803
Email: info@lawnguesthouse.co.uk
Web: www.lawnguesthouse.co.uk

Luxury Victorian house set in a mature garden, five minutes to Gatwick, two minutes to the centre of Horley, and close to mainline rail station. Holiday parking. No smoking.
Rooms: 12 all ensuite 🐾 ⊗
Pricing: Sgl £45–50 Dbl £55–55 CC: Accepted
Room facilities: ☐ ☎ ⊿ ⬰
Children: Welcome
Dogs: Welcome
Parking: Off-street
Directions: Exit M23 Junction 9. Follow A23 Redhill. ESSO station 3rd exit. 300 yards right Massetts Road. Lawn 400 yards on left.

Gillingham, Kent

Travelodge Medway (MOTO)

Travel Accommodation
M2 Moto Service Area, M2 Motorway, Rainham, Gillingham, Kent, ME8 8PQ
Web: www.travelodge.co.uk
Rooms: 52 all ensuite ⊗
Pricing: Sgl £54.40 Dbl £58.85
CC: Accepted Room facilities: ☐ ⊿ Access: ♿

Godalming, Surrey

Kings Arms and Royal Hotel

♦ ♦ ♦

High Street, Godalming, Surrey, GU7 1DZ
Tel: 01483 421545 Fax: 01483 415403
Rooms: 18 all ensuite 🖾
Room facilities: ☐ ☎ ⊿
Children: Welcome ♠
Licences: ♦♦♦
Parking: Off-street and monitored

Gosport, Hampshire

Belle Vue Hotel

★★★

39 Marine Parade East, Lee-on-the-Solent, Gosport, Hampshire, PO13 9BW
Tel: 023 9255 0258 Fax: 023 9255 2624
Email: information@bellevue-hotel.co.uk
Web: www.bellevue-hotel.co.uk
Seasonal closure: Christmas
Rooms: 27 all ensuite
Pricing: Dinner from £19.50 (2002 rate) CC: Accepted
Room facilities: Access:
Children: Welcome
Dogs: Welcome Licences:
Parking: Off-street
Directions: From the M27 (Junction 9 or 11), follow signs to Gosport, then Lee-on-the-Solent. The hotel is situated on the seafront just past shops.

Grays, Essex

Travelodge Thurrock (MOTO)

Travel Accommodation
Moto Service Area, off A1306, Thanent Way, Arterial Road, West Thurrock, Grays, Essex, RM16 3BG
Web: www.travelodge.co.uk
Rooms: 48 all ensuite
Pricing: Sgl £64.40 Dbl £68.85
CC: Accepted Room facilities: Access:

Great Milton, Oxfordshire

Le Manoir Aux Quat'Saisons

Gold Ribbon Winner

★★★★★

Church Road, Great Milton, Oxford, Oxfordshire, OX44 7PD
Tel: 01844 278881 Fax: 01844 278847
Email: lemanoir@blanc.co.uk
Web: www.manoir.com
Rooms: 32 all ensuite
Pricing: Sgl £245–260 Dbl £245–280 Dinner from £95
CC: Accepted Room facilities:
Access: Children: Welcome
Dogs: Guide dogs only Licences:
Parking: Off-street and monitored
Directions: From London, leave M40 at Junction 7. Turn towards Wallingford. Le Manoir is signposted on the right 2 miles further on.

Hailsham, East Sussex

Travelodge Hellingly, Eastbourne

Travel Accommodation
A22, Boship Farm Roundabout, Hellingly, Hailsham, East Sussex, BN27 4DT
Web: www.travelodge.co.uk
Rooms: 58 all ensuite
Pricing: Sgl £54.40 Dbl £58.85
CC: Accepted Room facilities: Access:

Harlow, Essex

Swallow Churchgate

★★★★

Churchgate Street Village, Old Harlow, Essex, CM17 0JT
Tel: 01279 420246 Fax: 01279 437720
Email: oldharlow.swallow@whitbread.com
Web: www.swallowhotels.co.uk

SWALLOW HOTELS

Rooms: 85 all ensuite
Pricing: Sgl £95–106 Dbl £105–135
Dinner from £25 CC: Accepted
Room facilities:
Conference: 7 meeting rooms (Thtr 160 max), 24hr-delegate from £150, day-delegate rate from £45
Children: Welcome
Dogs: Welcome
Licences:
Leisure: Indoor pool, Gym, Health spa
Parking: Off-street and monitored
Directions: Leave M11 at Junction 7. Take A414 to Harlow. At fourth roundabout turn right, onto B183. Follow signs to Churchgate Street.

Need help booking?

RAC Hotel Reservations will find the accommodation that's right for you – and book it too.
Call today on 0870 603 9109 and quote 'Guide 2003'

Ask the experts

To book a Hotel or Guest Accommodation, or for help and advice, call RAC Hotel Reservations on 0870 603 9109 and quote 'Guide 2003'

Southeast

Harpenden, Hertfordshire

Hanover International Hotel Harpenden

★★★

1 Luton Road, Harpenden, Hertfordshire, AL5 2PX
Tel: 0870 241 7080 Fax: 01582 460819
Email: reception.harpenden@hanover.international.com
Web: www.hanover-international.com

HANOVER INTERNATIONAL
HOTELS & CLUBS

An attractive hotel that retains many original features and offers excellent attention to detail. Transport links are superb via the M1 and M25 motorways.
Rooms: 60 all ensuite 🛏 🎱 🚭
Pricing: Sgl £69.95–170 Dbl £77.50–200
Dinner from £15 CC: Accepted
Room facilities: 📺 ☎ 🍵 ☕ Access: 🛗 🚹
Conference: 4 meeting rooms (Thtr 120 max), 24hr-delegate from £149.50, day-delegate rate from £47.50
Children: Welcome 🍴 Dogs: Welcome
Licences: ◇ 🎭
Parking: Off-street and monitored
Directions: Close to the town centre on the left-hand side of Luton Road if coming from Junction 9 of M1, or right-hand side when coming from Junction 10.

Harrow, Middlesex

Cumberland Hotel

★★★★ 🍴

1 St John's Road, Harrow, Middlesex, HA1 2EF
Tel: 020 8863 4111 Fax: 020 8861 5668
Web: www.cumberlandhotel.co.uk
Rooms: 84 all ensuite 🛏 🚭
Pricing: Sgl £60–98 Dbl £75–110 Dinner from £16.95
CC: Accepted
Room facilities: 📺 ☎ 🍵 ☕
Conference: 7 meeting rooms (Thtr 130 max), 24hr-delegate from £130, day-delegate rate from £36
Children: Welcome 🍴 🍽
Dogs: Guide dogs only
Licences: 🎭 Leisure: Gym
Parking: Off-street and monitored
Directions: Leave M1 at Junction 5. Take A41 and then A409 to Harrow town centre. Hotel is 1, St John's Road (reached via Lyon Road).
See advert on next page

Grim's Dyke

★★★★ 🍴 🍴

Old Redding, Harrow Weald, Middlesex, HA3 6SH
Tel: 020 8385 3100 Fax: 020 8954 4560
Email: reservations@grimsdyke.com
Web: www.grimsdyke.com
Rooms: 44 all ensuite 🛏 🎱 🚭
Pricing: Sgl £80–300 Dbl £90–300 Dinner from £20
CC: Accepted Room facilities: 📺 ☎ 🍵 ☕ Access: 🚹
Conference: 5 meeting rooms (Thtr 90 max), 24hr-delegate from £155, day-delegate rate from £51
Children: Welcome 🍽 Dogs: Welcome
Licences: ◇ 🎭 Parking: Off-street and monitored
Directions: From north, leave M1 at Junction 5. Take A41 towards A409 Harrow. After Kiln Nursery on right, turn right. Hotel is 300 yards on right.

Quality Harrow Hotel

★★★★ 🍴

12/22 Pinner Road, Harrow, Middlesex, HA1 4HZ
Tel: 020 8427 3435 Fax: 020 8861 1370
Email: info@harrowhotel.co.uk
Web: www.harrowhotel.co.uk

Winner of the Quality Hotel of the Year 2001. 50 rooms plus new 28 room luxury wing (see our advert), Lanfranc's award winning restaurant, serving International and French Cuisine open to non-residents 7 days a week, conferences, meetings, weddings and private dinners. Licensed to hold civil ceremonies.
Rooms: 78 all ensuite 🛏 🎱 🚭
Pricing: Sgl £60–98 Dbl £75–135 CC: Accepted
Room facilities: 📺 ☎ 🍵 ☕ Access: 🚹
Conference: 4 meeting rooms (Thtr 120 max)
Children: Welcome 🍴 🍽 Licences: ◇ 🎭
Parking: Off-street
Directions: Situated at junction of A312 and A404 on A404, leaving Harrow towards Pinner and Rickmansworth.
See advert on next page

Bogarts Bar and Lindal Hotel

★★

2 Hindes Road, Harrow, Middlesex, HA1 1SJ
Tel: 020 88633164 Fax: 020 84275435
Email: e.j.egan@amserve.net
Rooms: 24 (22 ensuite) 🛏 🚭
Pricing: Sgl £52–56 Dbl £69–75 Dinner from £8.95
CC: Accepted Room facilities: 📺 ☎ 🍵
Children: Welcome 2yrs min age
Dogs: Guide dogs only Licences: 🎭
Leisure: Games room

Parking: Off-street and monitored
Directions: Opposite Tesco/Wicks Harrow, off Station road, 7 mins walk from Harrow on the Hill tube station or Harrow Wealdstone.

Central Hotel

6 Hindes Road, Harrow, Middlesex, HA1 1SJ
Tel: 020 8427 0893 Fax: 020 8424 0673
Email: central@hindeshotel.com
Web: www.hindeshotel.com
Rooms: 15 (7 ensuite) Pricing: Sgl £39–49 Dbl £50–59
CC: Accepted Room facilities: ☐ ☞
Children: Welcome Parking: Off-street
Directions: Hindes Road is off Station Road (A409), in Harrow town centre. Hotel is opposite entrance to Tesco superstore in central Harrow.

Crescent Hotel

58-62 Welldon Crescent, Harrow, Middlesex, HA1 1QR
Tel: 020 8863 5491 Fax: 020 8427 5965
Email: jivraj@crsnthtl.demon.co.uk
Web: www.crsnthtl.demon.co.uk
Rooms: 21 (16 ensuite) ☜ Pricing: Sgl £40–50
Dbl £55–65 CC: Accepted Room facilities: ☐ ☎ ☞
Children: Welcome ⒣ ⒤ Licences: ⵊ
Parking: Off-street
Directions: In centre of Harrow. Five minutes from Harrow-on-the-Hill underground.

Hindes Hotel

8 Hindes Road, Harrow, Middlesex, HA1 1SJ
Tel: 020 8427 7468 Fax: 020 8424 0673
Email: reception@hindeshotel.com
Web: www.hindeshotel.com
Rooms: 14 (7 ensuite) Pricing: Sgl £39–49 Dbl £50–59
CC: Accepted Room facilities: ☐ ☞
Children: Welcome Parking: Off-street and monitored
Directions: Leave M1 at Junction 5, follow Harrow signs (A409). Or leave M4/A40 at exit A312 and follow signs.

Harwich, Essex

Pier at Harwich

The Quay, Harwich, Essex, CO12 3HH
Tel: 01255 241212 Fax: 01255 551922
Email: reception@thepieratharwich.com
Web: www.thepieratharwich.com
Rooms: 14 all ensuite ☜ Pricing: Sgl £62.50–75
Dbl £80–150 Dinner from £20.50 CC: Accepted
Room facilities: ☐ ☎ ☞ ⌇
Conference: 1 meeting room (Thtr 50 max), 24hr-delegate from £110, day-delegate rate from £30
Children: Welcome ⒣ Dogs: Guide dogs only
Licences: ⬙ ⵊ Parking: Off-street
Directions: From A12, follow A120 down to the quay (18 miles). Hotel opposite lifeboat station.

Southeast

Cliff Hotel

 ★★

Marine Parade, Dovercourt, Harwich, Essex, CO12 3RE
Tel: 01255 503345 Fax: 01255 240358
Email: reception@cliffhotelharwich.fsnet.co.uk
Web: www.thecliffhotelharwich.co.uk
Rooms: 26 all ensuite
Pricing: Sgl £55–65 Dbl £65–80 Dinner from £16
CC: Accepted
Room facilities:
Conference: 2 meeting rooms (Thtr 200 max), 24hr-
delegate from £64.75, day-delegate rate from £24.75
Children: Welcome
Dogs: Guide dogs only
Licences:
Leisure: Games room
Parking: Off-street
Directions: Leave A120 at Harwich International. At
roundabout take last exit to Dovercourt, then left at
next mini-roundabout. Take 10th turning on right to
seafront, then right 200 yards along.

Tower Hotel

★★

Main Road, Dovercourt, Harwich, Essex, CO12 3PJ
Tel: 01255 504952 Fax: 01255 504952
Email: admin@towerharwich.fsnet.co.uk
Rooms: 14 all ensuite
Pricing: Dinner from £6 (2002 rate) CC: Accepted
Room facilities:
Access: Children: Welcome
Licences:
Parking: Off-street
Directions: On the main road towards Dovercourt and
Harwich.

New Farm House

  ◆◆◆◆

Spinnel's Lane, Wix, Manningtree, Essex, CO11 2UJ
Tel: 01255 870365 Fax: 01255 870837
Email: newfarmhouse@which.net
Web: www.newfarmhouse.com
Rooms: 11 (9 ensuite)
Pricing: Sgl £28–38 Dbl £46–58 Dinner from £12
CC: Accepted
Room facilities:
Access:
Children: Welcome
Dogs: Guide dogs only Licences:
Parking: Off-street
Directions: 7 miles from Harwich, from A120 follow
signs to Wix. At village crossroads, take Bradfield
Road. Go under bridge and take next right.

Lythe Hill Hotel & Spa

★★★★★ ✦✦✦

Haslemere, Surrey, GU27 3BQ
Tel: 01428 651251 Fax: 01428 644131
Email: lythe@lythehill.co.uk
Web: www.lythehill.co.uk
Rooms: 41 all ensuite   Pricing: Sgl £112–249
Dbl £153–263 Dinner from £40 CC: Accepted
Room facilities: Access:
Conference: 8 meeting rooms (Thtr 110 max), 24hr-
delegate from £189, day-delegate rate from £60
Children: Welcome   Dogs: Welcome
Licences: Leisure: Indoor pool, Gym,
Health spa, Beauty salon, Tennis, Fishing, Games room
Parking: Off-street
Directions: Situated 1 mile east of Haslemere on B2131.

The Wheatsheaf Inn

 ✤

Grayswood Road, Grayswood, Haslemere,
Surrey, GU27 2DE
Tel: 01428 644440 Fax: 01428 641285
Rooms: 7 all ensuite Pricing: Sgl £55 Dbl £75
Dinner from £6.95 CC: Accepted Room facilities:
Children: Welcome   Dogs: Guide dogs only
Licences: Parking: Off-street
Directions: Leave A3 at junc 10 signed Milford Haven
follow A286 to Haslemere, we are in Grayswood.

Royal Victoria Hotel

★★★

Marina, St Leonards, Hastings, East Sussex, TN38 0BD
Tel: 01424 445544 Fax: 01424 721995
Email: reception@royalvichotel.co.uk
Web: www.royalvichotel.co.uk

A grand historic building located on the seafront of St
Leonards makes an ideal base to explore 1066
country. All rooms have a seating area, many with
seaviews and some split-level.
Rooms: 50 all ensuite
Pricing: Sgl £70–140 Dbl £70–150 Dinner from £19
CC: Accepted Room facilities: Access:
Conference: 6 meeting rooms (Thtr 150 max), 24hr-
delegate from £90, day-delegate rate from £35
Children: Welcome   Dogs: Welcome Licences:
Directions: On the A259 seafront, one mile west of
Hastings Pier. From M25 follow A21 to Hastings, then
right onto seafront.

Eagle House Hotel

◆◆◆◆

12 Pevensey Road, St Leonards, East Sussex, TN38 0JZ
Tel: 01424 430535 Fax: 01424 437771
Email: eaglehouse@cwcom.net
Web: www.eaglehousehotel.com

Town centre hotel with car park. A Victorian house in
period style. All bedrooms ensuite; restaurant
overlooking walled garden. Near the main London
Road, but in a quiet residential area.
Rooms: 19 all ensuite ⊗ Pricing: Dinner from £24 CC:
Accepted Room facilities: ▢ ☎ ☕ Access: ♿
Children: Welcome ☂ Licences: ⚤
Parking: Off-street and monitored
Directions: Follow signs to St Leonards, London Road.
At the church opposite office building Ocean House,
turn sharp right into Pevensey Road.

Hatfield, Hertfordshire

Quality Hotel Hatfield

★★★

Roehyde Way, Hatfield, Hertfordshire, AL10 9AF
Tel: 01707 275701 Fax: 01707 266033
Email: admin@gb059.u-net.com
Web: www.choicehotels.com
Rooms: 76 all ensuite ⊗⊗
Pricing: Sgl £56.60–140.75 Dbl £63–161.50
Dinner from £15.95 CC: Accepted
Room facilities: ▢ ☎ ☕ 📞 Access: ♿
Conference: 11 meeting rooms (Thtr 120 max), 24hr-
delegate from £140, day-delegate rate from £40
Children: Welcome ☂ Dogs: Welcome Licences: ⚤
Parking: Off-street and monitored
Directions: Exit Junction 3 of A1(M). Follow signs for
University of Hertfordshire. Hotel on Roehyde Way, half
mile from junction roundabout.

Havant, Hampshire

Green Cottage

◆◆◆

23 Park Lane, Bedhampton, Havant, Hampshire, PO9 3HG
Tel: 023 9247 5670
Seasonal closure: December and January
Rooms: 2 all ensuite ⊗ Pricing: Sgl £25–30
Dbl £45–50 Room facilities: ▢ ☕ Parking: Off-street
Directions: From M27/A27/A3M follow signs to
Bedhampton to B2177. At lights turn left into Hulbert
Road, immediately right into Park Lane.

Travelodge Chichester West

Travel Accommodation
A27 Eastbound, Emsworth, Nr. Havant, Hampshire,
PO10 7RB
Web: www.travelodge.co.uk
Rooms: 36 all ensuite ⊗
Pricing: Sgl £54.40 Dbl £58.85
CC: Accepted Room facilities: ▢ ☕ Access: ♿

Hayes, Middlesex

London Heathrow Marriott Hotel

★★★★ ⌘

Bath Road, Hayes, Middlesex, UB3 5AN
Tel: 020 8990 1100 Fax: 020 8990 1110
Web: www.marriotthotels.com/lhrhr
Rooms: 390 all ensuite ⊗⊗ ⊗
Pricing: Sgl £90–200 Dbl £90–200 Dinner from £20
CC: Accepted
Room facilities: ▢ ☎ ☕ 📞 ❄ Access: ⬆ ♿
Conference: 13 meeting rooms (Thtr 540 max), 24hr-
delegate from £170, day-delegate rate from £45
Children: Welcome ☂
Dogs: Guide dogs only Licences: ⚡ ⚤
Leisure: Indoor pool, Gym, Health spa
Parking: Off-street
Directions: Exit J4 M4, follow signs for Heathrow
terminals 123; turn onto A4; hotel is on left.

Shepiston Lodge Guest House

◆◆◆

31 Shepiston Lane, Hayes, Middlesex, UB3 1LJ
Tel: 020 8573 0266 Fax: 020 8569 2536
Email: shepistonlodge@aol.com
Web: www.shepistonlodge.co.uk
Rooms: 22 all ensuite
Pricing: Sgl £45–50 Dbl £60–65 Dinner from £6
CC: Accepted
Room facilities: ▢ ☕
Access: ♿ Children: Welcome ☂ 🐕 Licences: ⚤
Parking: Off-street and monitored
Directions: Exit J4 M4, follow signs for Hayes.
50 yards from Comfort Inn and Hayes fire station, in
Shepiston Lane.

Hayling Island, Hampshire

Cockle Warren Cottage

◆◆◆◆ ⚡

36 Seafront, Hayling Island, Hampshire, PO11 9HL
Tel: 02392 464961 Fax: 02392 464838
Rooms: 5 all ensuite ⊗⊗ ⊗
Pricing: Sgl £35–50 Dbl £55–80 CC: Accepted
Room facilities: ▢ ☕ Access: ♿
Children: Welcome ⚡
Dogs: Welcome
Licences: ⚤ Leisure: Outdoor pool
Parking: Off-street
Directions: On Hayling Island, follow signs to seafront,
passing through Mengham Village. Take road to the left
signed with brown signposts.

Redwalls

◆ ◆ ◆

66 Staunton Avenue, Hayling Island,
Hampshire, PO11 0EW
Tel: 023 9246 6109
Email: daphne@redwalls66.freeserve.co.uk
Web: www.redwalls.co.uk
Rooms: 3 (2 ensuite) ⊛ Pricing: Sgl £30 Dbl £40–45
Room facilities: ☐ ♨ Parking: Off-street
Directions: Follow main road across island signposted
Beachlands. Turn right into seafront road. Staunton
Avenue is fourth on the right.

Haywards Heath, West Sussex

Oakfield Cottage

◆ ◆ ◆

Brantridge Lane, Staplefield, Haywards Heath,
West Sussex, RH17 6JR
Tel: 01444 401121 Fax: 01444 401121
Email: joyoakfieldcot@aol.com
Web: www.smoothhound.co.uk/hotels/oakfieldcottagehtml
Rooms: 2 (1 ensuite) ⊛
Pricing: Sgl £25 Dbl £45 Room facilities: ☐ ♨
Dogs: Guide dogs only
Parking: Off-street and monitored
Directions: Handcross (N) take B2110 (Turners Hill),
after 2 miles turn right and right again into Brantridge
Lane. Property 1½ miles on right-hand side.

Headcorn, Kent

Four Oaks Bed & Breakfast

◆ ◆ ◆

Four Oaks Road, Headcorn, Kent, TN27 9PB
Tel: 01622 891224 Fax: 01622 890630
Email: info@fouroaks.uk.com
Web: www.fouroaks.uk.com

Restored, 500-year-old farmhouse in quiet rural
location. Close to Leeds Castle, Sissinghurst Gardens
and mainline rail services. London 1 hour, Eurolink 30
minutes.
Rooms: 3 (1 ensuite) ⊛
Room facilities: ☐ ♨ Children: Welcome �│
Dogs: Welcome Parking: Off-street
Directions: South from Maidstone on A274, right at
Weald of Kent Golf Club. One mile on right.

Heathrow Airport

Le Méridien Heathrow

★ ★ ★ ★

Bath Road, Heathrow, Middlesex, UB7 0DU
Tel: 0800 028 2840 Fax: 020 8759 3421
Email: reservations.heathrow@lemeridien.com
Web: www.lemeridien.com
Rooms: 567 all ensuite ⊛ ⊛
Pricing: Sgl £146.87 Dbl £146.87 Dinner from £19.95
CC: Accepted
Room facilities: ☐ ☎ ♨ ⌕ ❄
Access: ⇞ ♿
Conference: 37 meeting rooms (Thtr 250 max), 24hr-
delegate from £260, day-delegate rate from £72
Children: Welcome �│ ◦
Dogs: Guide dogs only
Licences: ◁ ⫼
Leisure: Indoor pool, Gym, Health spa, Beauty salon
Parking: Off-street and monitored
Directions: Exit J5 M4, follow signs for A4 London.
Hotel is on the left as the slip road joins the A4.

Renaissance London Heathrow Hotel

★ ★ ★ ★ ⊛

Bath Road, Hounslow, Middlesex, TW6 2AQ
Tel: 020 8897 6363 Fax: 020 8897 1113
Email: lhrrenaissance@cs.com
Web: www.renaissancehotels.com/lhrbr

Comfortable and relaxing accommodation, some
rooms with spectacular runway views. Plane Spotter
break available. Other services include: Icarus Lounge
Bar, Business Centre, Hairdressers, Bureau de Change
and Gift Shop.
Rooms: 649 all ensuite ⊛
Pricing: Dinner from £17.50 CC: Accepted
Room facilities: ☐ ☎ ♨ ⌕ ❄
Access: ⇞ ♿
Conference: 28 meeting rooms (Thtr 520 max)
Children: Welcome �│ ◦
Dogs: Guide dogs only
Licences: ◁ ⫼
Leisure: Gym, Health spa, Beauty salon
Parking: Off-street and monitored
Directions: Junction 4, M4. Follow signs for Heathrow,
terminals 1-3, via the M4/Heathrow access road.
Straight over roundabout, immediate left next
roundabout. Hotel is second exit.

Osterley Four Pillars Hotel

★★★

764 Great West Road, Isleworth, Middlesex, TW7 5NA
Tel: 020 8568 7781 Fax: 020 8569 7819
Email: osterley@four-pillars.co.uk
Web: www.four-pillars.co.uk
Seasonal closure: 25–30 December
Rooms: 61 all ensuite
Pricing: Sgl £59–101.25 Dbl £74–123.50
Dinner from £15.95 CC: Accepted
Room facilities:
Conference: 9 meeting rooms (Thtr 250 max), 24hr-delegate from £140, day-delegate rate from £32
Children: Welcome
Dogs: Welcome Licences:
Parking: Off-street
Directions: J3 M4; follow signs for A4. Pass Osterley Tube Station; hotel is 1 mile on left.

St Giles Hotel

★★★

Hounslow Hotel, Feltham, Middlesex, TW14 9AD
Tel: 020 8890 2358 Fax: 020 8751 6103
Email: book@stgiles.com
Web: www.stgiles.com
Rooms: 300 all ensuite
Pricing: Sgl £135–155 Dbl £145–165 Dinner from £14
CC: Accepted
Room facilities:
Access:
Conference: 10 meeting rooms (Thtr 150 max), 24hr-delegate from £155, day-delegate rate from £45
Children: Welcome
Dogs: Guide dogs only Licences:
Leisure: Gym
Parking: Off-street and monitored
Directions: Take A312 to Feltham, then A244 to town centre. Hotel is visible after 600 yards, opposite the train station.

Stanwell Hall Hotel

★★

Town Lane, Stanwell, Staines, Middlesex, TW19 7PW
Tel: 01784 252292 Fax: 01784 245250
Web: www.stanwell-hall.co.uk
Seasonal closure: 24–29 December
Rooms: 18 all ensuite
Pricing: Sgl £50–115 Dbl £70–145 Dinner from £18
CC: Accepted
Room facilities:
Conference: 1 meeting room (Thtr 16 max)
Children: Welcome
Dogs: Guide dogs only Licences:
Parking: Off-street and monitored
Directions: Leave M25 at Junction 14. Follow signs to Heathrow Terminal 4. At roundabout, turn right to Staines. At traffic lights turn left to Stanwell. At mini roundabout turn right. Hotel on right.

Channins Hounslow Hotel

★

41 Hounslow Road , Feltham, Middlesex, TW14 0AV
Tel: 020 8890 2358 Fax: 020 8751 6103
Rooms: 23 all ensuite
Room facilities:
Conference: 1 meeting room (Thtr 20 max), 24hr-delegate from £25, day-delegate rate from £15
Children: Welcome
Dogs: Welcome
Parking: Off-street and monitored

Hemel Hempstead, Hertfordshire

Hyde Lane Farm

♦ ♦ ♦

Hyde Lane, Hemel Hempstead, Hertfordshire, HP3 8SA
Tel: 01923 267380
Rooms: 2 (1 ensuite)
Pricing: Sgl £35–45
Room facilities:
Parking: Off-street and monitored
Directions: Situated in quiet country lane. Easy access to M1 and M25 Watford, St Albans and Hemel Hempstead.

Travelodge Hemel Hempstead (SA)

Travel Accommodation
Wolsey House, Wolsey Road, Hemel Hempstead, Hertfordshire, HP2 4SS
Web: www.travelodge.co.uk
Rooms: 53 all ensuite
Pricing: Sgl £47.40–74.40 Dbl £51.85–78.85
CC: Accepted Room facilities: Access:

Henley-on-Thames, Oxfordshire

Thamesmead House Hotel

◆ ◆ ◆ ◆ ◆ ◆ ✕ ✂ ✆

Remenham Lane, Henley-on-Thames, Oxon, RG9 2LR
Tel: 01491 574745 Fax: 01491 579944
Email: thamesmead@supanet.com
Web: www.thamesmeadhousehotel.co.uk
Seasonal closure: Christmas

Delightful house overlooking cricket green, 3 minutes walk from centre of Henley and river. Relaxed friendly atmosphere, stylish interior combining contemporary feel with period features. Luxurious beds, crisp linen, sparkling bathrooms.
Rooms: 6 all ensuite
Pricing: Sgl £105–115 Dbl £125–140 CC: Accepted
Room facilities: ▢ ☎ ☕ ✎
Access: ♿
Conference: 1 meeting room
Children: Welcome 10yrs min age
Licences: ♦♦♦
Parking: Off-street and monitored
Directions: From M4, junction 8/9, A404 (M) to Burchett's Green. Left on A4130, signed Henley 5 miles, turn right by Little Angel pub, house on left.

Hertford, Hertfordshire

Salisbury Arms Hotel

★★★

Fore Street, Hertford, Hertfordshire, SG14 1BZ
Tel: 01992 583091 Fax: 01992 552510
Email: reception@salisbury-arms-hotel.co.uk
Web: www.salisburyarmshotel.co.uk
Rooms: 31 all ensuite
Pricing: Sgl £39.50–70 Dbl £79–90 CC: Accepted
Room facilities: ▢ ☎ ☕ ✎
Access: ♿
Conference: 2 meeting rooms (Thtr 40 max)
Children: Welcome ♰
Dogs: Guide dogs only
Licences: ♦♦♦
Parking: Off-street and monitored
Directions: Situated in the centre of Hertford, off the A414 on Fore Street.

The White Horse

★★★

Hertingfordbury, Hertford, Hertfordshire, SG14 2LB
Tel: 0870 400 8114 Fax: 01992 550809
Email: whitehorsehertingfordbury@heritage-hotels.co.uk
Web: www.macdonaldhotels.co.uk
Rooms: 42 all ensuite
Pricing: Sgl £49 Dbl £98 Dinner from £20
CC: Accepted
Room facilities: ▢ ☎ ☕ ✎
Conference: 2 meeting rooms (Thtr 60 max), 24hr-delegate from £120, day-delegate rate from £35
Children: Welcome Dogs: Welcome
Licences: ♦♦♦ Parking: Off-street

Hickstead, West Sussex

Travelodge Hickstead

Travel Accommodation
A23, Jobs Lane, West Sussex, RH17 5NX
Web: www.travelodge.co.uk
Rooms: 55 all ensuite
Pricing: Sgl £54.40–64.40 Dbl £58.85–68.85
CC: Accepted Room facilities: ▢ ☕ Access: ♿

High Wycombe, Buckinghamshire

Bird in Hand

◆ ◆ ◆

West Wycombe Road, High Wycombe,
Buckinghamshire, HP11 2LR
Tel: 01494 523502 Fax: 01494 459449
Rooms: 6 (5 ensuite)
Pricing: Dinner from £5 (2002 rate) CC: Accepted
Room facilities: ▢ ☎ ☕ ✎
Children: Welcome ♰ ✂ Licences: ♦♦♦
Parking: Off-street
Directions: The Bird in Hand is on the A40 West Wycombe to Oxford Road, just a few minutes from the town centre.

Blue Flag

◆ ◆ ◆

Marlow Road, Cadmore End, High Wycombe,
Buckinghamshire, HP14 3PF
Tel: 01494 881183 Fax: 01494 882269
Email: blueflag.cadmoreend@eldridge-pope.co.uk
Rooms: 17 all ensuite
Pricing: Sgl £79 Dbl £89.50 Dinner from £8
CC: Accepted
Room facilities: ▢ ☎ ☕ ✎
Access: ♿
Children: Welcome ♰ Dogs: Guide dogs only
Licences: ♦♦♦ Parking: Off-street
Directions: Come off M4 to M40, take junction 5, turn right through Stocken Church village, pass Kings Arms and shop. Turn right onto Cadmore End to lane end, carry on down road to white gates and on for about 1½ to 2 miles. Hotel on the left after bend.

Clifton Lodge Hotel

 ◆ ◆ ◆

210 West Wycombe Road, High Wycombe,
Buckinghamshire, HP12 3AR
Tel: 01494 440095 Fax: 01494 536322
Email: mail@cliftonlodgehotel.com
Web: www.cliftonlodgehotel.com

Rooms: 32 (22 ensuite) ♨ 🛏
Pricing: Sgl £40–75 Dbl £58–99 Dinner from £15
CC: Accepted
Room facilities: 📺 ☎ 🍵
Children: Welcome 🍴 Licences: ♟♟♟
Parking: Off-street and monitored
Directions: Clifton Lodge is situated on the A40 West
Wycombe Road, 1 mile from the M40 and the centre of
High Wycombe.

Drake Court Hotel

 ◆ ◆

141 London Road, High Wycombe,
Buckinghamshire, HP11 1BT
Tel: 01494 523639 Fax: 01494 472696
Rooms: 20 (5 ensuite) ♨
Pricing: Dinner from £7 (2002 rate) CC: Accepted
Room facilities: 📺 ☎ 🍵
Children: Welcome 🍴 Dogs: Guide dogs only
Licences: ♟♟♟
Leisure: Outdoor pool Parking: Off-street
Directions: Approx 1¹/₂ miles from M40 on A40 London
Road ¹/₂ mile from town centre towards London and
Beaconsfield.

Hindhead, Surrey

Devils Punch Bowl

 ◆ ◆ ◆

London Road, Hindhead, Surrey, GU26 6AG
Tel: 01428 606565 Fax: 01428 605713
Rooms: 31 all ensuite 🛏 ⊗
Pricing: Sgl £61.90 Dbl £73.10
Dinner from £6.95 CC: Accepted
Room facilities: 📺 ☎ 🍵 📞
Access: ♿
Conference: 1 meeting room (Thtr 80 max)
Children: Welcome 🍴 Dogs: Welcome
Licences: ◭ ♟♟♟ Parking: Off-street and monitored
Directions: 12 miles south of Guildford on the A3 main
road to Portsmouth.

Hitchin, Hertfordshire

Firs Hotel & Restaurant

 ★ ★

83 Bedford Road, Hitchin, Hertfordshire, SG5 2TY
Tel: 01462 422322 Fax: 01462 432051
Email: info@firshotel.co.uk
Web: www.firshotel.co.uk
Rooms: 29 all ensuite ♨ ⊗
Pricing: Sgl £52–57 Dbl £62–75
Dinner from £10
CC: Accepted Room facilities: 📺 ☎ 🍵 📞
Access: ♿
Conference: 1 meeting room (Thtr 32 max), 24hr-
delegate from £95
Children: Welcome Dogs: Guide dogs only
Licences: ♟♟♟
Parking: Off-street
Directions: Exit M1 at J10; A505 to Hitchin. Exit A1 at
J8; A602 to Hitchin. Follow directions for Bedford.
Hotel is outside Hitchin town centre on A600.

Redcoats Farmhouse Hotel

◆ ◆ ◆ ◆

Redcoats Green, near Hitchin, Hertfordshire, SG4 7JR
Tel: 01438 729500 Fax: 01438 723322
Email: sales@redcoats.co.uk
Web: www.redcoats.co.uk
Rooms: 12 all ensuite ♨ ⊗
Pricing: Sgl £85–95 Dbl £95–115 Dinner from £35
CC: Accepted Room facilities: 📺 ☎ 🍵 📞
Access: ♿
Conference: 2 meeting rooms (Thtr 25 max), 24hr-
delegate from £145, day-delegate rate from £35
Children: Welcome Dogs: Welcome
Licences: ◭ ♟♟♟
Parking: Off-street and monitored
Directions: Leave A1(M) at Junction 8, follow road to
village of Little Wymondley. At end of village turn left at
roundabout into Blakemore End Road (to Redcoats
Green).

Southeast

Tudor Oaks Lodge

♦♦♦

Taylors Road, Astwick, near Hitchin, Hertfordshire, SG5 4AZ
Tel: 01462 834133 Fax: 01462 834133
Email: tudoroakslodge@aol.com
Web: www.thetudoroakslodge.co.uk

15th-century lodge around secluded courtyard. Ensuite rooms, fresh food daily from bar snacks to à la carte. Real Ales.
Rooms: 13 all ensuite
Pricing: Sgl £49.50–59.50 Dbl £62–72 Dinner from £10
CC: Accepted
Room facilities:
Conference: 2 meeting rooms (Thtr 30 max)
Children: Welcome 6yrs min age
Licences:
Parking: Off-street and monitored
Directions: Conveniently placed by the side of the A1, 1 mile north past Junction 10. Within easy reach of Letchworth, Baldock and Stevenage.

Hook, Hampshire

Tylney Hall Hotel

Gold Ribbon Winner

★★★★

Rotherwick, Hook, Hampshire, RG27 9AZ
Tel: 01256 764881 Fax: 01256 768141
Email: reservations@tylneyhall.com
Web: www.tylneyhall.com

Set in manicured, historic gardens, Tylney Hall is a perfect location – elegant lounges, stunning views, fine leisure facilities, exquisite bedrooms and a breathtaking setting. A tranquil, romantic country house of distinction.

Rooms: 112 all ensuite
Pricing: Sgl £125–385 Dbl £159–410 Dinner from £35
CC: Accepted
Room facilities:
Conference: 12 meeting rooms (Thtr 120 max), 24hr-delegate from £250, day-delegate rate from £80
Children: Welcome
Dogs: Guide dogs only
Licences:
Leisure: Indoor pool, Outdoor pool, Gym, Health spa, Beauty salon, Tennis, Snooker/billiards
Parking: Off-street and monitored
Directions: M3 J5, A287 to Basingstoke, over A30 into Old School Road. Left at T-junction, right at crossroads, one mile along.

Horsham, West Sussex

Ye Olde King's Head Hotel

★★

Carfax, Horsham, West Sussex, RH12 1EG
Tel: 01403 253126 Fax: 01403 242291
Web: www.kingsheadhorsham.co.uk
Rooms: 42 all ensuite
Pricing: Sgl £85–95 Dbl £98–125 CC: Accepted
Room facilities:
Access:
Conference: 3 meeting rooms (Thtr 40 max)
Children: Welcome
Dogs: Welcome
Licences:
Parking: Off-street
Directions: At junction of the Carfax (town centre) and East Street, having followed the brown tourist signs.

Hounslow, Middlesex

Master Robert Hotel

★★★

Great West Road, Hounslow, Middlesex, TW5 0BD
Tel: 020 8570 6261 Fax: 020 8569 4016
Email: stay@masterrobert.co.uk
Web: www.masterrobert.co.uk
Rooms: 96 all ensuite
Room facilities:
Access:
Children: Welcome
Licences:
Leisure: Games room
Parking: Off-street

Travelodge Heston Heathrow Eastbound (MOTO)

Travel Accommodation
M4 Moto Service Area, Phoenix Way, Hounslow, Middlesex, TW5 9NB
Web: www.travelodge.co.uk
Rooms: 66 all ensuite
Pricing: Sgl £54.40–74.40 Dbl £58.85–78.85
CC: Accepted Room facilities: Access:

Travelodge Heston Heathrow Westbound (MOTO)

Travel Accommodation
M4 Moto Service Area, Phoenix Way, Hounslow, Middlesex, TW5 9NB
Web: www.travelodge.co.uk
Rooms: 145 all ensuite
Pricing: Sgl £54.40–74.40 Dbl £58.85–78.85
CC: Accepted Room facilities: ☐ ☕ Access: ♿

Hove, East Sussex

Courtlands Hotel

★★★
15–27 The Drive, Hove, East Sussex, BN3 3JE
Tel: 01273 731055 Fax: 01273 328295
Email: info@courtlandshotel.com
Web: www.courtlandhotel.com
Rooms: 67 all ensuite 🍴 🖥 ⊗
Pricing: Sgl £65–75 Dbl £130–150 Dinner from £16.95
CC: Accepted
Room facilities: ☐ ☎ ☕ Access: ⬆ ♿
Conference: 3 meeting rooms (Thtr 70 max), 24hr-delegate from £80, day-delegate rate from £30
Children: Welcome ⑂ Dogs: Guide dogs only
Licences: ♟ Leisure: Indoor pool
Parking: Off-street
Directions: From A23 follow signs to Hove. Second turning at roundabout, follow Dyke Road, then Upper Drive and The Drive.

Imperial Hotel

★★★
First Avenue, Hove, East Sussex, BN2 2GU
Tel: 01273 777320 Fax: 01273 777310
Email: info@imperial-hove.com
Web: www.imperial-hove.com
Rooms: 76 all ensuite 🍴 ⊗
Pricing: Sgl £50–75 Dbl £85–105 Dinner from £16.50
CC: Accepted
Room facilities: ☐ ☎ ☕ Access: ⬆
Conference: 5 meeting rooms (Thtr 110 max), 24hr-delegate from £30, day-delegate rate from £85
Children: Welcome ⑂ ☕ Dogs: Guide dogs only
Licences: ♟
Directions: Enter Brighton on A23, proceed to seafront. Turn right (west) onto A259. First Avenue 1 mile on right.

Langfords Hotel

★★★★ ⊜
Third Avenue, Hove, East Sussex, BN3 2PX
Tel: 01273 738222 Fax: 01273 779426
Email: langfords@pavilion.co.uk
Web: www.langfordshotel.com
Rooms: 60 all ensuite 🍴 🖥 ⊗
Pricing: Sgl £50–75 Dbl £80–105 Dinner from £15
CC: Accepted
Room facilities: ☐ ☎ ☕ Access: ⬆
Conference: 6 meeting rooms (Thtr 200 max), 24hr-delegate from £105, day-delegate rate from £35
Children: Welcome ⑂ ☕

Dogs: Guide dogs only
Licences: ♟
Directions: From A23 follow signs to Hove. Turn left on seafront road (A259). Continue east until you reach third avenue on left.

Princes Marine Hotel

★★★
153 Kingsway, Hove, East Sussex, BN3 4GR
Tel: 01273 207660 Fax: 01273 325913
Email: princesmarine@bestwestern.co.uk
Web: www.princesmarinehotel.co.uk

Seafront hotel with well-equipped ensuite bedrooms. Rooftop function suites, seaview restaurant and bar. Large private car park. Situated close to all attractions, bowling greens and the King Alfred Leisure Centre. Open for Christmas and New Year.
Rooms: 48 all ensuite 🍴 🖥 ⊗
Pricing: Sgl £50–70 Dbl £80–120 Dinner from £15.95
CC: Accepted
Room facilities: ☐ ☎ ☕ Access: ⬆ ♿
Conference: 3 meeting rooms (Thtr 80 max), 24hr-delegate from £90, day-delegate rate from £25
Children: Welcome ⑂ ☕
Dogs: Welcome
Licences: ♟
Parking: Off-street and monitored
Directions: From M23, go straight to seafront. Turn right at Palace Pier. Continue along main seafront road. Hotel is 200 yards west of King Alfred swimming pool.

Hungerford, Berkshire

Marshgate Cottage Hotel

♦ ♦ ♦ ♦ ⊠
Marsh Lane, Hungerford, Berkshire, RG17 0QX
Tel: 01488 682307 Fax: 01488 685475
Email: reservations@marshgate.co.uk
Web: www.marshgate.co.uk
Rooms: 10 all ensuite 🍴 🖥 ⊗
Pricing: Sgl £45 Dbl £55–60 CC: Accepted
Room facilities: ☐ ☎ ☕
Conference: 1 meeting room (Thtr 20 max)
Children: Welcome Dogs: Welcome
Licences: ♟ Parking: Off-street and monitored
Directions: M4 J14. From High Street, turn into Church Street. Half a mile along, turn right into Marsh Lane. Hotel is at end.

Hythe, Kent

Hythe Imperial Hotel

★★★★★ ℞ ℞

Prince's Parade, Hythe, Kent, CT21 6AE
Tel: 01303 267441 Fax: 01303 264610
Email: hytheimperial@marstonhotels.com
Web: www.marstonhotels.com

100 bedroom majestic hotel situated on sea front of historic Hythe. Superb leisure facilities including heated indoor pool, spa, gym, tennis, and a 9 hole links golf course, AA rosette restaurant.
Rooms: 100 all ensuite ☕ 🖥 Ⓢ
Pricing: Sgl £102 Dbl £149 Dinner from £28
CC: Accepted
Room facilities: ▭ ☎ ☕ 🍴
Access: ⅃↥ ♿
Conference: 19 meeting rooms (Thtr 250 max), 24hr-delegate from £155, day-delegate rate from £50
Children: Welcome ♨ 🐴 ☕
Dogs: Guide dogs only
Licences: ◈ ♟
Leisure: Indoor pool, Gym, Health spa, Beauty salon, Tennis, Golf, Games room, Snooker/billiards
Parking: Off-street and monitored
Directions: Leave M20 southbound at Junction 11. Follow A261 to Hythe. When in Hythe follow signs to Folkestone. Turn right into Twiss Road.

Stade Court Hotel

★★★ ℞

West Parade, Hythe, Kent, CT21 6DT
Tel: 01303 268263 Fax: 01303 261803
Email: stadecourt@marstonhotels.com
Web: www.marstonhotels.com

A delightful hotel on sea front of historic Hythe, enjoying panoramic views of English Channel. Use of leisure facilities at sister hotel 600 meters away, convenient for Eurotunnel and channel ports.
Rooms: 42 all ensuite ☕
Pricing: Sgl £70 Dbl £99 Dinner from £23
CC: Accepted
Room facilities: ▭ ☎ ☕ 🍴
Access: ⅃↥
Conference: 5 meeting rooms (Thtr 40 max), 24hr-delegate from £110, day-delegate rate from £37.50
Children: Welcome ♨ 🐴 ☕
Dogs: Welcome
Licences: ♟
Leisure: Indoor pool, Gym, Health spa, Beauty salon, Tennis, Golf, Games room, Snooker/billiards
Parking: Off-street and monitored
Directions: Leave M20 southbound at Junction 11. Follow A261 to Hythe. When in Hythe, turn right into Stade Street (by canal).

Ilford, Essex

Park Hotel

◆ ◆ ◆

327 Cranbrook Road, Ilford, Essex, IG1 4UE
Tel: 020 8554 9616 Fax: 020 8518 2700
Email: parkhotelilford@netscapeonline.co.uk
Web: www.the-park-hotel.co.uk
Rooms: 20 all ensuite ☕ 🖥
Room facilities: ▭ ☕
Access: ♿
Children: Welcome
Dogs: Welcome
Licences: ♟
Parking: Off-street and monitored
Directions: Opposite Valentines Park, five minutes walk from Gants Hill Underground and Ilford railway stations.

Woodville Guest House

 ◆ ◆ ◆

10–12 Argyle Road, Ilford, Essex, IG1 3BQ
Tel: 020 8478 3779 Fax: 020 8478 6282
Email: cass@woodville-guesthouse.co.uk
Rooms: 16 (7 ensuite)
Pricing: Sgl £35–47 Dbl £45–60
Room facilities: ▢ ♨
Children: Welcome
Parking: Off-street and monitored
Directions: Leave M25 for M11 southbound to A406.
Leave at Ilford Junction. Past Ilford Station, take
second left off Cranbrook Road into Beal Road, then
second left into Argyle Road.
See advert on this page

Cranbrook Hotel

◆ ◆

24 Coventry Road, Ilford, Essex, IG1 4QR
Tel: 020 8554 6544 Fax: 020 8518 1463

Travelodge London, Ilford Central (SA)

Travel Accommodation
A118, Clements Road, Ilford, Essex, RM10 9YQ
Web: www.travelodge.co.uk
Rooms: 32 all ensuite ⊛
Pricing: Sgl £64.40 Dbl £68.85
CC: Accepted Room facilities: ▢ ♨ Access: ♿

Travelodge London, Ilford North (SA)

Travel Accommodation
B192, The Beehive, Beehive Hill, Gants Hill, Ilford,
Essex, IG4 5DR
Web: www.travelodge.co.uk
Rooms: 91 all ensuite ⊛
Pricing: Sgl £64.40 Dbl £68.85
CC: Accepted Room facilities: ▢ ♨ Access: ♿

Isle of Wight

Burlington Hotel

★ ★ ★

Bellevue Road, Ventnor, Isle of Wight, PO38 1DB
Tel: 01983 852113 Fax: 01983 853862
Email: @burlingtonhotel.freeserve.co.uk
Web: www.burlingtonhotel.uk.com
Seasonal closure: Nov to March
Rooms: 24 all ensuite
Pricing: Dinner from £15 CC: Accepted
Room facilities: ▢ ☎ ♨
Children: Welcome 3yrs min age ⵏ
Licences: ⅲ
Leisure: Outdoor pool, Games room
Parking: Off-street

Country Garden Hotel

 ★ ★ ★ ★

Church Hill, Totland Bay, Isle of Wight, PO39 0ET
Tel: 01983 754521 Fax: 01983 754521
Email: countrygardeniow@aol.com
Web: www.thecountrygardenhotel.co.uk
Seasonal closure: January-Feb 13
Rooms: 16 all ensuite
Pricing: Sgl £44–62 Dbl £75–124 Dinner from £18.50
CC: Accepted
Room facilities: ▢ ☎ ♨ Access: ♿
Children: Welcome 12yrs min age Dogs: Welcome
Licences: ⅲ
Parking: Off-street
Directions: Eight minutes' drive west from Yarmouth.

Eversley Hotel

★★★

Park Avenue, Ventnor, Isle of Wight, PO38 1LB
Tel: 01983 852244 Fax: 01983 856534
Email: eversleyhotel@yahoo.co.uk
Web: www.eversleyhotel.com
Seasonal closure: January

A family run hotel serving good food in comfortable
surroundings. Situated in an acre of grounds next to
the park and coastal paths. An ideal base for exploring
the island.
Rooms: 30 all ensuite
Pricing: Sgl £35–50 Dbl £69–89 Dinner from £15
CC: Accepted
Room facilities: 💻 ☎ 🍵
Children: Welcome ♁ ✆
Dogs: Welcome
Licences: ⛊⛊⛊
Leisure: Outdoor pool
Parking: Off-street
Directions: Situated to the west of Ventnor on the Niton
road A3055 next to Ventnor park.

Farringford Hotel

★★★

Bedbury Lane, Freshwater Bay, Isle of Wight, PO40 9PE
Tel: 01983 752500 Fax: 01983 756515
Email: enquiries@farringford.co.uk
Web: www.farringford.co.uk
Rooms: 18 all ensuite 🍵 🖥
Pricing: Sgl £35–70 Dbl £70–140 Dinner from £23
CC: Accepted
Room facilities: 💻 ☎ 🍵
Conference: 4 meeting rooms (Thtr 150 max), 24hr-
delegate from £90, day-delegate rate from £30
Children: Welcome ♁ ✆
Dogs: Welcome
Licences: ⚑ ⛊⛊⛊
Leisure: Outdoor pool, Tennis, Golf, Snooker/billiards
Parking: Off-street and monitored
Directions: Take A3054 towards Freshwater. Turn left to
Norton Green, left at roundabout to Freshwater Bay,
then right onto Bedbury Lane.
See advert on next page

George Hotel   Gold Ribbon Winner

★★★★ 🏵 🏵 🏵 🏵

Quay Street, Yarmouth, Isle of Wight, PO41 0PE
Tel: 01983 760331 Fax: 01983 760425
Email: res@thegeorge.co.uk
Web: www.thegeorge.co.uk
Rooms: 17 all ensuite 🖥 ⊛
Pricing: Sgl £125 Dbl £175–225 Dinner from £25
CC: Accepted
Room facilities: 💻 ☎
Conference: 1 meeting room (Thtr 30 max), 24hr-
delegate from £185, day-delegate rate from £65
Children: Welcome 10yrs min age
Dogs: Welcome
Licences: ⚑ ⛊⛊⛊
Directions: Situated in Yarmouth, between pier and castle.

Holliers Hotel

★★★

Church Road, Old Village, Shanklin,
Isle of Wight, PO37 6NU
Tel: 01983 862764 Fax: 01983 867134
Email: enquires@holliers-hotel.com
Web: www.holliers-hotel.com
Rooms: 30 all ensuite
Pricing: Sgl £55–60 Dbl £70–75 Dinner from £16.95
CC: Accepted
Room facilities: 💻 ☎ 🍵
Children: Welcome ♁ ✆
Dogs: Guide dogs only
Licences: ⛊⛊⛊
Leisure: Indoor pool, Outdoor pool, Snooker/billiards
Parking: Off-street
Directions: Holliers Hotel is situated on the main
A3055.

Keats Green Hotel

★★★

3 Queens Road, Shanklin, Isle of Wight, PO37 6AN
Tel: 01983 862742 Fax: 01983 868572
Email: enquiries@keatsgreenhoteliow.co.uk
Web: www.keatsgreenhoteliow.co.uk
Seasonal closure: January to March
Rooms: 33 all ensuite 🍵
Pricing: Sgl £31–39 Dbl £62–78 Dinner from £15.30
CC: Accepted
Room facilities: 💻 ☎ 🍵
Access: ⥮ ♿
Children: Welcome ♁
Dogs: Welcome
Licences: ⛊⛊⛊
Leisure: Outdoor pool
Parking: Off-street and monitored
Directions: Driving from Lake take A3055 towards
Ventnor (Queens Road). Hotel is approx 400 yards
on left.
See advert on next page

Luccombe Hall Hotel

★★★

Luccombe Road, Shanklin, Isle of Wight, PO37 6RL
Tel: 01983 869000 Fax: 01983 863082
Email: reservations@luccombehall.co.uk
Web: www.luccombehall.co.uk
Rooms: 30 all ensuite ⚅ 🏖
Pricing: Sgl £37–82 Dbl £74–140 Dinner from £18
CC: Accepted Room facilities: 🖥 ☎ 🍵, Access: ♿
Children: Welcome ⋔ 🛏 ⅍ Dogs: Guide dogs only
Licences: ♙♙♙
Leisure: Indoor pool, Outdoor pool, Gym, Games room
Parking: Off-street and monitored
Directions: From Shanklin, take B3020 towards
Ventnor. Take road towards Luccombe. Turn left at top.
Hotel 100 yards on right.
See advert on following page

New Holmwood

★★★

Queens Road, Egypt Point, Cowes,
Isle of Wight, PO31 8BW
Tel: 01983 292508 Fax: 01983 295020
Web: www.newholmwoodhotel.co.uk
Rooms: 26 all ensuite ⚅ ⊗
Pricing: Dinner from £16.50 (2002 rate) CC: Accepted
Room facilities: 🖥 ☎ 🍵 Children: Welcome ⋔
Dogs: Welcome Licences: ♙♙♙
Leisure: Outdoor pool Parking: Off-street

Seaview Hotel & Restaurant

★★★★ 🎧 🎧

High Street, Seaview, Isle of Wight, PO34 5EX
Tel: 01983 612711 Fax: 01983 613729
Email: reception@seaviewhotel.co.uk
Web: www.seaviewhotel.co.uk
Seasonal closure: 3/4 days Christmas
Rooms: 16 all ensuite ⊗
Pricing: Sgl £55 Dbl £70 CC: Accepted
Room facilities: 🖥 ☎ 🍵
Conference: 2 meeting rooms (Thtr 30 max)
Children: Welcome ⋔ ⅍ Dogs: Welcome
Licences: ♙♙♙
Leisure: Indoor pool, Gym, Health spa, Tennis
Parking: Off-street

Sentry Mead

★★★★ 🎧

Madeira Road, Totland Bay, Isle of Wight, PO39 0BJ
Tel: 01983 753212 Fax: 01983 753212
Email: enq@sentry-mead.co.uk
Web: www.sentry-mead.co.uk
Rooms: 14 all ensuite
Pricing: Sgl £50–59 Dbl £100–105 Dinner from £10
CC: Accepted
Room facilities: 🖥 ☎ 🍵 Children: Welcome ⅍
Dogs: Welcome
Licences: ♙♙♙ Parking: Off-street
Directions: A3054 to Totland turn right at roundabout
by Broadway Inn, continue to end of road, Sentry
Mead on right.

Southeast

Shanklin Manor House Hotel

★★★

Church Road, Old Village, Shanklin,
Isle of Wight, PO37 6QX
Tel: 01983 862777 Fax: 01983 863464
Web: www.hotelsiow.co.uk

Rooms: 44 all ensuite
Pricing: Dinner from £16 CC: Accepted
Room facilities:
Children: Welcome 5yrs min age
Licences:
Leisure: Indoor pool, Outdoor pool, Gym, Tennis,
Snooker/billiards
Parking: Off-street and monitored

Aqua Hotel

★★

17 The Esplanade, Shanklin, Isle of Wight, PO37 6BN
Tel: 01983 863024 Fax: 01983 864841
Email: info@aquahotel.co.uk
Web: www.aquahotel.co.uk
Seasonal closure: November to March
Rooms: 22 all ensuite
Pricing: Sgl £25–32 Dbl £50–70 Dinner from £10
CC: Accepted Room facilities:
Children: Welcome Licences:
Leisure: Games room
Directions: Turn down Hope Road from Arthurs Hill,
North Road or Atherley Road. Drive down to seafront
until you arrive at the hotel.

Bay House Hotel

★★

8 Chine Avenue, Shanklin, Isle of Wight, PO37 6AG
Tel: 01983 863180 Fax: 01983 868934
Email: bay-house@netguides.co.uk
Web: www.bayhouse-hotel.co.uk
Rooms: 21 all ensuite
Pricing: Sgl £27–37 Dbl £54–74 Dinner from £6
CC: Accepted Room facilities:
Access: Children: Welcome
Dogs: Welcome
Licences: Leisure: Indoor pool
Parking: Off-street
Directions: Follow A3055 from Sandown to traffic
lights. Take Queen's Road to the end, then turn left into
Chine Avenue.
See advert on this page

Fernbank Hotel

★★

Highfield Road, Shanklin, Isle of Wight, PO37 6PP
Tel: 01983 862790 Fax: 01983 864412
Email: enquiries@fernbankhotel.com
Web: www.fernbankhotel.com
Seasonal closure: Christmas to New Year
Rooms: 20 all ensuite
Pricing: Sgl £34–40 Dbl £68–80 Dinner from £14.95
CC: Accepted
Room facilities: Access:
Conference: 1 meeting room (Thtr 30 max), 24hr-
delegate from £65, day-delegate rate from £35
Children: Welcome 5yrs min age Licences:
Leisure: Indoor pool, Health spa, Games room
Parking: Off-street
Directions: On enterng Shanklin, follow signs to old
Village at traffic lights turn right , third turning left at the
end of road on the left.

Hambledon Hotel

★★

11 Queens Road, Shanklin, Isle of Wight, PO37 6AW
Tel: 01983 862403 Fax: 01983 867894
Email: enquiries@hambledon-hotel.co.uk
Web: www.hambledon-hotel.co.uk
Rooms: 12 all ensuite
Room facilities: Access:
Children: Welcome Licences:
Parking: Off-street
Directions: Please call to request a map.

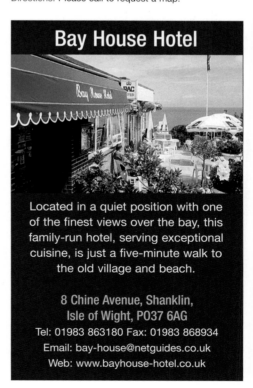

Southeast

Heatherleigh Hotel

★★

17 Queens Road, Shanklin, Isle of Wight, PO37 6AW
Tel: 01983 862503 Fax: 01983 861373
Email: enquires@heatherleigh.co.uk
Web: www.heatherleigh.co.uk
Rooms: 7 all ensuite
Pricing: Sgl £26 Dbl £52 Dinner from £11.50 CC:
Accepted
Room facilities:
Children: Welcome
Dogs: Guide dogs only
Licences:
Parking: Off-street
Directions: On entering Shanklin, follow signs for
Beach Lift. Heatherleigh is just 100 yards from cliff
walk and lift.

Hillside Hotel

★★

Mitchell Avenue, Ventnor, Isle of Wight, PO38 1DR
Tel: 01983 852271 Fax: 01983 852271
Email: rac@hillside-hotel.co.uk
Seasonal closure: Christmas
Rooms: 12 all ensuite
Pricing: Sgl £25–27 Dbl £50–54 Dinner from £12
CC: Accepted
Room facilities:
Children: Welcome 5yrs min age
Dogs: Welcome
Licences:
Parking: Off-street
Directions: Take B2257 off A3055 at junction between
Leeson Hill and St Boniface Road – hotel is behind
tennis courts.

Malton House Hotel

★★

8 Park Road, Shanklin, Isle of Wight, PO37 6AY
Tel: 01983 865007 Fax: 01983 865576
Email: couvoussis@totalise.co.uk
Web: maltonhouse.co.uk
Rooms: 15 all ensuite
Room facilities:
Access:
Children: Welcome
Licences:
Parking: Off-street
Directions: From Sandown on A3055, enter Shanklin.
At the traffic lights (Hope Road), go straight up hill.
Take third road on the left.

Melbourne-Ardenlea Hotel

★★

Queens Road, Shanklin, Isle of Wight, PO37 6AP
Tel: 01983 862283 Fax: 01983 862865
Email: melbourne-ardenlea@virgin.net
Web: www.hotel-isleofwight.co.uk
Seasonal closure: November to February

Long-established, family-run hotel in pleasant gardens,
giving personal service. Centrally situated in peaceful
area, yet close to all of Shanklin's amenities.
Rooms: 50 all ensuite
Pricing: Sgl £28–40 Dbl £56–80 Dinner from £15
CC: Accepted Room facilities: Access:
Children: Welcome Dogs: Welcome
Licences:
Leisure: Indoor pool, Health spa, Games room
Parking: Off-street
Directions: From Sandown, bear left at Fiveways
Crossroads heading towards Ventnor. Hotel is 150
yards on right after passing church spire.

Montrene

★★

Avenue Road, Sandown, Isle of Wight, PO36 8BN
Tel: 01983 403722 Fax: 01983 405553
Email: montrenehotel@ic24.net
Web: www.montrene.co.uk
Seasonal closure: January
Rooms: 41 all ensuite
Pricing: Sgl £36–40 Dbl £72–80 CC: Accepted
Room facilities:
Children: Welcome Dogs: Welcome
Licences:
Leisure: Indoor pool, Games room, Snooker/billiards
Parking: Off-street
Directions: Travel from Ryde via Brading, under railway
bridge. Keep to left at roundabout. Hotel at end on
right. Look out for yellow sign.

Orchardcroft

★★

Victoria Avenue, Shanklin, Isle of Wight, PO37 6LT
Tel: 01983 862133 Fax: 01983 862133
Email: nicklaffan@hotmail.com
Web: www.orchardcroft-hotel.co.uk
Seasonal closure: January to March
Rooms: 16 all ensuite
Pricing: Sgl £26–30 Dbl £52–60 Dinner from £12
CC: Accepted Room facilities:
Children: Welcome 1yr min age
Dogs: Welcome Licences:
Leisure: Indoor pool, Gym, Health spa, Games room,
Snooker/billiards Parking: Off-street
Directions: From Newport on Sandown Road, turn right
to Shanklin through Godshill into Victoria Avenue.
Orchardcroft is first hotel on left.

Sandpipers Country House Hotel

★★

Entrance through main car park, Freshwater Bay,
Isle of Wight, PO40 9QX
Tel: 01983 758500 Fax: 01983 754364
Email: sandpipers@fatcattrading.demon.co.uk
Web: www.fatcattrading.co.uk
Rooms: 12 all ensuite
Pricing: Dinner from £6.75 (2002 rate) CC: Accepted
Room facilities: 🖵 ☎ 🍵 💻
Children: Welcome 🍴 ⅛
Dogs: Welcome
Licences: 👥
Leisure: Games room
Parking: Off-street
Directions: Enter Freshwater Bay, drive into main
council park. Drive between two brick pillars at the
back to enter private car park.

Villa Mentone

★★

11 Park Road, Shanklin, Isle of Wight, PO37 6AY
Tel: 01983 862346 Fax: 01983 862130
Rooms: 30 all ensuite
Pricing: Dinner from £15
Room facilities: 🖵 ☎ 🍵
Children: Welcome 🍴 ⅛
Dogs: Welcome
Licences: ⟨⟩ 👥
Parking: Off-street and monitored
Directions: Follow A3055 to Sandown, then Shanklin.
Follow Beach Lift signs.

Altavia Hotel

✤

18, Beachfield Road, Sandown, Isle of Wight, PO36 8NA
Tel: 01983 403767 Fax: 01983 404981

Empress of the Sea

◆◆◆◆◆

10 Luccombe Road, Shanklin, Isle of Wight, PO37 6RQ
Tel: 01983 862178 Fax: 01983 868636
Email: empress.sea@btopenworld.com
Web: www.empressofthesea.com
Rooms: 15 all ensuite ⊗
Pricing: Dinner from £10 (2002 rate) CC: Accepted
Room facilities: 🖵 ☎ 🍵
Access: ♿ Dogs: Welcome
Licences: 👥
Leisure: Outdoor pool
Parking: Off-street
Directions: Follow signs to Shanklin, through towards
Ventnor. Turn onto Priory Road off Church Road
opposite Big Mead and arrive right.

Denewood Hotel

◆◆◆◆

7 Victoria Road, Sandown, Isle of Wight, PO36 8AL
Tel: 01983 402980 Fax: 01983 402980
Email: holiday@denewoodhotel.co.uk
Rooms: 14 all ensuite 🍵 🖵
Pricing: Sgl £22–26.50 Dbl £44–53 Dinner from £10.50
CC: Accepted
Room facilities: 🖵 🍵 Children: Welcome 🍴 ⅛
Dogs: Welcome
Licences: 👥 Leisure: Health spa
Parking: Off-street

Lake Hotel

◆◆◆◆

Shore Road, Lower Bonchurch, Ventnor,
Isle of Wight, PO38 1RF
Tel: 01983 852613
Email: richard@lakehotel.co.uk
Web: www.lakehotel.co.uk
Seasonal closure: November to February
Rooms: 20 all ensuite 🍵 🖵 ⊗
Pricing: Sgl £30–40 Dbl £60–80 Dinner from £10
Room facilities: 🖵 🍵
Children: Welcome 3yrs min age 🍴
Dogs: Welcome Licences: 👥
Parking: Off-street and monitored
Directions: The Lake Hotel is situated opposite
Bonchurch Pond, within easy reach of Shanklin.

Rockstone Cottage

◆◆◆◆

Colwell Chine Road, Freshwater,
Isle of Wight, PO40 9NR
Tel: 01983 753723 Fax: 01983 753721
Email: enquiries@rockstonecottage.co.uk
Web: www.rockstonecottage.co.uk

Built 1790, full of character, lovely gardens. Lounge,
licenced bar. 300 yards from Colwell Bay's sandy
beach. Lovely walks along sea front, over downs.
Nearby leisure centre, golf, horse riding etc.
Rooms: 5 all ensuite 🍵 ⊗
Pricing: Sgl £34–38 Dbl £48–56 Dinner from £15
Room facilities: 🖵 🍵
Children: Welcome 12yrs min age 🍴
Licences: 👥 Parking: Off-street
Directions: From Yarmouth over bridge for one mile. At
Colwell Bay Inn, turn right. Cottage is on right hand side.

Southeast

St Catherine's Hotel

◆◆◆◆

1 Winchester Park Road, Sandown,
Isle of Wight, PO36 8HJ
Tel: 01983 402392 Fax: 01983 402392
Email: stcathhotel@hotmail.com
Web: www.isleofwight-holidays.co.uk
Rooms: 19 all ensuite
Room facilities: ▢ ☎ ☕
Access: ♿ Children: Welcome ⊁ ☀
Licences: ⦀ Parking: Off-street
Directions: By car from Fishbourne to Sandown, turn
right at mini roundabout up Broadway. St Catherine's is
at top of hill on left, on corner of Broadway and
Winchester Park Road.

St Leonard's Hotel

◆◆◆◆

22 Queens Road, Shanklin, Isle of Wight, PO37 6AW
Tel: 01983 862121 Fax: 01983 868895
Email: info@wight-breaks.co.uk
Web: www.wight-breaks.co.uk
Rooms: 7 all ensuite
Pricing: Sgl £23–25 Dbl £46–50 Dinner from £10
CC: Accepted Room facilities: ▢ ☕
Children: Welcome 3yrs min age ⊁ ☀
Dogs: Guide dogs only Licences: ⦀
Parking: Off-street
Directions: Approach Shanklin on A3054. At Fiveways
lights take left-hand fork (signed Ventnor). Hotel is on
right after ¼ mile.

The Lodge

◆◆◆◆

Main Road, Brighstone, Isle of Wight, PO30 4DJ
Tel: 01983 741272 Fax: 01983 741144
Email: paul@thelodgebrighstone.com
Web: www.thelodgebrighstone.com
Rooms: 7 all ensuite
Pricing: Sgl £32–54 Dbl £54–54
Room facilities: ▢ ☕
Children: Welcome ⊁
Parking: Off-street and monitored
Directions: Leave Newport via Carisbrooke. Take
B3323 then B3399 to Brighstone. Proceed through
village, past Three Bishops Pub. The Lodge is ½ mile
on left-hand side.

Albert Cottage Hotel

◆◆◆

York Avenue, East Cowes, Isle of Wight, PO32 6BD
Tel: 01983 299309 Fax: 01983 299957
Email: james@scully-syer.fsnet.co.uk
Web: www.albertcottagehotel.co.uk
Rooms: 14 all ensuite
Pricing: Dinner from £18 (2002 rate) CC: Accepted
Room facilities: ▢ ☕ ⌁ Access: ♿
Children: Welcome Dogs: Guide dogs only
Licences: ⦀ Parking: Off-street
Directions: Situated very close to Osbourne House in
York Avenue.

Belmore Private Hotel

◆◆◆

101 Station Avenue, Sandown,
Isle of Wight, PO36 8HD
Tel: 01983 404189 Fax: 01983 405942
Email: iowbelmore@talk21.com
Web: www.islandbreaks.co.uk/belmore
Seasonal closure: 25–26 December
Rooms: 9 all ensuite
Pricing: Sgl £18–22 Dbl £36–44 CC: Accepted
Room facilities: ▢ ☕
Children: Welcome 5yrs min age ⊁ ☀
Dogs: Welcome
Licences: ⦀
Parking: Off-street and monitored
Directions: From Fishbourne car ferry, turn left at traffic
lights, take 3055 road to Sandown. Driving along
Broadway, turn left at antique shop. Belmore is on left,
past Conservative Club.

Braemar Hotel

◆◆◆

1 Grange Road, Shanklin, Isle of Wight, PO37 6NN
Tel: 01983 863172 Fax: 01983 863172
Rooms: 11 all ensuite
Pricing: Sgl £25 Dbl £50 Dinner from £10
CC: Accepted
Room facilities: ▢ ☕
Children: Welcome ⊁ Dogs: Welcome
Licences: ⦀
Parking: Off-street

Georgian House Guest House

◆◆◆

22 George Street, Ryde, Isle of Wight, PO33 2EW
Tel: 01983 563588
Email: d.cooke1@ntlworld.com
Web: www.georgian-guesthouse.co.uk
Rooms: 6 (5 ensuite)
Pricing: Sgl £18–25 Dbl £40–43
Room facilities: ▢ ☕
Children: Welcome
Directions: George Street is opposite Bus/Railway
Station and Hovercraft terminal. Hotel is 100 yards up
George Street on right hand side.

Latton House

◆◆◆◆

Madeira Road, Totland Bay, Isle of White, PO39 0BJ
Tel: 01983 754868 Fax: 01983 754868
Email: enqlattonhouse@aol.com
Seasonal closure: Christmas
Rooms: 4 all ensuite
Pricing: Sgl £30–35 Dbl £55–60 Dinner from £20
Room facilities: ▢ ☕
Children: Welcome 12yrs min age
Licences: ⦀
Parking: Off-street
Directions: A3054 from Yarmouth Ferry Terminal
towards Freshwater/Totland. Straight on at first
roundabout, right at next.

Little Span Farm

Rew Lane, Wroxall, Ventnor, Isle of Wight, PO38 3AU
Tel: 01983 852419 Fax: 01983 852419
Email: info@spanfarm.co.uk
Web: www.spanfarm.co.uk
Rooms: 4 (3 ensuite)
Pricing: Sgl £30–40 Dbl £38–50
Room facilities:
Children: Welcome Dogs: Welcome Parking: Off-street
Directions: From B3327 to Wroxall turn into West Street (by Post Ofice); drive out into countryside around sharp bend. First farm on right.

Mount House Hotel

20 Arthurs Hill, Shanklin, Isle of Wight, PO37 6EE
Tel: 01983 862556 Fax: 01983 867551
Web: www.netguides.co.uk/wight/mount.html
Seasonal closure: January
Rooms: 9 all ensuite
Pricing: Dinner from £8 CC: Accepted
Room facilities:
Children: Welcome Dogs: Welcome Licences:
Parking: Off-street
Directions: Hotel is on the main road from Sandown to Shanklin (A3055), on the corner between Clarance Road and Arthurs Hill.

Richmond Hotel

23 Palmerston Road, Shanklin,
Isle of Wight, PO37 6AS
Tel: 01983 862874 Fax: 01983 862874
Email: richmondhotel.shanklin@virgin.net
Web: www.richmondhotel-shanklin.co.uk
Seasonal closure: November to February
Rooms: 10 (9 ensuite)
Pricing: Sgl £25 Dbl £50 Dinner from £10
CC: Accepted
Room facilities:
Children: Welcome Dogs: Guide dogs only
Licences:
Parking: Off-street and monitored
Directions: Turn off Shanklin High Street opposite Boots. Hotel facing you.

Shangri-La Hotel

30 Broadway, Sandown, Isle of Wight, PO36 9BY
Tel: 01983 403672 Fax: 01983 403672
Email: shangrilahotel@aol.com
Web: www.shangrilahotel.co.uk
Rooms: 14 (11 ensuite)
Pricing: Sgl £22–28 Dbl £44–56 CC: Accepted
Room facilities:
Access: Children: Welcome
Licences: Leisure: Games room
Parking: Off-street
Directions: On A3055. Turn left at traffic lights from Newport Road. Hotel is on right after approx 3/4 of a mile.

White House Hotel

Eastcliffe Promenade, Carpark entrance 7, Park Road, Shanklin, Isle of Wight, PO37 6AY
Tel: 01983 862776 Fax: 01983 865980
Rooms: 11 all ensuite
Pricing: Sgl £27–29 Dbl £54–58
Dinner from £12.50 CC: Accepted
Room facilities:
Children: Welcome
Dogs: Guide dogs only
Parking: Off-street
Directions: Shanklin – North Road (main road) turn into Clarendon road, drive to top. Turn right into Park Road, 3rd carpark entrance on left.

Channel View Hotel

4-8 Royal Street, Sandown, Isle of Wight, PO36 8LP
Tel: 01983 402347 Fax: 01983 404128

The Burlington Hotel

6 Chine Avenue, Shanklin, Isle of Wight, PO37 6AG
Tel: 01983 862090 Fax: 01983 862190

Isleworth, Middlesex

The Bridge Inn

457 London Road, Isleworth, Middlesex, TW7 5AA
Tel: 020 8568 0088 Fax: 020 8568 0088
Rooms: 10 (3 ensuite)
Pricing: Sgl £35 Dbl £50–55 CC: Accepted
Room facilities:
Children: Welcome
Dogs: Guide dogs only
Leisure: Games room
Directions: Next to Isleworth BR station bus routes 237, 235 between Hounslow and Brentford.

Southeast

Kidlington, Oxfordshire

Bowood House

 ◆ ◆ ◆

238 Oxford Road, Kidlington, Oxfordshire, OX5 1EB
Tel: 01865 842288 Fax: 01865 841858
Email: bowoodhouse@kidlingtontotalserve.co.uk
Web: www.2stay.com/uk/hotels/bowood.html
Seasonal closure: Christmas- New Year

Rooms: 20 all ensuite 🥂 🚭
Pricing: Sgl £47.50–54.50 Dbl £62.50
Dinner from £10 CC: Accepted
Room facilities: 🖵 ☎ 🍵
Access: ♿
Conference: 1 meeting room (Thtr 10 max)
Children: Welcome ⍟ Dogs: Welcome
Licences: ♦♦♦ Parking: Off-street
Directions: From north M40 exit 9 onto A34 exit
Kidlington. From south M40 exit 8 onto A40 follow
signs Kidlington.

Kingston-upon-Thames, Surrey

The Kingston Lodge

 ★ ★ ★ ®

94 Kingston Hill, Kingston-upon-Thames,
Surrey, KT2 7NP
Tel: 020 8541 4481 Fax: 020 8547 1013
Email: kingstonlodge@heritage-hotels.co.uk
Web: www.macdonaldhotels.co.uk
Rooms: 63 all ensuite 🥂 🚭
Pricing: Sgl £54 Dbl £108 Dinner from £20
CC: Accepted
Room facilities: 🖵 ☎ 🍵 ☏
Conference: 2 meeting rooms (Thtr 60 max)
Children: Welcome ⍟ ⁓ Dogs: Welcome
Licences: ⚱ ♦♦♦
Parking: Off-street and monitored
Directions: From M25 Junction 10 to A3, up to Robin
Hood roundabout, after 14¹/₂ miles. Sharp left onto
Kingston Hill. Hotel 1¹/₂ miles on left.

Hotel Antoinette

 ★ ★

26 Beaufort Road, Kingston-upon-Thames,
Surrey, KT1 2TQ
Tel: 020 8546 1044 Fax: 020 8547 2595
Email: hotelantoinette@btconnect.com
Web: www.hotelantoinette.co.uk

Well-established family-owned hotel situated close to
London and many tourist attractions. Comfortable
accommodation, inviting atmosphere and large car
park. Brasserie restaurant. Landscaped gardens.
Rooms: 100 all ensuite 🚭
Pricing: Sgl £65–74 Dbl £75–81 Dinner from £12
CC: Accepted
Room facilities: 🖵 ☎ 🍵
Access: ⏐⏐ ♿
Conference: 7 meeting rooms (Thtr 120 max), 24hr-
delegate from £30, day-delegate rate from £60
Children: Welcome ⍟
Dogs: Guide dogs only
Licences: ♦♦♦
Parking: Off-street and monitored
Directions: From Junction 9 of M25 follow A243 to
Kingston/Surbiton. At Surbiton take second right after
railway bridge, Maple Road, then turn left at third set of
traffic lights.

Travelodge London, Kingston

Travel Accommodation
21-23 London Road, Kingston, Surrey, KT2 6ND
Web: www.travelodge.co.uk
Pricing: Sgl £74.40 Dbl £78.85
CC: Accepted Room facilities: 🖵 🍵

Leatherhead, Surrey

Bookham Grange

 ★★

Little Bookham Common, Bookham, Leatherhead,
Surrey, KT23 3HS
Tel: 01372 452742 Fax: 01372 450080
Email: bookhamgrange@easynet.co.uk
Web: www.bookham-grange.co.uk

Country house hotel in rural setting, yet conveniently
located for Leatherhead, Guildford, Heathrow, Gatwick,
Central London and touring the south east by car.
Good food and friendly service.
Rooms: 27 all ensuite ✤
Pricing: Sgl £75–85 Dbl £90–95 Dinner from £16.50
CC: Accepted
Room facilities: ☐ ☎ ☕
Conference: 2 meeting rooms (Thtr 80 max), 24hr-
delegate from £122.50, day-delegate rate from £27.50
Children: Welcome
Dogs: Welcome
Licences: ♨ ♦♦♦
Parking: Off-street
Directions: Exit 9 of M25 into Leatherhead and A246
towards Guildford. In Bookham, turn right into High
Street, straight on into Church Road and first right after
Bookham Station.

Leighton Buzzard, Bedfordshire

Travelodge Dunstable, Hockcliffe

Travel Accommodation
A5, Watling Street, Hockliffe, Leighton Buzzard,
Bedfordshire, LU7 9LZ
Web: www.travelodge.co.uk
Rooms: 28 all ensuite ⊛
Pricing: Sgl £54.40 Dbl £58.85
CC: Accepted Room facilities: ☐ ☕ Access: ♿

Lewes, East Sussex

Shelleys Hotel

★★★★ ♞ ♞

High Street, Lewes, East Sussex, BN7 1XS
Tel: 01273 472361 Fax: 01273 483152
Email: info@shelleys-hotel-lewes.com
Web: www.shelleys-hotel-lewes.com

This beautifully appointed country house style hotel
overlooks it's own peaceful garden, whilst being
situated at the historic heart of Lewes. Convenient for
Glydebourne, the South Downs and Brighton, award
winning restaurant.
Rooms: 19 all ensuite ✤ ⊟ ⊛
Pricing: Sgl £90–148.50 Dbl £120–202 Dinner from £30
CC: Accepted Room facilities: ☐ ☎ ☕
Conference: 2 meeting rooms (Thtr 50 max), 24hr-
delegate from £165, day-delegate rate from £45
Children: Welcome ⅛
Dogs: Guide dogs only
Licences: ♨ ♦♦♦
Parking: Off-street
Directions: From A23 London to Brighton Road, turn
on A27 north of Brighton, sign posted Lewes. Hotel in
High Street.

White Hart Hotel

★★★

High Street, Lewes, East Sussex, BN7 1XE
Tel: 01273 476694 Fax: 01273 476695
Rooms: 52 all ensuite ✤ ⊟
Pricing: Sgl £68–68 Dbl £98–98 Dinner from £7.50
CC: Accepted
Room facilities: ☐ ☎ ☕ Access: ♿
Children: Welcome
Dogs: Welcome Licences: ♦♦♦
Leisure: Indoor pool, Gym, Beauty salon
Parking: Off-street
Directions: Hotel is in the town centre, facing the law
courts. The A27 Eastbourne to Brighton Road skirts
Lewes.
See advert on following page

Berkeley House Hotel

◆◆◆◆ ⌘

2 Albion Street, Lewes, East Sussex, BN7 2ND
Tel: 01273 476057 Fax: 01273 479575
Email: rp.berkeleyhse@lineone.net
Web: www.berkeleyhousehotel.co.uk
Seasonal closure: Christmas
Rooms: 5 all ensuite
Pricing: Sgl £45–65 Dbl £55–80 CC: Accepted
Room facilities: ☐ ☕ Licences: ♦♦♦
Parking: Off-street
Directions: Albion Street is a turning off School Hill,
which is part of the High Street in the town centre.

White Hart Hotel

A charming 16th-century coaching inn which has been magnificently extended to comprise an indoor leisure complex with pool, sauna, steam room and gym. Accommodation is available in the main house or in our contemporary annexe.

This privately owned, family run hotel offers a friendly and lively though relaxed atmosphere.

High Street, Lewes,
East Sussex BN7 1XE
Tel: 01273 476694   Fax: 01273 476695
www.whitehartlewes.co.uk

Lightwater, Surrey

Carlton Guest House

63-65 Macdonald Road, Lightwater, Surrey, GU18 5XY
Tel: 01276 473580 Fax: 01276 453595

Liphook, Hampshire

Travelodge Liphook

Travel Accommodation
A3 North, Liphook, Hampshire, GU30 7TT
Web: www.travelodge.co.uk
Rooms: 40 all ensuite
Pricing: Sgl £57.40 Dbl £61.85
CC: Accepted Room facilities: 🖳 ☕ Access: ♿

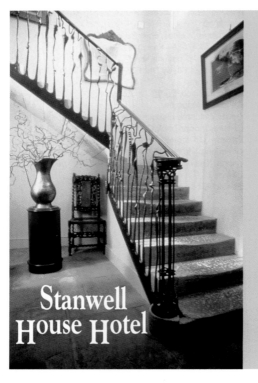

The Stanwell House Hotel

This charming Georgian Townhouse is friendly, informal and comfortable.

The 28 bedrooms, which include five suites and a self contained cottage, are individually designed, some with four posters, roll top bath and dramatic velvets and silks.

Dine by candlelight in the award-winning Bistro or snack in the lofty conservatory or garden.

**15 High Street, Lymington,
Hampshire SO14 9AA
Tel: 01590 677123
Fax: 01590 677756
Email: sales@stanwellhousehotel.co.uk
Website: www.stanwellhousehotel.co.uk**

Little Horsted, East Sussex

Horsted Place Sporting Estate & Hotel

★ ★ ★ ★ 🦌 🦌 🦌   *Blue Ribbon Winner*

Little Horsted, Uckfield, East Sussex, TN22 5TS
Tel: 01825 750581 Fax: 01825 750459
Email: hotel@horstedplace.co.uk
Web: www.horstedplace.co.uk

Horsted Place is a luxury country house hotel
overlooking the South Downs and the East Sussex
national golf club. The elegant restaurant opens each
day for lunch and dinner.
Rooms: 20 all ensuite 📠
Pricing: Sgl £130–330 Dbl £130–330 Dinner from £32
CC: Accepted
Room facilities: 🖵 ☎
Access: |↕↑ 🚻 ♿
Conference: 3 meeting rooms (Thtr 80 max), 24hr-
delegate from £160, day-delegate rate from £40
Children: Welcome 8yrs min age 🍴
Dogs: Guide dogs only
Licences: ♨ ⚑⚑⚑
Leisure: Tennis, Golf, Fishing
Parking: Off-street and monitored
Directions: Exit M23 Jct 10 to East Grinstead then A22
to Uckfield/Eastbourne. Hotel is one mile south of
Uckfield on A26 to Lewes.

Littlehampton, West Sussex

Rustington House Hotel

◆ ◆ ◆ ◆ ✳

Broadmark Lane, Rustington, Littlehampton,
West Sussex, BN16 2HH
Tel: 01903 771198
Email: rustingtonhousehotel@yahoo.com
Web: www.rustingtonhousehotel.com
Seasonal closure: November
Rooms: 8 all ensuite ⊗
Pricing: Sgl £39–39 Dbl £69–69 CC: Accepted
Room facilities: 🖵 ☎ ☕
Conference: 1 meeting room (Thtr 50 max)
Children: Welcome
Dogs: Welcome
Licences: ⚑⚑⚑
Parking: Off-street
Directions: Follow signs for Rustington. At traffic lights,
look for tourist signs pointing to hotel; Property is 400
yards on right from traffic lights.

Travelodge Littlehampton

Travel Accommodation
A259, Worthing Road, Rustlington, Littlehampton,
Sussex, BN17 6LZ
Web: www.travelodge.co.uk
Rooms: 36 all ensuite ⊗
Pricing: Sgl £54.40 Dbl £58.85
CC: Accepted Room facilities: 🖵 ☕ Access: ♿

Luton, Bedfordshire

Leaside Hotel & Restaurant

◆ ◆ ◆ 🦌

72 New Bedford Road, Luton, Bedfordshire, LU3 1BT
Tel: 01582 417643 Fax: 01582 734961
Web: www.leasidehotel.co.uk
Seasonal closure: 25–26, 31 December
Rooms: 16 all ensuite ⊗
Pricing: Sgl £40–60 Dbl £55–75 Dinner from £19.50
CC: Accepted
Room facilities: 🖵 ☎ ☕
Children: Welcome 🍴
Licences: ⚑⚑⚑
Leisure: Games room
Parking: Off-street and monitored
Directions: Situated near town centre approx 3 miles
from airport. Access to the car park is via Old Bedford
and Villa roads.

Pines Hotel

◆ ◆ ◆

10 Marsh Road, Luton, Bedfordshire, LU3 2NH
Tel: 01582 651130 Fax: 01582 615182

Travelodge Luton (SA)

Travel Accommodation
M1 Motorway, 641 Dunstable Road, Luton,
Bedfordshire, LU4 8RQ
Web: www.travelodge.co.uk
Rooms: 140 all ensuite ⊗
Pricing: Sgl £47.40–64.40 Dbl £51.85–68.85
CC: Accepted Room facilities: 🖵 ☕

Lymington, Hampshire

Stanwell House Hotel

★ ★ ★ 🦌 🦌

14–15 High Street, Lymington, Hampshire, SO41 9AA
Tel: 01590 677123 Fax: 01590 677756
Web: www.stanwellhousehotel.co.uk
Rooms: 29 all ensuite ⊗ 📠 ⊗
Pricing: Sgl £85–160 Dbl £110–160 CC: Accepted
Room facilities: 🖵 ☎ ☕ ⚓
Children: Welcome 🍴 ✂
Dogs: Welcome
Licences: ♨ ⚑⚑⚑
Directions: Take Junction 1 M27, then A397 Lyndhurst
and Brockenhurst into Lymington High Street, hotel
halfway along.
See advert on previous page

See advert on previous page

Southeast

Efford Cottage

♦ ♦ ♦ ♦ ♦ ☆ ♈

Everton, Lymington, Hampshire, SO41 0JD
Tel: 01590 642315 Fax: 01590 641030
Email: effordcottage@aol.com
Web: www.effordcottage.co.uk

Spacious Georgian cottage. Award-winning
guesthouse with an acre of garden. Luxury bedrooms.
Four course breakfast from a wide and varied menu,
with home-made bread/preserves. Patricia (qualified
chef) offers high class country cooking. England for
Excellence 2000 Regional Winner. Gold award.
RAC 5 Diamond with Sparkling Diamonds & Warm
Welcome Awards.
Rooms: 3 all ensuite 🖨 Ⓢ
Pricing: Dbl £50–65 Room facilities: 🖵 ☎ ☕
Children: Welcome 14yrs min age
Dogs: Welcome Parking: Off-street
Directions: Two miles west of Lymington on A337 on
the eastern edge of village of Everton.

The Angel Inn

♦ ♦ ♦

108 High Street, Lymington, Hampshire, SO41 9AP
Tel: 01590 672050 Fax: 01590 671661
Web: www.eldridge-pope-inns.co.uk
Rooms: 12 all ensuite 🍴 🖨 Ⓢ
Pricing: Sgl £55–70 Dbl £67–85 Dinner from £7.95
CC: Accepted
Room facilities: 🖵 ☎ ☕ ☎
Conference: 1 meeting room (Thtr 60 max)
Children: Welcome ⋔
Dogs: Guide dogs only
Licences: ▮▮▮
Leisure: Games room
Parking: Off-street and monitored
Directions: From the M27 junction 4 on the A337,
follow through Lyndhurst to Lymington.

Lyndhurst, Hampshire

Forest Lodge Hotel

★ ★ ★

Pikes Hill, Romsey Road, Lyndhurst,
Hampshire, SO43 7AS
Tel: 02380 283677 Fax: 02380 282940
Email: forest@carehotels.co.uk
Web: www.carehotels.co.uk
Rooms: 28 all ensuite 🍴 🖨
Pricing: Dinner from £21.50 CC: Accepted
Room facilities: 🖵 ☎ ☕
Access: ♿
Children: Welcome ⋔ ☾
Dogs: Welcome
Licences: ◁ ▮▮▮
Leisure: Indoor pool, Gym
Parking: Off-street and monitored
Directions: Exit M27 at J-1. Take A337, and after
approximately 3 miles turn right into Pikes Hill. Forest
Lodge is on left.
See advert on this page

Knightwood Lodge

★

Southampton Road, Lyndhurst, Hampshire, SO43 7BU
Tel: 02380 282502 Fax: 02380 283730
Web: www.knightwoodlodge.co.uk
Rooms: 18 all ensuite 🖨
Pricing: Sgl £30–50 Dbl £60–90 Dinner from £17.95
CC: Accepted
Room facilities: 🖵 ☎ ☕
Access: ♿
Children: Welcome ⋔ ☾
Dogs: Welcome
Licences: ▮▮▮
Leisure: Indoor pool, Gym
Parking: Off-street
Directions: From Junction 1 of M27, take A337 for
Lyndhurst. Turn left at traffic lights in Lyndhurst. Hotel
is ¼ mile along A35 Southampton Road.

Little Hayes

◆◆◆◆

43 Romsey Road, Lyndhurst, Hampshire, SO43 7AR
Tel: 02380 283816
Rooms: 5 all ensuite
Pricing: Dbl £28–30 CC: Accepted
Room facilities:
Children: Welcome
Parking: Off-street and monitored
Directions: From Junction 1 of M27, take A337
signposted Lyndhurst. Little Hayes is on right as you
enter village.

Lyndhurst House

◆◆◆◆

35 Romsey Road, Lyndhurst, Hampshire, SO43 7AR
Tel: 023 8028 2230 Fax: 023 8028 3190
Email: lyndhursthouse@aol.com
Web: www.lyndhursthousebab.co.uk
Rooms: 5 all ensuite
Pricing: Sgl £28 Dbl £50 CC: Accepted
Room facilities:
Children: Welcome
Parking: Off-street
Directions: M27 Junction 1, A337 to Lyndhurst. Approx
¼ mile inside 30mph limit, on right-hand side, laying
back off road.

Penny Farthing Hotel

◆◆◆◆

Romsey Road, Lyndhurst, Hampshire, SO43 7AA
Tel: 023 80284422 Fax: 023 80284488
Email: stay@pennyfarthinghotel.co.uk
Web: www.pennyfarthinghotel.co.uk
Seasonal closure: Christmas

A cheerful small hotel, ideally situated in the village of
Lyndhurst. Offering licenced bar, bicycle store,
comfortable ensuite rooms with colour TV, telephone
and tea/coffee making facilities and large car park.
Ideal base for touring New Forest.
Rooms: 21 all ensuite
Pricing: Sgl £35–45 Dbl £59–90 CC: Accepted
Room facilities:
Children: Welcome
Licences:
Parking: Off-street and monitored
Directions: Leave M27 at Junction 1. Take A337 to
Lyndhurst. Hotel is on left as you enter village.

Maidenhead, Berkshire

Monkey Island

★★★★★

Bray-on-Thames, Maidenhead, Berkshire, SL6 2EE
Tel: 01628 623400 Fax: 01628 675432
Email: ev.monkeyisland@btconnect.co
Web: www.monkeyisland.co.uk
Rooms: 26 all ensuite
Pricing: Dinner from £35 CC: Accepted
Room facilities:
Access:
Conference: 6 meeting rooms (Thtr 120 max), 24hr-
delegate from £230, day-delegate rate from £80
Children: Welcome
Dogs: Welcome
Licences:
Parking: Off-street
Directions: J8/9 M4 to Maidenhead central, second
exit roundabout Windsor A308, second left Bray
village, right Old Mill lane. Signposted to hotel.

Thames Hotel

★★

Ray Mead Road, Maidenhead, Berkshire, SL6 8NR
Tel: 01628 628721 Fax: 01628 773921
Email: reservations@thameshotel.co.uk
Web: www.thameshotel.co.uk

Idyllically situated on the banks of the River Thames.
The hotel has 35 ensuite rooms, many with superb
views of the river.
Rooms: 35 all ensuite
Pricing: Sgl £73–113 Dbl £116–121 CC: Accepted
Room facilities:
Conference: 1 meeting room (Thtr 60 max)
Children: Welcome
Dogs: Guide dogs only
Licences:
Parking: Off-street
Directions: Leave M4 at Junction 7. Signed to
Maidenhead. Over bridge and turn right at mini
roundabout. Hotel is 200yds on left.

Southeast

The Inn on The Green

◆◆◆◆♦ ♛ ♛

The Old Cricket Common, Cookham Dean,
Berkshire, SL6 9NZ
Tel: 01628 482638 Fax: 01628 487474
Email: enquiries@theinnonthegreen.com
Web: www.theinnonthegreen.com
Rooms: 9 all ensuite 🛏
Pricing: Sgl £100–130 Dbl £110–160 Dinner from £25
CC: Accepted Room facilities: 🖵 ☎ 🗗 📶 Access: ♿
Conference: 2 meeting rooms (Thtr 34 max), 24hr-
delegate from £160, day-delegate rate from £45
Children: Welcome ⼻ Dogs: Welcome
Licences: ⚱ ⅲ Parking: Off-street and monitored
Directions: A404(M) Bisham exit. Follow signs
Cookham Dean. Inn is down lane by war memorial in
centre of Cookham Dean.
See advert on this page

Clifton Guest House

◆◆◆

21 Crauford Rise, Maidenhead, Berkshire, SL6 7LR
Tel: 01628 620086 Fax: 01628 623572
Email: clifton@aroram.freeserve.co.uk
Web: www.cliftonguesthouse.co.uk
Rooms: 20 (12 ensuite) ⊛
Room facilities: 🖵 🗗 Access: ♿
Children: Welcome Licences: ⅲ
Parking: Off-street and monitored
Directions: Leave M4 at Junction 8/9. Follow A308 to
Maidenhead Central and on towards Marlow. Crauford
Rise is off Marlow Road.

THE INN on the green

Wonderful rooms each decorated and
furnished individually for that special touch.
Flat-screen TV, Sky, DVD player in every room.
Wonderful restaurant with emphasis on
excellent food in relaxing surroundings.
Children welcome, special rates on weekends
in Winter and on Friday and Sunday. Phone for
detailed directions before arrival.

The Old Cricket Common, Cookham
Dean, Berkshire SL6 9NZ
Tel: 01628 482638   Fax: 01628 487474
Email: enquiries@theinnonthegreen.com
Website: www.theinnonthegreen.com

Maidstone, Kent

Grange Moor Hotel

★★

St Michael's Road, Maidstone, Kent, ME16 8BS
Tel: 01622 677623 Fax: 01622 678246
Email: reservations@grangemoor.co.uk
Web: www.grangemoor.co.uk
Seasonal closure: 26–30 December
Rooms: 51 all ensuite 🐾 🛏 ⊛
Pricing: Sgl £44–48 Dbl £54–55 Dinner from £16
CC: Accepted Room facilities: 🖵 🗗
Conference: 3 meeting rooms (Thtr 120 max)
Children: Welcome ⼻ ⅉ
Dogs: Welcome Licences: ⅲ
Parking: Off-street and monitored
Directions: From Maidstone town centre approx. 1 mile
to A26 Tonbridge road; turn left just after church.

Ringlestone Inn and Farmhouse Hotel

◆◆◆◆

Ringlestone Hamlet, Nr. Harrietsham, Maidstone,
Kent, ME17 1NX
Tel: 01622 859900 Fax: 01622 859966
Email: bookings@ringlestone.com
Web: www.ringlestone.com
Rooms: 3 all ensuite 🛏 ⊛
Pricing: Sgl £104–140 Dbl £114–140 Dinner from £7.95
CC: Accepted Room facilities: 🖵 ☎ 🗗
Conference: 3 meeting rooms (Thtr 50 max), 24hr-
delegate from £140, day-delegate rate from £18
Children: Welcome ⼻ Dogs: Guide dogs only
Licences: ⅲ Parking: Off-street
Directions: Exit J8 M20 to A20 south. Take
Hollingbourne turn and go through village to top of
the hill. Turn right at crossroads.

Marlow, Buckinghamshire

Danesfield House Hotel & Spa

Blue Ribbon Winner

★★★★ ♛ ♛ ♛
Henley Road, Marlow, Buckinghamshire, SL7 2EY
Tel: 01628 891010 Fax: 01628 890408
Email: sales@danesfieldhouse.co.uk
Web: www.danesfieldhouse.co.uk

Built at the turn of the century, the hotel stands in 65
acres of grounds overlooking the River Thames.
Luxurious extensive spa includes 50 treatments, 20m
pool, fitness studio etc.

Rooms: 87 all ensuite 🛏 🚗
Pricing: Sgl £185–260 Dbl £225–300
Dinner from £26.50 CC: Accepted
Room facilities: 📺 ☎ 🍵 Access: 🔝 ♿
Conference: 8 meeting rooms (Thtr 100 max)
Children: Welcome 🍴 🕯 Dogs: Guide dogs only
Licences: 🍷 👥
Leisure: Indoor pool, Gym, Health spa, Tennis,
Snooker/billiards
Parking: Off-street
Directions: Leave M4 at Junction 8/9 or M40 at
Junction 4 and take A404 to Marlow. Then take A4155
towards Henley.

The Compleat Angler

★★★★★ 🎀🎀🎀
Marlow Bridge, Marlow, Buckingamshire, SL7 1RG
Tel: 0870 400 8100 Fax: 01628 486388
Email: general.compleatangler@heritage-hotels.co.uk
Web: www.macdonaldhotels.co.uk
Rooms: 64 all ensuite 🛏 🚗 🚭
Pricing: Sgl £109 Dbl £218 Dinner from £34.50
CC: Accepted
Room facilities: 📺 ☎ 🍵 🍵
Access: 🔝 ♿
Children: Welcome 🍴 🕯
Dogs: Welcome
Licences: 🍷 👥
Parking: Off-street and monitored
Directions: From A404, at the first roundabout follow
signs for Bisham. Hotel is on right immediately before
Marlow Bridge.

Holly Tree House

♦♦♦♦ ✼
Burford Close, Marlow Bottom,
Buckinghamshire, SL7 3NF
Tel: 01628 891110 Fax: 01628 481278
Email: hollytreeaccommodation@yahoo.co.uk
Seasonal closure: Christmas to New Year
Rooms: 5 all ensuite 🚗 🚭
Room facilities: 📺 ☎ 🍵
Access: ♿
Children: Welcome 🕯
Leisure: Outdoor pool
Parking: Off-street and monitored
Directions: Leave M4 at Junction 8/9 and take A404
towards High Wycombe. Take Marlow turn to second
mini-roundabout. Turn right. Proceed until sign
indicates Marlow Bottom. Take second on left.

Marton Moreataine, Bedfordshire

Travelodge Bedford Southwest

Travel Accommodation
A421, Beancroft Road Junction, Marton Mortaine,
Bedfordshire, MK43 0PZ
Web: www.travelodge.co.uk
Rooms: 54 all ensuite 🚭
Pricing: Sgl £54.40 Dbl £58.85
CC: Accepted Room facilities: 📺 🍵 Access: ♿

Milford-on-Sea, Hampshire

Westover Hall Hotel

Blue Ribbon Winner

★★★★ 🎀🎀🎀
Park Lane, Milford-on-Sea, Hampshire, SO41 0PT
Tel: 01590 643044 Fax: 01590 644490
Email: info@westoverhallhotel.com
Web: www.westoverhallhotel.com

A grade II listed Victorian mansion on the edge of the New
Forest, 200 yards from the beach with stunning
uninterrupted views to The Needles and Isle of Wight.
Family owned and run with a relaxed, friendly atmosphere.
Rooms: 12 all ensuite 🛏 🚗 🚭 Pricing: Sgl £85–110
Dbl £145–200 Dinner from £29.50 CC: Accepted
Room facilities: 📺 ☎ 🍵 🍵 Conference: 2 meeting
rooms (Thtr 50 max), 24hr-delegate from £130, day-
delegate rate from £35
Children: Welcome 10yrs min age 🕯 Dogs: Welcome
Licences: 🍷 👥 Parking: Off-street and monitored
Directions: Leave M27 at Junction 1. Follow A337 via
Lyndhurst, Brockenhurst, Lymington, Pennington then
Everton where you take B3058 to Milford-on-Sea.
See advert on below

Southeast

Milton Keynes, Buckinghamshire

Moore Place Hotel

★★★★ ☙ ☙

The Square, Aspley Guise, near Milton Keynes,
Buckinghamshire, MK17 8DW
Tel: 01908 282000 Fax: 01908 281888
Email: manager@mooreplace.co.uk
Web: www.mooreplace.co.uk

Moore Place is a charming Georgian Manor in a
delightful village location. The award-winning
restaurant overlooks a beautiful courtyard garden with
rockery and waterfall.
Rooms: 54 all ensuite
Pricing: Sgl £60–100 Dbl £80–125 Dinner from £22
CC: Accepted
Room facilities: 🖳 ☎ 🍵 Access: ♿
Conference: 5 meeting rooms (Thtr 40 max), 24hr-
delegate from £155, day-delegate rate from £48
Children: Welcome 🍼
Dogs: Welcome
Licences: 🍷 ♟ Parking: Off-street
Directions: Exit M1 at Junction 13. Take A507 and then
follow signs to Aspley Guise. Moore Place is on left-
hand side in the village.

Quality Hotel & Suites Milton Keynes

★★★

Monks Way, Two Mile Ash, Milton Keynes,
Buckinghamshire, MK8 8LY
Tel: 01908 561666 Fax: 01908 568303
Email: admin@gb616.u-net.com
Web: www.choicehotels.com
Rooms: 88 all ensuite 🍴 🚭 🚬
Pricing: Sgl £50–127 Dbl £65–140 Dinner from £16
CC: Accepted
Room facilities: 🖳 ☎ 🍵 📞
Access: ♿
Conference: 7 meeting rooms (Thtr 120 max), 24hr-
delegate from £150, day-delegate rate from £35
Children: Welcome 🍼
Dogs: Welcome
Licences: 🍷 ♟
Leisure: Indoor pool, Gym, Health spa
Parking: Off-street and monitored
Directions: Exit M1 at Junction 14, follow until the A5.
Go north and take next exit and follow signs for A422,
Two Mile Ash.

Shires Motel

★★

Open Pastures, Buckingham Road, Deanshanger,
Milton Keynes, Deanshanger,
Northamptonshire, MK19 6JU
Tel: 01908 262925 Fax: 01908 263642
Email: info@shiresmotel.co.uk
Web: www.shiremotel.co.uk
Rooms: 47 all ensuite 🚭
Pricing: Sgl £43.50 Dbl £46.95–51.95
Dinner from £6.95 CC: Accepted
Room facilities: 🖳 ☎ 🍵 📞
Access: ♿
Licences: ♟
Directions: M1 junction 14 take A509 to Milton Keynes,
follow A5 till roundabout showing A422 to
Buckingham. We are at Deanshanger on Buckingham
Road.
See advert on next page

Swan Revived Hotel

★★ ☙

High Street, Milton Keynes,
Buckinghamshire, MK16 8AR
Tel: 01908 610565 Fax: 01908 210995
Email: swanrevived@btinternet.com
Web: www.swanrevived.co.uk

Former coaching inn modernised to provide 40
comfortable guest rooms, fine a la carte restaurant,
conferences for a maximum of 70 and full wedding
services. Holders of civil marriage licence.
Rooms: 42 all ensuite 🍴 🚭
Pricing: Sgl £50–85 Dbl £70–95 Dinner from £16
CC: Accepted
Room facilities: 🖳 ☎ 🍵
Access: ♿
Conference: 2 meeting rooms (Thtr 80 max), 24hr-
delegate from £120, day-delegate rate from £35
Children: Welcome 🍼
Dogs: Welcome
Licences: 🍷 ♟
Parking: Off-street and monitored
Directions: From M1 Junction 14 take A509 to Newport
Pagnell (1³/₄ miles). The hotel is on the high street
opposite the post office.

Campanile Hotel

Travel Accommodation
40 Penn Road, Fenny Stratford, Bletchley,
Milton Keynes, MK2
Tel: 01908 649819 Fax: 01908 649818
Email: mk@envergure.co.uk
Web: www.envergure.fr

Typical Campanile bedroom

Campanile hotels offer comfortable and convenient budget accommodation and a traditional French style Bistro providing freshly-cooked food for breakfast, lunch and dinner. All rooms ensuite with tea/coffee making facilities, DDT and TV with Sky channels.
Rooms: 80 all ensuite ⊗
Pricing: Sgl £44.45–49.90 Dbl £50.40–55.80
Dinner from £11.55 CC: Accepted
Room facilities: 🖵 ☎ 🍵 🔌
Access: ♿
Conference: 2 meeting rooms (Thtr 90 max), 24hr-delegate from £68, day-delegate rate from £19.50
Children: Welcome 🍴
Dogs: Welcome
Licences: 🍾🍾🍾
Parking: Off-street and monitored
Directions: Follow A5 south, towards Dunstable. At Little Chef roundabout, take fourth exit, on right to Fenny Stratford. Take first left turn.

Travelodge Milton Keynes (SA)

Travel Accommodation
V6, 198 Grafton Gate, Milton Keynes,
Buckinghamshire, MK9 1AL
Web: www.travelodge.co.uk
Rooms: 80 all ensuite ⊗
Pricing: Sgl £57.40–64.40 Dbl £61.85–68.85
CC: Accepted Room facilities: 🖵 🍵 Access: ♿

Morden, Surrey

Travelodge London, Wimbledon (SA)

Travel Accommodation
A24, Epsom Road, Morden, Surrey, SM4 5PH
Web: www.travelodge.co.uk
Rooms: 32 all ensuite ⊗
Pricing: Sgl £74.40 Dbl £78.85
CC: Accepted Room facilities: 🖵 🍵 Access: ♿

The Shires Motel

The Shires Motel is a family owned and operated private motel, set in the rolling landscape of the Bucks/Northants countryside. Whether you are the traveller on business, or the tourist exploring the historic towns of England, you are welcomed with the assurance of homely comforts in pleasant surroundings at affordable prices.

Open Pastures, Buckingham Road,
Deanshanger, Milton Keynes
MK19 6JU

Website: www.shiresmotel.co.uk
Tel: 01908 262925   Fax: 01908 263642

Moulsford-on-Thames, Oxfordshire

Beetle & Wedge

★★🍾🍾

Blue Ribbon Winner

Ferry Lane, Moulsford-on-Thames, Oxfordshire, OX10 9JF
Tel: 01491 651381 Fax: 01491 651376
Web: www.beetleandwedge.co.uk

On the banks of the Thames in an idyllic location overlooking the water meadows, The Beetle and Wedge, which is run by the owners, has two award-winning restaurants and beautiful accommodation.
Rooms: 10 all ensuite 🛏 ⊗
Pricing: Sgl £99–135 Dbl £160–175 Dinner from £35
CC: Accepted Room facilities: 🖵 ☎ 🍵 Access: ♿
Conference: 2 meeting rooms (Thtr 50 max), 24hr-delegate from £160, day-delegate rate from £50
Children: Welcome 🍼 Dogs: Guide dogs only
Licences: 🍾🍾🍾 Parking: Off-street and monitored
Directions: From M4 Junction 12 take A4 south. At 2nd roundabout turn right and take A340 to Pangbourne – this becomes A329 follow to Moulsford, turn right into Ferry Lane.

New Alresford, Hampshire

Swan Hotel

★★

11 West Street, New Alresford, Hampshire, SO24 9AD
Tel: 01962 732302 Fax: 01962 735274
Email: swanhotel@btinternet.com
Web: www.smoothhound.co.uk/hotels/swanhotel2.html
Rooms: 23 all ensuite
Pricing: Sgl £42.50–47.50 Dbl £60–80 CC: Accepted
Room facilities: Access:
Conference: 2 meeting rooms (Thtr 60 max)
Children: Welcome Licences: Parking: Off-street
Directions: Situated between Winchester and Alton
take the A31 and follow signs for Alresford.

New Milton, Hampshire

Chewton Glen Hotel
Gold Ribbon Winner

★★★★★★ ⓡ ⓡ ⓡ

Christchurch Road, New Milton, Hampshire, BH25 6QS
Tel: 01425 275341 Fax: 01425 272310
Email: reservations@chewtonglen.com
Web: www.chewtonglen.com

Chewton Glen is the only privately owned hotel in the
UK with RAC 5-Star Rating plus Gold Ribbon, together
with 3 RAC Dining Awards, and voted Best Country
House Hotel in the World by the American magazine,
Gourmet, in 2000.
Rooms: 59 all ensuite Pricing: Sgl £270–715
Dbl £290–735 Dinner from £55 CC: Accepted
Room facilities: Access:
Conference: 5 meeting rooms (Thtr 150 max), 24hr-
delegate from £330, day-delegate rate from £95
Children: Welcome 6yrs min age
Dogs: Guide dogs only Licences:
Leisure: Indoor pool, Outdoor pool, Gym, Health spa,
Beauty salon, Tennis, Golf Snooker/billiards
Parking: Off-street and monitored
Directions: On A35 from Lyndhurst, drive 10 miles and
turn left at staggered junction. Follow brown tourist
signs for hotel through Walkford.
See advert on next page

Newbury, Berkshire

Vineyard at Stockcross
Blue Ribbon Winner

★★★★★★ ⓡ ⓡ ⓡ

Stockcross, Newbury, Berkshire, RG20 8JU
Tel: 01635 528770 Fax: 01635 528398
Email: general@the-vineyard.co.uk
Web: www.the-vineyard.co.uk

The Vineyard at Stockcross blends charm and elegant
surroundings and exquisite furniture with beautiful art and
sculptures. All guest rooms and suites are individually
named after wines. Chef John Campbell will seduce your
palate with famously exciting matches of favours.
Rooms: 31 all ensuite
Pricing: Sgl £188–269 Dbl £188–269 Dinner from £49
CC: Accepted Room facilities:
Access:
Conference: 3 meeting rooms (Thtr 100 max), 24hr-
delegate from £295, day-delegate rate from £80
Children: Welcome Licences:
Leisure: Indoor pool, Gym, Health spa, Beauty salon
Parking: Off-street and monitored
Directions: Exit J13 M4. Take A34 southbound and
take exit to Stockcross. At next roundabout take the
second exit. The Vineyard is ¼ mile on right.

Donnington Valley Hotel & Golf Course
Blue Ribbon Winner

★★★★ ⓡ ⓡ

Old Oxford Road, Donnington, Newbury,
Berkshire, RG14 3AG
Tel: 01635 551199 Fax: 01635 551123
Email: general@donningtonvalley.co.uk
Web: www.donningtonvalley.co.uk

A luxurious privately owned 4-star hotel surrounded by
its own 18-hole golf course. Superb food in the 'Wine
Press' restaurant with an extensive wine list.
Rooms: 58 all ensuite
Pricing: Sgl £150 Dbl £150 Dinner from £25
CC: Accepted Room facilities: Access:
Conference: 10 meeting rooms (Thtr 140 max), 24hr-
delegate from £185, day-delegate rate from £65
Children: Welcome Licences:
Leisure: Golf Parking: Off-street and monitored
Directions: Leave M4 at Junction 13. Take A34
southbound to Newbury. Leave at first exit signed
Donnington Castle. Take first right, then left. Hotel is 1
mile on right.

CHEWTON GLEN

THE HOTEL, HEALTH & COUNTRY CLUB

Chewton Glen is a splendid country house hotel set in a tranquil landscape of park and woodland ten minutes from the sea. Located 145km from London it was voted Best Country House Hotel in the World by readers of the American Magazine Gourmet and is the only privately owned Hotel in Britain with RAC 5-star rating plus Gold ribbon. The hotel's luxurious spa has recently been voted Best Hotel Spa in Europe by the German magazine, Gala. There is a par 3, 9-hole golf course within the grounds and ten 18-hole golf courses within easy reach of the hotel.

Christchurch Road, New Milton, Hampshire BH25 6QS
Tel: 01425 275341 Fax: 01425 272310
reservations@chewtonglen.com
www.chewtonglen.com

Regency Park Hotel

★★★★★ 🛎 🛎

Bowling Green Road, Thatcham, Nr. Newbury,
Berkshire, RG18 3RP
Tel: 01635 871555 Fax: 01635 871571
Email: info@regencyparkhotel.co.uk
Web: www.regencyparkhotel.co.uk

Recently refurbished luxury hotel renowned for its high
standards of service. Extensive indoor leisure facilities
with pool and gymnasium. Executive standard
bedrooms and award-winning restaurant.
Rooms: 82 all ensuite 🚭
Pricing: Sgl £85–348 Dbl £95–381 Dinner from £21
CC: Accepted
Room facilities: 🖵 ☎ ☕ ℄
Access: ᴵᴵᴵ ♿
Conference: 10 meeting rooms (Thtr 200 max), 24hr-
delegate from £165, day-delegate rate from £60
Children: Welcome ☂ ⸬℃
Dogs: Guide dogs only
Licences: ♨ ᴙᴙᴙ
Leisure: Indoor pool, Gym, Health spa, Beauty salon,
Tennis
Parking: Off-street
Directions: From Newbury take A4 signed
Thatcham/Reading. At second roundabout follow signs
to Cold Ash. Hotel 1 mile on left.

Bacon Arms Hotel

♦ ♦ ♦

Oxford Street, Newbury, Berkshire, RG14 1JB
Tel: 01635 31822 Fax: 01635 552496
Email: baconarms.newbury@eldridge-pope.co.uk
Web: www.eldridge-pope.co.uk
Rooms: 14 all ensuite 🥤 🖋 🚭
Pricing: Sgl £70–80 Dbl £75–85 Dinner from £10
CC: Accepted
Room facilities: 🖵 ☎ ☕ ℄
Conference: 1 meeting room (Thtr 36 max)
Children: Welcome ☂
Dogs: Guide dogs only
Licences: ᴙᴙᴙ
Parking: Off-street and monitored
Directions: From town centre head along London Road
past clock tower monument onto Oxford Street. We
are on the right.

Queens Hotel

♦ ♦ ♦

8 The Market Place, Newbury, Berkshire, RG14 5BD
Tel: 01635 47447 Fax: 01635 569626
Rooms: 15 all ensuite 🥤 🖋
Pricing: Sgl £60–80 Dbl £75–95
Room facilities: 🖵 ☎ ☕ ❄
Conference: 1 meeting room (Thtr 50 max)
Children: Welcome ☂ Dogs: Welcome
Licences: ♨ Parking: Off-street and monitored
Directions: Join M4, turn off to A4, head towards
Newbury. At large roundabout, the Queens is next to
Sainsburys.

The Swan Public House

♦ ♦ ♦

Station Road, Thatcham, Newbury,
Berkshire, RG19 4QL
Tel: 01635 871847 Fax: 01635 871851
Rooms: 6 all ensuite 🚭
Pricing: Sgl £55 Dbl £65–75 Dinner from £6
CC: Accepted Room facilities: 🖵 ☕ Access: ♿
Children: Welcome ☂ Dogs: Guide dogs only
Licences: ᴙᴙᴙ Leisure: Games room
Parking: Off-street
Directions: Exit J12 M4 towards Newbury. After 9 miles
turn left at Sony roundabout; the Swan is about ¹/₂ mile
on.

Travelodge Newbury, Chievely (MOTO)

Travel Accommodation
M4/A34 Moto Service Area, A34 Oxford Road,
Chieveley, Newbury, Berkshire, RG18 9XX
Web: www.travelodge.co.uk
Rooms: 63 all ensuite 🚭
Pricing: Sgl £54.40 Dbl £58.85
CC: Accepted Room facilities: 🖵 ☕ Access: ♿

Travelodge Newbury South

Travel Accommodation
Tot Hill Services, Newbury By-Pass, A34 Trunk Road,
Newbury, Berkshire, RG20 9ED
Web: www.travelodge.co.uk
Rooms: 52 all ensuite 🚭
Pricing: Sgl £54.40 Dbl £58.85
CC: Accepted Room facilities: 🖵 ☕ Access: ♿

Newport Pagnell, Buckinghamshire

Thurstons

♦ ♦ ♦ ⁂

90 High Street, Newport Pagnell,
Buckinghamshire, MK16 8EH
Tel: 01908 611377 Fax: 01908 611394
Rooms: 8 all ensuite
Room facilities: 🖵 ☕ Access: ♿
Children: Welcome ☂ Licences: ᴙᴙᴙ
Parking: Off-street and monitored
Directions: Located in the middle of town centre in
High Street, just off M21 Junction 14.

North Mymms, Hertfordshire

Little Gables Guest House

Little Gables, 3 Swanland Road, North Mymms,
Hatfield, Herts, AL9 7TG
Tel: 01707 660804 Fax: 020 8449 3559
Rooms: 4 (2 ensuite) ⊛
Pricing: Sgl £40–50 Dbl £50–70
Room facilities: ☐ ☕
Children: Welcome
Dogs: Welcome
Leisure: Golf, Riding
Parking: Off-street and monitored
Directions: Enter south Mimms services from A1 M/M25
junction 23, take directions to Colney Heath via
Swanland road. Little Gables is situated in Service road
on right side approx 2 minutes from motorway junction.

Norwood Hill, Surrey

Collendean Barn

Collendean Farm, Collendean Lane, Norwood Hill,
Nr. Horley, Surrey, RH6 0HP
Tel: 01293 862433 Fax: 01293 863102
Email: collendean.barn@amserve.net
Rooms: all ensuite ⇔ ⊛
Pricing: Sgl £30 Dbl £50
Room facilities: ☐ ☕
Children: Welcome ⴕ
Dogs: Guide dogs only
Licences: ⟐
Leisure: Health spa, Beauty salon, Fishing
Parking: Off-street
Directions: From J8 M25 to A217 turn right onto
Norwood Hill, take 2nd turn right Collendean lane, then
Collendean farm 1st on right.

Old Stratford, Buckinghamshire

Travelodge Old Stratford (July 02)

Travel Accommodation
A5, Old Stratford Roundabout, Old Stratford,
Buckinghamshire
Web: www.travelodge.co.uk
Pricing: Sgl £54.40 Dbl £58.85
CC: Accepted
Room facilities: ☐ ☕

Oxford, Oxfordshire

Cotswold Lodge Hotel

★★★★★ ⵃ ⵃ

66a Banbury Road, Oxford, Oxfordshire, OX2 6JP
Tel: 01865 512121 Fax: 01865 512490
Email: info@cotswoldlodgehotels.co.uk
Web: www.cotswoldlodgehotel.co.uk

Beautiful Victorian building, half a mile from the city
centre in a quiet conservation area. Recently
refurbished to a very high standard. Award-winning
restaurant. Bar with log fires, ample parking.
Rooms: 49 all ensuite ⊠ ⊛
Pricing: Dinner from £17 CC: Accepted
Room facilities: ☐ ☎ ☖ Children: Welcome
Dogs: Guide dogs only Parking: Off-street
Directions: From A40 ring road north of Oxford, take
A4165 into city. Cotswold Lodge is on Banbury Road,
2 miles into city on left.

Oxford Belfry

★★★★ ⵃ

Milton Common, Thame, Oxfordshire, OX9 2JW
Tel: 01844 279381 Fax: 01844 279624
Email: oxfordbelfry@marstonhotels.com
Web: www.marstonhotels.com

Delightful hotel with stunning views of the Cotswold
countryside, yet convenient for M40, minutes from
Oxford centre. AA rosette restaurant, leisure facilities
include heated indoor pool and all weather tennis courts.
Rooms: 130 all ensuite ⇔ ⊛ Pricing: Sgl £115
Dbl £149 Dinner from £28 CC: Accepted
Room facilities: ☐ ☎ ☕ ☖ Access: ⵽ ⴑ
Conference: 20 meeting rooms (Thtr 350 max), 24hr-
delegate from £170, day-delegate rate from £52.50
Children: Welcome ⴕ ⵙ Dogs: Guide dogs only
Licences: ⟐ ⵄ Leisure: Indoor pool, Gym, Tennis
Parking: Off-street and monitored
Directions: Leave M40 northbound at Junction 7.
Travelling southbound leave at Junction 8a. Hotel
situated on A40, 1.5 ½miles from either junction.

Oxford Spires Four Pillars Hotel

★★★★

Abingdon Road, Oxford, Oxfordshire, OX1 4PS
Tel: 01865 324324 Fax: 01865 324325
Email: spires@four-pillars.co.uk
Web: www.four-pillars.co.uk

Four star luxury hotel set amongst 40 acres of
outstanding parkland. Oxford City Centre is a short
walk away via a pleasant riverside walk. Facilities
include car parking and leisure.
Rooms: 115 all ensuite 🛏 🖨 ⊗
Pricing: Sgl £75–152.45 Dbl £99–198.90
Dinner from £23.95 CC: Accepted
Room facilities: ▢ ☎ ⊙ ✆
Access: ⇞ ♿
Children: Welcome ♁ ☕
Dogs: Welcome
Licences: ◬ ♔
Leisure: Indoor pool, Gym, Health spa, Beauty salon,
Fishing, Games room
Parking: Off-street and monitored
Directions: Exit J9 M40 A34 towards Oxford; then A423
turn left; left next roundabout, hotel 1 mile on the right.

Oxford Thames Four Pillars Hotel

★★★★

Henley Road, Sandford-on-Thames, Oxford,
Oxfordshire, OX4 4GX
Tel: 01865 334444 Fax: 01865 334400
Email: thames@four-pillars.co.uk
Web: www.four-pillars.co.uk
Rooms: 60 all ensuite 🛏 🖨 ⊗
Pricing: Sgl £75–152.45 Dbl £99–198.90
Dinner from £23.95 CC: Accepted
Room facilities: ▢ ☎ ⊙ ✆
Access: ♿
Conference: 12 meeting rooms (Thtr 160 max), 24hr-
delegate from £169, day-delegate rate from £59
Children: Welcome ♁ ☕
Dogs: Welcome
Licences: ◬ ♔
Leisure: Indoor pool, Gym, Health spa, Tennis
Parking: Off-street and monitored
Directions: J9 M40 A34 towards Oxford. Take A423
exit, then follow A4074 to Sandford. At T-junction, turn
right; hotel is on left.

The Oxford Hotel

★★★★

Wolvercote Roundabout, Oxford, Oxfordshire, OX2 8AL
Tel: 01865 489988 Fax: 01865 310259
Email: oxford@paramount-hotels.co.uk
Web: www.paramount-hotels.co.uk

PARAMOUNT
GROUP OF HOTELS

Rooms: 168 all ensuite
Pricing: Dbl £149–169 CC: Accepted
Room facilities: ▢ ☎ ⊙ ✆ ❄
Access: ⇞
Conference: 27 meeting rooms (Thtr 300 max), 24hr-
delegate from £185, day-delegate rate from £65
Children: Welcome ♁
Dogs: Guide dogs only Licences: ♔
Leisure: Indoor pool, Gym, Beauty salon
Parking: Off-street
Directions: From the M40 take the A34 south, leave
A34 at Oxford turn, take left turn at sliproad
roundabout. Right at Wolvercoate roundabout, the
hotel is on the right.

The Randolph

★★★★★ 🍴 🍴

Beaumont Street, Oxford, Oxfordshire, OX1 2LN
Tel: 0870 400 8200 Fax: 01865 791678
Email: randolph@heritage-hotels.co.uk
Web: www.macdonald-hotels.co.uk
Rooms: 114 all ensuite 🛏 🖨 ⊗
Pricing: Sgl £95 Dbl £190 Dinner from £30
CC: Accepted
Room facilities: ▢ ☎ ⊙ ✆ Access: ⇞ ♿
Conference: 6 meeting rooms (Thtr 300 max)
Children: Welcome ♁ Dogs: Welcome
Licences: ◬ ♔ Parking: Off-street and monitored
Directions: M40 to junction 8, signs to Oxford, take
A40 for approxiamately 5 miles, through set of traffic
lights to ring road roundabout. Take right exit to
Kidlington and at the next roundabout take left exit to
summertown. Follow Banbury Road all the way into
Oxford, the Randolph is on the right.

Fallowfields Country House Hotel
★★★★ ⓡ ⓡ ⓡ

Faringdon Road, Kingsrow Bagpuize Southmoor,
Oxford, Oxfordshire, OX13 5BH
Tel: 01865 820416 Fax: 01865 821275
Email: stay@fallowfield.com
Web: www.fallowfield.com

A beautiful country house, former home to Begum Aga
Ilhan, in twelve magnificent acres. Everything here is
exceptional. Outstanding bedrooms, delicious food,
warm hospitality and that rarest of assets – tranquility.
Rooms: 10 all ensuite Ⓦ ⓩ ⓢ
Pricing: Sgl £130–150 Dbl £140–190 Dinner from £25
CC: Accepted
Room facilities: ▢ ☎ ⓢ ⓛ
Conference: 2 meeting rooms (Thtr 60 max), 24hr-
delegate from £190, day-delegate rate from £43
Children: Welcome ⓗ
Dogs: Welcome Licences: ◭ ⓲ Leisure: Tennis
Parking: Off-street and monitored
Directions: From A420 take A415 direction Abingdon
for 100m, turn right, Fallowfields is 1 mile on left.

The Eastgate
★★★★ ⓡ

The High Street, Oxford, Oxfordshire, OX1 4BE
Tel: 0870 400 8201 Fax: 01865 791681
Email: eastgate@heritage-hotels.co.uk
Web: www.macdonald-hotels.co.uk
Rooms: 63 all ensuite Ⓦ ⓩ ⓢ
Pricing: Sgl £75 Dbl £150 Dinner from £10.95
CC: Accepted
Room facilities: ▢ ☎ ⓢ ⓛ Access: ⓵ ⓖ
Children: Welcome Dogs: Welcome
Licences: ⓲ Parking: Off-street and monitored
Directions: J8A from M40, follow signs into Oxford city
centre. Ignore the signs that say you can't drive up the
High Street and turn left into Merton street for carpark
access.

Balkan Lodge Hotel
★★

315 Iffley Road, Oxford, Oxfordshire, OX4 4AG
Tel: 01865 244524 Fax: 01865 251090
Email: balkanlodge@aol.co.uk
Web: www.oxfordcity.co.uk/hotels/balkan
Rooms: 13 all ensuite ⓩ ⓢ
Pricing: Sgl £62.50–70 Dbl £72–82.50

Dinner from £17.50 CC: Accepted
Room facilities: ▢ ☎ ⓢ
Children: Welcome ⓗ
Dogs: Welcome Licences: ⓲
Parking: Off-street and monitored
Directions: M40/A40 take eastern bypass A4158, bus
from city centre 4/A/B/C or service 3 from Queens St
to Howard St, hotel on left hand side.

Foxcombe Lodge Hotel
★★

Fox Lane, Boars Hill, Oxford, Oxfordshire, OX1 5DP
Tel: 01865 326326 Fax: 01865 730628
Email: res@foxcombe.demon.co.uk
Web: www.foxcombelodge.co.uk
Rooms: 19 all ensuite Ⓦ ⓩ
Pricing: Sgl £50–65 Dbl £65–90 Dinner from £18
CC: Accepted
Room facilities: ▢ ☎ ⓢ ⓛ Access: ⓖ
Conference: 4 meeting rooms (Thtr 80 max), 24hr-
delegate from £91.50, day-delegate rate from £23.50
Children: Welcome ⓗ
Dogs: Welcome Licences: ⓲
Leisure: Games room, Snooker/billiards
Parking: Off-street and monitored
Directions: At Hinksey Hill junction A34/A4142 follow
signs for Wootton. At top of hill (½ mile) turn right.
Hotel 1 mile on left.

Palace Hotel
★★

250–250a Iffley Road, Oxford, Oxfordshire, OX4 1SE
Tel: 01865 727627 Fax: 01865 200478
Web: www.stayoxford.co.uk
Rooms: 8 all ensuite ⓢ
Pricing: Sgl £69 Dbl £80 Dinner from £7.50
CC: Accepted
Room facilities: ▢ ☎ ⓢ
Children: Welcome ⓗ
Licences: ⓲
Parking: Off-street
Directions: From city centre take A4158; property is
half a mile on the right-hand side.

Victoria Hotel
★★

180 Abingdon Road, Oxford, Oxfordshire, OX1 4RA
Tel: 01865 724536 Fax: 01865 794909
Web: www.localhost/hotels/victoria
Rooms: 20 all ensuite ⓩ ⓢ
Pricing: Sgl £62.50–68.50 Dbl £78.50–85.50
Dinner from £18.50 CC: Accepted
Room facilities: ▢ ☎ ⓢ
Conference: 1 meeting room (Thtr 20 max), 24hr-
delegate from £195, day-delegate rate from £95
Children: Welcome ⓗ
Dogs: Welcome
Licences: ⓲
Parking: Off-street

Southeast

Chestnuts Guest House

♦ ♦ ♦ ♦ ♦

45 Davenant Road, Woodstock Road, Oxford,
Oxfordshire, OX2 8BU
Tel: 01865 553375 Fax: 01865 513712
Email: stay@chestnutsguesthouse.co.uk
Rooms: 6 all ensuite ⊗
Room facilities: ⊡ ☕
Children: Welcome 12yrs min age
Parking: Off-street
Directions: Leave A40/A34 at Peartree roundabout for
Woodstock Road, then sign for city centre, we are on
left hand side.

Bath Place Hotel

♦ ♦ ♦ ♦

4/5 Bath Place, Holywell Street, Oxford,
Oxfordshire, OX1 3SU
Tel: 01865 791812 Fax: 01865 791834
Email: info@bathplace.com
Web: www.bathplace.co.uk
Rooms: 14 all ensuite ⊗ ⊞ ⊗
Pricing: Sgl £90–125 Dbl £100–150 CC: Accepted
Room facilities: ⊡ ☎ ☕ ⬟
Access: ♿
Children: Welcome
Dogs: Welcome
Licences: ⬤⬤⬤
Parking: Off-street and monitored
Directions: Follow signs to the city centre, Bath Place
is situated off Holywell Street between Mansfield Road
and Broad Street.

Eltham Villa

♦ ♦ ♦ ♦

148 Woodstock Road, Yarnton, Oxford,
Oxfordshire, OX5 1PW
Tel: 01865 376037 Fax: 01865 376037
Seasonal closure: Christmas to New Year
Rooms: 6 all ensuite ⊗ ⊗
Room facilities: ⊡ ☕
Children: Welcome 5yrs min age
Parking: Off-street and monitored
Directions: On the A44 between Oxford and
Woodstock, minutes from Blenheim Palace.

Galaxie Hotel

♦ ♦ ♦ ♦

180 Banbury Road, Summertown, Oxford,
Oxfordshire, OX2 7BT
Tel: 01865 515688 Fax: 01865 556824
Email: info@galaxie.co.uk
Web: www.galaxie.co.uk
Seasonal closure: Jan 5 – March 1
Rooms: all ensuite ⊗
Pricing: Sgl £120 Dbl £200 CC: Accepted
Room facilities: ⊡ ☎ ❄ Access: ⬆ ♿
Children: Welcome 8yrs min age
Dogs: Guide dogs only
Licences: ⬤⬤⬤
Parking: Off-street and monitored

Marlborough House Hotel

♦ ♦ ♦ ♦

321 Woodstock Road, Oxford, Oxfordshire, OX2 7NY
Tel: 01865 311321 Fax: 01865 515329
Email: enquiries@marlbhouse.win-uk.net
Web: www.oxfordcity.co.uk/hotels/marlborough
Rooms: 17 all ensuite ⊗ ⊗
Pricing: Sgl £73 Dbl £84 CC: Accepted
Room facilities: ⊡ ☎ ☕
Access: ♿
Children: Welcome 5yrs min age
Licences: ⬤⬤⬤
Parking: Off-street
Directions: Located in north Oxford, 6 miles from
Junction 9, M40. 1½ miles from city centre.

Pickwick's

♦ ♦ ♦ ♦

15/17 London Road, Headington, Oxfordshire, OX3 7SP
Tel: 01865 750487 Fax: 01865 742208
Email: pickwicks@tiscali.co.uk
Web: www.pickwicks.oxfree.com
Seasonal closure: Christmas and New Year
Rooms: 15 (13 ensuite) ⊗
Pricing: Sgl £30–50 Dbl £65–75 CC: Accepted
Room facilities: ⊡ ☎ ☕
Access: ♿
Children: Welcome
Dogs: Welcome
Licences: ⬤⬤⬤
Parking: Off-street
Directions: From M40 and Oxford ring road, follow city
centre directions through Headington. Pickwicks is on
the right after 1 mile.

Acorn Guest House

♦ ♦ ♦

260–262 Iffley Road, Oxford, Oxfordshire, OX4 1SE
Tel: 01865 247998 Fax: 01865 247998
Email: acorn_gh_oxford@freezone.co.uk
Seasonal closure: Christmas to New Year
Rooms: 12 (5 ensuite) ⊗
Pricing: Sgl £29–31 Dbl £52–62 CC: Accepted
Room facilities: ⊡ ☕
Access: ⬆
Children: Welcome 9yrs min age
Parking: Off-street
Directions: From Oxford ring road, follow A4158 north
towards city centre. From roundabout go 1 mile; hotel
is on left, just after Motorworld VW Garage on right.

Traffic news

Sign up now for one month's free
trial of RAC Route Minder for
personalised traffic information.
Visit www.rac.co.uk/routeminder

Coach and Horses

◆ ◆ ◆

Watlington Road, Chislehampton, Oxford,
Oxfordshire, OX44 7UX
Tel: 01865 890255 Fax: 01865 891995
Email: david-mcphillips@lineone.net
Web: www.coachhorsesinn.co.uk
Seasonal closure: 26–30 December

A charming 16th-century oak-beamed inn and free
house set in splendid Oxfordshire countryside.
Excellent reputation for food and service.
Rooms: 9 all ensuite 🖃
Pricing: Sgl £53.50 Dbl £60–70 Dinner from £20
CC: Accepted Room facilities: ☐ ☎ ☕ Access: ♿
Conference: 1 meeting room (Thtr 12 max)
Children: Welcome Ħ Dogs: Guide dogs only
Licences: ♦♦♦ Leisure: Fishing, Riding,
Parking: Off-street and monitored

River Hotel

◆ ◆ ◆

17 Botley Road, Oxford, Oxfordshire, OX2 0AA
Tel: 01865 243475 Fax: 01865 724306
Email: reception@riverhotel.co.uk
Web: www.riverhotel.co.uk
Seasonal closure: Christmas and New Year

Originally a master builder's home built in the 1870s,
having been a small hotel for many years, now
independently run by proprietor and staff, offering well-
equipped bedrooms, all own bathroom, mostly full
ensuite facilities. Excellent location by River Thames at
Osney Bridge. Easy walk to city.
Rooms: 20 (18 ensuite)
Pricing: Sgl £57.50–67.50 Dbl £70–86 CC: Accepted
Room facilities: ☐ ☎ ☕ 🍽

Conference: 1 meeting room (Thtr 30 max)
Dogs: Guide dogs only
Licences: ♦♦♦
Parking: Off-street and monitored
Directions: For Botley Road, exit A420 west off ring
road (A34). 1 mile towards city and rail station. Hotel
on right beside Osney Bridge.

The Talk House

◆ ◆ ◆ 🍷

Wheatley Road, Stanton St John, near Oxford,
Oxfordshire, OX33 1EX
Tel: 01865 351648 Fax: 01865 351085
Email: talkhouse@traditionalfreehouses.com
Rooms: 4 all ensuite ♿
Pricing: Sgl £40 Dbl £60 Dinner from £8.95
CC: Accepted
Room facilities: ☐ ☎ ☕
Children: Welcome Ħ
Dogs: Guide dogs only
Licences: ♦♦♦
Parking: Off-street
Directions: Find Oxford ring road intersection with A40
– the Headington roundabout. At the last exit
(crematorium) continue to T-junction and turn right.

Tilbury Lodge

◆ ◆ ◆

5 Tilbury lane, Botley, Oxford, Oxfordshire, OX2 9NB
Tel: 01865 862138 Fax: 01865 863700
Email: tilburylodge@yahoo.co.uk
Web: www.oxfordcity.co.uk/hotels/tilbury
Rooms: 9 all ensuite 🖃
Pricing: Sgl £45–55 Dbl £65–70 Dinner from £5
CC: Accepted
Room facilities: ☐ ☎ ☕
Conference: 1 meeting room (Thtr 20 max)
Children: Welcome Dogs: Welcome
Parking: Off-street and monitored
Directions: From A34 take A420 Oxford. Right at traffic
lights, right into Eynsham Road, first right is Tilbury
Lane.

Travelodge Oxford East (SA)

Travel Accommodation
A40, London Road, Wheatley, Oxford,
Oxford, OX33 1JH
Web: www.travelodge.co.uk
Rooms: 36 all ensuite ♿
Pricing: Sgl £57.40 Dbl £61.85–68.85
CC: Accepted Room facilities: ☐ ☕ Access: ♿

Travelodge Oxford (MOTO)

Travel Accommodation
Peartee Roundabout, Woodstock Road, Oxford,
Oxfordshire, OX2 8JZ
Web: www.travelodge.co.uk
Rooms: 150 all ensuite ♿
Pricing: Sgl £64.40–69.40 Dbl £68.85–73.85
CC: Accepted Room facilities: ☐ ☕ Access: ♿

Southeast

Travelodge Thame

Travel Accommodation
A418, Thame, Nr. Oxford, Oxfordshire, OX9 7XA
Web: www.travelodge.co.uk
Rooms: 31 all ensuite ⊛
Pricing: Sgl £64.40 Dbl £68.85
CC: Accepted Room facilities: □ ☕ Access: ♿

Pagham, West Sussex

Inglenook Hotel

★ ★ ★

253–255 Pagham Road, Pagham,
West Sussex, PO21 3QB
Tel: 01243 262495 Fax: 01243 262668
Email: reception@the-inglenook.com
Web: www.the-inglenook.com
Rooms: 18 all ensuite ⊠ ⊛
Pricing: Sgl £50–75 Dbl £90–200 Dinner from £16.95
CC: Accepted
Room facilities: □ ☎ ☕ ⤸
Access: ♿
Children: Welcome ♀
Dogs: Welcome
Licences: ◁◇ ⅲ
Leisure: Golf, Fishing, Riding
Parking: Off-street
Directions: Ten minutes from A27, travelling south,
signposted Pagham.
See advert on this page

Inglenook Hotel

Family owned and run, sixteenth-century
hotel, restaurant and free house.
Cosy bars with inglenook log fireplaces.
Attractive restaurant
overlooking and opening onto the
gardens, with seafood specialities. Wedding
ceremonies and receptions, conferences.
Car parking at rear.

253–255 Pagham Road, Pagham, West
Sussex, PO21 3QB
Tel: 01243 262495   Fax: 01243 262668
reception@the-inglenook.com
www.the-inglenook.com

RAC ★ ★ ★   AA Tourist Board

Pangbourne, Berkshire

George Hotel

★ ★ ★

The Square, Pangbourne, Berkshire, RG8 7AJ
Tel: 0118 984 2237 Fax: 0118 984 4354
Email: info@georgehotelpangbourne.co.uk
Web: www.georgehotelpangbourne.co.uk
Rooms: 24 all ensuite ⇔ ⊠ ⊛
Pricing: Sgl £85–95 Dbl £95–105 Dinner from £6
CC: Accepted
Room facilities: □ ☎ ☕ ⤸
Conference: 4 meeting rooms (Thtr 60 max), 24hr-
delegate from £140, day-delegate rate from £40
Children: Welcome ♀ ⅈ
Dogs: Welcome
Licences: ⅲ
Parking: Off-street and monitored
Directions: Leave M4 at Junction 12. Follow signs for
A340 towards Pangbourne. On arrival in village, turn
right at mini roundabout. Hotel 50 yards on left.

Pevensey, East Sussex

Priory Court Hotel

◆ ◆ ◆

Castle Road, Pevensey, East Sussex, BN24 5LG
Tel: 01323 763150 Fax: 01323 769030
Email: priorycourthotel@aol.com
Web: priorycourthotel.com
Rooms: 10 (8 ensuite) ⇔ ⊠ ⊛
Pricing: Sgl £40–50 Dbl £53–85 Dinner from £15
CC: Accepted
Room facilities: □ ☎ ☕
Access: ♿
Conference: 2 meeting rooms (Thtr 25 max), day-
delegate rate from £99.50
Children: Welcome ♀
Dogs: Welcome
Licences: ⅲ
Parking: Off-street
Directions: At the roundabout at junction of A27 and
A259, follow sign for Pevensey. We are located
opposite Pevensey Castle on right.

Providence Cottage

◆ ◆ ◆ ⧗

45 Coast Road, Pevensey, Pevensey Bay,
East Sussex, BN24 6LP
Tel: 01323 769993
Web: www.providencecottage.co.uk
Rooms: 2 (1 ensuite) ⊛
Pricing: Dbl £40–50
Room facilities: □ ☕
Children: Welcome ♀ ⅈ
Dogs: Guide dogs only
Parking: Off-street
Directions: From A22 Polegate turn onto A27; at
roundabout turn onto A259, then first left Wallsend
Road, and first left again onto coast road.

Portsmouth, Hampshire

Queen's Hotel

★★★

Clarence Parade, Southsea, Portsmouth,
Hampshire, PO5 3LJ
Tel: 023 9282 2466 Fax: 023 9282 1901
Email: bestwestqueens@aol.com
Web: www.queenshotel-southsea.co.uk
Rooms: 100 all ensuite
Pricing: Sgl £65–95 Dbl £85–135 Dinner from £21.95
CC: Accepted Room facilities: Access:
Conference: 3 meeting rooms (Thtr 90 max), 24hr-
delegate from £99.50, day-delegate rate from £35.50
Children: Welcome Licences:
Leisure: Outdoor pool
Parking: Off-street and monitored
Directions: Leave M27 for M275 to Portsmouth. Follow
signs to Southsea seafront. Hotel is opposite war
memorial.
See advert on this page

The Sandringham House Hotel

★★

7 Osborne Road, Southsea, Hampshire, PO5 3LR
Tel: 023 9282 6969 Fax: 023 9282 2330
Email: reception@s-h-h.co.uk
Web: www.s-h-h.co.uk
Rooms: 44 all ensuite
Pricing: Sgl £35–56 Dbl £52–75 Dinner from £11.45
CC: Accepted Room facilities: Access:
Conference: 3 meeting rooms (Thtr 180 max), 24hr-
delegate from £75, day-delegate rate from £20
Children: Welcome Dogs: Guide dogs only
Licences:
Directions: At end of M275 follow signs for sea front
and hovercraft. At Southsea Common turn left; hotel is
300 yards on left.

Uppermount House Hotel

◆◆◆◆

The Vale, off Clarendon Road, Southsea, Portsmouth,
Hampshire, PO5 2EQ
Tel: 023 9282 0456 Fax: 023 9282 0456

An attractive, family-run Victorian villa with rooms of
character, some with four-poster or canopy beds.
Within easy walking distance of the city centre.
Rooms: 12 all ensuite

The Queens Hotel

Splendid Edwardian style hotel with
panoramic views of the Solent, offering a
selection of bars and an award winning
restaurant. 72 ensuite bedrooms. Easily
accessible from M275 and continental ferry
port. Ample secure, free parking

**Clarence Parade, Southsea,
Portsmouth PO5 3LJ**
Tel: 02392 822466   Fax: 02392 821901
Website: www.queenshotel-southsea.co.uk

Pricing: Sgl £30–32 Dbl £50–54 Dinner from £14
CC: Accepted Room facilities: Access:
Children: Welcome Licences:
Parking: Off-street and monitored
Directions: Exit M27; head for D-Day musem. Turn
down road opposite. Drive over crossroad; right at T-
junction and take first right.

Travelodge Portsmouth (SA)

Travel Accommodation
Kingston Crescent, Darfield Road, North End,
Portsmouth, Hants, PO2 8AB
Web: www.travelodge.co.uk Rooms: 78 all ensuite
Pricing: Sgl £59.40 Dbl £63.85
CC: Accepted Room facilities: Access:

Princes Risborough, Buckinghamshire

Rose & Crown

★★

Wycombe Road, Saunderton, Princes Risborough,
Buckinghamshire, HP27 9NP
Tel: 01844 345299 Fax: 01844 343140
Email: info@rosecrowninn.com
Rooms: 15 all ensuite
Pricing:73.2587 Dinner from £5.95 CC: Accepted
Room facilities: Children: Welcome
Dogs: Guide dogs only Licences: Parking: Off-street
Directions: Situated on the A4010 midway between
High Wycombe and Aylesbury.

Southeast

Ramsgate, Kent

Grove End Hotel

♦ ♦ ♦

2 Grange Road, Ramsgate, Kent, CT11 9NA
Tel: 01843 587520 Fax: 01843 853666
Email: reservation@groveendhotel.demon.co.uk
Web: www.groveendhotel.demon.co.uk
Rooms: 11 all ensuite ⛳
Pricing: Sgl £25 Dbl £40 CC: Accepted
Room facilities: 🖵 🗦 Children: Welcome ♀
Parking: Off-street

Reading, Berkshire

Millennium Madejski Hotel Reading

★ ★ ★ ★ 🍴 🍴 🍴

Madejski Stadium, Junction 11 M4, Reading,
Berkshire, RG2 0FL
Tel: 0118 925 3500 Fax: 0118 925 3501
Email: sales.reading@mill-cop.com
Web: www.millenniumhotels.com

Prestigious hotel with superb luxury facilities ideally
located in Royal Berkshire for business trips and
leisure weekends. Nearby attractions include Legoland
and Windsor Castle.
Rooms: 140 all ensuite ⛳ ⊗
Pricing: Sgl £70–195 Dbl £90–195 Dinner from £25
CC: Accepted Room facilities: 🖵 ☎ 🗦 📞 ❄ Access: ⬆
Children: Welcome ♀ Dogs: Welcome
Licences: ⚶ Leisure: Indoor pool, Gym, Health spa
Parking: Off-street and monitored
Directions: Take the M4 junction 11. Follow the A33
towards Reading. Follow signs to the Madejski
Stadium. 1 mile from M4.

Copper Inn Hotel

★ ★ ★ 🍴 🍴 🍴

Church Road, Pangbourne-on-Thames,
Berkshire, RG8 7AR
Tel: 0118 984 2244 Fax: 0118 984 5542
Email: reservations@copper-inn.co.uk
Web: www.copper-inn.co.uk

Ideal for a peaceful stay. The award-winning restaurant
will take you for a walk through flavours and fresh
produce, and the staff will make you feel at home.
Rooms: 22 all ensuite ⛳ 🖊 ⊗
Pricing: Sgl £60–110 Dbl £80–130 Dinner from £19.95
CC: Accepted Room facilities: 🖵 ☎ 🗦 📞 Access: ♿
Conference: 3 meeting rooms (Thtr 60 max), 24hr-
delegate from £140, day-delegate rate from £40
Children: Welcome ♀ ❄ Dogs: Welcome
Licences: ⚶ ⚶ Parking: Off-street
Directions: Exit M4 J12 follow sign for Theale, then
follow A340 to Pangbourne Hotel on left.

Hanover International Hotel & Club Reading

★ ★ ★

Pingewood, Reading, Berkshire, RG30 3UN
Tel: 0870 241 7083 Fax: 0118 939 1996
Email: crso@hanover-international.com
Web: www.hanover-international.com

HANOVER INTERNATIONAL
HOTELS & CLUBS

Stunning modern hotel in a spectacular lakeside
setting, convenient for London, Windsor Castle,
Legoland, M4, Heathrow and Gatwick. Extensive indoor
and outdoor leisure facilities, including watersports.
Rooms: 81 all ensuite ⊗ Pricing: Sgl £45–170
Dbl £90–170 Dinner from £19.50 CC: Accepted
Room facilities: 🖵 ☎ 🗦 📞 Access: ⬆ ♿
Conference: 14 meeting rooms (Thtr 110 max), 24hr-
delegate from £175, day-delegate rate from £57.50
Children: Welcome ♀ Dogs: Guide dogs only
Licences: ⚶ ⚶ Leisure: Indoor pool, Gym, Tennis,
Snooker/billiards
Parking: Off-street and monitored
Directions: M4 Junction 11, A33 south (Basingstoke).
Right at first roundabout then second right. Follow lane
for 2 miles, through traffic lights. Hotel on left.

Mill House Hotel

★★

Old Basingstoke Road, Swallowfield, Reading,
Berkshire, RG7 1PY
Tel: 0118 988 3124 Fax: 0118 988 5550
Email: info@themillhousehotel.co.uk
Web: www.themillhousehotel.co.uk
Seasonal closure: 25 Dec 2002 to 3 Jan 2003
Rooms: 12 (11 ensuite)
Pricing: Sgl £60–90 Dbl £80–100 Dinner from £22.50
CC: Accepted Room facilities:
Conference: 3 meeting rooms (Thtr 250 max), 24hr-
delegate from £135, day-delegate rate from £35
Children: Welcome Dogs: Welcome
Licences: Parking: Off-street and monitored
Directions: On M4, J11, take A33 to Basingstoke. At
roundabout 1st exit, 2 miles RHS. M3 J5, signs to
Reading, B3349 to Swallowfield.

Rainbow Corner Hotel

★★

132–138 Caversham Road, Reading, Berkshire, RG1 8AY
Tel: 0118 955 6902 Fax: 0118 958 6500
Email: info@rainbowhotel.co.uk
Web: www.rainbowhotel.co.uk
Rooms: 24 all ensuite
Pricing: Sgl £44–85 Dbl £59–105 Dinner from £11.95
CC: Accepted Room facilities:
Conference: 2 meeting rooms (Thtr 30 max)
Children: Welcome Dogs: Guide dogs only
Licences: Parking: Off-street and monitored
Directions: From M4 junction 11 follow signs for
Reading town centre, follow A4155 for Caversham and
Henley, we are on this road.

Travelodge Reading Central (SA)

Travel Accommodation
60 Oxford Road, Reading, Berkshire, RG1 7LT
Web: www.travelodge.co.uk
Rooms: 80 all ensuite
Pricing: Sgl £54.40–74.40 Dbl £58.85–78.85
CC: Accepted Room facilities: Access:

Travelodge Reading M4 Eastbound (MOTO)

Travel Accommodation
M4 Motorway, Burghfield, Reading, Berks, RG30 3UQ
Web: www.travelodge.co.uk
Rooms: 86 all ensuite
Pricing: Sgl £47.40–74.40 Dbl £51.85–78.85
CC: Accepted Room facilities: Access:

Travelodge Reading M4 Wesbound (MOTO)

Travel Accommodation
M4 Motoway, Burghfield, Reading, Berks, RG30 3UQ
Web: www.travelodge.co.uk
Rooms: 102 all ensuite
Pricing: Sgl £47.40–74.40 Dbl £51.85–78.85
CC: Accepted Room facilities: Access:

Travelodge Reading (SA)

Travel Accommodation
387 Basingstoke Road, Reading, Berkshire, RG2 0JE
Web: www.travelodge.co.uk
Rooms: 36 all ensuite
Pricing: Sgl £54.40–74.40 Dbl £58.85–78.85
CC: Accepted Room facilities: Access:

Redhill, Surrey

Ashleigh House Hotel

◆◆◆◆

39 Redstone Hill, Redhill, Surrey, RH1 4BG
Tel: 01737 764763 Fax: 01737 780308
Seasonal closure: Christmas and New Year
Rooms: 8 (6 ensuite)
Pricing: Sgl £40–55 Dbl £56–60 CC: Accepted
Room facilities:
Children: Welcome Dogs: Guide dogs only
Parking: Off-street
Directions: Gatwick 15 minutes by car, 10 minutes by
train. London 30 minutes by train.

Reigate, Surrey

Reigate Manor Hotel

★★★

Reigate Hill, Reigate, Surrey, RH2 9PF
Tel: 01737 240125 Fax: 01737 223883
Email: hotel@reigatemanor.co.uk
Web: www.reigatemanor.co.uk
Rooms: 50 all ensuite
Pricing: Sgl £117–132 Dbl £144–164 Dinner from £15
CC: Accepted
Room facilities:
Conference: 5 meeting rooms (Thtr 200 max), 24hr-
delegate from £150, day-delegate rate from £50
Children: Welcome
Licences: Leisure: Gym
Parking: Off-street
Directions: Leave M25 at Junction 8 and head south
on A217. Hotel is 1 mile on right.

Ringwood, Hampshire

Tyrrells Ford Country House Hotel

★★★

Avon, New Forest, Hampshire, BH23 7BH
Tel: 01425 672646 Fax: 01425 672262
Email: tyrrellsford@aol.com
Web: www.tyrrellsfordhotel.com
Rooms: 16 all ensuite
Pricing: Sgl £70–80 Dbl £120–130 Dinner from £25
CC: Accepted Room facilities:
Conference: 3 meeting rooms (Thtr 100 max)
Children: Welcome
Licences:
Parking: Off-street
Directions: From M3/M27/A31 to Ringwood take
B3347, 3 miles south signs for Sopley Winkton
entrance on left hand side.

Southeast

The Original White Hart

◆ ◆ ◆

Market Place, Ringwood, Hampshire, BH24 1AW
Tel: 01425 472702 Fax: 01425 471993
Email: originalwhitehart.ringwood@eldridge-pope.co.uk
Rooms: 15 all ensuite 🕮 📠 ⊛
Pricing: Sgl £49 Dbl £60 Dinner from £8.50
CC: Accepted Room facilities: ☐ ☎ ◷ ☎ ✻
Access: ♿ Conference: 1 meeting room (Thtr 20 max)
Children: Welcome Dogs: Welcome
Licences: ♦♦♦ Parking: Off-street
Directions: Off the A31 at Ringwood, come to a
roundabout, aim for Ringwood town centre. Turn right
at next roundabout and left at next. The road will veer
to the left, but take the turning straight ahead. At the
end of here turn right and we are situated immediately
on the right, car park at rear for customer use.

Travelodge Ringwood

Travel Accommodation
A31, St Leonard, Ringwood, Hampshire, BH24 2NR
Web: www.travelodge.co.uk
Rooms: 31 all ensuite ⊛
Pricing: Sgl £59.40 Dbl £63.85
CC: Accepted Room facilities: ☐ ◷ Access: ♿

Rochester, Kent

Bridgewood Manor

★ ★ ★ ★ ★ ♟ ♟

Bridgewood Roundabout, Walderslade Woods,
Chatham, Kent, ME5 9AX
Tel: 01634 201333 Fax: 01634 201330
Email: bridgewoodmanor@marstonhotels.com
Web: www.marstonhotels.com

Modern hotel, built around a classical courtyard, with
Gothic influences reflected in beautiful woodwork.
Leisure facilities include heated indoor pool, gym,
tennis and beauty treatment, 2AA rosette restaurant.
Rooms: 100 all ensuite 🕮 ⊛
Pricing: Sgl £115 Dbl £149 Dinner from £28
CC: Accepted Room facilities: ☐ ☎ ◷ ☎ Access: ⬆ ♿
Conference: 24 meeting rooms (Thtr 200 max), 24hr-
delegate from £145, day-delegate rate from £47.50

Children: Welcome ♏ ☪
Dogs: Guide dogs only
Licences: ◈ ♦♦♦
Leisure: Indoor pool, Gym, Health spa, Beauty salon,
Tennis, Snooker/billiards
Parking: Off-street and monitored
Directions: Leave M2 at Junction 3 or M20 at Junction
6. Follow A229 towards Rochester. At Bridgewood
roundabout take third exit.

Royal Victoria & Bull Hotel

★

High Street, Rochester, Kent, ME1 1PX
Tel: 01634 846266 Fax: 01634 832312
Email: enquiries@rvandb.co.uk
Web: www.rvandb.co.uk
Rooms: 28 (24 ensuite) 📠
Pricing: Dinner from £10 (2002 rate) CC: Accepted
Room facilities: ☐ ☎ ◷
Children: Welcome ☪ Dogs: Welcome
Licences: ♦♦♦ Parking: Off-street and monitored
Directions: Follow A2 into Rochester. Go across bridge
and get into middle lane. After lights, turn right into
Northgate at first dual carriageway intersection. Turn
right into High Street; hotel is on left.

Romsey, Hampshire

The White Horse

★ ★ ★

Market Place, Romsey, Hampshire, SO51 8ZJ
Tel: 0870 400 8123 Fax: 01794 517485
Email: whitehorseromsey@heritage-hotels.co.uk
Web: www.macdonaldhotels.co.uk
Rooms: 33 all ensuite ⊛
Pricing: Sgl £59 Dbl £118 Dinner from £18.95
CC: Accepted
Room facilities: ☐ ☎ ◷ ☎
Access: ♿
Conference: 2 meeting rooms (Thtr 130 max)
Children: Welcome ☪ Dogs: Welcome
Licences: ♦♦♦
Parking: Off-street and monitored
Directions: From junction 11 of M3 or junction 3 of M2
follow signs to Romsey, then to Town Centre. Drive
past hotel, take first left then left into car park.

The Sun Inn

◆ ◆ ◆ ◆ ☒

116 Winchester, Romsey, Hants, SO51 7JG
Tel: 01794 512255 Fax: 01794 521887
Rooms: 4 (3 ensuite) ⊛
Pricing: Sgl £52.50–57.50 Dbl £65–65
Dinner from £8.95 CC: Accepted
Room facilities: ☐ ◷
Children: Welcome 12yrs min age
Dogs: Guide dogs only
Licences: ♦♦♦
Parking: Off-street and monitored
Directions: Junction 3 M27 follow road to Romsey, we
are on main Winchester road.

Ruislip, Middlesex

The Barn Hotel

★★★

West End Road, Ruislip, Middlesex, HA4 6JB
Tel: 01895 636057 Fax: 01895 638379
Email: info@thebarnhotel.co.uk
Web: www.thebarnhotel.co.uk
Rooms: 59 all ensuite 🖨 ⊘
Pricing: Sgl £80–130 Dbl £90–165 Dinner from £15
CC: Accepted Room facilities: ▢ ☎ ⏺ 📞
Access: ♿
Conference: 5 meeting rooms (Thtr 80 max), 24hr-
delegate from £140, day-delegate rate from £50
Children: Welcome ⍭ Dogs: Guide dogs only
Licences: ⚒ ♙♙♙ Parking: Off-street and monitored
Directions: A40 – exit Ruislip/Polish War memorial, exit
roundabout to Ruislip (A4180 – West End Road).
Continue 2 miles, turn right at mini-roundabout.
See advert on this page

Rye, East Sussex

Flackley Ash

★★★

Peasmarsh, near Rye, East Sussex, TN31 6YH
Tel: 01797 230651 Fax: 01797 230510
Email: enquiries@flackleyashhotel.co.uk
Web: www.flackleyashhotel.co.uk

Friendly Georgian country house hotel set in beautiful
grounds, candlelit restaurant with fine wines and fresh
local fish. Indoor pool and leisure centre, beauty &
massage, visit local castles and gardens.
Rooms: 45 all ensuite ⚓ 🖨
Pricing: Sgl £79–89 Dbl £124–154 Dinner from £22.50
CC: Accepted
Room facilities: ▢ ☎ ⏺ 📞 Access: ♿
Conference: 3 meeting rooms (Thtr 100 max), 24hr-
delegate from £116.38, day-delegate rate from £38.19
Children: Welcome ⍭ ⃫
Dogs: Welcome
Licences: ⚒ ♙♙♙
Leisure: Indoor pool, Gym, Health spa,
Beauty salon
Parking: Off-street and monitored
Directions: Leave M25 at Junction 5, take A21
signposted Tunbridge Wells. Take A268 towards Rye.
Hotel on left when entering Peasmarsh.

Rye Lodge Hotel

★★★ 🛡

Hilder's Cliff, Rye, East Sussex, TN31 7LD
Tel: 01797 223838 Fax: 01797 223585
Email: info@ryelodge.co.uk
Web: www.ryelodge.co.uk

Attractive ensuite rooms. Every amenity. Room service
– breakfast in bed! Delicious candlelit dinners in the
elegant, marble-floored terrace room. Relaxed
atmosphere. Indoor swimming pool, spabath, sauna –
really caring service.
Rooms: 18 all ensuite ⚓ Pricing: Sgl £55–95
Dbl £90–150 Dinner from £25 CC: Accepted
Room facilities: ▢ ☎ ⏺ Access: ♿
Children: Welcome ⍭ Dogs: Welcome Licences: ♙♙♙
Leisure: Indoor pool, Health spa
Parking: Off-street and monitored
Directions: Follow town centre signs to Landgate Arch
(ancient monument); continue through Landgate Arch –
hotel is 100 yards on right.

Southeast

The Mermaid Hotel

★★★★ ⍰ ⍰

Mermaid Street, Rye, East Sussex, TN31 7EY
Tel: 01797 223065 Fax: 01797 225069
Email: mermaidinnrye@btclick.com
Web: www.mermaidinn.com

From a picturesque cobbled street step back in time and experience the unique atmosphere of one of England's oldest and loveliest inns with highly acclaimed restaurant.
Rooms: 31 all ensuite ⍰ ⍰
Pricing: Sgl £75–80 Dbl £150–190 Dinner from £35
CC: Accepted Room facilities: ⍰ ⍰
Conference: 2 meeting rooms (Thtr 50 max), 24hr-delegate from £150, day-delegate rate from £30
Children: Welcome ⍰ ⍰
Dogs: Guide dogs only
Licences: ⍰⍰⍰ Parking: Off-street and monitored
Directions: Rye is situated on the A259 east of Hastings, leave M20 at Ashford on the A2070 from A21 take B2089.

Durrant House Hotel

♦♦♦♦♦ ⍰

Market Street, Rye, East Sussex, TN31 7LA
Tel: 01797 223182 Fax: 01797 226940
Email: kingslands@compuserve.com
Web: www.durranthouse.com

A charming listed building located in the heart of Rye. It has six individually decorated bedrooms, all equipped to a high standard, including four-poster and triple rooms. Informal atmosphere.
Rooms: 6 all ensuite ⍰ ⍰ ⍰
Pricing: Sgl £45–65 Dbl £60–85 Dinner from £18
CC: Accepted

Room facilities: ⍰ ⍰
Children: Welcome ⍰ Dogs: Welcome
Licences: ⍰⍰⍰
Directions: Follow signs for town centre. Pass through the Landgate up to the High Street, then first left up East Street.

Jeake's House

♦♦♦♦♦ ⍰ ⍰

Mermaid Street, Rye, East Sussex, TN31 7ET
Tel: 01797 222828 Fax: 01797 222623
Email: jeakeshouse@btinternet.com
Web: www.jeakeshouse.com
Rooms: 12 (10 ensuite) ⍰ ⍰
Pricing: Sgl £34 Dbl £84 CC: Accepted
Room facilities: ⍰ ⍰ ⍰
Children: Welcome 11yrs min age
Dogs: Welcome Licences: ⍰⍰⍰
Parking: Off-street and monitored
Directions: Approach Rye from A259 or A2070. Follow town centre signs. From High Street turn right into West Street, which leads to Mermaid Street.
See advert on next page

The Benson

♦♦♦♦♦ ⍰ ⍰ ⍰

15 East Street, Rye, East Sussex, TN31 7JY
Tel: 01797 225131 Fax: 01797 225512
Email: info@bensonhotel.co.uk
Web: www.bensonhotel.co.uk

Situated in the heart of historic Rye, Benson offers sumptuous period-style bedrooms, most four-posters, with all-modern conveniences, attractive lounge, conservatory and terrace overlooking the River Rother and Romney Marshes.
Rooms: 4 all ensuite ⍰ ⍰
Pricing: Dbl £80–94 CC: Accepted
Room facilities: ⍰ ⍰ ⍰ Dogs: Guide dogs only
Licences: ⍰⍰⍰ Parking: Off-street
Directions: For East Street, follow town centre signs. Pass through landgate and after 300 yards take first left. Hotel 75 yards up hill on left.

White Vine House

◆ ◆ ◆ ◆ ◆ ✻ ❦

24 High Street, Rye, East Sussex, TN31 7JF
Tel: 01797 224748 Fax: 01797 223599
Email: irene@whitevinehouse.freeserve.co.uk
Seasonal closure: 30 Dec to 5 Jan

Tudor town house in the heart of ancient Rye with comfortable bedrooms, oak beams, stone fireplaces, books and paintings. Excellent breakfasts. Ideal for antique hunting, castles and gardens.
Rooms: 7 all ensuite 🐾 📺 ⊗
Pricing: Sgl £50–70 Dbl £80–115 CC: Accepted
Room facilities: ▢ ☕ Children: Welcome ⼌
Dogs: Welcome Licences: ⟁ ⅲ
Directions: At Rye follow signs to town centre and enter under Landgate Arch. Follow road into High Street and hotel is on right.

Hope Anchor Hotel

◆ ◆ ◆ ◆

Watchbell Street, Rye, East Sussex, TN31 7HA
Tel: 01797 222216 Fax: 01797 223796
Email: info@hotel-rye.freeserve.co.uk
Web: www.rye-tourism.co.uk/hopeanchor

Dating from the mid-18th century, this delightful hotel has 2 bars, welcoming log lounge, elegant restaurant and 12 lovely bedrooms. Situated in the heart of Rye it has stunning views over the Marshes.
Rooms: 12 (11 ensuite) 🐾 📺 ⊗ Pricing: Sgl £50–70
Dbl £65–115 CC: Accepted Room facilities: ▢ ☕
Children: Welcome ⼌ Dogs: Welcome Licences: ⅲ

Jeake's House

17th-century Jeake's House stands on the most famous cobbled street in Rye's medieval town centre. Each stylishly restored bedroom with brass, mahogany or Four-Poster bed creates a very special atmosphere, combining traditional elegance with modern comforts.

Breakfast served in the galleried dining room is traditional or vegetarian and the roaring fire and timeless atmosphere will combine to make your stay truly memorable.

There is a comfortable drawing room and book-lined bar. Private car park nearby.

RAC ◆ ◆ ◆ ◆ ◆
✻ ❦

Mermaid Street, Rye, East Sussex
TN31 7ET
Tel: 01797 222828   Fax: 01797 222623
Email: jeakeshouse@btinternet.com
Website: www.jeakeshouse.com

Old Borough Arms

◆◆◆◆

The Strand, Rye, East Sussex, TN31 7DB
Tel: 01797 222128 Fax: 01797 222128
Email: info@oldborougharms.co.uk
Web: www.oldborougharms.co.uk
Rooms: 9 all ensuite 🛏 🚭
Pricing: Sgl £30–45 Dbl £60–90 CC: Accepted
Room facilities: 📺 ☕ Access: ♿
Children: Welcome 🍴 Dogs: Guide dogs only
Licences: 🍸 Parking: Off-street and monitored
Directions: The hotel is located at the foot of Rye's
famous Mermaid Street, opposite the antique centres
on the Strand Quay.

Strand House

◆◆◆◆

The Strand, Tanyard's Lane, Winchelsea, Rye, East
Sussex, TN36 4JT
Tel: 01797 226276 Fax: 01797 224806
Email: strandhouse@winchelsea98.fsnet.co.uk
Web: www.smoothhound.co.uk/hotels/strand.html
Seasonal closure: Christmas

Fine old 15th century house with many original oak
beams and inglenooks, previously Winchelseas work
house, full of atmosphere, well furnished rooms, bar &
lounge, pretty gardens, overlooks National Trust
farmland.
Rooms: 10 (9 ensuite) 🛏 🚭
Pricing: Sgl £34–40 Dbl £52–76 CC: Accepted
Room facilities: 📺 ☕
Conference: 1 meeting room (Thtr 12 max)
Children: Welcome 3yrs min age 🍴
Licences: 🍸
Parking: Off-street
Directions: From Rye take A259 towards Hastings.
Property is first house on left side after passing village
sign, set back from road, approx 1½ miles from Rye.

Magnolia House

◆◆◆

15 Udimore Road, Rye, East Sussex, TN31 7DS
Tel: 01797 222561 Fax: 01797 227525
Web: www.magnoliaguesthouse.co.uk

Licenced premises, situated a few minutes' level walk
to Medieval Rye. A family-run guest house with
spacious accommodation.
Rooms: 6 all ensuite 🍴 🚭
Pricing: Dinner from £5.50 CC: Accepted
Room facilities: 📺 ☕ Children: Welcome 🍴 ☕
Licences: 🍸 Parking: Off-street
Directions: Going out of Rye on the B2089 to Battle:
just over the river bridge on the right.

Simmons of the Mint

❖

68-69 The Mint, Rye, East Sussex, TN31 7EW
Tel: 01797 226862 Fax: 01797 226862
Seasonal closure: Christmas
Centrally situated in the heart of Rye town within the
conservation area and easy walking distance to local
pubs and restaurants, the accommodation is in a 16th
century house full of character with oak beams and an
inglenook.
Bedrooms enjoy either ensuite or private bathrooms
with four poster or canopied beds which are stylishly
and elegantly furnished.
Gourmet breakfasts are served in the Inglenook
breakfast room with a choice of full English breakfast
and continental breakfasts.
For guests use there is a pretty, south facing, patio
garden with furniture. Early booking is advised.
Rooms: 5 all ensuite 🛏 🚭
Pricing: Dbl £90 CC: Accepted Room facilities: 📺 ☕
Children: Welcome 5yrs min age 🍴

Saffron Walden, Essex

Crown House

★★ 🍴

Great Chesterford, Saffron Walden, Essex, CB10 1NY
Tel: 01799 530515 Fax: 01799 530683
Web: www.virtualhotels.com
Rooms: 18 all ensuite 🍴 🛏
Pricing: Sgl £55–69.50 Dbl £79.50–120 CC: Accepted
Room facilities: 📺 ☎ ☕ 📞
Access: ♿
Children: Welcome Dogs: Welcome
Licences: 🍸 Parking: Off-street and monitored
Directions: Close to M11 Junction 9, on B1383 (old
A11), 1 mile from Stump Cross roundabout.
See advert on next page

Sanderstead, Surrey

Le Meridien Selsdon Park & Golf course

★★★★ ®

Addington Road, Sanderstead, South Croydon,
Surrey, CR2 8YA
Tel: 0800 028 2840 Fax: 020 8651 6171
Email: selsdonpark@principalhotels.co.uk
Web: www.lemeridien.com
Rooms: 204 all ensuite 🍴 🖥 ⊗
Pricing: Sgl £120.95–141.95 Dbl £169.90–215.90
Dinner from £27 CC: Accepted
Room facilities: ▢ ☎ 🖥 ☕ Access: ♿ ♿
Conference: 27 meeting rooms (Thtr 350 max), 24hr-
delegate from £229, day-delegate rate from £79
Children: Welcome ♀ Dogs: Guide dogs only
Licences: ◈ ♦♦♦
Leisure: Indoor pool, Outdoor pool, Gym, Beauty salon,
Tennis, Golf
Parking: Off-street and monitored
Directions: On A2022 10 minutes from East Croydon
railway station, 20 minutes from M25 junction 6, 13
miles from central London.

Sandwich, Kent

Bell Hotel

★★★ ®

The Quay, Sandwich, Kent, CT13 9EF
Tel: 01304 613388 Fax: 01304 615308
Email: hotel@princes-leisure.co.uk
Web: www.princes-leisure.co.uk
Rooms: 33 all ensuite 🍴 ⊗
Pricing: Sgl £80–100 Dbl £105–155 Dinner from £15.95
CC: Accepted Room facilities: ▢ ☎ 🖥
Conference: 3 meeting rooms (Thtr 200 max), 24hr-
delegate from £86.50, day-delegate rate from £25.50
Children: Welcome ♀ ☕
Dogs: Welcome Licences: ♦♦♦
Parking: Off-street and monitored
Directions: Via M20/A20 to Dover then A258 to Sandwich.
See advert on this page

Sedlescombe, East Sussex

Brickwall Hotel

★★★ ®

The Green, Sedlescombe, East Sussex, TN33 0QA
Tel: 01424 870253 Fax: 01424 870785
Email: reception@brickwallhotel.totalserve.co.uk
Web: www.smoothhound.co.uk/hotels/brickwall.html
Rooms: 26 all ensuite 🍴 🖥 ⊗
Pricing: Sgl £60 Dbl £90 Dinner from £24
CC: Accepted
Room facilities: ▢ ☎ 🖥 Access: ♿
Conference: 1 meeting room (Thtr 40 max)
Children: Welcome ♀ ☕
Dogs: Welcome Licences: ♦♦♦
Leisure: Outdoor pool
Parking: Off-street
Directions: The Brickwall Hotel is situated in the village
of Sedlescombe on the B2244, 3 miles east of Battle.

The Crown House

The hotel is set in an elegant
Georgian building in the beautiful
award-winning village of Great
Chesterford, Essex "Village of the
Year 2002". A friendly, informal
atmosphere with a superb restaurant
and great rooms. Close to Duxford,
Newmarket and Cambridge.

**Great Chesterford,
Saffron Walden CB10 1NY**
Tel: 01799 530515 Fax: 01799 530683
Website: www.virtualhotels.com

The Bell Hotel

Situated in the heart of classic championship
golf links country, The Bell Hotel enjoys an
international reputation for its hospitality and
cuisine. Exclusive golf breaks combine the
traditional comforts of this 3-star hotel with
golf at the famous Prince's Golf Club.

The Quay, Sandwich, Kent CT13 9EF
Tel: 01304 613388   Fax: 01304 615308
hotel@princes-leisure.co.uk
www.princes-leisure.co.uk

Sevenoaks, Kent

No 4 Old Timbertop Cottages

◆ ◆ ◆ ◆

Bethel Road, Sevenoaks, Kent, TN13 3UE
Tel: 01732 460506 Fax: 01732 464484
Email: anthony@ruddassociates.co.uk
Seasonal closure: Christmas to New Year
Delightful self-contained cottage, sleeping 4. Twin bedroom, bath/shower, sitting-room with sofabed, TV, fully-fitted kitchen, patio garden and parking.
Pricing: 1 person £40, 2 persons £55, 3 persons £75, 4 persons £88; all include a self-serve continental breakfast (English breakfast: £5 pp extra).
Rooms: 1🚭
Children: Welcome Parking: Off-street
Directions: Directions will be given by e-mail, fax or telephone.

Bramber

◆ ◆ ◆

45 Shoreham Lane, Riverhead, Sevenoaks,
Kent, TN13 3DX
Tel: 01732 457466 Fax: 01732 457466
Rooms: 2🚭
Pricing: Sgl £24–26.50 Dbl £40–45
Room facilities:
Children: Welcome 7yrs min age
Parking: Off-street
Directions: A25 Riverhead roundabout towards Maidstone; up a slight incline, then turn first right; Bramber is the middle chalet bungalow and garage on the right.

Moorings Hotel

◆ ◆ ◆

97 Hitchen Hatch Lane, Sevenoaks, Kent, TN13 3BE
Tel: 01732 452589 Fax: 01732 456462
Email: theryans@mooringshotel.co.uk
Web: www.mooringshotel.co.uk
Rooms: 23 all ensuite 🍽 🚭
Pricing: Sgl £49–59 Dbl £73–83 Dinner from £7.50
CC: Accepted
Room facilities: Access: ♿
Conference: 1 meeting room (Thtr 12 max), 24hr-delegate from £90, day-delegate rate from £25
Children: Welcome ⅋ Dogs: Guide dogs only
Licences: ⅋⅋⅋
Parking: Off-street and monitored
Directions: Follow signs for Sevenoaks from M25 Junction 5. For one mile, head towards Sevenoaks and Riverhead. At the roundabout, turn right and after one mile turn left into Hitchen Hatch Lane opposite railway station.

Shaftesbury, Dorset

Ye Olde Wheelwrights

Birdbush, Ludwell, Shaftesbury, Dorset, SP7 9NH
Tel: 01747 828955
Rooms: 2🚭 Room facilities: 💻
Parking: Off-street
Directions: We are on the A30 3 miles East of Shaftesbury and 17 miles West of Salisbury.

Shepperton-On-Thames, Middlesex

Warren Lodge Hotel

★ ★ ★

Church Square, Shepperton, Middlesex, TW17 9JZ
Tel: 01932 242972 Fax: 01932 253883
Email: info@warrenlodgehotel.co.uk
Web: www.warrenlodgehotel.co.uk

Pretty riverside hotel with gardens and river terrace. Well-appointed bedrooms, some with river view. Good English and continental cuisine. Weekend rates available.
Rooms: 50 all ensuite 🍽
Pricing: Dinner from £16.95 CC: Accepted
Room facilities: 💻 ☎ 🚭
Children: Welcome Licences: ⅋⅋⅋
Parking: Off-street
Directions: From J11 M25 Chertsey, take B375 to Shepperton. At roundabout at bottom of High Street take sign for Church Square.

Shipton-Under-Wychwood, Oxfordshire

The Lamb Inn

◆ ◆ ◆ ◆ ◆ ® ✗

Shipton-under-Wychwood, Oxon, OX7 6DQ
Tel: 01993 830465 Fax: 01993 832025
Email: info@thelambinn.net
Web: www.thelambinn.net
Rooms: 5 all ensuite 📺 🚭
Pricing: Sgl £119–149 Dbl £119–149 Dinner from £15
CC: Accepted Room facilities: 💻 ☎ 🚭 ⬈
Conference: 1 meeting room (Thtr 20 max), 24hr-delegate from £163
Children: Welcome Dogs: Welcome
Licences: ⅋⅋⅋ Parking: Off-street and monitored
Directions: 50 yds off the main A361 Banbury to Burford road at Shipton-under-Wychwood 4 miles northeast of Burford.

Sittingbourne, Kent

Hempstead House

♦ ♦ ♦ ♦ ♦

London Road, Bapchild, Sittingbourne, Kent, ME9 9PP
Tel: 01795 428020 Fax: 01795 436362
Email: info@hempsteadhouse.co.uk
Web: www.hempsteadhouse.co.uk
Rooms: 15 all ensuite
Pricing: Sgl £75 Dbl £85 Dinner from £19.50
CC: Accepted Room facilities:
Conference: 2 meeting rooms (Thtr 70 max)
Children: Welcome Dogs: Welcome
Licences: Leisure: Outdoor pool
Parking: Off-street
Directions: 1½ miles east of Sittingbourne along main A2.
See advert on this page

Beaumont

♦ ♦ ♦

74 London Road, Sittingbourne, Kent, ME10 1NS
Tel: 01795 472536 Fax: 01795 425921
Email: info@thebeaumont.co.uk
Web: www.thebeaumont.co.uk
Rooms: 9 (7 ensuite)
Pricing: Sgl £35–55 Dbl £55–70 CC: Accepted
Room facilities: Access:
Children: Welcome Dogs: Welcome
Licences: Parking: Off-street
Directions: From M2 or M20, take A249 north towards
Sheerness. Take A2 exit, turn right at roundabout and
follow A2 for 1 mile towards Sittingbourne.

Slough, Berkshire

Copthorne Hotel Slough Windsor

★ ★ ★ ★

Cippenham Lane, Slough, Berkshire, SL1 2YE
Tel: 01753 516222 Fax: 01753 516237
Email: sales.slough@mill-cop.com
Web: www.millenniumhotels.com

This hotel is situated just 15 minutes drive form
London Heathrow airport. Enjoy a meal in the Veranda
restaurant with views of Windsor castle. Weekend rates
are also available.
Rooms: 219 all ensuite
Pricing: Sgl £195.25 Dbl £210.50 Dinner from £23.75
CC: Accepted
Room facilities: ❄ Access:
Conference: 9 meeting rooms (Thtr 250 max), 24hr-
delegate from £195, day-delegate rate from £65

Hempstead House

• Private Victorian Country House Hotel set in
three acres of beautifully landscaped gardens.
• Individually designed luxurious guest suites.
• Award winning restaurant serving classic
English and French cuisine.
• Spacious, elegant reception and
conference rooms.
• Outdoor heated swimming pool
and floodlit terraces.

RƎC ♦ ♦ ♦ ♦ ♦

London Road, Bapchild,
Sittingbourne, Kent ME9 9PP
Tel: 01795 428020 Fax: 01795 436362
Email: info@hempsteadhouse.co.uk
Website: www.hempsteadhouse.co.uk

Children: Welcome Dogs: Guide dogs only
Licences: Leisure: Indoor pool, Gym,
Health spa, Beauty salon
Parking: Off-street and monitored
Directions: Exit M4 J6. Follow A355 Slough. Turn left at
roundabout. The hotel is on the left.

Upton Park Guest House

♦ ♦ ♦

41 Upton Park, Slough, Berkshire, SL1 2DA
Tel: 01753 528797 Fax: 01753 550208

Sonning-on-Thames, Berkshire

The Great House at Sonning

★ ★ ★

Thames Street, Sonnng-on-Thames, Nr. Reading,
Berkshire, RG4 6UT
Tel: 0118 969 2277 Fax: 0118 944 1296
Email: greathouse@btconnect.com
Web: www.greathouseatsonning.co.uk
Rooms: 49 all ensuite Pricing: Sgl £64.50–149
Dbl £99–165 Dinner from £28 CC: Accepted
Room facilities: Conference: 7 meeting rooms
(Thtr 100 max), 24hr-delegate from £179, day-delegate
rate from £51.50 Children: Welcome
Dogs: Welcome Licences: Leisure: Tennis
Parking: Off-street and monitored
Directions: From A4 take B378 into village over mini
roundabout, turn right before bridge into car park.
See advert on following page

Southeast

Southampton, Hampshire

Botleigh Grange Hotel

★★★★ ♛ ♛

Hedge End, Southampton, Hampshire, SO30 2GA
Tel: 01489 787700 Fax: 01489 788535
Email: enquiries@botleighgrangehotel.co.uk
Web: www.botleighgrangehotel.co.uk
Rooms: 59
Pricing: Sgl £90 CC: accepted
Dogs: Welcome
Parking: Off-street
Directions: From M27 follow A334 to Botleigh; we are 1 mile on the left.

Elizabeth House Hotel

★★

42–44 The Avenue, Southampton,
Hampshire, SO17 1XP
Tel: 023 8022 4327 Fax: 023 8022 4327
Email: mail@elizabethhousehotel.com
Web: www.elizabethhousehotel.com
Rooms: 28 all ensuite ☕
Pricing: Sgl £47.50 Dbl £57.50
Dinner from £8 CC: Accepted
Room facilities: ▢ ☎ ☕ Access: ♿
Conference: 1 meeting room (Thtr 40 max), 24hr-delegate from £80, day-delegate rate from £20
Children: Welcome ⑂ Dogs: Welcome
Licences: ♨ Parking: Off-street
Directions: From M3, take A33 towards town centre. Hotel on left after common but before main traffic lights.

Acacia Lodge Guest House

♦ ♦ ♦

Providence Hill, Bursledon, Southampton,
Hampshire, SO31 8AT
Tel: 023 8056 1155 Fax: 023 8056 1161
Email: petekenway@aol.com
Rooms: 5 all ensuite ⊗
Pricing: Sgl £35 Dbl £50
Room facilities: ▢ ☕
Access: ♿
Children: Welcome
Parking: Off-street
Directions: Exit J8 M27; follow signs for Southampton East and Hamble. Take first exit off roundabout.

Landguard Lodge

♦ ♦ ♦ ♦

21 Landguard Road, Southampton,
Hampshire, SO15 5DL
Tel: 023 8063 6904 Fax: 023 8063 2258
Email: landguardlodge@141.com
Web: www.landguardlodge.co.uk
Rooms: 10 all ensuite ⊗
Room facilities: ▢ ☕
Children: Welcome 5yrs min age
Parking: Off-street
Directions: North of railway station, between Hill Lane and Shirley Road.

Hunters Lodge Hotel

25 Landguard Road, Shirley, Southampton,
Hampshire, SO15 5DL
Tel: 02380 227919 Fax: 02380 230913
Email: hunterslodge.hotel@virgin.net
Web: hunterslodgehotel.net
Rooms: 14 all ensuite
Pricing: Sgl £35–45 Dbl £55–55 CC: Accepted
Room facilities: ▢ ☎ ☕
Children: Welcome ♫ ☾
Dogs: Welcome
Licences: ▮▮▮
Parking: Off-street and monitored
Directions: North of railway station, down Hill Lane, 4th
left half way down Landguard Road.

Travelodge Southampton (SA)

Travel Accommodation
A33, 144 Lodge Road, Southampton,
Hampshire, SO14 6QR
Web: www.travelodge.co.uk
Rooms: 59 all ensuite
Pricing: Sgl £59.40 Dbl £63.85
CC: Accepted Room facilities: ▢ ☕ Access: ♿

Southend-on-Sea, Essex

Balmoral Hotel

★ ★

32–36 Valkyrie Road, Westcliff-on-Sea, Essex, SS0 8BU
Tel: 01702 342947 Fax: 01702 337828
Email: enquiries@balmoralsouthend.com
Web: www.balmoralsouthend.com
Rooms: 32 all ensuite
Pricing: Sgl £48–68 Dbl £74–190 Dinner from £9.95
CC: Accepted
Room facilities: ▢ ☎ ☕
Access: ♿
Children: Welcome ♫
Dogs: Welcome
Licences: ▮▮▮
Parking: Off-street and monitored
Directions: We can send a location map on request.
Easy access from the A127 and the A13
See advert on this page

Mayflower Hotel

◆ ◆ ◆

6 Royal Terrace, Southend-on-Sea, Essex, SS1 1DY
Tel: 01702 340489
Seasonal closure: Christmas
Rooms: 23 (8 ensuite)
Pricing: Sgl £28.85 Dbl £39.95 CC: Accepted
Room facilities: ▢ ☕
Children: Welcome ♫
Dogs: Welcome
Leisure: Games room
Directions: Along sea front to pier; up pier hill into
Royal Terrace; The Mayflower Hotel is on the right side.

Terrace Hotel

◆ ◆ ◆ ☟

8 Royal Terrace, Southend-on-Sea, Essex, SS1 1DY
Tel: 01702 348143 Fax: 01702 348143
Seasonal closure: Christmas
Rooms: 9 (3 ensuite) ☕ ▨
Pricing: Sgl £25.85–39.95 Dbl £39.95–49.35
Room facilities: ▢ ☕
Children: Welcome
Dogs: Welcome
Licences: ▮▮▮
Directions: Royal Terrace is a one-way street and can
only be approached by vehicle along the seafront via
Pier Hill.

Tower Hotel and Restaurant

◆ ◆ ◆

146 Alexandra Road, Southend-on-Sea, Essex, SS1 1HE
Tel: 01702 348635 Fax: 01702 433044
Email: tower.rest@virgin.net
Rooms: 32 (31 ensuite)
Room facilities: ▢ ☎ ☕
Access: ♿
Children: Welcome
Dogs: Welcome
Licences: ▮▮▮
Directions: Turn off A13 into Milton Road, turn left into
Cambridge Road and take third right at mini-
roundabout into Wilson Road. Hotel on right at
crossroads.

Balmoral Hotel

Located in a quiet area of Westcliff-on-Sea, the
Balmoral Hotel offers the discerning business
traveller quality accommodation, high levels of
comfort and service in an environment that is
friendly and welcoming. Ideally positioned for
central Southend and its many commercial areas,
the hotel also offers fully enclosed
off-street parking, cable TV, ensuite rooms,
24-hour room service, exclusive à la carte or
simple table d'hôte menus, and is within easy
reach of major local leisure facilities.

**32–36 Valkyrie Road, Westcliff-on-Sea,
Essex SS0 8BU**
Tel: 01702 342947   Fax: 01702 337828
Email: enq@balmoralsouthend.com
Web: balmoralsouthend.com

Southeast

Regency Hotel

♦ ♦

The White House, 18 Royal Terrace, Southend-on-Sea,
Essex, SS1 1DU
Tel: 01702 340747
Seasonal closure: Nov-Dec
Rooms: 10 (8 ensuite) Pricing: Sgl £20–30 Dbl £30–50
CC: Accepted Room facilities: 💻 🖘
Children: Welcome ♫ Licences: ⚙
Directions: Follow seafront signs, turn right towards
pier, just before pier cross over roundabout and up pier
hill to Royal Terrace.

The Gleneagles Hotel

❖

5-6 Clifftown Parade, Southend-on-Sea, Essex, SS1 1DP
Tel: 01702 333635 Fax: 01702 332207
Web: www.thegleneagleshotel.co.uk
Rooms: 16 (10 ensuite) ❀
Pricing: Sgl £25–30 Dbl £45–60 CC: Accepted
Room facilities: 💻 🖘
Children: Welcome Dogs: Guide dogs only
Parking: Off-street and monitored
Directions: Follow A127 (Victoria Avenue) into
Southend, right at Victoria Plaza roundabout, 2nd left
into Princess Street, then phone.

St Albans, Hertfordshire

Sopwell House Hotel, Country Club & Spa

★ ★ ★ ★ 🏵 🏵 🏵

Cottonmill Lane, Sopwell, St Albans,
Hertfordshire, AL1 2HQ
Tel: 01727 864477 Fax: 01727 844741
Email: enquiries@sopwellhouse.co.uk
Web: www.sopwellhouse.co.uk

Set within 12 acres of grounds, this country house
hotel is the former home of Lord Mountbatten and
retains many original Georgian features. Ideal for
leisure breaks, conferences or weddings.
Rooms: 128 all ensuite 🖶
Pricing: Sgl £137.95–140 Dbl £190.90–250
Dinner from £15.50 CC: Accepted
Room facilities: 💻 ☎ 🖘 📞 Access: ⚿ ♿
Conference: 21 meeting rooms (Thtr 450 max), 24hr-
delegate from £199, day-delegate rate from £62
Children: Welcome ♫ Dogs: Guide dogs only
Licences: 🔔 ⚙

Leisure: Indoor pool, Gym, Health Spa,
Beauty salon Parking: Off-street and monitored
Directions: M25 jct J22, follow A1081 St Albans, left at
"Grill Bar" / traffic lights, over mini–roundabout into
Cottonmill Lane.

Quality Hotel St Albans

★ ★ ★

232-236 London Road, St Albans,
Hertfordshire, AL1 1JQ
Tel: 01727 857858 Fax: 01727 855666
Email: st.albans@quality-hotels.net
Web: www.stalbans-hotels.co.uk
Rooms: 43 all ensuite ❀ 🖶 ⊗
Pricing: Sgl £49–95 Dbl £69–110 Dinner from £14.25
CC: Accepted
Room facilities: 💻 ☎ 🖘
Conference: 4 meeting rooms (Thtr 200 max), 24hr-
delegate from £135, day-delegate rate from £32
Children: Welcome ♫ Dogs: Guide dogs only
Licences: ⚙ Parking: Off-street
Directions: Leave M25 at Junction 22. Follow A1081 to
St Albans. After 3 miles, hotel is on left-hand side.

St Michael's Manor   Blue Ribbon Winner

★ ★ ★ ★ 🏵 🏵 🏵

Fishpool Street, St Albans, Hertfordshire, AL3 4RY
Tel: 01727 864444 Fax: 01727 848909
Email: smmanor@globalnet.co.uk
Web: www.stmichaelsmanor.com
Rooms: 22 all ensuite 🖶 ⊗
Pricing: Sgl £120–130 Dbl £120–280 Dinner from
£37.50 CC: Accepted
Room facilities: 💻 ☎ 🖘 📞
Conference: 3 meeting rooms (Thtr 30 max), 24hr-
delegate from £205, day-delegate rate from £52
Children: Welcome ♫ ⚘
Licences: 🔔 ⚙
Parking: Off-street and monitored
Directions: Leave M25 at Junction 21a. Go through
Chiswell Gn. Turn left at King Harry pub and right at
roundabout. Past Waitrose, turn right again at next
roundabout and next right then left.
See advert on next page

Ardmore House Hotel

♦ ♦ ♦

54 Lemsford Road, St Albans, Hertfordshire, AL1 3PR
Tel: 01727 859313 Fax: 01727 859313
Email: info@ardmorehousehotel.co.uk
Web: www.ardmorehousehotel.altodigital.co.uk
Rooms: 40 all ensuite ❀ 🖶 ⊗
Room facilities: 💻 ☎ 🖘
Children: Welcome ♫ ⚘
Licences: 🔔 ⚙
Parking: Off-street and monitored
Directions: M25 Junction 22, A1081 to St Albans. At
London Colney roundabout, take A1081 (London
Road). Through two sets of traffic lights: right at
second mini-roundabout. Hotel 800 yards on right.
See advert on next page

Staines, Middlesex

The Thames Lodge

★★★★

Thames Street, Staines, Middlesex, TW18 4SJ
Tel: 0870 400 8121 Fax: 01784 454858
Email: thameslodge@heritage-hotel.co.uk
Web: www.macdonaldhotels.co.uk
Rooms: 78 all ensuite ⊗
Pricing: Sgl £54 Dbl £108 CC: Accepted
Room facilities: ▢ ☎ ⊿ ⌗
Access: ⟐
Conference: 18 meeting rooms (Thtr 50 max)
Children: Welcome ⼌ ☽
Dogs: Welcome
Licences: ⼝⼝⼝
Parking: Off-street and monitored
Directions: Leave M25 at junction 13. Take A30 to
London. At Crooked Billet roundabout, follow signs for
Staines town centre.

Travelodge Staines

Travel Accommodation
Two Rivers, Staines
Web: www.travelodge.co.uk
Room facilities: ▢ ⊿

Stansted Airport

Stansted Manor Hotel

★★★

Birchanger Lane, Birchanger, Nr Bishop's Stratford,
Essex, CM23 5ST
Tel: 01279 859800 Fax: 01279 467245
Email: info@stanstedmanor-hotel.co.uk
Web: www.stanstedmanor-hotel.co.uk

Rooms: 70 all ensuite ⛱ ⊗
Pricing: Sgl £110.95 Dbl £125.95 CC: Accepted
Room facilities: ▢ ☎ ⊿ ⌗
Access: ⼁⼁ ⟐
Conference: 1 meeting room (Thtr 36 max), 24hr-
delegate from £145, day-delegate rate from £45
Children: Welcome ⼌
Parking: Off-street and monitored

Vintage Court Hotel

 ★★★

Vintage Corner, Puckeridge, near Ware,
Hertfordshire, SG11 1SA
Tel: 01920 822722 Fax: 01920 822877
Rooms: 30 all ensuite
Pricing: Sgl £67.95 (2002 rate) Dbl £76.90 (2002 rate)
Dinner from £19.95 (2002 rate) CC: Accepted
Room facilities:
Children: Welcome
Dogs: Welcome
Licences:
Leisure: Snooker/billiards
Parking: Off-street

Steyning, West Sussex

The Old Tollgate Restaurant and Hotel

 ★★★

The Street, Bramber, Steyning,
West Sussex, BN44 3WE
Tel: 01903 879494 Fax: 01903 813399
Email: otr@fastnet.co.uk
Web: www.oldtollgatehotel.com
Rooms: 31 all ensuite
Pricing: Sgl £82.95–132.95 Dbl £90.90–140.90
Dinner from £21.95 CC: Accepted
Room facilities:
Access:
Conference: 7 meeting rooms (Thtr 50 max)
Children: Welcome
Dogs: Guide dogs only
Licences:
Parking: Off-street
Directions: From A24 or A27, take A283 signposted to
Steyning, then follow signposts to Bramber. Brown
tourist signs advertise hotel.

Penfold Gallery Guest House

Little Gem

 ♦♦♦♦♦

30 High Street, Steyning, West Sussex, BN44 3GG
Tel: 01903 815595 Fax: 01903 816686
Email: johnturner57@cs.com
Web: artyguesthouse.co.uk

A medieval dwelling full of architectural interest, the
Penfold Gallery has the beautiful backdrop of the
South Downs. Personal attention to all guests. Creative
cooking. Non-smoking.

Rooms: 3 all ensuite
Pricing: Sgl £49 Dbl £78 Dinner from £24
CC: Accepted
Room facilities:
Children: Welcome 12yrs min age
Directions: Leave A27 at junction with A283 and follow
signs to Steyning. The Penfold Gallery Guest House is
east of the mini-roundabout in the High Street.

Springwells Hotel

♦♦♦♦

9 High Street, Steyning, West Sussex, BN44 3GG
Tel: 01903 812446 Fax: 01903 879823
Email: contact@springwells.co.uk
Web: www.springwells.co.uk
Seasonal closure: Christmas to New Year

A former Georgian Merchant House in a picturesque
village. All rooms are individually furnished with TV and
telephone; the bar and adjoining conservatory lead to a
patio and outdoor heated swimming pool.
Rooms: 11 (9 ensuite)
Pricing: Sgl £34–49 Dbl £58–93 CC: Accepted
Room facilities:
Conference: 20 meeting rooms (Thtr 30 max)
Children: Welcome
Dogs: Welcome
Licences:
Leisure: Outdoor pool
Parking: Off-street
Directions: From M25 take A24 at Washington turn
onto A283 for 3 miles. Turn right into town, Springwells
is on the right.

Stockbridge, Hampshire

Carbery Guest House

◆◆◆

Salisbury Hill, Stockbridge, Hampshire, SO20 6EZ
Tel: 01264 810771 Fax: 01264 811022
Seasonal closure: 3 weeks around Christmas

Carbery Guest House is 2 minutes' walk from the old
market village of Stockbridge overlooking the River
Test in one acre of landscaped gardens.
Rooms: 11 (8 ensuite)
Pricing: Sgl £30–37 Dbl £52–56 Dinner from £14.50
CC: Accepted Room facilities: ☐ ᠔
Children: Welcome Licences: ♦♦♦
Leisure: Outdoor pool, Snooker/billiards
Parking: Off-street
Directions: Hotel at Salisbury end of Stockbridge on A30.

Stokenchurch, Buckinghamshire

Kings Arms Hotel

★★★

Oxford Road, Stokenchurch, Buckinghamshire, HP14 3TA
Tel: 01494 609090 Fax: 01494 484582
Rooms: £69 Pricing: Sgl £85 CC: accepted

Stoney Cross, Hampshire

Travelodge New Forest, Stoney Cross

Travel Accommodation
A31, Westbound, Stoney Cross, Hampshire, SO43 7GN
Web: www.travelodge.co.uk
Rooms: 32 all ensuite ⊛
Pricing: Sgl £59.40 Dbl £63.85
CC: Accepted Room facilities: ☐ ᠔ Access: ♿

Streatley-on-Thames, Berkshire

The Swan at Streatley

★★★★★ ⟐ ⟐

Streatley-on-Thames, Berkshire, RG8 9HR
Tel: 01491 878800 Fax: 01491 872554
Email: sales@swan-at-streatley.co.uk
Web: www.swan-at-streatley.co.uk
Rooms: 46 all ensuite ⊛ ⊠ ⊛
Pricing: Sgl £95–125 Dbl £130–190 Dinner from £24.50
CC: Accepted Room facilities: ☐ ☎ ᠔ ⚲ Access: ♿
Conference: 5 meeting rooms (Thtr 120 max), 24hr-
delegate from £180, day-delegate rate from £65

Children: Welcome ♁ Dogs: Welcome Licences: ⚱ ♦♦♦
Leisure: Indoor pool, Gym, Beauty salon
Parking: Off-street and monitored
Directions: Leave M4 at Junction 12, take exit towards
Theale, then take A340 to Pangbourne. Once there
take A329 to Streatley.

The Bull at Streatley

◆◆◆

Reading Road, Streatley, Reading, Berkshire, RG8 9JJ
Tel: 01491 872392 Fax: 01491 875231
Email: bull.streatley@eldridge-pope.co.uk
Rooms: 6 all ensuite ⊠ ⊛
Pricing: Sgl £60 Dbl £70 Dinner from £7.95
CC: Accepted Room facilities: ☐ ☎ ᠔ ⚲ Access: ♿
Children: Welcome ♁ Dogs: Welcome
Licences: ♦♦♦ Parking: Off-street
Directions: On the junction of A329 and B4009 in
Streatley.

Surbiton, Surrey

Pembroke Lodge Guest House

◆◆◆ ✎

35 Cranes Park, Surbiton, Surrey, KT5 8AB
Tel: 020 8399 8636 Fax: 020 8390 0731
Rooms: 6⚲ ⊛ Room facilities: ☐ ᠔
Children: Welcome ♁ Dogs: Welcome Parking: Off-street

Sutton, Surrey

Thatched House Hotel

★★

135 Cheam Road, Sutton, Surrey, SM1 2BN
Tel: 020 8642 3131 Fax: 020 8770 0684
Rooms: 32 (29 ensuite) ⊠
Pricing: Dinner from £13.50 (2002 rate) CC: Accepted
Room facilities: ☐ ☎ ᠔ Children: Welcome ♁ ⚮
Dogs: Guide dogs only Licences: ♦♦♦ Parking: Off-street
Directions: Leave M25 at Junction 8. Follow A217
towards Sutton. At junction with A232, turn right. Hotel
is 500 yards on right, before town centre.

Eaton Court Hotel

◆◆

49 Eaton Road, Sutton, Surrey, SM2 5ED
Tel: 020 8643 6766 Fax: 020 8642 4580
Email: manager@eatoncourthotel.co.uk
Web: www.eatoncourthotel.co.uk
Seasonal closure: 2 weeks over Christmas
Rooms: 13 (8 ensuite) ⚲ ⊛ Pricing: Sgl £38–59
Dbl £55–90 CC: Accepted Room facilities: ☐ ☎ ᠔
Conference: 1 meeting room (Thtr 20 max), 24hr-
delegate from £1, day-delegate rate from £500
Children: Welcome 3yrs min age Licences: ♦♦♦
Parking: Off-street
Directions: Leave M25 at Junction 8. Take A217 to
Sutton, then B2230. Take first right after BP filling
station into Cedar Road. Turn right into Eaton Road
and hotel is number 49.

Swanley, Kent

Hillview Guest House

◆ ◆ ◆ ◆

Wood Street, Swanley Village, Kent, BR8 8DX
Tel: 01322 666612
Rooms: 3 (2 ensuite) 🐾 📺 ⊘
Room facilities: ▢ 🍵
Children: Welcome ᚻ
Dogs: Guide dogs only
Leisure: Riding
Parking: Off-street and monitored
Directions: Exit J3 M25 A20, follow signs to Brands Hatch. Second left into Button Street; at T-junction turn left, then first left.

Sway, Hampshire

The Nurse's Cottage   Little Gem

◆ ◆ ◆ ◆ ◆ ◆ 🍴 🍴 ⋇ 🍷

Station Road, Sway, Lymington, Hampshire, SO41 6BA
Tel: 01590 683402 Fax: 01590 683402
Email: nurses.cottage@lineone.net
Web: www.nursescottage.co.uk
Seasonal closure: 2 weeks in March, 3 in November.

One of the New Forest's most highly acclaimed guest accommodations, selected universally by the UK's leading hospitality guides. Open to non-residents for breakfast, afternoon tea, dinner and Sunday luncheon. Booking essential.
Rooms: 3 all ensuite ⊘
Pricing: Sgl £62.50–72.50 Dbl £105
Dinner from £18.25 CC: Accepted
Room facilities: ▢ ☎ 🍵 🍵
Conference: 1 meeting room (Thtr 29 max), 24hr-delegate from £95, day-delegate rate from £25
Children: Welcome 10yrs min age
Dogs: Welcome Licences: ⋔
Parking: Off-street
Directions: Off B3055 in village centre, next to Post Office.
See advert on next page

Making a booking?

Don't forget to mention RAC Hotels and Bed & Breakfast 2003.

Swindon, Wiltshire

Cricklade Hotel & Country Club

★ ★ ★ ★ 🍴 🍴

Common Hill, Cricklade, Swindon, Wiltshire, SN6 6HA
Tel: 01793 750751 Fax: 01793 751767
Email: sharon@crickladehotel.fsnet.co.uk
Web: www.crickladehotel.co.uk
Rooms: 46 📺
Pricing: Sgl £105 CC: accepted
Leisure: Indoor swimming, Gym, Health spa, Beauty salon, Tennis, Golf, Games room, Snooker/billiards,
Parking: Off-street
Directions: Leave M4 at junction 15 and take the A419 towards Cirencester. After approx. 8 miles turn left to Cricklade, then follow the B4040 towards Malmesbury.

Taplow, Berkshire

Cliveden House   Gold Ribbon Winner

★ ★ ★ ★ ★ 🍴 🍴 🍴

Taplow, Berkshire, SL6 0JF
Tel: 01628 668561 Fax: 01628 661837
Email: reservations@clivedenhouse.co.uk
Web: www.clivedenhouse.co.uk

Set in 376 acres of the National Trust's finest gardens, a mere 20 minutes from Heathrow, 40 minutes from central London, Cliveden boasts 39 magnificent bedrooms, the Michelin-starred Waldo's and the terrace dining room, the beautiful pavillion spa, vintage launches, a championship golf course and the Lambourne Club.
Rooms: 39 all ensuite 🐾 📺 ⊘
Pricing: Dbl £190–495 Dinner from £42 CC: Accepted
Room facilities: ▢ ☎ 🍵
Access: ⏏
Conference: 2 meeting rooms (Thtr 40 max), 24hr-delegate from £375, day-delegate rate from £95
Children: Welcome ᚻ ⋇
Dogs: Welcome
Licences: ⟁ ⋔
Leisure: Indoor pool, Outdoor pool, Gym, Health spa, Beauty salon, Tennis, Golf, Snooker/billiards
Parking: Off-street and monitored
Directions: From Junction 7 of M4, follow brown National Trust signs to Taplow. From M40 Junction 2, follow signs to Taplow.

Thame, Oxfordshire

Spread Eagle Hotel

★★★★

16 Cornmarket, Thame, Oxfordshire, OX9 2BR
Tel: 01844 213661 Fax: 01844 261380
Email: enquiries@spreadeaglehotelthame.co.uk
Web: www.spreadeaglehotelthame.co.uk

Carefully-modernised former coaching inn, set in town centre. Large car park. Good centre for visiting Oxford and the Vale of Aylesbury. Hospitality is the speciality.
Rooms: 33 all ensuite 🐾 🖼
Pricing: Sgl £99.95–115.95 Dbl £115.95–139.95
Dinner from £25 CC: Accepted
Room facilities: 🖳 ☎ 🗂 ⤵ Access: ⚹
Children: Welcome 🍴 🎏 Dogs: Guide dogs only
Licences: ⚘ ⛉ Parking: Off-street and monitored
Directions: In town centre of Thame, on A418 between Aylesbury and Oxford. Leave M49 at Junction 6 southbound, Junction 8 northbound. Car park at rear of hotel.

Toddington, Bedfordshire

Travelodge Toddington, Luton North (MOTO)

Travel Accommodation
M1, Moto Service Area, Toddington, Bedfordshire, LU5 6HR
Web: www.travelodge.co.uk
Rooms: 66 all ensuite 🐾
Pricing: Sgl £47.40–64.40 Dbl £51.85–68.85
CC: Accepted Room facilities: 🖳 🗂 Access: ⚹

Tonbridge, Kent

Langley Hotel

★★

18–20 London Road, Tonbridge, Kent, TN10 3DA
Tel: 01732 353311 Fax: 01732 771471
Email: langley.hotel@virgin.net
Web: www.smoothhound.co.uk/hotels/langley
Rooms: 34 all ensuite
Pricing: Sgl £70 Dbl £70–90 CC: Accepted
Room facilities: 🖳 ☎ 🗂 Access: ⛉
Conference: 2 meeting rooms (Thtr 60 max), 24hr-delegate from £130, day-delegate rate from £30
Children: Welcome 🎏
Dogs: Guide dogs only Licences: ⚘ ⛉
Parking: Off-street
Directions: Leave M25 at Junction 5 and take A21 southbound, then B245 through Hildenborough. Hotel is on left as you approach Tonbridge.

Southeast

Tring, Hertfordshire

Pendley Manor

★★★★

Cow Lane, Tring, Hertfordshire, HP23 5QY
Tel: 01442 891891 Fax: 01442 890687
Email: info@pendley-manor.co.uk
Web: www.pendley-manor.co.uk
Grade II Listed luxury country house hotel, 71 bedrooms, many with four-poster beds. Excellent conference facilities, all meeting rooms have natural light. Award-winning restaurant with new magnificent leisure complex.
Rooms: 74 all ensuite
Pricing: Sgl £110–130 Dbl £140–160 Dinner from £30
CC: Accepted
Room facilities:
Access:
Conference: 20 meeting rooms (Thtr 300 max), 24hr-delegate from £230, day-delegate rate from £68
Children: Welcome
Dogs: Welcome
Licences:
Leisure: Indoor pool, Gym, Health spa, Tennis, Snooker/billiards
Parking: Off-street and monitored
Directions: M25 Jct 20 take A41 Aylesbury from Tring, exit, join A4251 Berkhamsted (200m), first left, Cow Lane, Pendley Manor on right-hand side.

Old Forge

◆◆◆◆

5 High Street, Ivinghoe, Leighton Buzzard, Berkshire, LU7 9EP
Tel: 01296 668122 Fax: 01296 668122
Rooms: 6 all ensuite
Room facilities:
Access:
Children: Welcome 6yrs min age
Parking: Off-street and monitored
Directions: Situated less than 30 minutes from the M1 motorway (Junctions 8 or 11). Five minutes from Tring railway station.

Tunbridge Wells, Kent

Royal Wells Inn Hotel

★★★

Mount Ephraim, Tunbridge Wells, Kent, TN4 8BE
Tel: 01892 511188 Fax: 01892 511908
Email: info@royalwells.co.uk
Web: www.royalwells.co.uk
Rooms: 18 all ensuite
Pricing: Sgl £55–85 Dbl £85–120 Dinner from £21.50
CC: Accepted
Room facilities:
Access:
Conference: 3 meeting rooms (Thtr 80 max), 24hr-delegate from £104.50, day-delegate rate from £32.50
Children: Welcome
Dogs: Welcome Licences:
Parking: Off-street and monitored
Directions: Junctions M25 join A21 forth exit take A26 Tunbridge Wells keep straight to junction A264 Royal Wells 100 meters on right.

Spa Hotel

★★★★

Mount Ephraim, Tunbridge Wells, Kent, TN4 8XJ
Tel: 01892 520331 Fax: 01892 510575
Email: info@spahotel.co.uk
Web: www.spahotel.co.uk
Rooms: 71 all ensuite
Pricing: Sgl £99.95–109.25 Dbl £132.50–187.50
Dinner from £25 CC: Accepted
Room facilities:
Access:
Conference: 6 meeting rooms (Thtr 300 max), 24hr-delegate from £130, day-delegate rate from £39
Children: Welcome
Dogs: Guide dogs only
Licences:
Leisure: Indoor pool, Gym, Beauty salon, Tennis, Riding
Parking: Monitored
Directions: Leave M25 at Junction 5 and join A21. Take fourth exit for A26 Tunbridge Wells. Fork right onto A264. Hotel is ½ a mile on right.
See advert on next page

Russell Hotel

★★

80 London Road, Tunbridge Wells, Kent, TN1 1DZ
Tel: 01892 544833 Fax: 01892 515846
Email: sales@russell-hotel.com
Web: www.russell-hotel.com
Rooms: 24 all ensuite
Pricing: Sgl £70–85 Dbl £85–99 CC: Accepted
Room facilities:
Access: Conference: 12 meeting rooms
Children: Welcome
Dogs: Guide dogs only
Licences:
Parking: Off-street and monitored
Directions: In the centre of Tunbridge Wells, opposite the common on the main London Road.

Summit Hotel

◆ ◆ ◆ ◆ ◆ ※

57 Mount Ephraim, Tunbridge Wells, Kent, TN4 8BB
Tel: 01892 522 225 Fax: 01892 523 233
Email: enquires@thesummithotel.co.uk
Web: www.summithotel.co.uk

Elegant town house hotel overlooking the Royal Spa town, interestingly different and very comfortable, surrounded by good food and drink establishments.
Rooms: 10 all ensuite 🛏 Ⓢ
Pricing: Sgl £95–115 Dbl £115–175 Dinner from £15
CC: Accepted Room facilities: ☐ ☎ 🕭 ☎
Conference: 2 meeting rooms (Thtr 8 max)
Children: Welcome Dogs: Guide dogs only
Licences: ♦♦♦ Parking: Off-street and monitored
Directions: On Mount Ephraim, overlooking the spa centre (A264).

Uckfield, East Sussex

Hooke Hall

◆ ◆ ◆ ◆ ◆

250 High Street, Uckfield, East Sussex, TN22 1EN
Tel: 01825 761578 Fax: 01825 768025
Email: a.percy@virgin.net
Web: www.hookehall.co.uk
Seasonal closure: Christmas/New Year
Rooms: 10 all ensuite 🛏 🛏
Pricing: Sgl £55–95 Dbl £82–140 CC: Accepted
Room facilities: ☐ ☎ 🕭 ☎
Children: Welcome 12yrs min age 🐴 ☕
Licences: ♦♦♦ Parking: Off-street
Directions: Hooke Hall is at the northern end of the High Street, set back from the road.

Wallingford, Oxfordshire

George Hotel

★ ★ ★ ☖

High Street, Wallingford, Oxfordshire, OX10 0BS
Tel: 01491 836665 Fax: 01491 825359
Email: info@george-hotel-wallingford.com
Web: www.george-hotel-wallingford.com
Rooms: 39 all ensuite 🛏 Ⓢ
Pricing: Sgl £52–110 Dbl £82–135 Dinner from £17.50
CC: Accepted Room facilities: ☐ ☎ 🕭 Access: ♿
Conference: 3 meeting rooms (Thtr 120 max), 24hr-delegate from £135, day-delegate rate from £39
Children: Welcome 🛏 ☕ Dogs: Guide dogs only

Licences: ♿ ♦♦♦ Parking: Off-street and monitored
Directions: M4 (junction 12) – 13 miles, follow A34 then A4130. M40 (junction 6) – 8 miles, follow A329. Cholsey rail station 1½ miles, Didcot Rail Station 6 miles. Heathrow 35 miles.

Springs Hotel + Golf Club

★ ★ ★ ★ ☖ ☖

Wallingford Road, North Stoke, Wallingford, Oxfordshire, OX10 6BE
Tel: 01491 836687 Fax: 01491 836877
Email: info@thespringshotel.com
Web: www.thespringshotel.com
Rooms: 31 all ensuite 🛏 🛏 Ⓢ
Pricing: Sgl £90–120 Dbl £110–130 Dinner from £25
CC: Accepted Room facilities: ☐ ☎ 🕭 Access: ♿
Conference: 4 meeting rooms (Thtr 100 max), 24hr-delegate from £150, day-delegate rate from £40
Children: Welcome 🛏 ☕ Dogs: Welcome
Licences: ♿ ♦♦♦ Leisure: Outdoor pool, Golf, Fishing, Games room
Parking: Off-street and monitored
Directions: M40 Join the A423 towards Reading and after the Wallingford roundabout take the B4009 towards Goring. The hotel is situated on the right hand side.

Spa Hotel

Situated in 14 acres of beautiful grounds, paddocks and stables, the Spa has 71 ensuite bedrooms. The Chandelier Restaurant offers French cuisine, with an English influence, complemented by an international wine list. Extensive Health and Beauty facilities are available. The Spa is very accessible and is within easy reach of the M25, Tunbridge Wells railway station and both Gatwick and Heathrow airports. You can now book online!

Mount Ephraim, Tunbridge Wells, Kent TN4 8XJ
Tel: 01892 520331   Fax: 01892 510575
Email: info@spahotel.co.uk
Website: www.spahotel.co.uk

Southeast

Ware, Hertfordshire

Vintage Court Hotel

★★★

Vintage Corner, Puckeridge, near Ware,
Hertfordshire, SG11 1SA
Tel: 01920 822722 Fax: 01920 822877
Rooms: 30 all ensuite
Pricing: Dinner from £19.95 (2002 rate) CC: Accepted
Room facilities:
Children: Welcome Dogs: Welcome
Licences: Leisure: Snooker/billiards
Parking: Off-street
Directions: At the junction of the A10 and A120.

Watford, Hertfordshire

White House Hotel

★★★

Upton Road, Watford, Hertfordshire, WD18 0JF
Tel: 01923 237316 Fax: 01923 233109
Email: info@whitehousehotel.co.uk
Web: www.whitehousehotel.co.uk
Rooms: 58 all ensuite
Pricing: Sgl £45–145 Dbl £70–160 Dinner from £17.95
CC: Accepted
Room facilities:
Access:
Conference: 3 meeting rooms (Thtr 250 max), 24hr-
delegate from £115, day-delegate rate from £40
Children: Welcome
Dogs: Welcome
Licences: Parking: Off-street and monitored
Directions: Follow signs to town centre ring road. Take
centre lane past lights at Market Street. Upton Road is
on left.
See advert on next page

Welwyn, Hertfordshire

Quality Hotel Welwyn

★★★

Aim Junction 6, The Link, Welwyn,
Hertfordshire, AL6 9XA
Tel: +44 1438 716911 Fax: +44 1438 714065
Email: admin@gb623.u-net.com
Web: www.choicehotels.com
Rooms: 96 all ensuite
Pricing: Sgl £99 Dbl £105 Dinner from £17.95
CC: Accepted
Room facilities:
Access:
Conference: 5 meeting rooms (Thtr 300 max), 24hr-
delegate from £100, day-delegate rate from £30
Children: Welcome
Dogs: Welcome
Licences:
Parking: Monitored
Directions: The hotel can be found just off the A1(M) at
Junction 6. There is a railway station at Welwyn
Garden City.

Wembley, Middlesex

Adelphi Hotel

◆◆◆

4 Forty Lane, Wembley, Middlesex, HA9 9EB
Tel: 020 8904 5629 Fax: 020 8908 5314
Email: enquiry@adelphihotel.fsnet.co.uk
Web: www.hoteladelphi.co.uk
Rooms: 13 (9 ensuite)
Pricing: Sgl £35–42 Dbl £45–55 CC: Accepted
Room facilities:
Children: Welcome
Parking: Off-street and monitored
Directions: M1 last exit onto A406, after about 2 miles
take exit to Kingsbury, about 5 minutes only.

Arena Hotel

◆◆◆

6 Forty Lane, Wembley, Middlesex, HA9 9EB
Tel: 020 8908 0670 Fax: 020 8908 2007
Email: enquiry@arenahotel.fsnet.co.uk
Web: www.arena-hotel.co.uk
Rooms: 13 all ensuite
Pricing: Sgl £45 Dbl £55 CC: Accepted
Room facilities:
Children: Welcome
Dogs: Welcome
Parking: Monitored
Directions: Ten minutes from Wembley park tube. One
& a half miles from the M1 and 500 yards from the
A406.
See advert on next page

Elm Hotel

◆◆◆

Elm Road, Wembley, Middlesex, HA9 7JA
Tel: 020 8902 1764 Fax: 020 8903 8365
Email: info@elmhotel.co.uk
Web: www.elmhotel.co.uk
Rooms: 33 all ensuite
Room facilities:
Access:
Children: Welcome
Dogs: Welcome
Licences:
Parking: Off-street
Directions: Wembley Central Station 150 yards (main
line and Tube). From North Circular (A406), turn west.
Turn right at Woolwich Building Society, Elm Road
first left.

West Drayton, Middlesex

Travelodge Heathrow Airport (SA)

Travel Accommodation
A4, Sipson Road, West Drayton, Middlesex, UB7 0DU
Web: www.travelodge.co.uk
Rooms: 289 all ensuite
Pricing: Sgl £54.40–74.40 Dbl £58.85–78.85
CC: Accepted Room facilities: Access:

Westcliff-on-Sea, Essex

Rose House Hotel

21–23 Manor Road, Westcliff-on-Sea, Essex, SS0 7SR
Tel: 01702 341959 Fax: 01702 390918
Rooms: 21 (11 ensuite) 🛏 📺 ⊗
Pricing: Sgl £27.50 (2002 rate) Dbl £50 (2002 rate)
Dinner from £7 (2002 rate) CC: Accepted
Room facilities: 🖥 📷 Access: ♿
Children: Welcome 🍴 🧸
Dogs: Welcome
Leisure: Snooker/billiards
Parking: Off-street and monitored

Weybridge, Surrey

Oatlands Park Hotel

★★★★ ℞
146 Oatlands Drive, Weybridge, Surrey, KT13 9HB
Tel: 01932 847242 Fax: 01932 842252
Email: info@oatlandsparkhotel.com
Web: www.oatlandsparkhotel.com

Set in 10 acres of parkland this historic country house
hotel offers 144 comfortable bedrooms and extensive
conference and banqueting facilities, only 10 miles
from Heathrow airport.
Rooms: 144 all ensuite 🛏 📺 ⊗
Pricing: Sgl £148.50–188.50 Dbl £207–227
Dinner from £29 CC: Accepted
Room facilities: 🖥 ☎ 📷 🍷
Access: 🛗 ♿
Conference: 12 meeting rooms (Thtr 300 max), 24hr-
delegate from £215, day-delegate rate from £75
Children: Welcome 🍴
Licences: ⚓ 🍺
Leisure: Gym, Tennis, Golf
Parking: Off-street and monitored
Directions: From Weybridge town centre, follow road
up Monument Hill to mini roundabout. Turn left into
Oatlands Drive. Hotel 500 yards on left.

Ship Hotel

★★★

Monument Green, Weybridge, Surrey, KT13 8BQ
Tel: 01932 848364 Fax: 01932 857153
Email: info@shiphotel.weybridge.com
Web: www.peelhotel.com
Rooms: 39 all ensuite 🛏 Ⓢ
Pricing: Sgl £139.50–162 Dbl £171–216
Dinner from £22.50 CC: Accepted
Room facilities: ▢ ☎ ☕
Conference: 6 meeting rooms (Thtr 140 max), 24hr-delegate from £171, day-delegate rate from £63
Children: Welcome Licences: ⦙⦙⦙
Parking: Off-street and monitored
Directions: From M25 Junction 11, take A317 to Weybridge. Straight over two roundabouts to T-junction: turn left into High Street. Hotel approx 300 yards on left.

Winchester, Hampshire

The Wessex Hotel

★★★★

Paternoster Row, Winchester, Hampshire, SO23 9LQ
Tel: 0870 4008126 Fax: 01962 841503
Email: wessex@heritage-hotels.co.uk
Web: www.macdonaldhotels.co.uk
Rooms: 94 all ensuite 🛏 Ⓢ
Pricing: Sgl £59 Dbl £118 Dinner from £15
CC: Accepted Room facilities: ▢ ☎ ☕ ☏
Access: ⦙⦙⦙ ♿
Conference: 4 meeting rooms (Thtr 80 max)
Children: Welcome ⅋ ✂ Dogs: Welcome
Licences: ⦙⦙⦙ ⦙⦙⦙ Leisure: Beauty salon
Parking: Off-street and monitored
Directions: Leave M3 at Junction 9 and head towards Winnall. Go straight over main roundabout. Turn left, stay in left lane. Turn right at King Alfred's statue roundabout. Turn left into Colebrook Street. Hotel on right.

The Winchester Royal

★★★★ ♖ ♖

St Peter Street, Winchester, Hampshire, SO23 8BS
Tel: 01962 840840 Fax: 01962 841582
Email: royal@marstonhotels.com
Web: www.marstonhotels.com

Formerly a private house, Bishop's residence and convent. All 75 bedrooms have private bathrooms, 24 hour room service. Pleasant garden and terrance, car parking at rear of hotel, rosette restaurant.

Rooms: 75 all ensuite 🛏 Ⓢ
Pricing: Sgl £110 Dbl £129 Dinner from £25
CC: Accepted Room facilities: ▢ ☎ ☕ ☏
Conference: 7 meeting rooms (Thtr 120 max), 24hr-delegate from £140, day-delegate rate from £45
Children: Welcome ⅋ Dogs: Welcome
Licences: ⟁ ⦙⦙⦙
Parking: Off-street and monitored
Directions: Leave M3 at Junction 9 towards town centre, at bottom of hill take first right through one way system, take second right.

Shawlands

◆◆◆◆ ✄

46 Kilham Lane, Winchester, Hampshire, SO22 5QD
Tel: 01962 861166 Fax: 01962 861166
Email: kathy@pollshaw.u-net.com

Attractive, modern house in quiet elevated position overlooking countryside. 1½ miles from city centre. Colour TV, hairdryers and welcome tray in bedrooms. Breakfast includes homemade bread and preserves with fruit from garden.
Rooms: 5 (1 ensuite) Ⓢ
Pricing: Sgl £32–36 Dbl £42–52 CC: Accepted
Room facilities: ▢ ☕
Access: ♿ Children: Welcome 5yrs min age
Parking: Off-street
Directions: A3090 from Winchester. Straight over roundabout, right at second set of lights.

Wykeham Arms

◆◆◆◆ ♖ ♖

75 Kingsgate Street, Winchester, Hampshire, SO23 9PE
Tel: 01962 853834 Fax: 01962 854411
Email: doreen@wykehamarms.sfnet.co.uk
Rooms: 14 all ensuite Ⓢ
Pricing: Dinner from £12.95 (2002 rate) CC: Accepted
Room facilities: ▢ ☎ ☕ ☏
Children: Welcome 14yrs min age Dogs: Welcome
Licences: ⦙⦙⦙
Parking: Off-street and monitored
Directions: Immediately south of the cathedral by Kingsgate, at junction of Canon Street and Kingsgate Street.

Stanmore Hotel

◆ ◆ ◆

Stanmore Lane, Winchester, Hampshire, SO22 4BL
Tel: 01962 852720 Fax: 01962 850467
Rooms: 6 all ensuite
Pricing: Sgl £55–75 Dbl £65–75
Room facilities:
Conference: 2 meeting rooms (Thtr 110 max)
Children: Welcome ⱦ
Dogs: Welcome
Licences: ⚖
Parking: Off-street and monitored
Directions: M3 junction 11, signs to Winchester, at
second roundabout follow signs to Olivers Battery
continue to Romsey road roundabout, exit right then
first right into Stanmore lane.

Sandy Lodge

◆ ◆

47 Christchurch Road, Hampshire, SO23 9TE
Tel: 01962 853385
Web: www.acomm.uksandylodge
Seasonal closure: Christmas
Rooms: 6 (5 ensuite) ⊛
Pricing: Sgl £45–50 Dbl £60–65
Room facilities: ⬜ ⊚
Access: ♿
Conference: 1 meeting room (Thtr 10 max)
Children: Welcome ⱦ
Dogs: Welcome
Parking: Off-street
Directions: From M3 turn off at J9, at 2nd roundabout
take the St Cross sign down Garnier Road. At the end
turn left into St Cross road. Turn right and sharp left
into Landdown Road, and into Christchurch road, turn
right and drive to number 47.

Travelodge Winchester, Sutton Scotney Northbound

Travel Accommodation
A34 Truck Road, Winchester, Hampshire, SO21 3JY
Web: www.travelodge.co.uk
Room facilities: ⬜ ⊚

Travelodge Winchester, Sutton Scotney Southbound

Travel Accommodation
A34 Truck Road, Winchester, Hampshire, SO21 3JY
Web: www.travelodge.co.uk
Room facilities: ⬜ ⊚

Mobile traffic information

Just dial 1740* from any mobile
phone to get up-to-the-minute
RAC traffic information on
motorways and major A roads.
Try it now! *Calls to 1740 cost up to 59p
per minute. Check with your network.

Windsor, Berkshire

The Castle Hotel

★ ★ ★ ⌖

High Street, Windsor, Berkshire, SL4 1LJ
Tel: 0870 400 8300 Fax: 01753 856930
Email: castle@heritage-hotels.co.uk
Web: www.macdonald-hotels.com
Rooms: 111 all ensuite
Pricing: Sgl £65 Dbl £130 Dinner from £24.95
CC: Accepted Room facilities: ⬜ ☎ ⊚ ⚱ Access: ⌊⌊↑
Conference: 10 meeting rooms (Thtr 370 max)
Children: Welcome ⱦ ⁑ Dogs: Welcome
Licences: ⚖ ⁂ Parking: Off-street and monitored
Directions: Leave M4 at Junction 6 and follow the
signs for Windsor Castle. The hotel is on the left at the
top of High Street.

Park Farm

◆ ◆ ◆ ◆

St Leonards Road, Windsor, Berkshire, SL4 3EA
Tel: 01753 866823 Fax: 01753 850869
Email: stay@parkfarm.com
Web: www.parkfarm.com
Rooms: 4 all ensuite ⊛ Pricing: Sgl £40–60 Dbl £60
Room facilities: ⬜ ⊚ Access: ♿
Children: Welcome ⱦ
Parking: Off-street and monitored
Directions: From M4 (Junction 6), head towards
Windsor. At roundabout with traffic lights, take third
exit. At T-junction, turn right. Park Farm is on left.

Netherton Hotel

◆ ◆ ◆

96–98 St Leonard's Road, Windsor, Berkshire, SL4 3DA
Tel: 01753 855508 Fax: 01753 621267
Email: netherton@btconnect.com
Web: www.nethertonhotel.co.uk
Rooms: 20 all ensuite ⊛ ⊛
Room facilities: ⬜ ☎ ⊚ ⚱
Access: ♿ Children: Welcome ⱦ
Parking: Off-street and monitored
Directions: From M4, Junction 6, take A355 to large
roundabout. Take second exit into Goslar Way.
Continue over and take first left immediately after
traffic lights.

Oscar Hotel

◆ ◆ ◆

65 Vansittart Road, Windsor, Berkshire, SL4 5DB
Tel: 01753 830613 Fax: 01753 833744
Email: info@oscarhotel.com
Web: www.oscarhotel.com
Rooms: 13 all ensuite ⊛
Pricing: Sgl £45–58 Dbl £55–75 CC: Accepted
Room facilities: ⬜ ☎ ⊚
Children: Welcome
Licences: ⁂
Parking: Off-street and monitored
Directions: M4 J6 to Windsor, first slip road to
roundabout, left, then first right into Vansittart Road.

Clarence Hotel

 ◆ ◆

9 Clarence Road, Windsor, Berkshire, SL4 5AE
Tel: 01753 864436 Fax: 01753 857060
Web: www.clarence-hotel.co.uk

Located in town centre and walking distance to Windsor Castle, river and Eton. Licenced bar and steam-sauna. All rooms ensuite, TV, tea maker, radio: alarm and hair dryer. Convenient for Heathrow airport and Legoland.
Rooms: 20 all ensuite
Pricing: Sgl £48–59 Dbl £55–70 CC: Accepted
Room facilities: 🛏 ☕ 📻
Children: Welcome
Dogs: Welcome
Licences: 🍾
Parking: Off-street
Directions: Leave M4 at Junction 4 and follow dual carriageway towards Windsor. Turn left at roundabout onto Clarence Road.

Witney, Oxfordshire

Witney Four Pillars Hotel

★ ★ ★

Ducklington Lane, Witney, Oxfordshire, OX8 7TJ
Tel: 01993 779777 Fax: 01993 703467
Email: witney@four-pillars.co.uk
Web: www.four-pillars.co.uk
Rooms: 83 all ensuite
Pricing: Sgl £65–101.25 Dbl £79–123.50
Dinner from £15.95 CC: Accepted
Room facilities: 🛏 ☎ 📻 🍵 Access: ♿
Conference: 15 meeting rooms (Thtr 160 max), 24hr-delegate from £130, day-delegate rate from £32
Children: Welcome
Dogs: Welcome
Licences: 🍾
Leisure: Indoor pool, Gym, Health spa
Parking: Off-street and monitored
Directions: A40 towards Cheltenham; 2nd exit for Witney A415; hotel is on the left.

The Fleece Hotel and Brasserie

Restaurant with Rooms 🛏 🛏

11 Church Green, Witney, Oxon, OX28 4AZ
Tel: 01993 892270 Fax: 01993 892284
Email: reservations@thefleecehotelandbrasserie.co.uk
Web: www.thefleecehotelandbrasserie.co.uk
Modern decor, comfortable surroundings in a traditional setting overlooking the church green. A classic yet creative menu combining traditional flavours with Mediterranean influences available in the 90-seat brasserie.
Rooms: 11 all ensuite
Pricing: Sgl £75–95 Dbl £95–110 CC: Accepted
Room facilities: 🛏 ☎ 📻 🍵 Access: ♿
Conference: 1 meeting room (Thtr 20 max), day-delegate rate from £35
Children: Welcome Dogs: Guide dogs only
Licences: 🍾 Parking: Off-street and monitored

The Bird In Hand

◆ ◆ ◆ ◆

Whiteoak Green, Hailey, Witney, Oxfordshire, OX29 9XP
Tel: 01993 868321 Fax: 01993 868702
Email: birdinhand@heavitreeinns.co.uk
Rooms: 16 all ensuite Pricing: Dinner from £2.95
(2002 rate) CC: Accepted Room facilities: 🛏 ☎ ☕
Access: ♿ Licences: 🍾

Woburn, Bedfordshire

The Inn at Woburn

★ ★ ★

George Street, Woburn, Milton Keynes, Bedfordshire, MK17 9PX
Tel: 01525 290441 Fax: 01525 290432
Email: enquires@theinnatwoburn.com
Web: www.theinnatwoburn.com
Rooms: 58 all ensuite
Pricing: Sgl £166 Dbl £136–159 CC: Accepted
Room facilities: 🛏 ☎ 📻 🍵 Access: ♿
Conference: 13 meeting rooms (Thtr 60 max), 24hr-delegate from £135, day-delegate rate from £38
Children: Welcome Dogs: Guide dogs only
Licences: 🍾 Parking: Off-street
Directions: M1 at Junction 13 Northbound – Turn left. Southbound – Turn right. You pass a petrol station, then come to a small village called Husborne Crawley. Go through the village to a T-junction where you turn right, follow that road straight to Woburn.

Woodstock, Oxfordshire

The Bear

★★★★ ☕ ☕

Park Street, Woodstock, Oxfordshire, OX20 1SZ
Tel: 0870 4008202 Fax: 01993 813380
Email: bear@heritage-hotels.co.uk
Web: www.macdonaldhotels.co.uk
Rooms: 54 all ensuite ☜ 🖥 ⊗
Pricing: Sgl £89.50 Dbl £179 Dinner from £25
CC: Accepted
Room facilities: ▢ ☎ ☕
Access: ♿
Conference: 6 meeting rooms (Thtr 40 max)
Children: Welcome ♄
Dogs: Welcome
Licences: ♟♟♟
Parking: Off-street
Directions: From London, take M40 to Oxford and
leave at Junction 8. Then take A40 to Oxford North.
Take A44 to Woodstock and turn left into town centre.

The Feathers

Blue Ribbon Winner

★★★★ ☕ ☕ ☕

Market Street, Woodstock, Oxfordshire, OX20 1SX
Tel: 01993 812291 Fax: 01993 813158
Email: enquiries@feathers.co.uk
Web: www.feathers.co.uk

17th-century country town house. Situated in the heart
of Woodstock, nestled by the gates of Blenheim
Palace. A comfortable friendly atmosphere pervades
throughout with charm and character
Rooms: 20 all ensuite ☜
Pricing: Sgl £89–150 Dbl £135–290 Dinner from £35
CC: Accepted
Room facilities: ▢ ☎
Conference: 2 meeting rooms (Thtr 25 max), 24hr-
delegate from £176.25, day-delegate rate from £58.75
Children: Welcome ☀
Dogs: Welcome
Licences: ♟♟♟
Directions: Exit J8 M40. Take A40 towards Oxford; A44
towards Woodstock. Take 2nd left into town centre,
first hotel on left.

Gorselands Hall

◆ ◆ ◆ ◆ ☀ ☕

Boddington Lane, North Leigh, Witney,
Oxfordshire, OX29 6PU
Tel: 01993 882292 Fax: 01993 883629
Email: hamilton@gorselandshall.com
Web: www.gorselandshall.com

Lovely old Cotswold stone country house with oak
beams and flagstone floors in delightful rural location.
Large secluded garden. Ideal for Blenheim Palace,
Oxford and Cotswolds. Lovely river walks nearby.
Rooms: 6 all ensuite ☜ ⊗
Pricing: Sgl £35 Dbl £22.50–25.50 CC: Accepted
Room facilities: ▢ ☕ ☏
Access: ♿
Conference: 1 meeting room (Thtr 9 max), 24hr-
delegate from £66, day-delegate rate from £35
Children: Welcome
Dogs: Welcome
Leisure: Tennis, Snooker/billiards
Parking: Off-street
Directions: Gorselands Hall is 150 yards from A4095
between North Leigh and Long Hanborough. 4 miles
from Woodstock, 9 miles from Oxford.

Worthing, West Sussex

Beach Hotel

★★★ ☕

Marine Parade, Worthing, West Sussex, BN11 3QJ
Tel: 01903 234001 Fax: 01903 234567
Email: thebeachhotel@btinternet.com
Web: www.thebeachhotel.co.uk
Rooms: 79 all ensuite ☜ 🖥 ⊗
Pricing: Sgl £52–71 Dbl £32.50–100
Dinner from £19.50 CC: Accepted
Room facilities: ▢ ☎ ☏ ☏
Access: ♨ ♿
Conference: 7 meeting rooms (Thtr 250 max), 24hr-
delegate from £75
Children: Welcome ♄
Licences: ♟♟♟
Parking: Off-street and monitored
Directions: Follow A27 or A24 to Worthing, follow signs
to seafront and hotel, ½ mile west of the pier.

Southeast

Best Western Berkeley Hotel

★★★

86-95 Marine Parade, Worthing,
West Sussex, BN11 3QD
Tel: 01903 820000 Fax: 01903 821333
Email: berkbn@aol.com
Web: www.berkeleyhotel-worthing.co.uk
Rooms: 80 all ensuite 📠 ⊗
Pricing: Sgl £82–85 Dbl £105–120 Dinner from £19.50
CC: Accepted
Room facilities: ▢ ☎ ☕ ☏
Access: ⫽⫽ ♿
Conference: 5 meeting rooms (Thtr 50 max), 24hr-delegate from £110, day-delegate rate from £40
Children: Welcome
Dogs: Guide dogs only
Licences: ◁ ▬▬▬
Parking: Off-street
Directions: Follow the signs to Worthing seafront. Travel west from the pier for ½ mile.

The Windsor Hotel

★★★

14/20 Windsor Road, Worthing,
West Sussex, BN11 2LX
Tel: 0800 980 4442 Fax: 01903 210763
Email: enquiries@thewindsor.co.uk
Web: www.thewindsor.co.uk
Seasonal closure: Christmas
Rooms: 30 all ensuite 🍴 📠 ⊗
Pricing: Dbl £90–130 Dinner from £16.95 CC: Accepted
Room facilities: ▢ ☎ ☕ ☏
Conference: 8 meeting rooms (Thtr 110 max)
Children: Welcome 🍴
Licences: ◁ ▬▬▬
Parking: Off-street
Directions: Westbound; follow Hotels East signs until directed down Windsor Road. Eastbound; coast road until tourist sign directs you down Windsor Road.

Cavendish

★★

115/116 Marine Parade, Worthing,
West Sussex, BN11 3QG
Tel: 01903 236767 Fax: 01903 823840
Email: thecavendish@mistral.co.uk
Web: www.mistral.co.uk/thecavendish
Rooms: 17 all ensuite ⊗
Pricing: Sgl £45–47.50 Dbl £67.50–77.50
Dinner from £12.50 CC: Accepted
Room facilities: ▢ ☎ ☕
Children: Welcome ⚬
Dogs: Welcome
Licences: ▬▬▬
Parking: Off-street
Directions: From the A27 or A24, follow signs to seafront. Hotel 600 yards west of pier.

Bonchurch House Hotel

1 Winchester Road, Worthing, West Sussex, BN11 4DJ
Tel: 01903 202492 Fax: 01903 202492
Email: bonchurch@enta.net
Web: www.smoothhound.co.uk/hotels/bonchurc.html
Seasonal closure: January
Rooms: 7 all ensuite 📠
Pricing: Sgl £25–27 Dbl £50–54 CC: Accepted
Room facilities: ▢ ☕
Children: Welcome 3yrs min age
Parking: Off-street
Directions: When entering Worthing, follow road sign A259 to Littlehampton and tourist direction signage 'Hotels West'. Hotel situated on junction betwen Richmond and Wykeham Road.

MARSTON HOTELS

... helping you to relax in style

Central Reservations 0845 1300 700 www.marstonhotels.com

There are sixteen, four and three star Marston Hotels in the UK. all set within delightful locations; you can choose from the country, the town or by the sea.

Each hotel is unique and has its own friendly style and range of fine services. Our aim is to make certain that your stay with Marston Hotels is a memorable one.

**AWARD WINNING RESTAURANTS SUPERB LEISURE FACILITIES CORPORATE ENTERTAINMENT
LEISURE BREAKS GOLF TENNIS SHOPPING BEAUTY TREATMENTS CONFERENCE ROOMS
WEDDINGS AND BANQUETS DELIGHTFUL LOCATIONS FRIENDLY SERVICE & HOSPITALITY**

The Mews Prince's Parade Hythe Kent CT21 6AQ Tel: 01303 269900 Fax: 01303 263600 www.marstonhotels.com

Southwest

Glasgow • •Edinburgh

Belfast •
•Newcastle

Dublin •
•Manchester

Birmingham •

Cardiff • • London

Lundy

BRISTOL

Combe   Lynton Lynmouth Porlock
Ilfracombe Martin Weir
Morthoe
Woolacombe A3123 EXMOOR Wheddon Cre
A361 B3358
Barnstaple Croyde Braunton Exford
or Saunton Barnstaple Winsfor
Bideford Bay West Anstey Dulver
Northam B3227 A327
Hartland Point Westward Ho! South
Horns Umberleigh Molton A361
Clovelly Cross Bideford Chittlehamholt Tiv
Hartland Parkham Burrington Chulmleigh
Great Torrington B3042
R Taw DEVON
R Torridge Cheriton
Bude Stratton Fitzpaine B
Holsworthy Hatherleigh Tedburn
Crackington Virginstow Crediton St Mary
Haven Okehampton Whiddon Cheriton
Boscastle Sourton Cross Down Bishop Exeter
Tintagel Chagford
Trebarwith Strand Launceston Lifton Moretonhampstead
Port Isaac Camelford Lydford DARTMOOR Bovey Tracey
Rock Tamar Postbridge
Padstow Bodmin Tavistock Two Ashburton
Constantine Bay Moor Bridges Kingsteignton
Wadebridge Rilla Mill R Dart Newton
Bedruthan Steps CORNWALL Callington Buckfastleigh Abbot Alle
Newquay Bodmin Staverton Mills
Pentire St Columb Liskeard Plymouth Totnes
Major Carkeel Bow Bridge Sto
Perranporth Lostwithiel Saltash Ivybridge Ga
St Agnes Tregarrian Widegates Torpoint A385 Da
Par Looe Porthinkle Plymouth Modbury Star
Redruth Canyon Fowey Polperro Whitsand Down Bigbury-on-Sea Kingsbridge
St Ives Camborne St Bay Thomas Bigbury Hope Torcross
Austell Bay Cove Salcombe Start
Leland Mevagissey Soar Mill Cove
Hayle Truro Thurlestone
St Just Penryn Rosevine
Chysauster Redruth Carne Beach
Penzance Marazion St Mawes
Sennen Penzance Falmouth
Cove Mayon Helston Falmouth Bay
Land's Sennen Mount's
End Bay Mullion St Keverne
Lizard Point Lizard

ISLES OF SCILLY

Tresco St Martin's
Bryher Northwethel Lower Town
Hugh Town Tresco Pelistry Bay ISLES
The Garrison St Mary's OF
St Agnes St Mary's SCILLY

Note:
Dark blue dots represent the location of RAC-inspected accommodation

Southwest

Gold Ribbon Award

The Bath Priory, Bath	★★★★	187
Island Hotel, Tresco	★★★	228
Little Barwick House, Nr. Yeovil	★	288
Lucknam Park Hotel, Colerne	★★★★	186
Northcote Manor Hotel, Umberleigh	★★★	280
Percy's Country Hotel & Restaurant, Virginstow	★★	240
Priory Hotel, Wareham	★★★	280
Queensberry Hotel, Bath	★★★	188
St. Martin's on the Isle, St. Martin's	★★★	228
Stockhill House Hotel, Gillingham	★★★	224
Ston Easton Park, Nr. Bath	★★★★	187
Summer Lodge, Evershot	★★★	216
The Castle, Taunton	★★★	266
Thornbury Castle Hotel, Thornbury	★★★	268

Blue Ribbon Award

Beechleas, Wimborne Minster	★★	286
Bindon Country House Hotel, Wellington	★★★	266
Boscundle Manor House, St. Austell	★★	260
Howard's House Hotel, Salisbury	★★	251
Hotel Riviera, Sidmouth	★★★★	237
Oaks Hotel, Porlock	★★	248
Orestone Manor Hotel & Restaurant, Torquay	★★★	272

Pear Tree at Purton, Swindon	★★★	265
Soar Mill Cove Hotel, Salcombe	★★★	250
The Rosevine Hotel, Portscatho	★★★	249
The Royal Crescent Hotel, Bath	★★★★★	185
The Luggar Hotel, Truro	★★★	279
Treglos Hotel, Padstow	★★★	241

Little Gem

Allamanda, St. Ives	♦♦♦♦♦	261
County Hotel, Bath	♦♦♦♦♦	252
Croyde Bay House Hotel, Croyde	♦♦♦♦♦	216
Jubilee Farm, South Molton	♦♦♦♦	214
Lydgate House, Dartmoor	♦♦♦♦♦	233
Moor View House, Okehampton	♦♦♦♦♦	229
Seaview Moorings, St. Marys	♦♦♦♦♦	194
Tasburgh House Hotel, Bath	♦♦♦♦	193
The Ayrlington, Bath	♦♦♦♦♦	264
The Castleton Hotel, Swanage	♦♦♦♦	190
Websters, Salisbury	♦♦♦♦♦	204
Widbrook Grange, Bradford-on-Avon	♦♦♦♦♦	215
Yalbury Cottage Hotel & Restaurant, Dorchester	♦♦♦♦♦	213

Almondsbury, South Gloucestershire

Abbotts Way Guest House

♦ ♦ ♦ ♦ ⚡

Gloucester Road, Almondsbury, Bristol, BS32 4JB
Tel: 01454 613134 Fax: 01454 613134
Rooms: 6 (5 ensuite) ⊗
Pricing: Sgl £33–35 Dbl £50–55
CC: Accepted
Room facilities: ☐ ☕
Children: Welcome �📶
Dogs: Guide dogs only
Leisure: Indoor pool
Parking: Off-street and monitored
Directions: From M4/M5 junction at Almondsbury,
travel 2 miles north. Guest House on left. From M5
north, leave at Junction 14. Follow A38 for Bristol:
Guest House 7 miles on right.

Amesbury, Wiltshire

Travelodge Amesbury (Stonehenge)

Travel Accommodation
A303, Countess Services, Amesbury, Wiltshire, SP4 7AS
Web: www.travelodge.co.uk
Rooms: 48 all ensuite ⊗
Pricing: Sgl £57.40 Dbl £61.85
CC: Accepted Room facilities: ☐ ☕ Access: ♿

Axbridge, Somerset

The Webbington Hotel

★★★

Loxton, Nr Axbridge, Somerset, BS26 2XA
Tel: 01934 750100
Email: webbington@latonahotels.co.uk
Web: catonahotels.co.uk
Rooms: 59 all ensuite 🍴 📠
Pricing: Sgl £37.50–65 Dbl £65–75
CC: Accepted
Room facilities: ☐ ☎ ☕
Conference: 6 meeting rooms (Thtr 1,000 max),
24hr-delegate from £100, day-delegate rate from £35
Children: Welcome �📶 ☕
Dogs: Guide dogs only
Licences: ◆
Leisure: Indoor pool, Gym, Health spa,
Beauty salon, Tennis
Parking: Off-street
Directions: From junction 22 of M5 follow A38 to
Bristol, at Lower Weare take left past Lamb Inn. At next
T-junction turn left and follow road for 3 miles.

Need help booking?

RAC Hotel Reservations will find
the accommodation that's right
for you – and book it too.
Call today on 0870 603 9109
and quote 'Guide 2003'

Axminster, Devon

Fairwater Head Hotel

★★★ ☕ ☕

Hawkchurch, Devon, EX13 5TX
Tel: 01297 678349 Fax: 01297 678459
Email: j.c.lowe@btinternet.com
Seasonal closure: January
Rooms: 20 all ensuite ⊗
Pricing: Sgl £88–95 Dbl £156–170
Dinner from £25
CC: Accepted
Room facilities: ☐ ☎ ☕ 🔌
Conference: 1 meeting room (Thtr 10 max)
Children: Welcome �📶 ☕
Dogs: Welcome
Licences: ⊪⊪⊪
Parking: Off-street and monitored
Directions: 2¹/₂ miles from A35 and 14 miles from
Crewkerne on the B3165. Signposted to hotel locally
from B3165.

Barnstaple, Devon

The Imperial Hotel

★★★★ ☕

Taw Vale Parade, Barnstaple, Devon, EX32 8NB
Tel: 01271 345861 Fax: 01271 324448
Email: info@brend-imperial.co.uk
Web: www.brend-imperial.co.uk

With luxury refurbishment now completed The Imperial
is Barnstaple's premier hotel and the only 4-star. The
hotel overlooks the River Taw and Barnstaple.
Rooms: 63 all ensuite 🍴
Pricing: Sgl £80–85 Dbl £95–155
Dinner from £24
CC: Accepted
Room facilities: ☐ ☎ ☕ 🔌
Access: |↓↑| ♿ Children: Welcome �📶 ☕
Dogs: Guide dogs only
Licences: ⊪⊪⊪
Leisure: Snooker/billiards
Parking: Off-street and monitored
Directions: Leave M5 at Junction 27 and take A361 to
Barnstaple. Follow signs to town centre passing Tesco.
Proceed straight over next two roundabouts. River is
on left, hotel on right.
See advert on following page

Barnstaple Hotel

★★★

Braunton Road, Barnstaple, Devon, EX31 1LE
Tel: 01271 376221 Fax: 01271 324101
Email: info@barnstaplehotel.co.uk
Web: www.barnstaplehotel.co.uk

On the coastal side of Barnstaple, offering easy access
to North Devon's beaches and Exmoor. The hotel has a
superb health and leisure complex.
Rooms: 60 all ensuite 🛏 Pricing: Sgl £59.50–84.50
Dbl £64–104 Dinner from £19.75 CC: Accepted
Room facilities: 🖥 ☎ 🍵 🔌 Access: ♿
Children: Welcome 🍴 ☕ Dogs: Welcome
Licences: 🍷 🍴 Leisure: Indoor pool, Outdoor pool,
Gym, Health spa, Games room Snooker/billiards
Parking: Off-street and monitored
Directions: Take A361 Braunton/Ilfracombe road from
Barnstaple. Hotel is located on left approximately 1
mile from town centre.

Park Hotel

★★★

New Road, Taw Vale, Barnstaple, Devon, EX32 9AE
Tel: 01271 372166 Fax: 01271 323157
Email: info@parkhotel.co.uk
Web: www.parkhotel.co.uk

With the whole of North Devon on your doorstep, the
Park Hotel combines luxury with excellent value.
Overlooking park and the River Taw, and an easy walk
to the town centre.
Rooms: 42 all ensuite 🛏 Pricing: Sgl £51.50–81.50
Dbl £61–91 Dinner from £19.50 CC: Accepted
Room facilities: 🖥 ☎ 🍵 🔌 Access: ♿
Children: Welcome 🍴 ☕ Dogs: Welcome
Licences: 🍷 🍴 Parking: Off-street and monitored
Directions: Leave M5 at Junction 27 and take A361 to
Barnstaple. Follow signs to town centre, passing
Tesco. Proceed straight ahead at next 2 roundabouts.
Rock Park is on left, the hotel entrance on right.

Royal and Fortescue Hotel

★★★★ R R

Boutport Street, Barnstaple, Devon, EX31 1HG
Tel: 01271 342289 Fax: 01271 340102
Email: info@royalfortescue.co.uk
Web: www.royalfortescue.co.uk

A former coaching inn, recent refurbishment has
retained this historic charm whilst adding fine modern
facilities. Lord Fortescue's restaurant, elegant balls,
beautiful bedrooms and the adjacent bar and brasserie
"62 the Bank" are all at your disposal.
Rooms: 50 all ensuite 🛏 Pricing: Sgl £51.50–81.50
Dbl £61–91 Dinner from £19.50 CC: Accepted
Room facilities: 🖥 ☎ 🍵 🔌 Access: 🛗 ♿
Children: Welcome 🍴 ☕ Dogs: Guide dogs only
Licences: 🍴 Parking: Off-street and monitored
Directions: Located in the town centre at the junction
of High Street and Boutport Street.

Rising Sun Inn

★ ★ ⓡ ⓡ

Umberleigh, near Barnstaple, North Devon, EX37 9DU
Tel: 01769 560447 Fax: 01769 560764
Email: risingsuninn@btinternet.com
Web: www.risingsuninn.com

Ideal for touring, 8 miles from busy Barnstaple, this quiet 13th-century inn overlooks the Taw River. Malcolm and Andrew Hogg offer warm hospitality, comfortable accommodation and award-winning food.
Rooms: 9 all ensuite ⬥ ⊗
Pricing: Dinner from £4.95 CC: Accepted
Room facilities: ▯ ☎ ⊙
Conference: 2 meeting rooms (Thtr 70 max)
Children: Welcome ⍭ Dogs: Welcome
Licences: ⬥ ⋔ Parking: Off-street
Directions: Junction of A377 and B3227, opposite Umberleigh Bridge.

Bath, Bath & NE Somerset

Royal Crescent Hotel
Blue Ribbon Winner

★ ★ ★ ★ ★

16 Royal Crescent, Bath,
Bath & NE Somerset, BA1 2LS
Tel: 01225 823333 Fax: 01225 339401
Email: reservations@royalcrescent.co.uk
Web: www.royalcrescent.co.uk
Rooms: 45 all ensuite ⬥ 🗂 ⊗
Pricing: Dbl £260–800 Dinner from £30
CC: Accepted
Room facilities: ▯ ☎ ⬥ ❄ Access: ▯▯ ♿
Children: Welcome ⍭ Dogs: Welcome
Licences: ⬥ ⋔
Leisure: Indoor pool, Outdoor pool, Gym, Health spa, Beauty salon
Parking: Off-street and monitored
Directions: Guests are provided with precise directions when making reservations.
See advert on this page

Southwest

RaC
★★★★

- Only 6 miles from Bath, conveniently located for both junctions 17 and 18 of the M4.

- 41 individually designed bedrooms and suites

- 500 acres of listed parkland and walled gardens

- Renowned Spa with a wide range of facilities, including indoor pool and tennis courts

- Dedicated Health and Beauty Salon

- Unique Equestrian facilities including all-weather arena and cross-country course

- Wide range of activities within the estate

RELAIS & CHATEAUX.

Colerne, near Bath, SN14 8AZ
Tel: 01225 742777   Fax: 01225 743536
reservations@lucknampark.co.uk
www.lucknampark.co.uk

The Bath Spa Hotel

★★★★★★ 🎀 🎀 🎀

Sydney Road, Bath, Somerset, BA2 6JF
Tel: 0870 4008222 Fax: 01225 444006
Email: bathspa@heritage-hotels.co.uk
Web: www.macdonald-hotels.co.uk
Rooms: 102 all ensuite 🖼 ⊗ Pricing: Sgl £149
Dbl £298 Dinner from £35 CC: Accepted
Room facilities: 🖳 ☎ 🍵 🔌 Access: ⬆ ♿
Conference: 6 meeting rooms (Thtr 130 max)
Children: Welcome ♟ 🐴 Dogs: Welcome
Licences: ◇ ⛲ Leisure: Indoor pool, Gym, Health spa Beauty salon, Tennis
Parking: Off-street and monitored
Directions: M4 Junction 18. Take A46 to Bath. 1st roundabout, right onto A4. Follow signs for city centre. Left onto A36 at lights. Right at mini roundabout, next left into Sydney Place. Hotel 200 yards up hill on right.

Combe Grove Manor

★★★★★ 🎀 🎀

Brassknocker Hill, Monkton Combe, Bath,
Bath & NE Somerset, BA2 7HS
Tel: 01225 834644 Fax: 01225 830669
Email: info@combegrovemanor.com
Web: www.combegrovemanor.com
Rooms: 40 all ensuite 🍵 🖼 Pricing: Sgl £110–180
Dbl £110–320 Dinner from £22 CC: Accepted
Room facilities: 🖳 ☎ 🍵 Conference: 6 meeting rooms (Thtr 100 max), 24hr-delegate from £155, day-delegate rate from £50 Children: Welcome ♟ 🐴
Dogs: Guide dogs only Licences: ◇ ⛲
Leisure: Indoor pool, Outdoor pool, Gym, Health spa, Beauty salon, Tennis, Golf
Parking: Off-street and monitored
Directions: From Bath city centre follow signs for the university. Go past the university for 1½ miles; hotel entrance is on the left.

Lucknam Park Hotel   Gold Ribbon Winner

★★★★★ 🎀 🎀 🎀

Colerne, Chippenham, Wiltshire, SN14 8AZ
Tel: 01225 742777 Fax: 01225 743536
Email: reservations@lucknampark.co.uk
Web: www.lucknampark.co.uk
One of Britain's leading country house hotels, offering superb facilities in a splendid Georgian setting. The highly motivated staff consistently provide guests with warm hospitality and exemplary standards of service.
Rooms: 41 all ensuite 🖼
Pricing: Sgl £223 Dbl £241–736 Dinner from £50
CC: Accepted Room facilities: 🖳 ☎ 🔌 Access: ♿
Conference: 4 meeting rooms (Thtr 40 max), 24hr-delegate from £240, day-delegate rate from £75
Children: Welcome ♟ Dogs: Guide dogs only
Licences: ◇ ⛲ Leisure: Indoor pool, Gym, Health spa, Beauty salon, Tennis, Riding, Games room, Snooker/billiards Parking: Off-street and monitored
Directions: Westbound, leave M4 at Junction 17. Take A350 to Chippenham, A420 to Ford, turn left to Colerne, and right at crossroads to the hotel.
See advert on this page

Ston Easton Park

Gold Ribbon Winner

★★★★ ♜ ♜ ♜

Ston Easton, Bath, Bath & NE Somerset, BA3 4DF
Tel: 01761 241631 Fax: 01761 241377
Email: stoneastonpark@stoneaston.co.uk
Web: www.stoneaston.co.uk
Rooms: 23 all ensuite
Pricing: Sgl £99 Dbl £185 Dinner from £39.50
CC: Accepted Room facilities:
Conference: 7 meeting rooms (Thtr 50 max),
24hr-delegate from £170, day-delegate rate from £55
Children: Welcome Dogs: Welcome
Licences: Leisure: Tennis, Snooker/billiards
Parking: Off-street
Directions: On the A37 10 minutes north of Shepton
Mallet in the village of Ston Easton, 11 miles from Bath
and Bristol.

The Bath Priory

Gold Ribbon Winner

★★★★ ♜ ♜ ♜ ♜

Weston Road, Bath, Bath & NE Somerset, BA1 2XT
Tel: 01225 331922 Fax: 01225 448276
Email: bathprioryhotel@compuserve.com
Web: www.thebathpriory.co.uk
Rooms: 34 all ensuite
Pricing: Sgl £145–190
Dbl £240–330 Dinner from £48 CC: Accepted
Room facilities: Access:
Conference: 3 meeting rooms (Thtr 60 max),
24hr-delegate from £190, day-delegate rate from £75
Children: Welcome Dogs: Guide dogs only

Licences: Leisure: Indoor pool, Outdoor pool, Gym,
Health spa, Beauty salon
Parking: Off-street and monitored
Directions: Situated in the north-west corner of the city,
Bath Priory Hotel is a 15-minute walk from city centre.
See advert on this page

Windsor Hotel

★★★★ Townhouse ♜

69 Great Pulteney Street, Bath,
Bath & NE Somerset, BA2 4DL
Tel: 01225 422100 Fax: 01225 422550
Email: sales@bathwindsorhotel.com
Web: www.bathwindsorhotel.com
Rooms: 14 all ensuite
Pricing: Sgl £85–115 Dbl £115–275 Dinner from £25
CC: Accepted Room facilities:
Conference: 1 meeting rooms (Thtr 14 max),
24hr-delegate from £175, day-delegate rate from £49
Children: Welcome, 12yrs min age
Dogs: Guide dogs only Licences:
Parking: Off-street
Directions: M4 J18, A46 to Bath, A4. Turn onto A36, 1/4
mile, right at roundabout, second right into Great
Pulteney Street.

Southwest

Abbey Hotel

★★★★ ♛ ♛

North Parade, Bath, Bath & NE Somerset, BA1 1LF
Tel: 01225 461603 Fax: 01225 447758
Email: ahres@compasshotels.co.uk
Web: www.compasshotels.co.uk
Rooms: 60 all ensuite ✎ Ⓢ
Pricing: Sgl £80 Dbl £125 Dinner from £22
CC: Accepted Room facilities: ▢ ☎ ☕ ↳
Access: ⇞ ⚬ Children: Welcome ⍾
Dogs: Welcome Licences: ⅲ
Directions: Approaching centre turn left signed Bristol, bear right at mini roundabout and right again under railway opposite top of road.

Lansdown Grove Hotel

★★★★ ♛ ♛

Lansdown Road, Bath, Bath & NE Somerset, BA1 5EH
Tel: 01225 483888 Fax: 01225 483838
Email: lansdown@marstonhotels.com
Web: www.marstonhotels.com

MARSTON HOTELS

A grade II listed building enjoying breathtaking views over the Georgian part of the city, free car parking. Excellent restaurant offering a varied menu, complemented by friendly and professional staff.
Rooms: 60 all ensuite ✎ ⊞ Ⓢ
Pricing: Sgl £105 Dbl £139 Dinner from £25
CC: Accepted Room facilities: ▢ ☎ ☕ ↳
Access: ⇞ ⚬
Conference: 6 meeting rooms (Thtr 100 max), 24hr-delegate from £130, day-delegate rate from £42.50
Children: Welcome ⍾ ⚇ Dogs: Guide dogs only
Licences: ⚬ ⅲ Parking: Off-street and monitored
Directions: Leave M4 at Junction 18. Follow A46 towards Bath city centre. Take Broad Street. Follow signs for Lansdown and Bath Races.

Limpley Stoke Hotel

★★★

Lower Limpley Stoke, Bath,
Bath & NE Somerset, BA3 6HZ
Tel: 01225 723333 Fax: 01225 722400
Email: latonalsh@aol.com
Web: latonahotels.co.uk
Rooms: 66 all ensuite ⊞ Ⓢ
Pricing: Sgl £52.50–68 Dbl £90–100 Dinner from £19
Room facilities: ▢ ☎ ☕ ↳ Access: ⇞
Conference: 4 meeting rooms (Thtr 85 max), 24hr-delegate from £110, day-delegate rate from £35
Children: Welcome ⍾ Dogs: Guide dogs only
Licences: ⚬ Parking: Off-street

Queensberry Hotel & Olive Tree Restaurant

Gold Ribbon Winner

★★★★ ♛ ♛ ♛

Russel Street, Bath, Somerset, BA1 2QF
Tel: 01225 447928 Fax: 01225 446065
Email: enquiries@bathqueensberry.com
Web: www.bathqueensberry.com
Seasonal closure: 4 days at Christmas

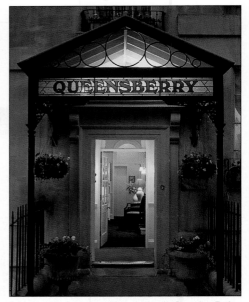

A luxury privately owned townhouse in Georgian Bath, minutes from Royal Crescent, Roman Baths and Pump Rooms. The Olive Tree restaurant is nationally renowned for informal contemporary British cooking.
Rooms: 29 all ensuite ⊞ Ⓢ
Pricing: Sgl £120–200 Dbl £140–250 Dinner from £26
CC: Accepted Room facilities: ▢ ☎ Access: ⇞ ⚬
Conference: 1 meeting rooms (Thtr 30 max), 24hr-delegate from £145, day-delegate rate from £47
Children: Welcome ⚇ Dogs: Guide dogs only
Licences: ⅲ Parking: Off-street
Directions: 2nd turn left, 1st turn right, from bottom of Landsdown Hill.

The Francis

★★★

Queen Square, Bath, Somerset, BA1 2HH
Tel: 0870 400 8223 Fax: 01225 319715
Email: francis@heritage-hotels.co.uk
Web: www.macdonald-hotels.co.uk
Rooms: 95 all ensuite 🛏 🚗 🚭
Pricing: Sgl £75 Dbl £150 Dinner from £23
CC: Accepted Room facilities: 🖵 ☎ 🍵 🐾
Access: |↕|
Conference: 2 meeting rooms (Thtr 90 max)
Children: Welcome ♀ Dogs: Welcome
Licences: ♦♦♦ P
arking: Off-street and monitored
Directions: Exit the M4 at Junction 18 and proceed
along the A46 to Bath city centre. Proceed to end of
George Street and turn left into Queen Square. The
Francis is on the south side of the square.

Compass Inn

★★

Tormarton, Nr Badminton,
South Gloucestershire, GL9 1JB
Tel: 01454 218242 Fax: 01454 218741
Email: info@compass-inn.co.uk
Web: www.compass-inn.co.uk
Rooms: 28 all ensuite 🛏 🚭
Pricing: Sgl £64.50–89 Dbl £84–108.50
Dinner from £5 CC: Accepted Room facilities:
🖵 ☎ 🍵 🐾 Access: ♿
Conference: 7 meeting rooms (Thtr 100 max)
Children: Welcome ♀ 🎠 Dogs: Welcome
Licences: ◇ ♦♦♦
Leisure: Games room
Parking: Off-street
Directions: Situated in the Cotwolds, the Compass Inn
has easy access to both Bath and Bristol, located on
Junction 18 of M4.

George's Hotel

★★

2-3 South Parade, Bath, Bath & NE Somerset, BA2 4AA
Tel: 01225 464923 Fax: 01225 425471
Email: info@georgeshotel.co.uk
Web: www.georgeshotel.co.uk
Rooms: 19 all ensuite 🛏 🚗
Pricing: Sgl £50–65 Dbl £65–95 CC: Accepted
Room facilities: 🖵 ☎ 🍵 Access: ♿
Children: Welcome ♀ 🎠
Licences: ♦♦♦
Directions: In city centre between Abbey and stations,
next to public car park.

Wentworth House Hotel

★★

106 Bloomfield Road, Bath,
Bath & NE Somerset, BA2 2AP
Tel: 01225 339193 Fax: 01225 310460
Email: stay@wentworthhouse.co.uk
Web: www.wentworthhouse.co.uk
Seasonal closure: Christmas
Rooms: 18 all ensuite 🛏 🚗 🚭
Pricing: Sgl £55–75 Dbl £75–105
Dinner from £8
CC: Accepted Room facilities: 🖵 ☎ 🍵
Conference: 1 meeting rooms
Children: Welcome, 5yrs min age
Licences: ♦♦♦
Leisure: Outdoor pool
Parking: Off-street
Directions: Exit Junction 18 M4 into city, A36 for
Bristol, then A367 Exeter/Wells for 1 mile. Turn right
just past The Bear pub.
See advert on this page

Southwest

Woolverton House Hotel

★ ★ ⏰

Woolverton, Bath, Bath & NE Somerset, BA2 7QS
Tel: 01373 830415 Fax: 01373 831243
Email: mail@bathhotel.com
Web: www.bathhotel.com

Rooms: 12 all ensuite 🐾 ⊗
Pricing: Dinner from £11.95 CC: Accepted
Room facilities: ▢ 🕾 🗐 🔥 Access: ♿
Children: Welcome, 10yrs min age Licences: ⛟
Leisure: Tennis Parking: Off-street and monitored
Directions: Located on the A36, 8 miles south of Bath
in direction of Warminster.

Athole Guest House

◆ ◆ ◆ ◆ ◆ ✻

33 Upper Oldfield Park, Bath,
Bath & NE Somerset, BA2 3JX
Tel: 01225 334307 Fax: 01225 320009
Email: bookings@atholehouse.co.uk
Web: www.atholehouse.co.uk

No Laura Ashley or dusty four-posters at Athole House.
Instead, a large Victorian home restored to give bright,
inviting, quiet bedrooms, sleek furniture, sparkling
bathrooms. Easy walking distance to town centre.
Rooms: 3 all ensuite 🐾 ⊗
Pricing: Sgl £48–58 Dbl £65–75 CC: Accepted
Room facilities: ▢ 🕾 🗐 🔥 Children: Welcome ⛟
Dogs: Guide dogs only Parking: Off-street and monitored
Directions: From M4 follow signs for through traffic/
Radstock/Wells into Wells Road. Take first turning on
right.

Cheriton House

◆ ◆ ◆ ◆ ◆ ✻ ⛤ ⏰

9 Upper Oldfield Park, Bath,
Bath & NE Somerset, BA2 3JX
Tel: 01225 429862 Fax: 01225 428403
Email: cheriton@which.net
Web: www.cheritonhouse.co.uk

South of the river in a quiet location off the A367,
Cheriton House offers a mix of Victorian charm and
modern amenities. Excellent breakfast, warm welcome
and a comfortable environment guaranteed.
Rooms: 10 all ensuite 🗐 ⊗
Pricing: Sgl £50–65 Dbl £66–95 CC: Accepted
Room facilities: ▢ 🕾 🗐 🔥
Children: Welcome, 12yrs min age Parking: Off-street
Directions: South of the city centre, just off A367.

County Hotel
Little Gem

◆ ◆ ◆ ◆ ◆ ✻ ⏰

18/19 Pulteney Road, Bath,
Bath & NE Somerset, BA2 4EZ
Tel: 01225 425003 Fax: 01225 466493
Email: reservations@county-hotel.co.uk
Web: www.county-hotel.co.uk
Seasonal closure: Christmas
Rooms: 22 all ensuite 🗐 ⊗ Room facilities: ▢ 🕾 🗐 🔥
Children: Welcome, 13yrs min age Licences: ◭ ⛟
Parking: Off-street and monitored
Directions: Follow A46. Before reaching city centre,
turn left at traffic lights following signposts for Exeter
on A36. Turn right to Holborne Museum on left and
proceed over roundabout. Hotel 50m on right.

See advert on next page

Dorian House

◆ ◆ ◆ ◆ ◆ ✻ ⏰

1 Upper Oldfield Park, Bath,
Bath & NE Somerset, BA2 3JX
Tel: 01225 426336 Fax: 01225 444699
Email: info@dorianhouse.co.uk
Web: www.dorianhouse.co.uk
Rooms: 8 all ensuite 🐾 🗐 ⊗
Pricing: Sgl £42–78 Dbl £60–140 CC: Accepted
Room facilities: ▢ 🕾 🗐 🔥 Access: ♿
Children: Welcome ⛟
Parking: Off-street and monitored
Directions: Exit M4 J-18, A46, A4 to Bath. Follow A36
signposted Bristol. Left on A367. First right is Upper
Oldfield Park.

See advert on following page

Dorian House

Enter an atmosphere of period charm, c.1880. All ensuite bedrooms feature telephone, TV, tea and coffee. Traditional solid oak four-poster beds, panoramic views over Bath or our beautiful garden. Ten minutes' walk to the centre.

1 Upper Oldfield Park, Bath BA2 3JX
Tel: 01225 426336   Fax: 01225 444699
Email: info@dorianhouse.co.uk
www.dorianhouse.co.uk

RAC

Oldfields Hotel

Elegant and traditional bed & breakfast with panoramic views of Bath and only 8 minutes walk to Bath city centre. A delicious choice of breakfast to include full English, fresh seasonal fruits and smoked salmon with scrambled eggs are served in the magnificent dining room. Car park and residents' garden.

102 Wells Road, Bath BA2 3AL
Tel: 01225 317984   Fax: 01225 444471
info@oldfields.co.uk
www.oldfields.co.uk

The Ayrlington

24/25 Pulteney Road, Bath BA2 4EZ
Tel: 01225 425495 Fax: 01225 469029
Email: mail@ayrlington.com Web: www.ayrlington.com

RAC ♦♦♦♦♦ Little Gem AA ♦♦♦♦♦ ETC Gold

A handsome listed Victorian house set in an award-winning walled garden with exceptional views of the Abbey. Bath's centre and historic sites are just a five-minute level stroll away. The elegant interior is a graceful blend of English and Asian antiques, artwork and fine fabrics. All bedrooms have an individual theme and are beautifully furnished, some with 4-poster beds and spa baths. The Hotel has a residents' bar, private parking and is entirely non smoking.

Closed 23rd December to 7th January

Oldfields

102 Wells Road, Bath, Bath & NE Somerset, BA2 3AL
Tel: 01225 317984 Fax: 01225 444471
Email: info@oldfields.co.uk
Web: www.oldfields.co.uk
Seasonal closure: December 20 to February
Rooms: 14 all ensuite 🖨
Pricing: Sgl £59–65 Dbl £65–95 CC: Accepted
Room facilities: 🖵 ☎ 🥃   Children: Welcome
Dogs: Guide dogs only Parking: Off-street
Directions: Oldfields is situated 1½ miles from the city
centre on the A367, Wells road at the corner of Upper
Oldfield park
See advert on previous page

The Ayrlington
Little Gem

24/25 Pulteney Road, Bath, Bath & NE Somerset, BA2
4EZ Tel: 01225 425495 Fax: 01225 469029
Email: mail@ayrlington.com
Web: www.ayrlington.com
Seasonal closure: Christmas to New Year

Conveniently located close to Bath city centre, this
small, tranquil, luxury hotel boasts an elegant interior,
excellent views, private parking, and access to the
nearby golf course.
Rooms: 12 all ensuite 🖨 ⊘
Pricing: Sgl £75–135 Dbl £75–135 CC: Accepted
Room facilities: 🖵 ☎ 🥃 Children: Welcome
Dogs: Guide dogs only Licences: 👫
Parking: Off-street and monitored
Directions: M4 Junction 18, take A46 then A4 into city.
Turn left at lights (signed A36) and right at end of road.
Straight over roundabout, hotel 100 yards on right.
See advert on previous page

Ainsborough

Weston Lane, Bath, Bath & NE Somerset, BA1 4AB
Tel: 01225 311380 Fax: 01225 447411
Email: ainsboroughhotel@aol.com
Web: www.ainsboroughhotel.co.uk
Rooms: 17 all ensuite 🖐 🖨 ⊘
Pricing: Sgl £45–60 Dbl £50–90 CC: Accepted
Room facilities: 🖵 ☎ 🥃 📞
Children: Welcome Licences: 👫 Parking: Off-street
Directions: On the north-west side of the city, west of
Royal Crescent and Circus near the R.U.H. hospital.

Ashley Villa Hotel

26 Newbridge Road, Bath,
Bath & NE Somerset, BA1 3JZ
Tel: 01225 421683 Fax: 01225 313604
Email: ashleyvilla@clearface.co.uk
Web: www.ashleyvilla.co.uk

Friendly, family-run hotel with relaxing informal
atmosphere. Close to city centre, private car park, bar,
restaurant, lovely gardens and outdoor pool. Premier
rooms include four-poster and large family
accommodation.
Rooms: 18 (17 ensuite) 🖐 🖨 ⊘
Pricing: Sgl £49–69 Dbl £59–130 Dinner from £15
CC: Accepted Room facilities: 🖵 ☎ 🥃 📞
Children: Welcome Dogs: Guide dogs only
Licences: 👫 Leisure: Outdoor pool
Parking: Off-street and monitored
Directions: Leaving Bath on A4 Bristol, take Upper
Bristol Road west onto left fork. At second set of traffic
lights turn into Newbridge Road. Hotel 200m on right.

Brompton House (B&B)

St John's Road, Bath, Somerset, BA2 6PT
Tel: 01225 420972 Fax: 01225 420505
Email: bromptonhouse@btinternet.com
Web: www.bromptonhouse.co.uk
Seasonal closure: Christmas and New Year
Rooms: 16 all ensuite 🖨 ⊘
Pricing: Sgl £48–60 Dbl £70–95 CC: Accepted
Room facilities: 🖵 ☎ 🥃
Children: Welcome, 15yrs min age Licences: 👫
Parking: Off-street
Directions: Leave M4 at Junction 18, take A46 for 12
miles. Then take A4 for city centre, then A36. Turn into
St Johns Road, Brompton House is adjacent to church.
See advert on following page

Southwest

Brompton House

Charming Georgian house (former rectory 1777). Family owned and run. Car park and beautiful secluded gardens. 6 minutes level walk to main historic sights and restaurants. 16 tastefully furnished and fully equipped ensuite bedrooms. Delicious choice of breakfasts. No smoking.

St John's Road, Bath BA2 6PT
Tel: 01225 420972   Fax: 01225 420505
Email: bromptonhouse@btinternet.com
Website: www.bromptonhouse.co.uk

Laura Place Hotel

◆◆◆◆

3 Laura Place, Great Pulteney Street, Bath, Bath & NE Somerset, BA2 4BH
Tel: 01225 463815 Fax: 01225 310222
Seasonal closure: December 22 to March 1

Charming Georgian town house hotel in central location. Eight spacious bedrooms. Private car parking. No-smoking policy.
Rooms: 8 (7 ensuite) 🏆 🖬 ⊗
Pricing: Dbl £72–95 CC: Accepted
Room facilities: ❑ ☎ ⊿
Children: Welcome, 8yrs min age Parking: Off-street
Directions: From A4 via Bathwick Street, along Henrietta Street. Laura Place is a square with a central fountain.

Oakleigh House

◆◆◆◆

19 Upper Oldfield Park, Bath, Somerset, BA2 3JX
Tel: 01225 315698 Fax: 01225 448223
Email: oakleigh@which.net
Web: www.oakleigh-house.co.uk
Rooms: 3 all ensuite ⊗
Pricing: Sgl £50–60 Dbl £68–78 CC: Accepted
Room facilities: ❑ ⊿ Dogs: Guide dogs only
Parking: Off-street
Directions: Take A367 from centre of Bath, then first turning on right. Oakleigh is 100m on right.

Sydney Gardens

◆◆◆◆

Sydney Road, Bath, Bath & NE Somerset, BA2 6NT
Tel: 01225 464818 Fax: 01225 484347
Email: pete@sydneygardens.co.uk
Web: www.sydneygardens.co.uk
Seasonal closure: Christmas to January
Rooms: 6 all ensuite ⊗ Room facilities: ❑ ☎ ⊿
Children: Welcome, 10yrs min age
Parking: Off-street and monitored
Directions: From M4 Junction 18, follow A46. Turn left at sign for Exeter-Warminster (A36), cross river, turn right at Sydney Gardens, then next left.

Tasburgh House Hotel   Little Gem

◆◆◆◆ 🍴🍴 ⊗ 🐾

Warminster Road, Bath, NE Somerset, BA2 6SH
Tel: 01225 425096 Fax: 01225 463842
Email: hotel@bathtasburgh.co.uk
Web: www.bathtasburgh.co.uk

Charming Victorian mansion in seven acres of lovely gardens and meadowpark — along the Kennet and Avon Canal. Spectacular views and convenient for the city centre. Gourmet evening meals. Personal, caring service. Country house comforts in a city setting.
Rooms: 12 all ensuite 🏆 🖬 ⊗
Pricing: Sgl £60–75 Dbl £85–115 Dinner from £25
CC: Accepted Room facilities: ❑ ☎ ⊿ 🔌
Children: Welcome Licences: 👬👬
Parking: Off-street and monitored
Directions: Follow signs for A36 to Warminster from city centre. Hotel stands on north side of A36, adjacent to Bathampton Lane junction, approx ½ mile from Bathwick Street roundabout and Sydney Gardens.

Bonheur B & B

◆ ◆ ◆

52 Box Road, Bathford, Bath,
Bath & NE Somerset, BA1 7QH
Tel: 01225 859537 Fax: 01225 859537
Email: bonheur@waitrose.com
Web: www.visitus.co.uk/bath/hotel/bonheur
Rooms: 5 (3 ensuite) ⚲ Ⓢ Room facilities: ▢ ☕
Children: Welcome Parking: Off-street
Directions: From Bath, follow A4 to Bathford. Take
Box/Chippenham road. Bonheur is 200m past
Dunsford Land Rovers.

Lamp Post Villa

◆ ◆ ◆

3 Crescent Gardens, Bath,
Bath & NE Somerset, BA1 2NA
Tel: 01225 331221 Fax: 01225 426783
Seasonal closure: Christmas
Rooms: 4 all ensuite Ⓢ Pricing: Sgl £30–35
Dbl £40–55 CC: Accepted Room facilities: ▢ ☎ ☕
Children: Welcome �𝔥 Dogs: Welcome
Parking: Off-street
Directions: On A4 Bristol road, in western side of city
centre close to Victoria Park.

Travelodge Bath, Royal York (SA)

Travel Accommodation
1 York Buildings, George Street, Bath, Avon, BA1 2EB
Web: www.travelodge.co.uk
Pricing: Sgl £74.40 Dbl £78.85
CC: Accepted Room facilities: ▢ ☕ Access: ⚲

Travelodge Beckington

Travel Accommodation
A36, Trowbridge Road, Beckington, Bath,
Avon, BA3 6SF
Web: www.travelodge.co.uk Rooms: 40 all ensuite Ⓢ
Pricing: Sgl £59.40 Dbl £63.85
CC: Accepted Room facilities: ▢ ☕ Access: ⚲

Bideford, Devon

Royal Hotel

★ ★ ★

Barnstaple Street, Bideford, Devon, EX39 4AE
Tel: 01237 472005 Fax: 01237 478957
Email: info@royalbideford.co.uk
Web: www.royalbideford.co.uk

The Royal Hotel overlooks ancient Bideford Bridge and
the River Torridge and is a good base for exploring the
countryside and coastline of North Devon.
Rooms: 31 all ensuite ⚲
Pricing: Sgl £51.50–71.50 Dbl £61–91
Dinner from £19.50 CC: Accepted
Room facilities: ▢ ☎ ☕ ✆ Access: ⊞ ⚲
Children: Welcome �𝔥 ⛱ Dogs: Welcome
Licences: ◁ ♟ Parking: Off-street and monitored
Directions: At the eastern end of old Bideford bridge.

Hoops Country Inn and Hotel

★ ★

Hoops, Nr Clovelly, Bideford, Devon, EX39 5DL
Tel: 01237 451222 Fax: 01237 451247
Email: reservations@hoopsinn.co.uk
Web: www.hoopsinn.co.uk
Seasonal closure: Christmas/New Year

13th century hotel set in pretty gardens close to coast
path, renowned for exceptional food served in a variety
of dining rooms complemented by fine wines, real ales,
and personal service. All rooms individually furnished
to a high standard.
Rooms: 12 all ensuite ✏ Ⓢ
Pricing: Sgl £55–95 Dbl £90–160 Dinner from £23
CC: Accepted Room facilities: ▢ ☎ ☕ ✆
Conference: 4 meeting rooms (Thtr 60 max),
24hr-delegate from £85, day-delegate rate from £30
Children: Welcome, 3yrs min age ⚲
Dogs: Welcome Licences: ♟ Leisure: Games room,
Snooker/billiards Parking: Off-street
Directions: Take A361 from junction 27 M5 then A39
directions Bideford and Clovelly. Hotel is 6 miles west
of Bideford on A39.

Riversford Hotel

★ ★ ★ ℞

Limers Lane, Bideford, Devon, EX39 2RG
Tel: 01237 474239 Fax: 01237 421661
Email: riversford@aol.com
Web: www.riversford.co.uk
Rooms: 16 all ensuite ✏ Ⓢ
Pricing: Sgl £45 Dbl £65 Dinner from £7.50
CC: Accepted Room facilities: ▢ ☎ ☕
Conference: 1 meeting rooms (Thtr 30 max)
Children: Welcome ⚲ Dogs: Welcome Licences: ♟
Directions: From M5 turn at junction 27 onto the North
Devon Link Rd. Stay until you cross the Torridge Bridge,
right at the roundabout, take 1st right into Limers Lane.

Blandford Forum, Dorset

Crown Hotel

★★★ ☆
West Street, Blandford Forum, Dorset, DT11 7AJ
Tel: 01258 456626 Fax: 01258 451084
Rooms: 32 all ensuite ⛳ 📺 ⊗
Pricing: Dinner from £15.95 (2002 rate) CC: Accepted
Room facilities: 🖥 ☎ ⬛ Access: ⬆
Children: Welcome ☙ Dogs: Welcome
Licences: ⬥ ♔ Parking: Off-street
Directions: Located in the centre of Blandford Forum,
by the River Stour.

Boscastle, Cornwall

The Wellington Hotel

★★★ ☆ ☆
Old Road, Boscastle, Cornwall, PL35 0AQ
Tel: 01840 250202 Fax: 01840 250621
Email: vtobutt@enterprise.net
Web: www.wellingtonboscastle.co.uk

A listed 16th-century coaching inn situated in glorious
National Trust countryside in an area of outstanding
natural beauty, with picturesque Elizabethan harbour
nearby. Excellent Anglo-French Georgian restaurant.
Rooms: 17 (16 ensuite) 📺
Pricing: Sgl £34–43 Dbl £58–76 Dinner from £16.50
CC: Accepted Room facilities: 🖥 ☎ ⬛
Conference: 2 meeting rooms (Thtr 20 max),
24hr-delegate from £35, day-delegate rate from £5
Children: Welcome, 7yrs min age Dogs: Welcome
Licences: ♔ Leisure: Games room
Parking: Off-street
Directions: From Exeter A30 to Launceston, at
Kennards House A395 to Camelford, at Davidstow
B3262 to A39, left then right onto B3266, follow signs
to Boscastle.

Bournemouth, Dorset

Norfolk Royale Hotel

★★★★
Richmond Hill, Bournemouth, Dorset, BH2 6EN
Tel: 01202 551521 Fax: 01202 299729
Email: norfolkroyale@englishrosehotels.co.uk
Web: www.englishrosehotels.co.uk

Rooms: 95 all ensuite 📺 ⊗
Pricing: Sgl £105 Dbl £145 Dinner from £22.50
CC: Accepted Room facilities: 🖥 ☎ ⬛ Access: ⬆
Conference: 9 meeting rooms, 24hr-delegate from
£130, day-delegate rate from £37.50
Children: Welcome ☙ ☙ Licences: ♔
Leisure: Indoor pool, Health spa
Parking: Off-street and monitored
Directions: M3 from London area then A27 via A33.
Take A31 to Wessex Way and at A34 junction left into
Richmond Hill.

See advert on next page

Bay View Court Hotel

★★★
35 East Overcliff Drive, East Cliff, Bournemouth,
Dorset, BH1 3AH
Tel: 01202 294449 Fax: 01202 292883
Email: enquiry@bayviewcourt.co.uk
Web: www.bayviewcourt.co.uk
Rooms: 64 all ensuite ⛳
Pricing: Sgl £42–50 Dbl £84–100 Dinner from £18
CC: Accepted Room facilities: 🖥 ☎ ⬛ Access: ⬆
Conference: 2 meeting rooms (Thtr 120 max),
24hr-delegate from £65, day-delegate rate from £20
Children: Welcome ☙ ☙ Dogs: Welcome
Licences: ♔ Leisure: Indoor pool, Gym,
Health spa, Games room, Snooker/billiards
Parking: Off-street and monitored
Directions: Turn off A338 at St Paul's roundabout. Head
for clifftop. Go over two roundabouts, head for clifftop.

Burley Court Hotel

★★★
Bath Road, Bournemouth, Dorset, BH1 2NP
Tel: 01202 552824 Fax: 01202 298514
Email: info@burleycourthotel.co.uk
Web: www.burleycourthotel.co.uk
Seasonal closure: early January
Rooms: 38 all ensuite ⛳ 📺 ⊗
Pricing: Sgl £31–47 Dbl £62–90 CC: Accepted
Room facilities: 🖥 ☎ ⬛ Access: ⬆
Children: Welcome ☙ ☙ Dogs: Welcome
Licences: ♔
Leisure: Outdoor pool, Games room
Parking: Off-street
Directions: Leave A338 at St Paul's roundabout. Take
third exit at next two roundabouts. Burley Court is the
first hotel after the crossing.

Chesterwood Hotel

★★★

East Overcliff Drive, East Cliff, Bournemouth,
Dorset, BH1 3AR
Tel: 01202 558057 Fax: 01202 556285
Email: enquiry@chesterwoodhotel.co.uk
Web: www.chesterwoodhotel.co.uk
Rooms: 51 all ensuite
Pricing: Sgl £42–50 Dbl £84–100 Dinner from £18
CC: Accepted Room facilities:
Access:
Conference: 4 meeting rooms (Thtr 120 max),
24hr-delegate from £65, day-delegate rate from £20
Children: Welcome Dogs: Welcome
Licences: Leisure: Outdoor pool
Parking: Off-street and monitored
Directions: Go along A338 in to Bournemouth. Follow
signs for East Cliff. Situated on clifftop between the
two piers.

Chine Hotel

★★★★

25 Boscombe Spa Road, Bournemouth,
Dorset, BH5 1AX
Tel: 01202 396234 Fax: 01202 391737
Email: reservations@chinehotel.co.uk
Web: www.chinehotel.co.uk

Attractive Victorian Hotel with award-winning cuisine,
located in three acres of mature gardens with direct
access to the beach. Indoor and outdoor pools,
jacuzzi, outdoor hot-tub, sauna and gymnasium.
Rooms: 89 all ensuite
Pricing: Sgl £55–85 Dbl £110–170 Dinner from £19
CC: Accepted Room facilities: Access:
Conference: 33 meeting rooms (Thtr 140 max), 24hr-
delegate from £113, day-delegate rate from £37.50
Children: Welcome Dogs: Guide dogs only
Licences: Leisure: Indoor pool, Outdoor pool,
Gym, Games room
Parking: Off-street
Directions: On A338, follow signs for town centre. Take
first exit at St Paul's roundabout, then second exit,
then first exit. Turn right into Boscome Spa Road.

Cliffeside Hotel

★★★

East Overcliff Drive, Bournemouth, Dorset, BH1 3AQ
Tel: 01202 555724 Fax: 01202 314534
Email: mail@cliffesidehotel.uk.com
Web: www.arthuryoung.co.uk
Rooms: 62 all ensuite Pricing: Sgl £48–63
Dbl £96–126 Dinner from £18.95 CC: Accepted
Room facilities: Access:
Children: Welcome Dogs: Welcome Licences:
Leisure: Outdoor pool, Games room
Parking: Off-street and monitored
Directions: Five minutes from A338. Follow signs to the
East Cliff.

Cumberland Hotel

★★★

East Overcliff Drive, Bournemouth, Dorset, BH1 3AF
Tel: 01202 290722 Fax: 01202 311394
Email: reservations@cumberlandhotel.uk.com
Web: www.arthuryoung.co.uk
Rooms: 102 all ensuite
Pricing: Sgl £54–65 Dbl £108–130 Dinner from £18.95
CC: Accepted Room facilities: Access:
Conference: 8 meeting rooms (Thtr 100 max), 24hr-
delegate from £79.50, day-delegate rate from £29.50
Children: Welcome, 6yrs min age
Dogs: Welcome Licences: Leisure: Outdoor pool,
Games room Parking: Off-street and monitored
Directions: Take A338 to Bournemouth, left at first round-
about. At next, take 3rd exit, at next take 2nd exit, at next
take 2nd exit to T-junction. Turn left. Hotel 200m on left.

Elstead Hotel

50 ensuite rooms, many refurbished. Set in a quiet tree-lined avenue with superb leisure complex. Good fresh home-cooked food and friendly attentive service offered.

Knyveton Road, Bournemouth, Dorset, BH1 3QP

Tel: 01202 293071 Fax: 01202 293827

Email: info@the-elstead.co.uk

Web: www.the-elstead.co.uk

Durley Hall Hotel
★★★
Durley Chine Road, Bournemouth, Dorset, BH2 5JS
Tel: 01202 751000 Fax: 01202 757535
Email: sales@durleyhall.co.uk
Web: www.durleyhall.co.uk
Rooms: 78 all ensuite 🛏
Pricing: Sgl £35–80 Dbl £75–150 Dinner from £18.50
CC: Accepted
Room facilities: 🖵 ☎ 🛗 📶 Access: ⎸⎸⎸ ♿
Conference: 11 meeting rooms (Thtr 200 max)
Children: Welcome 🍴 🐾 Dogs: Guide dogs only
Licences: ⚓ ♦♦♦
Leisure: Indoor pool, Outdoor pool, Gym, Health spa, Beauty salon, Games room
Parking: Off-street and monitored
Directions: Approaching on the A338 Wessex Way, follow signs to the West Cliff and Bournemouth International Centre.

East Anglia Hotel (Best Western)
★★★
6 Poole Road, Bournemouth, Dorset, BH2 5QX
Tel: 01202 765163 Fax: 01202 752949
Email: info@eastangliahotel.com
Web: www.eastangliahotel.com
Rooms: 70 all ensuite 🛏 🚭
Pricing: Sgl £52 Dbl £96 Dinner from £21
CC: Accepted Room facilities: 🖵 ☎ 🛗 📶
Access: ⎸⎸⎸ ♿
Conference: 4 meeting rooms (Thtr 150 max),

24hr-delegate from £90, day-delegate rate from £30
Children: Welcome 🍴 🐾 Dogs: Guide dogs only
Licences: ♦♦♦ Leisure: Outdoor pool, Health spa, Games room Parking: Off-street and monitored
Directions: From A338, take exit signposted BIC & West Cliff. Take 3rd exit at next roundabout into Poole Road. Hotel is on right.

Elstead Hotel
★★★
Knyveton Road, Bournemouth, Dorset, BH1 3QP
Tel: 01202 293071 Fax: 01202 293827
Email: info@the-elstead.co.uk
Web: www.the-elstead.co.uk
Rooms: 50 all ensuite 🛏 🚭 🚭
Pricing: Sgl £56–75 Dbl £90–130 Dinner from £18.50
CC: Accepted Room facilities: 🖵 ☎ 🛗 Access: ⎸⎸⎸ ♿
Conference: 5 meeting rooms (Thtr 90 max), 24hr-delegate from £85, day-delegate rate from £22.50
Children: Welcome 🍴 🐾 Dogs: Welcome
Licences: ♦♦♦
Leisure: Indoor pool, Gym, Snooker/billiards
Parking: Off-street and monitored
Directions: From A338 follow signs to Bournemouth. Turn into St Paul's Road off the main Wessex way. Turn first left into Knyveton Road.
See advert on this page

Grosvenor Hotel
★★★
Bath Road, Bournemouth, Dorset, BH1 2EX
Tel: 01202 558858 Fax: 01202 298332
Email: enquires@grosvenor-bournemouth.co.uk
Web: www.grosvenor-bournemouth.co.uk

The Grosvenor offers style combined with a caring hospitality. Located close to town centre and beaches. Facilities include leisure complex, conferencing, charming restaurant complemented by our national award-winning chef.
Rooms: 40 all ensuite 🚭
Pricing: Dbl £38–75 Dinner from £8.95 CC: Accepted
Room facilities: 🖵 ☎ 🛗 📶 Access: ⎸⎸⎸ ♿
Conference: Meeting rooms (Thtr 3 max)
Children: Welcome 🍴 Dogs: Welcome Licences: ♦♦♦
Leisure: Indoor pool, Gym, Health spa, Beauty salon, Games room
Parking: Off-street and monitored
Directions: Turn left off A338 towards railway station, then right at roundabout, Holdenhurst Road at roundabout 3, exit at roundabout hotel.

Heathlands Hotel

★★★

12 Grove Road, East Cliff, Bournemouth,
Dorset, BH1 3AY
Tel: 01202 553336 Fax: 01202 555937
Email: info@heathlandshotel.com
Web: www.heathlandshotel.com

115-bedroom hotel located on the East Cliff within
easy walking distance to sandy beaches, cosmopolitan
town centre and award-winning gardens. The hotel is
justly proud of its reputation for fine cuisine and
friendly, efficient staff.
Rooms: 115 all ensuite 🛏 🚭
Room facilities: 🖵 ☎ 🍵 🗢 Access: ⇅ ♿
Children: Welcome ⅂ Dogs: Welcome
Licences: ◇ ⅄
Leisure: Outdoor pool, Gym, Health spa
Parking: Off-street and monitored
Directions: Follow signs to East Cliff. At roundabout,
turn into Gervis Road.

Hotel Miramar

★★★

East Overcliff Drive, Bournemouth, Dorset, BH1 3AL
Tel: 01202 556581 Fax: 01202 291242
Email: sales@miramar-bournemouth.com
Web: www.miramar-bournemouth.com

Situated atop the prestigious East Cliff. Magnificent
views overlooking landscaped gardens and
Bournemouth Bay. An elegant hotel with traditional
English interior.
Rooms: 43 all ensuite 🛏 🖶 🚭
Pricing: Dinner from £20.95 CC: Accepted
Room facilities: 🖵 ☎ 🍵 🗢 Access: ⇅ ♿
Conference: 5 meeting rooms (Thtr 200 max)
Children: Welcome ⅂ 🐾 Dogs: Welcome

Licences: ◇ ⅄ Parking: Off-street
Directions: Turn into St Paul's Road off the main
Wessex Way roundabout. Turn right at the next
roundabout. Take third exit at the next roundabout and
second at the next. Hotel 50 metres on right.

Mayfair Hotel

★★★

27 Bath Road, Bournemouth, Dorset, BH1 2NW
Tel: 01202 551983 Fax: 01202 298459
Email: info@themayfair.com
Web: www.themayfair.com
Rooms: 40 all ensuite 🛏
Pricing: Dinner from £13.95 (2002 rate) CC: Accepted
Room facilities: 🖵 ☎ 🍵 Access: ⇅
Children: Welcome ⅂ 🐾 Licences: ⅄
Leisure: Games room Parking: Off-street and monitored
Directions: Take A338 southbound to first roundabout.
Take last exit off, and at next roundabout 3rd exit off
into Bath Road.

Queens Hotel

★★★★ 📡

Meyrick Road, East Cliff, Bournemouth,
Dorset, BH1 3DL
Tel: 01202 554415 Fax: 01202 294810
Email: mail@queenshotel.uk.com
Web: www.arthuryoung.co.uk
Rooms: 109 all ensuite 🛏 🖶
Pricing: Sgl £61.50–64.50 Dbl £123–129
Dinner from £17.95 CC: Accepted
Room facilities: 🖵 ☎ 🍵 Access: ⇅ ♿
Conference: 3 meeting rooms (Thtr 220 max), 24hr-
delegate from £82.50, day-delegate rate from £29.50
Children: Welcome ⅂ 🐾 Dogs: Welcome Licences: ⅄
Leisure: Indoor pool, Gym, Health spa, Beauty salon,
Games room, Snooker/billiards
Parking: Off-street
Directions: Follow signs into Bournemouth from the
A338 to Landsdowne or East Cliff. The Queens Hotel is
situated one road back from seafront.

Trouville Hotel

★★★★ 📡

5 Priory Road, Westcliff, Bournemouth, Dorset, BH2 5DH
Tel: 01202 552262 Fax: 01202 293324
Email: mail@trouvillehotel.uk.com
Web: www.arthuryoung.co.uk
Rooms: 77 all ensuite 🛏 🖶
Pricing: Sgl £52–59.50 Dbl £104–119
Dinner from £18.95 CC: Accepted
Room facilities: 🖵 ☎ 🍵 Access: ⇅ ♿
Conference: 7 meeting rooms (Thtr 110 max), 24hr-
delegate from £82.50, day-delegate rate from £29.50
Children: Welcome ⅂ 🐾 Dogs: Welcome
Licences: ⅄ Leisure: Indoor pool, Gym,
Health spa Parking: Off-street and monitored
Directions: Leave M3 for M27 Bournemouth. On
entering Bournemouth, follow directions for
Bournemouth International Centre. At roundabout turn
second left. Hotel is on right.

Southwest

Winterbourne Hotel

★★★

Priory Road, Westcliff, Bournemouth, Dorset, BH2 5DJ
Tel: 01202 296366 Fax: 01202 780073
Email: reservations@winterbourne.co.uk
Web: www.winterbourne.co.uk

Enjoying a prime position on the West Cliff with magnificent sea views. Adjacent to the Bournemouth International Centre and within 400m of pier, beaches and town centre.
Rooms: 41 all ensuite 🍴
Pricing: Sgl £37–49 Dbl £64–92 Dinner from £14.50
CC: Accepted Room facilities: ▢ ☎ 🍵
Access: |↓↑ ♿
Conference: 3 meeting rooms (Thtr 100 max), 24hr-delegate from £50, day-delegate rate from £20
Children: Welcome ♨ ⅋ Licences: ♣
Leisure: Outdoor pool, Games room
Parking: Off-street
Directions: Follow signs to the Bournemouth International Centre (BIC). Exit Wessex Way to the BIC. As you approach the BIC, Winterbourne is halfway down hill on the right-hand side (Priory Road).

Arlington Hotel

★★

Exeter Park Road, Lower Gardens, Bournemouth, Dorset, BH2 5BD
Tel: 01202 552879 or 553012 Fax: 01202 298317
Email: enquiries@arlingtonbournemouth.co.uk
Web: www.arlingtonbournemouth.co.uk
Rooms: 28 all ensuite
Pricing: Sgl £32.50–39.50 Dbl £65–79
Dinner from £12.50 CC: Accepted
Room facilities: ▢ ☎ 🍵 🔌 Access: |↓↑
Children: Welcome, 2yrs min age ♨
Licences: ♣ Parking: Off-street
Directions: Follow all signs to Bournemouth International Centre, town centre, pier, beach. Exeter Park Road runs behind Royal Exeter Hotel.

Chequers Hotel

★★

17 West Cliff Road, Bournemouth, Dorset, BH2 5EX
Tel: 01202 553900 Fax: 01202 551015
Email: myra@chequershotel.net
Web: www.chequershotel.net

Seasonal closure: First 2 weeks January
Rooms: 23 (22 ensuite)
Pricing: Sgl £20–33 Dbl £40–66 CC: Accepted
Room facilities: ▢ 🍵 Children: Welcome ♨
Dogs: Welcome Licences: ⚸ ♣ Parking: Off-street
Directions: Follow signs to BIC, Chequers Hotel is then up the hill from mini roundabout and on the right after next roundabout.

Chinehurst Hotel

★★

Studland Road, Westbourne, Bournemouth, Dorset, BH4 8JA
Tel: 01202 764583 Fax: 01202 762854
Rooms: 30 all ensuite 🍴 📺 ⊗
Pricing: Sgl £30–50 Dbl £60–100 CC: Accepted
Room facilities: ▢ ☎ 🍵 Access: ♿
Conference: 3 meeting rooms (Thtr 60 max)
Children: Welcome, 2yrs min age ♨
Dogs: Welcome Licences: ♣
Leisure: Games room, Snooker/billiards
Parking: Off-street
Directions: From A338/A35, take 3rd junction off Frizzel roundabout into The Avenue. Turn left at lights, then right at roundabout into Alumhurst Road. Take last turning left into Studland Road.

Croham Hurst Hotel

★★

9 Durley Road, West Cliff, Bournemouth, Dorset, BH2 5JH
Tel: 01202 552353 Fax: 01202 311484
Email: enquiries@crohamhurst.co.uk
Web: www.crohamhurst.co.uk
Rooms: 40 all ensuite 🍴
Pricing: Sgl £25–45 Dbl £50–90 Dinner from £13.50
CC: Accepted Room facilities: ▢ ☎ 🍵 Access: |↓↑
Children: Welcome ⅋ Dogs: Guide dogs only
Parking: Off-street
Directions: Follow main A338 to Cambridge Road roundabout, follow directions to Westcliff and the hotel is situated next to Durley roundabout.

Fircroft Hotel

★★

Owls Road, Bournemouth, Dorset, BH5 1AE
Tel: 01202 309771 Fax: 01202 395644
Email: info@fircrofthotel.co.uk
Web: www.fircrofthotel.co.uk
Rooms: 50 all ensuite 🍴 ⊗
Room facilities: ▢ ☎ 🍵 Access: |↓↑
Conference: 2 meeting rooms (Thtr 150 max), 24hr-delegate from £60, day-delegate rate from £20
Children: Welcome ♨ ⅋ Dogs: Welcome
Licences: ♣ Leisure: Indoor pool, Gym
Parking: Off-street
Directions: Off A338 over flyover. At next exit follow signs for Boscombe Pier. The hotel is situated on corner of St John's Road and Owls Road. Second turning right along pier.

Grange Hotel

Overcliff Drive, Southbourne, Bournemouth, Dorset, BH6 3NL
Tel: 01202 433093 Fax: 01202 424228
Web: www.bournemouthgrangehotel.co.uk
Rooms: 31 all ensuite
Pricing: Dinner from £15.50 (2002 rate) CC: Accepted
Room facilities: Access:
Children: Welcome Licences:
Leisure: Snooker/billiards Parking: Off-street
Directions: Follow Overcliff Drive to clifftop.

Russell Court Hotel

Bath Road, Bournemouth, Dorset, BH1 2EP
Tel: 01202 295819 Fax: 01202 293457
Email: russellcrt@aol.com
Web: www.russellcourthotel.com
Rooms: 56 all ensuite
Pricing: Sgl £49–67.50 Dbl £78–119
Dinner from £14.95 CC: Accepted
Room facilities: Access:
Conference: 2 meeting rooms (Thtr 80 max),
24hr-delegate from £49, day-delegate rate from £15
Children: Welcome
Dogs: Welcome Licences:
Parking: Off-street
Directions: Follow onto the A31 at the end of the M27. Turn left just past Ringwood onto A338 for Bournemouth. Turn off at roundabout for town centre. At next roundabout turn right and follow signs for BIC. Hotel on left on Bath Road.

Tower House Hotel

West Cliff Gardens, Bournemouth, Dorset, BH2 5HP
Tel: 01202 290742 Fax: 01202 553505
Email: towerhousehotel@macartney.fsnet.co.uk

Splendid family-run hotel with superb English cuisine. All bedrooms offer ensuite, TV, direct dial phones, tea/coffee tray. Romantic four-posters and larger suites, seaviews and ground floor rooms available.
Rooms: 32 all ensuite
Pricing: Sgl £25–35 Dbl £50–70 Dinner from £10

CC: Accepted Room facilities:
Access: Children: Welcome
Dogs: Welcome Licences:
Parking: Off-street and monitored
Directions: A338 for Bournmouth, take town centre west exit for BIC and seafront parking. 2nd exit off Durley roundabout towards the sea.

Ullswater Hotel

West Cliff Gardens, Bournemouth, Dorset, BH2 5HW
Tel: 01202 555181 Fax: 01202 317896
Email: enq@ullswater.uk.com
Web: www.ullswater.uk.com

A family-run hotel, centrally situated close to all amenities. Comfortable and tastefully furnished with an emphasis on good food and personal service.
Rooms: 42 all ensuite
Pricing: Sgl £25–35 Dbl £50–70 Dinner from £12
CC: Accepted Room facilities: Access:
Conference: 2 meeting rooms (Thtr 40 max),
24hr-delegate from £50, day-delegate rate from £20
Children: Welcome Dogs: Welcome
Licences: Leisure: Games room, Snooker/billiards
Parking: Off-street and monitored
Directions: From any major route into Bournemouth, follow the signs for the West Cliff. The Ullswater Hotel is situated in West Cliff Gardens, just off the main West Cliff Road.

Whitehall Hotel

Exeter Park Road, Bournemouth, Dorset, BH2 5AX
Tel: 01202 554682 Fax: 01202 554682
Rooms: 49 (48 ensuite)
Pricing: Dinner from £14 (2002 rate) CC: Accepted
Room facilities: Access:
Children: Welcome Dogs: Welcome

Carisbrooke Hotel

◆◆◆◆

42 Tregonwell Road, Bournemouth, Dorset, BH2 5NT
Tel: 01202 290432 Fax: 01202 310499
Email: info@carisbrooke.co.uk
Web: www.carisbrooke.co.uk
Rooms: 22 (20 ensuite) 🦪 🔳 ⊗
Pricing: Sgl £23–30 Dbl £48–66 Dinner from £9.75
CC: Accepted Room facilities: ⬜ ☎ 🔳 Access: ♿
Children: Welcome ⅄ Dogs: Welcome
Licences: ⅲ Parking: Off-street
Directions: A338 Bournemouth, signs for BIC and West
Cliff. Past roundabout, third left, second hotel on right.

Durley Court Hotel

◆◆◆◆

5 Durley Road, West Cliff, Bournemouth,
Dorset, BH2 5JQ
Tel: 01202 556857 Fax: 01202 554455
Email: durleycourthotel@lineone.net
Web: www.hotelmaster.co.uk
Rooms: 16 (13 ensuite) 🦪 ⊗
Pricing: Sgl £28–38 Dbl £52–72 Dinner from £9.50
CC: Accepted Room facilities: ⬜ 🔳
Children: Welcome, 5yrs min age ⅄ Licences: ⅲ
Parking: Off-street
Directions: Leave A338 at Bournemouth west
roundabout, at next roundabout take 2nd exit, take 1st
left then 1st right into Durley Road.

The Lodge At Meyrick Park

◆◆◆◆

Central Drive, Bournemouth, Dorset, BH2 6LH
Tel: 01202 786000 Fax: 01202 786020
Email: Meyrickpark.lodge@dubhaus.com
Web: www.mayrickpark.com
Rooms: 17 all ensuite ⊗
Pricing: Dbl £65–95 Dinner from £17
CC: Accepted Room facilities: ⬜ ☎ 🔳 Access: ♿
Conference: 1 meeting room (Thtr 50 max)
Licences: ⅲ
Leisure: Indoor pool, Gym, Health spa, Golf
Parking: Off-street
Directions: Follow A338 to Bournemouth to Wessex
way roundabout, straight over to Richmond Hill, 3rd
exit to Wimborne Road, first left to Braidley Road, turn
right at T-junction.

Tudor Grange Hotel

◆◆◆◆

31 Gervis Road, Bournemouth, Dorset, BH1 3EE
Tel: 01202 291472 Fax: 01202 311503
Email: info@tudorgrangehotel.co.uk
Web: www.tudorgrangehotel.co.uk
Seasonal closure: 24 December to 2 January
Rooms: 12 (11 ensuite)
Pricing: Sgl £28–35 Dbl £56–70 CC: Accepted
Room facilities: ⬜ ☎ 🔳 Children: Welcome
Parking: Off-street
Directions: Five minutes from A338 follow signs for
East Cliff, at roundabout turn into Gervis Road.

Denewood Hotel

◆◆◆

1 Percy Road, Bournemouth, Dorset, BH5 1BQ
Tel: 01202 309913 Fax: 01202 391155
Email: res@denewood.co.uk
Web: www.denewood.co.uk
Rooms: 11 all en-suite Pricing: Sgl £20–27 Dbl £40–55
CC: accepted Room facilities: ⬜ 🔳
Conference: 1 meeting rooms (Thtr 20 max)
Children: Welcome ⊁ Dogs: Welcome
Leisure: Beauty salon Parking: Off-street
Directions: On entering Bournemouth, follow signs for
Boscombe Pier. We are 500 metres away from the pier.

Ravenstone Hotel

◆◆◆

36 Burnaby Road, Alum Chine, Westbourne,
Bournemouth, Dorset, BH4 8JG
Tel: 01202 761047 Fax: 01202 761047
Email: holidays@ravenstone36.freeserve.co.uk
Web: www.ravenstone36.freeserve.co.uk
Seasonal closure: November to March

Situated in quiet road, yet close to wooded chine and
safe sandy beach. Easy access to Bournemouth and
Poole town centres. Same owner since 1986.
Rooms: 9 all ensuite
Pricing: Sgl £20–26 Dbl £40–52 Dinner from £10
CC: Accepted Room facilities: ⬜ 🔳
Children: Welcome Licences: ⅲ
Leisure: Games room Parking: Off-street
Directions: Follow A338 to Westbourne, then signs for
Alum Chine. From Alumhurst Road, turn left into
Beaulieu Road. Then turn right into Burnaby Road.

The Roselyn Hotel

◆◆◆

55 West Cliff Road, Alum Chine, Bournemouth,
Dorset, BH4 8BA
Tel: 01202 761037 Fax: 01202 767554
Email: theroselynhotel@yahoo.co.uk
Web: www.asdwebs.com/roselyn
Seasonal closure: January
Rooms: 9 (7 ensuite) 🦪 ⊗ Pricing: Sgl £18–23
Dbl £20–25 Dinner from £4.50 CC: Accepted
Room facilities: ⬜ 🔳 📞 Access: ♿ Children: Welcome ⅄
Dogs: Welcome Licences: ⅲ Leisure: Games room
Parking: Off-street
Directions: From A338 or A35 follow signs to
Westbourne Hotel is off Alum Chine Road.

Washington Hotel

3 Durley Road, West Cliff, Bournemouth,
Dorset, BH2 5JQ
Tel: 01202 557023 Fax: 01202 315562
Web: www.hotelwashington.co.uk
Rooms: 19 (18 ensuite) ⌖ ☕ ⊗
Pricing: Sgl £20–35 Dbl £40–60 Dinner from £8
CC: Accepted Room facilities: ▢ ☕ Children: Welcome ☍
Dogs: Guide dogs only Licences: ♦♦♦ Parking: Off-street
Directions: M3 – M27 then A31 to Bournemouth
airport. Wessex Way, over 1st roundabout, turn left at
2nd roundabout, left again.

Boltons Hotel

9 Durley Chine Road South, Westcliff, Bournemouth,
Dorset, BH2 5JT
Tel: 01202 751517 Fax: 01202 751629
Email: info@boltonshotel.co.uk
Web: www.boltonshotel.co.uk
Rooms: 13 all ensuite ⌖ ⊗
Pricing: Sgl £38.50 Dbl £65 Dinner from £12.50
CC: Accepted Room facilities: ▢ ☎ ☕
Conference: 1 meeting rooms (Thtr 30 max)
Children: Welcome ☍ Dogs: Guide dogs only
Licences: ♦♦♦ Leisure: Outdoor pool
Parking: Off-street

Bovey Tracey, Devon

Edgemoor
★★★ ♟ ♟

Lowerdown Cross, Haytor Road, Bovey Tracey,
Devon, TQ13 9LE
Tel: 01626 832466 Fax: 01626 834760
Email: edgemoor@btinternet.com
Web: www.edgemoor.co.uk
Seasonal closure: New Year
Rooms: 16 all ensuite ☕
Pricing: Sgl £57.50–60 Dbl £95–105 Dinner from £20
CC: Accepted Room facilities: ▢ ☎ ☕ Access: ♿
Conference: 3 meeting rooms (Thtr 60 max),
24hr-delegate from £75, day-delegate rate from £25
Children: Welcome 10yrs min age ☍ ⌖
Dogs: Welcome Licences: ♦♦♦ Parking: Off-street
Directions: From A38, take A382 towards Bovey Tracey.
Then take B3387 towards Haytor and Widecombe. Fork
left after $^1/_4$ mile. Hotel is $^1/_2$ mile on right.

Ilsington Country House Hotel
★★★ ♟ ♟
Ilsington Village, Newton Abbot, Devon, TQ13 9RR
Tel: 01364 661452 Fax: 01364 661307
Email: hotel@ilsington.co.uk
Web: www.ilsington.co.uk
Rooms: 25 all ensuite ⌖
Pricing: Dinner from £26.95 CC: Accepted
Room facilities: ▢ ☎ ☕ Access: ⊥⊥
Conference: 3 meeting rooms (Thtr 40 max),
24hr-delegate from £130, day-delegate rate from £35

Children: Welcome ☍ ⌖ Dogs: Welcome
Licences: ♦♦♦ Leisure: Indoor pool, Gym,
Health spa, Beauty salon
Parking: Off-street
Directions: Follow A38 towards Plymouth. Take exit to
Bovey Tracey, then third exit from roundabout, first
right to Ilsington. Hotel 5 miles on, on right.
See advert on this page

Bradford-on-Avon, Wiltshire

Leigh Park Hotel
★★★

Leigh Road West, Bradford-on-Avon,
Wiltshire, BA15 2RA
Tel: 01225 864885 Fax: 01225 862315
Email: latonalph@aol.com
Web: latonahotels.co.uk
Rooms: 22 all ensuite ☕ ⊗
Pricing: Sgl £75 Dbl £95–140 CC: Accepted
Room facilities: ▢ ☎ ☕ ⚲
Conference: 3 meeting rooms (Thtr 120 max),
24hr-delegate from £110, day-delegate rate from £35
Children: Welcome Dogs: Guide dogs only
Licences: ⊲ ♦♦♦ Parking: Off-street

Southwest

Widbrook Grange

Little Gem

Trowbridge Road, Bradford-on-Avon,
Wiltshire, BA15 1UH
Tel: 01225 863173 Fax: 01225 862890
Email: stay@widbrookgrange.com
Web: www.widbrookgrange.com
Rooms: 20 (19 ensuite) Pricing: Sgl £65–95
Dbl £110–125 Dinner from £27 CC: Accepted
Room facilities: Access: Conference: 3
meeting rooms (Thtr 50 max), 24hr-delegate from £140,
day-delegate rate from £35 Children: Welcome
Licences: Leisure: Indoor pool, Gym
Parking: Off-street and monitored
Directions: Located 1 mile ouside Bradford-on-Avon on
A363 Trowbridge road. 250 metres south of Kennet
and Avon Canal.
See advert on this page

Bridgwater, Somerset

Admirals Table

Bristol Road, Dunball, Bridgwater, Somerset, TA6 4TN
Tel: 01278 685671
Rooms: 13 all ensuite
Pricing: Sgl £47–47 Dbl £52.50–60 CC: Accepted
Room facilities: Access:
Children: Welcome Dogs: Guide dogs only
Licences: Parking: Off-street
Directions: From M5 J23 (west) to Bridgwater, 3rd exit
at roundabout. Next roundabout, 1st exit onto A38,
100 yards on left.

Widbrook Grange

An elegant yet homely Georgian house in eleven
acres surrounded by peaceful gardens and
countryside only seventeen minutes from Bath.
Beautifully decorated ensuite bedrooms and cosy
sitting rooms. Relax in our heated indoor swimming
pool or work-out in the gymnasium. Then enjoy
fine dining in the Medlar Tree restaurant.

Trowbridge Road, Bradford-on-Avon,
Wiltshire, BA15 1UH
Tel: 01225 863173 Fax: 01225 862890
Email: stay@widbrookgrange.com
Website: www.widbrookgrange.com

Travelodge Bridgwater

M5 Moto Service Area, Bridgwater, TA6 6TS
Web: www.travelodge.co.uk
Rooms: 29 all ensuite
Pricing: Sgl £54.40 Dbl £58.85
CC: Accepted Room facilities: Access:

Bridport, Dorset

Haddon House Hotel

★★★

West Bay, Bridport, Dorset, DT6 4EL
Tel: 01308 423626 Fax: 01308 427348
Web: www.haddonhousehotel.co.uk
Rooms: 12 all ensuite
Room facilities: Access:
Children: Welcome
Licences:
Parking: Off-street and monitored
Directions: At the Crown Inn roundabout take the
B3157 West Bay Road, travel to mini roundabout.
Hotel on right-hand side of road.

Roundham House Hotel

★★

Roundham Gardens, West Bay Road, Bridport,
Dorset, DT6 4BD
Tel: 01308 422753 Fax: 01308 421500
Email: cyprencom@compuserve.com
Web: www.roundhamhouse.co.uk
Seasonal closure: January to February
Rooms: 8 all ensuite
Pricing: Sgl £35–40 Dbl £60–80
Dinner from £18.95 CC: Accepted Room facilities:

Children: Welcome, 7yrs min age
Dogs: Welcome
Licences:
Parking: Off-street and monitored
Directions: From A35, as you enter Bridport, find the
Crown Inn roundabout and take signpost to West Bay.
Take 2nd turning left into Roundham Gardens.

Marquis of Lorne

◆ ◆ ◆ ◆

Nettlecombe, Bridport, Dorset, DT6 3SY
Tel: 01308 485236 Fax: 01308 485666
Email: enquires@marquisoflorne.com
Web: www.marquisoflorne.com

Idyllic 16th century pub in unspoilt countryside —
seven comfortable ensuite bedrooms. Homemade food
— members of the campaign for real food — fine
wines and ales. Family garden beautiful views, walking
and touring area.
Rooms: 7 all ensuite ⊗
Pricing: Sgl £25–35 Dbl £50–70 Dinner from £11.50
CC: Accepted Room facilities: ⬜ ☎ ⊗ ⬏
Children: Welcome, 10yrs min age �
Dogs: Guide dogs only Licences: ⚏
Parking: Off-street
Directions: North from Bridport on A3066 after 1¹/₂
miles, after mini roundabout turn right through West
Milton, straight over junction, premises up hill.

Bristol

Aztec Hotel

★ ★ ★ ★ ℞

Aztec West Business Park, Almondsbury,
Bristol, BS12 4TS
Tel: 01454 201090 Fax: 01454 201593
Email: aztec@shirehotels.co.uk
Web: www.shirehotels.co.uk
Rooms: 128 all ensuite ⬜ ⊗
Pricing: Sgl £155 Dbl £110 CC: Accepted
Room facilities: ⬜ ☎ ⊗ ⬏ ❄ Access: �ⅲ ♿
Conference: 22 meeting rooms (Thtr 200 max)
Children: Welcome � ⁋℃ Dogs: Guide dogs only
Licences: ⚏ ⚏
Leisure: Indoor pool, Gym, Beauty salon
Parking: Off-street and monitored
Directions: Close to M4/M5 intersection. Leave M5 at
Junction 16. Follow signs for Aztec West.

Jurys Bristol Hotel

★ ★ ★ ★

Prince Street, Bristol, BS1 4QF
Tel: +353(0)1 6070000 Fax: +353(0)1 6316999
Email: bookings@jurysdoyle.com
Web: www.jurysdoyle.com

JURYS DOYLE
HOTELS

Rooms: 191 all ensuite
Pricing: Sgl £124–154 Dbl £138–168 Dinner from £23
CC: Accepted Room facilities: ⬜ ☎ ⊗ ⬏
Access: ⅲ ♿ Children: Welcome 12yrs min age � ⁋℃
Dogs: Guide dogs only Licences: ⚏ ⚏
Parking: Off-street and monitored
Directions: Situated along River Quayside in the centre
of city.

Tortworth Court Four Pillars Hotel

★ ★ ★ ★

Tortworth, Wotton-under-Edge,
South Gloucestershire, GL12 8HH
Tel: 01454 263000 Fax: 01454 263001
Email: bristol@four-pillars.co.uk
Web: www.four-pillars.co.uk
Rooms: 189 all ensuite ⊗ ⬜ ⊗
Pricing: Sgl £75–152.45 Dbl £99–198.90
Dinner from £23.95 CC: Accepted
Room facilities: ⬜ ☎ ⊗ ⬏
Access: ⅲ ♿
Children: Welcome � ⁋℃ Dogs: Guide dogs only
Licences: ⚏ ⚏
Leisure: Indoor pool, Gym, Health spa, Beauty salon
Parking: Off-street and monitored
Directions: J14 M5 onto B4509, past visitors' centre, take
next right. Hotel is on right approximately ¹/₂ mile.
See advert on following page

Alveston House Hotel

★ ★ ★ ★ ℞ ℞

Alveston, Thornbury, Bristol, BS35 2LA
Tel: 01454 415050 Fax: 01454 415425
Email: info@alvestonhousehotel.co.uk
Web: www.alvestonhousehotel.co.uk
Rooms: 30 all ensuite ⊗
Pricing: Sgl £89.50–99.50
Dbl £99.50–109.50
Dinner from £19.75 CC: Accepted
Room facilities: ⬜ ☎ ⊗ ⬏
Conference: 8 meeting rooms (Thtr 85 max),
24hr-delegate from £135, day-delegate rate from £35
Children: Welcome ⁋℃
Dogs: Welcome
Licences: ⚏ ⚏
Parking: Off-street
Directions: 3¹/₂ miles north of M4/M5 junction on main
A38 at Alveston.

Avon Gorge Hotel

★★★

Sion Hill, Bristol, BS8 4LD
Tel: 0117 973 8955 Fax: 0117 923 8125
Email: info@avongorge-hotel-bristol.com
Web: www.peelhotel.com

Superbly located in fashionable Clifton Village, with stunning views of the Clifton Suspension Bridge. 76 luxurious bedrooms, including four-posters, studios and flats, equipped with satellite television. Free parking for overnight guests.
Rooms: 76 all ensuite ✥ ⬚ ⊗
Pricing: Sgl £112–122 Dbl £122–140
Dinner from £16.50 CC: Accepted
Room facilities: ⬚ ☎ ☕ Access: ⌊↑ ♿

Conference: 6 meeting rooms (Thtr 100 max), 24hr-delegate from £145, day-delegate rate from £42
Children: Welcome ⅂ Dogs: Guide dogs only
Licences: ◁ ⅰⅰⅰ Parking: Off-street
Directions: From M5, use Junction 19, signposted Clifton; go over suspension bridge, turn right. From M4, use Junction 19 and take M32 to city; follow signs to Clifton and bridge.

Berkeley Square Hotel

★★★

15 Berkeley Square, Clifton, Bristol, BS8 1HB
Tel: 0117 925 4000 Fax: 0117 925 2970
Email: berkeley@cliftonhotels.com
Web: www.cliftonhotels.com
Rooms: 42 all ensuite ⊗
Pricing: Dinner from £15 (2002 rate) CC: Accepted
Room facilities: ⬚ ☎ ☕ ♨ Access: ⌊↑↑
Children: Welcome ⅂ Dogs: Welcome
Licences: ⅰⅰⅰ Parking: Off-street and monitored

Henbury Lodge Hotel

★★★★

Station Road, Henbury, Bristol, BS10 7QQ
Tel: 0117 950 2615 Fax: 0117 950 9532
Email: enquiries@henburylodge.com
Web: www.henburylodge.com
Rooms: 21 all ensuite ✥ ⊗
Pricing: Sgl £59–106.50 Dbl £92–116.50
Dinner from £19.75 CC: Accepted
Room facilities: ⬚ ☎ ☕
Access: ♿
Conference: 1 meeting rooms (Thtr 32 max), 24hr-delegate from £120, day-delegate rate from £20
Children: Welcome ⅂
Dogs: Welcome
Licences: ⅰⅰⅰ Leisure: Gym
Parking: Off-street and monitored
Directions: From M5 Junction 17, follow A4018 to 3rd roundabout. Turn right. At T-junction, turn right. Hotel is 200m up on corner.

Best Western Victoria Square Hotel

★★

Victoria Square, Clifton, Bristol, BS8 4EW
Tel: 0117 973 9058 Fax: 0117 973 9058
Email: victoriasquare@btopenworld.com
Web: vicsquare.com
Seasonal closure: Christmas
Rooms: 40 all ensuite ✥ ⊗
Pricing: Sgl £70–80 Dbl £85–95 Dinner from £12.50
CC: Accepted Room facilities: ⬚ ☎ ☕
Conference: 2 meeting rooms (Thtr 36 max)
Children: Welcome ⅂
Dogs: Welcome
Licences: ⅰⅰⅰ
Parking: Off-street and monitored
Directions: From M5 Junction 19, follow signs for Clifton. Proceed over bridge and turn right into Clifton Down, turn left into Merchants Road.
See advert on next page

Clifton Hotel

★★

St Paul's Road, Clifton, Bristol, BS8 1LX
Tel: 0117 973 6882 Fax: 0117 974 1082
Email: clifton@cliftonhotels.com
Web: www.cliftonhotels.com
Rooms: 59 all ensuite
Pricing: Sgl £45–75 Dbl £69–89 CC: Accepted
Room facilities: Access:
Conference: 7 meeting rooms (Thtr 150 max)
Children: Welcome Licences:
Parking: Off-street and monitored
Directions: From M4: leave M4 junction 19 onto M32,
follow Clifton signs to Whiteladies Road, left at first set
traffic lights.

Rodney Hotel

★★

4 Rodney Place, Clifton, Bristol, BS8 4HY
Tel: 0117 973 5422 Fax: 0117 946 7092
Email: rodney@cliftonhotels.com
Web: www.cliftonhotels.com
Rooms: 31 all ensuite Pricing: Dinner from £15
(2002 rate) CC: Accepted Room facilities:
Children: Welcome Dogs: Welcome Licences:

Seeley's Hotel

★★

17-27 St Paul's Road, Clifton, Bristol, BS8 1LX
Tel: 0117 973 8544 Fax: 0117 973 2406
Email: admin@seeleys.demon.co.uk
Web: www.seeleyshotel.co.uk
Seasonal closure: Christmas and New Year
Rooms: 54 all ensuite Pricing: Sgl £50–70
Dbl £65–85 Dinner from £14 CC: Accepted
Room facilities: Conference: 3 meeting
rooms (Thtr 70 max), 24hr-delegate from £92, day-
delegate rate from £32 Children: Welcome
Dogs: Guide dogs only Licences: Leisure: Gym
Parking: Off-street
Directions: From city centre, up Park Street towards
Clifton. Head towards BBC studios on Whiteladies
Road and turn left opposite into St Paul's Road.
See advert on this page

Westbourne Hotel

★★

40-44 St Pauls Road, Clifton, Bristol, BS8 1LR
Tel: 0117 973 4214 Fax: 0117 974 3552
Email: westbournehotel@bristol8.fsworld.co.uk
Web: www.westbournehotel-bristol.co.uk
Rooms: 31 (27 ensuite) Pricing: Sgl £45–60
Dbl £65–70 Dinner from £4.50 CC: Accepted
Room facilities: Access: Conference: 1
meeting room (Thtr 6 max) Children: Welcome
Dogs: Guide dogs only Licences:
Leisure: Games room Parking: Off-street and monitored
Directions: City centre, up Park Street, at top take
right-hand lane to Whiteladies Road, turn left at first
traffic lights opposite BBC into St Paul's Road.
See advert on following page

Southwest

Westbourne Hotel

40-44 St Pauls Road
Clifton, Bristol
BS8 1LR
Tel: 0117 973 4214   Fax: 0117 974 3552

Westbourne Hotel is off Whiteladies Road in the heart
of upmarket Clifton, with its bars, clubs and
restaurants a few minutes walk away. Five minutes
from the Bristol University, ten minutes from the
famous Clifton Suspension Bridge and the zoo. It
offers 24-hour reception, bar and restaurant, room
service. All rooms with ensuite bathrooms and
modern facilities. Well placed for a night out.
Group bookings welcome

**Email: westbournehotel@bristol8.fsworld.co.uk
www.westbournehotel-bristol.co.uk**

Downs View Guest House

♦ ♦ ♦

38 Upper Belgrave Road, Clifton, Bristol, BS8 2XN
Tel: 0117 973 7046
Email: bookings@downsviewguesthouse.co.uk
Web: www.downsviewguesthouse.co.uk
Seasonal closure: Christmas and New Year
Rooms: 15 (7 ensuite)
Room facilities: 🖵 🍵
Children: Welcome Dogs: Guide dogs only
Directions: Exit J17 M5, follow signs to Zoo; on left
after 5 miles. From centre, top of Whiteladies Road,
turn left.

Oakfield Hotel

♦ ♦ ♦

52/54 Oakfield Road, Clifton, Bristol, BS8 2BG
Tel: 0117 973 5556 Fax: 0117 974 4141
Rooms: 27
Pricing: Sgl £30–35 Dbl £40–45 Dinner from £7.50
Room facilities: 🖵 🍵 Children: Welcome
Dogs: Welcome Licences: 👥
Parking: Off-street

Plan your route

Visit www.rac.co.uk for RAC's
interactive route planner, including
up to the minute traffic reports.

Washington Hotel

♦ ♦ ♦

St Paul's Road, Clifton, Bristol, BS8 1LX
Tel: 0117 973 3980 Fax: 0117 973 4740
Email: washington@cliftonhotels.com
Web: www.cliftonhotels.com
Seasonal closure: Christmas

With its excellent service and facilities, this budget
hotel has two-star quality. Close to shops and
restaurants, it also has a secure garage.
Rooms: 46 (40 ensuite)
Pricing: Sgl £35–49 Dbl £52–64 CC: Accepted
Room facilities: 🖵 ☎ 🍵 📺
Conference: Meeting rooms (Thtr 150 max)
Children: Welcome Dogs: Welcome
Parking: Off-street and monitored
Directions: Leave M4 at junction 19 onto M32. Follow
Clifton signs to Whiteladies Road. Left at first lights.

Travelodge Bristol Central (SA)

Travel Accommodation
A4, Anchor Road, Bristol, Avon, BS1 5TT
Web: www.travelodge.co.uk
Rooms: 119 all ensuite
Pricing: Sgl £64.40 Dbl £68.85
CC: Accepted Room facilities: 🖵 🍵 Access: ♿

Travelodge Bristol, Cribbs Causeway (SA)

Travel Accommodation
A4018, Cribbs Causeway, Bristol, Avon, BS10 7TL
Web: www.travelodge.co.uk
Rooms: 56 all ensuite
Pricing: Sgl £57.40–64.40 Dbl £61.85–68.85
CC: Accepted Room facilities: 🖵 🍵 Access: ♿

Travelodge Severn View (MOTO)

Travel Accommodation
M48 Moto Service Area, Seven Bridge, Aust,
Bristol, BS35 4BH
Web: www.travelodge.co.uk
Rooms: 50 all ensuite
Pricing: Sgl £57.40 Dbl £61.85
CC: Accepted Room facilities: 🖵 🍵 Access: ♿

Brixham, Devon

The Smugglers Haunt Hotel

★

Church Hill, Brixham, Devon, TQ5 8HH
Tel: 01803 853050 Fax: 01803 858738
Email: enquiries@smugglershaunt-hotel-devon.co.uk
Web: www.smugglershaunt-hotel-devon.co.uk
Rooms: 14 all ensuite
Pricing: Sgl £31–34 Dbl £52–58 Dinner from £6.95
CC: Accepted Room facilities:
Children: Welcome Dogs: Welcome
Licences:
Directions: Take the A3022 Brixham road to town centre, turn left at the light and T-junction. Our hotel directly in front of you, up a small hill on the left.

Brookside Guest House

♦♦♦

160 New Road, Brixham, Devon, TQ5 8DA
Tel: 01803 858858
Email: joythompson@onetel.net.uk
Rooms: 5 (2 ensuite)
Pricing: Sgl £18 Dbl £36–44 Dinner from £7
Room facilities: Parking: Off-street
Directions: Follow A3022 from Paignton to Brixham at traffic lights, fork left to town centre, Brookside 200 yards on right.

Harbour View Hotel

♦♦♦

65 King Street, Brixham, Devon, TQ5 9TH
Tel: 01803 853052 Fax: 01803 853052
Rooms: 8 all ensuite
Pricing: Sgl £25–29 Dbl £40–48 CC: Accepted
Room facilities: Children: Welcome
Parking: Off-street
Directions: A3022 Brixham road to town centre/harbour, left at lights, right at T-junction. Hotel is on right of inner harbour.

Bude, Cornwall

Hartland Hotel

★★★

Hartland Terrace, Bude, Cornwall, EX23 8JY
Tel: 01288 355661 Fax: 01288 355664
Web: www.hartlandhotel.co.uk
Seasonal closure: December to February
Rooms: 28 all ensuite
Pricing: Sgl £42–56 Dbl £74–90 Dinner from £22
Room facilities: Access:
Children: Welcome Dogs: Welcome
Licences: Leisure: Outdoor pool
Parking: Off-street
Directions: Turn left into Hartland Terrace from main street (opposite Boots). Hotel signposted in main street.

Camelot Hotel

★★

Downs View, Bude, Cornwall, EX23 8RE
Tel: 01288 352361 Fax: 01288 355470
Email: stay@camelot-hotel.co.uk
Web: www.camelot-hotel.co.uk
Seasonal closure: Christmas and New Year

Overlooking Bude Golf Course. A short walk from beaches and town centre. Elegantly refurbished to a high standard with first class, friendly service and superb freshly-prepared food.
Rooms: 24 all ensuite
Pricing: Sgl £39–55 Dbl £78–86 Dinner from £19
CC: Accepted Room facilities: Access:
Children: Welcome Licences:
Leisure: Games room Parking: Off-street and monitored
Directions: Follow one-way system past post office. Stay in left lane; Camelot is at bottom of hill on left.

Cliff Hotel

♦♦♦♦

Maer Down Road, Bude, Cornwall, EX23 8NG
Tel: 01288 353110 Fax: 01288 353110
Web: www.cliffhotel.co.uk
Seasonal closure: November to March
Rooms: 15 all ensuite
Pricing: Sgl £35.40–40.20 Dbl £59–67
Dinner from £12.50 CC: Accepted
Room facilities: Children: Welcome
Dogs: Welcome Licences: Leisure: Indoor pool, Gym, Tennis, Games room, Snooker/billiards
Parking: Off-street
Directions: Through High Street, past post office on left. Second left. First right to crossroads. Straight on, hotel on right-hand side.

Coombe Barton Inn

♦♦♦

Nr. Bude, Cornwall, EX23 0JG
Tel: 01840 230345 Fax: 01840 230788
Seasonal closure: November to March
Rooms: 6 (3 ensuite) Pricing: Sgl £30–35 Dbl £50–90 Dinner from £12.50 CC: Accepted
Room facilities: Children: Welcome
Dogs: Guide dogs only Licences:
Leisure: Games room Parking: Off-street and monitored
Directions: From Bude head south on A39, turn right at Wainhouse Corner junction and follow lane down to the beach.

Budleigh Salterton, Devon

Long Range Hotel

◆◆◆◆◆ ® ※

5 Vales Road, Budleigh Salterton, Devon, EX9 6HS
Tel: 01395 443321 Fax: 01395 442132
Email: info@thelongrangehotel.co.uk
Web: www.thelongrangehotel.co.uk
Rooms: 7 (6 ensuite) ⊛
Pricing: Sgl £35–40 Dbl £65–75 Dinner from £15.95
CC: Accepted Room facilities: ▢ ⌂
Children: Welcome, 10yrs min age
Licences: ╫╫╫ Parking: Off-street
Directions: From Exeter approach Budleigh Salterton.
Turn left at traffic lights. Continue to T-junction, turn
left. Take first right and first right again. Hotel on left.

Burnham-on-Sea, Somerset

Battleborough Grange Country Hotel

★★

Bristol Road, Brent Knoll, Nr Highbridge,
Somerset, TA9 4HJ
Tel: 01278 760208 Fax: 01278 760208
Email: info@battleboroughgrangehotel.co.uk
Web: www.battleboroughgrangehotel.co.uk
Seasonal closure: 26 December to 2 January
Rooms: 16 (15 ensuite) ⌱ ⊿
Pricing: Sgl £52–88 Dbl £68–108 Dinner from £16
CC: Accepted Room facilities: ▢ ☎ ⌂ ☎
Conference: 3 meeting rooms (Thtr 85 max),
24hr-delegate from £75, day-delegate rate from £25
Children: Welcome ᛚ ﹪℃ Dogs: Guide dogs only
Licences: ⚐ ╫╫╫ Parking: Off-street and monitored
Directions: Junction 22 M5, turn right at roundabout 1
mile on main A38 Hotel on left-hand side. 300 yards
from Garden World.
See advert on next page

Callington, Cornwall

Woodpeckers

◆◆◆◆ ※

Rilla Hill, Callington, Cornwall, PL17 7NT
Tel: 01579 363717

Woodpeckers offers relaxation in beautiful
surroundings, all rooms with views of babbling brook
and wooded hillside, in conservation village, centre for
Eden Project, Traso Mills, Looe, Tintash, 10 mins from
Bodmin Moor, Liskard, Callington.

Rooms: 3 all ensuite ⌱ ⊛
Pricing: Dbl £20–23 Dinner from £10
Room facilities: ▢ ⌂ Children: Welcome ᛚ
Parking: Off-street
Directions: M5–A30 past Oakhampton, Launceston
follow B3254 towards Liskeard, go through. Daws
House, South Pethorwin, straight over at Congdons
shop, north hill. Left at crossroads in Upton Cross for
Rilla Mill, first left after sign, Woodpeckers right house.

Castle Combe, Wiltshire

Castle Inn

★★★

Castle Combe, Wiltshire, SN14 7HN
Tel: 01249 783030 Fax: 01249 782315
Email: res@castle-inn.co.uk
Web: www.castle-inn.co.uk
Rooms: 11 all ensuite ⌱ ⊛
Pricing: Sgl £71.50 Dbl £105 Dinner from £10
CC: Accepted Room facilities: ▢ ☎ ⌂ ☎
Children: Welcome ᛚ ﹪℃ Dogs: Guide dogs only
Licences: ╫╫╫
Directions: In the centre of Castle Combe village,
overlooking the village cross.
See advert on next page

Chagford, Devon

Three Crowns Hotel

★★

High Street, Chagford, Devon, TQ13 8AJ
Tel: 01647 433444 Fax: 01647 433117
Email: threecrowns@msn.com
Web: www.chagford-accom.co.uk
Rooms: 18 all ensuite ⌱ ⊛
Pricing: Sgl £50–90 Dbl £55–80 Dinner from £17.50
CC: Accepted Room facilities: ▢ ☎ ⌂
Conference: 1 meeting room (Thtr 100 max)
Children: Welcome ᛚ Dogs: Welcome
Licences: ╫╫╫ Leisure: Games room
Parking: Off-street and monitored
See advert on next page

Cheriton Bishop, Exeter

The Old Thatch Inn

◆◆◆ ®

Cheriton Bishop, Exeter, Devon, EX6 6JH
Tel: 01647 24204 Fax: 01647 24584
Email: oldthatchinn@aol.com
Seasonal closure: Christmas Eve and day
Rooms: 3 all ensuite
Pricing: Sgl £35–35 Dbl £49–49 CC: Accepted
Room facilities: ▢ ⌂
Children: Welcome, 2yrs min age ᛚ
Dogs: Guide dogs only Licences: ╫╫╫
Parking: Off-street
Directions: Situated off A36 10 miles west of Exeter at
Cheriton Bishop, Woodleigh junction on left as you
enter the village car park opposite.

Chideock, Dorset

Betchworth House

Main Street, Chideock, Dorset, DT6 6JW
Tel: 01297 489478 Fax: 01297 489932
Rooms: 5 (3 ensuite)
Pricing: Sgl £30–40 Dbl £50–60 CC: Accepted
Room facilities: ☐ ⌂. Children: Welcome, 10yrs min age
Parking: Off-street
Directions: Located on A35, 2 miles from Bridport and
6 miles from Lyme Regis.

Chimneys

Main Street, Chideock, Bridport, Dorset, DT6 6JH
Tel: 01297 489368
Email: chimneys@ chideock.co.uk
Rooms: 5 (4 ensuite)
Pricing: Sgl £30 Dbl £50–60
Room facilities: ☐ ⌂. Children: Welcome
Dogs: Welcome Parking: Off-street
Directions: Found on A35 in Chideock Village.

It's easier online

For all your motoring and travel
needs, www.rac.co.uk

Battleborough Grange Hotel

Surrounded by mellow Somerset countryside,
the hotel is just 1 mile from M5, making it a
convenient location for both business and
leisure guests. Bedrooms are well equipped
and some offer extensive views of the historic
Iron Age fort of Brent Knoll. Public rooms
include a convivial bar, conservatory restaurant
and extensive function facilities.
Civil ceremonies also available.

Bristol Road, Highbridge,
Somerset TA9 4HJ

Tel: 01278 760208   Fax: 01278 760208
Website: www.battleboroughgrange.com

Castle Inn

Set in the market place, this famous hostelry
can trace its origins back to the 12th century
and many features of the original construction
remain today. Nestled in a wooded Cotswold
valley, Castle Combe is a truly delightul example
of a traditional English village. Architecturally,
little has changed since the 15th century and all
properties are listed as ancient monuments.

Castle Combe, Wilshire SN14 7HN
Tel: 01249 783030   Fax: 01249 782315
Email: res@castle-inn.co.uk
Website: www.castle-inn.co.uk

Three Crowns Hotel

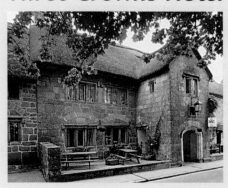

A warm and friendly 13th-century inn
situated in a picturesque village within
Dartmoor. Oak beams, four-poster
beds. Noted for good food and ale.

High Street, Chagford,
Devon, TQ13 8AJ
Tel: 01647 433444 Fax: 01647 433117
Email: threecrowns@msn.com
Web: www.chagford-accom.co.uk

Chippenham, Wiltshire

White Hart Inn

Ford, Chippenham, Wiltshire, SN14 8RP
Tel: 01249 782213 Fax: 01249 783075
Email: whitehart.ford@eldridge-pope.co.uk
Rooms: 11 all ensuite
Pricing: Sgl £60–80 Dbl £70–90 Dinner from £10.95
CC: Accepted Room facilities:
Conference: 1 meeting room (Thtr 10 max)
Children: Welcome Dogs: Welcome
Licences: Leisure: Games room
Parking: Off-street and monitored
Directions: M4 J18, A46 Bath. First roundabout, left at
A420 Chippenham, 6 miles. From London J17 to
Chippenham, A420 Bristol, 5 miles to Ford.

Travelodge Chippenham, Leigh Delamere East (MOTO)

Travel Accommodation
M4 Moto Service Area, Leigh Delarmere, Chippenham,
Wilshire, SN14 6LB
Web: www.travelodge.co.uk
Rooms: 69 all ensuite
Pricing: Sgl £54.40 Dbl £58.85
CC: Accepted Room facilities: Access:

Christchurch, Dorset

The Avonmouth Hotel

★★★

95 Mudeford, Mudeford, Christchurch,
Dorset, BH23 3NT
Tel: 0870 400 8120 Fax: 01202 479004
Email: avonmouth@heritage-hotels.co.uk
Web: www.macdonaldhotels.co.uk
Rooms: 40 all ensuite
Pricing: Sgl £82 Dbl £164 Dinner from £23.95
CC: Accepted Room facilities:
Conference: 2 meeting rooms (Thtr 110 max)
Children: Welcome Dogs: Welcome
Licences:
Leisure: Outdoor pool, Golf, Riding
Parking: Monitored
Directions: Take M27 to J1, then A35 to Christchurch.
Follow ample signs to Mudeford, hotel situated on right.

Waterford Lodge Hotel

★★★★

87 Bure Lane, Friars Cliff, Christchurch,
Dorset, BH23 4DN
Tel: 01425 278801 Fax: 01425 279130
Email: waterford@bestwestern.co.uk
Web: www.waterfordlodge.com
Rooms: 18 all ensuite
Room facilities: Children: Welcome
Dogs: Welcome Licences: Parking: Off-street
Directions: 2 miles east of Christchurch on A337, turn
south towards Mudeford and hotel is half a mile on left.

Cirencester, Gloucestershire

The Black Horse

17 Castle Street, Cirencester, Gloucestershire, GL7 1QD
Tel: 01285 653187
Rooms: 4 all ensuite
Pricing: Sgl £46–46 Dbl £51–51 CC: Accepted
Room facilities: Children: Welcome
Dogs: Welcome Licences:
Directions: Head for town centre, pass church and go
across traffic lights on the left hand side.

Clevedon, Somerset

Walton Park Hotel

★★★

1 Wellington Terrace, Clevedon,
North Somerset, BS21 7BL
Tel: 01275 874253 Fax: 01275 343577
Email: latonawph@aol.com
Web: latonahotels.co.uk
Rooms: 45 all ensuite
Pricing: Sgl £48–77 Dbl £83–95
Room facilities: Access:
Conference: 5 meeting rooms (Thtr 120 max),
24hr-delegate from £109, day-delegate rate from £33
Children: Welcome Dogs: Guide dogs only
Licences: Parking: Off-street

Combe Martin, Devon

Acorns Guest House

2 Woodlands, Combe Martin, Devon, EX34 0AT
Tel: 01271 882769 Fax: 01271 882769
Email: info@acorns-guesthouse.co.uk
Web: www.acorns-guesthouse.co.uk
Rooms: 8 all ensuite
Pricing: Sgl £25–29 Dbl £41–50 Dinner from £10
CC: Accepted Room facilities:
Children: Welcome Dogs: Guide dogs only
Licences: Parking: Off-street
Directions: M5 then A361 towards Barnstaple A399 to
Combe Martin, 300 yards past bay on left, private
parking at rear.

Plan your route

Visit www.rac.co.uk for RAC's
interactive route planner, including
up to the minute traffic reports.

Are you covered?

For competitively priced travel
insurance, buy online at
www.rac.co.uk or call RAC Travel
Sales on 0800 55 00 55. Quote GUI3

Blair Lodge Hotel

 ◆ ◆ ◆ ✕

Moory Meadow, Seaside, Combe Martin,
North Devon, EX34 0DG
Tel: 01271 882294
Email: info@blairlodge.co.uk
Web: www.blairlodge.co.uk
Seasonal closure: November to January

Suberb family-run, non-smoking hotel overlooking bay.
10 bedrooms, licensed, quiet position alongside
coastal path. Private car park, regret no pets. Perfect
for exploring Exmoor, golf nearby, mountain biking.
Rooms: 10 (6 ensuite) ⊗
Pricing: Sgl £23–23 Dbl £46–50 Dinner from £12
CC: Accepted Room facilities: ▢ ☐
Children: Welcome, 10yrs min age
Dogs: Guide dogs only Licences: ▮▮▮ Parking: Off-street
Directions: A399 straight through long high street in
Combe Martin. UK garage on left, turn right then
immediately right again.

Corsham, Wiltshire

Methuen Arms Hotel

★ ★ ★ ☕

High Street, Corsham, Wiltshire, SN13 0HB
Tel: 01249 714867 Fax: 01249 712004
Email: latonamah@aol.com
Web: latonahotels.co.uk
Rooms: 25 all ensuite ▱ ⊗
Pricing: Dinner from £9.95 CC: Accepted
Room facilities: ▢ ☎ ☐ Access: ♿
Conference: 1 meeting rooms (Thtr 30 max),
24hr-delegate from £90, day-delegate rate from £30
Children: Welcome ⁏ Dogs: Guide dogs only
Licences: ⟁ ▮▮▮ Leisure: Games room,
Snooker/billiards Parking: Off-street
Directions: On A4 between Chippenham and Bath.
Follow signs for town centre.

Crediton, Devon

Lower Burrow Coombe

◆ ◆ ◆

Cheriton Fitzpaine, Crediton, Devon, EX17 4JS
Tel: 01363 866220
Seasonal closure: December to February
Rooms: 3 (1 ensuite) ⊗
Pricing: Sgl £20–25 Dbl £36–40
Room facilities: ▢ ☐ Children: Welcome ⼝ ⁏

Parking: Off-street and monitored
Directions: M5 to Tiverton; follow signs to Exeter. At
Bickleigh take the A3072 towards Crediton; 3 miles on
the right, sign for the farm.

Croyde, Devon

Croyde Bay House Hotel   Little Gem

◆ ◆ ◆ ◆ ◆ ✕ ☏

Moor Lane, Croyde, Devon, EX33 1PA
Tel: 01271 890270
Seasonal closure: December to February

Warm, friendly hotel with seven confortable well
furnished ensuite rooms, ideally situated beside beach
with glorious views of bay. Rain or shine a place to
enjoy the magnificent sea.
Rooms: 7 all ensuite ⊛
Pricing: Dbl £64–80 CC: Accepted
Room facilities: ▢ ☐ Access: ♿
Children: Welcome Dogs: Welcome
Licences: ▮▮▮ Parking: Off-street
Directions: M5 Junction 27. Follow A361 to Barnstaple,
then signs for Braunton. Left in Braunton to Croyde
village. Left in centre of Croyde, then left again into
Moor Lane. Follow road to slipway 3/4 miles.

Cullompton, Devon

Manor House Hotel

★ ★

2/4 Fore Street, Cullompton, Devon, EX15 1JL
Tel: 01884 32281
Rooms: 11 (10 ensuite) ⊛ ▱
Room facilities: ▢ ☎ ☐ ❄ Children: Welcome ⼝
Dogs: Welcome Licences: ▮▮▮ Leisure: Snooker/billiards
Parking: Off-street and monitored

Waterloo Cross Inn

◆ ◆ ◆

Waterloo Cross, Uffculme, Cullompton, Devon, EX15 3ES
Tel: 01884 840328 Fax: 01884 840908
Email: waterloocross.uffculme@eldridge-pope.co.uk
Rooms: 10 all ensuite ⊛ ⊗
Pricing: Sgl £40 Dbl £50 Dinner from £6.95
CC: Accepted Room facilities: ▢ ☎ ☐ ☏
Children: Welcome ⼝ Dogs: Guide dogs only
Licences: ▮▮▮ Parking: Off-street
Directions: M5 J27, A38 towards Wellington/Willand.
Inn is situated 500 metres on the right.

Southwest

Dartmoor, Devon

Two Bridges Hotel

★★★

Two Bridges, Devon, PL20 6SW
Tel: 01822 890581 Fax: 01822 890575
Email: tb@warm-welcome-hotels.co.uk
Web: www.warm-welcome-hotels.co.uk

Historic 18th century hotel with a beautiful riverside location at the heart of Dartmoor. Award-winning restaurant, cosy bars and comfortable lounges. Warmest welcome guaranteed.
Rooms: 33 all ensuite 🐕 🍳 🚭
Pricing: Sgl £60–80 Dbl £90–130 Dinner from £25
CC: Accepted Room facilities: 📺 ☎ 🍵 Access: 🚶
Conference: 2 meeting rooms (Thtr 140 max),
24hr-delegate from £125, day-delegate rate from £35
Children: Welcome ♿ 🚼 Dogs: Welcome
Licences: 🍷 ♟ Parking: Off-street
Directions: At junction of B3357 (Ashburton/Tavistock) and B3212 (Moretonhampstead/Yelverton).

Lydgate House
Little Gem

◆◆◆◆◆ 🐕 ⚒ 🍷

Postbridge, Dartmoor, Devon, PL20 6TJ
Tel: 01822 880209 Fax: 01822 880202
Email: lydgatehouse@email.com
Web: www.lydgatehouse.co.uk

Refurbished Victorian country house set in 36 acres beside the East Dart River in the heart of the Dartmoor National Park, 500 yards from the road and overlooking the valley.
Rooms: 7 all ensuite 🚭 Pricing: Sgl £37–40
Dbl £40–50 Dinner from £24 CC: Accepted
Room facilities: 📺 🍵 Children: Welcome, 12yrs min age
Dogs: Welcome Licences: ♟
Parking: Off-street and monitored
Directions: Between Moreton Hampstead and Princetown on B3212. Turn south just by bridge over East Dart. 400 yards down lane.

Dartmouth, Devon

Dart Marina Hotel

★★★★

Sandquay, Dartmouth, Devon, TQ6 9PH
Tel: 01803 832580 Fax: 01803 835040
Email: info@dartmarinahotel.com
Web: www.dartmarinahotel.com
Rooms: 50 all ensuite 🚭
Pricing: Sgl £67.50–79.50 Dbl £135–159
Dinner from £18.50 CC: Accepted
Room facilities: 📺 ☎ 🍵 Access: ⬆ 🚶
Children: Welcome ♿ 🚼 Dogs: Welcome
Licences: 🍷 ♟ Parking: Off-street
Directions: Take A3122 from Totnes and follow signs for 'Dart Marina'. Hotel overlooks the marina itself, beside the 'Higher Ferry'.

Royal Castle Hotel

★★★

11 The Quay, Dartmouth, Devon, TQ6 9PS
Tel: 01803 833033 Fax: 01803 835445
Email: enquiry@royalcastle.co.uk
Web: www.royalcastle.co.uk

Two bars serving choice bar meals, ales and wines. Adam room restaurant specialising in local seafood. 25 luxuriously appointed ensuite bedrooms to choose from.
Rooms: 25 all ensuite 🍳
Pricing: Sgl £55–90 Dbl £100–200 Dinner from £15.50
CC: Accepted Room facilities: 📺 ☎ 🍵 ☎
Conference: 2 meeting rooms (Thtr 25 max),
24hr-delegate from £60, day-delegate rate from £14
Children: Welcome ♿ 🚼 Dogs: Welcome
Licences: 🍷 ♟ Parking: Off-street and monitored
Directions: Leave M5 and take A38 to Totnes. Once in Totnes, turn right towards Dartmouth at first lights. The hotel is in the town centre.

Dawlish, Devon

Langstone Cliff Hotel

★★★

Dawlish Warren, Dawlish, Devon, EX7 0NA
Tel: 01626 868000 Fax: 01626 868006
Email: rac@langstone-hotel.co.uk
Web: www.langstone-hotel.co.uk
Rooms: 65 all ensuite
Pricing: Sgl £58–67 Dbl £100–140
Dinner from £16.50 CC: Accepted
Room facilities:
Access:
Conference: 6 meeting rooms (Thtr 400 max),
24hr-delegate from £85, day-delegate rate from £28
Children: Welcome   Dogs: Welcome
Licences:
Leisure: Indoor pool, Outdoor pool, Gym, Beauty salon,
Tennis, Games room, Snooker/billiards
Parking: Off-street and monitored
Directions: From M5 Junction 30, follow A379 for
Dawlish. Turn left at Harbour for Dawlish Warren. At
beach turn right up hill. Hotel 500 metres.
See advert on this page

Dorchester, Dorset

The Wessex Royale Hotel

★★★★

High West Street, Dorchester, Dorset, DT1 1UP
Tel: 01305 262660 Fax: 01305 251941
Email: info@wessex-royale-hotel.com
Web: www.wessex-royale-hotel.com
Rooms: 23 all ensuite
Pricing: Dinner from £15 CC: Accepted
Room facilities:
Access:
Conference: 1 meeting rooms (Thtr 80 max),
24hr-delegate from £99, day-delegate rate from £19
Children: Welcome
Dogs: Welcome
Licences: Parking: Off-street and monitored

Yalbury Cottage Hotel & Restaurant

Little Gem

◆◆◆◆◆

Lower Bockhampton, Dorchester, Dorset, DT2 8PZ
Tel: 01305 262382 Fax: 01305 266412
Email: yalburycottage@aol.com
Web: www.smoothhound.co.uk/hotels/yalbury
Rooms: 8 all ensuite
Pricing: Sgl £58 Dbl £90
Dinner from £29.95
CC: Accepted Room facilities:
Children: Welcome
Dogs: Welcome
Licences: Parking: Off-street and monitored
Directions: Turn off Thomas Hardy's Cottage straight
over crossroads, 400 yards on left, just past red
telephone box, opposite village pump.
See advert on this page

Southwest

Junction Hotel

 ◆ ◆ ◆

42 Great Western Road, Dorchester, Dorset, DT1 1UF
Tel: 01305 268826 Fax: 01305 751947
Rooms: 6 all ensuite
Pricing: Sgl £52.50–52.50 Dbl £59–59
Room facilities: Access:
Conference: 2 meeting rooms (Thtr 300 max)
Dogs: Guide dogs only Licences:
Parking: Off-street
Directions: In the centre of Dorchester on the corner of Great Western Road and Weymouth Avenue.

Dulverton, Devon

Jubilee House   Little Gem

 ◆ ◆ ◆ ◆

Highaton Farm, West Anstey, South Molton,
Devon, EX36 3PJ
Tel: 01398 341312 Fax: 01398 341323
Email: denton@exmoorholiday.co.uk
Web: www.exmoorholiday.co.uk
Rooms: 4 (2 ensuite)
Pricing: Sgl £19.50 Dbl £50–50 Dinner from £12
CC: Accepted Room facilities:
Children: Welcome Dogs: Guide dogs only
Leisure: Health spa, Tennis
Parking: Off-street and monitored
Directions: Situated on B3227 midway between South Molton/Bampton. Take turning to West Anstey/Yeo Mill at side of the Jubilee Inn. Jubilee House is 400 metres along lane on right.

Dunster, Somerset

The Luttrell Arms

 ★ ★ ★

High Street, Dunster, Somerset, TA24 6SG
Tel: 0870 400 8110 Fax: 01643 821567
Email: luttrellarms@heritage-hotels.co.uk
Web: www.macdonald-hotels.co.uk
Rooms: 28 all ensuite
Pricing: Sgl £69 Dbl £138 Dinner from £24.50
CC: Accepted Room facilities:
Conference: 1 meeting room (Thtr 20 max)
Children: Welcome Dogs: Welcome
Licences:
Directions: Follow Dunster village sign from A39. Hotel is on the left in the High Street.

Evercreech, Somerset

Pecking Mill Inn

 ◆ ◆ ◆

A371, Evercreech, Shepton Mallett, Somerset, BA4 6PG
Tel: 01749 830336 Fax: 01749 831316
Email: peckingmill@peckingmill.freeserve.co.uk
Rooms: 6 all ensuite
Pricing: Sgl £35 Dbl £55 Dinner from £10
CC: Accepted Room facilities:
Dogs: Guide dogs only Licences:

Parking: Off-street and monitored
Directions: 4 miles south-east of Shepton Mallett on A371, 1 mile from Bath & West Showground. 9 miles north of Wincanton.

Evershot, Dorset

Summer Lodge   Gold Ribbon Winner

★ ★ ★

Evershot, Dorset, DT2 0JR
Tel: 01935 83424 Fax: 01935 83005
Email: reservations@summerlodgehotel.com
Web: www.summerlodgehotel.com
Rooms: 17 all ensuite
Pricing: Sgl £95–155 Dbl £155–355 Dinner from £24.75
CC: Accepted Room facilities: Access:
Conference: 3 meeting rooms (Thtr 20 max),
24hr-delegate from £205
Children: Welcome Dogs: Welcome
Licences:
Leisure: Outdoor pool, Tennis
Parking: Off-street
Directions: Exit J8 M3, A303, then A37 towards Dorchester, then Evershot, Summer Lane.

Exeter, Devon

Manor House Hotel & Golf Course

 ★ ★ ★ ★

Moretonhampstead, Devon, TQ13 8RE
Tel: 01647 445000 Fax: 01647 440355
Email: reception@principalhotels.co.uk
Web: www.principalhotels.co.uk
Rooms: 90 all ensuite
Pricing: Dinner from £24.95 CC: Accepted
Room facilities:
Access:
Conference: 1 meeting room (Thtr 100 max),
24hr-delegate from £135, day-delegate rate from £30
Children: Welcome Dogs: Welcome
Licences: Leisure: Beauty salon, Tennis, Golf, Fishing, Riding, Snooker/billiards
Parking: Off-street
Directions: 2 miles from Morehampstead towards Princetown on B3212. Nearest railway station: Exeter.

The Southgate

★ ★ ★ ★

Southernhay East, Exeter, Devon, EX1 1QF
Tel: 0870 400 8333 Fax: 01392 413549
Email: southgate@heritage-hotels.co.uk
Web: www.macdonaldhotels.com
Rooms: 110 all ensuite
Pricing: Sgl £57 Dbl £114 Dinner from £22
CC: Accepted Room facilities:
Access: Children: Welcome
Dogs: Welcome
Licences: Leisure: Indoor pool, Gym
Parking: Off-street and monitored
Directions: M5 junction 30 A379 to Exeter. Follow signs to city centre. After 2 miles hotel is on your right.

Woodbury Park Hotel Golf & Country Club
★★★★

Woodbury Castle, Woodbury, Exeter, Devon, EX5 1JJ
Tel: 01395 233382 Fax: 01395 234701
Email: enquiries@woodburypark.co.uk
Web: www.woodburypark.co.uk

One of the UK's top sporting retreats. This luxurious hotel, set in idyllic Devonshire countryside, offers the best of everything with the renowned warmth and hospitality of the West Country.
Rooms: 56 all ensuite
Pricing: Sgl £98–148 Dbl £136–186 Dinner from £25
CC: Accepted Room facilities:
Access:
Conference: 4 meeting rooms, 24hr-delegate from £138, day-delegate rate from £32
Children: Welcome Dogs: Guide dogs only
Licences:
Leisure: Indoor pool, Gym, Health spa, Beauty salon, Tennis, Golf, Fishing, Riding, Snooker/billiards
Parking: Off-street and monitored
Directions: Exit M5 J30. Follow A376, then A3052 towards Sidmouth; join B3180 where hotel is signed.

Barton Cross Hotel
★★★★ R R

Huxham, Stoke Canon, Exeter, Devon, EX5 4EJ
Tel: 01392 841245 Fax: 01392 841942
Email: bartonxhuxham@aol.com
Rooms: 9 all ensuite
Pricing: Sgl £65.50–72.50 Dbl £90–120
Dinner from £16.50 CC: Accepted
Room facilities: Access:
Conference: 2 meeting rooms (Thtr 40 max)
Children: Welcome Dogs: Welcome
Licences: Parking: Off-street and monitored

Devon Hotel
★★★

Exeter bypass, Matford, Exeter, Devon, EX2 8XU
Tel: 01392 259268 Fax: 01392 413142
Email: info@devonhotel.co.uk
Web: www.devonhotels.co.uk

Luxurious standards of comfort, personal service and fine wine in the hotel's bar and brasserie 'Carriages'. The Devon Hotel is conveniently located within easy reach of the M25 and Exeter city centre.
Rooms: 41 all ensuite Pricing: Sgl £57–59
Dbl £72–89 Dinner from £18 CC: Accepted
Room facilities: Access:
Children: Welcome Dogs: Welcome
Licences: Parking: Off-street and monitored
Directions: Leave M5 at Junction 30. Take 3rd exit, signposted Torquay. On old Exeter bypass at Matford.

Queen's Court Hotel
★★★★ R

6-8 Bystock Terrace, Exeter, Devon, EX4 4HY
Tel: 01392 272709 Fax: 01392 491390
Email: sales@queenscourt-hotel.co.uk
Web: www.queenscourt-hotel.co.uk
Seasonal closure: New Year
Rooms: 18 all ensuite
Pricing: Sgl £62.50–65 Dbl £71–86 Dinner from £8.50
CC: Accepted Room facilities: Access:
Conference: 2 meeting rooms (Thtr 60 max), 24hr-delegate from £108, day-delegate rate from £27
Children: Welcome Dogs: Welcome
Licences: Parking: Off-street
Directions: In city centre between Central and St David's stations; opposite clock tower on far side of square.

The White Hart Hotel
★★★

66 South Street, Exeter, Devon, EX1 1EE
Tel: 01392 279897 Fax: 01392 250159
Rooms: 55 all ensuite
Pricing: Sgl £45 Dbl £55 Dinner from £10
CC: Accepted Room facilities: Access:
Conference: 5 meeting rooms (Thtr 60 max)
Children: Welcome Dogs: Guide dogs only
Licences: Parking: Off-street
Directions: From junction 30 (Granada Services) follow signs for City Centre A379 on to the B3182 Topsham Road into South Street.

Fingle Glen Hotel Golf & Country Club

Old Tedburn Road, Tedburn St Mary, Exeter,
Devon, EX6 6AF
Tel: 01647 61817

Great Western Hotel

St David's Station Approach, Exeter, Devon, EX4 4NU
Tel: 01392 274039 Fax: 01392 425529
Email: reception@greatwesternhotel.co.uk
Web: www.greatwesternhotel.co.uk
Rooms: 35 all ensuite
Pricing: Sgl £42–45 Dbl £64–68 Dinner from £14
CC: Accepted Room facilities: □ ☎ ⬚
Conference: 2 meeting rooms (Thtr 80 max)
Children: Welcome ♀ Dogs: Welcome
Licences: ♦♦♦ Parking: Off-street
Directions: M5 exit at junction 29. Head towards city
centre and follow directions to St Davids Railway Station.

Red House Hotel

2 Whipton Village Road, Whipton, Exeter,
Devon, EX4 8AR
Tel: 01392 256104 Fax: 01392 666145
Email: red.house.hotel@eclipse.co.uk
Rooms: 12 all ensuite
Pricing: Dinner from £14.95 (2002 rate) CC: Accepted
Room facilities: □ ☎ ⬚ ⬚
Access: ⬚ Children: Welcome ♀
Dogs: Welcome Licences: ♦♦♦ Parking: Off-street
Directions: The Red House Hotel is on the B3212
Pinhoe to Exeter road.

St Andrews Hotel

28 Alphington Road, Exeter, Devon, EX2 8HN
Tel: 01392 276784 Fax: 01392 250249
Seasonal closure: Christmas to New Year

St Andrews is a long-established, family-run hotel
offering a high standard of comfort and service in a
friendly relaxing atmosphere. Excellent home cooking.
Rooms: 17 all ensuite
Pricing: Sgl £40–54 Dbl £60–72 CC: Accepted
Room facilities: □ ☎ ⬚ ⬚ Access: ⬚
Children: Welcome ♀ ⬚ Dogs: Guide dogs only
Licences: ♦♦♦ Parking: Off-street

Directions: Leave M5 at Junction 31, signposted Exeter.
Follow signs to city centre and Marsh Barton along
Alphington Road (A377). St Andrews is on the left.

Telstar Hotel

75-77 St David's Hill, Exeter, Devon, EX4 4DW
Tel: 01392 272466 Fax: 01392 272466
Email: reception@telstar-hotel.co.uk
Web: www.telstar-hotel.co.uk
Seasonal closure: Christmas
Rooms: 20 (13 ensuite)
Pricing: Sgl £22–35 Dbl £40–60 CC: Accepted
Room facilities: □ ☎ ⬚ ⬚ Access: ⬚
Children: Welcome ♀ Dogs: Welcome
Parking: Off-street and monitored
Directions: Drive through city centre from A30 or
Junction 30 of M5. Hotel is between city centre and St
David's Station.

Hotel Gledhills

32 Alphington Road, Exeter, Devon, EX2 8HN
Tel: 01392 430469 Fax: 01392 430469
Email: hotelgledhills@netscapeonline.co.uk
Web: www.uk-explorer.co.uk/gledhills
Seasonal closure: December 22 to January 19
Rooms: 12 (10 ensuite)
Pricing: Sgl £25–39 Dbl £45–51 CC: Accepted
Room facilities: □ ⬚ Children: Welcome
Licences: ♦♦♦ Parking: Off-street
Directions: From M5 at J31 take A30 Okehampton for
one mile, then A377 Exeter, Hotel Gledhills is 1 mile on
left after Sainsburys.

Park View Hotel

8 Howell Road, Exeter, Devon, EX4 4LG
Tel: 01392 271772
Email: philbatho@parkviewhotel.freeserve.co.uk
Web: www.parkviewhotel.freeserve.co.uk
Rooms: 13 (9 ensuite)
Pricing: Sgl £24–38 Dbl £42–55 CC: Accepted
Room facilities: □ ☎ ⬚ Children: Welcome
Parking: Off-street
Directions: M5 J29, follow A3015 to city centre until
clocktower. Take fourth exit (Elm Grove Road). At end,
turn left into Howell Road. Park View 100m on right.

Braeside

21 New North Road, Exeter, Devon, EX4 4HF
Tel: 01392 256875 Fax: 01392 256875
Rooms: 7 (2 ensuite)
Pricing: Sgl £22–28 Dbl £36–38 CC: Accepted
Room facilities: □ ⬚ Children: Welcome
Dogs: Welcome
Directions: From M5 J29 follow all signs to town
centre, straight through to New North Road. We are
between the clock tower and the prison.

Travelodge Exeter (MOTO)
Travel Accommodation
M5 Moto Service Area, Sandygate, Exeter, Devon, EX2 7HF
Web: www.travelodge.co.uk
Rooms: 102 all ensuite ⊗ Pricing: Sgl £64.40 Dbl £68.85
CC: Accepted Room facilities: Access:

Exford, Somerset
Stockleigh Lodge
◆◆◆
Exmoor, Somerset, TA24 7PZ
Tel: 01643 831500 Fax: 01643 831595
Email: myra@stockleighexford.freeserve.co.uk
Web: www.stockleighexford.freeserve.co.uk
Rooms: 9 all ensuite
Pricing: Sgl £25–35 Dbl £40–50 Dinner from £15
CC: Accepted Room facilities: Children: Welcome
Dogs: Guide dogs only Licences: Parking: Off-street
Directions: Exit M5 at Junction 25, Taunton. Follow
signs to Minehead on A358. At Bishops Lydeard turn
left onto B3224. Follow signs to Exford. Take Simons
Bath Road out of Exford. Lodge on right.

Exmoor, Somerset
Rest and Be Thankful Inn
◆◆◆◆
Wheddon Cross, nr. Minehead, Exmoor,
Somerset, TA24 7DR
Tel: 01643 841222 Fax: 01643 841813
Email: enquiries@restandbethankful.co.uk
Web: www.restandbethankful.co.uk
Rooms: 5 all ensuite
Pricing: Sgl £30–30 Dbl £52–60 Dinner from £12
CC: Accepted Room facilities: Conference: Meeting rooms (Thtr 30 max)
Children: Welcome, 11yrs min age
Dogs: Guide dogs only Licences: Parking: Off-street
Directions: 9 miles south of Minehead. Situated on
crossroads of A396 (Minehead-Tiverton Road) and
B3224 (Taunton-Exford).

Exmouth, Devon
Royal Beacon Hotel
★★★
The Beacon, Exmouth, Devon, EX8 2AF
Tel: 01395 264886 Fax: 01395 268890
Email: reception@royalbeaconhotel.co.uk
Web: www.royalbeaconhotel.co.uk
Rooms: 30 all ensuite
Pricing: Sgl £50–70 Dbl £90–110 Dinner from £17
CC: Accepted Room facilities: Access: Conference: 5 meeting rooms (Thtr 150 max),
24hr-delegate from £79, day-delegate rate from £21
Children: Welcome Dogs: Welcome
Licences: Parking: Off-street and monitored
See advert on this page

Royal Beacon Hotel

Former Georgian posting house
overlooking the sea, with 25 guest rooms,
spacious lounge and bar, and a charming
restaurant featuring superbly prepared
fresh local cuisine.

The Beacon, Exmouth, Devon, EX8 2AF
Tel: 01395 264886 Fax: 01395 268890

Email: reception@royalbeaconhotel.co.uk
Web: www.royalbeaconhotel.co.uk

Manor Hotel
★★
The Beacon, Exmouth, Devon, EX8 2AG
Tel: 01395 272549 Fax: 01395 225519
Web: www.manorexmouth.co.uk
Rooms: 40 all ensuite
Pricing: Dinner from £9.50 (2002 rate) CC: Accepted
Room facilities: Access:
Children: Welcome Dogs: Guide dogs only
Licences: Parking: Off-street
Directions: From M5 take A376 to Exmouth: signs for
seafront, then left at T-junction at end of Imperial Road.

Southwest

Falmouth, Cornwall

Budock Vean — The Hotel On The River

★★★★★ ☊ ☊

Mawnan Smith, near Falmouth, Cornwall, TR11 5LG
Tel: 01326 252100 Fax: 01326 250892
Email: relax@budockvean.co.uk
Web: www.budockvean.co.uk
Seasonal closure: 2–25 January

Friendly, peaceful, family-run 4-star hotel in 65 acres
with sub-tropical gardens, golf course, large indoor pool,
boat, jetty, health spa and award-winning restaurant.
Rooms: 56 all ensuite 🛏 ⊗ Pricing: Sgl £56–85
Dbl £112–170 Dinner from £27.50 CC: Accepted
Room facilities: ⬜ ☎ ☕ Access: |↕|
Children: Welcome, 7yrs min age ⅎ ⅊ Dogs: Welcome
Licences: ⚓ ⅲ Leisure: Indoor pool, Health spa,

Beauty salon, Tennis, Golf, Fishing, Snooker/billiards
Parking: Off-street
Directions: From A39 Truro to Falmouth road, follow
brown tourist signs to Trebah Garden. Continue for half
a mile past Trebah to the hotel.

Royal Duchy Hotel

★★★★ ☊ ☊

Cliff Road, Falmouth, Cornwall, TR11 4NX
Tel: 01326 313042 Fax: 01326 319420
Email: info@royalduchy.com
Web: www.royalduchy.com

On the seafront, Falmouth's only 4-star hotel is
renowned for award-winning cuisine, warm attentive
service and luxurious accommodation.
Rooms: 43 all ensuite 🛏
Pricing: Sgl £65–91 Dbl £122–202 Dinner from £26
CC: Accepted
Room facilities: ⬜ ☎ ☕ ☍
Access: |↕| ♿
Children: Welcome ⅎ ⅊
Dogs: Guide dogs only
Licences: ⚓ ⅲ
Leisure: Indoor pool, Games room, Snooker/billiards
Parking: Off-street and monitored
Directions: Situated at the castle end of the seafront on
the left-hand side.
See advert on this page

Falmouth Beach Resort Hotel

★★★

Gyllyngvase Beach, Seafront, Falmouth,
Cornwall, TR11 4NA
Tel: 01326 310500 Fax: 01326 319147
Email: info@falmouthbeachhotel.co.uk
Web: www.falmouthbeachhotel.co.uk
Rooms: 123 all ensuite 🛏 🖨 ⊗
Pricing: Sgl £63–87 Dbl £95–65 Dinner from £18
CC: Accepted Room facilities: ⬜ ☎ ☕ ☍ Access: |↕| ♿
Conference: 6 meeting rooms (Thtr 30 max),
24hr-delegate from £88, day-delegate rate from £25
Children: Welcome ⅎ ⅊ Dogs: Welcome
Licences: ⚓ ⅲ Leisure: Indoor pool, Gym, Health
spa, Tennis, Games room Parking: Off-street
Directions: From Truro take A39 to Falmouth. Follow
signs to seafront and beaches. The hotel is right
opposite Gyllyngcase beach.
See advert on next page

Falmouth Hotel

★★★

Castle Beach, Falmouth, Cornwall, TR11 4NZ
Tel: Freephone 0800 0193121 Fax: 01326 319533
Email: info@falmouthhotel.com
Web: www.falmouthhotel.com
Seasonal closure: Christmas and New Year
Rooms: 69 all ensuite 🛏 📶 Ⓢ
Pricing: Sgl £51–63 Dbl £92–166 CC: Accepted
Room facilities: 🖵 ☎ 🍵 📞
Access: ⬆ ♿
Conference: 6 meeting rooms (Thtr 300 max)
Children: Welcome 🍴 ▒
Dogs: Welcome
Licences: 🔶 ⛻
Leisure: Indoor pool, Gym, Health spa, Beauty salon,
Games room, Snooker/billiards
Parking: Off-street and monitored
Directions: Upon entering Falmouth from any direction,
follow signs for the seafront. Located at the castle end
of Cliff Road.
See advert on this page

Green Lawns Hotel

★★★★ 🏵 🏵

Western Terrace, Falmouth, Cornwall, TR11 4QJ
Tel: 01326 312734 Fax: 01326 211427
Email: info@greenlawnshotel.com
Web: www.greenlawnshotel.com
Rooms: 39 all ensuite 🛏 📶 Ⓢ
Pricing: Sgl £60–110 Dbl £120–170 Dinner from £22
CC: Accepted
Room facilities: 🖵 ☎ 🍵 📞 Access: ♿
Conference: 3 meeting rooms (Thtr 200 max),
24hr-delegate from £95, day-delegate rate from £24
Children: Welcome 🍴 ▒ Dogs: Welcome
Licences: 🔶 ⛻
Leisure: Indoor pool, Gym, Health spa
Parking: Off-street
Directions: Follow A39 to Falmouth. Continue to main
beaches; hotel is on right by mini-roundabout.
See advert on following page

Greenbank

★★★★ 🏵 🏵

Harbourside, Falmouth, Cornwall, TR11 2SR
Tel: 01326 312440 Fax: 01326 211362
Email: sales@greenbank-hotel.com
Web: www.greenbank-hotel.com
Rooms: 60 all ensuite 📶 Ⓢ
Pricing: Sgl £55–78 Dbl £98–160 Dinner from £18
CC: Accepted
Room facilities: 🖵 ☎ 🍵 📞 Access: ⬆ ♿
Conference: 2 meeting rooms (Thtr 60 max), 24hr-
delegate from £85, day-delegate rate from £19.75
Children: Welcome ▒ Dogs: Welcome
Licences: 🔶 ⛻
Parking: Off-street and monitored
Directions: Approach Falmouth from Penryn. Follow
the Greenbank sign from roundabout along North
Parade. Hotel is ¹/₂ mile past Marina on left.
See advert on following page

Green Lawns Hotel

Chateau-style hotel set in prize-winning gardens situated midway between the main sandy beaches and town. The hotel is privately owned but still retains and prides itself on the traditional standards associated with first-class cuisine, comfort and service. Hotel residents enjoy free membership of the Garras Leisure Club.

Western Terrace, Falmouth TR11 4QJ
Tel: 01326 312734   Fax: 01326 211427
info@greenlawnshotel.com
www.greenlawnshotel.com

St Michael's Hotel

★★★

Gyllyngvase Beach, Seafront, Falmouth, Cornwall, TR11 4NB
Tel: 01326 312707 Fax: 01326 211772
Email: sales@stmichaelshotel.com
Web: www.stmichaelshotel.com

Rooms: 65 all ensuite
Pricing: Sgl £54–62 Dbl £108–124 Dinner from £15
CC: Accepted Room facilities:
Conference: 4 meeting rooms (Thtr 200 max), 24hr-delegate from £18.50, day-delegate rate from £74
Children: Welcome Dogs: Guide dogs only
Licences:
Leisure: Indoor pool, Gym, Health spa
Parking: Off-street and monitored
Directions: From A39 into Falmouth follow signs for beaches, we are in Stracey Road directly opposite Gyllyngvase beach.

Greenbank

On the water's edge of one of the world's largest natural harbours, The Greenbank provides the ideal base from which to explore Cornwall's spectacular gardens and historical sites of interest.

Harbourside, Falmouth, Cornwall, TR11 2SR
Tel: 01326 312440 Fax: 01326 211362
Email: sales@greenbank-hotel.com
Web: www.greenbank-hotel.com

Bosanneth Hotel

◆◆◆◆

Gyllyngvase Hill, Falmouth, Cornwall, TR11 4DW
Tel: 01326 314649 Fax: 01326 314649
Email: bosanneth.falmouth@tinyworld.co.uk
Web: www.bosannethhotel.com
Seasonal closure: November to March
Rooms: 8 all ensuite
Pricing: Sgl £25–28 Dbl £50–56 Dinner from £15
Room facilities:
Children: Welcome, 10yrs min age
Dogs: Guide dogs only
Licences: Parking: Off-street and monitored
Directions: Enter Falmouth on A39, follow signs for beaches. Take Dracaena Avenue, Western Terrace, Melvill Road. Turn right after rail bridge into Gyllyngvase Hill.

Chellowdene

◆◆◆◆

Gyllyngvase Hill, Falmouth, Cornwall, TR11 4DN
Tel: 01326 314950
Seasonal closure: October to February
Rooms: 6 all ensuite
Pricing: Dbl £40–52 Dinner from £10
Room facilities:
Parking: Off-street and monitored
Directions: Take A39 into Falmouth. Follow road signed Beaches, Gyllyngvase Beach. Chellowdene 60 metres from main beach.

Ivanhoe Guest House

 ◆ ◆ ◆ ◆

7 Melvill Road, Falmouth, Cornwall, TR11 4AS
Tel: 01326 319083 Fax: 01326 319083
Email: ivanhoe@enterprise.net
Web: www.bedbreakfastcornwall.com
Rooms: 6 (4 ensuite)
Pricing: Sgl £20–24 Dbl £48–54
Room facilities: ▢ ◷
Children: Welcome, 5yrs min age
Parking: Off-street
Directions: A39 to Falmouth, follow signs to the docks.
Road becomes Melvill Road and Ivanhoe is near the
end on the right.

Rathgowry Hotel

 ◆ ◆ ◆ ◆

Gyllyngvase Hill, Gyllyngvase Beach, Falmouth,
Cornwall, TR11 4DN
Tel: 01326 313482
Email: a.ranford@virgin.net
Seasonal closure: October to April
Rooms: 10 all ensuite
Pricing: Sgl £20–27 Dbl £40–54 Dinner from £10.50
Room facilities: ▢ ◷
Children: Welcome
Dogs: Guide dogs only Licences: ♦♦♦
Parking: Off-street
Directions: Enter Falmouth on A39. Follow signs for
beaches along Dracaena Avenue, Western Terrace,
Melville Road; turn right into Gyllynvase Hill.

Trevaylor Hotel

◆ ◆ ◆ ◆

8 Pennance Road, Falmouth, Cornwall, TR11 4EA
Tel: 01326 313041 Fax: 01326 316899
Email: stay@trevaylor.co.uk
Web: www.trevaylor.co.uk
Rooms: 8 all ensuite ⊛
Pricing: Sgl £22–30 Dbl £42–50 Dinner from £9.50
CC: Accepted Room facilities: ▢ ◷ Access: ♿
Children: Welcome Dogs: Welcome
Parking: Off-street
Directions: Take signs for the beaches. Go along
Western Terrace, Green Lawns Hotel on right, turn right
at mini-roundabout.

Tudor Court Hotel

 ◆ ◆ ◆ ◆

55 Melvill Road, Falmouth, Cornwall, TR11 4DF
Tel: 01326 312807 Fax: 01326 312807
Email: peterb@tudor-court-hotel.freeserve.co.uk
Web: www.cornwall-online.co.uk/tudor-court-hotel
Rooms: 10 all ensuite ⊛ ⊛
Pricing: Sgl £20–25 Dbl £40–48 CC: Accepted
Room facilities: ▢ ◷
Children: Welcome, 6yrs min age
Licences: ♦♦♦
Parking: Off-street and monitored
Directions: From Truro, continue on main road and
head for docks. Hotel on right-hand side of Melvill Rd.

Gyllyngvase House Hotel

◆ ◆ ◆

Gyllyngvase Road, Falmouth, Cornwall, TR11 4GH
Tel: 01326 312956 Fax: 01326 316166
Email: gyllyngvase@btinternet.com
Web: www.smoothhound.co.uk/hotels/gyllyngv.html
Seasonal closure: Christmas
Rooms: 15 (12 ensuite) ⊛ Pricing: Sgl £29.50–40
Dbl £30–71 CC: Accepted Room facilities: ▢ ☎ ◷
Children: Welcome, 12yrs min age Dogs: Guide dogs only
Licences: ⬩ ♦♦♦ Parking: Off-street
Directions: From A30, follow signs to Truro, then from
Truro to Falmouth. Follow sign to beaches and dock.
Hotel is on the corner of Gyllyngvase and Melvill roads.

Hawthorn Dene Hotel

◆ ◆ ◆ ◆

12 Pennance Road, Falmouth, Cornwall, TR11 4EA
Tel: 01326 311 427 Fax: 01326 311 994
Email: hawthornedene@hotel12.fsbusiness.co.uk
Seasonal closure: Christmas

The Hawthorne Dene is a small Edwardian hotel, most
rooms have sea views, all have ensuite and room
facilities, our food is fresh, local and mainly organic.
Rooms: 8 all ensuite ⊛ ⊛
Pricing: Sgl £25–30 Dbl £30–60 Dinner from £12
CC: Accepted Room facilities: ▢ ◷
Children: Welcome ⍵ Dogs: Guide dogs only
Licences: ♦♦♦ Leisure: Indoor pool
Parking: Off-street
Directions: Approach Falmouth on A39, following signs
for town centre and beaches. Go straight across at the
traffic lights, at first mini roundabout take the right-hand
exit to Pennance Road. Hotel is on the right.

Fowey, Cornwall

Fowey Marine Guest House

◆ ◆ ◆

21 Station Road , Fowey, Cornwall, PL23 1DF
Tel: 01726 833920
Email: frances.rose@ukonline.co.uk
Web: www.foweyguesthouse.co.uk
Rooms: 4 all ensuite ⊛ ⊛
Pricing: Sgl £35 Dbl £50 CC: Accepted
Room facilities: ▢ ◷ Children: Welcome
Dogs: Welcome Parking: Off-street
Directions: From mini roundabout on outskirts of
Fowey, follow B3269 to Fowey signed Caffa Mill, car
park on left, guesthouse opposite.

Southwest

Frome, Somerset

Mendip Lodge Hotel

★★★

Bath Road, Frome, Somerset, BA11 2HP
Tel: 01373 463223 Fax: 01373 463990
Email: latonamlh@aol.com
Web: latonahotels.co.uk
Rooms: 40 all ensuite Pricing: Sgl £39.50–59.50
Dbl £49.50–95 Dinner from £15 CC: Accepted
Room facilities: 🖵 ☎ 🍵
Conference: 3 meeting rooms (Thtr 80 max),
24hr-delegate from £95, day-delegate rate from £35
Children: Welcome ᵀ 🍖 Dogs: Guide dogs only
Licences: 🔞 👯 Parking: Off-street
Directions: From London leave M4 at junction 17
Chippenham, to Trowbridge on the A350. A361 out of
Trowbridge, Mendip Lodge on the B3090.

The Sun Inn

◆◆◆

6 Catherine Street, Frome, Somerset, BA11 1DA
Tel: 01373 471913
Rooms: 6 (4 ensuite) ⊗
Pricing: Sgl £25–30 Dbl £45–50 CC: Accepted
Room facilities: 🖵 🍵 Children: Welcome
Licences: 👯

Gillingham, Dorset

Stock Hill House   Gold Ribbon Winner

★★★ 🎗 🎗 🎗

Stock Hill, Gillingham, Dorset, SP8 5NR
Tel: 01747 823626 Fax: 01747 825628
Email: reception@stockhillhouse.co.uk
Web: www.stockhillhouse.co.uk

Set in 11 acres, this hotel has an impressive beech-
lined driveway. Bedrooms are luxurious and individully-
styled. There is a sumptuously-furnished lounge for
you to relax in, and our cuisine shows a blend of
Austrian and International influences.
Rooms: 8 all ensuite 🍴 🚗 ⊗
Pricing: Sgl £130–150 Dbl £220–270 Dinner from £35
CC: Accepted Room facilities: 🖵 ☎
Children: Welcome, 7yrs min age Licences: 👯
Leisure: Tennis Parking: Monitored
Directions: 3 miles off the A303, situated on the B3081.
1 mile from Gillingham Rail Station.

Glastonbury, Somerset

Lower Farm

◆◆◆◆ ✿

Kingsweston, Somerton, Somerset, TA11 6BA
Tel: 01458 223237 Fax: 01458 223276
Email: lowerfarm@kingsweston.demon.co.uk
Web: www.lowerfarm.net
Seasonal closure: Christmas and New Year
Rooms: 3 (2 ensuite) ⊗
Pricing: Sgl £25–40 Dbl £55–60 CC: Accepted
Room facilities: 🖵 🍵
Children: Welcome ᵀ Dogs: Guide dogs only
Parking: Off-street and monitored
Directions: From A303 take A37 north to Lydford-on-
Fosse. Turn left onto B3153 to Kingsweston
Farmhouse on right by sharp bend.

Helston, Cornwall

Nansloe Manor Hotel

★★ 🎗 🎗

Meneage Road, Helston, Cornwall, TR13 0SB
Tel: 01326 574691 Fax: 01326 564680
Email: info@nansloe-manor.co.uk
Web: www.nansloe-manor.co.uk
Rooms: 7 (6 ensuite)
Pricing: Sgl £39–59 Dbl £70–140 Dinner from £24.95
CC: Accepted
Room facilities: 🖵 ☎ 🍵
Children: Welcome, 10yrs min age
Dogs: Guide dogs only
Licences: 👯 Parking: Off-street
Directions: 300 metres on the left from Helston/Lizard
roundabout A394/A3083.

Holford, Somerset

Alfoxton Park Hotel

★★

Holford, Somerset, TA5 1SG
Tel: 01278 741211
Email: alfoxton.park@tinyworld.co.uk
Web: alfoxtonpark.co.uk
Seasonal closure: December to March
Rooms: 18 all ensuite 🚗
Pricing: Sgl £39–41 Dbl £79–82 Dinner from £18.50
CC: Accepted
Room facilities: 🖵 🍵 Access: ♿
Children: Welcome ᵀ Dogs: Guide dogs only
Licences: 👯 Parking: Off-street
Directions: J23 M5, take A39 Minehead Road for 10
miles, take first left after "Holford" sign, follow road
approx 1½ miles through woods.

Plan your route

Visit www.rac.co.uk for RAC's
interactive route planner, including
up to the minute traffic reports.

Honiton, Devon

The Deer Park Country Hotel

★★★★

Buckerell Village, Honiton, Devon, EX14 0PG
Tel: 01404 41266 Fax: 01404 46598
Web: www.deerparkcountryhotel.com
Rooms: 26 all ensuite
Pricing: Sgl £40–90 Dbl £60–120 Dinner from £25
CC: Accepted
Room facilities: ☐ ☎ ☐ ☎ Access: ☐
Conference: 3 meeting rooms (Thtr 70 max)
Children: Welcome ♯ ☼ Dogs: Welcome
Licences: ⚐ ♙ Leisure: Outdoor pool, Tennis,
Fishing, Games room, Snooker/billiards
Parking: Off-street and monitored
Directions: From east take first left off A30 immediately
after Honiton, "Iron Bridge" sign. As you come down
slip road, please follow brown signs to Deer Park
Hotel, from west follow signs to Fenny Bridges then
brown signs appear by New Bridge.
See advert on this page

Ilfracombe, Devon

Arlington Hotel

★★

Sommers Crescent, Ilfracombe, Devon, EX34 9DT
Tel: 01271 862002 Fax: 01271 862803
Email: bookings@devoniahotels.co.uk
Web: www.devoniahotels.co.uk
Rooms: 32 (31 ensuite)
Pricing: Sgl £26–46 Dbl £52–72 Dinner from £15
CC: Accepted
Room facilities: ☐ ☎ ☐ Access: �॥↑
Children: Welcome ☼ Dogs: Welcome
Licences: ♙ Leisure: Outdoor pool
Parking: Off-street
Directions: Leave M5 at Junction 27. Take A361 to
Barnstaple, then to Ilfracombe. Straight across two
sets of traffic lights, then left-hand fork and first left.

Darnley Hotel

★★

3 Belmont Road, Ilfracombe, Devon, EX34 8DR
Tel: 01271 863955 Fax: 01271 864076
Email: darnleyhotel@yahoo.co.uk
Web: www.northdevon.co.uk/darnley
Rooms: 10 (7 ensuite)
Pricing: Sgl £27–27 Dbl £22–30 Dinner from £10.50
CC: Accepted
Room facilities: ☐ ☐ Children: Welcome ♯
Dogs: Welcome Licences: ♙
Leisure: Games room
Parking: Off-street and monitored
Directions: M5 J27 A361 Barnstaple, follow signs for
Ilfracombe.

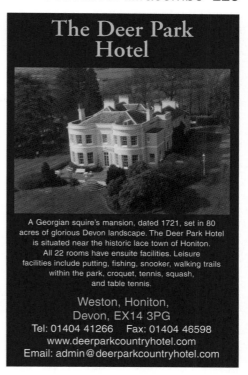

Elmfield Hotel

★★★ ®

Torrs Park, Ilfracombe, Devon, EX34 8AZ
Tel: 01271 863377 Fax: 01271 866828
Email: ann@elmfieldhotelilfracombe.co.uk
Web: www.elmfieldhotelilfracombe.co.uk
Seasonal closure: November to March
Rooms: 13 all ensuite 🖥 ⊛
Pricing: Sgl £40–50 Dbl £80–100 Dinner from £16
CC: Accepted
Room facilities: 🖵 ⊗ Licences: ♦♦♦
Leisure: Indoor pool, Gym, Games room
Parking: Off-street
Directions: Take A361 from Barnstaple, at first lights in
Ilfracombe turn left, at second lights turn left, 10
metres left again, hotel at top of hill on the left.
See advert on previous page

Ilfracombe Carlton Hotel

★★

Runnacleave Road, Ilfracombe, Devon, EX34 8AR
Tel: 01271 862446 Fax: 01271 865379
Web: www.ilfracombecarton.co.uk
Seasonal closure: January to February

Lovely Victorian-style hotel. Central location adjacent
to coastal walks, beach, gardens and theatre. We aim
to please — somewhere special for you!
Rooms: 48 all ensuite
Pricing: Sgl £27.50–29.50 Dbl £50–55
Dinner from £13.50 CC: Accepted
Room facilities: 🖵 ☎ ⊗
Access: |↓↑ Children: Welcome ♇ ⫲℃
Licences: ♦♦♦ Parking: Off-street
Directions: From M5 Junction 27, take A361 to
Barnstaple, then A361 to Ilfracombe. Turn left at lights
(seafront), and left again.

St Brannock's House

★★

61 St Brannock's Road, Ilfracombe, Devon, EX34 8EQ
Tel: 01271 863873 Fax: 01271 863873
Email: stbrannocks@aol.com
Web: www.stbrannockshotel.co.uk

At St Brannock's House we really welcome your K9
friends. We offer first class accommodation, good food
and service with a smile. The perfect base for touring
North Devon.
Rooms: 12 all ensuite ⊛
Pricing: Sgl £24–26 Dbl £48–52 Dinner from £11.50
CC: Accepted
Room facilities: 🖵 ⊗ Children: Welcome ♇
Dogs: Welcome Licences: ♦♦♦
Parking: Off-street
Directions: Leave M5 at Junction 27. Take A361
through Barnstaple to Ilfracombe. The hotel is on A361
on left as you approach town.

St Helier

★★

Hillsborough Road, Ilfracombe, Devon, EX34 9QQ
Tel: 01271 864906 Fax: 01271 864906
Email: st_helier_hotel@yahoo.com
Seasonal closure: October to April
Rooms: 10 all ensuite
Pricing: Sgl £29–30 Dbl £54–56 Dinner from £12
CC: Accepted Room facilities: 🖵 ⊗
Children: Welcome ⫲℃ Dogs: Welcome Licences: ♦♦♦
Parking: Off-street and monitored
Directions: From M5, leave at Junction 27 taking A361
towards Barnstaple to Ilfracombe. Through High Street
towards Combe Martin, hotel is on the left.

Tracy House Hotel

★★

Belmont Road, Ilfracombe, Devon, EX34 8DR
Tel: 01271 863933
Rooms: 9 all ensuite ⊛ Room facilities: 🖵 ☎ ⊗
Children: Welcome ♇ ⫲℃ Dogs: Welcome
Licences: ♦♦♦ Parking: Off-street and monitored
Directions: Approx 200 metres from end of High Street.
Ascend Church Hill from A361. Turn left into Belmont
Road, property is fourth on left.

Torrs Hotel

Torrs Park, Ilfracombe, Devon, EX34 8AY
Tel: 01271 862334
Email: info@thetorrshotel.co.uk
Web: www.thetorrshotel.co.uk
Rooms: 12 all ensuite 🛏
Pricing: Sgl £25–35 Dbl £50–70 Dinner from £10
CC: Accepted Room facilities: 📺 ☕
Children: Welcome 🍴 Dogs: Welcome
Licences: 🎭 Parking: Off-street
Directions: From Barnstaple (A361), turn left at first set
of traffic lights in Ilfracombe. At second set turn left
and then left again.

Westwell Hall Hotel

Torrs Park, Ilfracombe, Devon, EX34 8AZ
Tel: 01271 862792 Fax: 01271 862792
Email: westwellhall@btconnect.com
Seasonal closure: November to March
Rooms: 10 all ensuite 📺
Pricing: Sgl £24–26 Dbl £48–52 Dinner from £12
CC: Accepted Room facilities: 📺 ☕
Children: Welcome Dogs: Welcome
Licences: 🎭 Parking: Off-street
Directions: Take A361 from Barnstaple. Turn left at
both first and second traffic lights, then immediately
left. Take second on right into Upper Torrs.

The Palm Court Hotel

Wilder Road, Ilfracombe, Devon, EX34 9AS
Tel: 01271 866644 Fax: 01271 863581
Web: www.palmcourthotel.net

Palm Court Hotel, family-run 50 bed hotel, all rooms
ensuite, TV, lift, bar, entertainment, bowls, skittles,
large ballroom dancing, 5-course meal.
Rooms: 50 all ensuite 🛏 📺 ♿
Pricing: Sgl £24–26 Dbl £48–52 Dinner from £32
CC: Accepted Room facilities: 📺 ☕ Access: 🚪 ♿
Conference: 2 meeting rooms (Thtr 100 max)
Children: Welcome 🍴 Licences: 🎭
Leisure: Gym, Games room

Parking: Off-street and monitored
Directions: Come off A39 link road follow Sien Barn –
Ilfracombe. Take sign to seafront on entering
Ilfracombe, hotel on left-hand side.

Strathmore Hotel

57 St Brannock's Road, Ilfracombe, Devon, EX34 8EQ
Tel: 01271 862248 Fax: 01271 862243
Email: strathmore@ukhotels.com
Web: www.strathmoreukhotels.com

Relax in our delightful Victorian Hotel furnished with
lovely paintings and antiques. Enjoy a hearty breakfast
followed by a day of sightseeing in Devon's beautiful
countryside, then sample a fabulous home-cooked
dinner.
Rooms: 9 (8 ensuite) 🛏 ♿
Pricing: Sgl £35–45 Dbl £50–70 Dinner from £21.50
CC: Accepted Room facilities: 📺 ☕
Children: Welcome 🍴 ♿ Dogs: Welcome
Licences: 🎭 Parking: Off-street
Directions: Exit J27 M5, A361 Barnstaple/Ilfracombe.
Straight across Mullacott roundabout — hotel on left
side after 1³⁄₄ miles.

Avalon Hotel

6 Capstone Crescent, Ilfracombe, Devon, EX34 9BT
Tel: 01271 863325 Fax: 01271 866543
Email: ann@avalon-hotel.co.uk
Web: www.avalon-hotel.co.uk
Seasonal closure: December to Jan
Rooms: 10 all ensuite 🛏 ♿
Pricing: Sgl £25–60 Dbl £50–60 Dinner from £10
CC: Accepted Room facilities: 📺 ☕
Children: Welcome 🍴 Dogs: Welcome Licences: 🎭
Parking: Off-street and monitored
Directions: Seafront to harbour. Turn left into Capstone
when the Sandpiper Yellow pub is in front of you; hotel
is on right.

Capstone Hotel & Restaurant

◆ ◆ ◆

15/16 St James' Place, Ilfracombe, Devon, EX34 9BJ
Tel: 01271 863540 Fax: 01271 862277
Email: capstonehotel@ilfracombe2000.co.uk
Web: www.ilfracombe2000.co.uk.freeserve.co.uk
Seasonal closure: November to Easter
Rooms: 12 all ensuite
Pricing: Sgl £20–24 Dbl £38–46 Dinner from £5
CC: Accepted Room facilities: 🖵 🕭
Children: Welcome ♅ Dogs: Guide dogs only
Licences: ∰ Parking: Off-street
Directions: Entering Ilfracombe, turn left at lights.
Follow seafront, past Landmark Theatre, to St James'
Place. Look for bow-windowed restaurant on left.

South Leigh Hotel

◆ ◆ ◆

Runnacleave Road, Ilfracombe, Devon, EX34 8AQ
Tel: 01271 863976 Fax: 01271 863322
Email: reception@south-leigh.co.uk
Web: www.south-leigh.co.uk

Lovely family-run hotel, ideal for coastal walks, close to
harbour, beach, gardens and theatre, ideal for small
groups or individuals.
Rooms: 26 all ensuite 🐾 🕭
Pricing: Sgl £20–30 Dbl £40–50 Dinner from £12
CC: Accepted Room facilities: 🖵 🕭
Access: |↓↑ Children: Welcome ♅ 🐾
Dogs: Guide dogs only Licences: ∰
Leisure: Games room, Snooker/billiards
Parking: Off-street and monitored
Directions: Approach Ilfracombe via 361A, take signs
for sea front, turn left for tunnels bead, we are on left.

Ilminster, Somerset

Travelodge Ilminster

Travel Accommodation
A303, Southfield Roundabout, Horton Cross, Ilminster,
Somerset, TA19 9PT
Web: www.travelodge.co.uk
Rooms: 32 all ensuite 🕭
Pricing: Sgl £57.40 Dbl £58.85–61.85
CC: Accepted Room facilities: 🖵 🕭 Access: 🕭

Instow, Devon

The Commodore Hotel

★ ★ ★ ★ 🕭

Marine Parade, Instow, Bineford, Devon, EX39 4JN
Tel: 01271 860347 Fax: 01271 861233
Email: admin@the-commodore.freeserve.co.uk
Web: www.commodore-instow.co.uk
Rooms: 20 all ensuite
Pricing: Sgl £55–75 Dbl £90–130 Dinner from £25.50
CC: Accepted Room facilities: 🖵 ☎ 🕭
Conference: 1 meeting rooms (Thtr 180 max), 24hr-
delegate from £185.50, day-delegate rate from £17.50
Children: Welcome ♅ 🐾 Dogs: Guide dogs only
Licences: ∰
Parking: Off-street and monitored
Directions: M5 Junction 27, onto North Devon Link
Road. Instow turn-off signposted just before Torridge
Bridge. Follow signs for Instow to reach Marine Parade.

Isles of Scilly

Island Hotel   Gold Ribbon Winner

★ ★ ★ ★ 🕭 🕭 🕭

Tresco, Isles of Scilly, TR24 0PU
Tel: 01720 422883 Fax: 01720 423008
Email: islandhotel@tresco.co.uk
Seasonal closure: November to February
Rooms: 48 all ensuite 🐾 🕭
Pricing: Sgl £96–128 Dbl £96–236 Dinner from £33
CC: Accepted Room facilities: 🖵 ☎ 🕭
Conference: 3 meeting rooms (Thtr 60 max)
Children: Welcome ♅ 🐾 Dogs: Guide dogs only
Licences: ∰
Leisure: Outdoor pool, Tennis, Games room
Directions: Departure from Penzance via British
International Helicopters. Direct to Tresco Heliport for
collection. Departure St Mary's via boat to Tresco for
collection. Flights by skybus from Exeter, Bristol,
Newquay or Lands End to St Mary's via boat to Tresco.
See advert on next page

St Martin's on the Isle   Gold Ribbon Winner

★ ★ ★ 🕭 🕭 🕭 🕭

St Martin's, Isles of Scilly, Cornwall, TR25 0QW
Tel: 01720 422090 Fax: 01720 422298
Email: stay@stmartinshotel.co.uk
Web: www.stmartinshotel.co.uk
Seasonal closure: November to February
Rooms: 30 all ensuite 🐾
Pricing: Sgl £100–130 Dbl £180–260
Dinner from £35 CC: Accepted Room facilities:
🖵 ☎ 🕭
Access: 🕭
Conference: 3 meeting rooms (Thtr 60 max)
Children: Welcome ♅ 🐾 Dogs: Welcome
Licences: 🕭 ∰
Leisure: Indoor pool, Tennis, Snooker/billiards
Directions: 20-minute helicopter journey from
Penzance, and then 20-minute boat trip to St Martin's
from St Mary's.
See advert on second page following

Star Castle Hotel

★★★

The Garrison, St Mary's, Isles of Scilly, TR21 0JA
Tel: 01720 422317 Fax: 01720 422343
Seasonal closure: Mid October to mid March
Rooms: 34 all ensuite 🛏 🖾
Pricing: Dinner from £23 (2002 rate) CC: Accepted
Room facilities: 🖵 ☎ 🅐 🕹 Access: ⛼
Children: Welcome ♇ 🕸 Dogs: Welcome Licences: ♙♙♙
Leisure: Indoor pool, Tennis, Games room,
Snooker/billiards Parking: Off-street
Directions: A five-minute walk from the quay. A
courtesy car will collect all guests from the airport.

Tregarthen's Hotel

★★★

Hughtown, St Mary's, Isles of Scilly, TR21 0PP
Tel: 01720 422540 Fax: 01720 422089
Email: reception@tregarthens-hotel.co.uk
Web: www.tregarthens-hotel.co.uk
Seasonal closure: October to March
Rooms: 33 all ensuite 🛏 🅢
Pricing: Dinner from £24.50 (2002 rate) CC: Accepted
Room facilities: 🖵 ☎ 🅐 Children: Welcome ♇
Licences: ♙♙♙ Parking: Off-street

Hotel Godolphin

★★

St Mary's, Isles of Scilly, Cornwall, TR21 0JR
Tel: 01720 422316 Fax: 01720 422252
Email: enquiries@hotelgodolphin.co.uk
Web: www.hotelgodolphin.co.uk
Seasonal closure: November to March
Rooms: 31 (28 ensuite) Pricing: Dinner from £20 (2002
rate) CC: Accepted Room facilities: 🖵 ☎ 🅐
Children: Welcome ♇ Dogs: Guide dogs only Licences: ♙♙♙

Seaview Moorings
Little Gem

♦♦♦♦♦ ❀ ☕

The Strand, St Mary's, Isles of Scilly, TR21 0PT
Tel: 01720 422327 Fax: 01720 422211

We are alongside St Mary's Harbour, with sea views
from all our four suites of rooms. Extensive range of

accessories for your comfort. Breakfast menu to cater
for all tastes.
Rooms: 4 all ensuite Pricing: Sgl £40–80 Dbl £70–80
Room facilities: 🖵 ☎ 🅐
Children: Welcome 14yrs min age
Dogs: Welcome Licences: ♙♙♙
Directions: Hotel is situated directly opposite St Mary's
harbour quay.

Carnwethers Country House

♦♦♦♦ ❀ ☕

Pelistry Bay, St Mary's, Isles of Scilly, TR21 0NX
Tel: 01720 422415 Fax: 01720 422415
Seasonal closure: Oct to April
Rooms: 9 all ensuite 🖾 🅢
Pricing: Sgl £65–75 Dbl £100–120 Room facilities: 🖵 🅐
Children: Welcome, 12yrs min age Dogs: Welcome
Licences: ♙♙♙ Leisure: Outdoor pool, Games room
Parking: Off-street and monitored
Directions: 2½ miles from Hughtown and quay; 2 miles
from St Mary's heliport. Guests met by taxi or minibus.

Amaryllis

Buzza Hill, St Mary's, Isles of Scilly, TR21 0NQ
Tel: 01720 423387
Rooms: 3 all en-suite 🅢 Pricing: Dbl £100
Room facilities: 🖵 🅐 Licenses: ♙♙♙
Parking: Off-street
Directions: Situated 5 minutes from St Mary's Town on
secluded hillside overlooking sea. Transport available
from airport or boat quay.

Southwest

Ivybridge, Devon

Sportsmans Inn

★ ★

Exeter Road, Ivybridge, Devon, PL21 0BQ
Tel: 01752 892280 Fax: 01752 690714
Rooms: 14 all ensuite 🛏 🚭
Pricing: Sgl £45–50 Dbl £55–60 Dinner from £6
CC: Accepted Room facilities: 📺 ☎ ☕ 🍷
Access: ♿ Children: Welcome ⊤
Licences: ♦♦♦ Leisure: Games room
Parking: Off-street
Directions: Just off A38, 10 miles from Plymouth,
centre of Ivybridge town.

Keynsham, Bristol

Grasmere Court

♦ ♦ ♦ ♦ 🏵 ✕

22 Bath Road, Keynsham, Bristol, BS31 1SN
Tel: 01179 862662 Fax: 01179 862762
Email: grasmerecourthotel@aol.com
Web: www.grasmerecourthotel.co.uk

Superior family-run hotel conveniently situated
between Bristol and Bath. The hotel has been recently
refurbished to a high standard. All rooms are well-
appointed with private facilities. Free parking for all.
Rooms: 16 all ensuite 🛏
Pricing: Sgl £42–63 Dbl £61–75 Dinner from £15
CC: Accepted Room facilities: 📺 ☎ ☕
Conference: 1 meeting room Children: Welcome
Licences: ⚓ ♦♦♦ Parking: Off-street
Directions: Situated on main A4 road, midway between
the cities of Bristol and Bath.

Kingsbridge, Devon

Cottage Hotel, Hope Cove

★ ★ 🏵 🏵

Hope Cove, Devon, TQ7 3HJ
Tel: 01548 561555 Fax: 01548 561455
Email: info@hopecove.com
Web: www.hopecove.com
Seasonal closure: January
Rooms: 35 (25 ensuite) 🍽
Pricing: Sgl £24–53.50 Dbl £48–87 Dinner from £15.50
CC: Accepted Room facilities: ☎ ☕ 🍷

Access: ♿ Conference: 1 meeting room (Thtr 50 max)
Children: Welcome ⊤ 🎨 Dogs: Welcome
Licences: ♦♦♦ Leisure: Games room
Parking: Monitored
Directions: From Kingsbridge take A381 towards
Salcombe; Hope Cove signposted. Continue towards
Hope Cove, turn left for Inner Hope. Hotel is on right.

Launceston, Cornwall

Hurdon Farm

♦ ♦ ♦ ♦ ✕

Launceston, Cornwall, PL15 9LS
Tel: 01566 772955
Seasonal closure: November to April
Rooms: 6 all ensuite 🍽 🚭
Pricing: Sgl £21–25 Dbl £42–50
Room facilities: 📺 ☕ Children: Welcome ⊤
Dogs: Guide dogs only Parking: Off-street
Directions: Leave A30 at first Launceston exit. From
Bodmin turn right, second exit off roundabout. From
Exeter take first exit from roundabout, second right
signed Trebullet. Hurdon first right.

Leigh Delamere, Wiltshire

Travelodge Chippenham, Leigh Delamere West (Moto)

Travel Accommodation
M4 Moto Service Area, Leigh Delamere,
Wiltshire, SN14 6LB
Web: www.travelodge.co.uk
Rooms: 31 all ensuite 🚭
Pricing: Sgl £54.40 Dbl £58.85
CC: Accepted Room facilities: 📺 ☕ Access: ♿

Lifton, Devon

Arundell Arms Hotel

★ ★ ★ 🏵 🏵

Lifton, Devon, PL16 0AA
Tel: 01566 784666 Fax: 01566 784494
Email: reservations@arundellarms.com
Web: www.arundellarms.com
Seasonal closure: Christmas
Rooms: 27 all ensuite
Pricing: Sgl £50–82 Dbl £100–124 Dinner from £32
CC: Accepted Room facilities: 📺 ☎ ☕ 🍷
Conference: 2 meeting rooms (Thtr 100 max),
24hr-delegate from £130, day-delegate rate from £25
Children: Welcome ⊤ Dogs: Welcome
Licences: ♦♦♦ Leisure: Fishing, Games room
Parking: Off-street
Directions: Leave M5 at Junction 31. Take A30 towards
Launceston. Hotel is 2 miles east of Launceston in
Lifton village.

Lizard, Cornwall

Housel Bay Hotel

★★★

Housel Cove, Lizard, Cornwall, TR12 7PL
Tel: 01326 290417/917 Fax: 01326 290359
Email: info@houselbay.com
Web: www.houselbay.com
Rooms: 21 all ensuite 🍴 📶 🚭
Pricing: Dinner from £17 (2002 rate) CC: Accepted
Room facilities: ▢ ☎ 🍵 Access: |↕| 🚻
Children: Welcome ⋔ ۞ Licences: ⅲ
Parking: Off-street and monitored
Directions: At the Lizard signpost, take the left fork.
Follow hotel signs.

Parc Brawse House Hotel

◆◆◆◆

Penmenner Road, Lizard, Cornwall, TR12 7NR
Tel: 01326 290466 Fax: 01326 290466
Email: parcbrawsehouse@netscapeonline.co.uk
Web: www.cornwall-online.co.uk/parcbrawse
Rooms: 7 (5 ensuite) 🍴 🚭
Pricing: Sgl £19–36 Dbl £32–52 CC: Accepted
Room facilities: ▢ 🍵 Children: Welcome ⋔
Dogs: Welcome Licences: ⅲ Parking: Off-street
Directions: In Lizard Village just past carpark on Green,
turn right at newsagents on corner. Hotel is 400 metres
on right.

Looe, Cornwall

Klymiarven

★★

Barbican Hill, Looe, Cornwall, PL13 1BH
Tel: 01503 262333 Fax: 01503 262333
Email: reception@klymiarren.co.uk
Web: www.klymiarven.co.uk
Seasonal closure: January
Rooms: 14 all ensuite 🍴 📶 🚭
Pricing: Sgl £33–57 Dbl £54–104 Dinner from £9.95
CC: Accepted Room facilities: ▢ ☎ 🍵
Children: Welcome ⋔ ۞ Dogs: Welcome
Licences: ⅲ Leisure: Outdoor pool
Parking: Off-street
Directions: From M5 South take A38 Plymouth-Liskeard
road. After 10 miles take A374 towards Looe, then
B3253. Turn left after Looe Garden Centre onto Barbican.
Take tourist bed sign Barbican Hill to Klymiarven.

Coombe Farm Hotel

◆◆◆◆ ۞ ⚑

Widegates, Looe, Cornwall, PL13 1QN
Tel: 01503 240223 Fax: 01503 240895
Email: coombe_farm@hotmail.com
Web: www.coombefarmhotel.co.uk
Seasonal closure: November to February
Rooms: 10 all ensuite 🍴 🚭
Pricing: Dinner from £17.50 (2002 rate) CC: Accepted
Room facilities: ▢ ☎ 🍵 Access: 🚻
Children: Welcome ⋔ Dogs: Welcome Licences: ⅲ

Leisure: Outdoor pool, Games room, Snooker/billiards
Parking: Off-street and monitored
Directions: Take M4/A38 to Plymouth and A38 towards
Liskeard. Take A387 to Looe at Trerulefoot roundabout.
Continue on A387 to Hessenford, hotel 1 mile beyond
on left.

Deganwy Hotel

◆◆◆◆ ۞ ⚑

Station Road, Looe, Cornwall, PL13 1HL
Tel: 01503 262984
Email: deganwyhotel@freeserve.co.uk
Web: www.deganwyhotel.co.uk
Seasonal closure: November to December
Rooms: 6 all ensuite 🍴
Pricing: Sgl £20–25 Dbl £40–50 CC: Accepted
Room facilities: ▢ 🍵 Children: Welcome ⋔ ۞
Dogs: Guide dogs only Licences: ⅲ
Parking: Off-street and monitored
Directions: In East Looe, 100 metres from East/West
Looe Bridge, on the A387, opposite doctors' surgery.

Panorama Hotel

◆◆◆◆ ۞

Hannafore Road, Looe, Cornwall, PL13 2DE
Tel: 01503 262123 Fax: 01503 265654
Email: alan@looe.co.uk
Web: www.looe.co.uk
Rooms: 10 all ensuite 🍴 📶
Pricing: Sgl £27.50–39 Dbl £48–75 Dinner from £14.50
CC: Accepted Room facilities: ▢ 🍵
Children: Welcome, 5yrs min age
Licences: ⅲ Parking: Off-street
Directions: Hotel is in west Looe overlooking pier and
beach.

Lostwithiel, Cornwall

Lostwithiel Hotel Golf & Country Club

★★★

Lower Polscoe, Lostwithiel, Cornwall, PL22 0HQ
Tel: 01208 873550 Fax: 01208 873479
Email: reception@golf-hotel.co.uk
Web: www.golf-hotel.co.uk
Rooms: 21 all ensuite 🍴 🚭
Pricing: Sgl £36–47 Dbl £72–94 Dinner from £15.95
CC: Accepted Room facilities: ▢ ☎ 🍵
Access: 🚻 Children: Welcome ⋔ ۞
Dogs: Welcome Licences: ⬦ ⅲ
Leisure: Indoor pool, Gym, Tennis, Golf, Fishing,
Games room, Snooker/billiards
Parking: Off-street and monitored
Directions: Off A390 eastern side of Lostwithiel. Tourist
signposted.

Royal Oak Inn

Duke Street, Lostwithiel, Cornwall, PL22 0AH
Tel: 01208 872552 Fax: 01208 872552
Rooms: 6 all ensuite
Pricing: Sgl £38–40 Dbl £65–68.50 Dinner from £10
CC: Accepted Room facilities: 🖵 🍵
Children: Welcome ⊤ Dogs: Welcome
Licences: ♦♦♦ Leisure: Games room
Parking: Off-street
Directions: Hotel is in the centre of town off the A390.

Lulworth Cove, Dorset

Cromwell House Hotel

Lulworth Cove, Nr. Wareham, Dorset, BH20 5RJ
Tel: 01929 400253 Fax: 01929 400566
Email: catriona@lulworthcove.co.uk
Web: www.lulworthcove.co.uk
Seasonal closure: Christmas and New Year

Lulworth Cove 200 yards, spectacular sea views.
Direct Access Dorset coastal footpath. Swimming pool
(May–October), home cooking, fish specialities, bar,
wine list. Group bookings welcome. Special breaks.
Open all year.
Rooms: 17 all ensuite 🐾 🍵
Pricing: Sgl £30–52 Dbl £60–80 Dinner from £16
CC: Accepted Room facilities: 🖵 ☎ 🍵 ⚲ Access: ♿
Conference: 1 meeting rooms (Thtr 15 max), 24hr-
delegate from £60, day-delegate rate from £30
Children: Welcome ⊤ ≷℃ Dogs: Welcome
Licences: ♦♦♦ Leisure: Outdoor pool
Parking: Off-street
Directions: London M3 to Winchester, M27 to
Ringwood, A31 to Bere Regis, B3501 south to West
Lulworth, 200 yards after end of West Lulworth on left
high above main road before you reach Lulworth Cove.

Travelling abroad by car?

European Motoring Assistance can
help you out of a sticky situation
abroad. Buy online at www.rac.co.uk
or call RAC Travel Sales
on 0800 55 00 55. Quote GUI3

Lydford, Devon

Moor View House Little Gem

♦♦♦♦♦ 🍵 🍵 ⚹☾ ⚲

Vale Down, Lydford, Okehampton, Devon, EX20 4BB
Tel: 01822 820220 Fax: 01822 820220

Licensed Victorian country house in moorland.
Gardens, log fires, peace and quiet, lovely views, ideal
touring centre. NT property. Reputation for good
English food, sound wines.
Rooms: 4 all ensuite 🐾
Pricing: Sgl £45–50 Dbl £65–80 Dinner from £20
Room facilities: 🖵 🍵 Licences: ♦♦♦
Parking: Off-street and monitored
Directions: From M5 at Exeter A30 to Sourton Cross,
A386 Tavistock, Moor View House drive 4 miles on
right, 8 miles before Tavistock.

Lyme Regis, Dorset

Alexandra

★★★

Pound Street, Lyme Regis, Dorset, DT7 3HZ
Tel: 01297 442010 Fax: 01297 443229
Email: enquiries@hotelalexandra.co.uk
Web: www.hotelalexandra.co.uk
Seasonal closure: January
Rooms: 26 (25 ensuite) 🐾
Pricing: Dinner from £22.50 (2002 rate) CC: Accepted
Room facilities: 🖵 ☎ 🍵 Children: Welcome ⊤
Dogs: Welcome Licences: ♦♦♦
Parking: Off-street and monitored
Directions: Turn off M5 at Junction 25. Take A358 to
Axminster. Take B3261 to B3165 Lyme Regis. From
M5, take A303 to reach A358.

Dower House

★★★★ 🍵 🍵

Rousdon, Lyme Regis, Dorset, DT7 3RB
Tel: 01297 21047 Fax: 01297 24748
Email: mdowerhouse@aol.com
Seasonal closure: December to January
Rooms: 9 all ensuite 🐾 🍵 Room facilities: 🖵 ☎ 🍵
Children: Welcome ⊤ ≷℃ Dogs: Welcome
Licences: ♦♦♦ Leisure: Indoor pool
Parking: Off-street
Directions: Dower House is 3 miles outside of Lyme
Regis on the A3052 between Lyme Regis and Seaton.

Southwest

Kersbrook Hotel

Pound Road, Lyme Regis, Dorset, DT7 3HX
Tel: 01297 442596 Fax: 01297 442596
Web: www.lymeregis.com/kersbrook-hotel
Seasonal closure: November to March
Rooms: 10 all ensuite
Pricing: Sgl £40–40 Dbl £60–70 CC: Accepted
Room facilities: Access:
Children: Welcome Dogs: Welcome Licences:
Parking: Off-street and monitored
Directions: The road that leads to the harbour is Cobb
Road. Pound Road is at the top of Cobb Road
crossroads.

Lympsham, Somerset

Batch Country Hotel

Batch Lane, Lympsham, nr Weston-Super-Mare,
Somerset, BS24 0EX
Tel: 01934 750371 Fax: 01934 750501
Web: www.batchcountryhotel.co.uk

A short distance from Weston-Super-Mare and
Burnham-on-Sea this attractive hotel offers a relaxed and
friendly environment. The bedrooms are comfortable and
well equipped, and have views of the Mendip Hills. The
spacious lounges overlook the gardens, and extensive
range of dishes is served in the attractive restaurant.
Easy access from junction 22 of the M5.
Rooms: 10 all ensuite
Pricing: Sgl £48–53 Dbl £37–43 Dinner from £16
CC: Accepted Room facilities: Access:
Conference: 3 meeting rooms (Thtr 100 max),
24hr-delegate from £82, day-delegate rate from £19
Children: Welcome, 1yr min age
Dogs: Guide dogs only Licences:
Parking: Off-street and monitored
Directions: Leave M5 at junction 22, take last exit on
roundabout, signposted A370 to Weston-Super-Mare.
Keep on A370 for approx 3½ miles then turn left into
Lympsham village, follow tourist board signs to hotel.

Lynmouth, Devon

Tors Hotel

Lynmouth, Devon, EX35 6NA
Tel: 01598 753236 Fax: 01598 752544

Email: torshotel@torslynmouth.co.uk
Web: www.torslynmouth.co.uk
Seasonal closure: January to February
Rooms: 33 all ensuite
Pricing: Sgl £35–55 Dbl £70–110 Dinner from £25
CC: Accepted Room facilities: Access:
Children: Welcome Dogs: Welcome Licences:
Leisure: Outdoor pool, Games room
Parking: Off-street and monitored
Directions: Leave M5 at Junction 23. Take A39 for
Bridgwater. Travel west for 40 miles through Minehead
and Porlock. Down Countisbury Hill, the hotel is on left
as you enter Lynmouth.

Bath Hotel

Seafront, Lynmouth, Devon, EX35 6EL
Tel: 01598 752238 Fax: 01598 752544
Email: bathhotel@torslynmouth.co.uk
Web: www.torslynmouth.co.uk
Seasonal closure: December to Jan
Rooms: 24 all ensuite
Pricing: Sgl £32–45 Dbl £50–78 Dinner from £17
CC: Accepted Room facilities:
Children: Welcome Dogs: Welcome Licences:
Leisure: Games room, Snooker/billiards
Parking: Off-street
Directions: On A39 from Minehead, on entering
Lynmouth turn right towards the sea. Hotel on left by
harbour.

Lynton, Devon

Sandrock Hotel

Longmead, Lynton, Devon, EX35 6DH
Tel: 01598 753307 Fax: 01598 752665
Seasonal closure: November to January
Rooms: 8 all ensuite
Pricing: Sgl £24.50–27 Dbl £49–54 Dinner from £15
CC: Accepted Room facilities:
Children: Welcome Dogs: Welcome Licences:
Leisure: Games room Parking: Off-street
Directions: On arrival in Lynton, follow signs to The
Valley of Rocks.

Seawood

North Walk, Lynton, Devon, EX35 6HJ
Tel: 01598 752272 Fax: 01598 752272
Email: seawoodhotel@hotmail.com
Web: www.smoothhound.co.uk
Seasonal closure: November to April
Rooms: 12 all ensuite
Pricing: Sgl £29–32 Dbl £58–64 Dinner from £16
Room facilities:
Children: Welcome, 12yrs min age Dogs: Welcome
Licences: Parking: Off-street
Directions: Turn right at St Mary's Church in Lynton
High Street into the North Walk and Seawood is
second property on left.

Malmesbury, Wiltshire

Mayfield House Hotel

★★★

Crudwell, Malmesbury, Wiltshire, SN16 9EW
Tel: 01666 577409 Fax: 01666 577977
Email: reception@mayfieldhousehotel.co.uk
Web: www.mayfieldhousehotel.co.uk
Rooms: 24 all ensuite 🛏 ⊗
Pricing: Sgl £62–68 Dbl £80–85
Dinner from £18.50 CC: Accepted
Room facilities: ▢ ☎ ☺ 📞
Conference: 1 meeting rooms (Thtr 20 max),
24hr-delegate from £85, day-delegate rate from £24
Children: Welcome ⱦ ⁂ Dogs: Welcome
Licences: ♦♦♦ Parking: Off-street and monitored
Directions: Situated on the A429 between Malmesbury
and Cirencester. 7 miles north of Junction 17 on M4.

Marazion, Cornwall

Chymorvah Private Hotel

◆◆◆

Marazion, Cornwall, TR17 0DQ
Tel: 01736 710497 Fax: 01736 710508
Web: http://www.SmoothHound.co.uk
    /hotels/chymorva.html
Seasonal closure: Christmas and New Year

Rooms: 9 all ensuite 🛏 🚗 ⊗
Pricing: Sgl £27.50–29 Dbl £55–64 Dinner from £15
CC: Accepted Room facilities: ▢ ☎ ☺
Access: ♿ Children: Welcome ⱦ ⁂
Dogs: Welcome Parking: Off-street
Directions: Take A30 at Marazion/St Michael's Mount
roundabout, go through town, travel eastwards
towards Helston on A390 and turn right after Fire
Engine Inn.

Marlborough, Wiltshire

Ivy House Hotel

★★★

Marlborough, Wiltshire, SN8 1HJ
Tel: 01672 515333 Fax: 01672 515338
Email: ivyhouse@btconnect.com
Web: www.ivyhousemarlborough.co.uk

Overlooking Marlborough's famous High Street, this
hotel combines the luxuries of 3-star accommodation,
first-class food and friendly, efficient service with the
character of a listed Georgian building.
Rooms: 30 all ensuite 🛏 ⊗
Pricing: Sgl £65–85 Dbl £75–110 CC: Accepted
Room facilities: ▢ ☎ ☺ Access: ♿
Conference: 3 meeting rooms (Thtr 60 max), 24hr-
delegate from £125, day-delegate rate from £32
Children: Welcome ⱦ Licences: ♦♦♦
Parking: Off-street and monitored
Directions: Take Junction 15 from M4 then A346 to
Marlborough. Ivy House is situated on A4 in the main
high street of Marlborough.

Vines

◆◆◆◆

High Street, Marlborough, Wiltshire, SN4 1HJG
Tel: 01672 515333 Fax: 01673 515338

Merlin Hotel

◆◆◆

High Street, Marlborough, Wiltshire, SN8 1LW
Tel: 01672 512151 Fax: 01672 515310
Email: info@merlinhotel.co.uk
Web: www.merlinhotel.co.uk
Rooms: 14 all ensuite 🛏 ⊗
Pricing: Sgl £45–50 Dbl £60–70 CC: Accepted
Room facilities: ▢ ☺ Children: Welcome
Dogs: Welcome Parking: Off-street and monitored
Directions: Take junction 15 from M4 then A346 to
Marlborough, Merlin Hotel is situated on A4 in the main
High Street of Marlborough.

Southwest

Martock, Somerset

White Hart Hotel

◆ ◆ ◆ ◆

East Street, Martock, Somerset, TA12 6JQ
Tel: 01935 822005 Fax: 01935 822056
Email: mpjc@whitehearthotelmartock.co.uk
Web: www.whitehearthotelmartock.co.uk
Rooms: 10 (9 ensuite)
Pricing: Sgl £30–40 Dbl £45–60 Dinner from £5
CC: Accepted Room facilities:
Conference: 3 meeting rooms (Thtr 100 max)
Children: Welcome, 5yrs min age
Dogs: Guide dogs only Licences:
Parking: Off-street
Directions: From A303 follow sign for Martock, hotel
will be found in middle of village, by market house next
to post office.

Melksham, Wiltshire

Conigre Farm Hotel

★ ★ ★

Semington Road, Melksham, Wiltshire, SN12 6BZ
Tel: 01225 702229 Fax: 01225 707392
Email: conigrefarm.hotel@virgin.com
Web: www.cfhotel.co.uk

A charming 400-year-old farmhouse set in award-
winning gardens with a relaxed and warm atmosphere
and a popular restaurant with a good local reputation.
An ideal base for touring all local attractions.
Rooms: 8 all ensuite
Room facilities: Access:
Conference: Meeting rooms (Thtr 30 max)
Children: Welcome Dogs: Welcome
Parking: Off-street and monitored
Directions: Access to Melksham is via M4, exiting at
junction 17. Just 20 minutes to the south on the A350.

Mevagissey, Cornwall

The Fountain Inn

◆ ◆ ◆

Mevagissey, Cornwall, PL26 6QH
Tel: 01726 842320
Email: billymoore@ntlworld.com
Web: www.fountain-inn.cwc.com
Rooms: 3 (2 ensuite)

Pricing: Sgl £30–30 Dbl £50–50 Dinner from £9.75
CC: Accepted Room facilities:
Dogs: Welcome Licences:
Leisure: Games room
Directions: In center of village on south coast, 6 miles
from St Austell.

Minehead, Somerset

Gascony Hotel

◆ ◆ ◆ ◆

50 The Avenue, Minehead, Somerset, TA24 5BB
Tel: 01643 705939 Fax: 01643 709926
Seasonal closure: November to February
Rooms: 13 all ensuite
Pricing: Sgl £28.50–32.50 Dbl £52–56 CC: Accepted
Room facilities: Access: Children: Welcome
Dogs: Guide dogs only Licences:
Parking: Off-street and monitored
Directions: On main road between town centre and
seafront.

Newquay, Cornwall

Barrowfield Hotel

★ ★ ★

Hilgrove Road, Newquay, Cornwall, TR7 2QY
Tel: 01637 878878 Fax: 01637 879490
Email: booking@barrowfield.prestel.co.uk
Web: www.cranstar.co.uk

Rooms: 83 all ensuite
Pricing: Sgl £28–50 Dbl £56–130
Dinner from £16
CC: Accepted Room facilities:
Access:
Conference: 3 meeting rooms (Thtr 350 max),
24hr-delegate from £95, day-delegate rate from £95
Children: Welcome Dogs: Welcome
Licences:
Leisure: Indoor pool, Outdoor pool, Gym, Health spa,
Games room
Parking: Off-street and monitored
Directions: Enter Newquay via seafront. Turn left onto
Hilgrove Road. Situated on right-hand side.

Hotel Bristol

★★★

Narrowcliff , Newquay, Cornwall, TR7 2PQ
Tel: 01637 875181 Fax: 01637 879347
Email: info@hotelbristol.co.uk
Web: www.hotelbristol.co.uk
Rooms: 74 all ensuite 🍴
Pricing: Sgl £60–80 Dbl £100–140 Dinner from £21.50
CC: Accepted Room facilities: 🖵 ☎ 🍵
Access: 🔛
Children: Welcome 🍴 ⅛℃ Dogs: Welcome
Licences: 👬
Leisure: Indoor pool, Beauty salon, Games room,
Snooker/billiards Parking: Off-street
Directions: At Highgate Hill (A30), turn off to A39 then
A392. At Quintrell Downs take A3058, keep straight on
for 2½ miles.
See advert on this page

Hotel Riviera

★★★

Lusty Glaze Road, Newquay, Cornwall, TR7 3AA
Tel: 01637 874251 Fax: 01637 850823
Web: www.hotelrivieranewquay.com
Rooms: 48 all ensuite 🍴 📺
Pricing: Dinner from £15 CC: Accepted
Room facilities: 🖵 ☎ 🍵
Access: 🔛 ♿
Conference: 5 meeting rooms (Thtr 150 max), 24hr-
delegate from £59.95, day-delegate rate from £16.95
Children: Welcome 🍴 ⅛℃
Dogs: Guide dogs only
Licences: 🔔 👬
Leisure: Outdoor pool, Beauty salon
Parking: Off-street and monitored

Kilbirnie Hotel

★★★

Narrowcliffe, Newquay, Cornwall, TR7 2RS
Tel: 01637 875155 Fax: 01637 850769
Email: enquirykilbirnie@aol.com
Web: www.kilbirniehotel.co.uk
Rooms: 65 all ensuite 🍴
Pricing: Dinner from £14 CC: Accepted
Room facilities: 🖵 ☎ 🍵 Access: 🔛 ♿
Children: Welcome 🍴 ⅛℃
Dogs: Guide dogs only
Licences: 👬
Leisure: Indoor pool, Outdoor pool, Health spa,
Games room, Snooker/billiards
Parking: Off-street and monitored
Directions: When entering Quintrell Downs, turn right
and take the seafront road for approximately 3 miles.
Hotel is on left overlooking seafront.
See advert on this page

Making a booking?

Don't forget to mention RAC
Hotels and Bed & Breakfast 2003.

Hotel Bristol

This stylish family-run clifftop hotel
celebrated 75 years of service and
hospitality in 2002. Within easy driving
distance of the Eden Project and many
other attractions. Getaway breaks
available all year.

Narrowcliff , Newquay, Cornwall, TR7 2PQ
Tel: 01637 875181 Fax: 01637 879347
Email: info@hotelbristol.co.uk
Web: www.hotelbristol.co.uk

The Kilbirnie Hotel

The Kilbirnie occupies a position directly facing
the sea and has all the modern amenities which
once could wish to find. Centrally situated in town
and with easy access to beaches. Excellent
accommodation, cuisine and service. Heated
indoor/outdoor swimming pools, sauna, solarium,
hydro spa. Snooker room. Lift to all floors.

Narrowcliff, Newquay TR7 2RS
Tel: 01637 875155   Fax: 01637 850769
Email: enquirykilbirnie@aol.com
Website: www.kilbirniehotel.co.uk

Southwest

Trebarwith Hotel
"Probably the best views in Newquay"

There's more too! Gardens, sun terraces, private beach entrance, large indoor pool. All complemented by relaxing, comfortable, friendly atmosphere, high standards of housekeeping, excellent food and caring hospitality. Extensive indoor leisure facilities, entertainment, secure parking. Quiet, central location, an oasis in the heart of Newquay!

Newquay, Cornwall TR7 1BZ

Tel:
01637 872288
0800 387 520
Fax:
01637 875431

RɘC ★★★

Email: enquiry@trebarwith-hotel.co.uk
Website: www.trebarwith-hotel.co.uk

Trebarwith Hotel
★★★
Trebarwith Crescent, Newquay, Cornwall, TR7 1BZ
Tel: 01637 872288 Fax: 01637 875431
Email: enquiry@trebarwith-hotel.co.uk
Web: www.trebarwith-hotel.co.uk
Seasonal closure: November to March
Rooms: 41 all ensuite
Pricing: Sgl £35–70 Dbl £70–140 Dinner from £15
CC: Accepted Room facilities: 📺 ☎ 🍵
Children: Welcome ♁ ꞁℂ Licences: ⅲ
Leisure: Indoor pool, Fishing, Games room, Snooker/billiards Parking: Off-street and monitored
Directions: From town centre turn left just before bus station into Trebarwith Crescent. Hotel is located at end of crescent.
See advert on this page

Great Western Hotel
★★
Cliff Road, Newquay, Cornwall, TR7 2PT
Tel: 01637 872010 Fax: 01637 874435
Web: www.chycor.co.uk/greatwestern
Rooms: 72 all ensuite ⊛
Pricing: Dinner from £14 (2002 rate) CC: Accepted
Room facilities: 📺 ☎ 🍵 Access: ⅲ ♿
Children: Welcome ♁ Dogs: Welcome Licences: ⅲ
Leisure: Indoor pool Parking: Off-street
Directions: Take A30 'Indian Queens' to Quintrell Downs roundabout. Turn right, over level crossing, to seafront in Newquay. Hotel is on right.

Philema Hotel
★★
1 Esplanade Road, Pentire, Newquay, Cornwall, TR7 1PY
Tel: 01637 872571 Fax: 01637 873188
Email: info@philema.co.uk Web: www.philema.co.uk
Rooms: 32 (23 ensuite) ⊛
Pricing: Sgl £24–40 Dbl £40–80 CC: Accepted
Room facilities: 📺 ☎ 🍵 Children: Welcome ♁ ꞁℂ
Dogs: Welcome Licences: ⅲ
Leisure: Indoor pool, Health spa, Games room, Snooker/billiards Parking: Off-street
Directions: A392 to roundabout; left for Pentire Hotels. Continue down Pentire Road. Hotel situated on corner.

Priory Lodge Hotel
◆◆◆◆ ⊀
30 Mount Wise, Newquay, Cornwall, TR7 2BN
Tel: 01637 874111 Fax: 01637 851803
Email: fiona@priorylodgehotel.fsnet.co.uk
Seasonal closure: January to February
Rooms: 26 (24 ensuite) ⊛ Pricing: Sgl £30–40
Dbl £56–76 Dinner from £10 CC: Accepted
Room facilities: 📺 ☎ 🍵 Access: ♿
Children: Welcome ♁ ꞁℂ Licences: ⅲ Leisure: Outdoor pool, Health spa, Games room Parking: Monitored
Directions: Enter Newquay via seafront, left onto B3282; 500 metres on right, black-and-white telephone box in grounds.

Windward Hotel and Restaurant
◆◆◆◆ ⊛ ⊀ ꞁℂ
Alexandra Road, Porth Bay, Newquay, Cornwall, TR7 3NB
Tel: 01637 873185 Fax: 01637 873185
Email: enquires@windwardhotel.co.uk
Web: www.windwardhotel.co.uk

Enjoy fresh, exciting cuisine, eclectic mix of wines and beers, relaxed atmosphere, either in our conservatory restaurant or the stunning bar terrace, all complemented by breathtaking views of Porth bay.
Rooms: 14 all ensuite ⊛ Pricing: Sgl £45–80
Dbl £65–95 CC: Accepted Room facilities: 📺 🍵
Access: ♿ Conference: 1 meeting rooms (Thtr 10 max)
Children: Welcome ♁ ꞁℂ Dogs: Guide dogs only
Licences: ⬦ ⅲ Parking: Off-street and monitored
Directions: Join A392 at Indian Queens for 7 miles. Round–about at Quintell Downs, take A3058 to Newquay, then B3276 to Padstow at the double roundabout. Hotel is on right after 1 mile.

Carlton Hotel

◆ ◆ ◆

Towan Headland, 6 Dane Road, Newquay,
Cornwall, TR7 1HL
Tel: 01637 872658
Seasonal closure: November to Easter

Rooms: 10 (9 ensuite)
Pricing: Sgl £25–30 Dbl £46–54
Room facilities: ☐ ☕ Children: Welcome ⱨ ℃
Dogs: Welcome Licences: ▮▮▮ Parking: Off-street
Directions: Newquay on A30 onto A392, down Higher
Tower Road. Left at Red Lion. The Carlton Hotel is at
top of Dane Road.

Rolling Waves Hotel

◆ ◆ ◆ ✒

Alexandra Road, Porth, Newquay, Cornwall, TR7 3NB
Tel: 01637 873236 Fax: 01637 873236
Email: enquiries@rollingwaves.co.uk
Web: www.rollingwaves.co.uk
Rooms: 9 (8 ensuite) ❦ ⊛
Pricing: Sgl £17–21 Dbl £38–50 Dinner from £8
CC: Accepted Room facilities: ☐ ☕
Access: ♿ Children: Welcome ⱨ ℃
Dogs: Guide dogs only Licences: ▮▮▮ Parking: Off-street
Directions: From A30 turn into A3059 Newquay Road.
On entering Newquay at first roundabout turn right into
B3276 to Padstow. Hotel is on right past Porth beach.

Newton Abbot, Devon

Passage House Hotel

★ ★ ★

Hackney Lane, Kingsteignton, Newton Abbot,
Devon, TQ12 3QH
Tel: 01626 355515 Fax: 01626 363336
Email: mail@passagehousehotel.co.uk
Web: www.passagehousehotel.co.uk
Rooms: 38 all ensuite ❦ ⊛
Pricing: Sgl £69.50–79.50 Dbl £80–90
Dinner from £19.50 CC: Accepted
Room facilities: ☐ ☎ ☕ ☏ Access: ⌊↑⌉
Conference: 4 meeting rooms (Thtr 120 max),
24hr-delegate from £80, day-delegate rate from £22
Children: Welcome ⱨ ℃ Licences: ▮▮▮
Leisure: Indoor pool, Gym, Beauty salon
Parking: Off-street
Directions: Leave M5 at Junction 31 for A380. Leave at
A381 exit and follow racecourse signs.

Barn Owl Inn

◆ ◆ ◆ ◆

Aller Mills, Kings Kerswell, Newton Abbot,
Devon, TQ12 5AN
Tel: 01803 872130 Fax: 01803 875279
Email: barnowl.kingskerswell@eldridge-pope.co.uk
Rooms: 6 all ensuite ⊛ Pricing: Sgl £54 Dbl £69
Dinner from £6.95 CC: Accepted
Room facilities: ☐ ☎ ☕ ☏ Children: Welcome ⱨ
Dogs: Guide dogs only Licences: ▮▮▮ Parking: Off-street
Directions: Come up to roundabout head towards
Torquay, it's on the main road towards Torquay on the
right about 1½ mile from roundabout.

North Petherton, Somerset

The Walnut Tree Hotel

★ ★ ★ Ⓡ

Fore Street, North Petherton, nr Bridgwater,
Somerset, TA6 6QA
Tel: 01278 662255 Fax: 01278 663946
Email: info@walnut-tree-hotel.co.uk
Web: www.walnut-tree-hotel.co.uk
Rooms: 32 all ensuite ❦ 🖨 ⊛
Pricing: Sgl £62–79 Dbl £72–142 Dinner from £16.50
CC: Accepted Room facilities: ☐ ☎ ☕ ☏ ❄ Access: ♿
Conference: 4 meeting rooms (Thtr 120 max),
24hr-delegate from £119, day-delegate rate from £29
Children: Welcome ⱨ ℃ Dogs: Guide dogs only
Licences: ⚖ ▮▮▮ Parking: Off-street and monitored
Directions: Exit J24 M5; follow signs for North
Petherton, hotel is opposite the church.
See advert on this page

Southwest

The Boat & Anchor Inn

♦ ♦ ♦

Mead Crossing, Huntworth, Bridgewater,
Somerset, TA7 0AQ
Tel: 01278 662473 Fax: 01278 662542
Email: boatand.anchorinn@virgin.net

Canal side location, less than a mile from motorway
junction, excellent cuisine, full a la carte menu, family
run, ideal for cycling, walking and fishing. We cater for
large parties and have a function suite.
Rooms: 8 all ensuite 🦆 🛏 ⊗
Pricing: Sgl £42.50–55 Dbl £55–65 Dinner from £6.25
CC: Accepted Room facilities: ▢ 🗒
Conference: 1 meeting room Children: Welcome ⾼
Dogs: Welcome Licences: ▮▮▮
Parking: Off-street and monitored

Okehampton, Devon

Percy's Country
Hotel & Restaurant   Gold Ribbon Winner

★ ★ ®̂ ®̂ ®̂ ®̂

Coombeshead Estate, Virginstow, Devon, EX21 5EA
Tel: 01409 211236 Fax: 01409 211275
Email: info@percys.co.uk
Web: www.percys.co.uk

Organic produce, perfectly cooked dishes, Devon's top
female chef, GFG "Devon commended", excellent
accommodation and a history of prestigious
accolades. With this unique combination it's little
wonder that Percy's has just been made the "small
hotel of the year" for the west country!'
Rooms: 8 all ensuite ⊗
Pricing: Sgl £90–135 Dbl £120–175 Dinner from £37.50
CC: Accepted Room facilities: ▢ ☎ 🗒 ⅃ Access: ⅙
Conference: 1 meeting room (Thtr 10 max)
Dogs: Welcome Licences: ⚑ ▮▮▮
Leisure: Fishing, Riding Parking: Off-street and monitored
Directions: From Launceston A388, right at St Giles on
the Heath, then 2.2 miles on the right. See our website
for full directions.

Travelodge Okehampton East

Travel Accommodation
A30 Whiddon Down, Okehampton, Devon, EX20 2QT
Web: www.travelodge.co.uk
Rooms: 40 all ensuite ⊗
Pricing: Sgl £57.40 Dbl £61.85
CC: Accepted Room facilities: ▢ 🗒 Access: ⅙

Travelodge Okehampton West

Travel Accommodation
A30/A386, Sourton Cross, Nr. Okehampton,
Devon, EX20 4LY
Web: www.travelodge.co.uk
Rooms: 42 all ensuite ⊗
Pricing: Sgl 57.40–57.40 Dbl 61.85–61.85
CC: Accepted Room facilities: ▢ 🗒 Access: ⅙

Ottery St Mary, Devon

Pitt Farm

♦ ♦ ♦ ♦ ⚕ ⚘

Fairmile, Ottery St Mary, Devon, EX11 1NL
Tel: 01404 812439 Fax: 01404 812439
Email: pittfarm@tiscali.co.uk
Web: www.pitt-farm-devon-co.uk
Seasonal closure: Christmas and New Year

This 16th-century thatched farmhouse nestles in the
picturesque Otter Valley. Ideal centre for touring.
Devon/Exeter 10 miles, Honiton 6 miles.
Rooms: 5 (4 ensuite) ⊗
Pricing: Sgl £22–25 Dbl £44–50 CC: Accepted
Room facilities: ▢ 🗒 Children: Welcome ⾼
Parking: Off-street
Directions: Follow signs for Fairmile on A30. In Fairmile
turn into B3176 towards Cadhay House. After ½ mile,
Pitt Farm is on left. From Ottery St Mary, take Fairmile
Road. Farm 1 mile.

The Metropole

★★★ ♨

Station Road, Padstow, Cornwall, PL28 8DB
Tel: 0870 400 8122 Fax: 01841 532 867
Email: metropole@heritage-hotels.co.uk
Web: www.macdonald-hotel.co.uk
Rooms: 50 all ensuite ⛵ 🚬 ⊗
Pricing: Sgl £74 Dbl £148 Dinner from £23
CC: Accepted Room facilities: 🖵 ☎ 🅐 ⌁
Access: ⬇ Children: Welcome ⴕ ⸎ Dogs: Welcome
Licences: ⴕⴕⴕ Leisure: Outdoor pool
Parking: Off-street
Directions: Follow A30 from Bodmin to Wadebridge.
Locate B3890 to Padstow. Take 2nd on right (School
Hill). The Metropole is on the left.

Treglos Hotel

Blue Ribbon Winner

★★★★ ♨ ♨

Constantine Bay, Padstow, Cornwall, PL28 8JH
Tel: 01841 520727 Fax: 01841 521163
Email: enquiries@treglos-hotel.co.uk
Web: www.treglos-hotel.co.uk
Seasonal closure: Mid-November to beginning March

Situated near Padstow on the Atlantic coast of
Cornwall in an area of outstanding beauty, this
delightful country house hotel is said to be one of the
finest in the area. The hotel has been in the same
family ownership for over 30 years and the highest
standards are maintained and enhanced by the
personal touch of our friendly staff.
Rooms: 42 all ensuite ⛵
Pricing: Sgl £55–69 Dbl £110–138 Dinner from £25
CC: Accepted Room facilities: 🖵 ☎ 🅐 Access: ⬇ ⓰
Conference: 20 meeting rooms (Thtr 20 max)
Children: Welcome ⴕ ⸎ Dogs: Welcome Licences: ⴕⴕⴕ
Leisure: Indoor pool, Health spa, Beauty salon, Games
room, Snooker/billiards
Parking: Off-street and monitored
Directions: From Padstow follow signs to St Merryn,
then Constantine Bay (from St Marryn brown signs)
See advert on this page

Bedruthan House Hotel

◆ ◆ ◆ ◆ ✻🅐

Bedruthan Steps, St Eval, Cornwall, PL27 7UW
Tel: 01637 860346 Fax: 01637 860763
Email: reception@bedruthanhousehotel.co.uk
Web: www.bedruthanhousehotel.co.uk
Seasonal closure: December and January
Rooms: 6 (5 ensuite) ⊛
Pricing: Dinner from £9 CC: Accepted
Room facilities: 🅐
Children: Welcome, 3yrs min age ⴕ
Licences: ⴕⴕⴕ
Parking: Off-street and monitored
Directions: On B3276 coast road halfway between
Newquay and Padstow. Opposite Bedruthan Steps
and National Trust beauty spot Carnewas.

Woodlands Country House

◆ ◆ ◆ ◆ ◆ ✻🅐 ☕

Treator, Padstow, Cornwall, PL28 8RU
Tel: 01841 532426 Fax: 01841 533353
Email: woodlandsbrandb@hotmail.com
Web: www.padstow.com/woodlands
Seasonal closure: December to February
Rooms: 10 all ensuite
Room facilities: 🖵 ☎ 🅐
Children: Welcome ⴕ Dogs: Welcome
Licences: ⴕⴕⴕ
Parking: Off-street
Directions: Hotel is on B3276 between Padstow and
Trevone, half a mile from Padstow.

Southwest

Paignton, Devon

The Redcliffe Hotel

★★★

Marine Drive, Paignton, Devon, TQ3 2NL
Tel: 01803 526397 Fax: 01803 528030
Email: redclfe@aol.com Web: www.redcliffehotel.co.uk
Rooms: 65 all ensuite
Pricing: Sgl £49–54 Dbl £98–108
Dinner from £17.50 CC: Accepted
Room facilities:
Access:
Conference: 3 meeting rooms (Thtr 160 max)
Children: Welcome Dogs: Guide dogs only
Licences:
Leisure: Indoor pool, Outdoor pool, Gym, Health spa, Games room
Parking: Off-street and monitored
Directions: Follow the signs to Paignton seafront, the Redcliffe Hotel is at the Torquay end of Paignton Green.

Dainton Hotel

★★

95 Dartmouth Road, Three Beaches Goodrington,
Paignton, Devon, TQ4 6NA
Tel: 01803 550067 Fax: 01803 666339
Web: www.daintonhotel.com
Rooms: 11 all ensuite
Pricing: Dinner from £5.95 (2002 rate) CC: Accepted
Room facilities:
Access:
Children: Welcome Dogs: Guide dogs only
Licences: Parking: Off-street and monitored
Directions: Follow Zoo sign, after entrance next right Penwill Way at the bottom turn right, 400 yards on left is Dainton Hotel.

Preston Sands Hotel

★★

Marine Parade, Sea Front, Paignton, Devon, TQ3 2NU
Tel: 01803 558718 Fax: 01803 522875
Rooms: 31 all ensuite
Pricing: Sgl £28–36 Dbl £54–66 Dinner from £13
CC: Accepted Room facilities:
Children: Welcome, 9yrs min age Dogs: Welcome
Licences: Parking: Off-street
Directions: Preston Sands is situated on Preston Beach, off Maring Drive, Preston, Paignton.

Sea Verge Hotel

★★

Marine Drive, Preston, Paignton, Devon, TQ3 2NJ
Tel: 01803 557795
Seasonal closure: November to March
Rooms: 12 all ensuite
Pricing: Sgl £20–26 Dbl £36–44 Dinner from £9.50
Room facilities:
Children: Welcome, 9yrs min age Licences:
Parking: Off-street and monitored
Directions: On seafront overlooking Preston Beach and Green.

Torbay Holiday Motel

★★

Totnes Road, Paignton, Devon, TQ4 7PP
Tel: 01803 558226 Fax: 01803 663375
Email: enquiries@thm.co.uk
Web: www.thm.co.uk
Rooms: 16 all ensuite Pricing: Sgl £34–38
Dbl £52–60 Dinner from £8 CC: Accepted
Room facilities: Access:
Children: Welcome Dogs: Welcome Licences:
Leisure: Indoor pool, Outdoor pool, Gym, Games room
Parking: Off-street
Directions: Situated on the A385 Totnes road 2½ miles from Paignton.
See advert on next page

Roundham Lodge

♦♦♦♦♦

16 Roundham Road, Paignton, Devon, TQ4 6DN
Tel: 01803 558485 Fax: 01803 553090
Email: enquiries@roundhamlodge.co.uk
Web: www.roundham-lodge.co.uk
Seasonal closure: 2 weeks around Christmas/New Year
Rooms: 5 all ensuite
Pricing: Sgl £35–55 Dbl £50–75
Room facilities:
Conference: 1 meeting room (Thtr 16 max)
Parking: Off-street and monitored
Directions: Just off Eastern Esplanade at mini-roundabout Sands Road. Turn left. Follow road round then second turning on right. Hotel on left-hand side.

Redcliffe Lodge

♦♦♦

1 Marine Drive, Paignton, Devon, TQ3 2NJ
Tel: 01803 551394 Fax: 01803 551394
Email: holiday@redcliffelodgehotel.fsnet.co.uk

The family-run hotel that offers a great friendly atmosphere with excellent cuisine and breathtaking sea views. If it is a fun-packed holiday you want, or just to unwind and relax, Paignton's the place to be.
Rooms: 17 all ensuite
Pricing: Sgl £18–30 Dbl £40–60 Dinner from £15
CC: Accepted Room facilities: Access:
Children: Welcome, 3yrs min age
Dogs: Guide dogs only Licences:
Parking: Off-street
Directions: At northern end of Paignton seafront, opposite Paignton Green and close to the beach.

Sealawn Hotel

◆ ◆ ◆

20 Esplanade Road, Paignton, Devon, TQ4 6BE
Tel: 01803 559031
Seasonal closure: 21 Decemer to 4 January
Rooms: 12 all ensuite
Pricing: Sgl £24–31 Dbl £48–52 Dinner from £8
CC: Accepted Room facilities: ☐ ☎ ☕ Access: ♿
Children: Welcome Licences: ♟
Leisure: Games room Parking: Off-street
Directions: The Sealawn Hotel is situated between the
pier and the multiplex cinema on Paignton seafront.

Par, Cornwall

Elmswood House Hotel

◆ ◆ ◆ ◆

73 Tehidy Road, Tywardreath, Par, Cornwall, PL24 2QD
Tel: 01726 814221 Fax: 01726 814399
Rooms: 7 (6 ensuite)
Pricing: Dinner from £10 Room facilities: ☐ ☕
Access: ♿ Children: Welcome
Dogs: Guide dogs only Licences: ♟ Parking: Off-street
Directions: Turn off A390 at junction for Fowey. Follow
road for 3 miles B3269, turn right at junction for
Tywardreath & Par. Hotel opposite St Andrew's Church.

Parkham, Devon

Penhaven Country House Hotel

★ ★ ★ ★

Rectory Lane, Parkham, Devon, EX39 5PL
Tel: 01237 451711 Fax: 01237 451878
Email: reservations@penhaven.co.uk
Web: www.penhaven.co.uk
Rooms: 12 all ensuite
Pricing: Sgl £65–80 Dbl £130–160 Dinner from £18.50
CC: Accepted Room facilities: ☐ ☎ ☕
Children: Welcome, 10yrs min age Dogs: Welcome
Licences: ♟ Parking: Off-street
Directions: Turn left opposite Coach & Horses at Horns
Cross on A39. Follow signs to Parkham, continue up
hill to church then take second left.

Penzance, Cornwall

Queens Hotel

★ ★ ★

The Promenade, Penzance, Cornwall, TR18 4HG
Tel: 01736 362371 Fax: 01736 350033
Email: enquiries@queens-hotel.com
Web: www.queens-hotel.com
Rooms: 70 all ensuite
Pricing: Sgl £47–67 Dbl £94–134 Dinner from £16.95
CC: Accepted Room facilities: ☐ ☎ ☕ Access: ♿ ♿
Conference: 5 meeting rooms (Thtr 200 max)
Children: Welcome Dogs: Welcome
Licences: ♟ Parking: Off-street and monitored
Directions: Follow signs for Harbour and Promenade.
Follow to Promenade on seafront.
See advert on this page

Southwest

Tarbert Hotel & Restaurant

 ★★

11 Clarence Street, Penzance, Cornwall, TR18 2NU
Tel: 01736 363758 Fax: 01736 331336
Email: reception@tarbert-hotel.co.uk
Web: www.tarbert-hotel.co.uk
Seasonal closure: December and January

A superb example of a Georgian period hotel where personal attention and high standards of service are guaranteed. A warm welcome awaits you.
Rooms: 12 all ensuite
Pricing: Sgl £37–39 Dbl £66–72 Dinner from £14.75
CC: Accepted Room facilities:
Children: Welcome Dogs: Guide dogs only
Licences: Parking: Off-street
Directions: Approach Penzance via A30. At first roundabout after Heliport take ring road, signposted Land's End. At third roundabout turn left, then right into Clarence Street.

Sea & Horses Hotel

★

Seafront, 6 Alexandra Terrace, Penzance, Cornwall, TR18 4NX
Tel: 01736 361961 Fax: 01736 330499

Chy Bowjy

◆◆◆◆◆

Chysauster, Penzance, Cornwall, TR20 8XA
Tel: 01736 368815 Fax: 01736 363440
Web: www.chy-bowjy.co.uk
Rooms: 2
Pricing: Sgl £26–26 Dbl £42–42 Dinner from £23
Room facilities: Parking: Off-street and monitored
Directions: A30 turn right after Crowlas, follow signs Chysauster ancient village, 200 yards before village white sign on right Chy Bowjy.

Carlton Hotel

◆◆◆

Promenade, Penzance, Cornwall, TR18 4NW
Tel: 01736 362081 Fax: 01736 362081
Rooms: 12 (9 ensuite) Pricing: Sgl £18–25 Dbl £40–44
CC: Accepted Room facilities: Children: Welcome
Dogs: Guide dogs only
Directions: From Penzance railway/bus station follow signs for seafront and harbour. Carlton Hotel is 1 mile on the right.

Glendower

◆◆◆

5 Mennaye Road, Penzance, Cornwall, TR18 4NG
Tel: 01736 365991 Fax: 01736 365991
Seasonal closure: Christmas
Rooms: 4 (2 ensuite)
Pricing: Sgl £16–18 Dbl £36–40 Room facilities:
Children: Welcome, 5yrs min age
Directions: Follow around harbour and prom. From roundabout, Beachfield Hotel in front, turn right Alexandra Rd, 2nd turning right, 2nd guest house.

Keigwin Hotel

◆◆◆

Alexandra Road, Penzance, Cornwall, TR18 4LZ
Tel: 01736 363930 Fax: 0870 1673499
Email: info@keigwinhotel.co.uk
Web: www.keigwinhotel.co.uk
Rooms: 8 (5 ensuite)
Pricing: Sgl £16–20 Dbl £17–25 Dinner from £10.50
CC: Accepted Room facilities:
Children: Welcome Licences:
Directions: Proceed straight along the seafront to a mini-roundabout, turn right into Alexandra Road: hotel is halfway along on right.

Mount Royal Hotel

◆◆◆

Chyandour Cliff, Penzance, Cornwall, TR18 3LQ
Tel: 01736 362233 Fax: 01736 362233
Email: mountroyal@talk21.com
Web: www.s-h-systems.co.uk/hotels/mountroyal.html
Seasonal closure: November to February
Rooms: 7 all ensuite
Pricing: Sgl £35–55 Dbl £55–60
Room facilities: Children: Welcome
Dogs: Guide dogs only Leisure: Snooker/billiards
Parking: Off-street and monitored
Directions: Situated on the main road entering Penzance on the old A30.

Penmorvah Hotel

◆◆◆

Alexandra Road, Penzance, Cornwall, TR18 4LZ
Tel: 01736 363711 Fax: 01736 363711
Rooms: 8 all ensuite
Pricing: Sgl £20–30 Dbl £40–60 CC: Accepted
Room facilities: Children: Welcome
Dogs: Welcome Licences:
Directions: Approach Penzance promenade, turn right up Alexandra Road at mini-roundabout, hotel on right-hand side near top.

Making a booking?

(i) Don't forget to mention RAC Hotels and Bed & Breakfast 2003.

Woodstock

◆ ◆ ◆

29 Morrab Road, Penzance, Cornwall, TR18 4EZ
Tel: 01736 369049 Fax: 01736 369049
Email: woodstocp@aol.com
Web: www.cruising-america.com/woodstock
Rooms: 8 (5 ensuite) 📠 ⊗
Room facilities: ⬛ ☕ Children: Welcome, 5yrs min age
Dogs: Welcome
Directions: Enter Penzance, past railway station and
drive along sea front. Turn right after The Lugger Inn.
Woodstock 200 metres on right.

Plymouth, Devon

Copthorne Hotel Plymouth

★★★★★ ⏰

Armada Way, Plymouth, Devon, PL1 1AR
Tel: 01752 224161 Fax: 01752 670688
Email: sales.plymouth@mill-cop.com
Web: www.millenniumhotels.com

Located in the city centre, with sweeping views down
Armada Way towards the famous Hoe. The hotel is
easily accessible by road, rail and air. Weekend rates
are also available.
Rooms: 135 all ensuite ⊗
Room facilities: ⬛ ☎ ☕ ⚑ Access: ⬆ ⑇
Conference: 9 meeting rooms (Thtr 140 max)
Children: Welcome �␥ Dogs: Guide dogs only
Licences: ◈ ⑆ Leisure: Indoor pool, Gym
Parking: Off-street and monitored
Directions: Follow signs for Plymouth and then
Continental Ferry Port. At the 4th roundabout the hotel
is on the 1st left.

New Continental Hotel

★★★

Mill Bay Road, Plymouth, Devon, PL1 3LD
Tel: 01752 220782/276798 Fax: 01752 227013
Email: newconti@aol.com
Web: www.newcontinental.co.uk
Seasonal closure: December 24 to January 4
Rooms: 99 all ensuite ⊛ 📠 ⊗
Pricing: Sgl £65–95 Dbl £80–150
Dinner from £16.25 CC: Accepted
Room facilities: ⬛ ☎ ☕ ⚑
Access: ⬆ ⑇
Conference: 4 meeting rooms (Thtr 400 max),
24hr-delegate from £99, day-delegate rate from £28
Children: Welcome ⱨ ⑆
Dogs: Welcome
Licences: ◈ ⑆
Leisure: Indoor pool, Gym, Beauty salon
Parking: Off-street and monitored
Directions: From A38, follow signs for city centre,
Pavilions Conference Centre and Continental Ferryport.
Hotel is adjacent to Pavilions in Millbay Road.

The Duke of Cornwall Hotel

★★★★ ⏰ ⏰

Millbay Road, Plymouth, Devon, PL1 3LG
Tel: 01752 275850
Web: www.Bhere.co.uk
Seasonal closure: 26–30 December
Rooms: 72 all ensuite ⊛ 📠 ⊗
Pricing: Sgl £84.50–89.50 Dbl £105–150
Dinner from £20 CC: Accepted
Room facilities: ⬛ ☎ ☕ ⚑
Access: ⬆ ⑇
Conference: 7 meeting rooms (Thtr 300 max), 24hr-
delegate from £135, day-delegate rate from £35
Children: Welcome ⱨ ⑆
Dogs: Welcome
Licences: ◈ ⑆ Parking: Off-street and monitored
Directions: Plymouth is signposted from A38, then
follow signs for Plymouth Pavilions. We are opposite
with car park at rear.

Camelot Hotel

★★

5 Elliott Street, Plymouth, Devon, PL1 2PP
Tel: 01752 221255 Fax: 01752 603660
Email: camelotuk@supanet.com
Seasonal closure: 23 December to 2 January
Rooms: 18 all ensuite
Pricing: Sgl £43 Dbl £55
Dinner from £5.95
CC: Accepted Room facilities: ⬛ ☎ ☕
Children: Welcome ⱨ
Licences: ⑆
Directions: Leaving A38 at Plymouth, follow signs for
city centre, the Hoe, Citadel Road, then onto Elliot St.

Southwest

Invicta Hotel

★★

11/12 Osborne Place, Lockyer Street, The Hoe,
Plymouth, Devon, PL1 2PU
Tel: 01752 664997 Fax: 01752 664994
Email: info@invictahotel.co.uk
Web: www.invictahotel.co.uk
Seasonal closure: Christmas to New Year

Invicta has 23 well-appointed bedrooms. Is very close
to the city centre, historic Barbicon and Brittany
ferries. Friendly and personal service, and licensed
lock-up car park.
Rooms: 23 all ensuite ❤ ⊛ Pricing: Dinner from £10.50
CC: Accepted Room facilities: ☐ ☎ ⊜
Conference: 2 meeting rooms (Thtr 50 max), 24hr-
delegate from £55.50, day-delegate rate from £17.75
Children: Welcome �🍴 Dogs: Guide dogs only
Licences: ⅲ Parking: Off-street and monitored
Directions: Follow signs to city centre then look for Sir
Frances Drake Bowling Green. Invicta Hotel opposite
main entrance.

Langdon Court Hotel

★★ ⌘

Down Thomas, Wembury, Plymouth, PL9 0DY
Tel: 01752 862358 Fax: 01752 863428
Email: enquiries@langdoncourt.co.uk
Web: www.langdoncourt.co.uk
Rooms: 19 all ensuite ❤ ⌘
Pricing: Dinner from £15 (2002 rate) CC: Accepted
Room facilities: ☐ ☎ ⊜ 📞 Children: Welcome ⍔
Dogs: Welcome Licences: ◈ ⅲ
Parking: Off-street
Directions: Follow brown tourist signs to hotel from
Elburton on A379 (Plymouth to Kingsbridge road).
Approx. 6 miles from Plymouth city centre.

Strathmore Hotel

★★

Elliot Street, The Hoe, Plymouth, Devon, PL1 2PR
Tel: 01752 662101 Fax: 01752 223690
Rooms: 54 all ensuite ❤ Room facilities: ☐ ☎ ⊜
Access: |⊥| Children: Welcome ⍔ ⅈ℃
Dogs: Welcome Licences: ⅲ
Directions: Leave A38 at Plymouth, left at roundabout,
follow city centre then Hoe/Barbican. Left into
Athenaeum Street onto Elliot Street.

Victoria Court Hotel

★★

64 North Road East, Plymouth, Devon, PL4 6AL
Tel: 01752 668133 Fax: 01752 668133
Email: victoria.court@btinternet.com
Rooms: 13 all ensuite
Pricing: Sgl £40–45 Dbl £52–60
Dinner from £14.50 CC: Accepted Room facilities:
☐ ☎ ⊜ 📞
Children: Welcome Licences: ⅲ
Parking: Off-street
Directions: Follow signs for city centre northcross
roundabout, turn for railway station follow north road,
east for 200 yards, hotel on left.

Drake Hotel

★

1 Windsor Villas, Lockyer Street, The Hoe, Plymouth,
Devon, PL1 2QD
Tel: 01752 229730 Fax: 01752 255092
Email: drakehotel@themutual.net
Web: www.drakehotel.themutual.net
Seasonal closure: Christmas to New Year
Rooms: 35 all ensuite ❤
Pricing: Sgl £36–44 Dbl £48–56
Dinner from £13
CC: Accepted Room facilities: ☐ ☎ ⊜
Access: ♿
Children: Welcome ⍔ ⅈ℃ Licences: ⅲ
Parking: Off-street
Directions: Follow signs to city centre. Turn left at
Theatre Royal. Take last left and first right.

Imperial Hotel

★

Lockyer Street, The Hoe, Plymouth, Devon, PL1 2QD
Tel: 01752 227311 Fax: 01752 674986
Seasonal closure: December 23 to January 2
Rooms: 22 (17 ensuite) ❤
Pricing: Sgl £35–46 Dbl £46–58 Dinner from £12
CC: Accepted Room facilities: ☐ ☎ ⊜
Children: Welcome ⍔ ⅈ℃ Licences: ⅲ
Parking: Off-street
Directions: Head for city centre, at Theatre Royal turn
left up hill, turn left at traffic lights then first right.

Ashgrove Hotel

◆◆◆◆ ※⊠

218 Citadel Road, The Hoe, Plymouth, Devon, PL1 3BB
Tel: 01752 664046 Fax: 01752 252112
Email: ashgroveho@aol.com
Seasonal closure: Christmas and New Year
Rooms: 10 all ensuite ⊛
Pricing: Sgl £28–38 Dbl £38–45
CC: Accepted
Room facilities: ☐ ⊜ Children: Welcome
Dogs: Guide dogs only
Directions: Leave A38 head for city centre, continue
down Royal Parade, turn left at Theatre Royal. Right
into Notte Street, left into Athenaeum Street, then right
into Citadel Road.

Cranbourne Hotel

◆◆◆◆

Citadel Road, The Hoe, Plymouth, Devon, PL1 2PZ
Tel: 01752 263858/661400/224646 Fax: 01752 263858
Email: cran.hotel@virgin.net
Web: www.cranbournehotel.co.uk
Rooms: 37 (25 ensuite) Pricing: Sgl £35–45 Dbl £46–56
CC: Accepted Room facilities: ▢ ⏅ Children: Welcome
Dogs: Welcome Licences: ♦♦♦
Parking: Off-street and monitored

Rosaland Hotel

◆◆◆◆ ✁

32 Houndiscombe Road, Plymouth, Devon, PL4 6HQ
Tel: 01752 664749 Fax: 01752 256984
Email: manager@rosalandhotel.com
Web: www.rosalandhotel.com
Rooms: 9 (4 ensuite) ❧ Pricing: Dinner from £12
CC: Accepted Room facilities: ▢ ☎ ⏅
Children: Welcome Licences: ♦♦♦
Parking: Off-street
Directions: Sainsbury's roundabout, first exit. Left-hand
lane to Mutley. Through next three lights; right at fourth
and again at fifth.

Chester Hotel

◆◆◆ ✆

54 Stuart Road, Pennycomequick, Plymouth,
Devon, PL3 4EE
Tel: 01752 663706 Fax: 01752 663706

Headland Hotel

◆◆◆

1a Radford Road, West Hoe, Plymouth, Devon, PL1 3BY
Tel: 01752 660866 Fax: 01752 313339
Email: info@headlandhotelplymouth.co.uk
Web: www.headlandhotelplymouth.co.uk
Seasonal closure: Christmas and New Year

Family-run hotel overlooking the ferry terminal, walking
distance for city centre. Lift to both floors, evening bar,
standard and ensuite rooms. "Hotel facilities at Guest
House Prices."
Rooms: 29 (19 ensuite) ❧ ▤ ⊗
Pricing: Sgl £20–35 Dbl £35–45 CC: Accepted
Room facilities: ▢ ⏅ Access: ⌁ ♿
Children: Welcome ♱ Licences: ♦♦♦
Directions: From city centre, follow brown sign
"Pavilions". At mini-roundabout follow sign for West
Hoe & Seafront. Hotel is directly in front.

Poole, Dorset

Haven
★★★★★ ♜ ♜

Sandbanks, Poole, Dorset, BH13 7QL
Tel: 01202 707333 Fax: 01202 708796
Email: reservations@havenhotel.co.uk
Web: www.havenhotel.co.uk

An exclusive hotel located on the tip of Sandbanks
peninsula. Stunning sea views, award-winning cuisine,
first class service, fabulous leisure and beauty spa
facilities.
Rooms: 78 all ensuite ❧
Pricing: Sgl £95–135 Dbl £190–260 Dinner from £25
CC: Accepted Room facilities: ▢ ☎ ⏅ ✆
Access: ⌁ ♿
Conference: 9 meeting rooms (Thtr 160 max),
24hr-delegate from £170, day-delegate rate from £45
Children: Welcome ♱ ⅋℮ Dogs: Guide dogs only
Licences: ◁ ♦♦♦
Leisure: Indoor pool, Outdoor pool, Gym, Health spa,
Beauty salon, Tennis, Games room
Parking: Off-street and monitored
Directions: A31 towards Bournemouth, A338 Wessex
Way, onto B3065. At Sandbanks Bay turn left, follow
road to end of peninsula, hotel on left by Ferry Point.

Salterns
★★★★ ♜ ♜

38 Salterns Way, Lilliput, Poole, Dorset, BH14 8JR
Tel: 01202 707321 Fax: 01202 707488
Rooms: 20 all ensuite ❧ ▤ ⊗
Pricing: Dinner from £30 (2002 rate)
CC: Accepted
Room facilities: ▢ ☎ ⏅ Children: Welcome ♱ ⅋℮
Dogs: Welcome Licences: ◁ ♦♦♦
Parking: Off-street and monitored
Directions: From Poole, follow signs for Sandbanks, at
Lilliput turn right by Barclays Bank into Saltern Way.

Southwest

Sandbanks Hotel

★★★

15 Banks Road, Sandbanks, Poole, Dorset, BH13 7PS
Tel: 01202 707377 Fax: 01202 708885
Email: johnb@sandbankshotel.co.uk
Web: www.sandbankshotel.co.uk

On Blue Flag Award Golden Sands, the Sandbanks is perfect for holidays and short breaks. Special children's restaurant and play facilities, waterside brasserie and leisure centre.
Rooms: 109 all ensuite 🛏 🚭
Pricing: Sgl £65–110 Dbl £130–220 Dinner from £21.50
CC: Accepted Room facilities: 🖥 ☎ 🍵 ☕
Access: ⬆ ♿
Conference: 12 meeting rooms (Thtr 120 max), 24hr-delegate from £111.62, day-delegate rate from £41.13
Children: Welcome 🍴 🧸 ☕ Dogs: Guide dogs only
Licences: 👥 Leisure: Indoor pool, Gym, Health spa, Games room
Parking: Off-street and monitored
Directions: Take A31 towards Bournemouth. Turn onto A338. At Liverpool Victoria roundabout, keep far left and take B3065 to Sandbanks Beach. At T-junction, turn left. Hotel 500 metres on left.

The Mansion House

★★★★ 🎗 🎗 🎗

Thames Street, Poole, Dorset, BH15 1JN
Tel: 01202 685666 Fax: 01202 665709
Email: enquiries@themansionhouse.co.uk
Web: www.themansionhouse.co.uk

One of Dorset's most highly acclaimed hotels and restaurants. A Georgian house set in a quiet cobbled mews with an outstanding reputation for cuisine and service. Located within 5 minutes of the Channel ferries.

Rooms: 32 all ensuite 🛏 🚭 🚭
Pricing: Sgl £70–90 Dbl £110–130 Dinner from £24.95
CC: Accepted Room facilities: 🖥 ☎ 🍵
Conference: 2 meeting rooms Children: Welcome 🍴 ☕
Licences: 👥 👥 Parking: Off-street and monitored
Directions: Follow signs to Channel Ferry; at lifting bridge, turn left onto quayside; first road on the left.

Shah of Persia Hotel

♦♦♦♦ 🎗

173 Longfleet Road, Poole, Dorset, BH15 2HS
Tel: 01202 685346 Fax: 01202 679327
Web: www.eldridge-pope-inns.co.uk
Rooms: 15 all ensuite 🛏 🚭
Pricing: Sgl £67–67.50 Dbl £85–85
Dinner from £7.20 CC: Accepted
Room facilities: 🖥 ☎ 🍵 ☕
Children: Welcome 🍴 Licences: 👥 👥
Parking: Off-street
Directions: Follow the signs for the A338 to Bournemouth, then the A35 to Poole. The Shah of Persia is situated on left side of the crossroads of the A35 and B3068 leading to Poole town centre.

Porlock, Somerset

Oaks Hotel

★★ 🎗 🎗

Porlock, Somerset, TA24 8ES
Tel: 01643 862265 Fax: 01643 863131
Email: info@oakshotel.co.uk
Web: www.oakshotel.co.uk

Blue Ribbon Winner

Rooms: 8 all ensuite 🚭
Pricing: Dinner from £22.50 CC: Accepted
Room facilities: 🖥 ☎ 🍵
Children: Welcome, 8yrs min age Dogs: Welcome
Licences: 👥 Parking: Off-street
Directions: The hotel is on the A39 just as you enter the village from the west.

Andrews on the Weir

◆◆◆◆ ⌚⌚⌚

Porlock Weir, Porlock, Somerset, TA24 8PB
Tel: 01643 863300 Fax: 01643 863311
Email: information@andrewsontheweir.co.uk
Web: www.andrewsontheweir.co.uk
Seasonal closure: 2 weeks in November, all January.
Rooms: 5 all ensuite 🖥 ⊗
Pricing: Sgl £45–80 Dbl £65–100 Dinner from £32.50
CC: Accepted Room facilities: ▢ ☕
Children: Welcome, 12yrs min age Dogs: Welcome
Licences: ⛊ Parking: Off-street
Directions: Junction 25 M5 Taunton, A358 to
Minehead. A39 Porlock. Porlock Weir 1¹/₂ miles from
Porlock Village.

Ship Inn

◆◆◆

High Street, Porlock, Somerset, TA24 8QD
Tel: 01643 862507 Fax: 01643 863224
Email: mail@shipinnporlock.co.uk
Web: www.shipinnporlock.co.uk
Rooms: 10 (8 ensuite) ☕ ⊗
Pricing: Sgl £22–29 Dbl £44–58 CC: Accepted
Room facilities: ▢ ☕
Conference: 2 meeting rooms (Thtr 50 max)
Children: Welcome ⊼ Dogs: Welcome
Licences: ⛊ Leisure: Games room Parking: Off-street
Directions: Follow the A39 to Porlock, the Ship Inn is on
the High Street at the bottom of Porlock Hill.

Porlock Weir, Somerset

Anchor & Ship Hotel

★★★

Porlock Weir, Somerset, TA24 8PB
Tel: 01643 862753 Fax: 01643 862843
Email: anchorhotel@clara.net
Web: www.smoothhound.co.uk/hotels/anchorho.html
Rooms: 20 all ensuite ☕ 🖥
Pricing: Dinner from £24.75 (2002 rate) CC: Accepted
Room facilities: ▢ ☎ ☕ Children: Welcome ⊼ ☽
Dogs: Welcome Licences: ◇ ⛊ Parking: Off-street
Directions: M5 to Taunton, A358 Taunton to Williton, A39
Williton to Porlock, then B3224 to Porlock Harbour.

Redruth, Cornwall

Lyndhurst Guest House

◆◆◆

80 Agar Road, Illogan Highway, Redruth,
Cornwall, TR15 3NB
Tel: 01209 215146 Fax: 01209 217643
Email: sales@lyndhurst-guesthouse.net
Web: www.lyndhurst-guesthouse.net
Rooms: 6 (4 ensuite) ☕
Pricing: Sgl £18–20 Dbl £40–44 CC: Accepted
Room facilities: ▢ ☕ Children: Welcome
Parking: Off-street
Directions: On the A3047, betwen Redruth and Pool by
traffic lights at Railway Inn.

Rock, Cornwall

Tzitzikama Lodge

◆◆◆◆

Rock Road, Rock, Cornwall, PL27 6NP
Tel: 01208 862839
Email: tzitzikama.lodge@btinternet.com
Web: www.cornwall-online.co.uk/tzitzikama-lodge
Rooms: 8 all ensuite ☕ ⊗
Pricing: Sgl £32–39.50 Dbl £49–57.50 CC: Accepted
Room facilities: ▢ ☕ Children: Welcome ⊼
Dogs: Welcome Parking: Off-street
Directions: Follow the signs to Rock where we are in
the centre of the village.

Rosevine, Cornwall

Rosevine Hotel

Blue Ribbon Winner

★★★ ⌚⌚⌚

Rosevine, Porthscatho, St Mawes, Truro,
Cornwall, TR2 5EW
Tel: 01872 580206 Fax: 01872 580230
Email: info@rosevine.co.uk
Web: www.rosevine.co.uk
Seasonal closure: December to January, open
Christmas only

Set in beautiful sub-tropical gardens facing directly
over the safe sandy Porthcurnick beach. Ideally placed
for Eden and Heligan, indoor pool, award-winning
cuisine, children welcome.
Rooms: 17 all ensuite ☕ ⊗
Pricing: Sgl £120–180 Dbl £160–240 Dinner from £28
CC: Accepted Room facilities: ▢ ☎ ☕ Access: ♿
Children: Welcome ⊼ ☽ Dogs: Welcome Licences: ⛊
Leisure: Indoor pool, Games room
Parking: Off-street
Directions: Approaching St Mawes on A3078, turn right
at sign for Rosevine Hotel and Porthcurnic beach.

Salcombe, Devon

Thurlestone Hotel

★★★★
Thurlestone, Devon, TQ7 3NN
Tel: 01548 560382 Fax: 01548 561069
Email: enquiries@thurlestone.co.uk
Web: www.thurlestone.co.uk

Set in a peaceful thatched village, same ownership over 100 years, outstanding leisure indoor and outdoor facilities. Golf course, first class service, friendly staff, luxury, elegant, relaxing atmosphere, stunning coastal views.
Rooms: 68 all ensuite
Pricing: Dinner from £28 CC: Accepted
Room facilities: Access:
Conference: 6 meeting rooms (Thtr 120 max)
Children: Welcome Dogs: Welcome Licences:
Leisure: Indoor pool, Outdoor pool, Gym, Health spa, Beauty salon, Tennis, Golf, Riding, Games room, Snooker/billiards
Parking: Off-street and monitored
Directions: At Buckfastleigh (A38) take A384 to Totnes then A381 to Kingsbridge. At roundabout take A379 to Churchston. At second roundabout turn left into B3197, then right into lane to Thurlestone.

Bolt Head

★★★
South Sands, Salcombe, Devon, TQ8 8LL
Tel: 01548 843751
Email: info@boltheadhotel.com
Web: www.boltheadhotel.com
Seasonal closure: November to February
Rooms: 28 all ensuite
Pricing: Dinner from £27 (2002 rate) CC: Accepted
Room facilities: Children: Welcome
Dogs: Welcome Licences:
Leisure: Outdoor pool, Games room
Parking: Off-street
Directions: From M5, take A38 towards Plymouth. Then take A384/A381 towards Totnes/Kingsbridge. Then follow signs for South Sands and Salcombe.

Soar Mill Cove Hotel

Blue Ribbon Winner

★★★
Soar Mill Cove, Salcombe, Devon, TQ7 3DS
Tel: 01548 561566 Fax: 01548 561223
Email: info@makepeacehotels.co.uk
Web: www.makepeacehotels.co.uk
Seasonal closure: January

Wake up late and enjoy lemon presse and scrambled eggs with smoked salmon, on your private patio facing the Eddystone lighthouse.... Relax with Ingrid Bergman or chill with Quincy Jones from our free CD/video/DVD library.
Rooms: 21 all ensuite
Pricing: Sgl £78–130 Dbl £180–260 Dinner from £36
CC: Accepted Room facilities:
Children: Welcome Dogs: Welcome Licences:
Leisure: Indoor pool, Outdoor pool, Beauty salon, Tennis, Golf, Games room, Snooker/billiards
Parking: Off-street
Directions: From Totnes, follow A381 to Kingsbridge. Turn right towards Salcombe (on A381). Four miles at Malborough, turn right to Soar. After church, bear left.

Tides Reach Hotel

★★★
South Sands, Salcombe, Devon, TQ8 8LJ
Tel: 01548 843466 Fax: 01548 843954
Email: enquire@tidesreach.com
Web: www.tidesreach.com
Seasonal closure: December & January
Rooms: 35 all ensuite
Pricing: Sgl £74–100 Dbl £124–224
Dinner from £32 CC: Accepted
Room facilities:
Access: Children: Welcome, 8yrs min age
Dogs: Welcome Licences:
Leisure: Indoor pool, Gym, Health spa, Beauty salon, Games room, Snooker/billiards
Parking: Off-street and monitored
Directions: Leave A38 at Buckfastleigh. Follow A384 to Totnes, then A381 to Salcombe. Follow sandcastle symbol signs to South Sands.
See advert on next page

Devon Tor Hotel

◆ ◆ ◆ ◆

Devon Road, Salcombe, Devon, TQ8 8HJ
Tel: 01548 843106 Fax: 01548 842425
Email: malcolmbarlow@devontor.freeserve.co.uk
Web: www.salcombeinformation.co.uk
Rooms: 6 all ensuite 🄫 Room facilities: ▯ 🝑
Children: Welcome � Dogs: Guide dogs only
Licences: ♦♦♦ Parking: Off-street

Salisbury, Wiltshire

Red Lion

★★★★ 🄬

Milford Street, Salisbury, Wiltshire, SP1 2AN
Tel: 01722 323334 Fax: 01722 325756
Email: reception@the-redlion.co.uk
Web: www.the-redlion.co.uk
Rooms: 51 all ensuite 🍴 🖃 🄫
Pricing: Dinner from £19 CC: Accepted
Room facilities: ▯ ☎ 🝑 Access: ⬆ 🗴
Conference: 5 meeting rooms (Thtr 100 max),
24hr-delegate from £115, day-delegate rate from £35
Children: Welcome Licences: ♦♦♦ Leisure: Games room
Parking: Off-street and monitored
Directions: From A303 take A30 10 miles south, located
in central city off market square in Milford Street.

The White Hart

★★★★ 🄬

St John Street, Salisbury, Wiltshire, SP1 2SD
Tel: 0870 4008125 Fax: 01722 412761
Email: whitehartsalisbury@heritage-hotels.co.uk
Web: www.macdonald-hotels.co.uk
Rooms: 68 all ensuite 🍴 🖃 🄫
Pricing: Sgl £75 Dbl £150 Dinner from £22
CC: Accepted Room facilities: ▯ ☎ 🝑 🗲
Conference: 3 meeting rooms (Thtr 90 max)
Children: Welcome ♦ 🝑 Dogs: Welcome
Licences: ⬧ ♦♦♦ Parking: Off-street and monitored
Directions: Take Ring Road, heading towards city centre
and cathedral. Proceed into Exeter Street, and join St
John Street. Hotel is at the end of the road on right.

Howards House Hotel   Blue Ribbon Winner

★★ 🄬 🄬 🄬

Teffont Evias, Salisbury, Wiltshire, SP3 5RJ
Tel: 01722 716392 Fax: 01722 716820
Email: enq@howardshousehotel.com
Web: www.howardshousehotel.com
Rooms: 9 all ensuite 🍴 🖃 🄫
Pricing: Sgl £85 Dbl £135–155 Dinner from £23.95 CC:
Accepted Room facilities: ▯ ☎ 🝑 🗲
Conference: 1 meeting room (Thtr 30 max)
Children: Welcome ♦ 🝑 Dogs: Welcome
Licences: ⬧ ♦♦♦ Leisure: Golf, Fishing, Riding
Parking: Off-street
Directions: From London, turn left off A303, after A36
turn off for Wyle. Head for B3089, turn right after 1/3
mile, hotel on right 400 yards.
See advert on this page

Southwest

Websters

Little Gem

♦♦♦♦♦

11 Hartington Road, Salisbury, Wiltshire, SP2 7LG
Tel: 01722 339779 Fax: 01722 421903
Email: enquires@websters-bed-breakfast.com
Web: www.websters-bed-breakfast.com

Our guests say "wonderful B&B", "the best", "comfortable", "friendly", "helpful", "fantastic". Find out why so many guests return time and time again; to experience excellent hospitality delivered with good humour.
Rooms: 5 all ensuite
Pricing: Sgl £32–35 Dbl £42–45 Dinner from £12
CC: Accepted Room facilities: Access:
Children: Welcome, 12yrs min age
Dogs: Guide dogs only Parking: Off-street
Directions: From city centre head west towards Wilton. At St Paul's roundabout take A360 Devizes Road. 400 metres on left is Hartington Road.

Cricket Field House Hotel

♦♦♦♦

Wilton Road, Salisbury, Wiltshire, SP2 9NS
Tel: 01722 322595 Fax: 01722 322595
Email: cricketfieldhousehotel@btinternet.com
Web: www.cricketfieldhousehotel.co.uk
Rooms: 14 all ensuite
Pricing: Sgl £45–65 Dbl £60–75 Dinner from £14.95
CC: Accepted Room facilities: Access:
Conference: Meeting rooms (Thtr 25 max)
Children: Welcome, 14yrs min age
Dogs: Guide dogs only Licences:
Parking: Off-street and monitored
Directions: Take A36 west from Salisbury to Wilton.

Stratford Lodge

♦♦♦♦

4 Park Lane, Salisbury, Wiltshire, SP1 3NP
Tel: 01722 325177 Fax: 01722 325177
Email: enquiries@stratfordlodge.co.uk
Web: www.stratfordlodge.co.uk
Rooms: 8 all ensuite
Room facilities: Access:
Children: Welcome, 5yrs min age
Licences: Parking: Off-street
Directions: Take A345 towards Salisbury. Turn right after shop called Alldays. Park Lane is immediately on right. Stratford Lodge is second house on right.

Byways House

♦♦♦

31 Fowler's Road, City Centre, Salisbury, Wiltshire, SP1 2QP
Tel: 01722 328364 Fax: 01722 322146
Email: byways@bed-breakfast-salisbury.co.uk
Web: www.bed-breakfast-salisbury.co.uk
Seasonal closure: Christmas and New Year

Attractive family-run Victorian house close to cathedral in quiet area of city centre. Large car park. Traditional English or vegetarian breakfasts. Ideal for Stonehenge and Wilton House.
Rooms: 23 (19 ensuite) Room facilities:
Access: Children: Welcome Dogs: Welcome
Licences: Parking: Off-street
Directions: Arriving in Salisbury, follow A36, then follow youth hostel signs until outside hostel. Fowler's Road is opposite: Byways is a big Victorian house on the left.

Cornmarket Inn

♦♦♦

29-32 Cheesemarket, Salisbury, Wiltshire, P1 1TL
Tel: 01722 412925 Fax: 01722 412927
Rooms: 8 all ensuite
Pricing: Sgl £50–75 Dbl £60–80 CC: Accepted
Room facilities: Children: Welcome Licences:
Directions: In Salisbury town centre. Located on west side of market square, next to public library.

Hayburn Wyke Guest House

♦♦♦

72 Castle Road, Salisbury, Wiltshire, SP1 3RL
Tel: 01722 412627 Fax: 01722 412627
Email: hayburn.wyke@tinyonline.co.uk
Web: www.hayburnwykeguesthouse.co.uk
Rooms: 7 (4 ensuite)
Pricing: Sgl £30–56 Dbl £44–58 CC: Accepted
Room facilities: Children: Welcome
Dogs: Guide dogs only Parking: Off-street
Directions: Situated on Castle Road (A345), half a mile north of city centre at the junction with Stratford Road, by Victoria Park.

The Junipers

♦ ♦ ♦ ❧

3 Juniper Road, Firsdown, near Salisbury,
Wiltshire, SP5 1SS
Tel: 01980 862330 Fax: 01980 862071
Email: junipers.bb@tesco.net
Web: www.homepages.tesco.net/
~junipers.bb/junipers.bb/
Rooms: 2 all ensuite ☺ Pricing: Dbl £45
Room facilities: ☐ ♨, Dogs: Guide dogs only
Parking: Off-street and monitored
Directions: A30 to London 5 miles north-east of
Salisbury, follow brown signs to the Junipers.

Saltash, Cornwall

Travelodge Saltash

Travel Accommodation
Callington Road, Carkeel, Saltash, Cornwall, PL12 6LF
Web: www.travelodge.co.uk
Rooms: 53 all ensuite ☺ Pricing: Sgl £57.40 Dbl £61.85
CC: Accepted Room facilities: ☐ ♨, Access: ♿

Saunton, Devon

Saunton Sands Hotel

★ ★ ★ ★ ★ ⓡ ⓡ

Saunton, Devon, EX33 1LQ
Tel: 01271 890212 Fax: 01271 890145
Email: info@sauntonsands.com
Web: www.sauntonsands.com

North Devon's premier 4-star hotel commands
spectacular views, and provides a wealth of facilities.
Rooms: 92 all ensuite ☺ Pricing: Sgl £68–193
Dbl £136–216 Dinner from £25 CC: Accepted
Room facilities: ☐ ☎ ♨ ☜ Access: ⇞ ♿
Children: Welcome ♨ ☙ ☙ Dogs: Guide dogs only
Licences: ⚭ ♟ Leisure: Indoor pool, Outdoor pool,
Gym, Health spa, Beauty salon, Tennis, Games room,
Snooker/billiards
Parking: Off-street and monitored
Directions: From Barnstaple town centre take A361
Braunton road. From Braunton follow the Saunton sign.
See advert on this page

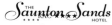
Preston House Hotel

★ ★ ⓡ ⓡ ⓡ

Preston House Hotel, Saunton,
Braunton, Devon, EX33 1LG
Tel: 01271 890472 Fax: 01271 890555
Email: prestonhouse-saunton@300m.co.uk
Web: www.prestonhouse-saunton.co.uk
Seasonal closure: Mid December/January

Set on the cliffs above the Atlantic rollers, Preston House
commands spectacular views. With the easy informality
of the house comes relaxation, the anticipation of award-
winning food and a warm welcome.
Rooms: 12 all ensuite ☵ ☺ Pricing: Sgl £60–65
Dbl £60–87 Dinner from £30 CC: Accepted
Room facilities: ☐ ☎ ♨ Conference: 1 meeting room
(Thtr 20 max) Children: Welcome, 15yrs min age
Dogs: Guide dogs only Licences: ♟
Leisure: Outdoor pool Parking: Off-street and monitored
Directions: M5 junction 27, to Barnstaple on A361.
Follow A361 through Barnstaple to Braunton. Turn left
at traffic lights in town centre, hotel 4 miles on left.

Southwest

The Crossroads Lodge

A family-owned establishment extending a warm welcome, offering friendly service and fine cuisine.
The Crossroads Lodge is set in the heart of the county, giving convenient access to all major resorts and attractions. Its accessibility makes it an ideal location for that executive conference, family function, or a welcome stop-over.
Lift to most bedrooms

Scorrier, Redruth, Cornwall TR16 5BP
Tel: 01209 820551 Fax: 01209 820392

Scorrier, Cornwall

The Crossroads Lodge
★★
Scorrier, Redruth, Cornwall, TR16 5BP
Tel: 01209 820551 Fax: 01209 820392
Rooms: 36 all ensuite
Pricing: Sgl £35–55 Dbl £57–70 Dinner from £12.50
CC: Accepted Room facilities: 📺 ☎ 🍵 Access: |↑↓
Conference: 3 meeting rooms (Thtr 120 max)
Children: Welcome ♀ ♨ Dogs: Welcome Licences: ♦♦♦
Leisure: Games room Parking: Off-street
Directions: Follow the A30 for Redruth, take the first exit left for Scorrier after the Chiverton roundabout.
See advert on this page

Sennen, Cornwall

Homefields
◆◆◆◆ ✍
Mayon, Sennen, Cornwall, TR19 7AD
Tel: 01736 871418 Fax: 01736 871666
Email: homefields1bandb@aol.com
Web: www.homefieldsguesthouse.co.uk
Seasonal closure: Christmas
Rooms: 5 (4 ensuite)
Pricing: Dbl £35–50 CC: Accepted
Room facilities: 📺 🍵 Access: ♿ Children: Welcome ♀
Dogs: Welcome Licences: ♦♦♦ Parking: Off-street
Directions: Follow A30 from Penzance for 8 miles to village of Sennen. Homefields is opposite the Post Office.

Sennen Cove, Cornwall

Old Success Inn
★★
Sennen Cove, Cornwall, TR19 7DG
Tel: 01736 871232 Fax: 01736 788354

Shaftesbury, Dorset

Royal Chase
★★★
Salisbury Road, Shaftesbury, Dorset, SP7 8DB
Tel: 01747 853355 Fax: 01747 851969
Email: royalchasehotel@btinternet.com
Web: www.theroyalchasehotel.co.uk
Rooms: 33 all ensuite
Pricing: Sgl £93–103.50 Dbl £117–132
Dinner from £24.50 CC: Accepted
Room facilities: 📺 ☎ 🍵 Access: ♿
Conference: 5 meeting rooms (Thtr 150 max), 24hr-delegate from £99.50, day-delegate rate from £29.50
Children: Welcome ♀ ♨ Dogs: Welcome
Licences: ⚖ ♦♦♦ Leisure: Indoor pool
Parking: Off-street and monitored
Directions: On the outskirts of Shaftesbury on the roundabout joining the A30 and A350 Salisbury and Blandford roads.

Grove Arms Inn
◆◆◆◆ ✍
Ludwell, near Shaftesbury, Dorset, SP7 9ND
Tel: 01747 828328 Fax: 01747 828960
Email: grovearms@talk21.com
Web: www.grovearms.co.uk

Award-winning Grade II listed thatched property, refurbished in 1999 to high standard. Surrounded by beautiful countryside for walks and picturesque scenery. Good food and friendly welcome.
Rooms: 6 all ensuite ♨ Room facilities: 📺 🍵
Licences: ♦♦♦ Parking: Off-street
Directions: On main A30 Shaftesbury to Salisbury road.

Shepton Mallet, Somerset

Shrubbery Hotel

 ★ ★ ★ ♙ ♙

17 Commercial Road, Shepton Mallet,
Somerset, BA4 5BU
Tel: 01749 346671 Fax: 01749 346581
Rooms: 11 all ensuite 🐾 🗊
Pricing: Sgl £52.50 Dbl £75 Dinner from £22.90
CC: Accepted Room facilities: 🖵 ☎ 🍵 📞
Children: Welcome ♬ 🍼 Dogs: Welcome
Licences: ♦♦♦ Parking: Off-street
Directions: Situated in the town centre, off A37 on main
A371, next to police station.

Belfield House

 ♦ ♦ ♦ ✍

34 Charlton Road, Shepton Mallet, Somerset, BA4 5PA
Tel: 01749 344353 Fax: 01749 344353
Email: andrea@belfield-house.co.uk
Web: www.belfield-house.co.uk
Rooms: 6 (4 ensuite) 🐾 ⊗
Pricing: Sgl £19 Dbl £42 CC: Accepted
Room facilities: 🖵 🍵 Children: Welcome ♬
Dogs: Guide dogs only Parking: Off-street
Directions: On main A361 Wells/Frome Road. Just 200
yards from main A37 junction, opposite leisure centre.

43 Maesdown Road

 ♦ ♦ 🐾

Evercreech, Shepton Mallet, Somerset, BA4 6LE
Tel: 01749 830721
Rooms: 3 ⊗ Room facilities: 🖵 🍵
Access: ♿ Children: Welcome, 5yrs min age
Dogs: Welcome Parking: Off-street
Directions: From Bath & West Showground on A37,
turn left, then first right for village, 1 mile. First left after
village name sign.

Sherborne, Dorset

The Sherborne

★ ★ ★

Horsecastles Lane, Sherborne, Dorset, DT9 6BB
Tel: 01935 813191 Fax: 01935 816493
Web: www.macdonaldhotels.co.uk
Rooms: 59 all ensuite 🐾 ⊗
Pricing: Dinner from £17.95 CC: Accepted
Room facilities: 🖵 ☎ 🍵
Conference: 2 meeting rooms (Thtr 80 max)
Children: Welcome ♬ Dogs: Welcome
Licences: ⚓ ♦♦♦ Parking: Off-street

The Half Moon

 ♦ ♦ ♦ ♦ ✍

Half Moon Street, Sherbourne, Dorset, DT9 6LP
Tel: 01935 812017 Fax: 01935 815295
Rooms: 16 all ensuite 🐾
Pricing: Sgl £54 Dbl £69 CC: Accepted
Room facilities: 🖵 ☎ 🍵 📞 Children: Welcome ♬

Dogs: Welcome Licences: ♦♦♦ Parking: Off-street
Directions: From London/south, A30. Turn left at
junction with A352 (Sherborne), follow A352 into
Sherborne. You eventually have to turn left, into Half
Moon Street. From north, M5 to junction 29, Exeter.
Exit here and follow signs for A30. Continue on A30
until you reach A352 Sherborne.

Shipham, Somerset

Daneswood House Hotel

 ★ ★ ★ ♙ ♙ ♙

Cuck Hill, Shipham, Somerset, BS25 1RD
Tel: 01934 843145 Fax: 01934 843824
Email: info@daneswoodhotel.co.uk
Web: www.daneswoodhotel.co.uk
Rooms: 17 all ensuite 🐾 🗊 ⊗
Pricing: Sgl £89.50–99.50 Dbl £105.50–150
Dinner from £29.95 CC: Accepted
Room facilities: 🖵 ☎ 🍵
Conference: 2 meeting rooms (Thtr 40 max),
24hr-delegate from £135, day-delegate rate from £35
Children: Welcome ♬ 🍼 Dogs: Guide dogs only
Licences: ♦♦♦ Parking: Off-street
Directions: One mile inland off A38 Bridgwater–Bristol
road, at far side of village on left.

Sidmouth, Devon

Belmont Hotel

 ★ ★ ★ ★ ♙

The Esplanade, Sidmouth, Devon, EX10 8RX
Tel: 01395 512555 Fax: 01395 579101
Email: info@belmont-hotel.co.uk
Web: www.belmont-hotels.co.uk

Located on Sidmouth's famous esplanade, the
Belmont offers all the amenities you would expect from
a 4-star hotel, while retaining the charm and character
of its origin.
Rooms: 50 all ensuite 🐾
Pricing: Sgl £61–111 Dbl £104–222 Dinner from £26.50
CC: Accepted Room facilities: 🖵 ☎ 🍵 📞
Access: ⬆ ♿ Children: Welcome ♬ 🍼
Dogs: Guide dogs only Licences: ⚓ ♦♦♦
Parking: Off-street and monitored
Directions: On Sidmouth seafront.
See advert on following page

Southwest

Hotel Riviera

★★★★ ⌖ ⌖ ⌖
Blue Ribbon Winner

The Esplanade, Sidmouth, Devon, EX10 8AY
Tel: 01395 515201 Fax: 01395 577775
Email: enquiries@hotelriviera.co.uk
Web: www.hotelriviera.co.uk

A majestic Regency hotel, situated on the Esplanade
with panoramic sea views and a splendid terrace
overlooking Lyme Bay.
Rooms: 27 all ensuite ⊛
Pricing: Sgl £84–114 Dbl £148–208 Dinner from £29
CC: Accepted Room facilities: ☐ ☎ ⊿ Access: ⌊⌊ ⌕
Conference: 1 meeting room (Thtr 85 max)
Children: Welcome ⼑ ⌇ Dogs: Welcome
Licences: ⫙ Parking: Off-street and monitored
Directions: M5 from London, Exit 30 follow A3052.
Hotel Riviera is situated in centre of the Esplanade.
See advert on previous page

Victoria Hotel

★★★★★ ⌖ ⌖

The Esplanade, Sidmouth, Devon, EX10 8RY
Tel: 01395 512651 Fax: 01395 579154
Email: info@victoriahotel.co.uk
Web: www.victoriahotel.co.uk

Overlooking the esplanade and the sea, magnificent
rooms, renowned cuisine and superb leisure facilities
make the Victoria one of England's finest hotels.
Rooms: 61 all ensuite ⊛⌇
Pricing: Sgl £72–102 Dbl £120–240 Dinner from £29
CC: Accepted Room facilities: ☐ ☎ ⊿ ⌇
Access: ⌊⌊ ⌕ Children: Welcome ⼑ ⌇
Dogs: Guide dogs only Licences: ⫙
Leisure: Indoor pool, Outdoor pool, Beauty salon,
Tennis, Games room, Snooker/billiards
Parking: Off-street and monitored
Directions: Located on Sidmouth seafront.
See advert on this page

Bedford Hotel

★★★

The Esplanade, Sidmouth, Devon, EX10 8NR
Tel: 01395 513047 Fax: 01395 578563
Seasonal closure: February
Rooms: 36 all ensuite ⊿ ⊛
Pricing: Sgl £42–70 Dbl £84–140 Dinner from £19.95
CC: Accepted Room facilities: ☐ ☎ ⊿ Access: ⌊⌊
Children: Welcome ⼑ ⌇ Dogs: Welcome
Licences: ⫙ Parking: Off-street and monitored
Directions: Centrally situated on Sidmouth seafront.

Royal Glen Hotel

★★★

Glen Road, Sidmouth, Devon, EX10 8RW
Tel: 01395 513221 Fax: 01395 514922
Email: sidmouthroyalglen.hotel@virgin.net
Web: www.royalglenhotel.co.uk

In a secluded position close to the sea front, this one-
time royal residence will appeal to those seeking old-
world charm, comfort, good catering and personal
service.
Rooms: 32 all ensuite ⊛⌇
Pricing: Sgl £32–46 Dbl £64–92 Dinner from £16
CC: Accepted Room facilities: ☐ ☎ ⊿
Children: Welcome ⼑ Dogs: Welcome Licences: ⫙
Leisure: Indoor pool Parking: Off-street
Directions: Follow signs to seafront. Turn right onto
Esplanade. Turn right into Glen Road at the end of the
Promenade.

Salcombe Hill House Hotel

★★★

Beatlands Road, Sidmouth, Devon, EX10 8JQ
Tel: 01395 514697 Fax: 01395 578310
Seasonal closure: 1 November to 1 March
Rooms: 28 all ensuite ⊛⌇
Pricing: Dinner from £16.50 CC: Accepted
Room facilities: ☐ ☎ ⊿ Access: ⌊⌊
Children: Welcome ⼑ Dogs: Welcome Licences: ⫙
Leisure: Outdoor pool, Tennis, Games room

Southwest

Westcliff Hotel

Enjoy our supreme position in lovely south-facing grounds, nearest to Connaught Gardens, Western Beach, Golf Course, and an easy stroll along the Esplanade to the main part of town. Beautifully appointed lounges, cocktail bar, restaurant, sun terrace, and most bedrooms have magnificent coastal views. Locally renowned cuisine and service.

Manor Road, Sidmouth,
Devon, EX10 8RU
Tel: 01395 513252   Fax: 01395 578203
stay@westcliffhotel.co.uk
www.westcliffhotel.co.uk

Westcliff Hotel
★★★★
Manor Road, Sidmouth, Devon, EX10 8RU
Tel: 01395 513252 Fax: 01395 578203
Email: stay@westcliffhotel.co.uk
Web: www.westcliffhotel.co.uk
Seasonal closure: November to March
Rooms: 40 all ensuite ✇ ⊛ Pricing: Dinner from £27.50
CC: Accepted Room facilities: ☐ ☎ ☺ ☏ Access: ⊞ ♿
Children: Welcome, 6yrs min age
Dogs: Guide dogs only Licences: ♦♦♦
Leisure: Outdoor pool, Gym, Games room,
Snooker/billiards Parking: Off-street and monitored
Directions: Turn right at Sidmouth seafront, then right into Manor Road; first right into hotel.
See advert on this page

Royal York & Faulkner Hotel
★★
Esplanade, Sidmouth, Devon, EX10 8AZ
Tel: 0800 220714 Fax: 01395 577472
Email: stay@royalyorkhotel.net
Web: www.royalyorkhotel.net
Seasonal closure: January
Rooms: 70 (68 ensuite) ✇ Pricing: Sgl £31–54
Dbl £62–108 Dinner from £15 CC: Accepted
Room facilities: ☐ ☎ ☺ Access: ⊞ Children:
Welcome ♨ ☕ Dogs: Welcome Licences: ♦♦♦
Leisure: Gym, Health spa, Games room,
Snooker/billiards Parking: Off-street and monitored
Directions: Exit M5 at junction 30 and follow signs for Sidmouth, hotel is situated at centre of Esplanade.

Groveside
◆◆◆◆ ※☐
Vicarage Road, Sidmouth, Devon, EX10 8UQ
Tel: 01395 513406
Email: groveside.sidmouth@virgin.net
Web: www.eastdevon.net/groveside
Seasonal closure: December to January
Rooms: 9 (8 ensuite) ⊛ Pricing: Sgl £24 Dbl £48
Room facilities: ☐ ☺ Children: Welcome ♨
Dogs: Guide dogs only
Parking: Off-street and monitored
Directions: From M5 or A303 follow signs to Honiton, then signs to Sidmouth. Hotel is just on the edge of town, to left on the main road.

South Cerney, Gloucestershire

The Eliot Arms Hotel
◆◆◆◆
Clarks Hay, South Cerney, Cirencester,
Gloucestershire, GL7 5UA
Tel: 01285 860215 Fax: 01285 861121
Email: eliotarms.cirencester@eldridge-pope.co.uk
Rooms: 11 all ensuite ✇ ▦ ⊛
Pricing: Sgl £45 Dbl £50 Dinner from £6.95
CC: Accepted Room facilities: ☐ ☎ ☺ ☏
Access: ♿ Children: Welcome ♨
Dogs: Guide dogs only Licences: ⟁ ♦♦♦
Parking: Off-street
Directions: From London M4 J15, follow signs to Swindon A419, 2nd exit to Cirencester, at Little Chef 2nd exit to spine road junction. Branch left and at roundabout take 1st exit for B4696, then turn right for Watermark Leisure Club. Hotel on left.

South Molton, Devon

Highbullen Hotel
★★★★
Chittlehamholt, Omberleijh, Devon, EX37 9HD
Tel: 01769 540561 Fax: 01769 540492
Email: info@highbullen.co.uk
Web: www.highbullen.co.uk
Rooms: 40 all ensuite
Pricing: Sgl £75–90 Dbl £140–160 Dinner from £25
CC: Accepted Room facilities: ☐ ☎ ☺
Dogs: Guide dogs only Licences: ♦♦♦
Leisure: Indoor pool, Outdoor pool, Gym, Health spa, Beauty salon, Tennis, Golf, Fishing, Snooker/billiards
Parking: Off-street
Directions: Leave M5 at Junction 27. Take A361 to South Molton. Take B3226. After 5 miles turn right up hill to Chittlehamholt. High Bullen is ½ mile beyond village, on left.

Plan your route

Visit www.rac.co.uk for RAC's interactive route planner, including up to the minute traffic reports.

Stumbles Hotel & Restaurant

 ◆ ◆ ◆ 🐾

134 East Street, South Molton, Devon, EX36 3BU
Tel: 01769 574145 Fax: 01769 572558
Email: colette@stumbles.co.uk
Web: www.stumbles.co.uk
In a thriving market town, a combination of quality
accommodation and top class cuisine. Al Fresco dining
in summer, ongoing offer of every fourth night free,
sporting/leisure facilities available nearby.
Rooms: 10 all ensuite
Pricing: Sgl £35–50 Dbl £45–80 Dinner from £12
CC: Accepted Room facilities: 🖵 ☎ 🝔 Access: ⛨
Conference: 1 meeting room (Thtr 50 max),
24hr-delegate from £50, day-delegate rate from £10
Children: Welcome ♒ Dogs: Welcome
Licences: ♦♦♦ Parking: Off-street
Directions: Leave M5 junction 27 Tiverton, follow A361
to South Molton, on left in main street. Just before
square, parking behind.

St Agnes, Cornwall

Rose-in-Vale Country House Hotel

★ ★ ★ ★ 🐾 🐾
Mithian, St Agnes, Cornwall, TR5 0QD
Tel: 01872 552202 Fax: 01872 552700
Email: reception@rose-in-vale-hotel.co.uk
Web: www.rose-in-vale-hotel.co.uk
Seasonal closure: January to February

Secluded Georgian manor house surrounded by 11
acres of wooded valley grounds, high standards of
service, comfort and cuisine. Close to Eden project,
good walking country, magnificent coastline and
stunning beaches nearby.
Rooms: 18 all ensuite 🐾 🚗
Pricing: Sgl £60–60 Dbl £105–125 Dinner from £25.95
CC: Accepted Room facilities: 🖵 ☎ 🝔 Access: ⛨
Conference: 2 meeting rooms (Thtr 50 max),
24hr-delegate from £82, day-delegate rate from £27.50
Children: Welcome ♒ ✾ Dogs: Welcome
Licences: ◁ ♦♦♦
Leisure: Outdoor pool, Games room, Snooker/billiards
Parking: Off-street
Directions: A30 through Cornwall turn right onto B3284
to Perranporth Cross, A3075 continue on B3284, take
3rd turning left to Rose-in-Vale.

Rosemundy House Hotel

★ ★ 🐾

8 Rosemundy, St Agnes, Cornwall, TR5 0UF
Tel: 01872 552101 Fax: 01872 554000
Email: info@rosemundy.co.uk
Web: www.rosemundy.co.uk
Rooms: 44 all ensuite 🐾 🚗
Pricing: Sgl £28–50 Dbl £56–100 Dinner from £33
CC: Accepted Room facilities: 🖵 🝔
Children: Welcome, 10yrs min age Licences: ♦♦♦
Leisure: Outdoor pool, Games room
Parking: Off-street and monitored
Directions: A30 until Chiverton Cross roundabout, 4th
exit signposted St Agnes, 2nd right, 2nd left,
Rosemundy House Hotel on left.

Penkerris

◆ ◆

Penwinnick Road, St Agnes, Cornwall, TR5 0PA
Tel: 01872 552262 Fax: 01872 552262
Email: info@penkerris.co.uk Web: www.penkerris.co.uk

Creeper-clad Edwardian residence with garden in
unspoilt Cornish village. A home-from-home with real
food and comfortable rooms. Licensed. Ample parking.
Cliff walks and beaches nearby.
Rooms: 7 (3 ensuite) 🐾
Pricing: Sgl £17.50–30 Dbl £30–50 Dinner from £12.50
CC: Accepted Room facilities: 🖵 🝔
Children: Welcome ♒ ✾ ✾ Dogs: Welcome
Licences: ♦♦♦ Parking: Off-street
Directions: From roundabout at Chivertoncross on A30,
take B3277 to St Agnes itself. Penkerris is first on right
after village sign and 30mph limit sign.

Southwest

St Austell, Cornwall

Carlyon Bay Hotel

★★★★★ 🍷 🍷

Sea Road, Carlyon Bay, St Austell, Cornwall, PL25 3RD
Tel: 01726 812304 Fax: 01726 814938
Email: reservations@carlyonbay.com
Web: www.carlyonbay.com

A superb hotel in a clifftop location offering spectacular views. The hotel's 18-hole golf course runs along the clifftop adjacent to the hotel.
Rooms: 73 all ensuite 🍽
Pricing: Sgl £81–98 Dbl £156–250 Dinner from £28
CC: Accepted Room facilities: 🖵 ☎ 🍵 🥂
Access: |↕| Children: Welcome 🍴 🎠 🌿
Dogs: Guide dogs only Licences: 🍷 👯
Leisure: Indoor pool, Outdoor pool, Health spa, Beauty salon, Tennis, Golf, Games room, Snooker/billiards
Parking: Off-street and monitored
Directions: From St Austell follow signs for Charlestown. Carlyon Bay is signposted on left. Hotel at end of sea road.

Cliff Head Hotel

★★★ 🍷

Sea Road, Carlyon Bay, St Austell, Cornwall, PL25 3RB
Tel: 01726 812345 Fax: 01726 815511
Email: cliffheadhotel@btconnect.com
Web: www.cliffheadhotel.com
Rooms: 60 all ensuite 🍽 🚭
Pricing: Sgl £55 Dbl £100 Dinner from £14.95
CC: Accepted Room facilities: 🖵 ☎ 🍵 Access: ♿
Children: Welcome 🍴 🌿 Licences: 🍷 👯
Leisure: Indoor pool, Gym, Health spa,
Games room Parking: Off-street
Directions: From Plymouth, take A390 to Dobwalls, then to St Austell. Just before entering St Austell, follow signs to Carlyon Bay.

The Porth Avallen Hotel

★★★ 🍷

Sea Road, Carlyon Bay, St Austell, Cornwall, PL25 3SG
Tel: 01726 812802 Fax: 01726 817097
Email: info@porthavallen.co.uk
Web: www.porthavallen.co.uk
Seasonal closure: 26 December to 2 January
Rooms: 27 all ensuite 🚭 🚭
Pricing: Sgl £62–77 Dbl £106–150 CC: Accepted
Room facilities: 🖵 ☎ 🍵 Conference: 1 meeting room (Thtr 100 max), 24hr-delegate from £105, day-delegate rate from £16 Children: Welcome 🍴 🌿
Dogs: Guide dogs only Licences: 👯 Parking: Off-street
Directions: A30 onto A391, follow signs to St Austell, Charlestown and Carlyon Bay. Turn right into Sea Road.
See advert on this page

Boscundle Manor

Blue Ribbon Winner

★★ 🍷

Tregrehan, St Austell, Cornwall, PL25 3RL
Tel: 01726 813557 Fax: 01726 814997
Email: stay@boscundlemanor.co.uk
Web: www.boscundlemanor.co.uk
Seasonal closure: November to March

A small country house hotel with luxurious accommodation, extensive facilities including indoor and outdoor swimming pools, woodland walks and a golf practice area. Beautifully prepared fresh food with oustanding wine list.
Rooms: 14 all ensuite 🚭 🚭 Pricing: Sgl £70–80
Dbl £160–180 Dinner from £27.50 CC: Accepted
Room facilities: 🖵 ☎ 🍵 Children: Welcome
Dogs: Welcome Licences: 🍷 👯 Leisure: Indoor pool, Outdoor pool, Gym Parking: Off-street
Directions: 2 miles east of St Austell, off A390 on road signposted 'Tregrehan'.

St Ives, Cornwall

Chy-an-albany Hotel

★★★

Albany Terrace, St Ives, Cornwall, TR26 2BS
Tel: 01736 796759 Fax: 01736 795584
Email: info@chyanalbanyhotel.com
Web: www.chynalbanyhotel.com
Rooms: 40 all ensuite
Pricing: Sgl £44–64 Dbl £88–128 Dinner from £17.95
CC: Accepted Room facilities: Access:
Conference: 2 meeting rooms (Thtr 60 max),
24hr-delegate from £80, day-delegate rate from £19
Children: Welcome Licences:
Parking: Off-street and monitored
Directions: A3074 road to St Ives, through Carbis Bay,
down Tregenna Hill past car sales; left-hand fork at
bottom of hill.

Porthminster

★★★

The Terrace, St Ives, Cornwall, TR26 2BN
Tel: 01736 795221 Fax: 01736 797043
Email: reception@porthminster-hotel.co.uk
Web: www.porthminster-hotel.co.uk
Seasonal closure: early January
Rooms: 43 all ensuite
Pricing: Dinner from £16 (2002 rate) CC: Accepted
Room facilities: Access:
Children: Welcome Dogs: Welcome Licences:
Leisure: Indoor pool, Outdoor pool, Gym, Health spa
Parking: Off-street
Directions: Porthminster Hotel is on A3074.

The Garrack Hotel & Restaurant

★★★★

Burthallan Lane, St Ives, Cornwall, TR26 3AA
Tel: 01736 796199 Fax: 01736 798955
Email: garrack@accuk.co.uk
Web: www.garrack.com

Small family-run hotel & restaurant. Secluded position
with 30 miles of coastal views overlooking St Ives. 4
poster beds, sea view rooms, private car parking and
indoor pool.
Rooms: 19 all ensuite
Pricing: Sgl £65.50–67.50 Dbl £110–160
Dinner from £24.50 CC: Accepted
Room facilities: Access:
Conference: 1 meeting room (Thtr 18 max)
Children: Welcome Dogs: Welcome Licences:

Leisure: Indoor pool, Gym Parking: Off-street
Directions: B3311 to St Ives, into town 1st mini roundabout, 1st left Carnellis Road, 5 km road bends right,
1st turning on left Burthallan Lane.

Chy-An-Dour Hotel

★★★

Trelyon Avenue, St Ives, Cornwall, TR26 2AD
Tel: 01736 796436 Fax: 01736 795772
Email: chyndour@aol.com
Web: www.connexions.co.uk/chyandourhotel
Rooms: 20 all ensuite
Pricing: Dbl £110–140 Dinner from £19 CC: Accepted
Room facilities: Access:
Children: Welcome Dogs: Guide dogs only
Licences: Parking: Off-street and monitored
Directions: From A30, take A3074 towards St Ives.
Hotel is on right 50 metres past Jet filling station.

Allamanda   Little Gem

♦♦♦♦♦

83 Back Road East, St Ives, Cornwall, TR26 1PF
Tel: 01736 793548 Email: hynd@allamanda.co.uk
Web: www.allamand.co.uk
Rooms: 2 all ensuite
Pricing: Sgl £50–60 Dbl £70–80 Room facilities:
Children: Welcome, 12yrs min age
Parking: Off-street and monitored
Directions: Entering St Ives, drive along harbour to
Sloop Inn, turn left into Fish Street, at T-junction turn
right into Back Road East.

Dean Court Hotel

♦♦♦♦

Trelyon Avenue, St Ives, Cornwall, TR26 2AD
Tel: 01736 796023 Fax: 01736 796233
Email: deancourt@amserve.net
Web: www.deancourthotel.com
Seasonal closure: Easter to 1 November
Rooms: 12 all ensuite
Pricing: Sgl £35–42 Dbl £70–84 Dinner from £12
CC: Accepted Room facilities: Access:
Children: Welcome, 14yrs min age
Dogs: Guide dogs only Licences:
Parking: Off-street
Directions: From A30 take A3074 through Carbis Bay
to St Ives. Dean Court is located on the right side of
Trelyon Avenue.

Hindon Hall

♦♦♦♦

Lelant Village, St Ives, Cornwall, TR26 3EN
Tel: 01736 753046 Fax: 01736 753046
Email: hindonhall@talk21.com Web: hindonhall.co.uk
Seasonal closure: Christmas and New Year
Rooms: 4 all ensuite Pricing: Dbl £52–62
Room facilities: Dogs: Guide dogs only
Licences: Parking: Off-street
Directions: From A30 follow St Ives (sign) A3074
Lelant, Hindon Hall is ¼ mile up hill on right.

Southwest

Longships Hotel

Talland Road, St Ives, Cornwall, TR26 2DF
Tel: 01736 798180 Fax: 01736 798180
Email: enquires@longships-hotel.co.uk
Web: www.longships-hotel.co.uk
Rooms: 25 all ensuite
Pricing: Sgl £20–30 Dbl £40–60 Dinner from £10.50
CC: Accepted Room facilities: ☐ ☕ Access: ♿
Children: Welcome ☇ ☕ Dogs: Guide dogs only
Licences: ♦♦♦ Parking: Off-street and monitored
Directions: Take left fork at Portminster Hotel. Follow
Talland Area Accommodation sign. Hotel is first in
Talland Road.

Regent Hotel

Fern Lea Terrace, St Ives, Cornwall, TR26 2BH
Tel: 01736 796195 Fax: 01736 794641
Email: enquiries@regenthotel.com
Web: www.regenthotel.com
Rooms: 9 (7 ensuite) ☺ Room facilities: ☐ ☕
Parking: Off-street and monitored

Rivendell

7 Porthminster Terrace, St Ives, Cornwall, TR26 2DQ
Tel: 01736 794923 Fax: 01736 794923
Email: rivendellstives@aol.com
Web: www.rivendell-stives.co.uk
Rooms: 7 (4 ensuite) ☕ ☺
Pricing: Sgl £18–23 Dbl £18–25 Dinner from £12
Room facilities: ☐ ☕ Children: Welcome ☇
Dogs: Guide dogs only Parking: Off-street
Directions: B3074 St Ives, bear left Albert Road, left
Dunmar Hotel uphill directly opposite Porthminster
Terrace, straight across 200 yards on right, blue sign.

The Nook Hotel

Ayr, St Ives, Cornwall, TR26 1EQ
Tel: 01736 795913 Fax: 01736 796536
Email: info@nookhotelstives.co.uk
Web: www.nookstives.co.uk

Escape to the Nook Hotel, a family-run licensed hotel
in a peaceful location of St Ives. Relax and enjoy the
home comforts — the perfect base for exploring
beautiful St Ives and beyond.

Rooms: 8 (6 ensuite) ☺
Pricing: Sgl £25–30 Dbl £25–30 Dinner from £5
CC: Accepted Room facilities: ☐ ☕
Children: Welcome ☇ Dogs: Guide dogs only
Licences: ♦♦♦ Parking: Off-street and monitored
Directions: A30 to St Ives, Porthmnster Hotel right, left
Gabriel Street, roundabout right Bullans Lane, left Aye
Terrace, second left private lane.

Trewinnard

4 Parc Avenue, St Ives, Cornwall, TR26 2DN
Tel: 01736 794168 Fax: 01736 798161
Email: sam.sears@btopenworld.com
Web: trewinnard-hotel-stives.co.uk
Seasonal closure: November to March
Rooms: 7 all ensuite ☕ ☕ ☺
Pricing: Sgl £25–35 Dbl £50–70 CC: Accepted
Room facilities: ☐ ☕ Children: Welcome, 6yrs min age
Licences: ♦♦♦
Parking: Off-street
Directions: Take A3074 to St Ives. Turn left at Natwest
Bank. Turn left at mini-roundabout, go past car park,
and house is 150 metres on right.

St Mawes, Cornwall

Idle Rocks Hotel

★★★★ ☕ ☕

Harbourside, St Mawes, Cornwall, TR2 5AN
Tel: 01326 270771 Fax: 01326 270062
Email: reception@idlerocks.co.uk
Web: www.idlerocks.co.uk
Rooms: 27 all ensuite ☕ ☺
Pricing: Sgl £63–119 Dbl £126–250 CC: Accepted
Room facilities: ☐ ☎ ☕ Children: Welcome ☇ ☕
Dogs: Welcome Licences: ♦♦♦
Parking: Off-street and monitored
Directions: M5 onto A30, then onto A39, A390 and
A3078. Hotel first on left in village.

Stoke Gabriel, Devon

Gabriel Court Hotel

★★★

Stoke Hill, Stoke Gabriel, near Totnes, Devon, TQ9 6SF
Tel: 01803 782206 Fax: 01803 782333
Email: obeacom@aol.com
Web: www.gabrielcourthotel.co.uk
Rooms: 19 all ensuite ☕
Pricing: Sgl £55 Dbl £84 Dinner from £30
CC: Accepted Room facilities: ☐ ☎ ☕ ☏
Conference: 20 meeting rooms (Thtr 20 max),
24hr-delegate from £30, day-delegate rate from £40
Children: Welcome ☇ ☕ Dogs: Welcome
Licences: ♦♦♦ Leisure: Outdoor pool, Tennis
Parking: Off-street and monitored
Directions: Turn off A385 (between Totnes and
Paignton) at Parkers Arms pub. Proceed towards
Stoke Gabriel. On entering village, stay left and you will
reach hotel.

Stourton, Wiltshire

Spread Eagle Inn

◆ ◆ ◆ ◆

Stourhead, Stourton, nr Warminster, Wiltshire, BA12 6QE
Tel: 01747 840587 Fax: 01747 840954
Rooms: 5 all ensuite
Pricing: Dinner from £15.95 (2002 rate) CC: Accepted
Room facilities: 🖵 ☎ 🍵 Children: Welcome ⪫ ⪡
Dogs: Guide dogs only Licences: ⫫ Parking: Off-street

Street, Somerset

Wessex Hotel

★★★

High Street, Street, Somerset, BA16 0EF
Tel: 01458 443383 Fax: 01458 446589
Email: wessex@hotel-street.freeserve.co.uk
Web: www.wessexhotel.com
Rooms: 50 all ensuite
Pricing: Sgl £56.50 Dbl £73 Dinner from £9.95
CC: Accepted Room facilities: 🖵 ☎ 🍵 Access: ⫲ ⪧
Conference: 3 meeting rooms (Thtr 250 max),
24hr-delegate from £80, day-delegate rate from £16.95
Children: Welcome ⪡ Dogs: Guide dogs only
Licences: ⫫ Parking: Off-street and monitored
Directions: From M5, Junction 23 to Bridgewater,
Glastonbury and Street. From A303, follow B3151 to
Street. Nearest railway station Castle Cary.

The Birches

◆ ◆ ◆ ◆

13 Housman Road, Street, Somerset, BA16 0SD
Tel: 01458 442902 Email: askins@ukonline.co.uk
Rooms: 2 all ensuite
Pricing: Sgl £28.50–32 Dbl £46–25
Room facilities: 🖵 🍵 Children: Welcome ⪫
Parking: Off-street
Directions: From A39: B3151, 2nd right after Millfield
traffic lights, then first left. From A303: B3151, first left
after 30 mph sign, then first right.

The Bear Inn

◆ ◆ ◆

High Street, Street, Somerset, BA16 0EF
Tel: 01458 442021 Fax: 01458 840007
Rooms: 25 all ensuite
Pricing: Sgl £30–63 Dbl £60–126 Dinner from £3.30
CC: Accepted Room facilities: 🖵 ☎ 🍵 Access: ⪧
Conference: 2 meeting rooms (Thtr 30 max)
Children: Welcome ⪫ Licences: ⫫
Parking: Off-street and monitored
Directions: 2 miles from Glastonbury just off the A39.

Swanage, Dorset

Pines Hotel

★★★

Burlington Road, Swanage, Dorset, BH19 1LT
Tel: 01929 425211 Fax: 01929 422075
Email: reservations@pineshotel.co.uk
Web: www.pineshotel.co.uk
Rooms: 48 all ensuite
Pricing: Sgl £49.50–64.50 Dbl £99–138
Dinner from £21 CC: Accepted
Room facilities: 🖵 ☎ 🍵 ⪡ Access: ⫲ ⪧
Conference: 4 meeting rooms (Thtr 80 max),
24hr-delegate from £79, day-delegate rate from £16.50
Children: Welcome ⪫ ⪡ Dogs: Welcome
Licences: ⫫ Parking: Off-street and monitored
Directions: At seafront, left then 2nd right to end of road.
See advert on this page

Havenhurst

★★

3 Cranborne Road, Swanage, Dorset, BH19 1EA
Tel: 01929 424224 Fax: 01929 422173
Rooms: 17 all ensuite
Pricing: Sgl £24.50–40 Dbl £49–80 Dinner from £16
CC: Accepted Room facilities: 🖵 ☎ 🍵
Children: Welcome ⪫ ⪡ Licences: ⫫
Parking: Off-street
Directions: Take A351 to Swanage along Victoria
Avenue. Turn right at traffic lights. First right into
Cranborne Road.

Southwest

The Castleton Hotel   Little Gem

♦ ♦ ♦ ♦ ※

1 Highcliffe Road, Swanage, Dorset, BH19 1LW
Tel: 01929 423972 Fax: 01929 422901

Family run non-smoking hotel situated 150 yards from
Swanage's Beach. All rooms ensuite and decorated to
high standard. Please telephone for brochure and tariff.
Rooms: 9 all ensuite ⊛
Pricing: Sgl £30–40 Dbl £60–96 Dinner from £17.95
CC: Accepted Room facilities: ▢ ☺
Children: Welcome, 8yrs min age
Dogs: Guide dogs only Licences: ⅲ
Directions: A351 via Wareham to Swanage, left at
seafront. Follow road up hill towards Studland. First
road on right off seafront.

Sandringham Hotel

♦ ♦ ♦

20 Durlston Road, Swanage, Dorset, BH19 2HX
Tel: 01929 423076 Fax: 01929 423076
Email: silk@sandhot.fsnet.co.uk
Rooms: 11 (9 ensuite) ⊛
Pricing: Sgl £27–33 Dbl £54–66 Dinner from £14
CC: Accepted Room facilities: ▢ ☺
Children: Welcome ⊦ ☕ Dogs: Guide dogs only
Licences: ⅲ Parking: Off-street
Directions: On entering Swanage, follow signs to
Durlston Country Park.

Swindon, Wiltshire

Blunsdon House Hotel

★ ★ ★ ★ ℞

The Ridge, Blunsdon, Swindon, Wiltshire, SN26 7AS
Tel: 01793 721701 Fax: 01793 720625
Email: info@blunsdonhouse.co.uk
Web: www.blunsdonhouse.co.uk
Rooms: 118 all ensuite ⊛ ▱ ⊛
Pricing: Sgl £107–137 Dbl £100–130 Dinner from £20
CC: Accepted Room facilities: ▢ ☎ ☺ ☏ ✳
Access: ⇵ ♿ Conference: 11 meeting rooms (Thtr
300 max) Children: Welcome ⊦ ⛀ ☕
Dogs: Guide dogs only Licences: ⌂ ⅲ
Leisure: Indoor pool, Gym, Health spa, Beauty salon,
Tennis, Golf, Games room
Parking: Off-street and monitored
Directions: Leave M4 at Junction 15. Take A419 to
Cirencester. After 7 miles you reach Broad Blunsdon.
200 yards past traffic lights, turn right into village.

Chiseldon House Hotel

★ ★ ★ ℞

New Road, Chiseldon, Swindon, Wiltshire, SN4 0NE
Tel: 01793 741010 Fax: 01793 741059
Email: chishoho@hotmail.com
Web: www.chiseldonhousehotel.co.uk
Rooms: 21 all ensuite ▱ ⊛
Pricing: Sgl £80–80 Dbl £100–120 Dinner from £25
CC: Accepted Room facilities: ▢ ☎ ☺ ☏
Conference: 2 meeting rooms (Thtr 50 max),
24hr-delegate from £136, day-delegate rate from £36
Children: Welcome ⊦ ☕ Dogs: Welcome
Licences: ⌂ ⅲ Leisure: Outdoor pool
Parking: Off-street
Directions: M4 J15 then A346 south. ¾ mile, right into
New Road. Hotel is 300 yards on the right.

Marsh Farm Hotel

★ ★ ★ ℞ ℞

Coped Hall, Wootton Bassett, Swindon,
Wiltshire, SN4 8ER
Tel: 01793 848044 Fax: 01793 851528
Email: marshfarmhotel@btconnect.com
Web: www.marshfarmhotel.co.uk
Seasonal closure: December 26–30

This beautiful grade 2 listed Victorian farm house has
been tastefully restored and converted into a luxury
country hotel. Reid's Conservatory Restaurant offers
excellent cuisine and fine wines.
Rooms: 38 all ensuite ⊛ ⊛
Pricing: Sgl £55–110 Dbl £70–140 Dinner from £22.50
CC: Accepted Room facilities: ▢ ☎ ☺ ☏ Access: ♿
Conference: 8 meeting rooms (Thtr 120 max),
24hr-delegate from £135, day-delegate rate from £38
Children: Welcome Licences: ⌂ ⅲ
Parking: Off-street and monitored
Directions: Leave M4 at Junction 16. Take A3102
towards Wootton Bassett, at 2nd roundabout turn
right. Hotel is immediately on your left.

Stanton House Hotel

★★★

The Avenue, Stanton, Fitzwarren, Swindon,
Wiltshire, SN6 7SD
Tel: 01793 861777 Fax: 01793 861857
Email: reception@stantonhouse.co.uk
Web: www.stantonhouse.co.uk
Rooms: 86 all ensuite ⊗
Pricing: Sgl £69 Dbl £109 Dinner from £15
CC: Accepted Room facilities: ☐ ☎ ◱ Access: ⏍ ⅏
Children: Welcome Dogs: Guide dogs only
Licences: ◬ ⅲ Leisure: Tennis
Parking: Off-street and monitored
Directions: M4 junction 15 A419, pass Honda factory
onto A361 towards Highworth Pass business park, turn
left towards Stanton Fitzwarren.
See advert on this page

The Pear Tree at Purton

★★★

Church End, Purton, Swindon, Wiltshire, SN5 4ED
Tel: 01793 772100 Fax: 01793 772369
Email: relax@peartreepurton.co.uk
Web: www.peartreepurton.co.uk
Seasonal closure: 26–30 December

This personally run Cotswold stone former vicarage is
set in 7½ acres and surrounded on all sides by rolling
Wiltshire farmland. Ideal for visiting the Cotswolds,
Bath, Oxford and Swindon.
Rooms: 18 all ensuite ◱ ⊗
Pricing: Sgl £110–130 Dbl £110–145
Dinner from £31.50 CC: Accepted
Room facilities: ☐ ☎ ⚘ Access: ⏍
Conference: 4 meeting rooms (Thtr 50 max),
24hr-delegate from £160, day-delegate rate from £45
Children: Welcome ⅌ ⅃ Dogs: Welcome
Licences: ◬ ⅲ Parking: Off-street and monitored
Directions: From M4 J16 follow signs to Purton. At
Spar grocers turn right. Hotel is half mile on left.

Villiers Inn

★★★

Moormead Road, Wroughton, Swindon,
Wiltshire, SN4 9BY
Tel: 01793 814744 Fax: 01793 814119
Email: wroughton@villiershotels.com
Web: www.villiershotels.com/wroughton
Rooms: 33 all ensuite ⚭ ◱ ⊗
Pricing: Sgl £49–79 Dbl £69–89 Dinner from £10
CC: Accepted Room facilities: ☐ ☎ ◱ Access: ⏍
Conference: 7 meeting rooms (Thtr 90 max)
Children: Welcome ⅌ ⅃ Dogs: Welcome
Licences: ◬ ⅲ Parking: Off-street and monitored
Directions: Leave M4 at Junction 15. Take A346 to
Chiseldon, turn right onto B4005 towards Wroughton.
Take A4361 to Swindon. Hotel 100 metres on right.

Fir Tree Lodge

◆ ◆ ◆ ⌁

17 Highworth Road, Stratton St Margaret, Swindon,
Wiltshire, SN3 4QL
Tel: 01793 822372 Fax: 01793 822372
Rooms: 13 (11 ensuite) ⚭
Pricing: Sgl £32.32–52.88 CC: Accepted
Room facilities: ☐ ◱ Children: Welcome
Dogs: Welcome Parking: Off-street and monitored
Directions: Opposite Rat Trap public house. Follow
A419 until A361 Highworth/Burford turn. Turn at
roundabout, approximately 100 metres on right.

Southwest

Taunton, Somerset

Bindon Country House

Blue Ribbon Winner

★★★ ⓡ ⓡ ⓡ

Langford Budville, Wellington, Somerset, TA21 0RU
Tel: 01823 4000 70 Fax: 01823 4000 71
Email: stay@bindon.com Web: www.bindon.com
Rooms: 12 all ensuite 🛏 📺 Ⓢ
Pricing: Dinner from £29.95 (2002 rate) CC: Accepted
Room facilities: 🖥 ☎ Children: Welcome ♨ ≋€
Dogs: Welcome Licences: ⚓ ♦♦♦
Leisure: Outdoor pool, Tennis Parking: Off-street
Directions: Exit M5 at Junction 26, take A38 to
Wellington. Take B3187 to Langford Budville, then
follow hotel signs.

Castle Hotel

Gold Ribbon Winner

★★★★ ⓡ ⓡ ⓡ ⓡ

Castle Green, Taunton, Somerset, TA1 1NF
Tel: 01823 272671 Fax: 01823 336066
Email: reception@the-castle-hotel.com
Web: www.the-castle-hotel.com

Welcoming travellers to Somerset's county town for
800 years, the Castle Hotel offers rare standards of
comfort and service and a restaurant now rated one of
the best in the country.
Rooms: 44 all ensuite 🛏 📺 Ⓢ
Pricing: Sgl £105 Dbl £175–255 Dinner from £33
CC: Accepted Room facilities: 🖥 ☎ 🔌 Access: ⌊↑ ⓓ
Conference: 4 meeting rooms (Thtr 100 max),
24hr-delegate from £155, day-delegate rate from £45
Children: Welcome Dogs: Welcome Licences: ♦♦♦
Parking: Off-street and monitored
Directions: From M5, take Junction 25 and follow signs
to town centre, then brown signs to Castle Hotel.

The Mount Somerset Hotel

★★★★ ⓡ ⓡ ⓡ

Lower Henlade, Taunton, Somerset, TA3 5NB
Tel: 01823 442500 Fax: 01823 442900
Email: info@mountsomersethotel.co.uk
Web: www.mountsomersethotel.com
Rooms: 11 all ensuite 📺 Ⓢ
Pricing: Sgl £95 Dbl £155 Dinner from £25.95
CC: Accepted Room facilities: 🖥 ☎ Access: ⌊↑ ⓓ
Conference: meeting rooms, 24hr-delegate from £140,
day-delegate rate from £27.50
Children: Welcome ♨ ≋€ Dogs: Welcome
Licences: ♦♦♦ Parking: Off-street
Directions: Junction 25, M5, take A358 for Chard, turn
right to Stoke St Mary, left at T-junction. Hotel on right.

Corner House Hotel

★★

Park Street, Taunton, Somerset, TA1 4DQ
Tel: 01823 284683 Fax: 01823 323464
Email: res@corner-house.co.uk
Web: www.corner-house.co.uk

The Corner house hotel is a five-minute walk from
Taunton town centre and has its own park. Rooms are
comfortably furnished and have DVD televisions,
tea/coffee facilities and are ensuite.
Rooms: 28 (2 ensuite) Ⓢ
Pricing: Sgl £45–65 Dbl £62–89 Dinner from £19.95
CC: Accepted Room facilities: 🖥 ☎ 🔌
Children: Welcome ♨ Dogs: Guide dogs only
Licences: ♦♦♦ Parking: Off-street and monitored
Directions: On the corner of the A38 Wellington Road
and Park Street.

Farthings Hotel and Restaurant

★★★ 🛡 🛡

Hatch Beauchamp, Taunton, Somerset, TA3 6SG
Tel: 01823 480664 Fax: 01823 481118
Email: farthings1@aol.com
Web: www.farthingshotel.com

Relaxing, friendly Georgian house owned and run by
Stephen (your chef) and Hilary (your host). Log fires in
winter, peaceful gardens in summer, but a wonderful
dinner all year round.
Rooms: 10 all ensuite 🏌 🚫
Pricing: Sgl £75–85 Dbl £105–115 Dinner from £28.95
CC: Accepted Room facilities: ☐ ☎ 🗒
Children: Welcome Dogs: Welcome
Licences: 🍸 🍴 Parking: Off-street
Directions: Exit J25 M5, A358 towards Ilminster. Go 3½
miles, then turn left at sign for Hatch Beauchamp.
Farthings Hotel is 1 mile from turn.

Langley House

★★ 🛡

Langley, Wiveliscombe, Taunton, Somerset, TA4 2UF
Tel: 01984 623318 Fax: 01984 624573
Email: langley.house@virgin.net
Web: www.langleyhousehotel.co.uk
Rooms: 8 all ensuite 🖋 🚫
Pricing: Sgl £50–70 Dbl £100–140 Dinner from £32.50
CC: Accepted Room facilities: ☐ ☎ 🔌
Conference: 1 meeting room (Thtr 25 max)
Children: Welcome, 12yrs min age 🍴 Dogs: Welcome
Licences: 🍴 Parking: Off-street and monitored
Directions: From junction 25 M5 follow B3224 to
Wiveliscombe, at traffic lights turn right to town square,
turn right ½ mile on right-hand side.

Elm Villa

◆◆◆◆◆ ⌁

Private Road, Staplegrove Road, Taunton,
Somerset, TA2 6AJ
Tel: 01823 336165
Email: ferguson@elmvilla10.freeserve.co.uk
Rooms: 2 all ensuite
Pricing: Sgl £30–35 Dbl £50–52
Room facilities: ☐ 🗒 Parking: Off-street
Directions: From Taunton centre, private road is off
A3027 near junction with A358 Minehead road.

Meryan House Hotel

◆◆◆◆ 🛡 🛡 ⌁

Bishops Hull, Taunton, Somerset, TA1 5EG
Tel: 01823 337445 Fax: 01823 322355
Email: meryanhouse@mywebpage.net
Web: www.mywebpage.net/meryanhouse
Rooms: 12 all ensuite 🖋 🚫
Pricing: Dinner from £16 CC: Accepted
Room facilities: ☐ ☎ 🗒 🔌 Access: ♿
Children: Welcome 🍴 🐾 Dogs: Welcome
Licences: 🍴 Parking: Off-street and monitored
Directions: Take A38 out of Taunton for about 1 mile,
after crematorium turn right into Bishops Hull Road.
Hotel approximately 600 yards.

Salisbury House Hotel

◆◆◆◆ ⌁

14 Billetfield, Taunton, Somerset, TA1 3NN
Tel: 01823 272083 Fax: 01823 365978
Email: res.salisbury@btinternet.com
Web: www.salisburyhousehotel.com

Victorian family-owned hotel is unrivalled town centre
location. Modern comforts combined with charm and
character will ensure a memorable stay. Four-poster
and ground floor rooms available. Car park.
Rooms: 17 all ensuite 🏌 🖋 🚫
Pricing: Sgl £48–53 Dbl £58–65 CC: Accepted
Room facilities: ☐ ☎ 🗒 🔌 Access: ♿
Conference: 1 meeting room (Thtr 15 max)
Children: Welcome Licences: 🍴 Parking: Off-street
Directions: Follow signs to Taunton town centre. From
East Reach, bear left and go past Sainsbury's and BP
garage. Hotel is on right, past church.

Canonsgrove Farm

◆◆◆

Trull, Taunton, Somerset, TA3 7PD
Tel: 01823 279720
Rooms: 2 🚫 Pricing: Sgl £25 Dbl £45
Room facilities: ☎ Children: Welcome 🍴
Dogs: Guide dogs only Leisure: Games room
Directions: Exit J25 M5, take A38 towards Wellington,
take Honiton Road. Signposted Trull, go 3 miles, turn
right at sign Sweethay before bridge, 100 metres on left.

Chitcombe Farm

◆ ◆ ◆

Huish Champflower, Taunton, Somerset, TA4 2EL
Tel: 01398 371274 Fax: 01398 371111
Email: jekennen@hotmail.com
Web: www.chitcombefarm.co.uk
Rooms: 2 🐾 🚭
Pricing: Sgl £25 Dbl £40 Dinner from £12.50
Room facilities: 📠 Children: Welcome 🍴
Dogs: Guide dogs only Parking: Off-street
Directions: From Taunton B3227 to Wiveliscombe; right
in square to Huish Champflower. Left to Upton.
Chitcombe Farm 2¹/₂ miles on right.

Lime House

◆ ◆ ◆ 🚭

6 Linden Grove, Taunton, Somerset, TA1 1EF
Tel: 01823 274686
Rooms: 2 🚭 Pricing: Sgl £25–30 Dbl £45–50
Room facilities: 📺 📠 Children: Welcome, 4yrs min age
Directions: J25 M5, follow signs for Cricket
Ground/Market. Left at T-junction, 3rd turning right
(Staplegrove Road), 2nd right (Linden Grove).

Travelodge Taunton (SA)

Travel Accommodation
A38, Riverside Retail Park, Hankridge Farm,
Blackbrook Park, Taunton, Somerset, TA1 2LR
Web: www.travelodge.co.uk
Rooms: 48 all ensuite 🚭
Pricing: Sgl £54.40 Dbl £58.85
CC: Accepted Room facilities: 📺 📠 Access: ♿

Tavistock, Devon

Browns Hotel

★ ★ ★ ★ Townhouse 🎗 🎗
80 West Street, Tavistock, Devon, PL19 8AQ
Tel: 01822 618686 Fax: 01822 618646
Email: enquiries@brownsdevon.co.uk
Web: www.brownsdevon.co.uk

A stylish townhouse hotel offering luxurious ensuite
bedrooms, superb food in the Brasserie and fine wines
and champagnes by the glass or bottle. Affordable
chic for the discerning west country visitor.
Rooms: 20 all ensuite 🐾 🚭 🚭
Pricing: Sgl £65–65 Dbl £90–120 Dinner from £17.95

CC: Accepted Room facilities: 📺 ☎ 📠 🔌 Access: ⬆️
Children: Welcome 🍴 Dogs: Guide dogs only
Licences: 🎎 Leisure: Indoor pool, Gym
Parking: Off-street and monitored
Directions: In town centre, on right-hand side of West
Street, which is one-way.

Bedford Hotel

★ ★ ★ 🎗 🎗
1 Plymouth Road, Tavistock, Devon, PL19 8BB
Tel: 01822 613221 Fax: 01822 618034
Email: jane@bedford-hotel.co.uk
Web: www.warm-welcome-hotels.co.uk
Rooms: 29 all ensuite 🐾 🚭 🚭
Pricing: Sgl £47.50–60 Dbl £90–105
Dinner from £19.95 CC: Accepted
Room facilities: 📺 ☎ 📠 🔌 Access: ♿
Children: Welcome 🍴 🍴 Dogs: Welcome Licences: 🎎
Parking: Off-street and monitored
Directions: In the centre of Tavistock, opposite the
parish church.
See advert on next page

Thornbury, Gloucestershire

Thornbury Castle   Gold Ribbon Winner

★ ★ ★ 🎗 🎗 🎗
Castle Street, Thornbury,
South Gloucestershire, BS35 1HH
Tel: 01454 281182 Fax: 01454 416188
Email: thornburycastle@compuserve.com
Web: www.thornburycastle.com
Seasonal closure: 4 days in early January

Beautiful 16th century castle-palace, once owned by
Henry VIII, offering 25 carefully restored bedchambers.
Renowned for its fine food, the castle has three dining
rooms, each baronial in style with open fires.
Rooms: 26 all ensuite 🚭
Pricing: Sgl £105 Dbl £135–400 Dinner from £42.50
CC: Accepted Room facilities: 📺 ☎ 📠
Conference: 3 meeting rooms (Thtr 50 max),
24hr-delegate from £230, day-delegate rate from £55
Children: Welcome 🍴 Dogs: Welcome
Licences: ⚜️ 🎎 Leisure: Snooker/billiards
Parking: Off-street and monitored
Directions: To Thornbury on A38. At traffic lights turn to
town centre. Through High Street and left into Castle
Street. Castle behind St Mary's Church (look for brown
castle signage).

Tintagel, Cornwall

Port William Inn

◆ ◆ ◆ ◆

Trebarwith Strand, Tintagel, Cornwall, PL34 0HB
Tel: 01840 770230 Fax: 01840 770936
Email: william@eurobell.co.uk
Rooms: 5 all ensuite 🐾 🛇
Pricing: Sgl £55–73 Dbl £75–90 CC: Accepted
Room facilities: ▭ ☎ 🗐 ✉ Children: Welcome 🍴 ☕
Dogs: Welcome Licences: ♦♦♦ Leisure: Games room
Parking: Off-street and monitored
See advert on this page

Tiverton, Devon

The Fishermans Cot

◆ ◆ ◆ ◆

Bickleigh, Tiverton, Devon, EX16 8RW
Tel: 01884 855289 Fax: 01884 855241
Email: fishermanscot@eldridge-pope.co.uk
Rooms: 21 all ensuite 🐾 🛇
Pricing: Sgl £45 Dbl £55 CC: Accepted
Room facilities: ▭ ☎ 🗐 Access: ♿
Conference: 1 meeting room (Thtr 35 max), 24hr-
delegate from £24.50, day-delegate rate from £79.50
Children: Welcome 🍴 Dogs: Welcome
Licences: ♦♦♦ Parking: Off-street and monitored
Directions: From junction 27 of M5 take link road to
Tiverton, from Tiverton follow A396 to Bickleigh, just
before bridge on right.

Bridge Guest House

◆ ◆ ◆ ☕

23 Angel Hill, Tiverton, Devon, EX16 6PE
Tel: 01884 252804 Fax: 01884 252804
Web: www.smoothhound.co.uk/hotels/bridgegh.html
Rooms: 10 (6 ensuite) 🛇
Pricing: Dinner from £16 (2002 rate)
Room facilities: ▭ 🗐 Children: Welcome 🍴 ☕
Licences: ♦♦♦ Leisure: Fishing, Games room
Parking: Off-street and monitored
Directions: Leave M5 at Junction 27. Take A361 north
for 7 miles. Leave A361 into Tiverton. Bridge Guest
House situated in centre of town, by river.

Lodgehill Farm Hotel

◆ ◆ ◆ ⚘ ☕

Tiverton, Devon, EX16 5PA
Tel: 01884 251200 Fax: 01884 242090
Email: lodgehill@dial.pipex.com
Web: www.lodgehill.co.uk
Rooms: 10 all ensuite 🐾 🛇
Pricing: Dinner from £17.50 (2002 rate) CC: Accepted
Room facilities: ▭ ☎ 🗐 Children: Welcome 🍴
Dogs: Welcome Licences: ♦♦♦
Parking: Off-street and monitored
Directions: Hotel is on A396 Bickleigh road leaving
Tiverton.

Southwest

Travelodge Tiverton

Travel Accommodation
M5 J27, Sampford Peverell Service Area, Sampford
Peverell, M5 Motorway, Nr. Tiverton, Devon, EX16 7HD
Web: www.travelodge.co.uk
Rooms: 40 all ensuite
Pricing: Sgl £54.40 Dbl £58.85
CC: Accepted Room facilities: ☐ ☕ Access: &

Torcross, Devon

Greyhomes Hotel

★★

Torcross, Devon, TQ7 2TH
Tel: 01548 580220 Fax: 01548 580832
Email: howard@greyhomeshotel.co.uk
Web: www.greyhomeshotel.co.uk
Seasonal closure: November to March
Rooms: 6 (5 ensuite)
Pricing: Dinner from £17.50 (2002 rate) CC: Accepted
Room facilities: ☐ ☕ Children: Welcome, 5yrs min age
Dogs: Welcome Licences: ♦♦♦
Leisure: Tennis Parking: Off-street
Directions: Torcross is on A379 between Kingsbridge
and Dartmouth. Leave A379 and enter village square.
Pass shops and take through-road up hill. Hotel
second turning on left.

Torpoint, Cornwall

Whitsand Bay

★★

Portwrinkle, Crafthole, Torpoint, Cornwall, PL11 3BU
Tel: 01503 230276 Fax: 01503 230329
Web: www.cornish-golf-hotels.co.uk
Rooms: 40 (38 ensuite) ♦ ⊗
Pricing: Sgl £35–50 Dbl £30–90 Dinner from £19.50
CC: Accepted Room facilities: ☐ ☎ ☕
Conference: 2 meeting rooms (Thtr 100 max),
24hr-delegate from £50, day-delegate rate from £25
Children: Welcome ♦ ⛄ ☕ Dogs: Welcome
Licences: ◊ ♦♦♦ Leisure: Indoor pool, Gym, Health
spa, Beauty salon, Golf, Games room,
Snooker/billiards Parking: Off-street
Directions: A38 past Plymouth. At Trerulefoot
roundabout, take A374 towards Torpoint and follow
signs after approximately 3 miles.

Torquay, Devon

The Imperial Hotel

★★★★★★

Park Hill Road, Torquay, Devon, TQ1 2DG
Tel: 01803 294301 Fax: 01803 298293
Email: imperialtorquay@paramount-hotels.co.uk
Web: www.paramount-hotels.co.uk

Rooms: 153 all ensuite ♦ ⊞ ⊗
Pricing: Sgl £106.25–132.25 Dbl £184.50–214.50
Dinner from £22.50 CC: Accepted
Room facilities: ☐ ☎ ☕ Access: ⊥⊥ &
Conference: 8 meeting rooms (Thtr 350 max),
24hr-delegate from £155, day-delegate rate from £135
Children: Welcome ♦ ⛄ Dogs: Welcome
Licences: ◊ ♦♦♦ Leisure: Indoor pool, Outdoor pool,
Gym, Health spa, Beauty salon, Tennis, Snooker/billiards
Parking: Off-street and monitored
Directions: From M5 follow signs for Torquay, head for
seafront and take coast road through town centre onto
Park Hill Road, hotel is on right.

Osborne Hotel

★★★★

Hesketh Crescent, Meadfoot, Torquay, Devon, TQ1 2LL
Tel: 01803 213311 Fax: 01803 296788
Email: enq@osborne-torquay.co.uk
Web: www.osborne-torquay.co.uk
Rooms: 29 all ensuite ♦ ⊞ Pricing: Sgl £55–123
Dbl £110–201 CC: Accepted Room facilities: ☐ ☎ ☕ ⚓
Access: ⊥⊥ Conference: 2 meeting rooms (Thtr 60 max),
24hr-delegate from £91, day-delegate rate from £29
Children: Welcome ♦ ☕ Licences: ♦♦♦
Leisure: Indoor pool, Outdoor pool, Gym, Tennis,
Games room, Snooker/billiards
Parking: Off-street and monitored
Directions: A380 via Newton Abbot, follow signs to
seafront, follow A3022 down and turn left, turn onto
B3199 and follow road up to hotel.
See advert on next page

Palace Hotel

★★★★

Babbacombe Road, Torquay, Devon, TQ1 3TG
Tel: 01803 200200 Fax: 01803 299899
Email: info@palacetorquay.co.uk
Web: www.palacetorquay.co.uk
Rooms: 141 all ensuite ♦ ⊗
Pricing: Sgl £71–81 Dbl £142–280 Dinner from £25
CC: Accepted Room facilities: ☐ ☎ ☕ Access: ⊥⊥ &
Conference: 11 meeting rooms (Thtr 1000 max), 24hr-
delegate from £127, day-delegate rate from £37.50
Children: Welcome ♦ ☕ Dogs: Guide dogs only
Licences: ♦♦♦ Leisure: Indoor pool, Outdoor pool, Gym,
Tennis, Golf, Games room, Snooker/billiards
Parking: Off-street and monitored
Directions: Exit M5 at Junction 30. Follow signs on
A380 to Newton Abbot, then signs to Torquay and
Babbacombe.
See advert on next page

The Grand

★★★★

Seafront, Torquay, Devon, TQ2 6NT
Tel: 0808 100 2529 Fax: 01803 213462
Email: grandhotel@netsite.co.uk
Web: www.grandtorquay.co.uk

Set in its own grounds with panoramic views over Torbay. Award-winning cuisine, sumptuous surroundings, indoor and outdoor swimming pools and friendly, attentive staff.

Rooms: 110 all ensuite ♨ Pricing: Sgl £72–85 Dbl £126–166 Dinner from £29.95 CC: Accepted
Room facilities: 🖥 ☎ ☕ 🔌 Access: ⬆↕
Conference: 4 meeting rooms (Thtr 300 max), 24hr-delegate from £99, day-delegate rate from £25
Children: Welcome ⴰ 🌟 Dogs: Welcome Licences: ⛲
Leisure: Indoor pool, Outdoor pool, Gym, Beauty salon, Tennis, Games room, Snooker/billiards
Parking: Off-street and monitored
Directions: End of M5, take A380 to Torquay seafront. At seafront turn right, The Grand is first building on the right. Take first right, then left for hotel main entrance.

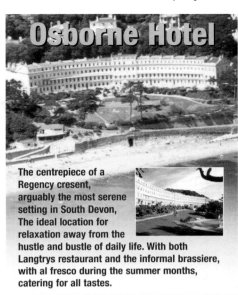

Belgrave Hotel

★★★

Sea Front, Torquay, Devon, TQ2 5HE
Tel: 01803 296666 Fax: 01803 211308
Email: info@belgrave-hotel.co.uk
Web: www.belgrave-hotel.co.uk
Rooms: 70 all ensuite Pricing: Sgl £50–75 Dbl £100–150 Dinner from £16.50 CC: Accepted
Room facilities: Access:
Conference: 5 meeting rooms (Thtr 200 max), 24hr-delegate from £58, day-delegate rate from £16
Children: Welcome Dogs: Welcome Licences:
Leisure: Outdoor pool Parking: Off-street
Directions: Follow signs to Torquay seafront. Turn left Belgrave 500 yards on left.

Corbyn Head Hotel

★★★

Seafront, Torquay, TQ2 6RH
Tel: 01803 213611 Fax: 01803 296152
Email: info@corbynhead.com
Web: www.corbynhead.com
Rooms: 50 all ensuite Pricing: Sgl £35–56 Dbl £70–112 Dinner from £19.95 CC: Accepted
Room facilities: Conference: 1 meeting room (Thtr 40 max) Children: Welcome
Dogs: Welcome Licences:
Leisure: Outdoor pool Parking: Off-street
Directions: At sea front, turn right towards Livermead and Cockington. Hotel is situated just past Cockington Lane on right opposite Livermead Beach.
See advert on next page

Hotel Gleneagles

★★★

Asheldon Road, Wellswood, Torquay, Devon, TQ1 2QS
Tel: 01803 293637 Fax: 01803 295106
Email: hotelgleneagles@lineone.net
Web: www.hotel-gleneagles.com

Under 3/4 mile from the harbour in a tree-lined avenue, overlooking Anstey's Cove, with path to the beach. All rooms are ensuite with balconies, TVs and telephones. Poolside restaurant.
Rooms: 41 all ensuite
Pricing: Sgl £35 Dbl £70 Dinner from £15.95
CC: Accepted Room facilities: Access:
Children: Welcome, 14yrs min age
Dogs: Welcome Licences: Leisure: Outdoor pool
Parking: Off-street and monitored
Directions: Babbacombe Road to St Mathias Church, on right, 300 yards, Hollies Hotel on right. Turn right into Asheldon Road and hotel is on left.

Livermead Cliff Hotel

★★★

Seafront, Torquay, Devon, TQ2 6RQ
Tel: 01803 299666 Fax: 01803 294496
Email: enquiries@livermeadcliff.co.uk
Web: www.livermeadcliff.co.uk
Rooms: 67 all ensuite
Pricing: Sgl £39.50–69.50 Dbl £79–139
Dinner from £16.95 CC: Accepted
Room facilities: Access:
Conference: 3 meeting rooms (Thtr 100 max), 24hr-delegate from £99, day-delegate rate from £29
Children: Welcome Dogs: Welcome Licences:
Leisure: Outdoor pool, Fishing, Games room
Parking: Off-street and monitored
Directions: From M5, take A379 to Torquay. Follow A3022 through town to seafront. Turn right, sign to Paignton. Hotel 600 yards seaward side.

Livermead House Hotel

★★★

Seafront, Torquay, Devon, TQ2 6QJ
Tel: 01803 294361 Fax: 01803 200758
Email: rewhotels@aol.com
Web: www.livermead.com
Rooms: 67 all ensuite
Pricing: Sgl £45–60 Dbl £90–120 Dinner from £21.75
CC: Accepted Room facilities: Access:
Conference: 5 meeting rooms (Thtr 300 max)
Children: Welcome Dogs: Welcome Licences:
Leisure: Outdoor pool, Snooker/billiards
Parking: Off-street
Directions: From Exeter, take A380 to Torquay then follow the signs for seafront.
See advert on next page

Orestone Manor Hotel & Restaurant

Blue Ribbon Winner

★★★

Rockhouse Lane, Maidencombe, Torquay, Devon, TQ1 4SX
Tel: 01803 328098 Fax: 01803 328336
Email: enquiries@orestone.co.uk
Web: www.orestone.co.uk
Rooms: 12 all en-suite
Pricing: Sgl £52–127.50 Dbl £104–190
Dinner from £32.50 CC: accepted
Room facilities:
Licenses:
Leisure: Outdoor swimming, Snooker/billiards,
Directions: The hotel is located 200 yards down Rockhouse Lane, off the A379 halfway between Torquay and Teignmouth.
See advert on next page

Southwest

Orestone Manor Hotel & Restaurant

Orestone Manor is an elegant yet contemporary country house hotel. Nestling in lovely grounds on the quiet, rural fringe of Torbay, the hotel offers superb service and sweeping views. The restaurant offers gracious country house dining with exceptionally good food.

Rockhouse Lane, Maidencombe, Torquay, Devon TQ1 4SX
Tel: 01803 328098   Fax: 01803 328336
enquiries@orestone.co.uk
www.orestone.co.uk

Toorak Hotel

★★★★
Chestnut Avenue, Torquay, Devon, TQ2 5JS
Tel: 01803 400400 Fax: 01803 400140
Email: rheale@tlh.co.uk Web: www.tlh.co.uk
Rooms: 92 all ensuite
Room facilities: 🖵 ☎ 🗍 Access: ↕↕
Children: Welcome ♨ ☃ Licences: ♟♟♟
Leisure: Indoor pool, Outdoor pool, Tennis, Games room, Snooker/billiards Parking: Off-street
Directions: Immediately opposite Riviera Centre, which is clearly signed from all major routes into the town.

Abbey Court Hotel

★★
Falkland Road, Torquay, Devon, TQ2 5JR
Tel: 01803 297316 Fax: 01803 297316

Allerdale Hotel

★★
Croft Road, Torquay, Devon, TQ2 5UD
Tel: 01803 292667 Fax: 01803 292667
Email: enquiry@allerdalehotel.co.uk
Web: www.allerdalehotel.co.uk
Seasonal closure: January

A Victorian villa nestling in own spacious south-facing garden with path to seafront. Family-run hotel with all rooms ensuite, excellent choice menus. Centrally situated for all amenities. Parking.
Rooms: 20 all ensuite
Pricing: Sgl £25–35 Dbl £50–70 Dinner from £18
CC: Accepted Room facilities: 🖵 🗍
Children: Welcome ♨ Dogs: Welcome Licences: ♟♟♟
Leisure: Games room, Snooker/billiards
Parking: Off-street
Directions: Follow A380 to seafront. Turn left, next traffic lights take left fork (Sheddon Hill). First turning on left is Croft Road.

Ansteys Cove Hotel

★★★
327 Babbacombe Road, Torquay, Devon, TQ1 3TB
Tel: 0800 0284953
Email: info@torquayengland.com
Web: www.torquayengland.com
Seasonal closure: November to March
Rooms: 9 all ensuite ☃ Pricing: Sgl £36–39
Dbl £66–80 Dinner from £10 CC: Accepted
Room facilities: 🖵 ☎ 🗍 ♨ Dogs: Guide dogs only
Licences: ♟ ♟♟♟ Parking: Off-street
Directions: Turn left onto B3199 at Babbacombe. Turn right onto Babbacombe Road. Hotel is on right opposite the Palace Hotel.

Ansteys Lea Hotel

★★
Babbacombe Road, Torquay, Devon, TQ1 2QJ
Tel: 01803 294843 Fax: 01803 214333
Email: stay@ansteys-lea.co.uk
Web: www.ansteys-lea.co.uk
Rooms: 24 all ensuite
Pricing: Sgl £26–35 Dbl £52–70 CC: Accepted
Room facilities: 🖵 ☎ 🗍 Children: Welcome ♨ ☃
Dogs: Welcome Licences: ♟ ♟♟♟
Leisure: Outdoor pool, Games room
Parking: Off-street and monitored
Directions: Only a short bus or taxi drive away from Torquay Railway Station and Torquay Coach Station.

Bute Court Hotel

Belgrave Road, Torquay, Devon, TQ2 5HQ
Tel: 01803 293771 Fax: 01803 213429
Email: bute-court-hotel@talk21.com
Web: www.bute-court-hotel.co.uk
Rooms: 45 all ensuite
Pricing: Dinner from £8.50 (2002 rate)
CC: Accepted Room facilities: 🖵 ☎ 🍵 Access: ⏐↕ ♿
Children: Welcome Dogs: Welcome Licences: ▮▮▮
Leisure: Outdoor pool, Games room, Snooker/billiards
Parking: Off-street and monitored
Directions: Right at South Devon College, passing police station. Belgrave Rd is 200 yards down on right.

Cavendish Hotel

Belgrave Road, Torquay, Devon, TQ2 5HN
Tel: 01803 293682 Fax: 01803 292802
Email: thecaven@lineone.net
Web: www.cavendishhotel.net
Rooms: 93 all ensuite
Pricing: Sgl £37–47 Dbl £70–95 Dinner from £12.95
CC: Accepted Room facilities: 🖵 ☎ 🍵 Access: ⏐↕ ♿
Conference: 2 meeting rooms (Thtr 150 max)
Children: Welcome 🍴 Dogs: Guide dogs only
Licences: ▮▮▮ Leisure: Indoor pool, Outdoor pool, Gym, Games room Parking: Off-street
Directions: From M5 take A380 to Torquay, follow seafront signs, at seafront turn left then first left is Belgrave Road.

Coppice Hotel

Babbacombe Road, Torquay, Devon, TQ1 2QJ
Tel: 01803 297786 Fax: 01803 211085
Email: peter@coppicehotel.demon.co.uk
Web: www.coppicehotel.co.uk
Seasonal closure: November to January
Rooms: 40 all ensuite Pricing: Sgl £29.50 Dbl £59
Room facilities: 🖵 ☎ 🍵 Children: Welcome 🍴
Dogs: Welcome Licences: ▮▮▮
Leisure: Indoor pool, Outdoor pool, Gym, Health spa, Snooker/billiards Parking: Off-street
Directions: Hotel is 1 mile on left from Torquay Harbour

Crofton House Hotel

Croft Road, Torquay, Devon, TQ2 5TZ
Tel: 01803 293761 Fax: 01803 211796
Email: enquires@croftonhouse.freeserve.co.uk
Web: www.croftonhousehotel.com
Seasonal closure: January
Rooms: 37 all ensuite
Pricing: Sgl £25–40 Dbl £50–80 Dinner from £9.95
CC: Accepted Room facilities: 🖵 🍵
Access: ♿ Children: Welcome 🍴 Dogs: Guide dogs only Licences: ▮▮▮ Leisure: Indoor pool, Outdoor pool, Health spa, Games room, Snooker/billiards
Parking: Off-street and monitored

Directions: Follow signs for town centre into Belgrave Road, turn left into Lucius Street at lights, and take first right into Croft Road.

Gresham Court Hotel

Babbacombe Road, Torquay, Devon, TQ1 1HG
Tel: 01803 293007 Fax: 01803 215951
Email: via web-site
Web: www.gresham-court-hotel.co.uk
Seasonal closure: January
Rooms: 30 all ensuite Pricing: Sgl £27–80 Dbl £54–100
Dinner from £13 CC: Accepted Room facilities: 🖵 🍵
Access: ⏐↕ Children: Welcome, 3yrs min age
Dogs: Guide dogs only Licences: ▮▮▮
Leisure: Games room Parking: Off-street
Directions: Bear left at clocktower (harbour/strand), cross set of lights into Babbacombe road, travel short distance, hotel on left near museum.

Hotel Burlington

462-466 Babbacombe Road, Torquay, Devon, TQ1 1HN
Tel: 01803 210950 Fax: 01803 200189
Email: info@burlingtonhotel.co.uk
Web: www.dukes-hotels.co.uk
Rooms: 55 all ensuite
Pricing: Sgl £37.50–40.50 Dbl £55–71 Dinner from £12
CC: Accepted Room facilities: 🖵 ☎ 🍵
Children: Welcome 🍴 🍵 Dogs: Welcome
Licences: ▮▮▮ Leisure: Indoor pool, Games room
Parking: Off-street
Directions: Take M5 to Exeter. Follow signs to Torquay. At Torquay seafront turn left. At clock tower turn left. Hotel ½ mile on right.

Howden Court Hotel

23 Croft Road, Torquay, Devon, TQ2 5UD
Tel: 01803 294844 Fax: 01803 211356
Rooms: 38 all ensuite
Pricing: Sgl £27.50–32.50 Dbl £45–55
Dinner from £12.75 Room facilities: 🖵 🍵
Access: ♿ Children: Welcome 🍴
Dogs: Welcome Licences: ▮▮▮
Leisure: Games room Parking: Off-street

Inglewood Hotel

★★

Belgrave Road, Torquay, Devon, TQ2 5HP
Tel: 01803 293800
Email: enquiry@theinglewoodhotel.co.uk
Web: www.theinglewoodhotel.co.uk
Rooms: 52 all ensuite Room facilities: 🖵 🍵
Access: ⏐↕ ♿ Children: Welcome 🍴
Leisure: Outdoor pool, Games room, Snooker/billiards
Parking: Off-street
Directions: From M5 take A380 to Torquay; follow seafront signs; at seafront turn left, then first left; hotel is second on the left.

Southwest

Norcliffe

Seafront, Babbacombe Downs Road, Torquay,
Devon, TQ1 3LF
Tel: 01803 328456 Fax: 01803 328023
Rooms: 27 all ensuite
Room facilities:
Access:
Children: Welcome
Dogs: Welcome
Licences:
Leisure: Indoor pool, Games room, Snooker/billiards
Parking: Off-street and monitored
Directions: Join A380 Exeter–Newton Abbot. Continue
along Newton Road. Turn left at traffic lights. Follow
signs to TUFC. Left at Manor Road lights, right at
crossroads. Turn left.

Roseland Hotel

Warren Road, Torquay, Devon, TQ2 5TT
Tel: 01803 210950 Fax: 01803 200189
Email: info@burlingtonhotel.co.uk
Web: www.torquayholidayhotels.co.uk
Rooms: 40 all ensuite
Pricing: Dinner from £10 (2002 rate)
CC: Accepted
Room facilities: Access:
Children: Welcome
Dogs: Welcome
Licences: Leisure: Indoor pool, Games room
Parking: Off-street
Directions: At seafront, turn left up Sheddon Hill and
turn right at Warren Road.

Shedden Hall Hotel

Shedden Hill, Torquay, Devon, TQ2 5TX
Tel: 01803 292964 Fax: 01803 295306
Email: sheddenhtl@aol.com
Web: www.sheddenhallhotel.co.uk
Seasonal closure: January
Rooms: 24 all ensuite
Pricing: Dinner from £12.95 CC: Accepted
Room facilities:
Children: Welcome, 4yrs min age Licences:
Leisure: Outdoor pool, Games room
Parking: Off-street
Directions: From M5, take A380 and follow signs to
Torquay seafront. Turn left at seafront traffic lights. At
next set proceed up Sheden Hill.

White Gables Hotel

Rawlyn Road, Chelston, Torquay, Devon, TQ2 6PQ
Tel: 01803 605233 Fax: 01803 606634
Email: stay@whitegableshotel.com
Web: www.whitegableshotel.com
Rooms: 23 all ensuite
Pricing: Sgl £20–36 Dbl £40–72 Dinner from £10.75
CC: Accepted Room facilities:

Conference: 1 meeting room (Thtr 50 max)
Children: Welcome
Dogs: Guide dogs only Licences:
Leisure: Outdoor pool, Gym, Games room
Parking: Off-street and monitored
Directions: Immediately behind Torquay's main railway
station, courtesy bus available to and from hotel.

Ashley Rise Hotel

18 Babbacombe Road, Torquay, Devon, TQ1 3SJ
Tel: 01803 327282 Fax: 01803 327177
Email: ashleyrisehotel@ukonline.co.uk
Web: www.ashleyrisehotel.co.uk
Rooms: 25 all ensuite
Pricing: Sgl £17–28 Dbl £34–56 Dinner from £6
CC: Accepted Room facilities: Access:
Children: Welcome Dogs: Welcome
Licences: Parking: Off-street
Directions: Follow signs to Babbacombe model village;
at St Mary Church turn left towards Torquay town
centre; on to Babbacombe Road, third left.

Anchorage Hotel

Babbacombe, Torquay, Devon, TQ1 3NQ
Tel: 01803 326175 Fax: 01803 316439

Colindale Hotel

20 Rathmore Road, Chelston, Torquay, Devon, TQ2 6NZ
Tel: 01803 293947
Email: broute@eurobell.co.uk
Web: www.colindatehotel.co.uk
Seasonal closure: Christmas to New Year
Rooms: 8 (6 ensuite)
Pricing: Sgl £25–27 Dbl £50–54 Dinner from £15
CC: Accepted Room facilities:
Children: Welcome, 6yrs min age
Dogs: Guide dogs only Licences:
Parking: Off-street
Directions: From seafront head for Torquay Station,
Colindale Hotel is approx 300m past station, on left.

Belmont Hotel

66 Belgrave Road, Torquay, Devon, TQ2 5HY
Tel: 01803 295028 Fax: 01803 211668
Email: belmont@murphytq2.fsnet.co.uk
Web: www.belmonthoteltorquay.co.uk
Rooms: 11 (8 ensuite)
Pricing: Sgl £18–25 Dbl £20–28 CC: Accepted
Room facilities:
Children: Welcome, 10yrs min age
Dogs: Guide dogs only
Licences: Parking: Off-street
Directions: Turn into Belgrave Road from seafront, by
Belgrave Hotel 250 yards on left side over traffic lights.

Haldon Priors

♦ ♦ ♦ ♦

Meadfoot Sea Road, Torquay, Devon, TQ1 2LQ
Tel: 01803 213365 Fax: 01803 215577
Web: www.haldonpriors.co.uk
Seasonal closure: November to February
Rooms: 6 all ensuite ⊗ Pricing: Sgl £40–44 Dbl £56–90
Room facilities: ▢ ☕ Children: Welcome
Leisure: Outdoor pool, Games room Parking: Off-street
Directions: Pass Torquay Harbour on right. Turn left at
the clocktower. Turn right at lights. Hotel on left, just
before the beach.

Haytor Hotel

♦ ♦ ♦ ♦

Meadfoot Road, Torquay, Devon, TQ1 2JP
Tel: 01803 294708 Fax: 01803 292511
Email: enq@haytorhotel.com
Web: www.haytorhotel.com
Rooms: 15 all ensuite ⊗
Room facilities: ▢ ☎ ☕ Access: ♿
Children: Welcome, 12yrs min age ⊮
Dogs: Guide dogs only Licences: ♙
Parking: Monitored
Directions: Turn left at seafront past Princess Theatre.
Head for inner harbour to clocktower roundabout. Turn
left, then right at lights.

Hotel Patricia

♦ ♦ ♦ ♦ ♟ ✖ ℃

64 Belgrave Road, Torquay, Devon, TQ2 5HY
Tel: 01803 293339
Email: hotelpatricia@freeuk.com
Web: www.hotelpatricia.freeuk.com
Rooms: 10 all ensuite ⊟ ⊗ Pricing: Sgl £20–45
Dbl £40–100 Dinner from £15 CC: Accepted
Room facilities: ▢ ☕ 📞 Dogs: Guide dogs only
Licences: ♙
Directions: Turn into Belgrave Road from seafront; 250
yards on left-hand side.

Morley Hotel

♦ ♦ ♦ ♦ ✖ ℃

16 Bridge Road, Torquay, Devon, TQ2 5BA
Tel: 01803 292955
Email: themorleyhotel@aol.com
Web: www.morleyhotel.co.uk
Rooms: 8 all ensuite ⊜ Pricing: Sgl £18–25
Dbl £36–25 Dinner from £9 CC: Accepted
Room facilities: ▢ ☕ Access: ♿ Children: Welcome ⊮ ℃
Licences: ♙ Parking: Off-street
Directions: Approaching Torquay, turn right into Avenue
Road. Proceed past traffic lights. Take first left into
Bampfylde Road. Bridge Road is second left.

The Marstan Hotel

♦ ♦ ♦ ♦ ♟ ✖ ℃

Meadfoot Sea Road, Torquay, Devon, TQ1 2LQ
Tel: 01803 292837 Fax: 01803 299202
Email: enquires@marstanhotel.co.uk

Web: www.marstanhotel.co.uk
Rooms: 10 all ensuite ⊜ ⊗
Pricing: Sgl £35–50 Dbl £35–55 Dinner from £23.50
CC: Accepted Room facilities: ▢ ☎ ☕ 📞 Access: ♿
Conference: 2 meeting rooms (Thtr 50 max)
Children: Welcome ⊮ ℃ Dogs: Guide dogs only
Licences: ♙ Leisure: Outdoor pool
Parking: Off-street and monitored
Directions: A380 towards Torquay sea front, at sea front
turn left, follow coastal road to second roundabout. Turn
left onto Babbacombe Road, right at next traffic lights
onto Meadfoot Sea Rd, 1½ miles on right.

Banksea Hotel

♦ ♦ ♦ ♟ ✖ ℃

51 Avenue Road, Torquay, Devon, TQ2 5LE
Tel: 01803 213911 Fax: 01803 213911
Rooms: 5 all ensuite
Pricing: Sgl £16–20 Dbl £32–40 Dinner from £10
CC: Accepted Room facilities: ▢ ☕
Children: Welcome, 8yrs min age Licences: ♙
Parking: Off-street and monitored
Directions: From Exeter M5 onto A380 onto A3002
Torquay: signs to seafront, hotel on left side of road.

Briarfields Hotel

♦ ♦ ♦

84-86 Avenue Road, Torquay, Devon, TQ2 5LF
Tel: 01803 297844 Fax: 01803 297844
Email: briarfieldshotel@aol.com
Web: briarfields.co.uk
Seasonal closure: December
Rooms: 10 all ensuite ⊜
Pricing: Sgl £17–30
Dbl £30–36 CC: Accepted Room facilities: ▢ ☕
Children: Welcome Dogs: Welcome Licences: ♙
Parking: Off-street and monitored
Directions: Approaching Torquay from Newton Abbot,
bear right at the junction of Torre Station and Halfords
down Avenue Road. Hotel is halfway down on right.

Devon Court Hotel

♦ ♦ ♦

Croft Road, Torquay, Devon, TQ2 5UE
Tel: 01803 293603 Fax: 01803 213660

Glenwood

♦ ♦ ♦

Rowdens Road, Torquay, Devon, TQ2 5AZ
Tel: 01803 296318 Fax: 01803 296462
Email: enquiries@glenwood-hotel.co.uk
Web: www.glenwood-hotel.co.uk
Rooms: 10 (9 ensuite) Pricing: Sgl £22–30 Dbl £40–52
Dinner from £8 CC: Accepted Room facilities: ▢ ☕
Access: ♿ Children: Welcome, 2yrs min age
Dogs: Welcome Licences: ♙
Leisure: Outdoor pool Parking: Off-street
Directions: Bear right by traffic lights at Torre rail
station. After next set of lights in Avenue Road, turn
left into Bampfylde Road. Take first left.

The Exton

◆ ◆ ◆

12 Bridge Road, Torquay, Devon, TQ2 5BA
Tel: 01803 293561
Email: extonhotel@lineone.net
Web: www.extonhotel.co.uk
Rooms: 5 (4 ensuite) 🐾 🚭
Pricing: Sgl £16–20 Dbl £32–40
Dinner from £9
CC: Accepted Room facilities: 📺 🗇
Children: Welcome 🍴 Dogs: Guide dogs only
Parking: Off-street
Directions: Bear right at Torre Station (Avenue Road). Through lights, then left into Bampfylde, then first left into Rowdens.

Totnes, Devon

Royal Seven Stars Hotel

★ ★

The Plains, Totnes, Devon, TQ9 5DD
Tel: 01803 862125 Fax: 01803 867925
Rooms: 16 (14 ensuite) 🐾 🎿
Pricing: Dinner from £18 (2002 rate) CC: Accepted
Room facilities: 📺 ☎ 🗇 Children: Welcome 🍴
Dogs: Welcome Licences: ⅲ Parking: Off-street
Directions: Follow signs for Totnes from A38 for 6 miles, then signs for town centre.

The Sea Trout Inn

★ ★ 🐦 🐦

Staverton, Nr Totnes, Devon, TQ9 6PA
Tel: 01803 762 274 Fax: 01803 762 506
Email: enquiries@seatroutinn.com
Web: www.seatroutinn.com
Seasonal closure: Christmas day
Rooms: 10 all ensuite 🐾 🎿 🚭
Pricing: Sgl £35–49.50 Dbl £55–79
Dinner from £12.50 CC: Accepted
Room facilities: 📺 ☎ 🗇
Conference: 1 meeting rooms (Thtr 32 max), day-delegate rate from £15 Children: Welcome 🍴 ℃
Dogs: Welcome Licences: ⅲ
Leisure: Health spa, Fishing, Games room, Snooker/billiards
Parking: Off-street
Directions: South Dartmoor, halfway between Exeter and Plymouth (A38 expressway), exit A38 at Buckfastleigh, take A384 south for 2 miles. After bridge over river, turn left before crest of hill, follow Seatrout Inn/Staverton signs, ¹/₂ mile.
See advert on next page

The Waterman's Arms

◆ ◆ ◆ ◆ ◆ 🐦 ⚔ 🍷

Bow Bridge, Ashprington, Totnes, Devon, TQ9 7EG
Tel: 01803 732214 Fax: 01803 732314
Email: watermansarms.ashprington
@elderidge-pope.co.uk
Rooms: 15 all ensuite 🎿
Pricing: Sgl £54 Dbl £69 Dinner from £6.95

CC: Accepted Room facilities: 📺 ☎ 🗇 🕾
Children: Welcome 🍴
Dogs: Welcome
Licences: ⅲ
Leisure: Games room
Parking: Off-street and monitored
Directions: From Totnes take Dartmouth/Kingsbridge road. At top of hill turn left, signposted Waterman's Arms.

Truro, Cornwall

Nare Hotel

★ ★ ★ ★ ★ 🐦 🐦 🐦

Carne Beach, Veryan-In-Roseland, Truro, Cornwall, TR2 5PF
Tel: 01872 501111 Fax: 01872 501856
Email: office@narehotel.co.uk
Web: www.narehotel.co.uk
Rooms: 36 all ensuite 🐾
Pricing: Sgl £76–145 Dbl £152–290
Dinner from £33 CC: Accepted Room facilities:
📺 ☎ 🗇
Access: ⅼⅼ ♿ Children: Welcome 🍴 🐎 ℃
Dogs: Welcome Licences: ⅲ
Leisure: Indoor pool, Outdoor pool, Gym, Health spa, Beauty salon, Tennis, Games room, Snooker/billiards
Parking: Off-street and monitored
Directions: From M5 and A30, take B3275. Turn right 2 miles after Ladock for Truro, left towards St Mawes. Right onto A3078, over Tregony bridge, left after 1¹/₂ miles for Veryan. Hotel is 1 mile beyond the village.

Alverton Manor

★ ★ ★ ★ 🐦

Tregolls Road, Truro, Cornwall, TR1 1ZQ
Tel: 01872 276633 Fax: 01872 222989
Email: reception@alvertonmanor.demon.co.uk
Rooms: 33 all ensuite 🐾 🎿 🚭
Pricing: Sgl £72–136 Dbl £109–165
Dinner from £23.50 CC: Accepted
Room facilities: 📺 ☎ 🗇 🕾 Access: ⅼⅼ ♿
Conference: 8 meeting rooms (Thtr 100 max), 24hr-delegate from £120, day-delegate rate from £30
Children: Welcome 🍴 Dogs: Welcome
Licences: 🔔 ⅲ
Leisure: Golf, Fishing
Parking: Off-street and monitored
Directions: Take M5 south/west to Exeter, then A30 for Oakhampton, leading to A39 into Truro, Aleverton hotel on the right.
See advert on next page

The Brookdale Hotel

★ ★ ★

Tregolls Road, Truro, Cornwall, TR1 1JZ
Tel: 01872 273513 Fax: 01872 272400
Email: Brookdale@hotelstruro.com
Web: www.hotelstruro.com
Rooms: 30 all ensuite 🐾 🚭
Pricing: Sgl £54.50–56.50 Dbl £75.50–79.50
Dinner from £12.50 CC: Accepted

Room facilities: ⬜ ☎ 🥤 🥢
Conference: 3 meeting rooms (Thtr 75 max),
24hr-delegate from £90, day-delegate rate from £13.50
Children: Welcome ♬ ⅞ Dogs: Welcome
Licences: ♦♦♦ Parking: Off-street
Directions: On A39 approach road into Truro, at lower end of Tregolls Road, 250 metres to the east of the roundabout.
See advert on this page

The Lugger Hotel

Blue Ribbon Winner

★★★ 🥤 🥤

Portloe, Truro, Cornwall, TR2 5RD
Tel: 01872 501322 Fax: 01872 501691
Email: office@luggerhotel.com
Web: www.luggerhotel.com
Seasonal closure: January
Rooms: 21 all ensuite
Pricing: Sgl £157–227 Dbl £180–260
Dinner from £32.50 CC: Accepted
Room facilities: ⬜ ☎ 🥤
Children: Welcome, 12yrs min age Licences: ♦♦♦
Parking: Off-street
Directions: M5–A30 or A38–A390, left to Trefony B3287 A3078 Veryan left Portloe. Air: Gatwick/Stansted to Newquay.

Carlton Hotel

★★

Falmouth Road, Truro, Cornwall, TR1 2HL
Tel: 01872 272450 Fax: 01872 223938
Email: reception@carltonhotel.co.uk
Web: www.carltonhotel.co.uk
Rooms: 29 all ensuite ⚹ ⊗
Pricing: Sgl £36–41 Dbl £52–58 Dinner from £11
CC: Accepted Room facilities: ▢ ☎ ⌧
Conference: 3 meeting rooms (Thtr 70 max)
Children: Welcome ⼑ Dogs: Welcome
Licences: ⫙ Leisure: Health spa Parking: Off-street
Directions: Take A39 to Truro. Proceed across two
roundabouts onto bypass. At top of hill, turn right into
Falmouth Road. Hotel is 100 metres on right.

Marcorrie Hotel

◆◆◆◆ ℘

20 Falmouth Road, Truro, Cornwall, TR1 2HX
Tel: 01872 277374 Fax: 01872 241666
Email: marcorrie@aol.com Web: www.hotelstruro.com

Family owned and managed late Victorian style hotel
centrally situated for touring Cornwall for business or
leisure, ample parking, 5 minutes walk to city centre.
Rooms: 12 all ensuite ⚹ ⊗
Pricing: Sgl £42 Dbl £52 CC: Accepted
Room facilities: ▢ ☎ ⌧ ☏
Children: Welcome ⼑ ℘ Dogs: Welcome
Licences: ⫙ Parking: Off-street
Directions: At Falmouth junction on Truro ring road,
turn to city centre. Hotel is 400 yards down Falmouth
Road on the left.

Umberleigh, Devon

Northcote Manor Hotel   Gold Ribbon Winner

★★★ ☖ ☖ ☖

Burrington, near Umberleigh, North Devon, EX37 9LZ
Tel: 01769 560501 Fax: 01769 560770
Email: rest@northcotemanor.co.uk
Web: www.northcotemanor.co.uk

The 18th century Manor and the grounds located high
above the Taw River Valley offer an atmosphere of
timeless tranquility. Professional, attentive but
unobtrusive service with excellent food is what
Northcote Manor aims to provide.
Rooms: 11 all ensuite ⌧
Pricing: Sgl £99–156 Dbl £165–272 Dinner from £35
CC: Accepted Room facilities: ▢ ☎
Children: Welcome, 10yrs min age Dogs: Welcome
Licences: ⟁ ⫙ Leisure: Tennis Parking: Off-street
Directions: Do not enter Burrington Village. Entrance to
Northcote Estate is on main A377 Barnstaple/Exeter road
opposite Portsmouth Arms Pub and railway station.

Wadebridge, Cornwall

Roskarnon House Hotel

◆◆◆

Rock, near Wadebridge, Cornwall, PL27 6LD
Tel: 01208 862785
Seasonal closure: October to March
Rooms: 12 (10 ensuite)
Pricing: Sgl £40 Dbl £68 CC: Accepted
Room facilities: ▢ ⌧ Children: Welcome ℘
Licences: ⫙ Parking: Off-street
Directions: From Wadebridge, follow road to Rock,
Trebetherick, Polzeath and then to St Enodoc Golf
Course. Hotel situated on road to golf course.

Wareham, Dorset

Priory Hotel   Gold Ribbon Winner

★★★ ☖ ☖ ☖

Church Green, Wareham, Dorset, BH20 4ND
Tel: 01929 551666 Fax: 01929 554519
Email: reservations@theprioryhotel.co.uk
Web: www.theprioryhotel.co.uk

One of the highest rated hotels in Dorset. Individually appointed bedrooms, fine food and wine, and superb standards of service, are complemented by a riverside location and open countryside views.
Rooms: 18 all ensuite
Pricing: Sgl £105–105 Dbl £135–285
Dinner from £32.50 CC: Accepted
Room facilities: 📺 ☎ ☕ ⚲
Conference: 1 meeting rooms (Thtr 24 max)
Children: Welcome 8yrs, min age
Licences: ⅢⅢ Parking: Off-street and monitored
Directions: Wareham is on the A351 to the west of Poole: hotel is at southern end of town between church and river.

Springfield Country Hotel
★★★ ⓡ
Grange Road, Stoborough, Wareham, Dorset, BH20 5AL
Tel: 01929 552177 Fax: 01929 551862
Email: enquiries@springfield-country-hotel.co.uk
Web: www.springfield-country-hotel.co.uk
Rooms: 50 all ensuite
Pricing: Sgl £75–85 Dbl £120–140 Dinner from £19.50
CC: Accepted Room facilities: 📺 ☎ ☕ ⚲
Access: ⇅ ♿
Conference: 12 meeting rooms (Thtr 200 max)
Children: Welcome ⴕ Dogs: Welcome Licences: ⅢⅢ
Leisure: Indoor pool, Outdoor pool, Gym, Health spa, Beauty salon, Tennis, Games room, Snooker/billiards
Parking: Off-street and monitored
Directions: A35 towards Wareham. At end of dual carriageway, 1st exit off roundabout (A351). At roundabout just outside Wareham, 2nd exit. Straight over next roundabout. After ³/₄ mile turn right. Hotel 300 yards on left.

Worgret Manor Hotel
★★
Worgret, Wareham, Dorset, BH20 6AB
Tel: 01929 552957 Fax: 01929 554804
Email: admin@worgretmanor.co.uk
Web: www.worgretmanorhotel.co.uk
Rooms: 12 all ensuite
Pricing: Dinner from £14.95 CC: Accepted
Room facilities: 📺 ☎ ☕ Access: ♿
Conference: 2 meeting rooms (Thtr 35 max)
Children: Welcome ⴕ Dogs: Welcome
Licences: ⅢⅢ Parking: Off-street
Directions: Follow A351 from Poole to Wareham, then signs for Wool on A352. Hotel on left-hand side of road.

Warminster, Wiltshire

The George Inn
♦ ♦ ♦ ♦ ⓡ ⓥ
Longbridge Deverill, Warminster,
Wiltshire, BA12 7DG
Tel: 01985 840396 Fax: 01985 841333
Web: www.thegeorgeinnlongbridgedeverill.co.uk
Rooms: 10 all ensuite
Pricing: Sgl £40–40 Dbl £60–95 Dinner from £7.95
CC: Accepted Room facilities: 📺 ☎ ☕

Licences: ⅢⅢ
Directions: Hotel is on the main A350 from Salisbury. Follow A36 then A350 Blandford. From London A303 then A350 to Warminister.

Travelodge Warminster
Travel Accommodation
A36/A350 By-Pass, Warminster, Wiltshire, BA12 7RU
Web: www.travelodge.co.uk
Rooms: 31 all ensuite ⊗
Pricing: Sgl £59.40 Dbl £63.85
CC: Accepted Room facilities: 📺 ☕ Access: ♿

Wells, Somerset

Swan Hotel
★★★ ⓡ
Sadler Street, Wells, Somerset, BA5 2RX
Tel: 01749 836300 Fax: 01749 836301
Email: swan@bhere.co.uk Web: www.bhere.co.uk

15th-century coaching hotel, with original four-poster beds and cheerful log fires, facing west front of Wells Cathedral. Traditional English food and an ideal location for touring.
Rooms: 50 all ensuite ⊛ 🖥 ⊗
Pricing: Sgl £89.50–94.50 Dbl £115–135
Dinner from £25 CC: Accepted
Room facilities: 📺 ☎ ☕ ⚲ Access: ♿
Conference: 5 meeting rooms (Thtr 80 max), 24hr-delegate from £99, day-delegate rate from £22.50
Children: Welcome ⴕ ☕
Dogs: Welcome
Licences: ◈ ⅢⅢ
Parking: Off-street and monitored
Directions: Hotel faces the west front of Wells Cathedral in city centre.

Southwest

White Hart Hotel

 ★ ★ ★

Sadler Street, Wells, Somerset, BA5 2RR
Tel: 01749 672056 Fax: 01749 671074
Email: info@whitehart-wells.co.uk
Web: www.whitehart-wells.co.uk

15th-century coaching hotel, situated directly opposite
Wells Cathedral, offering comfortable accommodation
and fine English food. Open fires and an ideal location
make this family-run hotel an excellent choice.
Rooms: 15 all ensuite
Pricing: Sgl £65–70 Dbl £85–95 Dinner from £16
CC: Accepted Room facilities: Access:
Conference: 2 meeting rooms (Thtr 100 max), 24hr-
delegate from £99, day-delegate rate from £20
Children: Welcome Dogs: Welcome
Licences: Parking: Off-street and monitored
Directions: Approaching Wells, follow signs for Hotels
and Deliveries. Hotel is the first one on the right as you
enter Wells.

Crossways on Avalon

Stocks Lane, North Wootton, Nr Wells,
Somerset, BA4 3EU
Tel: 01749 899000 Fax: 01749 890476

Bekynton House

 ◆ ◆ ◆ ◆

7 St Thomas Street, Wells, Somerset, BA5 2UU
Tel: 01749 672222 Fax: 01749 672222
Email: reservations@bekynton.freeserve.co.uk
Web: www.bekynton-house.co.uk
Seasonal closure: Christmas and New Year
Rooms: 4 all ensuite
Pricing: Sgl £34–44 Dbl £53–55 CC: Accepted
Room facilities: Children: Welcome, 7yrs min age
Parking: Off-street and monitored
Directions: St Thomas Street is the B3139 Wells to
Radstock road, via The Horringtons; we are three
doors from the Fountain Inn.

Double Gate Farm

 ◆ ◆ ◆ ◆

Godney, Wells, Somerset, BA5 1RX
Tel: 01458 832217 Fax: 01458 835612
Email: doublegatefarm@aol.com
Web: www.doublegatefarm.com
Seasonal closure: Christmas to New Year

Award-winning farmhouse accommodation — outdoor,
sunshine breakfasts in summertime — includes home-
made bread and local produce. Ideally situated for
sightseeing, walking and cycling. Two Golden
Retrievers and two mischievous moggies!
Rooms: 6 all ensuite
Pricing: Sgl £35–40 Dbl £55–60 CC: Accepted
Room facilities: Access:
Children: Welcome Dogs: Guide dogs only
Leisure: Games room, Snooker/billiards
Parking: Off-street and monitored
Directions: From Wells take A39 south. At Polsham
turn right. Continue approx 3 miles. Farmhouse on left.

Weston-Super-Mare, Somerset

Beachlands Hotel

 ★ ★ ★

17 Uphill Road North, Weston-Super-Mare,
Somerset, BS23 4NG
Tel: 01934 621401 Fax: 01934 621966
Email: info@beachlandshotel.com
Web: www.beachlandshotel.com

This delightful family-run hotel, situated overlooking the
18-hole golf course, only 300 yards from the sandy
beach, benefits from ample parking and an indoor
heated swimming pool and sauna.
Rooms: 24 all ensuite
Pricing: Sgl £47–63.50 Dbl £70–89.50 Dinner from £12
CC: Accepted Room facilities: Access:
Conference: Meeting rooms (Thtr 50 max),
24hr-delegate from £85, day-delegate rate from £19.50
Children: Welcome Dogs: Guide dogs only
Licences: Leisure: Indoor pool
Parking: Off-street and monitored
Directions: From Junction 21 on M5, follow signs for
beach. Hotel is 6½ miles from exit, overlooking golf
course 200 yards before beach.

The Commodore
★ ★ ★

Beach Road, Sand Bay, Kewstoke,
Weston-Super-Mare, Somerset, BS22 9UZ
Tel: 01934 415778 Fax: 01934 636483
Email: latonacomm@aol.com Web: latonahotels.co.uk
Rooms: 19 all ensuite 🛏 Room facilities: 🖵 ☎ 🍵
Conference: 2 meeting rooms (Thtr 120 max),
24hr-delegate from £100, day-delegate rate from £25
Children: Welcome � 🍼 Dogs: Guide dogs only
Licences: ⚲ ♔ Leisure: Fishing, Snooker/billiards
Parking: Off-street

Arosfa
★ ★

Lower Church Road, Weston-Super-Mare,
Somerset, BS23 2AG
Tel: 01934 419523 Fax: 01934 636084
Email: reception@arosfahotel.co.uk
Web: www.arosfahotel.co.uk
Rooms: 46 all ensuite 🛏
Pricing: Dinner from £16 (2002 rate) CC: Accepted
Room facilities: 🖵 ☎ 🍵 Access: ♿
Children: Welcome ♔ 🍼 Dogs: Welcome
Licences: ♔ Parking: Off-street
Directions: From sea front, take first right past Winter
Gardens; hotel is 100m on left beyond the college.

Dauncey's Hotel
★ ★

Claremont Crescent, Weston-Super-Mare,
Somerset, BS23 2ED
Tel: 01934 410180 Fax: 01934 410181
Email: reservations@daunceyshotel.fsnet.co.uk

Dauncey's has been run by the Hunt family for 40
years. Superb views across Weston Bay. Well-
appointed sea-view rooms. Open to non-residents.
Rooms: 74 all ensuite 🛏
Pricing: Sgl £34–38 Dbl £68–76 Dinner from £13
CC: Accepted Room facilities: 🖵 🍵 Access: ♿
Conference: 5 meeting rooms (Thtr 50 max)
Children: Welcome ♔ Dogs: Welcome
Licences: ♔ Leisure: Games room
Directions: Situated at the north end of the promenade,
in a Victorian crescent.

Queenswood
★ ★

Victoria Park, Weston-Super-Mare, Somerset, BS23 2HZ
Tel: 01934 416141 Fax: 01934 621759
Email: stay@queenswoodhotel.com
Web: www.queenswoodhotel.com
Rooms: 17 all ensuite 🛏 🚭
Pricing: Sgl £48–55 Dbl £70–85 Dinner from £17.50
CC: Accepted Room facilities: 🖵 ☎ 🍵
Children: Welcome ♔ 🍼 Dogs: Welcome
Licences: ♔ Parking: Off-street
Directions: The Queenswood is centrally situated in a
quiet cul-de-sac just off the seafront, in a slightly
elevated position.

The Old Colonial
◆ ◆ ◆ ◆

30 Knightstone Road, Weston-Super-Mare,
Somerset, BS23 2AW
Tel: 01934 620739 Fax: 01934 645725
Rooms: 10 all ensuite 🚭
Pricing: Sgl £62.50 Dbl £67.50
Room facilities: 🖵 ☎ 🍵 Children: Welcome ♔
Dogs: Guide dogs only
Parking: Off-street and monitored
Directions: Come off M4 at junction 21 follow signs to
seafront, turn right at seafront, can't miss then.

Wychwood Hotel
◆ ◆ ◆ ◆

148 Milton Road, Weston-Super-Mare,
Somerset, BS23 2UZ
Tel: 01934 627793
Seasonal closure: Christmas
Rooms: 9 all ensuite 🛏 🚭
Pricing: Sgl £28–30 Dbl £48–50 Dinner from £14
CC: Accepted Room facilities: 🖵 🍵
Access: ♿ Children: Welcome ♔
Dogs: Guide dogs only Licences: ♔
Leisure: Outdoor pool Parking: Off-street
Directions: From Junction 21 of M5, follow signs for
town centre. Take third exit at fifth roundabout and at
second traffic lights turn right into Milton Road — hotel
400 yards on right.

Baymead
◆ ◆ ◆

19-23 Longton Grove Road, Weston-Super-Mare,
Somerset, BS23 1LS
Tel: 01934 622951 Fax: 01934 620640
Rooms: 33 (31 ensuite) 🚭
Pricing: Dinner from £8.50
Room facilities: 🖵 🍵 Access: ♿
Children: Welcome ♔
Dogs: Welcome Licences: ♔
Leisure: Snooker/billiards Parking: Off-street
Directions: Exit M5 at Junction 21. At seafront, turn
right, then right again into Knightstone Road. Turn left
into West Street. At T-junction, turn left. Keep right,
hotel on right.

Southwest

Blakeney Guest House

 ◆ ◆ ◆

52 Locking Road, Weston-Super-Mare,
Somerset, BS23 3DN
Tel: 01934 624772
Rooms: 6 (2 ensuite) ⊗ Pricing: Sgl £15–20
Dbl £14–34 CC: Accepted Room facilities: ▢ ☕ ✴
Children: Welcome � Dogs: Guide dogs only
Licences: ⅲ Parking: Off-street and monitored
Directions: Leave M5 at Junction 21 heading south.
Follow signs for tourism accommodation into Weston-
Super-Mare.

L'Arrivee Guest House

 ◆ ◆ ◆

75 Locking Road, Weston-Super-Mare,
Somerset, BS23 3DW
Tel: 01934 625328 Fax: 01934 625328
Email: carolinetr@bun.co.uk
Rooms: 12 (10 ensuite) ⊲ ⊞
Pricing: Dinner from £9.50 (2002 rate) CC: Accepted
Room facilities: ▢ ☎ ☕ Access: ⅋
Children: Welcome Dogs: Welcome
Licences: ⅲ Parking: Off-street
Directions: Leave M5 at Junction 21. Follow B3440
Locking Road signs. L'Arrivee is on the right-hand side,
300 yards before Tesco store.

Oakover Guest House

 ◆ ◆ ◆ ✕

25 Clevedon Road, Weston-Super-Mare,
Somerset, BS23 1DA
Tel: 01934 620125
Email: info@oakover.co.uk Web: www.oakover.co.uk
Rooms: 7 all ensuite ⊲ ⊞
Pricing: Sgl £20–24 Dbl £40–48 CC: Accepted
Room facilities: ▢ ☕ Children: Welcome
Parking: Off-street
Directions: From M5 Junction 21, follow signs to
Tropicana/seafront. Turn left into Cleveden Road. Hotel
is on left, just before traffic lights.

Weymouth, Dorset

Hotel Rembrandt

★ ★ ★

12-18 Dorchester Road, Weymouth, Dorset, DT4 7JU
Tel: 01305 764000 Fax: 01305 764022
Email: reception@hotelrembrandt.co.uk
Web: www.hotelrembrandt.co.uk
Rooms: 75 all ensuite ⊞ ⊗
Pricing: Sgl £60–75 Dbl £80–98 Dinner from £14.95
CC: Accepted Room facilities: ▢ ☎ ☕ Access: ⅋ ⅋
Conference: 6 meeting rooms (Thtr 250 max),
24hr-delegate from £98, day-delegate rate from £22
Children: Welcome ⅋ ⅋
Dogs: Welcome Licences: ⅋ ⅲ
Leisure: Indoor pool, Gym Parking: Off-street
Directions: From Dorchester, along A354, straight on at
Manor roundabout (by Safeway). Hotel ³/₄ mile on left,
800 yards from seafront.

Hotel Rex

 ★ ★ ★ ★

29 The Esplanade, Weymouth, Dorset, DT4 8DN
Tel: 01305 760400 Fax: 01305 760500
Email: rex@kingshotels.f9.co.uk
Web: www.kingshotel.co.uk
Rooms: 31 all ensuite ⊲ ⊞
Pricing: Sgl £49–58 Dbl £74–100 Dinner from £13.75
CC: Accepted Room facilities: ▢ ☎ ☕ Access: ⅋
Children: Welcome ⅋ Dogs: Welcome
Licences: ⅲ Parking: Off-street and monitored
Directions: Take A354 to Weymouth. Head towards
seafront. Follow signs towards ferry and harbour. The
Rex overlooks beach and harbour.

Best Western Hotel Prince Regent

★ ★

139 The Esplanade, Weymouth, Dorset, DT4 7NR
Tel: 01305 771313 Fax: 01305 778100
Email: hprwey@aol.com

Newly refurbished seafront hotel with magnificent
views of the bay and coastline. A short level stroll to
the town centre and attactions. A good base to explore
Dorset.
Rooms: 50 all ensuite ⊲ ⊞ ⊗
Pricing: Sgl £40–80 Dbl £56–115 Dinner from £13.75
CC: Accepted Room facilities: ▢ ☎ ☕ ⅋
Access: ⅋ ⅋
Conference: 3 meeting rooms (Thtr 150 max),
24hr-delegate from £79, day-delegate rate from £21
Children: Welcome ⅋ ⅋ Dogs: Guide dogs only
Licences: ⅲ Parking: Off-street
Directions: At Dorchester, take A354 for Weymouth.
Follow signs for town centre. Turn left at clock tower
and proceed along Esplanade.

Central Hotel

★★

15 Maiden Street, Weymouth, Dorset, DT4 8BB
Tel: 01305 760700 Fax: 01305 760300
Email: central@kingshotels.co.uk
Web: www.kingshotels.co.uk
Seasonal closure: 15 December to 2 March
Rooms: 29 all ensuite
Pricing: Sgl £40–42 Dbl £68–73 Dinner from £9
CC: Accepted Room facilities:
Access: Children: Welcome
Dogs: Guide dogs only Licences:
Parking: Off-street
Directions: Take A354 from Dorchester. Head for seafront. At Marks & Spencer, take small road called New Street to rear of hotel.

Crown Hotel

★★

51/52 St Thomas Street, Weymouth, Dorset, DT4 8EQ
Tel: 01305 760800 Fax: 01305 760300
Email: crown@kingshotels.co.uk
Web: www.kingshotels.co.uk
Rooms: 86 all ensuite
Pricing: Sgl £38–45 Dbl £70–75 Dinner from £9.50
CC: Accepted Room facilities:
Access: Children: Welcome
Dogs: Guide dogs only Licences:
Parking: Off-street and monitored
Directions: From Dorchester, take the A354 to Weymouth. When you reach the back water on the left, follow this. Take the second bridge over the water. Crown Hotel is on left.

Fairhaven Hotel

★★

37 The Esplanade, Weymouth, Dorset, DT4 8DH
Tel: 01305 760200 Fax: 01305 760300
Email: fairhaven@kingshotels.co.uk
Web: www.kingshotels.co.uk
Seasonal closure: November to March
Rooms: 90 all ensuite
Pricing: Sgl £40–45 Dbl £68–74
Dinner from £8.50
CC: Accepted Room facilities:
Access: Children: Welcome
Dogs: Guide dogs only Licences:
Leisure: Games room
Parking: Off-street and monitored
Directions: Take A354 to Weymouth. Head towards seafront. Follow signs towards Ferry. Fairhaven Hotel is 200 yards before ferry terminal.

The Cottage

♦♦♦♦

Puddledock Lane, Preston, Weymouth, Dorset, DT3 6LZ
Tel: 01305 834729 Fax: 01305 834729
Email: mcribb.thecottage@tiscal:.co.uk
Seasonal closure: November to February
Rooms: 2 (1 ensuite)
Pricing: Sgl £25–40 Dbl £40–80
Room facilities: Children: Welcome
Dogs: Welcome Parking: Off-street
Directions: Map will be sent with confirmation letter.

Basil Towers (Birchfields)

♦♦♦

22 Abbotsbury Road, Weymouth, Dorset, DT4 0AE
Tel: 01305 773255 Fax: 01305 773255
Email: birchfieldshotel@lineone.net
Web: www.smoothhound.co.uk/hotels/birchfields.html
Seasonal closure: November to February
Rooms: 9 (3 ensuite)
Pricing: Sgl £18–21 Dbl £18–25 CC: Accepted
Room facilities: Children: Welcome
Dogs: Guide dogs only Licences:
Parking: Off-street and monitored
Directions: From Jubilee Clock on Esplanade, go down King Street. 2nd exit at Kings roundabout, and over Swannery Bridge. 2nd exit Westham roundabout onto Abbotsbury Road. Basil Towers 100 metres on right.

Concorde

♦♦♦

131 The Esplanade, Weymouth, Dorset, DT4 7EY
Tel: 01305 776900 Fax: 01305 776900
Email: theconcorde@aol.com
Rooms: 13 all ensuite
Pricing: Sgl £19–29.50 Dbl £38–59
Room facilities: Access:
Children: Welcome Dogs: Guide dogs only
Licences:
Directions: Hotel is situated on the Esplanade.

Greenhill Hotel

♦♦♦

8 Greenhill, Weymouth, Dorset, DT4 7SQ
Tel: 01305 786026 Fax: 01305 786026
Seasonal closure: December to January
Rooms: 17 (12 ensuite)
Pricing: Sgl £25–45 Dbl £50–75 Dinner from £7.50
CC: Accepted Room facilities: Access:
Children: Welcome Dogs: Guide dogs only
Licences: Parking: Off-street and monitored
Directions: Situated on Weymouth promenade at Junction of A353 and A354.

Sandcombe Hotel

♦♦♦

8 The Esplanade, Weymouth, Dorset, DT4 8EB
Tel: 01305 786833
Email: ann.mcveigh@virgin.net
Web: www.resort-guide.co.uk/sandcombe or www.sandcombehotel.co.uk
Rooms: 9 (5 ensuite)
Pricing: Sgl £20–24 Dbl £46–48
Room facilities:
Children: Welcome, 5yrs min age Licences:
Directions: Located on Esplanade between beach and harbour. Near to Pavilion theatre and Condor ferry port.

Sou'west Lodge Hotel

Rodwell Road, Weymouth, Dorset, DT4 8QT
Tel: 01305 783749
Web: www.weymouth.gov.co.uk
Rooms: 8 all ensuite
Pricing: Sgl £30–45 Dbl £49–60 Dinner from £12.50
CC: Accepted Room facilities: Access:
Children: Welcome Dogs: Guide dogs only
Licences: Parking: Off-street

The Redcliff

18/19 Brunswick Terrace, Weymouth, Dorset, DT4 7RW
Tel: 01305 784682 Fax: 01305 768886
Email: redcliffweymouth@hotmail.com
Web: www.smoothhound.co.uk/hotel/redcliff.html
Rooms: 12 (6 ensuite)
Pricing: Sgl £19–29 Dbl £44–58 Dinner from £12
CC: Accepted Room facilities:
Children: Welcome Dogs: Welcome
Licences: Parking: Off-street
Directions: A254 to Weymouth, turn left at clock tower,
drive 200 metres along Esplanade, turn right at old pier
into Brunswick Terrace.

Trelawney Hotel

1 Old Castle Road, Weymouth, Dorset, DT4 8QB
Tel: 01305 783188 Fax: 01305 783181
Email: trelawney@freeuk.com
Web: www.trelawneyhotel.com
Rooms: 10 all ensuite
Pricing: Sgl £40 Dbl £60 CC: Accepted
Room facilities: Access:
Children: Welcome Dogs: Guide dogs only
Licences: Parking: Off-street
Directions: Approximately 1 mile from town centre.
Follow A354 towards Portland. Hotel is 800 yards on
left from 'Harbour' roundabout.

Westwey Hotel

62 Abbotsbury Road, Weymouth, Dorset, DT4 0BJ
Tel: 01305 784564 Fax: 01305 770920
Email: westweyhotel@weymouthobj.fsnet.co.uk
Rooms: 9 (7 ensuite)
Pricing: Sgl £24–30 Dbl £44–52 Dinner from £10
CC: Accepted
Room facilities: Children: Welcome
Licences: Parking: Off-street
Directions: From Jubilee clock on Esplanade, turn right
into King Street. At roundabout take second exit, next
roundabout take second exit, hotel 50 yards on right.

The Chandlers Hotel

4 Westerhall Road, Weymouth , Dorset, DT4 7SZ
Tel: 01305 771341

White House Hotel

Long Street, Williton, Somerset, TA4 4QW
Tel: 01984 632306
Seasonal closure: November to May
Rooms: 10 (9 ensuite) Pricing: Sgl £49–71 Dbl £84–112
Dinner from £36 Room facilities: Access:
Children: Welcome Dogs: Welcome
Licences: Parking: Off-street
Directions: On A39 in centre of village.

Stilegate Bed & Breakfast

Staple Close, West Quantoxhead, Williton, Taunton,
Somerset, TA4 4DN
Tel: 01984 639119 Fax: 01984 639119
Email: stilegate@aol.com Web: www.stilegate.co.uk
Seasonal closure: Closed January
Rooms: 3 all ensuite
Pricing: Sgl £30–30 Dbl £50–50 Room facilities:
Access: Children: Welcome Dogs: Welcome
Leisure: Outdoor pool, Health spa, Games room
Parking: Off-street and monitored
Directions: Take A39 from Bridgwater to Minehead.
Take first left past Windmill public house, through West
Quantoxhead. Take second right into Staple Lane, first
right into Staple Close.

Beechleas Hotel and Restaurant

17 Poole Road, Wimborne Minster, Dorset, BH21 1QA
Tel: 01202 841684 Fax: 01202 849344
Email: beechleas@hotmail.com
Web: www.beechleas.com

A beautifully-restored Grade II listed Georgian house
with delightful walled garden, award-winning
restaurant, log fires in winter, sunny conservatory in
summer and a lovely ambience.
Rooms: 9 all ensuite
Pricing: Sgl £69–99 Dbl £79–119 Dinner from £24.75
CC: Accepted Room facilities: Access:
Children: Welcome Dogs: Welcome
Licences: Parking: Off-street
Directions: From A31 take road into Wimbourne. From
the centre, take A349 to Poole. House is 100m on right.

Winsford, Somerset

Royal Oak Inn

★★★★

Exmoor National Park, Winsford, Somerset, TA24 7JE
Tel: 01643 851455 Fax: 01643 851009
Email: enquiries@royaloak-somerset.co.uk
Web: www.royaloak-somerset.co.uk

On the edge of Exmoor National park in the centre of an ancient riverside village, you will find a very charming place — a 12th-century thatched inn with inglenook fireplaces and oak beams, two cheerful bars and comfortable ensuite rooms.
Rooms: 14 all ensuite
Room facilities: Children: Welcome
Dogs: Welcome Licences: Parking: Off-street
Directions: Take M5 south, exit Junction 27. At Tiverton roundabout take A396 north for 20 miles through Exbridge and Bridgetown. Next left to Winsford.

Woolacombe, Devon

Watersmeet Hotel

★★★★

Mortehoe, Woolacombe, Devon, EX34 7EB
Tel: 01271 870333 Fax: 01271 870890
Email: info@watersmeethotel.co.uk
Web: www.watersmeethotel.co.uk
Seasonal closure: January

Watersmeet enjoys panoramic sea views across Woolacombe Bay to Lundy Island. Award-winning cuisine and fine wines. Indoor and outdoor pools. Steps to private beach.
Rooms: 22 all ensuite
Pricing: Sgl £75–130 Dbl £140–230 Dinner from £21

CC: Accepted
Room facilities: Children: Welcome
Dogs: Guide dogs only Licences:
Leisure: Indoor pool, Outdoor pool, Tennis, Snooker/billiards
Parking: Off-street and monitored
Directions: Leave M5 at Junction 27. Take A361 to Barnstaple. Follow signs for Woolacombe. Take Esplanade along seafront. The hotel is on left.

Woolacombe Bay Hotel

★★★★

Woolacombe, Devon, EX34 7BN
Tel: 01271 870388 Fax: 01271 870613
Email: woolacombe.bayhotel@btinternet.com
Web: www.woolacombe-bay-hotel.co.uk
Seasonal closure: January to mid February
Rooms: 64 all ensuite
Pricing: Sgl £50–95 Dbl £100–190 Dinner from £24
CC: Accepted Room facilities: Access:
Conference: 4 meeting rooms (Thtr 150 max), day-delegate rate from £20
Children: Welcome Licences:
Leisure: Indoor pool, Outdoor pool, Gym, Health spa, Beauty salon, Tennis, Golf, Games room, Snooker/billiards
Parking: Off-street
Directions: Leave M5 at Junction 27. Follow A361 to Mullacott Cross. Take B3343 to Woolacombe. Hotel in centre of village.
See advert on following page

Lundy House Hotel

★★

Mortehoe, Woolacombe, North Devon, EX34 7DZ
Tel: 01271 870372 Fax: 01271 871001
Email: info@lundyhouse.co.uk
Web: www.lundyhousehotel.co.uk
Seasonal closure: January
Rooms: 9 all ensuite
Room facilities: Children: Welcome
Dogs: Welcome Licences:
Parking: Off-street and monitored
Directions: In Woolacombe, proceed to the end of the Esplanade, and Lundy House is the 3rd property on the seaside.

Crossways Hotel

★

The Seafront, Woolacombe, North Devon, EX34 7DJ
Tel: 01271 870395 Fax: 01271 870395
Web: www.s-h-systems.co.uk/hotels/crossway.html
Seasonal closure: November to February
Rooms: 9 (7 ensuite)
Pricing: Sgl £26–33 Dbl £52–66 Dinner from £5
Room facilities: Children: Welcome
Dogs: Welcome Licences: Parking: Off-street
Directions: Exit J27 M5. Follow A361 Barnstaple towards Ilfracombe, then left for Woolacombe. Turn right at seafront. Hotel ¹⁄₂ mile on right.

Cleeve House

 ◆ ◆ ◆ ◆

North Morte Road, Mortehoe, Woolacombe, Devon, EX34 7ED
Tel: 01271 870719 Fax: 01271 870719
Email: info@cleevehouse.co.uk
Web: www.cleevehouse.co.uk
Seasonal closure: November to March
Rooms: 7 all ensuite
Pricing: Sgl £30–44
Dbl £60–64 Dinner from £17
CC: Accepted
Room facilities:
Access:
Children: Welcome, 10yrs min age
Dogs: Guide dogs only
Licences:
Parking: Off-street
Directions: In the village of Mortehoe, 50 yards on the left side of the lighthouse road (North Morte Road).

A listed Georgian Dower House with a delightful garden offers exceptional comfort and charm. The restaurant, locally popular and nationally renowned, serves superb food and interesting wines at affordable prices — worth a detour!
Rooms: 6 all ensuite   Pricing: Sgl £60–65
Dbl £93–103 Dinner from £24.95 CC: Accepted
Room facilities: Children: Welcome
Dogs: Welcome Licences: Parking: Off-street and monitored
Directions: On A37 south from Yeovil, left at first roundabout (by Red House pub) through village. House signed left after 200 yards.

Yeovil, Somerset

Little Barwick House   Gold Ribbon Winner

★

Barwick Village, near Yeovil, Somerset, BA22 9TD
Tel: 01935 423902 Fax: 01935 420908
Email: reservations@barwick7.fsnet.co.uk
Web: www.littlebarwickhouse.co.uk

Travelodge Yeovil, Podimore

Travel Accommodation
A303 Roundabout, Podimore Services, Nr. Yeovil, Somerset, BA22 8JG
Web: www.travelodge.co.uk Rooms: 41 all ensuite
Pricing: Sgl £54.40–57.40 Dbl £58.85–61.85
CC: Accepted Room facilities: Access:

Luxury
British Hotels

A warm welcome awaits you at Paramount. Choose from 13 great locations and enjoy fabulous service and value for money at every one. From exciting city breaks to peaceful country settings, Paramount Group of Hotels has all you need.

LOCATION	HOTEL	DESCRIPTION	RAC RATING
Scotland			
Edinburgh	⚜ The Carlton	One of Edinburgh's finest	★★★★
Stirling	⚜ The Stirling Highland	Historic hotel in Stirling's Old Town	★★★★
Troon	⚜ The Marine	Coastal location, views of Isle of Arran	★★★★
England			
Harrogate	⚜ The Majestic	Elegant, historic hotel in Spa town	★★★★
County Durham	⚜ Redworth Hall	Stunning country manor	★★★★
Blackpool	⚜ The Imperial	Blackpool's Hotel of the Year 2002	★★★★
Nr. Manchester	⚜ Shrigley Hall	18 hole golf course on-site	★★★★
Buxton	⚜ The Palace	Famous Victorian hotel	★★★★
Cheltenham	⚜ The Cheltenham Park	Georgian hotel in Cotswolds	★★★★
Oxford	⚜ The Oxford	£11million refurbishment	★★★★
Brighton	The Old Ship	Stylish hotel on sea front	★★★★
Torquay	⚜ The Imperial	Area's only five star venue	★★★★★
Wales			
Cardiff	The Angel Hotel	Centrally located for attractions	★★★★

⚜ Leisure facilities available

East Anglia

Glasgow • • Edinburgh

Belfast •

• Newcastle

Dublin •

• Manchester

Birmingham •

Cardiff •   London •

Skeg

Wainfleet
All Saints

THE WASH

Boston

Bicker
Bar   Kirton

Donington   Hunsta

Gedney
Drove End

Holbeach   Long Sutton   King's
Lynn

Bourne   Spalding

Market
Deeping   Crowland   Terrington
St John

Stamford   Wisbech   Downham
Market

Belton   Morcott   Eye
Green   Thorney   Outwell

Uppingham   Guyhirn

RUTLAND   A47
R Nene   March

Alwalton   Whittlesey

Corby   Peterborough

Weldon   Stilton   B1096   Littlep

Oundle   CAMBRIDGESHIRE

Ramsey   Chatteris   Ely

Kettering   Thrapston
Burton Latimer

Huntingdon   Soham

Raunds   St Ives   Burwell
Irthlingborough   Swavesey
Higham   Brampton   Fenstanton   Waterbeach
Ferrers   Godmanchester   Buckden
Rushden   Lolworth

St Neots   Cambridge   Six Mile
Chawston   Bottom

Bedford   Great Shelford

Abington
Sandy   Great
Potton   Melbourn   Duxford   Chesterford
Biggleswade   Saffron W

Shefford

Astwick   Royston

Letchworth   Baldock

Hitchin   Buntingford   Church
London End
Stansted   Stansted
Mountfitchet

Stevenage
Puckeridge

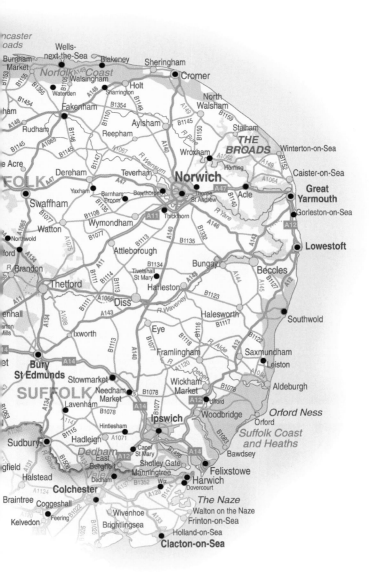

East Anglia

Abington, Cambridgeshire

Travelodge Cambridge South

Travel Accommodation
A11/A1307, Four Wentways, Abington,
Cambridgeshire, CB8 6AP
Web: www.travelodge.co.uk
Rooms: 40 all ensuite ⊗
Pricing: Sgl £64.40 Dbl £68.85
CC: Accepted Room facilities: ▢ ☕ Access: ♿

Acle, Norfolk

Travelodge Great Yarmouth, Acle

Travel Accommodation
A47, Acle Bypass, Acle, Norfolk, NR13 3BE
Web: www.travelodge.co.uk
Rooms: 40 all ensuite ⊗
Pricing: Sgl £54.40 Dbl £58.85
CC: Accepted Room facilities: ▢ ☕ Access: ♿

Blakeney, Norfolk

Blakeney Hotel

★★★★
Quayside, Blakeney, Norfolk, NR25 7NE
Tel: 01263 740797 Fax: 01263 740795
Email: reception@blakeney-hotel.co.uk
Web: www.blakeney-hotel.co.uk
Rooms: 59 all ensuite 🍽 📺 ⊗
Pricing: Sgl £64–107 Dbl £128–214 Dinner from £25
CC: Accepted Room facilities: ▢ ☎ ☕ Access: ▮↕ ♿
Conference: 6 meeting rooms (Thtr 100 max)
Children: Welcome ☌ ⅗ Dogs: Welcome
Licences: ♟♟♟
Leisure: Indoor pool, Gym, Games room,
Snooker/billiards Parking: Off-street and monitored
Directions: Situated on the quayside in Blackeney
just off the A149 coast road between Sheringham
and Wells.

Blakeney Manor Hotel

★★
The Quay, Blakeney, Holt, Norfolk, NR25 7ND
Tel: 01263 740376 Fax: 01263 741116
Seasonal closure: 6–27 January
Rooms: 37 all ensuite 📺
Pricing: Dinner from £17 (2002 rate) CC: Accepted
Room facilities: ▢ ☎ ☕ Access: ♿ Dogs: Welcome
Licences: ♟♟♟ Parking: Off-street
Directions: Blakeney Quay is located off the A149
coast road between Cromer and Wells.

Buckden, Cambridgeshire

The Lion

★★
High Street, Buckden, Cambridgeshire, PE19 5XA
Tel: 01480 810313 Fax: 01480 811070
Web: www.buckden-village.co.uk
Rooms: 15 all ensuite 🍽 📺
Pricing: Sgl £45–73.50 Dbl £60–90 Dinner from £12.50
CC: Accepted Room facilities: ▢ ☎ ☕ 🕻 Access: ♿
Conference: 1 meeting rooms (Thtr 8 max)
Children: Welcome Dogs: Guide dogs only
Licences: ♟♟♟ Parking: Off-street

Bury St Edmunds, Suffolk

Butterfly Hotel

★★★
Symonds Road, Moreton Hall Estate,
Bury St Edmunds, Suffolk, IP32 7BW
Tel: 01284 760884
Fax: 01284 755476
Email: burybutterfly@lineone.net
Web: www.butterflyhotels.co.uk
Rooms: 66 all ensuite ⊗
Pricing: Sgl £63.50–88 Dbl £72–96.50
Dinner from £17.50 CC: Accepted
Room facilities: ▢ ☎ ☕ 🕻 Access: ♿
Conference: 5 meeting rooms (Thtr 40 max)
Children: Welcome ☌ Dogs: Guide dogs only
Licences: ♟♟♟ Parking: Off-street
Directions: Take A14 towards Bury St Edmunds (Bury
East exit).

Cambridge, Cambridgeshire

Best Western Gonville Hotel

★★★★
Gonville Place, Cambridge, Cambridgeshire, CB1 1LY
Tel: 01223 221111 Fax: 01223 315470
Email: info@gonvillehotel.co.uk
Web: www.gonvillehotel.co.uk
Rooms: 78 all ensuite 🍽 ⊗
Pricing: Sgl £109–125 Dbl £139–159
Dinner from £12 CC: Accepted
Room facilities: ▢ ☎ ☕ 🕻 Access: ▮↕ ♿
Conference: 6 meeting rooms (Thtr 200 max),
24hr-delegate from £48, day-delegate rate from £38
Children: Welcome ☌ Dogs: Welcome
Licences: ♟♟♟ Parking: Off-street and monitored
Directions: Exit M11 at junction 11. Take A1309 to city
centre. At second mini-roundabout turn right into
Lensfield Road. Straight on at main junction. Hotel
20 yards on right.

Making a booking?

Don't forget to mention RAC
Hotels and Bed & Breakfast 2003.

East Anglia

Centennial Hotel

Modernised, recently refurbished, family-run hotel, opposite the Botanical Gardens, the Centennial Hotel offers a pleasing combination of home comforts and full conference facilities.

The Hotel is conveniently situated within walking distance of both the Railway Station and historic Cambridge City.

63–71 Hills Road
Cambridge CB2 1PG

Tel: 01223 314652   Fax: 01223 315443

Cambridge Lodge Hotel

Occupying a spacious Mock-Tudor house, Cambridge Lodge has an aura of quiet elegance reminiscent of more genteel times.

Your hosts Darren and Stephanie Chamberlain ensure that guests are made to feel totally at home.

The oak-beamed restaurant has an excellent reputation for high quality cuisine with locals and residents alike

139 Huntingdon Road, Cambridge, Cambridgeshire CB3 0DQ
Tel: 01223 352833 Fax: 01223 355166
Email: cambridge.lodge@btconnect.com

Arundel House Hotel

★★ ⬤ ⬤

Chesterton Road, Cambridge,
Cambridgeshire, CB4 3AN
Tel: 01223 367701 Fax: 01223 367721
Email: info@arundelhousehotels.co.uk
Web: www.arundelhousehotels.co.uk
Seasonal closure: Christmas

Beautifully located overlooking the River Cam and open parkland, this elegant Victorian terrace hotel offers some of the best food in the area. Close to the city centre and University colleges.
Rooms: 102 all ensuite ⬤ ⬤
Pricing: Sgl £72.50–89.50 Dbl £85–115
Dinner from £19.75 CC: Accepted
Room facilities: ⬚ ☎ ⬤
Conference: 3 meeting rooms (Thtr 50 max), 24hr-delegate from £107.50, day-delegate rate from £25
Children: Welcome ⷭ ⬤ Licences: ⬤
Parking: Off-street and monitored
Directions: The hotel is situated in the north of the city, overlooking the River Cam. From M11 J13, follow signs to Cambridge until mini-roundabout. Turn left then through traffic lights. Hotel 400 yards on left.

Centennial Hotel

★★

63/71 Hills Road, Cambridge,
Cambridgeshire, CB2 1PG
Tel: 01223 314652 Fax: 01223 315443
Email: reception@centennialhotel.co.uk
Web: www.centennialhotel.co.uk
Seasonal closure: Christmas to New Year
Rooms: 39 all ensuite ⬤
Pricing: Sgl £70–80 Dbl £88–96 Dinner from £13.50
CC: Accepted Room facilities: ⬚ ☎ ⬤ Access: ⬤
Conference: 1 meeting room (Thtr 20 max), day-delegate rate from £100
Children: Welcome ⷭ Licences: ⬤
Parking: Off-street and monitored
Directions: Opposite botanical gardens, conveniently near railway station and city centre.
See advert on this page

Hotel Felix

Whitehouse Lane, Huntingdon Road, Cambridge,
Cambridgeshire, CB3 0LX
Tel: 01223 277977 Fax: 01223 277973
Email: info@hotelfelix.co.uk
Web: www.hotelfelix.co.uk
Rooms: 52 all ensuite
Pricing: Sgl £125–150 Dbl £155–210 CC: Accepted
Room facilities: ▢ ☎ ◷ ✆ Access: ⬆ ♿
Conference: 4 meeting rooms (Thtr 60 max),
24hr-delegate from £170, day-delegate rate from £50
Children: Welcome ♩
Dogs: Welcome
Licences: ⬣
Parking: Off-street and monitored
Directions: From A1 take A14 turn off on A1307, at
sign city of Cambridge turn left at Whitehouse Lane.

Cambridge Lodge Hotel   Little Gem

◆◆◆◆◆ ⬮ ⬮ ❧

139 Huntingdon Road, Cambridge,
Cambridgeshire, CB3 0DQ
Tel: 01223 352833 Fax: 01223 355166
Email: cambridge.lodge@btconnect.com

Our mock-tudor hotel and restaurant prides itself on
providing a warm welcome to all. Fine dining in our
intimate beamed restaurant and comfortable
accommodation bring guests back time after time.
Rooms: 15 (12 ensuite) ⊗
Pricing: Sgl £66–67 Dbl £80–82 Dinner from £22.95
CC: Accepted Room facilities: ▢ ☎ ◷
Children: Welcome Licences: ⋮⋮⋮ Parking: Off-street
Directions: J13 M11, turn right onto Madingley Road,
then left into Storeys Way. From A14 onto A1307, then
onto Huntingdon Road.
See advert on facing page

Hills Guesthouse Cambridge

◆◆◆◆

157 Hills Road, Cambridge, CB2 2RJ
Tel: 01223 214216 Fax: 01223 214216
Rooms: 4 all ensuite ⊗
Pricing: Sgl £35–45 Dbl £50–55 CC: Accepted
Room facilities: ▢ ◷ Children: Welcome
Parking: Off-street

Lensfield Hotel

◆◆◆◆

53 Lensfield Road, Cambridge,
Cambridgeshire, CB2 1EN
Tel: 01223 355017 Fax: 01223 312022
Email: enquiries@lensfieldhotel.co.uk
Web: www.lensfieldhotel.co.uk
Seasonal closure: Christmas
Rooms: 30 (29 ensuite) ⊗ ⊗
Pricing: Sgl £55–85 Dbl £90–95 Dinner from £9
CC: Accepted Room facilities: ▢ ☎ ◷ ✆
Children: Welcome ♩ Licences: ⋮⋮⋮
Parking: Off-street and monitored
Directions: Take signposts to Cambridge centre and
join city ring road. Approach hotel via Silver Street or
Trumpington Street, turning into Lensfield Road.

Suffolk House

◆◆◆◆ ⊠

69 Milton Road, Cambridge, Cambridgeshire, CB4 1XA
Tel: 01223 352016 Fax: 01223 566816
Rooms: 8 all ensuite ⊗ Room facilities: ▢ ☎ ◷
Children: Welcome, 8yrs min age Parking: Off-street
Directions: 1¼ miles from A10/A14/A1309 junction.

Assisi Guest House

◆◆◆

193 Cherry Hinton Road, Cambridge,
Cambridgeshire, CB1 7BX
Tel: 01223 246648 Fax: 01223 412900
Rooms: 16 all ensuite ⊗ ⊗
Pricing: Sgl £35 Dbl £50 CC: Accepted
Room facilities: ▢ ☎ ◷ Access: ♿
Children: Welcome ♩ Dogs: Guide dogs only
Parking: Off-street
Directions: From the centre of Cambridge, take the
Hills Road toward Addenbrooke's Hospital. Cherry
Hinton Road is the first left after the railway station
turning.
See advert on following page

East Anglia

Cromer, Norfolk

Wellington Hotel

Garden Street, Cromer, Norfolk, NR27 9HN
Tel: 01263 511075 Fax: 01263 511914
Seasonal closure: Christmas
Rooms: 8 all ensuite ☺ Room facilities: ☐ ☕
Children: Welcome ☧ Licences: ♦♦♦
Leisure: Games room
Directions: Situated just above the pier and beaches.

Anglia Court Hotel

Seafront, Runton Road, Cromer, Norfolk, NR27 9AR
Tel: 01263 512443 Fax: 01263 513104
Email: cward31567@aol.com
Web: www.smoothhound.co.uk/hotels/angliaco.html
Rooms: 27 all ensuite ☺
Pricing: Sgl £34.50–39.50 Dbl £69–79
Dinner from £6.95 CC: Accepted
Room facilities: ☐ ☕
Conference: 2 meeting rooms (Thtr 60 max)
Children: Welcome ☧ Dogs: Welcome Licences: ♦♦♦
Parking: Off-street
Directions: From Norwich, enter Cromer on A140 and follow A149 for Sheringham. From King's Lynn enter Cromer on A148 and follow A149 to Sheringham.

Dereham, Norfolk

Yaxham Mill

Norwich Road, Yaxham, Dereham, Norfolk, NR19 1RP
Tel: 01362 693144 Fax: 01362 699801
Web: www.yaxham-mill.co.uk
Rooms: 8 all ensuite ☺
Pricing: Sgl £30–35 Dbl £39.50–45 Dinner from £5.95
CC: Accepted Room facilities: ☐ ☕ Access: ♿
Children: Welcome ☧ Dogs: Guide dogs only
Licences: ♦♦♦ Leisure: Outdoor pool
Parking: Off-street
Directions: From A47 Dereham follow signs for Wynmondham until you reach Yaxham, then continue on towards Mattishall, ½ mile on the right.

Downham Market, Norfolk

Castle Hotel

★★

High Street, Downham Market, Norfolk, PE38 9HF
Tel: 01366 384311 Fax: 01366 384311
Email: castle@castle-hotel.com
Web: www.castle-hotel.com
Rooms: 12 all ensuite ☺ 🖥
Pricing: Dinner from £17.95 (2002 rate) CC: Accepted
Room facilities: ☐ ☎ ☕ Children: Welcome ☧
Dogs: Welcome Licences: ♦♦♦
Parking: Off-street and monitored
Directions: From M11 take A10 for Ely into Downham Market. At traffic lights straight over. Hotel on next corner.

Duxford, Cambridgeshire

Duxford Lodge Hotel

★★★

Ickleton Road, Duxford, Cambridgeshire, CB2 4RU
Tel: 01223 836444 Fax: 01223 836444
Email: duxford@btclick.com
Web: duxfordlodgehotel.co.uk
Seasonal closure: 26–30 December
Rooms: 15 all ensuite
Pricing: Sgl £60–90 Dbl £104–114 CC: Accepted
Room facilities:
Conference: 1 meeting room (Thtr 30 max)
Children: Welcome Dogs: Welcome
Licences: Parking: Off-street
Directions: Leave M11 at Junction 10 and take A505
eastbound. Take 1st right turn. Hotel half a mile.
See advert on facing page

Ely, Cambridgeshire

Nyton

7 Barton Road, Ely, Cambridgeshire, CB7 4HZ
Tel: 01353 662459 Fax: 01353 666217
Email: nytonhotel@yahoo.co.uk
Rooms: 10 all ensuite
Pricing: Sgl £45–50 Dbl £70–75 CC: Accepted
Room facilities: Access:
Conference: 1 meeting room Children: Welcome
Dogs: Welcome Licences: Parking: Off-street
Directions: From A10, pass golf centre on right. Take
first turning on right, signposted 'Cathedral Car Park'.
Hotel is on right-hand side, 200 yards into turning.

Fakenham, Norfolk

Wensum Lodge Hotel

★★

Bridge Street, Fakenham, Norfolk, NR21 9AY
Tel: 01328 862100 Fax: 01328 863365
Email: enquiries@wensumlodge.fsnet.couk
Rooms: 17 all ensuite
Pricing: Sgl £50–60 Dbl £70–80 Dinner from £10
CC: Accepted Room facilities:
Conference: 2 meeting rooms (Thtr 100 max)
Children: Welcome Dogs: Guide dogs only
Licences: Parking: Off-street
Directions: Situated a few yards away from town
centre. Easily reached from Norwich on A1067, King's
Lynn on A148 and Swaffham on A1065.

Felixstowe, Suffolk

Orwell Hotel

★★★

Hamilton Road, Felixstowe, Suffolk, IP11 7DX
Tel: 01394 285511 Fax: 01394 670687
Email: welcome@orwellhotel.co.uk
Web: www.orwellhotel.co.uk
Rooms: 58 all ensuite
Pricing: Sgl £60–75 Dbl £72.50–95 Dinner from £18.50
CC: Accepted Room facilities: Access:
Conference: 11 meeting rooms (Thtr 250 max),
24hr-delegate from £90, day-delegate rate from £30
Children: Welcome, 13yrs min age
Dogs: Guide dogs only Licences: Parking: Off-street
Directions: A14 to Felixstowe. Straight at dock
roundabout. Straight at second roundabout. Right at
third roundabout into Beatrice Avenue. Hotel at end.

Grafton Guest House

◆◆◆◆

The Grafton, 13 Sea Road, Felixstowe,
Suffolk, IP11 2BB
Tel: 01394 284881 Fax: 01394 279101
Email: info@grafton-house.com
Web: www.grafton-house.com

Situated by the seafront, "The Grafton" offers quality
bed and breakfast accommodation. Owners Geoffrey
and Elizabeth are committed to providing a first class
service and extend a warm welcome to all guests,
non-smoking throughout.
Rooms: 8 (6 ensuite)
Pricing: Sgl £22–27.50 Dbl £38–45
Room facilities:
Conference: 1 meeting room (Thtr 1 max)
Children: Welcome
Directions: A14 to Felixstone, straight at first
roundabout, right at second. Straight over two traffic
lights, left at first roundabout, right at second. Guest
house 250 yards on right.

East Anglia

Gorleston-on-Sea, Norfolk

The Pier Hotel

★★

Harbour Mouth, Gorleston-on-Sea, Norfolk, NR31 6PL
Tel: 01493 662631 Fax: 01493 440263
Email: bookings@pierhotelgorleston.co.uk
Web: www.pierhotelgorleston.co.uk
Rooms: 19
Pricing: Sgl £40–55 Dbl £55–70 Dinner from £11.50
Room facilities: 🖵 ☎ 🍵 Children: Welcome ⼌
Directions: From A12 Lowestoft or A47 Norwich, Great
Yarmouth. 3 miles from Yarmouth. Ask for Harbour
mouth Gorleston-0n-Sea.

Great Yarmouth, Norfolk

Cliff Hotel

★★★

Cliff Hill, Gorleston-on-Sea, Norfolk, NR31 6DH
Tel: 01493 662179 Fax: 01493 653617
Email: cliff.hotel@elizabethhotels.co.uk
Web: www.elizabethhotels.co.uk
Rooms: 39 all ensuite 🍴 🚭
Pricing: Sgl £60–100 Dbl £80–150 Dinner from £18.95
CC: Accepted Room facilities: 🖵 ☎ 🍵 📞
Conference: 3 meeting rooms (Thtr 200 max)
Children: Welcome ⼌ ☕ Dogs: Welcome
Licences: ⟨⟩ ⚶ Parking: Off-street and monitored
Directions: From M11 take A11 to Norwich, then A47
to Great Yarmouth. Hotel is at north end of Gorleston's
Upper Marine Parade.

Imperial Hotel

★★★★ ⓡ

North Drive, Great Yarmouth, Norfolk, NR30 1EQ
Tel: 01493 842000 Fax: 01493 852229
Email: imperial@scs-datacom.co.uk
Web: www.imperialhotel.co.uk
Rooms: 39 all ensuite 🍴 🚭
Pricing: Sgl £55–75 Dbl £64–88 Dinner from £20.50
CC: Accepted Room facilities: 🖵 ☎ 🍵 📞 Access: ⼢
Conference: 6 meeting rooms (Thtr 140 max),
24hr-delegate from £95, day-delegate rate from £25
Children: Welcome ☕ Dogs: Welcome
Licences: ⟨⟩ ⚶ Parking: Off-street and monitored
Directions: Follow signs to seafront. Turn left into North
Drive. Hotel is ½ mile north of Britannia Pier.

Star Hotel

★★★

Hall Quay, Great Yarmouth, Norfolk, NR30 1HG
Tel: 01493 842294 Fax: 01493 330215
Email: star.hotel@elizabethhotels.co.uk
Web: www.elizabethhotels.co.uk
Rooms: 40 all ensuite 🍴 🖭 🚭
Pricing: Sgl £60–70 Dbl £70–90 Dinner from £14.95
CC: Accepted Room facilities: 🖵 ☎ 🍵 Access: ⼢
Conference: 3 meeting rooms (Thtr 150 max)
Children: Welcome ⼌ Dogs: Guide dogs only
Licences: ⚶ Leisure: Games room
Parking: Off-street and monitored
Directions: From A12 directly opposite Haven Bridge.
On entering Yarmouth from A47 take the third exit on
first roundabout on right

Burlington Palm Court Hotel

★★

North Drive, Great Yarmouth, NR30 1EG
Tel: 01493 844568 Fax: 01493 331848
Email: enquires@burlington-hotel.co.uk
Web: www.burlinton-hotel.co.uk
Seasonal closure: December to January

This family-run hotel has views of the sea and
recreation grounds. There is ample car parking and an
indoor swimming pool.
Rooms: 70 all ensuite 🍴 🚭
Pricing: Sgl £50–30 Dbl £70–100 Dinner from £13
CC: Accepted Room facilities: 🖵 ☎ 🍵 Access: ⼢ ⼤
Conference: 8 meeting rooms (Thtr 120 max)
Children: Welcome ⼌ ☕ Dogs: Guide dogs only
Licences: ⚶ Leisure: Indoor pool, Games room
Parking: Off-street
Directions: Follow signs for seafront. Hotel is 600 yards
from Britannia Pier, at the quieter end of town.

Sandringham Hotel

★★

74-75 Marine Parade, Great Yarmouth,
Norfolk, NR30 2DH
Tel: 01493 852427 Fax: 01493 852336
Rooms: 24 all ensuite 🍴 🚭
Pricing: Sgl £29.50 Dbl £56.50 Dinner from £9.50
CC: Accepted Room facilities: 🖵 ☎ 🍵
Children: Welcome ⼌ ☕ Dogs: Guide dogs only
Licences: ⚶
Directions: At seafront, turn inland opposite Britannia Pier.

Two Bears

★★

Southtown Road, Great Yarmouth, Norfolk, NR31 0HU
Tel: 01493 603198 Fax: 01493 440486

Admiral House Hotel

◆◆◆◆

12a Nelson Road South, Great Yarmouth,
Norfolk, NR30 3JL
Tel: 01493 843712
Email: sally@admiralhouse.co.uk
Web: www.admiralhouse.co.uk
Rooms: 8 all ensuite
Pricing: Sgl £20–30 Dbl £40–60 Dinner from £8.50
CC: Accepted
Room facilities: Children: Welcome
Licences:
Directions: From seafront turn right (Kings Road) at
Wellington Pier. Turn right into Nelson Road South, 5th
hotel on left side.

All Seasons Lodge Hotel

◆◆◆◆

55-56 Clarence Road, Gorleston, Great Yarmouth,
Norfolk, NR31 6DR
Tel: 01493 651111

Corner House Hotel

◆◆◆◆

Albert Square, Great Yarmouth, Norfolk, NR30 3JH
Tel: 01493 842773
Email: accommodation@thecornerhousehotel.co.uk
Web: thecornerhousehotel.co.uk
Seasonal closure: October to March
Rooms: 8 all ensuite
Pricing: Sgl £26–32 Dbl £52–64 Dinner from £10
Room facilities: Licences: Parking: Off-street
Directions: Follow signs to seafront. From Marine
Parade turn right opposite Wellington Pier/Winter
Gardens, then left into Albert Square.

Maluth Lodge

◆◆◆◆

40 North Denes Road, Great Yarmouth,
Norfolk, NR30 4LU
Tel: 01493 304652 Fax: 01493 308112
Email: maluthlodge@aol.com
Web: relaxed.at/maluthlodge
Rooms: 8 all ensuite
Pricing: Sgl £21–30 Dbl £42–60 Dinner from £8.95
CC: Accepted Room facilities:
Children: Welcome Dogs: Guide dogs only
Licences:
Directions: Left on seafront past waterways, left onto
Salisbury Road, right onto North Denes, Maluth Lodge
on your left.
See advert on this page

Alclive Hotel

◆◆◆

33-35 North Denes Road, Great Yarmouth,
Norfolk, NR30 4LU
Tel: 01493 844741
Seasonal closure: October to April
Rooms: 20 (18 ensuite)
Pricing: Sgl £22–28 Dbl £44–56 Dinner from £6
CC: Accepted Room facilities:
Children: Welcome Dogs: Welcome Licences:
Directions: Take the A47 to Great Yarmouth. Turn left at
roundabout onto A149. Turn right at traffic lights. Take
the first left into Salisbury Road. Turn left at North
Denes Road.

Anglia House Hotel

◆◆◆

56 Wellesley Road, Great Yarmouth, Norfolk, NR30 1EX
Tel: 01493 844395
Rooms: 10 (8 ensuite)
Pricing: Sgl £15–21 Dbl £30–42 Dinner from £8
Room facilities: Children: Welcome
Dogs: Guide dogs only Licences:
Directions: Follow seafront signs. Left at lights, keeping
Sainsbury's on left. Through traffic lights, next left
opposite Wellesley park.

East Anglia

Arch House

14 Wellington Road, Great Yarmouth,
Norfolk, NR30 3AQ
Tel: 01493 854258
Rooms: 8 (7 ensuite)
Pricing: Sgl £20–22 Dbl £25–35 Dinner from £25
Room facilities: Children: Welcome
Dogs: Guide dogs only Licences:
Parking: Off-street

Armani Hotel

14-15 Sandown Road, Great Yarmouth,
Norfolk, NR30 1EY
Tel: 01493 843870 Fax: 01493 843870
Email: armanihotel@talk21.com
Web: www.armanihotel.co.uk
Rooms: 22 (20 ensuite)
Pricing: Sgl £30–35 Dbl £25–30 Dinner from £9
Room facilities: Access:
Children: Welcome, 3yrs min age Licences:
Parking: Off-street and monitored
Directions: Follow signs to seafront. On seafront turn
left. Sandown Road is second, turn left opposite
entrance to Waterways Garden.

Beaumont House

52 Wellesley Road, Great Yarmouth, Norfolk, NR30 1EX
Tel: 01493 843957 Fax: 01493 855635
Email:
beaumonthouse@nelsonnr301ex.fsbusiness.co.uk
Rooms: 14 (9 ensuite)
Pricing: Sgl £18–23 Dbl £32–44 Dinner from £7
CC: Accepted Room facilities: Access:
Children: Welcome Licences:
Parking: Off-street
Directions: Beaumont House is situated one street
away from beach, overlooking Wellesley Park. Two
minutes from attractions and town centre.

Mobile traffic information

Just dial 1740* from any mobile
phone to get up-to-the-minute
RAC traffic information on
motorways and major A roads.
Try it now! *Calls to 1740 cost up to 59p
per minute. Check with your network.

Making a booking?

Don't forget to mention RAC
Hotels and Bed & Breakfast 2003.

Belvedere

90 North Denes Road, Great Yarmouth,
Norfolk, NR30 4LN
Tel: 01493 844200
Email: belvedere@talk21.com

Open all year. Car parking. Ensuite rooms available
with central heating, colour TVs, tea, coffee-making
facilities, radio alarm clocks and hairdryer. Own keys:
access at all times. Varied menu.
Rooms: 9 (5 ensuite)
Pricing: Sgl £14–22 Dbl £28–44 Room facilities:
Children: Welcome Dogs: Welcome
Parking: Off-street
Directions: At seafront, proceed north to 'Waterways'
— turn left into Beaconsfield Road. Turn right at mini
roundabout. Hotel fifth property on right.

Bonheur Hotel

3 Norfolk Square, Great Yarmouth, Norfolk, NR30 1EE
Tel: 01493 843042 Fax: 01493 745235
Email: enq@bonheur-hotel.co.uk
Web: www.bonheur-hotel.co.uk
Rooms: 10 (7 ensuite)
Pricing: Sgl £20–35 Dbl £35–45 Dinner from £8
CC: Accepted
Room facilities: Children: Welcome
Licences: Parking: Off-street
Directions: 200 yards north of Britannia Pier along
North Drive, turn left into Albemarle Road, Bonheur
50 yards on left.

Bramalea/Balmoral

114–115 Wellesley Road, Great Yarmouth,
Norfolk, NR30 2AR
Tel: 01493 844722
Rooms: 15 all ensuite
Pricing: Sgl £16–23 Dbl £32–46 Dinner from £6
Room facilities: Children: Welcome
Dogs: Guide dogs only Licences:
Directions: From bus station go left into Regent Road;
over traffic lights, turn left into Wellesley Road.
Property is 100 metres on right.

Cavendish House

◆ ◆ ◆

19/20 Princes Road, Great Yarmouth,
Norfolk, NR30 2DG
Tel: 01493 844829 Fax: 01493 843148
Rooms: 19 all ensuite
Pricing: Sgl £18–25 Dbl £36–50 Dinner from £7
Room facilities: ☐ ☕ Access: ⊔⊓ ♿
Children: Welcome ⅄ Licences: ⅄⅄⅄
Directions: Follow A12 into Great Yarmouth, follow
signs to seafront and Britannia Pier, Princes Road is
immediately left before pier.

Chateau Hotel

◆ ◆ ◆

1 North Drive, Great Yarmouth, Norfolk, NR30 1ED
Tel: 01493 859052
Seasonal closure: October to March
Rooms: 11 all ensuite
Pricing: Sgl £29.50–31.50 Dbl £46–56 CC: Accepted
Room facilities: ☐ ☕ Children: Welcome ⅄
Dogs: Welcome Licences: ⅄⅄⅄ Parking: Off-street
Directions: Opposite bowling greens on seafront, just
north of Britannia Pier.

Chequers Hotel

◆ ◆ ◆ ※

27 Nelson Road South, Great Yarmouth,
Norfolk, NR30 3JA
Tel: 01493 853091
Rooms: 8 all ensuite ⊗
Pricing: Sgl £20–22 Dbl £40–44 Dinner from £6
Room facilities: ☐ ☕ Children: Welcome ⅄ ☕
Licences: ⅄⅄⅄ Parking: Off-street and monitored
Directions: Drive to seafront. Turn opposite Wellington
Pier, then turn down Albert Square. At T junction,
Chequers is on opposite corner.

Dene House

◆ ◆ ◆

89 North Denes Road, Great Yarmouth,
Norfolk, NR30 4LW
Tel: 01493 844181
Email: pulham@denehouse.fsbusiness.co.uk
Rooms: 8 all ensuite ⊗
Pricing: Sgl £15–22 Dbl £30–44 CC: Accepted
Room facilities: ☐ ☕ Children: Welcome ⅄ ☕
Dogs: Guide dogs only Licences: ⅄⅄⅄
Parking: Off-street
Directions: Off A47, signs for sea front; at traffic lights
past Sainsbury's, left to roundabout; straight on past
six houses, on the right.

Fjaerland Hotel

◆ ◆ ◆ ※

24 Trafalgar Road, Great Yarmouth,
Norfolk, NR30 2LD
Tel: 01493 856339/0780 3859951 Fax: 01493 856339
Rooms: 12 all ensuite ⊗
Pricing: Sgl £25–35 Dbl £40–50 CC: Accepted

Room facilities: ☐ ☕ Children: Welcome ⅄
Dogs: Guide dogs only Licences: ⅄⅄⅄
Directions: From major roads follow signs to seafront.
Trafalgar Road located off Marina Parade opposite
Marina Centre. Hotel overlooking two grass squares.

Gable End Hotel

◆ ◆ ◆

30 North Drive, Great Yarmouth, Norfolk, NR30 4EW
Tel: 01493 842112

Gai-Sejour

◆ ◆ ◆

21 Princes Road, Great Yarmouth, Norfolk, NR30 2DG
Tel: 01493 843371
Rooms: 11 (7 ensuite)
Pricing: Dinner from £5 (2002 rate)
Room facilities: ☐ ☕ Children: Welcome ⅄ ☕
Licences: ⅄⅄⅄ Leisure: Snooker/billiards
Directions: Off Marine Parade, just opposite Britannia Pier.

Hamilton Hotel

◆ ◆ ◆

23/24 North Drive, Great Yarmouth, Norfolk, NR30 4EU
Tel: 01493 844662 Fax: 01493 332123
Email: enquiries@hamilton-hotel.co.uk
Web: www.hamilton-hotel.co.uk
Rooms: 25 all ensuite
Pricing: Sgl £28–36 Dbl £48–60 Dinner from £9
CC: Accepted
Room facilities: ☐ ☕ Children: Welcome ⅄ ☕
Dogs: Welcome Licences: ⅄⅄⅄ Leisure: Games room
Parking: Off-street
Directions: Follow signs for seafront. Turn left at
Britannia Pier. Hotel 800 yards along the seafront.

Hotel Victoria

◆ ◆ ◆

2 Kings Road, Great Yarmouth, Norfolk, NR30 3JW
Tel: 01493 843872 Fax: 01493 843872
Seasonal closure: January to Easter
Rooms: 35 (30 ensuite)
Pricing: Sgl £20–28 Dbl £22–50 CC: Accepted
Room facilities: ☐ ☕ Access: ⊔⊓
Children: Welcome ⅄ ☕ Dogs: Welcome Licences: ⅄⅄⅄
Leisure: Outdoor pool, Games room
Parking: Off-street
Directions: Kings Road is opposite the model village,
close to Wellington Pier. Second building in from
seafront.

East Anglia

Kentville Guest House

5 Kent Square, Great Yarmouth, Norfolk, NR30 2EX
Tel: 01493 844783
Rooms: 9 (5 ensuite)
Pricing: Sgl £15–17 Dbl £30–34 Dinner from £5
Room facilities: Access:
Children: Welcome Dogs: Welcome
Directions: Kent Square is just off the seafront. Take
Standard Road (opposite Marina Leisure Centre). Hotel
is in corner.

Kilbrannan

14 Trafalgar Road, Great Yarmouth, Norfolk, NR30 2LD
Tel: 01493 850383
Rooms: 5 all ensuite Room facilities:
Children: Welcome Parking: Off-street and monitored
Directions: Approach sea front past Britannia Pier.
Before the Marina Centre, turn right up Trafalgar Road.
Kilbrannan is half way up.

Kingsley House

68 King Street, Great Yarmouth, Norfolk, NR30 2PP
Tel: 01493 850948 Fax: 01493 850948
Email: brian.savoury@bt.internet.com
Rooms: 7 all ensuite
Pricing: Sgl £15–20 Dbl £30–40
Room facilities: Children: Welcome
Dogs: Welcome Licences:
Directions: Located at the southern end of King Street.
Kingsley House is a short walk from seafront and town
centre.

Lea-Hurst

117 Wellesley Road, Great Yarmouth, Norfolk, NR30 2AP
Tel: 01493 843063
Email: theleahurst@tiscali.co.uk
Rooms: 8 (6 ensuite) Pricing: Sgl £12–20 Dbl £24–40
Room facilities: Children: Welcome
Licences:
Directions: Take A47 to Great Yarmouth. Follow signs
to seafront. Turn right at Britannia Pier onto Regent
Road. Take first road on right (Wellesley Road).
Lea-Hurst 30 yards on right.

Little Emily Hotel

18 Princes Road, Great Yarmouth, Norfolk, NR30 2DG
Tel: 01493 842515
Rooms: 11 (5 ensuite)
Pricing: Sgl £17–20 Dbl £34–40 Dinner from £7.50
Room facilities: Children: Welcome
Dogs: Guide dogs only Licences:
Leisure: Games room Parking: Off-street
Directions: Follow A12 into Great Yarmouth. Follow
signs to seafront and Britannia Pier. Princes Road is
immediately left, before pier.

Marine Lodge

19-20 Euston Road, Great Yarmouth,
Norfolk, NR30 1DY
Tel: 01493 331120 Fax: 01493 332040
Email: marinelodge@aol.com
Web: marinelodge@burlington-hotel.co.uk
Seasonal closure: March to December

Overlooking the sea in a great location, this 19th
Century building has been updated providing good
quality accommodation and public areas.
Rooms: 38 all ensuite
Pricing: Sgl £35 Dbl £50 CC: Accepted
Room facilities: Access:
Conference: 2 meeting rooms (Thtr 60 max),
24hr-delegate from £50, day-delegate rate from £20
Children: Welcome Dogs: Welcome Licences:
Parking: Off-street and monitored
Directions: Following signs to seafront the Marine
Lodge is situated 300 yards north of the Britannia Pier
on Great Yarmouth seafront.

Maryland

53 Wellesley Road, Great Yarmouth, Norfolk, NR30 1EX
Tel: 01493 844409
Rooms: 7 all ensuite
Pricing: Sgl £18–25 Dbl £32–40 Room facilities:
Children: Welcome, 2yrs min age Licences:
Parking: Off-street and monitored
Directions: Follow seafront signs. Turn left at traffic
lights into St Nicholas Road. Go straight over traffic
lights, turn left. 400 yards on left.

Raynscourt Hotel

83 Marine Parade, Great Yarmouth, Norfolk, NR30 2DJ
Tel: 01493 856554 Fax: 01493 856554
Seasonal closure: January to March
Rooms: 55 (54 ensuite)
Pricing: Sgl £24–36 Dbl £24–30 Dinner from £7.50
CC: Accepted Room facilities: Access:
Children: Welcome Licences: Parking: Off-street
Directions: Follow signs for sea front. As approaching
sea front we are on the right-hand corner.

Richmond House

♦ ♦ ♦

113 Wellesley Road, Great Yarmouth,
Norfolk, NR30 2AR
Tel: 01493 853995
Seasonal closure: Christmas
Rooms: 8 all ensuite
Pricing: Sgl £15–20 Dbl £30–40 CC: Accepted
Room facilities: 🖵 🍵 Children: Welcome 3yrs min age ♛
Licences: ⚱ ♛♛♛ Parking: Monitored
Directions: Close to Britannia Pier and sea front.

Russell Private Hotel

♦ ♦ ♦

26 Nelson Road South, Great Yarmouth,
Norfolk, NR30 3JL
Tel: 01493 843788
Email: paul.mason@russell-private-hotel.co.uk
Web: www.russell-private-hotel.co.uk
Seasonal closure: October to April
Rooms: 10 all ensuite
Pricing: Sgl £20–26 Dbl £40–52 Dinner from £8
CC: Accepted Room facilities: 🖵 🍵
Children: Welcome ♛ ≀℃ Licences: ♛♛♛
Directions: Turn right past Wellington Pier, onto Kings
Road. Take next right onto Nelson Road South. Hotel
150 yards on left.

Sandholme Hotel

♦ ♦ ♦

12-13 Sandown Road, Great Yarmouth,
Norfolk, NR30 1EY
Tel: 01493 300001 Fax: 01493 842161
Email: sandholme@lineone.net
Web: www.sandholme-hotel.co.uk
Rooms: 19 (10 ensuite) 🍵 🖨
Room facilities: 🖵 ☎ 🍵
Children: Welcome, 3yrs min age ≀℃
Licences: ⚱ ♛♛♛ Parking: Off-street
Directions: Follow seafront signs. When sea is in front
of you, turn left. At the Imperial Hotel & Waterways turn
left. The Sandholme is 50 yards on right.

Sedley House

♦ ♦ ♦

5 St George's Road, Great Yarmouth,
Norfolk, NR30 2JR
Tel: 01493 855409
Rooms: 7 (4 ensuite)
Pricing: Sgl £14–18 Dbl £28–36
Room facilities: 🖵 🍵
Children: Welcome, 10yrs min age
Parking: Off-street and monitored
Directions: From A12, take bypass to A47. Enter town
via A47. Continue over roundabout. Cross 4 sets of
lights, turn left after park. Sedley House is 50 yards on
left.

Senglea Lodge

♦ ♦ ♦

7 Euston Road, Great Yarmouth, Norfolk, NR30 1DX
Tel: 01493 859632
Email: info@senglealodge.freeserve.co.uk
Web: www.uk-bedandbreakfasts.com
Rooms: 7 (4 ensuite) 🍵 🖨
Pricing: Sgl £15–17.50 Dbl £30–35 CC: Accepted
Room facilities: 🖵 🍵 Children: Welcome ≀℃
Licences: ♛♛♛
Directions: On entering Great Yarmouth on the A47 or
A12, go straight over 1st and 2nd roundabouts. Take a
left turn to seafront. Go straight through traffic lights.
Lodge on right-hand side.

Shemara Guest House

♦ ♦ ♦

11 Wellesley Road, Great Yarmouth, Norfolk, NR30 2AR
Tel: 01493 844054 Fax: 01493 844054
Seasonal closure: December
Rooms: 9 all ensuite 🐕 Room facilities: 🖵 🍵 ❄
Children: Welcome ♛
Directions: Take A47 to Yarmouth, past rail station.
Follow signs for seafront. Take fourth turning right.
Wellesley Road is halfway down on right.

Sienna Lodge

♦ ♦ ♦

17-18 Camperdown, Great Yarmouth, Norfolk, NR30 3JB
Tel: 01493 843361
Seasonal closure: November
Rooms: 14 all ensuite 🍵
Pricing: Sgl £24–26 Dbl £48–52 Dinner from £8
Room facilities: 🖵 🍵 Children: Welcome ♛ ≀℃
Dogs: Welcome Licences: ♛♛♛
Directions: Turn off seafront opposite Sea Life Centre
into Camperdown. Sienna Lodge is on the corner of
Nelson Road South and Camperdown.

Siesta Lodge

♦ ♦ ♦

53/54 York Road, Great Yarmouth, Norfolk, NR30 2NE
Tel: 01493 843207
Email: siesta-lodge@aol.com
Web: www.siestalodge.co.uk
Rooms: 7 (2 ensuite) 🍵 🐕
Pricing: Sgl £15–20 Dbl £30–40 Dinner from £5
Room facilities: 🖵 🍵 Children: Welcome ♛ ≀℃
Licences: ♛♛♛
Directions: Along the seafront going south, Marina
Centre on left and Maritime Museum on right, York
Road is next right.

Making a booking?

Don't forget to mention RAC
Hotels and Bed & Breakfast 2003.

East Anglia

Southern Hotel

◆◆◆

46 Queens Road, Great Yarmouth, Norfolk, NR30 3JR
Tel: 01493 843313 Fax: 01493 853047
Email: southern.hotel@tinyonline.co.uk
Web: www.southernhotel.co.uk
Seasonal closure: October to March
Rooms: 18 (16 ensuite) Pricing: Sgl £22–28 Dbl £44–50
Room facilities: 🖵 🛇 Children: Welcome ℏ ℘
Licences: ⚲ Parking: Off-street
Directions: Southern Hotel is situated close to
Wellington Pier and model village on Great Yarmouth's
Golden Mile.

Sunshine Lodge Hotel

◆◆◆ ☆

73 Marine Parade, Great Yarmouth, Norfolk, NR30 2DQ
Tel: 01493 842250 Fax: 01493 857521
Email: john@sunshine-lodge.co.uk
Web: www.sunshine-lodge.co.uk
Rooms: 11 all ensuite 🐾 🚲
Pricing: Sgl £20–22 Dbl £36–50 CC: Accepted
Room facilities: 🖵 🛇 Children: Welcome ℘
Licences: ⚲ Leisure: Games room
Directions: Sunshine Lodge is on the seafront opposite
the Britannia Pier and just before the Hollywood Cinema.

The Collingwood Hotel

◆◆◆

25/26 Princes Road, Great Yarmouth,
Norfolk, NR30 2DG
Tel: 01493 844398 Fax: 01493 844398
Web: www.smoothhound.co.uk/hotels/collingwood.html
Seasonal closure: November to January
Rooms: 19 (10 ensuite) 🐾 🛇
Pricing: Sgl £20–25 Dbl £40–55 CC: Accepted
Room facilities: 🖵 🛇 Children: Welcome, 6yrs min age
Licences: ⚲
Directions: Follow signs to the seafront. Turn right.
Princes Road is opposite the Britannia Pier.
Collingwood is the second hotel on the left.

The Shrewsbury non-smoking Guest House

◆◆◆

9 Trafalgar Road, Great Yarmouth, Norfolk, NR30 2LD
Tel: 01493 844788
Email: pstainton@lineone.net
Web: www.shrewsburyguesthouse.co.uk
Seasonal closure: 24 December to 2 January
Rooms: 8 (4 ensuite) 🛇
Pricing: Sgl £18–26 Dbl £36–52 Room facilities: 🖵 🛇
Children: Welcome ℏ Dogs: Guide dogs only

Thelton House Hotel

◆◆◆

60 Wellesley Road, Great Yarmouth, Norfolk, NR30 1EX
Tel: 01493 843288
Email: thelton@lineone.net
Rooms: 7 all ensuite 🐾 Room facilities: 🖵 🛇
Children: Welcome ℏ

Trevi Guest House

◆◆◆

57 Wellesley Road, Great Yarmouth, Norfolk, NR30 1EX
Tel: 01493 842821
Rooms: 9 (5 ensuite) Pricing: Sgl £15–18 Dbl £30–36
Room facilities: 🖵 🛇 Children: Welcome Licences: ⚲
Directions: Follow signs to seafront. Proceed through
traffic lights past Sainsbury's. Take first turning on left.
Trevi Guest House is opposite the recreation ground.

Windy Shore Hotel

◆◆◆

29 North Drive, Great Yarmouth, Norfolk, NR30 4EW
Tel: 01493 844145 Fax: 01493 852364
Email: hduffield@windyshore.freeserve.co.uk
Web: www.windyshorehotel.co.uk

Situated in one of the prettiest parts of the seafront,
overlooking the illuminated Venetian waterways and
rock gardens, The Windy Shore is the ideal seaview
hotel with ample car parking.
Rooms: 25 all ensuite
Pricing: Sgl £22–30 Dbl £40–52 Dinner from £9.50
Room facilities: 🖵 🛇 Children: Welcome
Dogs: Welcome Parking: Off-street
Directions: Head towards the seafront, turn left and
head north along North Drive.

Woods End

◆◆◆

49 Wellesley Road, Great Yarmouth, Norfolk, NR30 1EX
Tel: 01493 842229
Rooms: 8 all ensuite 🐾 🛇
Pricing: Sgl £16–23 Dbl £32–46 Room facilities: 🖵 🛇
Children: Welcome ℏ Dogs: Guide dogs only
Licences: ⚲ Parking: Off-street and monitored
Directions: Off Norwich roundabout, follow seafront
signs past Sainsburys, first turn on left into Wellesley
Road, proceed approx 200 yards opposite recreation
ground.

Plan your route

Visit www.rac.co.uk for RAC's
interactive route planner, including
up to the minute traffic reports.

Charron Guest House

 ◆ ◆

151 Nelson Road Central, Great Yarmouth,
Norfolk, NR30 2HZ
Tel: 01493 843177 Fax: 01493 843177
Seasonal closure: October – Easter
Rooms: 10 (7 ensuite) 🦽 Room facilities: 🖵 🍵
Children: Welcome, 2yrs min age 🍴 🍸
Dogs: Guide dogs only

Chatsworth Hotel

◆ ◆

32 Wellesley Road, Great Yarmouth, Norfolk, NR30 1EU
Tel: 01493 842890
Rooms: 17 all ensuite 🦽 🍽
Pricing: Sgl £25–36 Dbl £36–50
Room facilities: 🖵 ☎ 🍵 Access: |↓↑
Conference: 2 meeting rooms (Thtr 45 max)
Children: Welcome 🍴 🍸 Licences: ◬
Leisure: Indoor pool, Games room, Snooker/billiards
Parking: Off-street and monitored
Directions: 100 yards north of Britannia Pier.

Holt, Norfolk

Daubeney Hall Farm

 ◆ ◆ ◆ ◆ 🍸

Lower Hall Lane, Sharrington, Norfolk, NR24 2PQ
Tel: 01263 861412
Email: ninaogier@hotmail.com
Web: daubeneyhallfarm.co.uk
Rooms: 3 all ensuite 🚭 Pricing: Dbl £44–55
Room facilities: 🖵 🍵 Dogs: Welcome
Parking: Off-street
Directions: At Fakenham, take A148 eastbound for
9 miles. Turn right into lane for Sharrington. Take first
left past church. Daubeney Hall is 100 metres on left.

Hunstanton, Norfolk

Caley Hall Motel

★ ★

Old Hunstanton, Hunstanton, Norfolk, PE36 6HH
Tel: 01485 533486 Fax: 01485 533348
Rooms: 29 all ensuite 🦽 🍽 🚭
Pricing: Dinner from £18.75 CC: Accepted
Room facilities: 🖵 🍵 Access: ♿
Conference: 80 meeting rooms (Thtr 80 max)
Children: Welcome 🍸 Dogs: Welcome
Leisure: Snooker/billiards
Parking: Off-street and monitored

Need help booking?

RAC Hotel Reservations will find
the accommodation that's right
for you – and book it too.
Call today on 0870 603 9109
and quote 'Guide 2003'

Huntingdon, Cambridgeshire

The Grange Hotel

◆ ◆ ◆ ◆ 🍽 🍽

115 High Street, Brampton, Huntingdon,
Cambridgeshire, PE28 4RA
Tel: 01480 459516 Fax: 01480 459391
Email: enquiries@grangehotelbrampton.com
Web: www.grangehotelbrampton.com
Rooms: 8 (7 ensuite) 🚭
Pricing: Sgl £55–75 Dbl £75–95 CC: Accepted
Room facilities: 🖵 ☎ 🍵 🧺 Children: Welcome 🍴 🍸
Dogs: Guide dogs only Licences: ⛟ Parking: Off-street
Directions: Exit A14 Brampton Racecourse (B1514)
towards Huntingdon. After mini-roundabout, turn right
into Grove Lane. Hotel faces T-junction.

Ipswich, Suffolk

Hintlesham Hall
Gold Ribbon Winner

★ ★ ★ ★ ★ 🍽 🍽 🍽

Hintlesham, near Ipswich, Suffolk, IP8 3NS
Tel: 01473 652334 Fax: 01473 652463
Email: reservations@hintleshamhall.com
Web: www.hintleshamhall.com

An uncommon blend of formality and relaxation
conjured by a friendly professional staff in a glorious
hotel and restaurant. A unique health club and a top
class golf club.
Rooms: 33 all ensuite 🍽
Pricing: Sgl £98–125 Dbl £10–235 Dinner from £28
CC: Accepted Room facilities: 🖵 ☎ 🧺 Access: ♿
Conference: 3 meeting rooms (Thtr 80 max)
Children: Welcome 🍸 Dogs: Welcome
Licences: ⛟ ⛟
Leisure: Outdoor pool, Gym, Health spa,
Beauty salon, Tennis, Golf, Snooker/billiards
Parking: Off-street and monitored
Directions: 5 miles west of Ipswich on the A1071.

It's easier online

For all your motoring and travel
needs, www.rac.co.uk

Swallow Belstead Brook Hotel

★★★

Belstead Road, Ipswich, Suffolk, IP2 9HB
Tel: 01473 684241 Fax: 01473 681249
Email: sales@belsteadbrook.co.uk
Web: www.belsteadbrook.co.uk

SWALLOW HOTELS

This 16th-century former hunting lodge, found in the suburbs, offers superb grounds, original features and fine food, which has won an RAC Dining Award.

Rooms: 88 all ensuite
Pricing: Sgl £70–95 Dbl £80–104.75
Dinner from £20.50 CC: Accepted
Room facilities: Access:
Conference: 10 meeting rooms (Thtr 200 max), 24hr-delegate from £110, day-delegate rate from £27.50
Children: Welcome
Dogs: Welcome Licences:
Leisure: Indoor pool, Gym, Beauty salon
Parking: Off-street and monitored
Directions: Just south of Ipswich, 5 minutes from A12/A14 intersection.

Travelodge Ipswich, Capel

Travel Accommodation
A12 Southbound, Capel St Mary, Ipswich, Suffolk, IP9 2JP
Web: www.travelodge.co.uk
Rooms: 32 all ensuite
Pricing: Sgl £49.40 Dbl £53.85
CC: Accepted Room facilities: Access:

Travelodge Ipswich, Stowmarket

Travel Accommodation
A14 West Bound, Stowmarket, Suffolk, IP14 3PY
Web: www.travelodge.co.uk
Rooms: 40 all ensuite
Pricing: Sgl £49.40 Dbl 53.85
CC: Accepted Room facilities: Access:

King's Lynn, Norfolk

Butterfly Hotel

★★★

Beveridge Way, Hardwick Narrows Estate, King's Lynn, Norfolk, PE30 4NB
Tel: 01553 771707 Fax: 01553 768027
Email: kingsbutterfly@lineone.net
Web: www.butterflyhotels.co.uk
Rooms: 50 all ensuite
Pricing: Sgl £63.50–88 Dbl £72–96.50
Dinner from £17.50 CC: Accepted
Room facilities:
Conference: 4 meeting rooms (Thtr 90 max)
Children: Welcome Dogs: Guide dogs only
Licences: Parking: Off-street
Directions: A10/A147 roundabout.

Congham Hall Hotel

Gold Ribbon Winner

★★★

Grimston, King's Lynn, Norfolk, PE32 1AH
Tel: 01485 600250 Fax: 01485 601191
Email: reception@conghamhallhotel.co.uk
Web: www.conghamhallhotel.co.uk

Rooms: 14 all ensuite
Pricing: Sgl £85 Dbl £150 Dinner from £34
CC: Accepted Room facilities:
Conference: 5 meeting rooms (Thtr 50 max), 24hr-delegate from £155, day-delegate rate from £26
Children: Welcome Dogs: Welcome
Licences: Leisure: Outdoor pool, Tennis
Parking: Off-street and monitored
Directions: A148 towards Sandringham right-hand turn signposted Grimson and Congham Hall Hotel is 2½ miles on left as you enter Grimston Village.

Kismet Bed & Breakfast

◆ ◆ ◆ ◆

Main Road, Terrington St John, King's Lynn,
Norfolk, PE14 7RR
Tel: 01945 881364 Fax: 01945 881364
Email: francesg6@aol.com
Web: www.kismet-guest-house.com

Centrally located between King's Lynn and Wisbech in
bypassed village. Well-decorated, fully-equipped
ensuite bedrooms. 1/2-acre garden, excellent parking,
guests' lounge/diner. Holders of RAC Warm Welcome
and Sparkling Diamond awards.
Rooms: 3 all ensuite ⊛
Pricing: Sgl £30–35 Dbl £50–50 Room facilities: ▢ ⊜
Children: Welcome, 12yrs min age
Parking: Off-street and monitored
Directions: From King's Lynn take A47 to Wisbech.
Take 1st slip road off A47. Turn left, and after 150
yards left again. Hotel is white property 500yds on left.

Beeches Guest House

◆ ◆ ◆

2 Guanock Terrace, King's Lynn, Norfolk, PE30 5QT
Tel: 01553 766577 Fax: 01553 776664
Seasonal closure: Christmas/New Year
Rooms: 7 (4 ensuite) ⊛ ⊛
Pricing: Sgl £20–30 Dbl £20–28 Dinner from £8.50
CC: Accepted Room facilities: ▢ ☎ ⊜
Children: Welcome ⋔ Dogs: Welcome Licences: ⬧ ⋔⋔
Parking: Off-street and monitored
Directions: From A10 and A47 to town centre, 1st left
through Southgates and 1st right before statue.

Guanock Hotel

◆ ◆ ◆

South Gates, King's Lynn, Norfolk, PE30 5QJ
Tel: 01553 772959 Fax: 01553 772959
Email: guanockhotel@faxvia/net
Rooms: 17 ⊛
Pricing: Sgl £23–26 Dbl £39–41 Dinner from £5
CC: Accepted Room facilities: ▢ ⊜
Children: Welcome ⋔ Dogs: Guide dogs only
Licences: ⋔⋔ Leisure: Games room
Parking: Off-street and monitored
Directions: From A47 A17 follow signs to town centre.
We are on right immediately after passing through the
south gates.

Twinson Lee

◆ ◆ ◆

109 Tennyson Road, King's Lynn, Norfolk, PE30 5PA
Tel: 01553 762900 Fax: 01533 769944
Seasonal closure: Christmas Rooms: 3 (1 ensuite) ⊛
Pricing: Sgl £20–25 Dbl £40 Dinner from £6
Room facilities: ▢ ⊜ Children: Welcome ⋔
Dogs: Welcome Parking: Off-street

Lavenham, Suffolk

The Swan

★ ★ ★ ★

High Street, Lavenham, Suffolk, CO10 9QA
Tel: 0870 4008116 Fax: 01787 248286
Email: swanlavenham@heritage-hotels.co.uk
Web: www.macdonaldhotels.co.uk
Rooms: 51 all ensuite ⊛ ▨
Pricing: Sgl £89.50 Dbl £179 Dinner from £27.95
CC: Accepted Room facilities: ▢ ☎ ⊜ ⊛ ☏
Children: Welcome ⋔ Dogs: Welcome Licences: ⬧ ⋔⋔
Parking: Off-street and monitored
Directions: Follow the A14, then A134 Sudbury and
follow signs for Lavenham. The hotel is situated on the
High Street.

Leiston, Suffolk

White Horse Hotel

★ ★ ▨

Station Road, Leiston, Suffolk, IP16 4HD
Tel: 01728 830694 Fax: 01728 833105
Email: whitehorse@globalnet.co.uk
Web: www.whitehorsehotel.co.uk
Rooms: 14 all ensuite ⊛
Pricing: Sgl £37.50 Dbl £60 Dinner from £11.50
CC: Accepted Room facilities: ▢ ☎ ⊜
Children: Welcome ⋔ ⊛ Dogs: Welcome
Licences: ⋔⋔ Parking: Off-street

Lolworth, Cambridgeshire

Travelodge Lolworth

Travel Accommodation
A14, Hundington Road, Lolworth,
Cambridgeshire, CB3 8DR
Web: www.travelodge.co.uk
Pricing: Sgl £57.40 Dbl £61.85
CC: Accepted Room facilities: ▢ ⊜

East Anglia

Lowestoft, Suffolk

Albany Hotel

400 London Road South, Lowestoft,
Suffolk, NR33 0BQ
Tel: 01502 574394 Fax: 01502 581198
Email: geoffrey.ward@btclick.com
Web: www.albanyhotel-lowestoft.co.uk
Rooms: 8 (6 ensuite)
Pricing: Sgl £21.50–27.50 Dbl £44–56
Dinner from £7.95 CC: Accepted Room facilities:
Children: Welcome Dogs: Welcome Licences:
Directions: Situated on A12 northbound, the hotel is
approx 350 yards on right once you have entered the
one-way system.

Hazeldene

21 Marine Parade, Lowestoft, Suffolk, NR33 0QL
Tel: 01502 517 907
Rooms: 5
Pricing: Sgl £22–25 Dbl £36–40 CC: Accepted
Room facilities: Children: Welcome
Dogs: Welcome Parking: Off-street
Directions: Seafront location at South Beach and
opposite lifeguards' station. Five minutes walk from
town centre and railway station.

March, Cambridgeshire

The Olde Griffin Hotel

★★

High Street, March, Cambridgeshire, PE15 9JS
Tel: 01354 652517 Fax: 01354 650086
Email: griffhotel@aol.com
Web: www.smoothhound.co.uk/hotels/oldegrif.html

Rooms: 21 (20 ensuite)
Pricing: Sgl £45 Dbl £59.50
Dinner from £6.95 CC: Accepted
Room facilities:
Conference: 2 meeting rooms Children: Welcome
Licences: Parking: Off-street and monitored
Directions: Entering March from any direction, the hotel
is the biggest white building in the middle of the High
Street.

Mildenhall, Suffolk

Smoke House

★★★

Beck Row, Mildenhall, Suffolk, IP28 8DH
Tel: 01638 713223 Fax: 01638 712202
Email: enquiries@smoke-house.co.uk
Web: www.smoke-house.co.uk

Oak beams, log fires and a warm welcome await you
at the Smoke House. Facilities include modern
bedrooms, two bars, two lounges and a restaurant.
96 bedrooms, all ensuite.
Rooms: 96 all ensuite
Pricing: Sgl £80–140 Dbl £100–165 Dinner from £17.95
CC: Accepted Room facilities: Access:
Children: Welcome Dogs: Guide dogs only
Licences: Parking: Off-street

Cobbles Restaurant With Rooms

Little Gem

38 Market Place, Mildenhall, Suffolk, IP28 7EF
Tel: 01638 717022 Fax: 01638 712312
Email: gordon@thecobbles.netlineuk.net
Web: www.cobblesrestaurant.co.uk
Seasonal closure: 1–20 January
Rooms: 3 all ensuite
Pricing: Sgl £35–55 Dbl £55–95 Dinner from £25
CC: Accepted Room facilities: Access:
Conference: 1 meeting room (Thtr 50 max),
24hr-delegate from £100, day-delegate rate from £40
Children: Welcome, 3yrs min age Dogs: Welcome
Licences: Parking: Off-street and monitored
Directions: Exit A11 at Barton Mills roundabout, take
A1101 to Mildenhall. At second mini-roundabout turn
left, then take next left to Market Place.

Travelodge Barton Mills

Travel Accommodation
A11, Five Ways Roundabout, Barton Mills, Mildenhall,
Suffolk, IP28 6AE
Web: www.travelodge.co.uk
Rooms: 40 all ensuite
Pricing: Sgl £54.40–57.40 Dbl £58.85–61.85
CC: Accepted
Room facilities: Access:

Needham Market, Suffolk

Travelodge Ipswich, Beacon Hill

Travel Accommodation
A14/A140, Beacon Hill, Needham Market,
Suffolk, IP6 8LP
Web: www.travelodge.co.uk
Rooms: 40 all ensuite ⊛
Pricing: Sgl £49.40 Dbl £53.85
CC: Accepted Room facilities: ☐ ☺ Access: ♿

Newmarket, Suffolk

Bedford Lodge Hotel

★★★

Bury Road, Newmarket, Suffolk, CB8 7BX
Tel: 01638 663175 Fax: 01638 667391
Email: info@bedfordlodgehotel.co.uk
Web:www.bedfordlodgehotel.co.uk

For those who appreciate an elegant environment
together with fine cuisine, the Bedford Lodge Hotel is
the perfect place to visit. The hotel offers stylish
accommodation, excellent food and wine, and service
that exceeds all expectations.
Rooms: 55 ⚉ ⊛
Pricing: Sgl £105 Dbl £140 Dinner from £24.50
CC: Accepted
Room facilities: ☐ ☎ ☺ ❄ Access: |↕|
Conference: 7 meeting rooms (Thtr 200 max)
Children: Welcome ⅄ Licences: ⋔
Leisure: Indoor pool, Gym, Beauty salon
Parking: Off-street and monitored
Directions: On entering Newmarket and Bury Road,
hotel is 1/2 mile on the right-hand side.

Rutland Arms Hotel

★★★

High Street, Newmarket, Suffolk, CB8 8NB
Tel: 01638 664251 Fax: 01638 666298
Email: gapleisure@rutlandarmshotel.com
Web: www.rutlandarmshotel.com
Rooms: 46 all ensuite ⊠ ⊛
Pricing: Sgl £80.75–98.25 Dbl £101–136.50
Dinner from £17.50 CC: Accepted
Room facilities: ☐ ☎ ☺ ☎ Children: Welcome ⅄
Licences: ⋔ Parking: Off-street
Directions: From M11 take A11 (Junction 9) and signs
to Newmarket town centre. Hotel is on the High Street.

Swynford Paddocks Hotel

★★★ ⓡ

Six Mile Bottom, Newmarket, Suffolk, CB8 0UE
Tel: 01638 570234 Fax: 01638 570283
Email: sales@swynfordpaddocks.com
Web: www.swynfordpaddocks.com
Rooms: 15 all ensuite ⚉ ⊠
Pricing: Dinner from £28.50 (2002 rate) CC: Accepted
Room facilities: ☐ ☎ ☺ Children: Welcome ⅄ ⅟
Dogs: Welcome Licences: ⋖ ⋔ Leisure: Tennis
Parking: Off-street
Directions: From A14 take A1303 signposted
Newmarket. After 3/4 mile, turn right after Prince Albert
pub. Continue for 5 miles to crossroads at Six Mile
Bottom. Turn left.

Norwich, Norfolk

Annesley House Hotel

★★★ ⓡ

6 Newmarket Road, Norwich, Norfolk, NR2 2LA
Tel: 01603 624553 Fax: 01603 621577
Email: annesleyhouse@bestwestern.co.uk
Seasonal closure: Christmas and New Year
Rooms: 26 all ensuite
Pricing: Sgl £75 Dbl £90 CC: Accepted
Room facilities: ☐ ☎ ☺ ☎
Conference: 1 meeting rooms (Thtr 16 max)
Dogs: Guide dogs only Licences: ⋔ Parking: Off-street
Directions: On A11, 1/2 mile from city centre on
right-hand side.

Barnham Broom Hotel, Golf and Country Club

★★★ ⓡ

Honingham Road, Barnham Broom, Norwich,
Norfolk, NR9 4DD
Tel: 01603 759393 Fax: 01603 758224
Email: enquiry@barnhambroomhotel.co.uk
Web: www.barnham-broom.co.uk
Rooms: 52 all ensuite ⚉ ⊠ ⊛
Pricing: Sgl £90–150 Dbl £115–175 Dinner from £3.50
CC: Accepted Room facilities: ☐ ☎ ☺
Conference: 9 meeting rooms (Thtr 180 max),
24hr-delegate from £127.50, day-delegate rate from £82
Children: Welcome ⅄ ⅟ ⅟ Dogs: Guide dogs only
Licences: ⋖ ⋔
Leisure: Outdoor pool, Gym, Tennis, Golf,
Games room
Parking: Off-street and monitored
Directions: 10 miles west of Norwich, off A47/A11 trunk
routes. Follow brown tourist signs bearing a white golf
flag.

East Anglia

Oaklands Hotel

★★★

89 Yarmouth Road, Thorpe St Andrews,
Norfolk, NR7 0HH
Tel: 01603 434471 Fax: 01603 700318
Email: reception@oaklands-hotel.co.uk
Web: www.oaklands.hotel.co.uk
Rooms: 38 all ensuite
Pricing: Dinner from £17.95 (2002 rate) CC: Accepted
Room facilities: ☐ ☎ ☐ ☜ Children: Welcome ♁ ☾
Dogs: Guide dogs only Licences: ⚊ Parking: Off-street
Directions: Turn off the A47 onto the A1042. Then join
the A1242 towards Norwich. The Oaklands is on the
right-hand side.

Quality Hotel Norwich

★★★

2 Barnard Road, Bowthorpe, Norwich, Norfolk, NR5 9JB
Tel: 01603 741161 Fax: 01603 741500
Email: admin@gb619.u-net.com
Web: www.choicehotels.com
Rooms: 80 all ensuite ✈ ☺
Pricing: Sgl £89–110 Dbl £109–133 Dinner from £15.50
CC: Accepted Room facilities: ☐ ☎ ☐ ☜ Access: ♿
Conference: 7 meeting rooms (Thtr 200 max),
24hr-delegate from £105, day-delegate rate from £35
Children: Welcome ♁ ☾ Dogs: Welcome
Licences: ⚊ ⚊ Leisure: Indoor pool, Gym
Parking: Off-street and monitored
Directions: From A11, follow A47 towards Swaffham.
Situated on A1074 Norwich/Cromer road. At double
roundabout go straight over. Hotel next roundabout
on right.

Hotel Wroxham

★★

The Bridge, Wroxham, Norwich, Norfolk, NR12 8AJ
Tel: 01603 782061 Fax: 01603 784279
Email: enquiries@hotelwroxham.co.uk
Web: www.hotelwroxham.co.uk

Situated on the banks of the River Bure, in the capital
of Broadland, only seven miles from Norwich on the
A1151, the Hotel Wroxham is a riverside oasis catering
for both the leisure and business visitor. Its unique
"Waterside Terrace Bar and Restaurant" serves à la
carte, carvery and bar snack meals. Excellent wedding
and conference facilities, riverside suites with
balconies, private boat moorings and car parking.

Rooms: 18 all ensuite
Pricing: Sgl £47.50–67.50 Dbl £70–90 Dinner from £16
CC: Accepted Room facilities: ☐ ☎ ☐ ☜
Conference: 3 meeting rooms (Thtr 300 max)
Children: Welcome ♁ Dogs: Guide dogs only
Licences: ⚊ Parking: Off-street
Directions: Take A1151 from Norwich at Wroxham,
1st right after the River Bridge, then hard right again.
Car park is on the right.

Kings Head Inn

◆◆◆◆

The Street, Acle, Norwich, Norfolk, NR13 3DY
Tel: 01493 750204 Fax: 01493 750713
Email: info@kingsheadinnacle.co.uk
Rooms: 6 all ensuite
Pricing: Dinner from £7.95 (2002 rate) CC: Accepted
Room facilities: ☐ ☐ Children: Welcome ♁
Dogs: Welcome Licences: ⚊ Parking: Off-street
Directions: From A11 or A140, join A47 to Yarmouth.
Continue to Acle, turn off into Acle, Kings Head in
centre.

Edmar Lodge

◆◆◆

64 Earlham Road, Norwich, Norfolk, NR2 3DF
Tel: 01603 615599 Fax: 01603 495599
Email: mail@edmarlodge.co.uk
Web: www.edmarlodge.co.uk

Edmar Lodge is a family-run guest house where you
will find a warm welcome. Digital TV in rooms. We are
situated only 10 minutes walk from city centre. Non
smoking.
Rooms: 5 all ensuite ☺
Pricing: Sgl £30–35 Dbl £40–44 CC: Accepted
Room facilities: ☐ ☐ Children: Welcome ♁
Dogs: Welcome Parking: Off-street and monitored
Directions: Ring road or A47 take B1108 into city.
Edmar Lodge on the right towards city just past
controlled zone signs.

Wedgewood House

 ♦ ♦ ♦

42 St Stephen's Road, Norwich, Norfolk, NR1 3RE
Tel: 01603 625730 Fax: 01603 615035
Email: mail@wedgewoodhouse.co.uk
Web: www.wedgewoodhouse.co.uk
Rooms: 12 (9 ensuite)
Pricing: Sgl £27–40 Dbl £44–55 CC: Accepted
Room facilities: Children: Welcome
Parking: Off-street
Directions: Follow A11 or A140 towards city centre,
Wedgewood House is on right opposite old hospital.

Travelodge Norwich

Travel Accommodation
A11/A47 Interchange, Thickthorn Service Area,
Norwich Southern Bypass, Norwich, Norfolk, NR9 3AU
Web: www.travelodge.co.uk
Rooms: 62 all ensuite
Pricing: Sgl £57.40 Dbl £61.85
CC: Accepted Room facilities: Access:

Old Hunstanton, Norfolk

Lodge Hotel & Amrthyst Restaurant

 ★ ★

Old Hunstanton Road, Hunstanton,
Norfolk, PE36 6HX
Tel: 01485 532896 Fax: 01485 535007
Email: reception@thelodge-hotel.co.uk
Web: www.thelodge-hotel.co.uk
Rooms: 22 all ensuite
Pricing: Sgl £40–55 Dbl £80–106 Dinner from £23
CC: Accepted Room facilities:
Access: Children: Welcome Dogs: Welcome
Licences: Leisure: Games room Parking: Off-street
Directions: From King's Lynn, take A149 to Hunstanton
and on into Old Hunstanton. Hotel on right-hand side.

Peterborough, Cambridgeshire

Bull Hotel

★ ★ ★

Westgate, Peterborough,
Cambridgeshire, PE1 1RB
Tel: 01733 561364 Fax: 01733 557304
Email: info@bull-hotel-peterborough.com
Rooms: 118 all ensuite
Pricing: Sgl £47–104 Dbl £64–120 Dinner from £10
CC: Accepted Room facilities: Access:
Conference: 12 meeting rooms (Thtr 300 max),
24hr-delegate from £135, day-delegate rate from £35
Children: Welcome Dogs: Welcome
Licences: Parking: Off-street and monitored
Directions: From A1, follow city centre signs. Boures
Boulevard, St John's Road. First left at roundabout,
New Road, right along Northminster, hotel on left.

Butterfly Hotel

★ ★ ★

Thorpe Meadows, off Longthorpe Parkway,
Peterborough, Cambridgeshire, PE3 6GA
Tel: 01733 564240 Fax: 01733 565538
Email: peterbutterfly@lineone.net
Web: www.butterflyhotels.co.uk
Rooms: 70 all ensuite
Pricing: Sgl £63.50–88 Dbl £72–96.50 Dinner from £17.50
CC: Accepted Room facilities: Access:
Conference: 5 meeting rooms (Thtr 80 max)
Children: Welcome Dogs: Guide dogs only
Licences: Parking: Off-street
Directions: A1(M) follow signs to city centre, then
Thorpe Meadows and rowing course.

 Butterfly

Thorpe Lodge Hotel

♦ ♦ ♦

83 Thorpe Road, Peterborough,
Cambridgeshire, PE3 6JQ
Tel: 01733 348759 Fax: 01733 891598
Rooms: (18 ensuite)
Pricing: Sgl £39–53 Dbl £55–65 Dinner from £9
CC: Accepted Room facilities:
Conference: 2 meeting rooms (Thtr 30 max),
day-delegate rate from £20 Children: Welcome
Dogs: Guide dogs only Parking: Off-street
Directions: On main thoroughfare A1179 from A1/A47, ten
minutes walk to city centre and station and bus station.

Southwold, Suffolk

Mrs R D Hemsley

♦ ♦ ♦

28 Fieldstile Road, Southwold, Suffolk, IP18 6LD
Tel: 01502 723588 Fax: 01502 723588
Seasonal closure: open Easter till October
Rooms: 3 Pricing:Sgl £35 Dbl £50
Room facilities: Access:
Children: Welcome Dogs: Welcome
Directions: Southwold. Cross mini-roundabout, first
left. Past church & hospital towards seafront, No.28 left
side with sign and red door.

St Ives, Cambridgeshire

Dolphin Hotel

★ ★ ★

London Road, St Ives, Huntingdon,
Cambridgeshire, PE27 5EP
Tel: 01480 466966 Fax: 01480 495597
Web: www.dolphinhotelcambs.co.uk
Rooms: 67 all ensuite
Pricing: Sgl £75–95 Dbl £95–120 Dinner from £14.50
CC: Accepted Room facilities: Access:
Conference: 1 meeting room (Thtr 50 max)
Children: Welcome Licences:
Leisure: Gym, Fishing, Games room Parking: Off-street
Directions: From A14, take A1096 towards St Ives. Left
at first roundabout, then immediately right. The Dolphin
is 800 yards further on.

Oliver's Lodge Hotel

★★★

Needingworth Road, St, Ives, near Cambridge,
Cambridgeshire, PE17 4JP
Tel: 01480 463252 Fax: 01480 461150
Email: reception@oliverslodge.co.uk
Web: www.oliverslodge.co.uk
Rooms: 17 all ensuite
Pricing: Sgl £70–82 Dbl £75–110 Dinner from £16
CC: Accepted Room facilities: Access:
Conference: 4 meeting rooms (Thtr 65 max),
24hr-delegate from £110, day-delegate rate from £24.70
Children: Welcome Dogs: Welcome
Licences: Parking: Off-street
Directions: From M11/A1, take A14 then A1096 to
St Ives. At 1st roundabout, go straight across. At next
roundabout, turn left and first right. Hotel 500 yards
down the road on right.

Slepe Hall Hotel

★★★

Ramsey Road, St Ives, Cambridgeshire, PE27 5RB
Tel: 01480 463122 Fax: 01480 300706
Email: mail@slepehall.co.uk
Web: www.slepehall.co.uk
Seasonal closure: 25 December & 1 January
Rooms: 16 all ensuite
Pricing: Sgl £50–80 Dbl £65–107.50 Dinner from £15.95
CC: Accepted Room facilities:
Conference: 4 meeting rooms (Thtr 200 max),
24hr-delegate from £95, day-delegate rate from £23
Children: Welcome Dogs: Welcome
Licences: Parking: Off-street
Directions: Leave A14 on A1096. At roundabout with
Manchester Arms pub, take A1123 towards
Huntingdon. At traffic lights by Toyota garage turn left.
Slepe Hall 1/3 mile on left.

Sudbury, Suffolk

Mill Hotel

★★★

Walnut Tree Lane, Sudbury, Suffolk, CO10 1BD
Tel: 01787 375544/378928 Fax: 01787 373027
Web: www.millhotelsuffork.co.uk
Rooms: 56 all ensuite
Pricing: Sgl £69.50–69.50 Dbl £108–148 Dinner from £25
CC: Accepted Room facilities:
Conference: 5 meeting rooms (Thtr 70 max),
24hr-delegate from £79, day-delegate rate from £25
Children: Welcome Dogs: Welcome
Licences: Parking: Off-street
Directions: From A12 Colchester take A134 to Sudbury.
Follow signs for A131. Pass main square, 3rd on right.

The Old Bull Hotel

◆◆◆

Church Street, Sudbury, Suffolk, CO10 6BL
Tel: 01787 374120 Fax: 01787 379044
Web: www.theoldbullhotel.co.uk

We are a small family-run hotel with the emphasis on
hospitality and home comforts. Situated close to the
river and Meadow Walks, within walking distance of
the town centre.
Rooms: 10 all ensuite
Pricing: Sgl £45–50 Dbl £55–60 Dinner from £8
CC: Accepted Room facilities: Access:
Children: Welcome Dogs: Welcome Licences:
Parking: Off-street

Swaffham, Norfolk

Lydney House Hotel

★★

Norwich Road, Swaffham, Norfolk, PE37 7QS
Tel: 01760 723355 Fax: 01760 721410
Email: rooms@lydney-house.demon.co.uk
Web: www.lydney-house.demon.co.uk
Rooms: 12 all ensuite
Pricing: Sgl £65–67 Dbl £85–87.50 Dinner from £12
CC: Accepted Room facilities:
Conference: 2 meeting rooms (Thtr 14 max),
24hr-delegate from £82.50, day-delegate rate from £27.50
Children: Welcome Dogs: Welcome Licences:
Parking: Off-street
Directions: Lydney House can be found on Norwich
Road, 1/4 mile from traffic lights in centre of town.

Horse & Groom

◆◆◆

40 Lynn Street, Swaffham, Norfolk, PE37 7AX
Tel: 01760 721567

Thetford, Norfolk

Lynford Hall Hotel

★ ★ ★

Lynford Hall, Mundford, near Thetford,
Norfolk, IP26 5HW
Tel: 01842 878351 Fax: 01842 878252
Email: enquiries@lynfordhallhotel.co.uk
Web: www.lynfordhallhotel.co.uk

Rooms: 21 all ensuite 🛏 🖾 ⊗
Pricing: Sgl £99 Dbl £115–190 Dinner from £25
CC: Accepted Room facilities: 📺 ☎ 🖳 📞 Access: ♿
Conference: 4 meeting rooms (Thtr 600 max),
24hr-delegate from £135, day-delegate rate from £29.85
Children: Welcome ☂ Dogs: Guide dogs only
Licences: ⚓ ♨ Parking: Off-street
Directions: From A134 Mundford roundabout take
A1065 to Swaffham. Take first right.

Comfort Inn Thetford

★ ★

Thetford Road, Northwold, near Thetford,
Norfolk, IP26 5LQ
Tel: 01366 728888 Fax: 01366 727121
Email: admin@gb632.u-net.com
Web: www.choicehotels.com
Rooms: 34 all ensuite 🛏 ⊗
Pricing: Sgl £45–67.75 Dbl £50–80.50
Dinner from £12.95 CC: Accepted
Room facilities: 📺 ☎ 🖳 Access: ♿
Children: Welcome, 14yrs min age ☂
Dogs: Welcome Licences: ⚓ ♨
Leisure: Gym Parking: Off-street
Directions: From Thetford roundabout (A11/A134 north)
follow A134 north for 12 miles, over a roundabout and
past Northwold. Hotel then on left.

Tivetshall St Mary, Norfolk

Old Ram Coaching Inn

★ ★ ★ ®

Ipswich Road, Tivetshall St Mary, Norfolk, NR15 2DE
Tel: 01379 676794 Fax: 01379 608399
Email: theoldram@btinternet.com
Web: www.theoldram.com

Listed 17th century hotel, restaurant and free house.
Award winning food. Big on fish. Over sixties' and
children's menus. Superb accommodation, meeting
space. Ample car parking.
Rooms: 11 all ensuite 🖾
Pricing: Sgl £52.50–57.50 Dbl £72–80
Dinner from £11.95 CC: Accepted
Room facilities: 📺 ☎ 🖳 📞
Conference: 1 meeting room (Thtr 20 max),
24hr-delegate from £84.95, day-delegate rate from £19.95
Children: Welcome ☂ Dogs: Guide dogs only
Licences: ♨ Parking: Off-street
Directions: On the A140, 15 minutes south of Norwich
and the A47 bypass. Five miles from the market town
of Diss.

Walsingham, Norfolk

Old Rectory

◆ ◆ ◆

Waterden, Walsingham, Norfolk, NR22 6AT
Tel: 01328 823298
Rooms: 2 all ensuite 🛏 ⊗ Room facilities: 🖳
Access: ♿ Children: Welcome ☂ ⅀ Dogs: Welcome
Parking: Off-street and monitored
Directions: Take the B1355 Fakenham to Burnham
Market Road, turn right at Waterden sign before the
village centre of South Creake. One mile up lane on left
hand side.

East Anglia

Wells-next-the-Sea, Norfolk

Kilcoroon

Chancery Lane, Wells-next-the-Sea,
Norfolk, NR23 1ER
Tel: 01328 710270
Email: gues@kilcoroon.co.uk
Web: www.smoothhound.co.uk/hotels/kilcoroon.html
Rooms: 3 (1 ensuite) ⊛
Pricing: Dbl £40–48 CC: Accepted
Room facilities: ⬜ ⬛
Children: Welcome, 10yrs min age
Directions: At Wells town sign, turn towards town
centre. Third turning right onto Buttlands, Kilcoroon
situated left of Crown Hotel.

Oyster Cottage Bed & Breakfast

Oyster Cottage, 20 High Street, Wells-next-the-Sea,
Norfolk, NR23 1EP
Tel: 01328 711997
Email: bb@oystercottage.co.uk
Web: www.oystercottage.co.uk
Rooms: 4 all ensuite ⬛ ⊛
Pricing: Sgl £22–25 Dbl £18.50–22
Room facilities: ⬜ ⬛ Children: Welcome ⴕ
Dogs: Guide dogs only
Directions: From town sign take Mill Road to town
centre, at junction by Barclays Bank – High Street is on
the right.

Wisbech, Cambridgeshire

Crown Lodge Hotel

★★★ ⬛

Downham Road, Outwell, Wisbech,
Cambridgeshire, PE14 8SE
Tel: 01945 773391 Fax: 01945 772668
Email: crownlodgehotel@hotmail.com
Web: www.smoothhound.co.uk/hotels/crownl.html

Situated on the banks of Well Creek, in the village of
Outwell, this family-run hotel offers a warm, friendly
atmosphere with excellent standards of
accommodation and cuisine.
Rooms: 10 all ensuite ⊛
Pricing: Sgl £51.50–55 Dbl £67–75 Dinner from £16.50

CC: Accepted Room facilities: ⬜ ☎ ⬛ ⬛ Access: ♿
Children: Welcome ⴕ Dogs: Welcome Licences: ⅲ
Leisure: Games room, Snooker/billiards
Parking: Off-street and monitored
Directions: Situated on the A1122/A1101 Downham
Market to Wisbech road. Approximately 5 miles to
Wisbech and 7 miles to Downham Market.

Woodbridge, Suffolk

Ufford Park Hotel

★★★ ⬛

Yarmouth Road, Ufford, Woodbridge, Suffolk, IP12 1QW
Tel: 01394 383555 Fax: 01394 383582
Email: uffordparkltd@btinternet.com
Web: www.uffordpark.co.uk

Visit the tranquility of Ufford park, set in 120 acres —
voted top 40 winter golf course — with golf academy,
full leisure, beauty and hair salons, two restaurants,
50 ensuite bedrooms and conference/functions.
Rooms: 50 all ensuite ⬛ ⬛ ⊛
Pricing: Sgl £79–85 Dbl £99–129 Dinner from £17.95
CC: Accepted Room facilities: ⬜ ☎ ⬛ Access: ♿
Conference: 8 meeting rooms (Thtr 200 max)
Children: Welcome ⴕ ⬛ Dogs: Welcome
Licences: ⬛ ⅲ
Leisure: Indoor pool, Gym, Health spa, Beauty salon,
Golf, Games room Parking: Off-street
Directions: A1152, left at traffic lights, or southwards
slip road off A12, take two rights turn, and hotel on
right, approx 1 mile from Melton.

Plan your route

Visit www.rac.co.uk for RAC's
interactive route planner, including
up to the minute traffic reports.

Ask the experts

To book a Hotel or Guest
Accommodation, or for help
and advice, call RAC Hotel
Reservations on 0870 603 9109
and quote 'Guide 2003'

Relax and Unwind

Take the stress out of finding an hotel with RAC Hotel Reservations

On the move and looking for an hotel or a cosy B&B? Look no further than RAC Hotel Reservations.

With just one phone call, RAC Hotel Reservations gives you unique access to over 3000 quality hotels and B&Bs throughout the UK & Ireland. Each one is inspected, rated and the best ones awarded on your behalf by our team of discerning inspectors for quality and service.

We'll not only source the perfect hotel or B&B to suit your pocket and your needs, we'll also source the latest deals and make the booking for you, completely free of charge*.

So if you are looking for somewhere to relax and unwind, whether on business or leisure, call us now.

Call 0870 603 9109 and quote RAC 05
or visit www.rac.co.uk/hotels

*Calls will be charged at National rates

A to B - we RAC to it

RAC

East Midlands

Note:
Dark blue dots represent the location of RAC-inspected accommodation

East Midlands

Gold Ribbon Award

Stapleford Park Hotel, Melton Mowbray	★★★★	337

Blue Ribbon Award

Cavendish Hotel, Baslow	★★★	322
George of Stamford Hotel, Stamford	★★★	340

Little Gem

Rock Lodge, Stamford	♦♦♦♦♦	340
D'Isney Place Hotel, Lincoln	♦♦♦♦	332

Alfreton, Derbyshire

Travelodge Alfreton

Travel Accommodation
A38/A61, Old Swanwick Colliery Road, Alfreton,
Derbyshire, DE55 1HJ
Web: www.travelodge.co.uk
Rooms: 60 all ensuite ⊛
Pricing: Sgl £47.40 Dbl £51.85
CC: Accepted Room facilities: ☐ ☕ Access: ♿

Ashbourne, Derbyshire

Callow Hall Hotel
★★★★ ☂ ☂ ☂
Mappleton, Ashbourne,
Derbyshire, DE6 2AA
Tel: 01335 300900 Fax: 01335 300512
Email: reservations@callowhall.co.uk
Web: www.callowhall.co.uk
Seasonal closure: Christmas Day and Boxing Day

A unique atmosphere created in this family-run country
house hotel. Noted for its fine dining, using the
freshest of ingredients and superb wine list. Victorian
garden and woodland setting.
Rooms: 16 all ensuite ☕
Pricing: Sgl £85–110 Dbl £130–165 Dinner from £38.50
CC: Accepted
Room facilities: ☐ ☎ ☕ ☏
Access: ♿
Conference: 2 meeting rooms (Thtr 20 max)
Children: Welcome ☂
Dogs: Welcome
Licences: ⅲ
Parking: Off-street and monitored
Directions: Follow A515 through Ashbourne, after
Market Square turn left past Bowling Green pub. Take
first right for Mappleton, entrance on right after bridge.

One click does it all

For the latest special offers and
online booking, plus detailed
information on over 3,000
RAC inspected properties,
visit www.rac.co.uk/hotels

Hanover International Hotel & Club Ashbourne
★★★
Derby Road, Ashbourne, Derbyshire, DE6 1XH
Tel: 0870 241 7071 Fax: 01335 346549
Email: crso@hanover-international.com
Web: www.hanover-international.com

HANOVER INTERNATIONAL
HOTELS & CLUBS

Attractively purpose-built hotel and leisure club at the
'Gateway to Dovedale' with the highest standards of
traditional comfort and warm friendly service.
Rooms: 50 all ensuite ☕ ☕ ⊛
Pricing: Sgl £50–88 Dbl £100–108 Dinner from £21.95
CC: Accepted
Room facilities: ☐ ☎ ☕ ☏
Access: ⅲ ♿
Conference: 7 meeting rooms (Thtr 200 max),
24hr-delegate from £125, day-delegate rate from £35
Children: Welcome ☂
Dogs: Guide dogs only
Licences: ◭ ⅲ
Leisure: Indoor pool, Gym
Parking: Off-street
Directions: Take A52 to Ashbourne, first roundabout
turn right. Hotel approx half a mile on the left.

The Peveril of the Peak
★★★
Nr Ashbourne, Derbyshire, DE6 2AW
Tel: 0870 400 8109 Fax: 01335 350507
Email: Peveril@heritage-hotels.co.uk
Web: www.macdonaldhotels.co.uk
Rooms: 46 all ensuite ☕ ☕ ⊛
Pricing: Sgl £59 Dbl £119 Dinner from £22
CC: Accepted
Room facilities: ☐ ☎ ☕ ☏
Conference: 6 meeting rooms
Children: Welcome ☂
Dogs: Welcome
Licences: ⅲ
Leisure: Tennis
Parking: Off-street
Directions: Follow A515 from Ashbourne towards
Buxton. 1 mile out of Ashbourne turn left, signposted
Thorpe. Continue along this road and hotel is situated
in the village of Thorpe.

East Midlands

The Dog and Partridge Country Inn

★★

Swinscoe, Ashbourne, Derbyshire, DE6 2HS
Tel: 01335 343183 Fax: 01335 342742
Email: info@dogpartridge.co.uk
Web: www.dogandpartridge.co.uk
Rooms: 29 all ensuite 🛏 📠 ⊗ Pricing: Sgl £35–70
Dbl £65–85 Dinner from £15.95 CC: Accepted
Room facilities: 🖵 ☎ 🍵 Access: ♿
Conference: 5 meeting rooms (Thtr 25 max),
24hr-delegate from £75, day-delegate rate from £25
Children: Welcome ♩ ☕ Dogs: Welcome
Licences: ♦♦♦ Leisure: Fishing, Games room
Parking: Off-street
Directions: Follow A52 from Ashbourne towards Leek.
Located on the left-hand side, 3 miles from Ashbourne.

Omnia Somnia

♦♦♦♦♦☎ ☕

The Coach House, The Firs, Ashbourne,
Derbyshire, DE6 1HF
Tel: 01335 300145 Fax: 01335 300958
Email: alan@omniasomnia.co.uk
Web: www.omniasomnia.co.uk

Indulge yourselves in luxury and generous hospitality
unmatched in the Derbyshire Dales at the superlative
award-winning, licensed accommodation. Three very
special, very different rooms await your discovery....
Rooms: 3 all ensuite 📠 ⊗
Pricing: Sgl £50–60 Dbl £75–85
Dinner from £22.50 CC: Accepted
Room facilities: 🖵 🍵 Access: ♿
Dogs: Welcome Licences: ♦♦♦
Parking: Off-street
Directions: From Derby A52, descend hill, turn sharp left
into old hill at lights. First left into the Firs follow sign.

The Courtyard

♦♦♦♦ ✗ ☕

Dairy House Farm, Alkmonton, Longford, Ashbourne,
Derbyshire, DE6 3DG
Tel: 01335 330187 Fax: 01335 330187
Email: andy@dairyhousefarm.org.uk
Web: www.dairyhousefarm.org.uk/
Seasonal closure: December

The Courtyard is situated in a tranquil location and has
been converted from early Victorian cowsheds into
tastefully well appointed bedrooms, all rooms ensuite.
Rooms: 7 all ensuite Pricing: Sgl £30–35 Dbl £48–50
CC: Accepted Room facilities: 🖵 🍵 Access: ♿
Children: Welcome Dogs: Guide dogs only
Parking: Off-street
Directions: Follow signs of A50 for Church Broughton.
Follow signs of A515 for Alkmonton. Follow signs of
A52 for Longford.

Ashbourne, Derbyshire

Dairy House Farm

♦♦♦♦ ☕

Alkmontn, Longford, Derbyshire, DE6 3DG
Tel: 01335 330359 Fax: 01335 330359
Email: andy@dairyousefarm.org.uk
Web: www.dairyhousefarm.org.uk
Rooms: 5 all en-suite ⊗ Pricing: Sgl £25–25
Dbl £25–25 Dinner from £15 Room facilities: 🖵 🍵
Dogs: Guide dogs only Licenses: ♦♦♦
Parking: Off-street and monitored
Directions: Off A515 at Cubley: take road to
Alkmonton. Dairy House Farm is 1.5 miles south.

Ashby-de-la-Zouch, Leicestershire

Fallen Knight Restaurant & Hotel

★★★★ ☎ ☎

Kilwardby Street, Ashby de la Zouch,
Leicestershire, LE65 2FQ
Tel: 01530 412230 Fax: 01530 417596
Web: fallenknight.co.uk
Rooms: 27 all en-suite 📠 ⊗ Pricing: Sgl £70
Dbl £105 CC: accepted Room facilities: 🖵 ☎ 🍵
Access: ⬆ Children: Welcome ☕ Dogs: Welcome
Parking: Off-street
Directions: M42 - J12 follow sign for Ashby left a
roundabout hotel 150m on right J13. As above but go
straight over mini roundabouts.
See advert on this page

The Royal Hotel

Station Road, Ashby de la Zouch,
Leicestershire, LE65 2GP
Tel: 01530 412833 Fax: 01530 564548
Email: theroyalhotel@email.com
Web: www.royalhotelashby.co.uk

A grade II listed building having undergone a total refurbishment. Set in four acres of manicured gardens and also offers guests a warm and friendly atmosphere afforded to all.
Rooms: 34 all en-suite
Pricing: Sgl £30–70 Dbl £50–120 CC: accepted
Room facilities:
Conference: 3 meeting rooms (Thtr 70 max), 24hr-delegate from £105, day-delegate rate from £25
Children: Welcome ⴲ Dogs: Welcome
Licenses: ⟁ ⷮ Parking: Off-street and monitored
Directions: J12 on the A42/M42 continue towards Ashby-de-la-Zouch. The Royal Hotel is approximately 1 mile from J12 on the right hand side.

Ashford-in-the-Water, Derbyshire

Rowdale
◆ ◆ ◆ ⚹ ☕

Ashford-in-the-Water, Bakewell, Derbyshire, DE45 1NX
Tel: 01629 640260
Email: info@rowdale.co.uk
Web: www.rowdale.co.uk
Rooms: 5 (3 ensuite) Pricing: Dbl £55–66
Room facilities: ☕ Children: Welcome ⴲ Dogs: Welcome
Parking: Off-street and monitored
Directions: Turn off A6 at Ashford (2 miles north of Bakewell), follow A6020, farm on left after 1½ miles, entrance 100 yards past buildings.

Ashover, Derbyshire

Old School Farm
◆ ◆ ◆ ◆ ⚹

Uppertown, Ashover, Derbyshire, S45 0JF
Tel: 01246 590813
Seasonal closure: November to March
Rooms: 4 (2 ensuite)
Pricing: Sgl £22–24 Dbl £44–48 Room facilities: ☐ ☕
Children: Welcome Parking: Off-street
Directions: Take A362 Chesterfield to Matlock Road. Turn onto the B5057 Darley Dale Road. Turn left to Uppertown.

Barton-upon-Humber, Lincolnshire

Reeds Hotel
★ ★ ★

Far-Ings Road, Barton-upon-Humber,
Lincolnshire, DN18 5RG
Tel: 01652 632313 Fax: 01652 636361
Email: info@reedshotel.co.uk
Web: www.reedshotel.co.uk
Rooms: 31 all ensuite ⷮ ⷮ ⷮ
Pricing: Sgl £70–85 Dbl £85–95 Dinner from £11.95
CC: Accepted Room facilities: ☐ ☎ ☕ ⷮ
Access: ⷮ ⷮ
Conference: 6 meeting rooms (Thtr 300 max),
day-delegate rate from £28
Children: Welcome ⴲ ⷮ Dogs: Guide dogs only
Licences: ⟁ ⷮ Parking: Off-street
Directions: Exit M180 onto A15 at Barton-upon-Humber. Take first exit onto A1077. Take first right, hotel is straight on.

Making a booking?

Don't forget to mention RAC Hotels and Bed & Breakfast 2003.

East Midlands

Baslow, Derbyshire

Cavendish Hotel

★★★★ ₱ ₱ ₱

Church Lane, Baslow, Derbyshire, DE45 1SP
Tel: 01246 582311 Fax: 01246 582312
Email: info@cavendish-hotel.net
Web: www.cavendish-hotel.net

Occupying a glorious position overlooking the
Catsworth Estate, the Cavendish offers attentive
service, critically acclaimed food amidst an
atmosphere of art collections and antiques, under 27
years of continuous ownership.
Rooms: 24 all ensuite 📺 📼 ⊗
Pricing: Sgl £109–145 Dbl £149–190
Dinner from £26 CC: Accepted Room facilities: ☐ ☎ ⊡
Conference: 2 meeting rooms (Thtr 20 max), 24hr-
delegate from £174, day-delegate rate from £33.50
Children: Welcome Ⱨ ⅀ Licences: ♦♦♦
Leisure: Private fishing Parking: Off-street
Directions: From M1 exit 29 follow A617 from Chesterfield
take A619 to Baslow, Cavendish is on left-hand side.

Belper, Derbyshire

Shottle Hall Guest House

♦♦♦♦

Shottle, Belper, Derbyshire, DE56 2EB
Tel: 01773 550203 Fax: 01773 550276
Seasonal closure: Christmas to New Year
Rooms: 9 (7 ensuite) 📺
Pricing: Sgl £37–40 Dbl £60–75
Dinner from £15
Room facilities: ⊡ Access: ⅀
Children: Welcome Ⱨ ⅀
Dogs: Welcome
Licences: ♦♦♦ Parking: Off-street
Directions: Off B5023, 200 metres north of crossroads
with A517 Belper-Ashbourne road.

Blyth, Nottinghamshire

Travelodge Blyth Notts (MOTO)

Travel Accommodation
A1(M) Moto Service Area, Hilltop Roundabout, Blyth,
Nottinghamshire, S81 8HG
Web: www.travelodge.co.uk
Rooms: 38 all ensuite ⊗
Pricing: Sgl £47.40 Dbl £51.85
CC: Accepted Room facilities: ☐ ⊡ Access: ⅀

Boston, Lincolnshire

Comfort Inn Boston

★★

Bicker Bar roundabout, A17/A52 Junction, Boston,
Lincolnshire, PE20 3AN
Tel: 01205 820118 Fax: 01205 820228
Email: admin@gb607.u/net.com
Web: www.choicehotels.com
Rooms: 55 all ensuite 📼 ⊗
Pricing: Dinner from £10.75 (2002 rate) CC: Accepted
Room facilities: ☐ ☎ ⊡
Access: ⅀
Children: Welcome Ⱨ ⅀
Dogs: Welcome
Licences: ◈ ♦♦♦
Leisure: Gym, Snooker/billiards
Parking: Off-street and monitored

Bourne, Lincolnshire

Angel Hotel

♦♦♦

Market Place, Bourne, Lincolnshire, PE10 9AE
Tel: 01778 422346 Fax: 01778 426113

Rooms: 14 all ensuite 📺 📼 ⊗
Pricing: Sgl £40–50 Dbl £50–70 Dinner from £10
CC: Accepted Room facilities: ☐ ☎ ⊡
Conference: 1 meeting room (Thtr 120 max)
Children: Welcome Ⱨ ⅀ Dogs: Welcome
Licences: ◈ ♦♦♦ Parking: Off-street

Buxton, Derbyshire

Palace Hotel

★★★★

Palace Road, Buxton, Derbyshire, SK17 6AG
Tel: 01298 22001 Fax: 01298 72131
Email: palace@paramount-hotels.co.uk
Web: www.paramount-hotels.co.uk

PARAMOUNT
GROUP OF HOTELS

The Palace is an historic Victorian hotel situated within 5 acres of beautifully manicured gardens. The magnificent features and friendly service combine to ensure that your stay with us is truly memorable.
Rooms: 122 all ensuite 🛏 🚭
Pricing: Sgl £110 Dbl £125 Dinner from £18.50
CC: Accepted Room facilities: 🖥 ☎ 🍵 Access: Ⅱ↑ 👤
Conference: 7 meeting rooms (Thtr 300 max), 24hr-delegate from £148, day-delegate rate from £45
Children: Welcome 🍴 Dogs: Welcome
Licences: 🔔 👬
Leisure: Indoor pool, Gym, Beauty salon
Parking: Off-street and monitored
Directions: From M6 north, exit at junction 20, follow Stockport signs then A6 to Buxton, hotel is in Buxton town centre adjacent to railway station.

Best Western Lee Wood Hotel

★★★★ 🅡 🅡

The Park, Buxton, Derbyshire, SK17 6TQ
Tel: 01298 23002 Fax: 01298 23228
Email: leewoodhotel@btinternet.com
Web: www.leewoodhotel.co.uk
Rooms: 40 all ensuite 🚭
Pricing: Sgl £84–92 Dbl £105–129 CC: Accepted
Room facilities: 🖥 ☎ 🍵 🧳 Access: Ⅱ↑
Conference: 10 meeting rooms (Thtr 120 max), 24hr-delegate from £130, day-delegate rate from £45
Children: Welcome 🍴 🎾 Dogs: Welcome
Licences: 🔔 👬
Leisure: Games room, Snooker/billiards
Parking: Off-street
Directions: From North, leave M1 at Junction 29, Chesterfield–Baslow–Buxton. From South, leave M1 at Junction 23A/24: take A50 for approx 19 miles then A515 to Buxton.

Buckingham Hotel

★★★

1/2 Burlington Road, Buxton, Derbyshire, SK17 9AS
Tel: 01298 70481 Fax: 01298 72186
Email: frontdesk@buckinghamhotel.co.uk
Web: www.buckinghamhotel.co.uk
Rooms: 37 all ensuite 🛏 🚿 🚭
Pricing: Sgl £40–55 Dbl £70–130 Dinner from £18
CC: Accepted Room facilities: 🖥 ☎ 🍵 🧳
Access: Ⅱ↑ 👤 Conference: 3 meeting rooms (Thtr 75 max), 24hr-delegate from £90, day-delegate rate from £27.50 Children: Welcome 🍴 🎾 Dogs: Welcome
Licences: 🔔 👬 Parking: Off-street
Directions: Upon entering Buxton, the hotel lies opposite Pavillion Gardens carpark (signposted) at junction Burlington/St James Road (on A53).

Grove Hotel

★★

Grove Parade, Buxton, Derbyshire, SK17 6AJ
Tel: 01298 23804 Fax: 01298 77906
Email: brewery@frederic-robinson.co.uk
Web: www.frederic-robinson.com
Rooms: 14 all ensuite 🚭
Pricing: Dinner from £10.50 CC: Accepted
Room facilities: 🖥 🍵 Children: Welcome 🍴
Dogs: Guide dogs only Licences: 👬
Directions: Situated in town centre, opposite Spa Baths.

Hartington Hotel

★★

18 Broad Walk, Buxton, Derbyshire, SK17 6JR
Tel: 01298 22638 Fax: 01298 22638
Email: syl.mel@hartingtonhotel.co.uk
Web: www.hartingtonhotel.co.uk
Seasonal closure: 10 days at Christmas
Rooms: 16 (15 ensuite) 🛏 🚭
Pricing: Sgl £25–55 Dbl £50–75 Dinner from £14.50
CC: Accepted Room facilities: 🖥 🍵
Access: 👤 Children: Welcome
Dogs: Guide dogs only Licences: 👬
Parking: Off-street
Directions: From A515 end of Buxton, turn left after Swan pub down Bath Road. Near the bottom, right into Hartington Road.

Netherdale Guest House

◆◆◆◆ 🍴 🎾

16 Green Lane, Buxton, Derbyshire, SK17 9DP
Tel: 01298 23896 Fax: 01298 73771
Seasonal closure: November to January
Rooms: 10 (8 ensuite) 🛏 🚭
Pricing: Sgl £25–35 Dbl £50–60
Room facilities: 🖥 🍵
Children: Welcome, 10yrs min age 🍴
Dogs: Guide dogs only
Licences: 👬
Parking: Off-street and monitored
Directions: From London Road traffic lights, the hotel is 250 metres up Green Lane towards Pooles Cavern.

East Midlands

The Priest House On The River

Perched on the banks of the river Trent surrounded by woodland, the original watermills once on the site were mentioned in the Doomsday Book.

Idyllic for relaxation, fine dining and business.

The hotel is contemporary and minimal inside, with the latest technology and thoughtful planning.

**Kings Mills, Castle Donington, Derby,
Derbyshire DE74 2RR
Tel: 01332 810649 Fax: 01332 811141
Email: priesthouse@arcadianhotels.co.uk
Web: www.thepriesthouse.co.uk**

Roseleigh Hotel
19 Broad Walk
Buxton · Derbyshire · SK17 6JR
Tel/Fax: 01298 24904
Email: enquiries@roseleighhotel.co.uk
Website: www.roseleighhotel.co.uk

RAC

AA

*A Non-Smoking Hotel Overlooking The
Pavilion Gardens
Private Car Park · ensuite Rooms
Fully Licensed*

Roseleigh Hotel

◆◆◆◆

19 Broad Walk, Buxton, Derbyshire, SK17 6JR
Tel: 01298 24904 Fax: 01298 24904
Email: enquiries@roseleighhotel.co.uk
Web: www.roseleighhotel.co.uk
Rooms: 14 all ensuite ⊗
Pricing: Sgl £28 Dbl £56 CC: Accepted
Room facilities: ▢ ⌕
Children: Welcome Licences: ♦♦♦
Parking: Off-street
Directions: A6 to Safeway roundabout, turn onto Dale Road, right at lights, turn left by Swan pub, down Bath Road, right into Harlington Road.
See advert on previous page

Hawthorn Farm Guest House

◆◆◆

Fairfield Road, Buxton, Derbyshire, SK17 7ED
Tel: 01298 23230 Fax: 01298 71322
Email: alan.pimblett@virgin.net
Web: www.hawthorn-farm.co.uk
Rooms: 10 (6 ensuite) ⊘ ⊗
Room facilities: ▢ ⌕
Access: ♿ Children: Welcome ♨ ☙
Dogs: Welcome
Parking: Off-street and monitored
Directions: Hawthorn Farm is situated on the A6 towards Manchester on leaving Buxton.

Castle Donington, Leicestershire

Priest House on the River

★★★★ ♞ ♞ ♞

Kings Mills, Castle Donington, Derby,
Derbyshire, DE74 2RR
Tel: 01332 810649 Fax: 01332 811141
Email: priesthouse@arcadianhotels.co.uk
Web: www.thepriesthouse.co.uk
Rooms: 45 all ensuite ⊘ ⊞ ⊗
Pricing: Sgl £120–140 Dbl £130–150 Dinner from £15
CC: Accepted Room facilities: ▢ ☎ ⌕ ✆
Access: ♿
Conference: 7 meeting rooms (Thtr 120 max),
24hr-delegate from £150, day-delegate rate from £50
Dogs: Welcome Licences: ⊲ ♦♦♦
Parking: Off-street and monitored
Directions: Travelling south on the M1, take junction 24A, travelling north take junction 23A of the M1 and follow signs to hotel through Castle Donington.
See advert on this page

Donington Park Farmhouse Hotel

◆◆◆ ♖

Melbourne Road, Isley Walton, near Derby,
Leicestershire, DE74 2RN
Tel: 01332 862409 Fax: 01332 862364
Email: info@parkfarmhouse.co.uk
Web: www.parkfarmhouse.co.uk
Seasonal closure: Christmas
Rooms: 16 all ensuite ⊘ ⊗

Pricing: Sgl £69 Dbl £79 Dinner from £19
CC: Accepted
Room facilities: 🖵 ☎ 🍵 📞 Access: ♿
Conference: 2 meeting rooms (Thtr 60 max),
24hr-delegate from £99, day-delegate rate from £27
Children: Welcome ♫ ⁙ Dogs: Welcome
Licences: ◬ 👯 Parking: Off-street
Directions: From exit 23A or 24 on M1, proceed past
East Midlands airport to Isley Walton. Turn right, hotel
is ½ mile on right.

Travelodge Donington Park (MOTO)

Travel Accommodation
M1 Moto Service Area Junction 23A,
Castle Donington, Derby, DE74 2TN
Web: www.travelodge.co.uk
Rooms: 80 all ensuite ⊛
Pricing: Sgl £47.40–54.40 Dbl £51.85–58.85
CC: Accepted Room facilities: 🖵 🍵 Access: ♿

Chesterfield, Derbyshire

Travelodge Chesterfield

Travel Accommodation
A61, Birmingham Road, Chesterfield,
Derbyshire, S41 9BE
Web: www.travelodge.co.uk
Rooms: 20 all ensuite ⊛
Pricing: Sgl £54.40 Dbl £58.85
CC: Accepted Room facilities: 🖵 🍵 Access: ♿

Coalville, Leicestershire

Hermitage Park Hotel
★★★
Whitwick Road, Coalville, Leicestershire, LE67 3FA
Tel: 0870 4603 814 Fax: 01530 814202
Email: hotel@hermitagepark.com
Web: www.hermitagepark.com
Rooms: 25 all ensuite ⊛
Pricing: Sgl £49.50–65 Dbl £59.50–89.50
Dinner from £14.95 CC: Accepted
Room facilities: 🖵 ☎ 🍵 📞
Access: ♿
Conference: 5 meeting rooms (Thtr 60 max), 24hr-
delegate from £99.50, day-delegate rate from £19.50
Children: Welcome ♫ ⁙
Dogs: Guide dogs only
Licences: ◬ 👯
Parking: Off-street and monitored
Directions: Exit Junction 13/A42 or Junction 22/M1 and
take A511 to Coalville, then follow tourism signs from
A511 to Hermitage Park Hotel.
See advert on following page

Charnwood Arms
★★
Beveridge Lane, Bardon Hall, Coalville,
Leicestershire, LE67 2TB
Tel: 01530 813644 Fax: 01530 815425

Corby, Northamptonshire

Thatches-On-The-Green
◆ ◆ ◆ ◆ ⚒ ⚐
9 School Lane, Weldon, Corby,
Northamptonshire, NN17 3JN
Tel: 01536 266681 Fax: 01536 266659
Email: tom@thatches-on-the-green.fsnet.co.uk
Web: www.thatches-on-the-green.fsnet.co.uk
Rooms: 6 all ensuite 🐾 ⊛
Room facilities: 🖵 🍵
Children: Welcome ♫
Dogs: Welcome
Parking: Off-street
Directions: The house is to be found in the centre of
the village opposite the Woolpack on the A43 next to
the Weldon cricket ground.

Daventry, Northamptonshire

Hanover International Hotel & Club Daventry
★★★★
Sedgemoor Way, Ashby Road, Daventry,
Northamptonshire, NN11 5SG
Tel: 0870 241 7078 Fax: 01455 630030
Email: crso@hanover-international.com
Web: www.hanover-international.com

HANOVER INTERNATIONAL
HOTELS & CLUBS

Stylish and elegant, located in the Nene Valley close to
Silverstone, with a superb fully equipped leisure club.
The Waterside Restaurant overlooks beautiful Drayton
Water.
Rooms: 138 all ensuite ⊛
Pricing: Sgl £40–131.95 Dbl £80–143.95
Dinner from £21 CC: Accepted
Room facilities: 🖵 ☎ 🍵 📞 Access: ⑪ ♿
Conference: 20 meeting rooms (Thtr 600 max),
24hr-delegate from £155, day-delegate rate from £48
Children: Welcome ♫ Dogs: Guide dogs only
Licences: ◬ 👯 Leisure: Indoor pool, Gym, Beauty
salon, Games room, Snooker/billiards
Parking: Off-street and monitored
Directions: M1 south junction 16 A45 to Daventry, M1
north junction 18 A361 to Daventry, M40 junction 11
A361 to Daventry.

East Midlands

Hellidon Lakes Hotel, Golf & Country Club

★★★★

Hellidon, Daventry, Northamptonshire, NN11 6GG
Tel: 01327 262550 Fax: 01327 262559
Email: hellidon@marstonhotels.com
Web: www.marstonhotels.com

MARSTON HOTELS

Situated in 220 acres of countryside, 110 comfortable bedrooms and suites, AA rosette restaurant offering panoramic views. Fine leisure facilities including 27 holes of golf, 10-pin bowling, beauty salon.
Rooms: 111 all ensuite ⬤ ⊗
Pricing: Sgl £105 Dbl £139 Dinner from £26
CC: Accepted

Room facilities: ▢ ☎ ⬤ ⬤ Access: ♿
Conference: 20 meeting rooms (Thtr 300 max), 24hr-delegate from £170, day-delegate rate from £55
Children: Welcome ⍭
Dogs: Guide dogs only Licences:
Leisure: Indoor pool, Gym, Health spa, Beauty salon, Tennis, Golf, Fishing
Parking: Off-street and monitored
Directions: Leave M1 at junction 16, take A45 to Daventry, take A361 to Banbury, turn right towards Hellidon then 2nd right.

Derby, Derbyshire

Hotel La Gondola

★★★★ ⓡ

220 Osmaston Road, Derby, Derbyshire, DE23 8JX
Tel: 01332 332895 Fax: 01332 384512
Email: service@lagondola.co.uk
Web: www.lagondola.co.uk
Rooms: 20 all ensuite ⬤
Pricing: Sgl £54.50–56 Dbl £62–64
Dinner from £15.50 CC: Accepted
Room facilities: ▢ ☎ ⬤ Access: ♿
Conference: 4 meeting rooms (Thtr 120 max)
Children: Welcome ⍭ Licences: ⍭⍭⍭
Parking: Off-street and monitored
Directions: Leave M1 at Junction 25. Take A514 towards Melbourne. Hotel is 5 minutes from city centre and 10 minutes from Derby station.

The International Hotel

★★★

Burton Road, Derby, Derbyshire, DE23 6AD
Tel: 01332 369321 Fax: 01332 294430
Email: internationalhotel.derby@virgin.net
Rooms: 62 all ensuite ⬤ ⊗
Pricing: Sgl £42.50–64.50 Dbl £47.50–76.50
Dinner from £14.50 CC: Accepted
Room facilities: ▢ ☎ ⬤
Access: ⍭⍭
Conference: 7 meeting rooms (Thtr 60 max), day-delegate rate from £22.80
Children: Welcome ⍭
Dogs: Welcome Licences: ⍭⍭⍭
Parking: Off-street and monitored
Directions: The hotel is on the A5250, which is just off A5111 Derby Ring Road. Approx ½ mile from city centre.

Rose & Thistle

◆ ◆ ◆

21 Charnwood Street, Derby, Derbyshire, DE1 2GU
Tel: 01332 344103 Fax: 01332 291006
Email: rosethistle@gpanet.co.uk
Rooms: 13 (3 ensuite) ⊗
Pricing: Sgl £22–30 Dbl £42–50 CC: Accepted
Room facilities: ▢ ☎ ⬤
Parking: Off-street
Directions: Leave M1 at Junction 24, take A6 to Derby. Follow Inner Ring Road to Charnwood Street.

Travelodge Derby (SA)

Travel Accommodation
A5111, Kings Way Retail Park, Rowditch, Derby,
Derbyshire, DE22 3NN
Web: www.travelodge.co.uk
Rooms: 40 all ensuite ⊗ Pricing: Sgl £54.40 Dbl £58.85
CC: Accepted Room facilities: 📺 ☕ Access: ♿

Desborough, Northamptonshire

Travelodge Market Harborough

Travel Accommodation
A6, Harborough Road, Desborough,
Northamptonshire, NN14 2UG
Web: www.travelodge.co.uk
Rooms: 32 all ensuite ⊗ Pricing: Sgl 47.40 Dbl 51.85
CC: Accepted Room facilities: 📺 ☕ Access: ♿

Dovedale, Derbyshire

Izaak Walton Hotel

★★★ 🏵
Dovedale, Derbyshire, DE6 2AY
Tel: 01335 350555 Fax: 01335 350539
Email: reception@izaakwaltonhotel.com
Web: www.izaakwaltonhotel.com

Nestling in the Derbyshire Peaks, this converted 17th
century farmhouse, named after the famous author of
"The Compleat Angler", offers a unique combination of
warm hospitality, tranquillity and tradition.
Rooms: 30 all ensuite ⊛ 🔲 ⊗
Pricing: Sgl £89–105 Dbl £115–155
Dinner from £27.50 CC: Accepted
Room facilities: 📺 ☎ ☕ Access: ♿
Conference: 4 meeting rooms (Thtr 50 max),
24hr-delegate from £35, day-delegate rate from £125
Children: Welcome ⱦ 🍼 Dogs: Welcome
Licences: ⚓ ⅲ Parking: Off-street and monitored
Directions: Hotel is 5 miles NW of Ashbourne. Take
A515 towards Buxton. After 2 miles turn left on B5054
to Thorpe, Dovedale and Ilam. Hotel after 4 miles.

Edale, Derbyshire

The Rambler Country House Hotel

◆ ◆ ◆
Edale, Hope Valley, Derbyshire, S33 7SA
Tel: 01433 670268 Fax: 01433 670106
Email: therambler@dorbiere.co.uk
Web: www.theramblerinn.co.uk

Rooms: 9 all ensuite ⊛
Pricing: Sgl £36–50 Dbl £72 Dinner from £6.45
CC: Accepted
Room facilities: 📺 ☎ ☕ Children: Welcome ⱦ
Licences: ⅲ Parking: Off-street

Ely, Cambridgeshire

Travelodge Ely

Travel Accommodation
A10/142 Roundabout, Witchford Road, Ely,
Cambridgeshire, CB6 3NN
Web: www.travelodge.co.uk
Rooms: 39 all ensuite ⊗
Pricing: Sgl £57.40 Dbl £61.85
CC: Accepted Room facilities: 📺 ☕ Access: ♿

Fenstaton, Cambridgeshire

Travelodge Huntingdon, Fenstanton

Travel Accommodation
A14 Eastbound, Fenstaton, Cambridgeshire, PE18 9LP
Web: www.travelodge.co.uk
Rooms: 40 all ensuite ⊗
Pricing: Sgl £57.40 Dbl £61.85
CC: Accepted Room facilities: 📺 ☕ Access: ♿

Froggatt Edge, Derbyshire

The Chequers Inn

◆ ◆ ◆ ◆
Froggatt Edge, Hope Valley, Derbyshire, S32 3ZJ
Tel: 01423 630231 Fax: 01423 630231
Rooms: 5 all ensuite 🔲
Pricing: Sgl £45–55 Dbl £65–75 CC: Accepted
Room facilities: 📺 ☎ ☕ 🔌
Children: Welcome
Dogs: Welcome
Licences: ⅲ
Parking: Off-street
Directions: Situated on the A625 in Froggatt.

Glossop, Derbyshire

Wind in the Willows Hotel

★★ 🏵 🏵
Derbyshire Level, Glossop, Derbyshire, SK13 7PT
Tel: 01457 868001 Fax: 01457 853354
Email: info@windinthewillows.co.uk
Web: www.windinthewillows.co.uk
Rooms: 12 all ensuite 🔲
Pricing: Sgl £85–100 Dbl £105–140
Dinner from £27 CC: Accepted
Room facilities: 📺 ☎ ☕
Children: Welcome, 8yrs min age
Licences: ⅲ
Parking: Off-street and monitored
Directions: 1 mile east of Glossop centre on A57 to
Sheffield. Turn right opposite Royal Oak pub. Hotel 400
yards on right.

The George Hotel

◆ ◆

34 Norfolk Street, Glossop, Derbyshire, SK13 7QU
Tel: 01457 855449 Fax: 01457 857033
Email: george-hotel2000@hotmail.com
Web: www.georgehotelglossop.co.uk

Centrally situated family owned and run hotel, offering ensuite rooms, two public bar lounges serving cask ales. Café bar and à la Carte restaurant. Conferences, family occasions. 40 minutes Manchester airport.
Rooms: 8 all ensuite 🛏 🚭
Pricing: Sgl £30–35 Dbl £50–55 Dinner from £15
CC: Accepted
Room facilities: 🖵 ☎ 🍵
Conference: 2 meeting rooms (Thtr 40 max)
Children: Welcome ⅋
Dogs: Guide dogs only
Licences: ⅄⅄⅄
Directions: The George Hotel opposite railway station, Norfolk Street, B6105 in town centre, opposite free carpark.

Grantham, Lincolnshire

Black Bull

◆ ◆ ◆

Black Bull Farm, North Witham, Grantham, Lincolnshire, NG33 5LL
Tel: 01476 860086 Fax: 01476 860796

Travelodge Grantham, Colsterworth (MOTO)

Travel Accommodation
A1 Colsterworth, Grantham, Lincs, NG35 5JR
Web: www.travelodge.co.uk
Rooms: 31 all ensuite 🚭
Pricing: Sgl £47.40 Dbl £51.85
CC: Accepted Room facilities: 🖵 🍵 Access: ♿

Travelodge Grantham, New Fox

Travel Accommodation
A1, New Fox, South Witham, Grantham, Linc, NG33 5LN
Web: www.travelodge.co.uk
Rooms: 32 all ensuite 🚭
Pricing: Sgl £47.40 Dbl £51.85
CC: Accepted Room facilities: 🖵 🍵 Access: ♿

Travelodge Grantham North (MOTO)

Travel Accommodation
A1, Moto Service Area, Grantham North, A1 Gonley, Grantham, Lincs, NG32 2AB
Web: www.travelodge.co.uk
Rooms: 39 all ensuite 🚭
Pricing: Sgl £47.40 Dbl £51.85
CC: Accepted Room facilities: 🖵 🍵 Access: ♿

Grindleford, Derbyshire

Maynard Arms Hotel

★ ★ ★ ®

Main Road, Grindleford, Derbyshire, S32 2HE
Tel: 01433 630321 Fax: 01433 630445
Email: info@maynardarms.co.uk
Web: www.maynardarms.co.uk
Rooms: 10 all ensuite 🛏 🚭
Pricing: Sgl £69–89 Dbl £79–99
Dinner from £23.50 CC: Accepted
Room facilities: 🖵 ☎ 🍵 ⅃
Conference: 3 meeting rooms (Thtr 140 max), 24hr-delegate from £99, day-delegate rate from £27.50
Children: Welcome
Dogs: Welcome
Licences: ◭ ⅄⅄⅄
Parking: Off-street
Directions: Situated on the B6521 running through Grindleford. Accessible from M1 Junctions 29 and 33.

Hassop, Derbyshire

Hassop Hall Hotel

★ ★ ★ ® ®

Hassop, Bakewell, Derbyshire, DE45 1NS
Tel: 01629 640488 Fax: 01629 640577
Email: hassophallhotel@btinternet.com
Seasonal closure: Christmas
Rooms: 13 all ensuite 🛏 🚭
Pricing: Sgl £87–159 Dbl £95–169
Dinner from £27.75 CC: Accepted
Room facilities: 🖵 ☎ 🍵
Access: ⅃⅃ ♿
Conference: 5 meeting rooms (Thtr 200 max), 24hr-delegate from £149, day-delegate rate from £35
Children: Welcome ⅋
Dogs: Welcome
Licences: ◭ ⅄⅄⅄
Leisure: Tennis
Parking: Off-street
Directions: 2½ miles north of Bakewell, from M1 exit 29, Chesterfield town centre; A619 to Baslow, A623 to Calver, left at traffic lights onto B6001, Hassop 1 mile.

Hathersage, Derbyshire

George Hotel

★★★★

Main Road, Hathersage, Derbyshire, S32 1BB
Tel: 01433 650436 Fax: 01433 650099
Email: info@george-hotel.net
Web: www.george-hotel.net
Rooms: 19 all ensuite
Pricing: Sgl £70–120 Dbl £100–150 Dinner from £15
CC: Accepted Room facilities:
Conference: 2 meeting rooms (Thtr 80 max)
Children: Welcome Dogs: Welcome
Licences: Parking: Off-street
Directions: Leave M1 at Junction 29. Head west on
A619 to Baslow, then north onto B6001 to Hathersage.

Hayfield, Derbyshire

Pool Cottage

◆ ◆ ◆

Park Hall, Little Hayfield, High Peak,
Derbyshire, SK22 2NN
Tel: 01663 742463
Email: dean@poolcottage.fsbusiness.co.uk
Seasonal closure: Christmas to 1 April
Rooms: 3 (2 ensuite)
Pricing: Sgl £20–22 Dbl £40–44
Room facilities: Children: Welcome
Dogs: Welcome Parking: Off-street
Directions: Off A624 up unmade lane with a National
Trust sign at entrance marked 'Park Hall Woods', then
first on left.

Hinckley, Leicestershire

Hanover International Hotel & Club Hinckley

★★★★

A5 Watling Street, Hinckley, Leicestershire, LE10 3JA
Tel: 0870 241 7081 Fax: 01455 635370
Email: crso@hanover-international.com
Web: www.hanover-international.com

Unique, friendly modern hotel and extensive leisure
club set in lovely countryside, with easy access to
Midlands attractions, the NEC and motorway
connections.
Rooms: 349 all ensuite
Pricing: Sgl £115 Dbl £115 Dinner from £18.95
CC: Accepted
Room facilities:
Access:
Children: Welcome
Dogs: Guide dogs only
Licences:
Leisure: Indoor pool, Gym, Health spa,
Beauty salon, Snooker/billiards
Parking: Off-street and monitored
Directions: Hanover International is situated 300 yards
from Junction 1 of M69, which links the M1 and M6.

Kings Hotel

★★

13–19 Mount Road, Hinckley, Leicestershire, LE10 1AD
Tel: 01455 637193 Fax: 01455 636201
Email: kingshinck@aol.com
Web: www.kings-hotel.net

Rooms: 7 all ensuite
Pricing: Sgl £49.50–74.90 Dbl £59.50–84.90
Dinner from £20 CC: Accepted
Room facilities:
Children: Welcome, 10yrs min age
Licences:
Parking: Off-street
Directions: From Hinckley town centre, follow signs for
hospital. Hotel is at the bottom end of the same road.

Holbeach, Lincolnshire

Cackle Hill House

◆ ◆ ◆ ◆

Cackle Hill Lane, Holbeach, Lincolnshire, PE12 8BS
Tel: 01406 426721 Fax: 01406 424659
Seasonal closure: Christmas & New Year
Rooms: 3 (2 ensuite)
Pricing: Sgl £28 Dbl £44–46
Room facilities:
Dogs: Guide dogs only
Parking: Off-street
Directions: From A17 at Holbeach roundabout, take
B1168 to Cackle Hill. Hotel ½ mile on right.

East Midlands

Kettering, Northamptonshire

Kettering Park Hotel

★★★★ 🌳 🌳 🌳

Kettering Parkway, Kettering,
Northamptonshire, NN15 6XT
Tel: 01536 416666 Fax: 01536 416171
Email: kpark@shirehotels.co.uk
Web: www.shirehotels.co.uk
Rooms: 119 all ensuite 🖃 ⊛
Pricing: Sgl £130 Dbl £120 Dinner from £20
CC: Accepted Room facilities: 🖵 ☎ 🍵 📞 ❄
Access: ⬇ ♿
Conference: 14 meeting rooms (Thtr 200 max)
Children: Welcome 🍴 Dogs: Guide dogs only
Licences: ◇ 👯 Leisure: Indoor pool, Gym,
Snooker/billiards Parking: Off-street and monitored
Directions: Take Junction 9 on A14. Hotel is just off
roundabout.

Travelodge Kettering

Travel Accommodation
A14 Westbound, Kettering, Northamptonshire, NN14 1WR
Web: www.travelodge.co.uk
Rooms: 40 all ensuite ⊛
Pricing: Sgl £49.40 Dbl £53.85
CC: Accepted Room facilities: 🖵 🍵 Access: ♿

Leicester, Leicestershire

Leicester Stage Hotel

★★★

299 Leicester Road (A50), Wigston Fields, Leicester,
Leicestershire, LE18 1JW
Tel: 0116 288 6161 Fax: 0116 281 1874
Email: reservations@stagehotel.co.uk
Web: www.stagehotel.co.uk
Rooms: 75 all ensuite 🍽 🖃 ⊛
Room facilities: 🖵 ☎ 🍵 📞 Access: ♿
Children: Welcome 🍴 🕯 Licences: ◇ 👯
Leisure: Indoor pool, Gym, Health spa
Parking: Off-street and monitored
Directions: From Junction 21 M1 Outer Ring Road,
southeast (A563) towards Oadby, Wigston. Turn right
towards Northampton A50. Hotel ¼ mile on left.

Regency

★★★★ 🌳

360 London Road, Leicester, Leicestershire, LE2 2PL
Tel: 0116 270 9634 Fax: 0116 270 1375
Email: info@the-regency-hotel.com
Web: www.the-regency-hotel.com
Rooms: 32 all ensuite 🖃
Pricing: Sgl £38–54 Dbl £56–70 Dinner from £29
CC: Accepted Room facilities: 🖵 ☎ 🍵
Conference: 2 meeting rooms (Thtr 50 max),
24hr-delegate from £82, day-delegate rate from £25
Children: Welcome 🍴 Dogs: Guide dogs only
Licences: 👯 Parking: Off-street and monitored
Directions: Located on the main A6, approximately ½
mile from the city centre. Close to universities.

Red Cow Hotel

★★

Hinckley Road, Leicester Forest East, Leicester,
Leicestershire, LE3 3PG
Tel: 0116 238 7878 Fax: 0116 238 6539

Travelodge Leicester North

Travel Accommodation
A46 Thrussington, Leicestershire, LE7 8TF
Web: www.travelodge.co.uk
Rooms: 32 all ensuite ⊛
Pricing: Sgl £47.40 Dbl £51.85
CC: Accepted Room facilities: 🖵 🍵 Access: ♿

Lincoln, Lincolnshire

Bentley Hotel & Leisure Club

★★★

Newark Road, South Hykeham, Lincoln,
Lincolnshire, LN6 9NH
Tel: 01522 878000 Fax: 01522 878001
Email: info@thebentleyhotel.uk.com
Web: www.thebentleyhotel.uk.com
Rooms: 53 all ensuite 🍽 🖃 ⊛
Pricing: Sgl £62–83 Dbl £85–95 Dinner from £16
CC: Accepted
Room facilities: 🖵 ☎ 🍵 📞
Access: ⬇ ♿
Conference: 7 meeting rooms (Thtr 350 max),
24hr-delegate from £105, day-delegate rate from £27
Children: Welcome 🍴 🕯
Licences: ◇ 👯
Leisure: Indoor pool, Gym, Beauty salon
Parking: Off-street and monitored
Directions: From A1, take A46 towards Lincoln. After
10 miles, go straight over first roundabout on Lincoln
bypass. Hotel 50 yards on left.
See advert on next page

Branston Hall Hotel

★★★★

Branston Park, Lincoln Road, Branston, Lincoln,
Lincolnshire, LN4 1PD
Tel: 01522 793305 Fax: 01522 790734
Email: reservations@branstonhall.com
Web: www.branstonhall.com

Branston Hall is an elegant country house hotel set in
88 acres of wooded parkland, just five minutes drive
from Historic Lincoln. Our 'Parklands' Leisure Suite is
perfect for relaxation, with its impressive murals, indoor
heated pool, sauna and spa. We also offer a superb
array of conference and banqueting facilities.
Rooms: 45 all ensuite
Pricing: Sgl £69–85 Dbl £92–149
Dinner from £17.95 CC: Accepted
Room facilities:
Access:
Conference: 4 meeting rooms (Thtr 200 max),
24hr-delegate from £95, day-delegate rate from £28
Children: Welcome
Dogs: Guide dogs only
Licences:
Leisure: Indoor pool, Gym, Health spa
Parking: Off-street
Directions: Branston Hall Hotel is on the B1188, 3
miles south of Lincoln in the village of Branston.

Golf Hotel

★★★

The Broadway, Woodhall Spa, near Lincoln,
Lincolnshire, LN10 6SG
Tel: 01526 353535 Fax: 01526 353096
Email: reception.golf@principalhotels.co.uk
Web: www.thegolfhotellincoln.co.uk
Rooms: 50 (36 ensuite)
Pricing: Dinner from £19.45 CC: Accepted
Room facilities:
Access:
Conference: 4 meeting rooms (Thtr 150 max),
24hr-delegate from £85, day-delegate rate from £27
Children: Welcome
Dogs: Welcome
Licences:
Parking: Off-street and monitored
Directions: Take B1189 to Metheringham, then B1191
to Woodhall Spa. When approaching Woodhall, the
Golf Hotel is situated on the main street, "The
Broadway".

Bentley Hotel & Leisure Club

Lincoln's newest, and the only hotel sporting
a smart leisure club. Indoor pool and large
conference facilities. Popular with both
corporate and leisure markets.

Newark Road, South Hykeham,
Lincoln, Lincolnshire, LN6 9NH
Tel: 01522 878000 Fax: 01522 878001
Email: info@thebentleyhotel.uk.com
Web: www.thebentleyhotel.uk.com

The Grand Hotel

★★★

St Mary's Street, Lincoln, Lincolnshire, LN5 7EP
Tel: 01522 524211 Fax: 01522 878000
Email: reception@thegrandhotel.uk.com
Web: www.thegrandhotel.uk.com

Family-owned for over 70 years and renowned
throughout the county for its excellent cuisine. Situated
in the heart of the city.
Rooms: 46 all ensuite
Pricing: Sgl £56–73 Dbl £73–83 Dinner from £15
CC: Accepted
Room facilities:
Conference: 5 meeting rooms (Thtr 80 max)
Children: Welcome   Dogs: Guide dogs only
Licences: Parking: Off-street and monitored
Directions: From A1 take A46 towards Lincoln city
centre and then follow the signs for railway station.

The White Hart

 ★★★

Bailgate, Lincoln, Lincolnshire, LN1 3AR
Tel: 0870 400 8117 Fax: 01522 531798
Email: whitehartlincoln@heritage-hotels.co.uk
Web: www.macdonaldhotels.co.uk
Rooms: 48 all ensuite ▱ ⊗
Pricing: Sgl £66 Dbl £132 Dinner from £30
CC: Accepted
Room facilities: ▢ ☎ ◱ ✉
Access: |↕|
Conference: 4 meeting rooms (Thtr 120 max)
Children: Welcome ⋔
Dogs: Welcome
Licences: ◈ ⋔⋔⋔
Parking: Off-street and monitored
Directions: The White Hart is located in Bailgate, midway between the castle and the cathedral.

Castle Hotel

 ★★ ⓡ

Westgate, Lincoln, Lincolnshire, LN1 3AS
Tel: 01522 538801 Fax: 01522 575457
Email: rac@castlehotel.net
Web: www.castlehotel.net
Rooms: 19 all ensuite ▱ ⊗
Pricing: Sgl £65–87 Dbl £87–160 Dinner from £16
CC: Accepted
Room facilities: ▢ ☎ ◱ ✉
Access: ♿
Conference: 2 meeting rooms (Thtr 40 max)
Children: Welcome, 8yrs min age
Dogs: Welcome
Licences: ⋔⋔⋔
Parking: Off-street and monitored
Directions: Follow signs to 'Lawn Visitors Centre'. At mini-roundabout, turn left. Hotel is on left at end of Westgate.

Archers Lodge

 ◆◆◆◆ ✉

133 Yarborough Road, Lincoln, Lincolnshire, LN1 1HR
Tel: 01522 520201 Fax: 01522 520201
Email: info@archerslodge.co.uk
Web: www.archerslodge.co.uk
Rooms: 4 all ensuite ⊗
Room facilities: ▢ ◱
Children: Welcome
Dogs: Welcome
Parking: Off-street
Directions: Take A57 into Lincoln to main traffic lights. Turn left, follow road through two sets of lights. Halfway up on the right.

D'Isney Place Hotel   Little Gem

 ◆◆◆◆ ✉

Eastgate, Lincoln, Lincolnshire, LN2 4AA
Tel: 01522 538881 Fax: 01522 511321
Email: info@disneyplacehotel.co.uk
Web: www.disneyplacehotel.co.uk

Fine elegant town house with spacious gardens provides luxury bed and breakfast. All 17 rooms are ensuite and individually decorated. Breakfast served in bedrooms with three jacuzzi rooms available.
Rooms: 17 all ensuite ◔ ▱ ⊗
Pricing: Sgl £56.50–66.50 Dbl £89–109 CC: Accepted
Room facilities: ▢ ☎ ◱
Access: ♿ Children: Welcome ⋔
Dogs: Welcome
Parking: Off-street
Directions: Situated 150 yards from Lincoln Cathedral in the ancient part of the city, nearest main roads are A15 and A46.

Tennyson Hotel

 ◆◆◆◆ ✉

7 South Park, Lincoln, Lincolnshire, LN5 8EN
Tel: 01522 521624 Fax: 01522 521355
Email: tennyson.hotel@virgin.net
Web: www.tennysonhotel.com
Seasonal closure: Christmas
Rooms: 8 all ensuite
Pricing: Sgl £33–37 Dbl £45–47 CC: Accepted
Room facilities: ▢ ☎ ◱
Children: Welcome Licences: ⋔⋔⋔
Parking: Off-street
Directions: South of the city, on the A15, 15 metres from the high street roundabout.

The Gables

 ◆◆◆◆

546 Newark Road, North Hykeham, Lincoln, Lincolnshire, LN6 9NG
Tel: 01522 829102 Fax: 01522 850497
Email: gary.burnett@ntlworld.com
Web: www.gablesguesthouse.co.uk
Rooms: 4 (2 ensuite) ⊗
Pricing: Sgl £30–35 Dbl £45–50 CC: Accepted
Room facilities: ▢ ◱
Access: |↕|
Children: Welcome
Dogs: Welcome
Leisure: Games room
Parking: Off-street and monitored
Directions: A46 Newark to Lincoln bypass, follow (A1434) Lincoln south. We are 1½ miles on the right after McDonalds.

Admiral Guest House

 ♦ ♦ ♦

16–18 Nelson Street, Lincoln, Lincolnshire, LN1 1PJ
Tel: 01522 544467 Fax: 01522 544467
Email: tony@admiral63.freeserve.co.uk
Rooms: 9 (7 ensuite) ⊗
Pricing: Sgl £25 Dbl £38 CC: Accepted
Room facilities: ⬜ ☕
Access: ♿
Children: Welcome ♄
Dogs: Welcome
Parking: Off-street and monitored
Directions: Follow A57 to Carlholme Road situated on Nelson Street. Five minutes walk from the University and town.

Bradford Guest House

 ♦ ♦ ♦

67 Monks Road, Lincoln, Lincolnshire, LN2 5HP
Tel: 01522 523947
Rooms: 4 all ensuite ⊗
Pricing: Sgl £25 Dbl £40 Dinner from £8
Room facilities: ⬜ ☕
Children: Welcome ♄
Parking: Off-street and monitored
Directions: 300 yards east of Lindum Road/Silver Street junction. Opposite North Lincolnshire College on Monks Road.

Halfway Farm Motel

 ♦ ♦ ♦

A46 Swinderby, Lincoln, Lincolnshire, LN6 9HN
Tel: 01522 868749 Fax: 01522 868082
Seasonal closure: Christmas to New Year
Rooms: 17 (15 ensuite) ⊗
Pricing: Sgl £35 Dbl £42–52 CC: Accepted
Room facilities: ⬜ ☎ ☕
Access: ♿
Children: Welcome
Dogs: Guide dogs only
Parking: Off-street and monitored
Directions: On A46 Newark to Lincoln Road. Opposite disused RAF Swinderby airfield, five minutes from Lincoln bypass.

Hillside Guest House

 ♦ ♦ ♦ ✗

34 Yarborough Road, Lincoln, Lincolnshire, LN1 1HS
Tel: 01522 888671
Email: jean@jbixley.freeserve.co.uk
Web: www.hillsideguesthouse.co.uk
Rooms: 3 (2 ensuite) ⊗
Pricing: Sgl £25 Dbl £38 CC: Accepted
Room facilities: ⬜ ☕
Children: Welcome ♄
Dogs: Welcome
Parking: Off-street and monitored
Directions: We are five minutes walk from the city centre and cathedral area, at the lower end of Yarborough Road.

Pines Guest House

 ♦ ♦ ♦

104 Yarborough Road, Lincoln, Lincolnshire, LN1 1HR
Tel: 01522 532985 Fax: 01522 532985
Email: pines.guest.house@ntlworld.com
Web: www.smoothhound.co.uk
Rooms: 7 (4 ensuite) 🍴 ⊗
Pricing: Sgl £18–30 Dbl £36–45 Dinner from £6
Room facilities: ⬜ ☕
Access: ♿
Children: Welcome ♄
Dogs: Welcome
Licences: ⛲
Leisure: Games room
Parking: Off-street and monitored
Directions: West side of city. Accessible from Relief Road. A15 — A46, A158, A607, A57. Close to city centre and cathedral.

South Park Guest House

 ♦ ♦ ♦

11 South Park, Lincoln, Lincolnshire, LN5 8EN
Tel: 01522 528243 Fax: 01522 524603
Email: enquiries@southpark-lincoln.co.uk
Web: www.southpark-lincoln.co.uk
Rooms: 7 all ensuite
Room facilities: ⬜ ☕
Children: Welcome Dogs: Guide dogs only
Parking: Off-street
Directions: In the south of Lincoln, follow the High Street to the bottom turning left at the roundabout. 100 metres on the left.

Old Rectory Guest House

 ♦ ♦

19 Newport, Lincoln, Lincolnshire, LN1 3DQ
Tel: 01522 514774
Seasonal closure: Christmas and New Yer
Rooms: 7 (5 ensuite) ⊗
Pricing: Sgl £20–25 Dbl £40
Room facilities: ⬜ ☕
Children: Welcome
Parking: Off-street
Directions: From A46 ring road turn off at Lincoln North roundabout. Straight over next one to Newport. We are at the south end.

Tennyson Court

 ♦ ♦

3 Tennyson Street, Lincoln, Lincolnshire, LN1 1LZ
Tel: 0800 980 5408 Fax: 01522 887997
Email: sales@tennyson-court.co.uk
Web: www.tennyson-court.co.uk
Rooms: 3 all ensuite 🍴 ⊗
Pricing: Sgl £34.90–51 Dbl £39.90–51
Room facilities: ⬜ ☎ ☕
Access: ♿ Children: Welcome
Parking: Off-street and monitored
Directions: Follow A57 into Lincoln, left onto Hewson Road, right at top onto West Parade, then next left is Tennyson Street.

Travelodge Lincoln

Travel Accommodation
A46, Newark/Lincoln Road, Thorpe On The Hill,
Lincoln, Lincolnshire, LN6 9AJ
Web: www.travelodge.co.uk
Rooms: 32 all ensuite ⊗
Pricing: Sgl £47.40 Dbl £51.85
CC: Accepted Room facilities: ☐ ☕ Access: ♿

Loughborough, Leicestershire

Quorn Country Hotel

★★★★ ♨ ♨ ♨

66 Leicester Road, Quorn, Leicestershire, LE12 8BB
Tel: 01509 415050 Fax: 01509 415557
Email: sales@quorncountryhotel.co.uk
Rooms: 30 all ensuite ⊠ ⊗
Pricing: Sgl £92–140 Dbl £112–150
Dinner from £25 CC: Accepted
Room facilities: ☐ ☎ ☕ ☏ ❄
Access: ⫼ ♿
Conference: 11 meeting rooms (Thtr 350 max),
24hr-delegate from £150, day-delegate rate from £45
Children: Welcome ⅍
Licences: ⟁ ♟
Parking: Off-street and monitored
Directions: From A6 Loughborough to Leicester Road,
take exit for Quorn (Quorndon) Village. Hotel near
village hall and opposite police station.
See advert on this page

Originally Leicestershire's most exclusive private
club, created around the original 17th-century
listed building. This award winning 4-star hotel is
set amid 4 acres of beautiful landscaped gardens.
Stay in one of our 30 individually-designed
bedrooms, including 3 suites and 7 executive
rooms. Your stay will be enhanced by the hotel's
two RAC and AA award-winning restaurants where
you can choose between the intimate alcoves of
the Shires Restaurant with its classical cuisine or
the light conservatory atmosphere of the Orangery
Brasserie with its selection of contemporary dishes.

**Charnwood House, 66 Leicester Road,
Quorn, Leicestershire LE12 8BB**
Tel: 01509 415050   Fax: 01509 415557
Email:reservations@quorncountryhotel.co.uk

Quality Hotel & Suites Loughborough

★★★

Junction 23, M1, New Ashby Road, Loughborough,
Leicestershire, LE11 4EX
Tel: 01509 211800 Fax: 01509 211868
Email: admin@gb613.u-net.com
Web: www.choicehotels.com
Rooms: 94 all ensuite ♨ ⊠ ⊗
Pricing: Dinner from £14.95 CC: Accepted
Room facilities: ☐ ☎ ☕ ☏
Access: ♿
Conference: 9 meeting rooms (Thtr 250 max),
24hr-delegate from £130, day-delegate rate from £35
Children: Welcome ⅍ ☾
Dogs: Welcome
Licences: ⟁ ♟
Leisure: Indoor pool, Gym, Games room
Parking: Off-street and monitored
Directions: From Junction 23 M1, follow A512 towards
Loughborough town centre. Hotel is approx 800
metres on left-hand side.

Cedars Hotel

★★

Cedar Road, Loughborough, Leicestershire, LE11 2AB
Tel: 01509 214459 Fax: 01509 233573
Email: info@thecedarshotel.com
Web: www.thecedarshotel.com

Family-run hotel in quiet surroundings, specialising in
private functions. Cots available; family rooms
available. Rolls Royce available for weddings at no
extra charge on some packages.
Rooms: 36 all ensuite ♨ ⊗
Pricing: Sgl £50–70 Dbl £70–85 Dinner from £11
CC: Accepted
Room facilities: ☐ ☎ ☕
Conference: 3 meeting rooms (Thtr 40 max),
24hr-delegate from £95, day-delegate rate from £20
Children: Welcome ⅍ ☾
Dogs: Welcome
Licences: ♟
Leisure: Outdoor pool
Parking: Off-street and monitored
Directions: Proceed along the A6 towards Leicester,
turning left into Cedar Road opposite Loughborough
Crematorium. Situated along the A6 south of the town.

Great Central Hotel

★★

Great Central Road, Loughborough,
Leicestershire, LE11 1RW
Tel: 01509 263405 Fax: 01509 264130
Email: reception@greatcentralhotel.co.uk
Web: www.greatcentralhotel.co.uk
Rooms: 22 all ensuite
Room facilities: 🖵 ☎ 🍵 📞
Children: Welcome 🍴
Dogs: Welcome
Licences: ⅲ
Parking: Off-street and monitored
Directions: Enter Loughborough on the A6. Turn onto the A60 to Nottingham. Great Central Road is first on the right.

The Grange Courtyard

◆◆◆◆◆ ✳ ☕

The Grange, Forest Street, Shepshed, Loughborough, Leicestershire, LE12 9DA
Tel: 01509 600189 Fax: 01509 600189
Email: linda.lawrence@thegrangecourtyard.co.uk
Web: www.thegrangecourtyard.co.uk
Rooms: 12 all ensuite 🖼 🛇
Pricing: Sgl £65–70 Dbl £75–80 Dinner from £7.50
CC: Accepted
Room facilities: 🖵 ☎ 🍵 📞
Access: ♿
Children: Welcome, 8yrs min age
Dogs: Welcome
Licences: ⅲ
Parking: Off-street and monitored
Directions: Exit J23 M1, A512 towards Ashby. ³/₄ mile, traffic lights, turn right. ³/₄ mile, turn right at petrol station into Forest Street.

De Montfort Hotel

◆◆◆

88 Leicester Road, Loughborough,
Leicestershire, LE11 2AQ
Tel: 01509 216061 Fax: 01509 233667
Email: thedemontforthotel@amserve.com
Web: www.thedemontforthotel.co.uk
Rooms: 9 (7 ensuite)
Pricing: Sgl £30–40 Dbl £40–50 Dinner from £7
CC: Accepted
Room facilities: 🖵 🍵
Children: Welcome 🍴
Licences: ⅲ
Parking: Off-street
Directions: Situated on A6 Leicester Road, 5 minutes from the town centre.

Market Harborough, Leicestershire

Sun Inn Hotel

★★ ☕

Main Street, Marston Trussell, Market Harborough, Leicestershire, LE16 9TY
Tel: 01858 465531 Fax: 01858 433155

Email: manager@suninn.com
Web: www.suninn.com
Seasonal closure: Christmas and New Year
Rooms: 20 all ensuite 🖼 🛇
Pricing: Sgl £69 Dbl £69 Dinner from £19.95
CC: Accepted
Room facilities: 🖵 ☎ 🍵 Access: ♿
Conference: 1 meeting room (Thtr 70 max)
Children: Welcome 🍴
Dogs: Guide dogs only Licences: ⅲ
Parking: Off-street
Directions: Exit J20 M1, A4304. Marston Trussell is between Theddingworth and Lubenham. By rail, Market Harborough is 3 miles away.

Markfield, Leicestershire

Travelodge Leicester, Markfield

Travel Accommodation
A50/M1 Interchange, Littleshaw Lane,
Markfield, LE6 0PP
Web: www.travelodge.co.uk
Rooms: 60 all ensuite 🛇
Pricing: Sgl £54.40 Dbl £58.85
CC: Accepted Room facilities: 🖵 🍵 Access: ♿

Matlock, Derbyshire

Riber Hall

★★★★ ☕ ☕

Matlock, Derbyshire, DE4 5JU
Tel: 01629 582795 Fax: 01629 580475
Email: info@riber-hall.co.uk
Web: www.riber-hall.co.uk

Renowned historic and tranquil country manor house set in peaceful rolling Derbyshire hills. Gourmet cuisine — AA two rosettes, two RAC Dining Awards. Privately owned and proprietor-run for 30 years.
Rooms: 14 all ensuite 🖼 🛇
Pricing: Sgl £101–116 Dbl £136–182
Dinner from £29.75 CC: Accepted
Room facilities: 🖵 ☎ 🍵 📞
Conference: 3 meeting rooms (Thtr 20 max), 24hr-delegate from £148, day-delegate rate from £36.75
Children: Welcome, 10yrs min age
Dogs: Welcome Licences: ⬥ ⅲ
Leisure: Tennis Parking: Off-street
Directions: One mile off A615 at Tansley, signed to Riber.

The New Bath Hotel

★★★

New Bath Road, Matlock Bath, Derbyshire, DE4 3PX
Tel: 0870 400 8119 Fax: 01629 580268
Email: newbath@heritage-hotels.co.uk
Web: www.macdonaldhotels.co.uk
Rooms: 55 all ensuite 🍵 🚭 ⊗
Pricing: Sgl £59.50 Dbl £119 Dinner from £22
CC: Accepted
Room facilities: 🖥 ☎ 🍵 🕻 Access: ♿
Conference: 4 meeting rooms (Thtr 200 max)
Children: Welcome 🍴 ☕
Dogs: Welcome Licences: 🜊 ⚶
Leisure: Indoor pool, Outdoor pool,
Health spa, Tennis Parking: Off-street
Directions: Leave M1 at Junction 28. Follow A38, then A610. Proceed to Little Chef restaurant at Ambergate. Turn right. Hotel is approx 20 minutes along A6 on left.

Hillview

◆◆◆

80 New Street, Matlock, Derbyshire, DE4 3FH
Tel: 01629 583662 Fax: 0870 127 7822
Email: hillview@bizonline.co.uk
Seasonal closure: November to Easter
Rooms: 3 (1 ensuite) ⊗ Room facilities: 🖥 🍵
Children: Welcome, 5yrs min age
Parking: Off-street
Directions: From Matlock centre (A6, Crown Square), proceed up the hill, take fourth right into New Street. Hillview is on the corner.

Melbourne Arms
& Cuisine India

The historic Melbourne Arms, home to Cuisine India, where east meets west. Recommended by the AA & RAC with three diamonds, our comfortable accommodation is ideally situated for easy access to East Midlands International Airport, Donnington Park Race Track and the surrounding Derbyshire countryside.

92 Ashby Road, Melbourne DE73 1ES
Tel: 01332 864949/01332 345995
Fax: 01332 865525
Email: info@melbournearms.co.uk
Website: www.melbournearms.com.co.uk

Jackson Tor House

◆◆◆

76 Jackson Road, Matlock, Derbyshire, DE4 3JQ
Tel: 01629 582348 Fax: 01629 582348
Email: jacksontorhotel@uk2.net
Web: www.jacksontorhotel.co.uk
Rooms: 29 (14 ensuite) 🍵 🚭
Pricing: Sgl £20–35 Dbl £40–65 Dinner from £8.95
CC: Accepted
Room facilities: 🖥 🍵
Children: Welcome 🍴 Licences: ⚶
Leisure: Games room
Parking: Off-street
Directions: Take Bank Road exit from roundabout take first left after Wilkinsons, at end right, immediate left into far green.

The Coach House, Home Farm

◆◆◆

Main Road, Lea, near Matlock, Derbyshire, DE4 5GJ
Tel: 01629 534346
Email: barbarahobson@coachhouselea.co.uk
Web: www.coachhouselea.co.uk
Rooms: 3 (1 ensuite)
Pricing: Dinner from £6.50 CC: Accepted
Room facilities: 🍵
Children: Welcome 🍴
Dogs: Welcome
Licences: ⚶
Parking: Off-street
Directions: From A6 Cromford follow road to Crich. After a mile, turn left at Leabridge for Lea and Riber. The Coach House is ¾ mile on left.

Melbourne, Derbyshire

Melbourne Arms & Cuisine India

◆◆◆

92 Ashby Road, Melbourne, Derbyshire, DE73 1ES
Tel: 01332 864949/345995 Fax: 01332 865525
Email: info@melbournearms.co.uk
Web: www.melbournearms.com (co.uk)
Rooms: 7 all ensuite 🍵 ⊗
Pricing: Sgl £30–38 Dbl £50–55 Dinner from £10
CC: Accepted
Room facilities: 🖥 🍵
Conference: 1 meeting room (Thtr 20 max)
Children: Welcome 🍴
Dogs: Guide dogs only
Licences: ⚶
Parking: Off-street and monitored
See advert on this page

Melton Mowbray, Leicestershire

Stapleford Park Hotel ·········· Gold Ribbon Winner

★★★★ ♛ ♛ ♛

Stapleford, Melton Mowbray, Leicestershire, LE14 2EF
Tel: 01572 787522 Fax: 01572 787651
Web: www.stapleford.co.uk
Rooms: 51 all ensuite 🖥
Pricing: Dinner from £44 (2002 rate) CC: Accepted
Room facilities: 🖵 ☎
Access: |↕|
Children: Welcome ♿ ⛄
Dogs: Welcome
Licences: ⟨◇⟩ ♦♦♦
Leisure: Indoor pool, Gym, Health spa, Beauty salon,
Tennis, Golf, Fishing, Riding, Snooker/billiards
Parking: Off-street and monitored
Directions: From Melton Mowbray, follow ring road and
signs for Grantham. Stay in left-hand lane until
Grantham Road turns left: don't turn left, but drive
through traffic lights. Follow signs for B676 Stapleford.
After 4 miles, turn right at Stapleford signpost.

Newark, Nottinghamshire

Travelodge North Muskham, Newark

Travel Accommodation
A1 South Bound, North Muskham, Nr. Newark,
Nottinghamshire, NG23 6HT
Web: www.travelodge.co.uk
Rooms: 30 all ensuite 🚭
Pricing: Sgl £47.40 Dbl £51.85
CC: Accepted Room facilities: 🖵 ☕ Access: ♿

Northampton, Northamptonshire

Quality Hotel Northampton

★★★

Ashley Way, Weston Favell, Northampton,
Northamptonshire, NN3 3EA
Tel: 01604 739955 Fax: 01604 415023
Email: admin@gb070.u-net.com
Web: www.choicehotels.com
Rooms: 66 all ensuite 🚭
Pricing: Sgl £105–120 Dbl £126–196
Dinner from £17.95 CC: Accepted
Room facilities: 🖵 ☎ ☕ 🍴
Access: |↕|
Conference: 6 meeting rooms (Thtr 140 max),
24hr-delegate from £140, day-delegate rate from £35
Children: Welcome ♿ ⛄
Dogs: Welcome
Licences: ⟨◇⟩ ♦♦♦
Leisure: Games room
Parking: Off-street and monitored
Directions: Leave M1 motorway at junction 15, proceed
to Northampton along A508 for 2 miles, follow Kettering
& Wellingborough. Then A45 to Weston Favell (A43).

Travelodge Northampton, Upton Way

Travel Accommodation
A45, Upton Way, Northampton,
Northamptonshire, NN5 6EG
Web: www.travelodge.co.uk
Rooms: 62 all ensuite 🚭
Pricing: Sgl £54.40 Dbl £58.85
CC: Accepted Room facilities: 🖵 ☕ Access: ♿

Nottingham, Nottinghamshire

Bestwood Lodge Hotel

★★★

Bestwood Country Park, Arnold, Nottingham,
Nottinghamshire, NG5 8NE
Tel: 0115 920 3011 Fax: 0115 967 0409
Web: www.bestwestern.co.uk
Rooms: 39 all ensuite 🐾 🚭
Pricing: Sgl £38–75 Dbl £70–135 Dinner from £18.50
CC: Accepted
Room facilities: 🖵 ☎ ☕
Conference: 9 meeting rooms (Thtr 200 max),
24hr-delegate from £95, day-delegate rate from £30
Children: Welcome ♿ ⛄
Dogs: Welcome
Licences: ♦♦♦
Leisure: Tennis, Riding
Parking: Off-street and monitored
Directions: 3½ miles north of city centre off A60, in
Bestwood Country Park.

Westminster Hotel

★★★

312 Mansfield Road, Nottingham,
Nottinghamshire, NG5 2EF
Tel: 0115 955 5000 Fax: 0115 955 5005
Email: mail@westminster-hotel.co.uk
Web: www.westminster-hotel.co.uk
Rooms: 72 all ensuite 🖥 🚭
Pricing: Sgl £88.50–103.50 Dbl £112–127
Dinner from £17 CC: Accepted
Room facilities: 🖵 ☎ ☕ 🍴
Access: |↕| ♿
Conference: 5 meeting rooms (Thtr 60 max),
24hr-delegate from £105, day-delegate rate from £35
Children: Welcome
Licences: ♦♦♦
Parking: Off-street and monitored
Directions: M1 J26, take A610 to Nottingham centre.
Left onto A6130. Signs for A60 north (Mansfield Road).

Ask the experts

To book a Hotel or Guest
Accommodation, or for help
and advice, call RAC Hotel
Reservations on 0870 603 9109
and quote 'Guide 2003'

East Midlands

Hotel Des Clos

Restaurant with Rooms 🍴 🍴 🍴 🍴
Old Lenton Lane, Nottingham,
Nottinghamshire, NG7 2SA
Tel: 0115 986 6566 Fax: 0115 986 0343
Email: info@hoteldesclos.com
Web: www.hoteldesclos.com
Seasonal closure: Bank Holidays/1st week in January

Victorian farm conversion nestled on the banks of the river Trent, located five minutes from the city. Rooms furnished with British and French antiques. Excellent restaurant Sat Bains, cuisine presided over by Sat Bains (Roux Scholer). Small oasis in the city is perfect for any private function or wedding reception.
Rooms: 8 all ensuite 🖥 ⊗
Pricing: Sgl £79.50–99.50 Dbl £89.50–139.50
Dinner from £30 CC: Accepted
Room facilities: ☐ ☎ 🕾 📞 Access: ♿
Conference: 2 meeting rooms (Thtr 20 max),
24hr-delegate from £140, day-delegate rate from £60
Children: Welcome, 8yrs min age ⍩
Dogs: Guide dogs only
Licences: ♦♦♦ Leisure: Riding
Parking: Off-street
Directions: Junction 24 M1, take A453, continue on this road for approx 9 miles, take middle lane to large island left and immediate left again, Old Lenton Lane, "Blue hotel sign".

Travelodge Nottingham, Riverside (SA)

Travel Accommodation
A453, Riverside Retail Park, Tottle Road, Queens Drive, Nottingham, NG2 1RT
Web: www.travelodge.co.uk
Rooms: 61 all ensuite ⊗
Pricing: Sgl £57.40 Dbl £61.85
CC: Accepted Room facilities: ☐ 🕾 Access: ♿

Oakham, Rutland

Old Wisteria Hotel

★★★ 🍴
4 Catmose Street, Oakham, Rutland, LE15 6HW
Tel: 01572 722844 Fax: 01572 724473
Email: enquiries@wisteriahotel.co.uk
Web: www.wisteriahotel.co.uk

A welcoming country house ambience. Intimate lounge bar and restaurant. Private dining and meeting rooms. Friendly and attentive service. A minute's drive into rolling countryside.
Rooms: 25 all ensuite 🖥 ⊗
Pricing: Sgl £32.50–70 Dbl £65–90
Dinner from £18.50 CC: Accepted
Room facilities: ☐ ☎ 🕾 📞 Access: ♿
Conference: 5 meeting rooms (Thtr 60 max),
24hr-delegate from £100, day-delegate rate from £25
Children: Welcome
Dogs: Welcome Licences: ♦♦♦
Parking: Off-street
Directions: Hotel in Oakham town at junction A606/A6003. From A1 North join B668. From A1 South join A606. From Nottingham or Kettering join A6003.

Peterborough, Cambridgeshire

Travelodge Alwalton

Travel Accommodation
A1 South, Great North Road, Alwalton Village, Peterborough, Cambridgeshire, PE7 3UR
Web: www.travelodge.co.uk
Rooms: 32 all ensuite ⊗
Pricing: Sgl £47.40 Dbl £51.85
CC: Accepted Room facilities: ☐ 🕾 Access: ♿

Travelodge Peterborough

Travel Accommodation
Crowland Road, Eye Green, Peterborough, Cambridgeshire, PE6 7SZ
Web: www.travelodge.co.uk
Rooms: 42 all ensuite ⊗
Pricing: Sgl £47.40 Dbl £51.85
CC: Accepted Room facilities: ☐ 🕾 Access: ♿

Retford, Nottinghamshire

Travelodge Retford, Markham Moor

Travel Accommodation
A1 North Bound, Markham Moor, Nr. Retford, Nottinghamshire, DN22 0QU
Web: www.travelodge.co.uk
Rooms: 40 all ensuite ⊗
Pricing: Sgl £47.40 Dbl £51.85
CC: Accepted Room facilities: ☐ 🕾 Access: ♿

Rushden, Northamptonshire

Travelodge Wellingborough

Travel Accommodation
A45 Eastbound, Rushden, Northamptonshire, NN10 9AP
Web: www.travelodge.co.uk
Rooms: 40 all ensuite
Pricing: Sgl £47.40 Dbl £51.85
CC: Accepted Room facilities: ☐ ◻ Access: ♿

Scunthorpe, Lincolnshire

Forest Pines Hotel

★★★★ ⌘
Ermine Street, Broughton, Brigg,
North Lincolnshire, DN20 0AQ
Tel: 01652 650770 Fax: 01652 650495
Email: enquiries@forestpines.co.uk
Web: www.forestpines.co.uk

Set in woodland grounds, the hotel offers everything
for the discerning guest including golf and
leisure/beauty facilities. AA rosette-awarded restaurant.
Ideally situated for the historic city of Lincoln.
Rooms: 86 all ensuite
Pricing: Sgl £90 Dbl £100 CC: Accepted
Room facilities: ☐ ☎ ◻ ☎
Access: ⌕ ♿
Conference: 6 meeting rooms (Thtr 220 max),
24hr-delegate from £140, day-delegate rate from £30
Children: Welcome ⱨ ⅙ Dogs: Guide dogs only
Licences: ◇ ⅲ Leisure: Indoor pool, Gym, Health
spa, Beauty salon, Golf
Parking: Off-street and monitored
Directions: Exit J4 M180. Hotel is 200 metres to the
north at junction of A18 and A15.

Wortley House Hotel

★★★
Rowland Road, Scunthorpe,
North Lincolnshire, DN16 1SU
Tel: 01724 842223 Fax: 01724 280646
Rooms: 38 all ensuite ⬚ ◻
Pricing: Sgl £55–95 Dbl £70–110 CC: Accepted
Room facilities: ☐ ☎ ◻ Children: Welcome ⱨ ⅙
Dogs: Welcome Licences: ◇ ⅲ
Parking: Off-street and monitored
Directions: Leave M180 at Junction 3. Turn right at
roundabout. At next roundabout take third exit, take
second left into Brumby Wood Lane. Go straight over
next roundabout. Hotel is on right.

Skegness, Lincolnshire

Crown Hotel

★★★
Drummond Road, Skegness, Lincolnshire, PE25 3AB
Tel: 01754 610760 Fax: 01754 610847
Web: www.theaa.com/hotels/41427.html

3 star hotel offers the elegance of yesteryear combined
with the benefits of refurbishment to modern
standards, just 1½ miles from centre of Skegness, but
on the edge of the countryside.
Rooms: 29 all ensuite
Pricing: Sgl £50 Dbl £70 Dinner from £14.75
CC: Accepted Room facilities: ☐ ☎ ◻
Access: ⌕
Conference: 3 meeting rooms (Thtr 120 max)
Children: Welcome ⱨ ⅙ Dogs: Guide dogs only
Licences: ◇ Leisure: Indoor pool
Parking: Off-street
Directions: Turn right from Lumley Road into
Drummond Road. Crown Hotel is 1½ miles down
Drummond Road (signposted) nature reserve.

Vine Hotel

★★★
Vine Road, Skegness, Lincolnshire, PE25 3DB
Tel: 01754 763018 Fax: 01754 769845
Email: vinehotel@bateman.co.uk
Web: www.skegness-resort.co.uk/vine
Rooms: 25 all ensuite ⬚ ◻
Pricing: Sgl £68 Dbl £88 Dinner from £13.95
CC: Accepted Room facilities: ☐ ☎ ◻ ☎
Conference: 3 meeting rooms (Thtr 100 max),
24hr-delegate from £85, day-delegate rate from £20
Children: Welcome ⱨ ⅙
Dogs: Guide dogs only Licences: ◇ ⅲ
Parking: Off-street
Directions: Set in the Seacroft area of Skegness, close
to the beach, two golf courses and other attractions.

The Saxby Hotel

◆ ◆ ◆
Saxby Avenue, Skegness,
Lincolnshire, PE25 3LG
Tel: 01754 763905 Fax: 01754 763905
Seasonal closure: November — Easter
Rooms: 15 all ensuite ◻
Pricing: Sgl £24 (2002 rate) Dbl £48 (2002 rate)
Dinner from £8 (2002 rate) CC: Accepted
Room facilities: ☐ ◻ Access: ♿
Children: Welcome ⱨ Licences: ⅲ
Parking: Off-street

Sleaford, Lincolnshire

Carre Arms Hotel

1 Mareham Lane, Sleaford, Lincolnshire, NG34 7JP
Tel: 01529 303156 Fax: 01529 303139
Email: enquiries@carrearmshotel.co.uk
Web: www.carrearmshotel.co.uk
Rooms: 13 all ensuite
Pricing: Sgl £50–55 Dbl £70–75
Dinner from £15.50 CC: Accepted
Room facilities:
Conference: 2 meeting rooms (Thtr 100 max), 24hr-delegate from £60.50, day-delegate rate from £15.50
Children: Welcome
Dogs: Guide dogs only Licences:
Parking: Off-street and monitored
Directions: 3 mins from Sleaford rail station, easy access from Lincoln, Grantham (A1), Boston (A15) and Newark (A1).

Travelodge Sleaford

Travel Accommodation
A15/A17, Holdingham, Sleaford,
Lincolnshire, NG34 8PN
Web: www.travelodge.co.uk
Rooms: 40 all ensuite
Pricing: Sgl £47.40 Dbl £51.85
CC: Accepted Room facilities: Access:

Spalding, Lincolnshire

Cley Hall Hotel

22 High Street, Spalding, Lincolnshire, PE11 1TX
Tel: 01775 725157 Fax: 01775 710785
Email: cleyhall@enterprise.net
Web: www.cleyhallhotel.com
Rooms: 12 all ensuite
Pricing: Sgl £50–70 Dbl £65–100 CC: Accepted
Room facilities:
Access: Conference: 2 meeting rooms (Thtr 30 max)
Children: Welcome
Dogs: Welcome Licences:
Parking: Off-street and monitored
Directions: The hotel is situated on a one-way system, not in the town centre. Phone, fax, e-mail for a map.

Travel Stop

Locksmill Farm, 50 Cowbit Road, Spalding,
Lincolnshire, PE11 2RJ
Tel: 01775 767290 Fax: 01775 767716
Email: travelstopraclodg@btinternet.com
Rooms: 16 (14 ensuite)
Room facilities:
Access: Children: Welcome
Dogs: Welcome Licences:
Parking: Off-street and monitored
Directions: Located on B1173, ¾ mile from centre of Spalding, by the side of the River Welland.

Travelodge Kings Lynn, Long Sutton

Travel Accommodation
A17, Wisbech Road, Long Sutton, Spalding,
Lincolnshire, PE12 9AG
Web: www.travelodge.co.uk
Rooms: 40 all ensuite
Pricing: Sgl £54.40 Dbl £58.85
CC: Accepted Room facilities: Access:

Stamford, Lincolnshire

George of Stamford

Blue Ribbon Winner

71 St Martin's, Stamford, Lincolnshire, PE9 2LB
Tel: 01780 750750 Fax: 01780 750701
Email: reservations@georgehotelofstamford.com
Web: www.georgehotelofstamford.com
Rooms: 47 all ensuite
Pricing: Sgl £78–110 Dbl £105–220 Dinner from £7.65
CC: Accepted Room facilities:
Conference: 9 meeting rooms (Thtr 50 max),
24hr-delegate from £130, day-delegate rate from £32
Children: Welcome
Dogs: Welcome Licences:
Parking: Off-street and monitored
Directions: North of Peterborough. From A1, B1081 to Stamford at roundabout. Hotel situated on left at first set of traffic lights.

The Lady Anne's Hotel

37–38 High Street, Saint Martins Without, Stamford,
Lincolnshire, PE9 2LJ
Tel: 01780 470331 Fax: 01780 765422
Web: www.ladyanneshotel@activehotels.com
Rooms: 29 all ensuite
Pricing: Sgl £52–52 Dbl £75–95 Dinner from £10.95
CC: Accepted
Room facilities: Access:
Conference: 4 meeting rooms (Thtr 130 max),
24hr-delegate from £95.50, day-delegate rate from £25
Children: Welcome Dogs: Welcome
Licences:
Parking: Off-street
Directions: One mile from the A1

Rock Lodge

Little Gem

1 Empingham Road, Stamford, Lincolnshire, PE9 2RH
Tel: 01780 481758 Fax: 01780 481757
Email: rocklodge@innpro.co.uk
Web: www.innpro.co.uk
Rooms: 4 all ensuite
Pricing: Sgl £50–90 Dbl £65–90 CC: Accepted
Room facilities:
Children: Welcome
Dogs: Guide dogs only
Parking: Off-street and monitored
Directions: Leave A1 at A606, follow signs to Stamford 1¼ miles. Rock Lodge entrance on left at junction of A606 and B1081.

Candlesticks Hotel & Restaurant

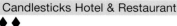 ◆ ◆

1 Church Lane, Stamford,
Lincolnshire, PE9 2JU
Tel: 01780 764033 Fax: 01780 756071
Email: pinto@breathmail.net
Web: www.candlestickshotel.co.uk

A small family hotel run by Mr & Mrs Pinto for 25 years
providing freshly cooked food and luxury bedrooms
with a fridge and Sky TV. Dine in comfortable and
elegant surroundings and enjoy excellent cuisine at a
price you can afford.
Rooms: 8 all ensuite
Pricing: Dinner from £16.50 CC: Accepted
Room facilities:
Children: Welcome
Licences:
Parking: Off-street
Directions: From A1 down St Martin's High Street. Turn
left into Church Street by St Martin's Church.

Stretton, Leicestershire

Ram Jam Inn

 ★ ★

Great North Road, Stretton, near Oakham,
Leicestershire, LE15 7QX
Tel: 01780 410776 Fax: 01780 410361
Email: rji@rutnet.co.uk
Rooms: 7 all ensuite
Pricing: Dinner from £7.95 CC: Accepted
Room facilities:
Children: Welcome
Licences:
Parking: Off-street
Directions: Travelling north on A1, look for hotel sign.
Through service station, just past B668 turn-off.
Southbound, take B668 exit and follow Oakham signs.

Sutton-on-Sea, Lincolnshire

Grange and Links Hotel

 ★ ★ ★

Sea Lane, Sandilands, Mablethorpe,
Lincolnshire, LN12 2RA
Tel: 01507 441334 Fax: 01507 443033
Email: grangelinks@ic24.net
Web: www.grangeandlinkshotel.com

Rooms: 23 all ensuite
Pricing: Sgl £59.50 Dbl £78 Dinner from £20
CC: Accepted
Room facilities:
Access:
Conference: 2 meeting rooms (Thtr 200 max),
24hr-delegate from £85, day-delegate rate from £30
Children: Welcome
Dogs: Welcome
Licences:
Leisure: Gym, Tennis, Golf, Snooker/billiards
Parking: Off-street
Directions: From south, take A16 to Spilsby and
Ulceby Cross. From north, take A16 to Louth and
Ulceby Cross, then A1104 to Alford and A1111 to
Sutton-on-Sea.

Swavesey, Cambridgeshire

Travelodge Cambridge West

Travel Accommodation
A14, Cambridge Road, Swavesey,
Cambridgeshire, CB4 5QR
Web: www.travelodge.co.uk
Rooms: 36 all ensuite
Pricing: Sgl £57.40 Dbl £61.85
CC: Accepted Room facilities: Access:

Thrapston, Northamptonshire

Travelodge Thrapston

Travel Accommodation
A14, Link Road, Thrapston Bypass, Thrapston,
Northamptonshire, NN14 4UR
Web: www.travelodge.co.uk
Rooms: 40 all ensuite
Pricing: Sgl £47.40 Dbl £51.85
CC: Accepted Room facilities: Access:

Towcester, Northamptonshire

Whittlebury Hall Hotel & Spa

Whittlebury Hall, Whittlebury, Nr. Towcester,
Northamptonshire, NN12 8QH
Tel: 01327 857857 Fax: 01327 857669

Travelodge Towcester, Silverstone

Travel Accommodation
A43 East, Towcester Bypass, Towcester,
Northamptonshire, NN12 6TQ
Web: www.travelodge.co.uk
Rooms: 55 all ensuite
Pricing: Sgl £47.40 Dbl £51.85
CC: Accepted Room facilities: Access:

East Midlands

Trowell, Nottingham

Travelodge Nottingham, Trowell (MOTO)

Travel Accommodation
M1 Moto Service Area, Trowell, Nottingham, NG9 3PL
Web: www.travelodge.co.uk
Rooms: 35 all ensuite ⊗
Pricing: Sgl £54.40 Dbl £58.85
CC: Accepted Room facilities: ☐ ☕ Access: ♿

Uppingham, Rutland

Lake Isle

★ ★ 🍴 🍴

16 High Street East, Uppingham, Rutland, LE15 9PZ
Tel: 01572 822951 Fax: 01572 824400
Email: info@lakeislehotel.com
Web: www.lakeislehotel.com

Personally run 18th century hotel situated in pretty
market town of Uppingham. Restaurant offers weekly
changing menus with a wine list of more than 300 wines.
Rooms: 12 all ensuite
Pricing: Sgl £45–62 Dbl £65–84
Dinner from £19.50 CC: Accepted
Room facilities: ☐ ☎ ☕ 🍷
Conference: 1 meeting room
Children: Welcome
Dogs: Welcome
Licences: ▮▮▮
Parking: Off-street
Directions: Via Queen Street to the rear of the property
for parking. On foot, via Reeves Yard.

Old Rectory

◆ ◆ ◆

Belton-in-Rutland, Oakham, Rutland, LE15 9LE
Tel: 01572 717279 Fax: 01572 717343
Email: bb@iepuk.com
Web: www.rutnet.co.uk/orb
Rooms: 6 (4 ensuite) ⊗
Pricing: Sgl £28–35 Dbl £45–60 CC: Accepted
Room facilities: ☐ ☕
Children: Welcome ☕
Dogs: Welcome
Parking: Off-street
Directions: From Leicester A47 take first turn to Belton-
in-Rutland village. Old Rectory is on left after 400
yards.

Travelodge Uppingham (Morcott)

Travel Accommodation
A47, Glaston Road, Morcott, Nr. Uppington, Rutland,
Leicestershire, LE15 8SA
Web: www.travelodge.co.uk
Rooms: 40 all ensuite ⊗
Pricing: Sgl £47.40 Dbl £51.85
CC: Accepted Room facilities: ☐ ☕ Access: ♿

Weedon Bec, Northamptonshire

Globe Hotel

★ ★

High Street, Weedon Bec, Northamptonshire, NN7 4QD
Tel: 01327 340336 Fax: 01327 349058
Email: theglobeatweedon@hotmail.com
Web: www.theglobeatweedon.co.uk
Rooms: 18 all ensuite ⊗
Pricing: Dinner from £7.95 (2002 rate) CC: Accepted
Room facilities: ☐ ☎ ☕
Access: ♿ Children: Welcome 🍴
Dogs: Welcome Licences: ▮▮▮ Parking: Off-street
Directions: From junction 16 M1, take Daventry road
for 3 miles, on junction of A5 and A45.

Woodhall Spa, Lincolnshire

Petwood Hotel

★ ★ ★ 🏅

Stixwould Road, Woodhall Spa, Lincolnshire, LN10 6QF
Tel: 01526 352411 Fax: 01526 353473
Email: reception@petwood.co.uk
Web: www.petwood.co.uk

Delightful Edwardian country house hotel set in 30
acres of secluded gardens and woodland. Home of the
Dambusters during the war. Extensive conference and
special event facilities, 50 bedrooms individually
designed.
Rooms: 50 all ensuite ⊗
Pricing: Sgl £70 Dbl £126 Dinner from £20.50
CC: Accepted Room facilities: ☐ ☎ ☕
Access: ▮▮ ♿ Children: Welcome 🍴 ☕
Dogs: Welcome Licences: ◈ ▮▮▮
Leisure: Beauty salon, Snooker/billiards
Parking: Off-street and monitored
Directions: From Sleaford, take A153 to Tattershall.
Turn left onto B1192 to Woodhall Spa. From Lincoln,
south on B1188 and B1191.

Worksop, Nottinghamshire

Charnwood Hotel

★★★

Sheffield Road, Blyth, Worksop,
Nottinghamshire, S81 8HF
Tel: 01909 591610 Fax: 01909 591429
Email: reception@charnwood-hotel.com
Web: www.charnwood-hotel.com
Rooms: 33 all ensuite
Pricing: Sgl £50–65 Dbl £65–85
Dinner from £19.95 CC: Accepted
Room facilities: 🖥 ☎ ☕
Conference: 3 meeting rooms (Thtr 126 max)
Children: Welcome 🍴
Dogs: Welcome
Licences: ◭ ▮▮▮
Leisure: Gym
Parking: Monitored
Directions: Just off the A1 outside the village of Blyth
on the A634 Sheffield Road.

Lion Hotel

★★★

112 Bridge Street, Worksop,
Nottinghamshire, S80 1HT ｜
Tel: 01909 477925 Fax: 01909 479038
Rooms: 45 all ensuite
Pricing: Dinner from £15 (2002 rate) CC: Accepted
Room facilities: 🖥 ☎ ☕ 🖥
Access: ⇅ Children: Welcome 🍴
Dogs: Welcome Licences: ◭ ▮▮▮
Parking: Off-street and monitored

Travelodge Worksop

Travel Accommodation
A57, St Anne's Drive, Dukeries Mill, Worksop,
Nottinghamshire, S80 3QD
Web: www.travelodge.co.uk
Rooms: 40 all ensuite ⊗
Pricing: Sgl £47.40 Dbl £51.85
CC: Accepted Room facilities: 🖥 ☕ Access: ♿

West Midlands

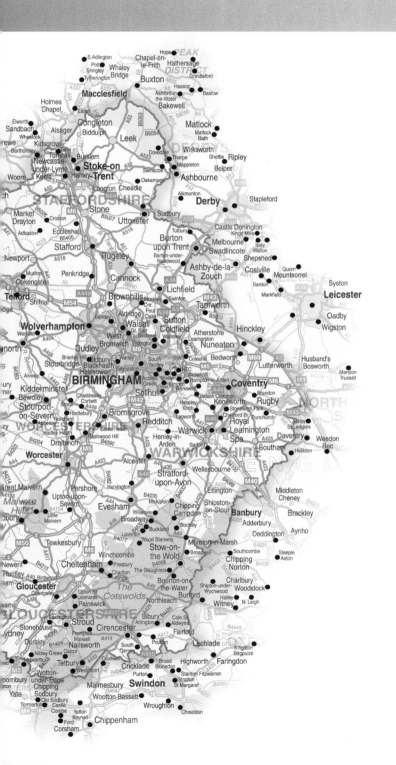

West Midlands

Gold Ribbon Award

Buckland Manor, Broadway	★★★	354
Calcot Manor Hotel, Nr. Tetbury	★★★	385
Castle House, Hereford	★★★	368
Hotel on the Park, Cheltenham	★★★	358
Lords of The Manor, Upper Slaughter	★★★	387
Lower Slaughter Manor, Lower Slaughter	★★★	371
New Hall, A Country House Hotel, Sutton Coldfield	★★★★	384
The Lygon Arms, Broadway	★★★★	354

Blue Ribbon Award

Brockencote Hall Hotel, Kidderminster	★★★	356
Charingworth Manor Hotel, Chipping Campden	★★★	359
Cotswold House, Chipping Campden	★★★	360
Greenway, Cheltenham	★★★	357
Mill At Harvington Hotel, Evesham	★★	365
Old Vicarage Hotel, Bridgnorth	★★★	353
The New Inn At Coln, Coln St-Aldwyns	★★	362
The Painswick Hotel, Painswick	★★★	375

Little Gem

Lower Brook House, Blockley	◆◆◆◆◆	352
Number Twenty-Eight, Ludlow	◆◆◆◆◆	371
Three Choirs Vineyards, Newent	◆◆◆◆◆	374

Alcester, Warwickshire

Travelodge Stratford, Alcester

Travel Accommodation
A46/A435, Birmingham Road, Oversley Mill
Roundabout, Alcester, Warwickshire, B49 6AA
Web: www.travelodge.co.uk
Rooms: 66 all ensuite ⊗
Pricing: Sgl £57.40 Dbl £61.85 CC: Accepted
Room facilities: ☐ ⊚ Access: ♿

Balsall Common, West Midlands

Haigs Hotel

★★ ⓡ ⓡ ⓡ
273 Kenilworth Road, Balsall Common,
West Midlands, CV7 7EL
Tel: 01676 533004 Fax: 01676 535132
Web: www.haigshotel.co.uk
Seasonal closure: Christmas to New Year

Family-run hotel recently refurbished to a high
standard. Award-winning restaurant. Ideally situated 5
miles from the NEC and at hub of Midland motorways.
Close to Warwick and Stratford-upon-Avon.
Rooms: 23 all ensuite ⊗
Pricing: Sgl £75 Dbl £110 Dinner from £21.50
CC: Accepted Room facilities: ☐ ☎ ⊚ ✆
Access: ♿
Conference: 1 meeting room (Thtr 30 max),
24hr-delegate from £130, day-delegate rate from £30
Children: Welcome Dogs: Guide dogs only
Licences: ♦♦♦ Parking: Off-street and monitored
Directions: Close to Junction 4 M6, Junction 6 M42
and Junction 15 M40. Close to Warwick and Stratford,
10 minutes from NEC/Birmingham Airport on A452.

Berkswell, Warwickshire

Nailcote Hall Hotel

★★★★ ⓡ ⓡ ⓡ
Nailcote Lane, Berkswell, Warwickshire, CV7 7DE
Tel: 02476 466174 Fax: 02476 470720
Email: info@nailcotehall.co.uk
Web: www.nailcotehall.co.uk

Charming Elizabethan house in 15 acres of grounds.
Relax in the Piano Bar Lounge, dine in the award-
winning Oak Room Restaurant or Mediterranean
Rick's. Swimming pool, gym, steam room, solarium,
tennis, 9-hole golf course.
Rooms: 40 all ensuite ⊛ ⊚
Pricing: Sgl £150–180 Dbl £160–220
Dinner from £32.50 CC: Accepted
Room facilities: ☐ ☎ ⊚ ✆ Access: ♿ ♿
Conference: 9 meeting rooms (Thtr 100 max),
24hr-delegate from £155, day-delegate rate from £45
Children: Welcome ⱶ ⟨
Dogs: Guide dogs only Licences: ⟨ ♦♦♦
Leisure: Indoor pool, Gym, Tennis, Golf,
Snooker/billiards Parking: Off-street and monitored

Bewdley, Worcestershire

George Hotel

★★ ⓡ
Load Street, Bewdley, Worcestershire, DY12 2AW
Tel: 01299 402117 Fax: 01299 401269
Email: enquiries@georgehotelbewdley.co.uk
Web: www.georgehotelbewdley.co.uk
Rooms: 11 all ensuite ⊟
Pricing: Sgl £49–59 Dbl £69–89 Dinner from £12.50
CC: Accepted Room facilities: ☐ ☎ ⊚
Conference: meeting rooms (Thtr 80 max),
24hr-delegate from £74, day-delegate rate from £25
Children: Welcome ⱶ ⟨ Dogs: Guide dogs only
Licences: ♦♦♦ Parking: Off-street and monitored
Directions: Town centre location, 300m from river. From
M5 Junction 3, A456 to Bewdley. From M5 Junction 6,
A449 to Kidderminster, A456 to Bewdley. From M42
Junction 1, A448 to Kidderminster, A456 to Bewdley.

West Midlands

Bibury, Gloucestershire

The Catherine Wheel

◆ ◆ ◆

Arlington, Bibury near Cirencester,
Gloucestershire, GL7 5ND
Tel: 01285 740250 Fax: 01285 740779
Email: catherinewheel.bibury@eldridge-pope.co.uk
Rooms: 4 all ensuite ⊗
Pricing: Sgl £40 Dbl £60 Dinner from £7.95
CC: Accepted Room facilities: ☐ ☎ ⊿ ☍
Access: ⎙ Children: Welcome ⍑
Dogs: Guide dogs only Licences: ┆┆┆
Leisure: Games room Parking: Off-street
Directions: Located 7 miles from Cirencester. Follow
signs to Burford and Stow from town centre along the
B4425.

Birmingham

Burlington Hotel

★★★★ ℞

6 Burlington Arcade, 126 New Street,
Birmingham, B2 4JQ
Tel: 0121 643 9191 Fax: 0121 628 5005
Rooms: 112 all ensuite ⊠ ⊗
Pricing: Sgl £152–152 Dbl £157–220
Dinner from £20 CC: Accepted
Room facilities: ☐ ☎ ⊿ ☍ Access: ⎙
Conference: 11 meeting rooms (Thtr 400 max),
24hr-delegate from £150, day-delegate rate from £50
Children: Welcome ⍑ ⍧ Dogs: Welcome
Licences: ⎈ ┆┆┆ Leisure: Gym

Copthorne Hotel Birmingham

★★★★ ℞

Paradise Circus, Birmingham, West Midlands, B3 3HJ
Tel: 0121 200 2727 Fax: 0121 200 1197
Email: sales.birmingham@mill-cop.com
Web: www.millenniumhotels.com

Located in the heart of the city centre, this hotel is
ideally located for the NEC, National Indoor Arena and
International Convention Centre. Weekend rates are
also available.
Rooms: 212 all ensuite ⊗
Pricing: Dinner from £18 CC: Accepted
Room facilities: ☐ ☎ ⊿ ☍ Access: ⎙ ⎙
Conference: 12 meeting rooms (Thtr 200 max),

24hr-delegate from £150, day-delegate rate from £50
Children: Welcome ⍑ Dogs: Guide dogs only
Licences: ┆┆┆ Leisure: Indoor pool, Gym
Parking: Off-street and monitored
Directions: Situated by Centenary Square,
approximately 10 minutes from M6 Junction 6, follow
city centre route (A38)

Crowne Plaza Birmingham NEC

★★★★ ℞ ℞

Pendigo Way, NEC, Birmingham,
West Midlands, B40 1PS
Tel: 0121 781 4000 Fax: 0121 781 4321
Email: sales@cpbirminghamnec.com
Web: www.crowneplaza.com
Rooms: 242 all ensuite ⊗ Pricing: Sgl £99–125
Dbl £99–295 Dinner from £30 CC: Accepted
Room facilities: ☐ ☎ ⊿ ☍ ✳ Access: ⎙ ⎙
Conference: 9 meeting rooms (Thtr 192 max),
24hr-delegate from £180, day-delegate rate from £60
Children: Welcome ⍑ Dogs: Guide dogs only
Licences: ⎈ ┆┆┆ Leisure: Gym Parking: Monitored
Directions: M42 exit off junction 6, from roundabout
take directions for NEC, take second exit on left, south
way, hotel entrance right-hand side.

Birmingham Great Barr Hotel

★★★

Pear Tree Drive, Newton Road, Great Barr, Bimingham,
West Midlands, B43 6HS
Tel: 0800 373 853 Fax: 0121 357 9197
Email: sales@thegreatbarrhotel.co.uk
Web: www.thegreatbarrhotel.co.uk

Situated in the leafy suburb of north Birmingham
offering tastefully furnished bedrooms, contemporary
classic designed. Restaurant with a fine range of
international cuisine complemented by a "country pub"
style bar with real open fire.
Rooms: 105 all ensuite ⊗
Pricing: Sgl £48.95–77.95 Dbl £67.90–102.90
Dinner from £17.50 CC: Accepted
Room facilities: ☐ ☎ ⊿
Conference: 10 meeting rooms (Thtr 200 max),
24hr-delegate from £105, day-delegate rate from £30
Children: Welcome ⍑ ⍧ Dogs: Guide dogs only
Licences: ┆┆┆ Parking: Monitored
Directions: Take M6 Exit 7, follow A34 to Birmingham.
Turn right at Scott Arms traffic lights onto Newton
Road. After 1¼ miles, turn right into Pear Tree Drive.

Jurys Inn Birmingham

★★★

245 Broad Street, Birmingham, B1 2HO
Tel: 0870 9072222 Fax: +353(0)1 631 6999
Email: bookings@jurysdoyle.com
Web: www.jurysdoyle.com
Seasonal closure: 24-26 December inclusive

JURYS DOYLE
HOTELS

Rooms: 445 all ensuite
Pricing: Sgl £67–125 Dbl £67–125 Dinner from £17
CC: Accepted Room facilities: ▢ ☎ ☺ ❄
Access: ⊔↑ Children: Welcome ⍵
Dogs: Guide dogs only Licences: ⅰⅰⅰ
Directions: Jurys Inn Birmingham is situated approx 8
miles from Birmingham International Airport, or 1 mile
from New Street train station.

Norfolk Hotel

★★★

267 Hagley Road, Edgbaston, Birmingham,
West Midlands, B16 9NA
Tel: 0121 454 8071 Fax: 0121 455 6149
Email: info@norfolkinn.co.uk
Web: www.norfolkinn.co.uk
Rooms: 169 all ensuite ❤ ☺
Room facilities: ▢ ☎ ☺ ❧ Access: ⊔↑ 占
Conference: 6 meeting rooms (Thtr 80 max),
24hr-delegate from £90, day-delegate rate from £32
Children: Welcome ⍵ Dogs: Welcome
Licences: ◈ ⅰⅰⅰ Parking: Off-street and monitored
Directions: From M6 take exit 6 and head for central
Birmingham. Turn right onto ring road. Turn right onto
A456 to Kidderminster (Hagley Road).

Portland Hotel

★★★

313 Hagley Road, Edgbaston, Birmingham,
West Midlands, B16 9LQ
Tel: 0121 455 0535 Fax: 0121 456 1841
Email: sales@portland-hotel.demon.co.uk
Web: www.portland-birmingham.co.uk
Rooms: 63 all ensuite ☺
Pricing: Dinner from £13.95 (2002 rate) CC: Accepted
Room facilities: ▢ ☎ ☺ Access: ⊔↑
Licences: ⅰⅰⅰ Parking: Monitored
Directions: Hotel is situated on A456, Hagley Road into
Birmingham city centre from M5 Junction 3.

Quality Hotel

★★★

166 Hagley Road, Edgbaston, Birmingham,
West Midlands, B16 9NZ
Tel: 0121 454 6621 Fax: 0121 456 2935
Email: admin@gb605.u-net.com
Web: www.choicehotels.com
Rooms: 215 all ensuite ▨ ☺
Pricing: Sgl £85 Dbl £140

Dinner from £14.50 CC: Accepted
Room facilities: ▢ ☎ ☺ ❧ Access: ⊔↑ 占
Conference: 8 meeting rooms (Thtr 100 max),
24hr-delegate from £95, day-delegate rate from £30
Children: Welcome ⍵ ⍣ Dogs: Guide dogs only
Licences: ◈ ⅰⅰⅰ
Leisure: Indoor pool, Gym, Health spa
Parking: Off-street and monitored
Directions: From M6 take exit 6 and head for central
Birmingham. Turn right onto ring road and right onto
A456 to Kidderminster (Hagley Road).

Quality Sutton Court Hotel

★★★

66 Lichfield Road, Sutton Coldfield,
West Midlands, B74 2NA
Tel: 0121 354 4991 Fax: 0121 355 0083
Email: res@sctt.co.uk Web: www.schotel.co.uk
Rooms: 54 all ensuite ❤ ▨ ☺
Pricing: Dinner from £17 CC: Accepted
Room facilities: ▢ ☎ ☺
Conference: 5 meeting rooms (Thtr 100 max),
24hr-delegate from £120, day-delegate rate from £40
Children: Welcome ⍵ ⍣ Dogs: Welcome
Licences: ◈ ⅰⅰⅰ Parking: Off-street and monitored
Directions: Leave M42 at Junction 9. Take A446
towards Lichfield. Take A453 towards Sutton Coldfield,
hotel is on left at second set of traffic lights.

Beechwood

★★

201 Bristol Road, Edgbaston, Birmingham, B5 7UB
Tel: 0121 440 2133 Fax: 0121 446 4549
Rooms: 28 (20 ensuite) ❤ ▨ ☺
Room facilities: ▢ ☎ ☺ Access: 占
Children: Welcome ⍵ ⍔ Licences: ◈ ⅰⅰⅰ
Parking: Off-street and monitored
Directions: From city centre, proceed on Bristol Road
past traffic lights at McDonalds, hotel is on right, 1 mile
from city centre.

Greswolde Park Hotel

★★

980 Warwick Road, Acocks Green, Birmingham,
West Midlands, B27 6QG
Tel: 0121 706 4068 Fax: 0121 706 0649
Email: jeff@greswolde.freeserve.co.uk
Web: www.greswolde.freeserve.co.uk
Rooms: 10 all ensuite ☺ Room facilities: ▢ ☎ ☺
Children: Welcome ⍵ ⍣ Dogs: Welcome
Licences: ⅰⅰⅰ Leisure: Snooker/billiards
Parking: Off-street and monitored
Directions: From M42 Junction 6 take A45 to
Birmingham. Fork left to Acocks Green, left at island.
Straight down to T-Junction, turn right. Second hotel
on right.

West Midlands

Paragon Birmingham

145 Alcester Street, Birmingham,
West Midlands, B12 OPJ
Tel: 0121 627 0627 Fax: 0121 627 0627

Woodlands Hotel & Restaurant

379–381 Hagley Road, Edgbaston, Birmingham,
West Midlands, B17 8DL
Tel: 0121 420 2341 Fax: 0121 429 3935
Email: hotel@woodlands2000.freeserve.co.uk
Web: www.thewoodlandshotel.co.uk
Rooms: 20 all ensuite 🛏 😊 Pricing: Sgl £45–50
Dbl £56–64 Dinner from £12.50 CC: Accepted
Room facilities: 🖵 ☎ 🍵 🗑
Conference: 1 meeting room (Thtr 40 max)
Children: Welcome Dogs: Guide dogs only
Licences: 🍴 Leisure: Snooker/billiards
Parking: Off-street and monitored

Bridge House Hotel

49 Sherbourne Road, Acocks Green, Birmingham,
West Midlands, B27 6DX
Tel: 0121 706 5900 Fax: 0121 624 5900

Central Guest House

1637 Coventry Road, South Yardley, Birmingham,
West Midlands, B26 1DD
Tel: 0121 706 7757 Fax: 0121 706 7757
Email: mmou826384@aol.com
Web: www.centralguesthouse.com

Small family-run guesthouse having 5 letting bedrooms,
all ensuite rooms. The establishment offers friendly
attentive service and a hearty, freshly cooked breakfast,
full or vegetarian. Bedrooms come in a variety of sizes;
all are nicely decorated & well equipped. Situated on
the main A45 Coventry Road, 4 miles into the
Birmingham city centre, New Street Station, 4 miles to
Birmingham International airport. International railway
station, international exhibition centre.
Rooms: 5 all ensuite 😊 😊
Pricing: Sgl £20–25 Dbl £40–55 CC: Accepted
Room facilities: 🖵 🍵 Children: Welcome 🍼

Dogs: Welcome Parking: Off-street and monitored
Directions: We are just down from the Swan shopping
centre, Yardley, opposite Jet garage.

La Caverna Restaurant and Hotel

23-27 Coventry Road, Sheldon, Birmingham, B26 3PG
Tel: 0121 743 7917/722 2725 Fax: 0121 722 3307
Rooms: 19 all ensuite 😊
Pricing: Sgl £42 Dbl £59 CC: Accepted
Room facilities: ☎ 🍵 Children: Welcome
Licences: 🍷 Parking: Off-street and monitored
Directions: 3 miles from NEC and Airport, close to
junction of Coventry Road and Wells Road.

Lyndhurst Hotel

135 Kingsbury Road, Erdington, Birmingham, B24 8QT
Tel: 0121 373 5695 Fax: 0121 373 5697
Email: info@lyndhurst-hotel.co.uk
Web: www.lyndhurst-hotel.co.uk
Seasonal closure: Christmas
Rooms: 14 all ensuite 😊 😊
Pricing: Sgl £35–45 Dbl £46–58 Dinner from £10
CC: Accepted Room facilities: 🖵 🍵
Children: Welcome Dogs: Guide dogs only
Licences: 🍴 Parking: Off-street
Directions: Exit J6 M6; A5127 to roundabout. Second
left up Gravelly Hill. Right-hand fork along Kingsbury
Road. Hotel on the right.

Tri-Star Hotel

Coventry Road, Elmdon, Birmingham, B26 3QR
Tel: 0121 782 1010 Fax: 0121 782 6131

Ideally situated 2 miles from Junction 6 of the M42,
and 1½ miles from Birmingham International Airport
and the NEC, the hotel maintains a homely atmosphere
at moderate charge. Licensed bar. Ample parking.
Rooms: 15 all ensuite 😊 😊
Pricing: Sgl £49 Dbl £59 CC: Accepted
Room facilities: 🖵 🍵 Children: Welcome 🍴
Licences: 🍴
Leisure: Games room, Snooker/billiards
Parking: Off-street and monitored
Directions: 2 miles from Junction 6 of M42, 1½ miles
from Birmingham International Airport, train station and
National Exhibition Centre.

Comfort Inn

◆ ◆

Station Street, City Centre, Birmingham, B5 4DY
Tel: 0121 643 1134 Fax: 0121 643 3209
Email: comfort.inn@talk21.com
Rooms: 40 (39 ensuite) ⊗
Pricing: Sgl £50–60 Dbl £65–75
Dinner from £15 CC: Accepted
Room facilities: ▢ ☎ ☕ ⬧ Access: |↓↑
Conference: 2 meeting rooms (Thtr 55 max),
24hr-delegate from £80, day-delegate rate from £30
Children: Welcome Dogs: Guide dogs only
Licences: ⟁ ♔♔♔
Directions: Leave M6 at Junction 6. Head for city
centre on A38(M). Follow Queensway to Bromsgrove.
Turn onto Hill Street (near New Street station).

Rollason Wood Hotel

◆ ◆

Wood End Road, Erdington, Birmingham, B24 8BJ
Tel: 0121 373 1230 Fax: 0121 382 2578
Email: rollwood@globknet.co.uk

Friendly family-run hotel with 35 bedrooms. Choose
from economy, with shower, or fully ensuite. Licensed
bar and à la carte restaurant. Weekend and weekly
reductions.
Rooms: 35 (17 ensuite) ⊗
Pricing: Dinner from 6 CC: Accepted
Room facilities: ▢ ☕ Children: Welcome
Licences: ♔♔♔ Leisure: Games room Parking: Off-street
Directions: Exit M6 at Junction 6 and take A5127 to
Erdington. At island turn right onto A4040. Hotel ¼
mile on left.

Campanile Hotel

Travel Accommodation
Chester Street, Aston Locks, Birmingham, B6 4BE
Tel: 0121 359 3330 Fax: 0121 359 1223

Campanile hotels offer comfortable and convenient
budget accommodation and a traditional French-style
Bistro providing freshly-cooked food for breakfast,
lunch and dinner. All rooms ensuite with tea/coffee-
making facilities, DDT and TV with pay movie channels.
Rooms: 111 all ensuite ⬧ ⊗
Pricing: Sgl £48.90 Dbl £54.85
Dinner from £6.95 CC: Accepted
Room facilities: ▢ ☎ ☕ ⬧ Access: |↓↑ ⚹
Conference: 5 meeting rooms (Thtr 270 max),
24hr-delegate from £68, day-delegate rate from £19.50
Children: Welcome ♏ Dogs: Welcome
Licences: ♔♔♔ Parking: Off-street and monitored
Directions: Junction 6 of M6, then A38. Take second
exit (ring road), go left at roundabout, then first left into
Richard Street. From city centre, take M6 direction
then ring road/NEC.

Travelodge Birmingham Central (SA)

Travel Accommodation
230 Broad Street, Birmingham, West Midlands, B15 1AY
Web: www.travelodge.co.uk
Rooms: 136 all ensuite ⊗
Pricing: Sgl £57.40–59.40 Dbl £61.85–63.85
CC: Accepted Room facilities: ▢ ☕ Access: ⚹

Travelodge Birmingham, Dudley (SA)

Travel Accommodation
A461, Dudley Road, Brierley Hill, Birmingham,
West Midlands, DY5 1LQ
Web: www.travelodge.co.uk
Rooms: 32 all ensuite ⊗
Pricing: Sgl £49.40 Dbl £53.85
CC: Accepted Room facilities: ▢ ☕ Access: ⚹

Travelodge Birmingham East (SA)

Travel Accommodation
A45, Coventry Road, Yardley, Birmingham,
West Midlands, B26 1DS
Web: www.travelodge.co.uk
Rooms: 40 all ensuite ⊗
Pricing: Sgl £57.40–59.40 Dbl £61.85–63.85
CC: Accepted Room facilities: ▢ ☕ Access: ⚹

Travelodge Birmingham North, Hilton Park

Travel Accommodation
M6 Moto Service Area, Essington, Nr. Wolverhampton,
Staffordshire, WV11 2AT
Web: www.travelodge.co.uk
Rooms: 64 all ensuite ⊗
Pricing: Sgl £54.40 Dbl £58.85–61.85
CC: Accepted Room facilities: ▢ ☕ Access: ⚹

West Midlands

Travelodge Birmingham South. Frankley (MOTO)

Travel Accommodation
M5 Motorway, Illey Lane, Birmingham, B32 4AR
Web: www.travelodge.co.uk
Rooms: 62 ensuite ⊛
Pricing: Sgl £54.40–57.40 Dbl £58.85–61.85
CC: Accepted Room facilities: ☐ ⬓ Access: ⓰

Blockley, Gloucestershire

Lower Brook House   Little Gem

♦ ♦ ♦ ♦ ♦ ♖ ♖ ✖ ♜

Lower Street, Blockley, Nr Moreton in Marsh,
Gloucestershire, GL56 9DS
Tel: 01386 700286 Fax: 01386 700286
Email: lowerbrookhouse@aol.com
Web: www.lowerbrookhouse.co.uk
Rooms: 7 all ensuite ⬓ ⊛
Pricing: Sgl £65–80 Dbl £80–145
CC: Accepted
Room facilities: ☐ ⬓
Conference: 1 meeting room
Children: Welcome ♥ ⬏ ⅋
Dogs: Guide dogs only
Licences: ♦♦♦ Parking: Off-street
Directions: On the A44 between Moreton-in-Marsh and
Broadway take turning to Blockley. Go down road and
into valley and car park.
See advert on this page

Lower Brook House

A 17th-century Country House
by a babbling brook set in an idyllic village.
Little Gem Winner together with numerous awards.
Seven tastefully appointed ensuite rooms filled with
little luxuries to ensure a memorable visit.
Wine & Dine in comfortable surroundings.
Good food, fine wine and unique hospitality.

Lower Street, Blockley,
Gloucestershire GL56 9DS

Tel: 01386 700286   Fax: 01386 700286
Email: lowerbrookhouse@aol.com
Website: www.lowerbrookhouse.co.uk

Little Gem

Bourton-on-the-Water, Gloucestershire

Chester House Hotel

★★

Victoria Street, Bourton-on-the-Water,
Gloucestershire, GL54 2BU
Tel: 01451 820286 Fax: 01451 820471
Email: juliand@chesterhouse.u-net.com
Web: www.chesterhouse.u-net.com
Seasonal closure: December to January
Rooms: 22 all ensuite ⬲ ⬚
Pricing: Sgl £65–65 Dbl £85–115 Dinner from £16.95
CC: Accepted Room facilities: ☐ ☎ ⬓ Access: ⓰
Children: Welcome ♥ ⅋ Dogs: Welcome
Licences: ♦♦♦ Parking: Off-street
Directions: In centre of village. Take left road bridge
spanning river, which leads to hotel car park.

The Old New Inn

★★

High Street, Bourton-on-the-Water,
Gloucestershire, GL54 2AF
Tel: 01451 820467 Fax: 01451 810236
Email: reception@theoldnewinn.co.uk
Web: www.theoldnewinn.co.uk

Rooms: 9 all ensuite ⬚
Pricing: Sgl £38 Dbl £76–80 Dinner from £15
CC: Accepted Room facilities: ☐ ⬓
Children: Welcome ♥ Dogs: Guide dogs only
Licences: ♦♦♦ Parking: Off-street
Directions: Situated on the left-hand side of the road at
the junction of the High Street and Rissington Road.

The Kingsbridge Inn

♦ ♦ ♦

The Riverside, Bourton-on-the-Water, Cheltenham,
Gloucestershire, GL54 2BS
Tel: 01451 820371
Rooms: 3 all ensuite ⊛
Pricing: Sgl £49 Dbl £64
Room facilities: ☐ ☎ ⬓ ⌘ ❄
Children: Welcome ♥ Dogs: Guide dogs only
Directions: From north, exit M5 junction 11 Cheltenham,
follow A40 signs for Oxford. Take A436 Stow-on-the-
Wold/Bourton turn-off, follow to A429 intersection, left
and immediate right to Bourton. From south, M40 to
Oxford then A40, A436 and A429, as before.

Bridgnorth, Shropshire

Mill Hotel

★★★★

Alveley, near Bridgnorth, Shropshire, WV15 6HL
Tel: 01746 780437 Fax: 01746 780850
Web: www.theaa.com/hotels/36837.html
Rooms: 21 all ensuite 🍴 💻 ⊗
Pricing: Sgl £77.50–112.50 Dbl £100–135
Dinner from £15 CC: Accepted
Room facilities: ⬜ ☎ 🍵 Access: 🔼 ♿
Children: Welcome 🍴 ⚬ Licences: 🔶 ♙♙
Leisure: Gym Parking: Off-street and monitored
Directions: Situated just off main A442, midway
between Kidderminster and Bridgnorth.

Old Vicarage

★★★★★ ♖ ♖ ♖ Blue Ribbon Winner

Worfield, Bridgnorth, Shropshire, WV15 5JZ
Tel: 01746 716497 Fax: 01746 716552
Email: admin@the-old-vicarage.co.uk
Web: www.oldvicarageworfield.com

Rural, peaceful, country house hotel overlooking rolling
Shropshire countryside. Award-winning wine list and
restaurant, fourteen luxuriously appointed bedrooms. A
warm welcome assured from David & Sarah Blakstad
and their dedicated team.
Rooms: 14 all ensuite 🍴 💻 ⊗
Pricing: Sgl £85–115 Dbl £125–175
Dinner from £22.50 CC: Accepted
Room facilities: ⬜ ☎ 🍵 📠 Access: ♿
Conference: 3 meeting rooms (Thtr 30 max),
24hr-delegate from £140, day-delegate rate from £40
Children: Welcome 🍴 ⚬ Dogs: Welcome
Licences: ♙♙♙ Parking: Off-street and monitored
Directions: The Old Vicarage is 1 mile from the A454
and 2 miles from the A442 to the east of Bridgnorth —
look for the brown signs.
See advert on this page

Parlors Hall Hotel

★★

Mill Street, Bridgnorth, Shropshire, WV15 5AL
Tel: 01746 761931 Fax: 01746 767058
Rooms: 13 all ensuite 📠
Pricing: Sgl £45–45 Dbl £60–66 Dinner from £15
CC: Accepted Room facilities: ⬜ ☎ 🍵
Children: Welcome Dogs: Guide dogs only
Licences: ♙♙♙ Parking: Off-street
See advert on this page

West Midlands

Broadway, Worcestershire

The Lygon Arms
Gold Ribbon Winner

★★★★★★ ⓜ ⓜ ⓡ ⓡ

Broadway, Worcestershire, WR12 7DU
Tel: 020 7950 5495 Fax: 020 7950 5485
Email: info@the-lygon-arms.co.uk
Web: www.the-lygon-arms.co.uk

The Savoy Group's fabulous 16th century inn at
Broadway on the north-west slopes of the Cotswolds,
with the only spa in the country offering Borghese
treatments and make-up by Versace.
Rooms: 69 all ensuite 🐾 🗲
Pricing: Sgl £119–159 Dbl £179–199 CC: Accepted
Room facilities: ▢ ☎ ⊙ ☎ Access: ♿
Conference: 6 meeting rooms (Thtr 80 max),
24hr-delegate from £200, day-delegate rate from £60
Children: Welcome � Dogs: Welcome
Licences: ◈ ⫴⫴⫴
Leisure: Indoor pool, Gym, Health spa, Beauty salon,
Tennis, Snooker/billiards Parking: Off-street
Directions: In the centre the village of Broadway, follow
signs to Broadway from the A44 Oxford–Worcester Road.

Buckland Manor
Gold Ribbon Winner

★★★★ ⓡ ⓡ ⓡ ⓡ

Buckland, Nr. Broadway, Worcestershire, WR12 7LY
Tel: 01386 852626 Fax: 01386 853557
Email: enquire@bucklandmanor.com
Web: www.bucklandmanor.com

13th-century manor situated in the heart of the
Cotswolds, in glorious grounds. Superb food and
wines in award-winning restaurant. Luxury bedrooms
with antiques and four-poster beds.
Rooms: 13 all ensuite 🐾 🗲 Pricing: Sgl £215–350
Dbl £225–360 Dinner from £45.50 CC: Accepted
Room facilities: ▢ ☎
Access: ♿ Children: Welcome, 12yrs min age
Licences: ⫴⫴⫴ Leisure: Outdoor pool, Tennis
Parking: Off-street and monitored
Directions: 2 miles south of Broadway, on B4632.

Dormy House

★★★★ ⓜ ⓡ ⓡ ⓡ

Willersey Hill, Broadway, Worcestershire, WR12 7LF
Tel: 01386 852711 Fax: 01386 858636
Email: reservations@dormyhouse.co.uk
Web: www.dormyhouse.co.uk
Seasonal closure: Christmas

Meticulously converted 17th-century Cotswold
farmhouse combining traditional charm with all the
modern comforts. Leisure facilities include: games room,
gym, sauna/steam room, putting green and croquet lawn.
Rooms: 48 all ensuite 🗲 Pricing: Sgl £82.50–115
Dbl £155–200 Dinner from £33.50 CC: Accepted
Room facilities: ▢ ☎ ⊙ ☎ Access: ♿
Children: Welcome ♙ ⅜ Dogs: Welcome
Licences: ◈ ⫴⫴⫴
Leisure: Gym, Games room, Snooker/billiards
Parking: Off-street
Directions: Off A44 at top of Fish Hill. 1½ miles from
Broadway, take turn signposted Saintbury/picnic area.
After ½ mile fork left. Dormy House on left.

Leasow House Hotel

◆◆◆◆ ⅗

Laverton Meadow, Broadway,
Worcestershire, WR12 7NA
Tel: 01386 584526 Fax: 01386 584596
Email: leasow@clara.net Web: www.leasow.co.uk
Rooms: 7 all ensuite 🐾 ⊘
Room facilities: ▢ ☎ ⊙ ☎ Access: ♿
Children: Welcome Dogs: Welcome
Parking: Off-street and monitored
Directions: From Broadway take B4632 towards
Winchcombe. After 2 miles turn right to Wormington
and Dumbleton. Hotel is first on the right.

Windrush House

◆◆◆◆ ※⚲ ☏

Station Road, Broadway, Worcestershire, WR12 7DE
Tel: 01386 853577
Email: richard@broadway-windrush.co.uk
Web: www.broadway-windrush.co.uk
Rooms: 5 all ensuite ⚙
Pricing: Sgl £45–55 Dbl £55–70 Dinner from £12.50
CC: Accepted Room facilities: ⬜ ☕ ☎
Conference: 1 meeting room (Thtr 20 max),
24hr-delegate from £50, day-delegate rate from £25
Children: Welcome ⼊ Dogs: Welcome
Parking: Off-street and monitored
Directions: Follow Broadway sign from roundabout on
A44 (bypass). Windrush House is near start of Station
Road, opposite junction with B4632.

Bromsgrove, Worcestershire

Hanover International Hotel & Club Bromsgrove

★★★★

Kidderminster Road, Bromsgrove,
Worcestershire, B61 9AB
Tel: 0870 241 7106 Fax: 01527 878981
Email: crso@hanover-international.com
Web: www.hanover-international.com

HANOVER INTERNATIONAL
HOTELS & CLUBS

This magnificent hotel has a distinctive Mediterranean
flavour and charm with an extensive leisure club and a
wealth of local attractions in easy reach.
Rooms: 114 all ensuite ⚙ ⬜ ⚙
Pricing: Sgl £140 Dbl £160
Dinner from £19.50 CC: Accepted
Room facilities: ⬜ ☎ ☕ ☎ Access: ⬆ ♿
Conference: 9 meeting rooms (Thtr 200 max)
Children: Welcome ⼊ ⊱ Dogs: Welcome
Licences: ◇ ♟
Leisure: Indoor pool, Gym, Beauty salon,
Snooker/billiards Parking: Off-street and monitored
Directions: From Junction 4 or 5 M5 or Junction 1
M42, follow A38 into Bromsgrove centre. Follow signs
to Kidderminster (A448). Hotel is 1/2 mile outside
Bromsgrove.

Avoncroft Guest House

◆◆◆◆ ※⚲

77 Redditch Road, Stoke Heath, Bromsgrove,
Worcestershire, B60 4JP
Tel: 01527 832819
Rooms: 4 all ensuite ⚙
Pricing: Sgl £35 Dbl £49.50 Room facilities: ⬜ ☕
Access: ♿ Children: Welcome ⼊ Parking: Off-street
Directions: Exit J1 M42, A38 south 3 miles. J5 M5 A38
north 2 miles, 300 yds from Hanbury turn crossroads.

Burton upon Trent, Staffordshire

Queens Hotel

★★★

One Bridge Street, Burton upon Trent,
Staffordshire, DE14 1SY
Tel: 0870 4603 800 Fax: 0870 4603 801
Email: hotel@burton-conferencing.com
Web: www.burton-conferencing.com
Rooms: 38 all ensuite ⬛ ⚙
Pricing: Sgl £55–95 Dbl £60–100 Dinner from £14.95
CC: Accepted Room facilities: ⬜ ☎ ☕ ☎ Access: ⬆
Conference: 5 meeting rooms (Thtr 100 max), 24hr-
delegate from £99.50, day-delegate rate from £22.50
Children: Welcome ⼊ ⊱ Dogs: Guide dogs only
Licences: ◇ ♟ Parking: Off-street and monitored
Directions: Town centre on corner of Bridge Street and
High Street. From M42 Junction 11 take A444. From
A38 follow town centre.
See advert on this page

West Midlands

Delter Hotel

♦ ♦ ♦ ♦ ⁕

5 Derby Road, Burton upon Trent,
Staffordshire, DE14 1RU
Tel: 01283 535115 Fax: 01283 845261
Email: delterhotel@burtonontrenthotels.co.uk
Web: www.burtonontrenthotels.co.uk
Rooms: 6 all ensuite
Pricing: Sgl £36–47 Dbl £47–60 CC: Accepted
Room facilities: ▢ ☕ Access: ♿
Children: Welcome Dogs: Guide dogs only
Licences: ▮▮▮ Parking: Off-street
Directions: From A511 turn into Derby Road at
roundabout. Hotel 50 yards on left. Or, from A38 join
A5121 Burton north, straight over two roundabouts.
Hotel ¹/₂ mile on right.

Travelodge Burton South

Travel Accommodation
A38 Southbound, Barton Under Needwood,
Burton upon Trent, Staffordshire, DE13 8EH
Web: www.travelodge.co.uk
Rooms: 40 all ensuite ⊗
Pricing: Sgl £49.40 Dbl £53.85
CC: Accepted Room facilities: ▢ ☕ Access: ♿

Travelodge Burton upon Trent (Barton under Needwood)

Travel Accommodation
A38 Northbound, Burton Under Needwood,
Burton upon Trent, Staffordshire, DE13 8EG
Web: www.travelodge.co.uk
Rooms: 20 all ensuite ⊗
Pricing: Sgl £49.40 Dbl £53.85
CC: Accepted Room facilities: ▢ ☕ Access: ♿

Chaddesley Corbett, Worcestershire

Brockencote Hall

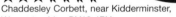
★ ★ ★ ☕ ☕ ☕ ☕   Blue Ribbon Winner

Chaddesley Corbett, near Kidderminster,
Worcestershire, DY10 4PY
Tel: 01562 777876 Fax: 01562 777872
Email: info@brockencotehall.com
Web: www.brockencotehall.com

A beautiful country house hotel set in 70 acres of
parkland, with it's own lake and 16th century dovecote.
Brockencote is full of Gallic charm serving excellent
French cuisine.

Rooms: 17 all ensuite ☕ ▤
Pricing: Sgl £120–140 Dbl £140–180 CC: Accepted
Room facilities: ▢ ☎ ☕ ♨ Access: |↕| ♿
Conference: 2 meeting rooms (Thtr 25 max),
24hr-delegate from £155, day-delegate rate from £38
Children: Welcome ♨ ℃ Dogs: Guide dogs only
Licences: ▮▮▮ Leisure: Tennis Parking: Off-street
Directions: From Exit 4 of M5 or Exit 1 of M42, go into
Bromsgrove and take A448 towards Kidderminster.
Hotel is 5 miles out of Bromsgrove, on left-hand side.

Cheltenham, Gloucestershire

Cheltenham Park Hotel

★ ★ ★ ★ ☕

Cirencester Road, Charlton Kings, Cheltenham,
Gloucestershire, GL53 8EA
Tel: 01242 222021 Fax: 01242 226935
Email: cheltenhampark@paramount-hotels.co.uk
Web: www.paramount-hotels.co.uk

PARAMOUNT
GROUP OF HOTELS

Rooms: 143 ☕ ⊗
Pricing: Sgl £117.25–217.25 Dbl £150.50–224.50
Dinner from £20 CC: Accepted
Room facilities: ▢ ☎ ☕ ♨ Access: ♿
Conference: 13 meeting rooms (Thtr 320 max),
24hr-delegate from £165, day-delegate rate from £51
Children: Welcome ♨ Dogs: Welcome Licences: ◁ ▮▮▮
Leisure: Indoor pool, Gym, Health spa,
Beauty salon, Golf Parking: Off-street
Directions: From M40, follow A40 to Cheltenham, on
approach to town follow A436 (A417) to Gloucester,
after 4¹/₂ miles turn right onto A435, hotel is on right.

The Queen's

★ ★ ★ ★

The Promenade, Cheltenham,
Gloucestershire, GL50 1NN
Tel: 0870 400 8107 Fax: 01242 224145
Email: queens@heritage-hotels.co.uk
Web: www.macdonald-hotels.com
Rooms: 79 all ensuite ▤ ⊗
Pricing: Sgl £69 Dbl £138 Dinner from £22
CC: Accepted Room facilities: ▢ ☎ ☕ ♨ Access: |↕|
Conference: 3 meeting rooms Children: Welcome ♨
Dogs: Welcome Licences: ◁ ▮▮▮
Parking: Off-street and monitored
Directions: Follow town centre signs from A40 (Oxford)
or A46. Situated behind the town hall.

Charlton Kings Hotel

London Road, Charlton Kings, Cheltenham,
Gloucestershire, GL52 6UU
Tel: 01242 231061 Fax: 01242 241900
Email: enquiries@charltonkingshotel.co.uk
Web: www.charltonkingshotel.co.uk

Privately owned hotel in an acre of grounds. Most
rooms have views of the Cotswolds. Bedrooms
beautifully refurbished, few minutes from town centre,
ample parking.
Rooms: 14 all ensuite
Pricing: Sgl £65 Dbl £95–120 Dinner from £13.95
CC: Accepted Room facilities: Access:
Conference: 1 meeting room (Thtr 20 max)
Children: Welcome Dogs: Welcome
Licences: Parking: Off-street and monitored
Directions: First property on left as you enter
Cheltenham from Oxford on A40, or M5 junction 11
then A40 to Oxford.

George Hotel

St George's Road, Cheltenham,
Gloucestershire, GL50 3DX
Tel: 01242 235751 Fax: 01242 224359
Email: hotel@stayatthegeorge.co.uk
Web: www.stayatthegeorge.co.uk

Town centre, privately-owned Regency-style hotel.
Two-minute walk to fashionable shopping areas,
theatre and antique shops. Perfect for both business
and pleasurable breaks. Seasons restaurant serves
modern British cuisine with an international influence.

Rooms: 38 all ensuite
Pricing: Sgl £60–70 Dbl £80–90 Dinner from £21.95
CC: Accepted Room facilities:
Conference: 4 meeting rooms (Thtr 40 max), 24hr-
delegate from £117.45, day-delegate rate from £32.50
Children: Welcome Dogs: Guide dogs only
Licences: Parking: Off-street
Directions: M5 junction 11 — signs to town centre, 1st
traffic lights left into Gloucester Road. Straight on next
lights, turn right into St George's Road, hotel ³/₄ mile on
left.

Greenway

Blue Ribbon Winner

Shurdington, Cheltenham, GL51 4UG
Tel: 01242 862352 Fax: 01242 862780
Email: greenway@btconnect.com
Web: www.the-greenway.co.uk

The Greenway is a charming Elizabethan manor house
dating back to 1587. The hotel enjoys an enviable
reputation throughout the country for its peerless style
and welcoming atmosphere.
Rooms: 21 all ensuite
Pricing: Sgl £89–99 Dbl £140–240
Dinner from £38.50 CC: Accepted
Room facilities: Access:
Conference: 2 meeting rooms (Thtr 45 max),
24hr-delegate from £150, day-delegate rate from £50
Children: Welcome Dogs: Welcome
Licences: Parking: Off-street and monitored
Directions: Located on the A46 Cheltenham to Stroud
Road, approx 1¹/₂ miles from city centre.

West Midlands

Hotel on The Park

★★★ ⓡ ⓡ ⓡ   Gold Ribbon Winner

Evesham Road, Cheltenham, Gloucestershire, GL52 2AH
Tel: 01242 518898 Fax: 01242 511526
Email: stay@hotelonthepark.co.uk
Web: www.hotelonthepark.co.uk

Hotel on the Park offers twelve individually designed
sumptuous bedrooms, the comfiest beds, two very
elegant public rooms, delicious imaginative cuisine,
discreet, unhurried hospitality, and fabulous shopping a
short walk away.
Rooms: 12 all ensuite 🖾
Pricing: Sgl £91.50 Dbl £122.50–172.50 CC: Accepted
Room facilities: 🖳 ☎ ☕ ⚒
Children: Welcome, 8yrs min age Parking: Off-street
Directions: Head for town centre, join one-way system.
Follow signs to Evesham (A435). Join Portland Street,
which becomes Evesham Road. Hotel is on left.

Prestbury House Hotel & Restaurant

★★★ ⓡ

The Burgage, Prestbury, Cheltenham,
Gloucestershire, GL52 3DN
Tel: 01242 529533 Fax: 01242 227076
Email: sandjw@freenetname.co.uk
Web: www.prestburyhouse.co.uk

300-year-old manor house hotel and restaurant (open
to non-residents), set in five acres of secluded
grounds. Cheltenham centre is 1½ miles away. Full
conference and wedding reception facilities.
Rooms: 17 all ensuite 🖾 ⊗
Pricing: Sgl £60–75 Dbl £70–90
Dinner from £23 CC: Accepted
Room facilities: 🖳 ☎ ☕ ⚒
Access: ♿
Conference: 4 meeting rooms (Thtr 70 max),
24hr-delegate from £118, day-delegate rate from £40
Children: Welcome ♀ ⚛ Dogs: Guide dogs only
Licences: ◬ ♦♦♦ Leisure: Gym, Golf, Riding
Parking: Off-street and monitored
Directions: Follow any sign for Cheltenham Racecourse
on entering Cheltenham. Hotel is ½ mile from race
course entrance, signposted from Prestbury village.

The Carlton Hotel

★★★

Parabola Road, Cheltenham, Gloucestershire, GL50 3AQ
Tel: 01242 514453 Fax: 01242 226487
Email: enquirie@thecarltonhotel.co.uk
Web: www.thecarltonhotel.co.uk
Rooms: 76 all ensuite ☕ 🖾 ⊗
Pricing: Sgl £37.50–66.50 Dbl £75–89
Dinner from £18.50 CC: Accepted
Room facilities: 🖳 ☎ ☕ ⚒ Access: ⦀
Children: Welcome ♀ ⚛ Dogs: Welcome
Licences: ◬ ♦♦♦ Parking: Off-street
Directions: Follow signs to Town Hall. At Town Hall,
take middle lane, across traffic lights, past Ladies'
College, left at lights and first right into Parabola Road.

Wyastone Hotel

★★★ ⓡ

Parabola Road, Montpellier, Cheltenham Spa,
Gloucester, GL50 3BG
Tel: 01242 245549 Fax: 01242 522659
Email: reservations@wyastonehotel.co.uk
Rooms: 13 all ensuite 🖾 ⊗
Pricing: Sgl £57–67 Dbl £98 Dinner from £21.25
CC: Accepted Room facilities: 🖳 ☎ ☕ ⚒
Children: Welcome Dogs: Guide dogs only
Licences: ♦♦♦
Parking: Off-street and monitored
Directions: Exit M5 J11; follow A40 to town centre. Turn
right, second roundabout at third exit. Take second exit
to Bayshill Road; Parabola Road bears off left.

Lypiatt House

♦ ♦ ♦ ♦ ♦

Lypiatt Road, Cheltenham, Gloucestershire, GL50 2QW
Tel: 01242 224994 Fax: 01242 224996
Email: stay@lypiatt.co.uk
Web: www.lypiatt.co.uk
Seasonal closure: 2 weeks at Christmas
Rooms: 10 all ensuite
Pricing: Sgl £58–70 Dbl £65–90 CC: Accepted
Room facilities: 🖳 ☎ ☕ ⚒ Dogs: Guide dogs only
Licences: ♦♦♦ Parking: Off-street

Milton House hotel

◆◆◆◆◆

12 Bayshill Road, Cheltenham,
Gloucestershire, GL50 3AY
Tel: 01242 582 601 Fax: 01242 222 326
Email: info@miltonhousehotel.com
Web: www.miltonhousehotel.com
Seasonal closure: 18 December to 10 January
Rooms: 8 all ensuite 🖨 ⊗ Pricing: Sgl £48–60
Dbl £68–92 CC: Accepted Room facilities: ▢ ☎ ⬥ 📞
Access: ♿ Children: Welcome Parking: Off-street
Directions: M5 junction 11, A40 from Oxford, A65 from
Bath/Stroud, at Cheltenham follow Town centre,
Montpellier, then Bayshill Road.

Beaumont House Hotel

◆◆◆◆

56 Shurdington Road, Cheltenham,
Gloucestershire, GL53 0JE
Tel: 01242 245986 Fax: 01242 520044
Email: rocking.horse@virgin.net
Web: www.smoothhound.co.uk/hotels/beauchel.html
Rooms: 16 all ensuite 🖨 ⊗ Pricing: Sgl £52–65
Dbl £68–109 CC: Accepted Room facilities: ▢ ☎ ⬥ 📞
Children: Welcome, 10yrs min age
Licences: ∎∎∎ Parking: Off-street
Directions: From A40 follow A6. From M4 follow
A419/417 then A46. From M5 exit 11, A40 then A46.

Moorend Park Hotel

◆◆◆◆

Moorend Park Road, Cheltenham,
Gloucestershire, GL53 0LA
Tel: 01242 224441 Fax: 01242 572413
Email: moorendpark@freeuk.com
Web: moorendpark.freeuk.com
Seasonal closure: Christmas to New Year
Rooms: 9 all ensuite ⊗ Pricing: Sgl £48–52
Dbl £58–69 CC: Accepted Room facilities: ▢ ☎ ⬥
Conference: 1 meeting room (Thtr 30 max)
Children: Welcome Dogs: Guide dogs only
Licences: ∎∎∎ Parking: Off-street
Directions: Located on the A46 off M5 Junction 11A.

Strayleaves

◆◆◆

282 Gloucester Road, Cheltenham,
Gloucestershire, GL51 7AG
Tel: 01242 572303 Fax: 01242 572303

This delightfully extended guest house is conveniently
located for railway station, town centre, bus routes,
GCHQ, M5 and Cotswolds. Evening meal and special
offers arranged, ensuite and ground floor rooms, parking.
Rooms: 3 all ensuite ⊗
Pricing: Sgl £25–50 Dbl £50–65
Dinner from £12.50 CC: Accepted
Room facilities: ▢ ⬥
Children: Welcome
Dogs: Guide dogs only Parking: Off-street
Directions: Turn left from rear entrance of Cheltenham
railway station. 300 yards, second house on left. Look
for Strayleaves sign.

Wood Stanway Farmhouse

◆◆◆

Wood Stanway, Nr. Winchcombe, Cheltenham,
Gloucestershire, GL54 5PG
Tel: 01386 584318
Rooms: 3 all ensuite ⊗
Pricing: Sgl £30 Dbl £50
Room facilities: ⬥ Children: Welcome
Dogs: Guide dogs only
Parking: Off-street
Directions: M5 junction 9 A46 (Evesham), approx 4
miles B4077 (Stow), approx 9 miles right crossroads
Wood Stanway Farmhouse right.

Travelodge Cheltenham

Travel Accommodation
Golden Valley Roundabout, Hartherley Lane,
Cheltenham, Gloucestershire
Web: www.travelodge.co.uk
Room facilities: ▢ ⬥ CC: Accepted
Opens 2003

Chipping Campden, Gloucestershire

Charingworth Manor

★★★★ ⬥ ⬥ ⬥   Blue Ribbon Winner

Chipping Campden,
Gloucestershire, GL55 6NS
Tel: 01386 593555 Fax: 01386 593353
Email: charingworthmanor@englishrosehotels.co.uk
Web: www.englishrosehotels.co.uk

Rooms: 26 all ensuite 🖨
Pricing: Sgl £115 Dbl £180
Dinner from £37.50
CC: Accepted Room facilities: ▢ ☎
Conference: 2 meeting rooms (Thtr 30 max), 24hr-
delegate rate from £175, day-delegate rate from £49.50
Children: Welcome ⼘ ⼘ Licences: ⬥ ∎∎∎
Leisure: Indoor pool, Gym, Health spa, Tennis
Parking: Off-street
Directions: From M40 leave at Junction 15. Take A429
towards Stow, then B4035 toward Chipping Camden.
Charingworth Manor is on the right.
See advert on following page

West Midlands

Charingworth Manor

Just 25 minutes from Stratford-upon-Avon, this 14th-century Manor House hotel with individually decorated bedrooms has a reputation for excellent cuisine and attractive accommodation. The hotel's Romanesque leisure spa with pool and gym is the place to unwind. Splendid views and exciting surprises for the avid explorer.

Chipping Campden, Gloucestershire GL55 6NS

RAC Dining Award

Tel: 01386 593555   Fax: 01386 593353
charingworthmanor@englishrosehotels.co.uk
www.englishrosehotels.co.uk

Cotswold House

★★★   Blue Ribbon Winner

The Square, Chipping Campden,
Gloucestershire, GL55 6AN
Tel: 01386 840330 Fax: 01386 840310
Email: reception@cotswoldhouse.com
Web: www.cotswoldhouse.com
Rooms: 20 all ensuite Pricing: Sgl £115–145
Dbl £195–350 Dinner from £20 CC: Accepted
Room facilities: Conference: 3 meeting rooms (Thtr 40 max), 24hr-delegate from £175, day-delegate rate from £50 Children: Welcome
Dogs: Welcome Licences: Leisure: Gym
Parking: Off-street and monitored
Directions: Leave M40 at Junction 15, taking the A429 south towards Cirencester. After 16 miles turn right onto B4035, signposted Campden.

Seymour House Hotel

★★★

High Street, Chipping Campden,
Gloucestershire, GL55 6AH
Tel: 01386 840429 Fax: 01386 840369
Email: enquiry@seymourhousehotel.com
Web: www.seymourhousehotel.com
Rooms: 15 all ensuite Pricing: Sgl £72.50–150
Dbl £95–180 Dinner from £20 CC: Accepted
Room facilities:
Conference: 3 meeting rooms (Thtr 65 max)
Children: Welcome Dogs: Guide dogs only
Licences: Parking: Off-street
Directions: Hotel to be found in town centre.

Three Ways House Hotel

★★★★

Mickleton, Chipping Campden,
Gloucestershire, GL55 6SB
Tel: 01386 438429 Fax: 01386 438118
Email: threeways@puddingclub.com
Web: www.puddingclub.com
Rooms: 41 all ensuite Pricing: Sgl £72–80
Dbl £98–135 Dinner from £25 CC: Accepted
Room facilities: Access:
Conference: 3 meeting rooms (Thtr 80 max), 24hr-delegate from £130, day-delegate rate from £38
Children: Welcome Dogs: Welcome
Licences: Parking: Off-street and monitored
Directions: Situated on the B4632 in the centre of Mickleton Village.

Nineveh Farm

♦ ♦ ♦ ♦

Campden Road, Mickleton, Chipping Campden,
Gloucestershire, GL55 6PS
Tel: 01386 438923
Email: stay@ninevehfarm.co.uk
Web: www.ninevehfarm.co.uk
Rooms: 5 all ensuite Pricing: Sgl £45–45
Dbl £55–55 CC: Accepted Room facilities:
Children: Welcome, 5yrs min age Parking: Off-street
Directions: Close to Mickleton Village, 3 miles from Chipping Campden (B4081) and 8 miles from Stratford-upon-Avon (B4632).

Church Stretton, Shropshire

Travellers Rest Inn

♦ ♦ ♦

Upper Affcot, Church Stretton, Shropshire, SY6 6RL
Tel: 01694 781275 Fax: 01694 781555
Email: reception@travellersrestinn.co.uk
Web: www.travellersrestinn.co.uk
Rooms: 12 all ensuite
Pricing: Dinner from £7 CC: Accepted
Room facilities: Access:
Children: Welcome Dogs: Welcome
Licences: Leisure: Games room Parking: Off-street
Directions: Situated on west side of A49, 5 miles south of Church Stretton, near the villages of Bushmore and Wistanstow.

Cirencester, Gloucestershire

Fleece Hotel

★★★

Market Place, Cirencester, Gloucestershire, GL7 2NZ
Tel: 01285 658507 Fax: 01285 651017
Email: relax@fleecehotel.co.uk
Rooms: 26 all ensuite
Pricing: Dinner from £13.95 CC: Accepted
Room facilities: Children: Welcome
Dogs: Welcome Licences: Parking: Off-street
Directions: Follow signs for the town centre. The Fleece has a black-and-white Tudor front.

Corinium Hotel & Marchants Restaurant

12 Gloucester Street, Cirencester,
Gloucestershire, GL7 2DG
Tel: 01285 659711 Fax: 01285 885807
Email: info@coriniumhotel.co.uk
Web: coriniumhotel.co.uk
Rooms: 15 all ensuite
Pricing: Sgl £75–95 Dbl £75–95 Dinner from £7.50
CC: Accepted Room facilities:
Children: Welcome
Dogs: Welcome Licences: Parking: Off-street
Directions: ¼ mile north of church in town centre, car
park off Spitalgate Lane, turn towards town from traffic
lights on A419.

Wild Duck Inn

Drakes Island, Ewen, Gloucestershire, GL7 6BY
Tel: 01285 770310 Fax: 01285 770924
Email: wduckinn@aol.com
Web: www.thewildduckinn.co.uk
Rooms: 11 all ensuite
Pricing: Sgl £60 Dbl £80–100 Dinner from £6.95
CC: Accepted Room facilities: Access:
Children: Welcome Dogs: Welcome
Licences: Parking: Off-street and monitored
Directions: From Cirencester take A429 towards
Malmesbury and M4. At Kemble turn left to Ewen. The
Wild Duck is in the centre of the village.
See advert on this page

Jolifleur

London Road, Poulton, Cirencester, Gloucestershire,
GL7 5JG
Tel: 01285 850118 Fax: 01285 850118
Email: jolifleur40@hotmail.com
Rooms: 2
Pricing: Sgl £28 Dbl £48
Room facilities: Access: Children: Welcome
Dogs: Guide dogs only Parking: Off-street
Directions: Midway between Cirencester and Fairford
on the A417.

The Bungalow

93 Victoria Road, Cirencester,
Gloucestershire, GL7 1ES
Tel: 01285 654179 Fax: 01286 656159
Email: cbeard7@compuserve.com
Rooms: 6 all ensuite
Room facilities: Access:
Children: Welcome Parking: Off-street
Directions: From town centre, church is on left,
proceed to traffic lights. Turn right into Victoria Road.
The Bungalow is two-thirds down road on left.

Travelodge Cirencester

Travel Accommodation
A417/A429, Burford Road, Cirencester,
Gloucestershire
Web: www.travelodge.co.uk
Pricing: Sgl £54.40 Dbl £58.85 CC: Accepted
Room facilities:

Coleshill, Warwickshire

Old Barn Guest House

◆ ◆ ◆

Birmingham Road, Coleshill, Warwickshire, B46 1DP
Tel: 01675 463692 Fax: 01675 466275
Rooms: 11 all ensuite ♨ Ⓢ
Pricing: Sgl £37.50–49 Dbl £63.50–75
CC: Accepted
Room facilities: Children: Welcome
Licences: ♦♦♦ Leisure: Indoor pool, Games room
Parking: Off-street
Directions: From M6 Junction 4, turn onto A446
towards Coleshill. Turn left at island onto B4114. Old
Barn ¼ mile on the left.

Coln St-Aldwyns, Gloucestershire

New Inn At Coln

★ ★ ★ ℞ ℞ ℞   *Blue Ribbon Winner*

Coln St-Aldwyns, near Cirencester,
Gloucestershire, GL7 5AN
Tel: 01285 750651 Fax: 01285 750657
Email: stay@new-inn.co.uk
Web: www.new-inn.co.uk

An exceptional 16th-century coaching inn set in an
idyllic Cotswold Village. Wonderful food in bar and
restaurant. Quality bedrooms and attentive, courteous
staff. Great walking countryside.
Rooms: 14 all ensuite 🗗
Pricing: Sgl £80–125 Dbl £110–140 Dinner from £25
CC: Accepted Room facilities: 🖵 ☎ 🛋
Conference: 1 meeting room (Thtr 20 max),
24hr-delegate from £135, day-delegate rate from £48
Children: Welcome, 10yrs min age �
Dogs: Welcome Licences: ♦♦♦
Parking: Off-street
Directions: From Burford (A40), take B4425 towards
Bibury; turn left after Aldsworth.
See advert on next page

Coventry, West Midlands

Brooklands Grange Hotel and Restaurant

★ ★ ★ ★ ℞ ℞

Holyhead Road, Coventry, West Midlands, CV5 8HX
Tel: 02476 601601 Fax: 02476 601277
Email: brooklands.grange@virgin.net
Web: www.brooklands-grange.co.uk

Originally a 16th century Jacobean farmhouse,
sympathetically restored and refurbished, to combine
original character with modern facilities. Set in a semi-
rural location, 8 miles from the NEC and within easy
access to all major Midland motorway networks.
Rooms: 31 all ensuite ♨ Ⓢ
Pricing: Sgl £50–90 Dbl £70–125
Dinner from £10 CC: Accepted
Room facilities: 🖵 ☎ 🛋
Access: ♿
Conference: 1 meeting room (Thtr 18 max),
24hr-delegate from £140, day-delegate rate from £30
Children: Welcome Ꝑ
Licences: ◭ ♦♦♦
Parking: Off-street and monitored
Directions: Situated on the A4114, just off the A45, five
minutes to the city's cathedral and only 8 miles from
NEC and Birmingham International Airport.

The Brandon Hall

★ ★ ★

Brandon, Coventry, Warwickshire, CV8 3FW
Tel: 0870 4008105 Fax: 02476 544909
Email: brandonhall@heritage-hotels.co.uk
Web: www.macdonald-hotels.co.uk
Rooms: 60 all ensuite 🗗 Ⓢ
Pricing: Sgl £52.50 Dbl £105 Dinner from £25
CC: Accepted Room facilities: 🖵 ☎ 🛋 📞
Access: ♿
Conference: 7 meeting rooms (Thtr 106 max)
Children: Welcome ☕
Dogs: Welcome
Licences: ◭ ♦♦♦ Leisure: Golf, Riding
Parking: Off-street and monitored

Tulip Inn Stoneleigh Park

National Agricultural Centre, Stoneleigh Park,
Nr. Coventry, Warwickshire, CV8 2LZ
Tel: 02476 690123 Fax: 02476 690789
Email: info@tulipinnstoneleigh.com
Web: www.tulipinnstoneleigh.com
Rooms: 58 all ensuite
Pricing: Sgl £45–94 Dbl £60–90 Dinner from £9.75
CC: Accepted Room facilities: 🖵 ☎ 🖳 📠 Access: ♿
Conference: 1 meeting room (Thtr 15 max),
24hr-delegate from £95, day-delegate rate from £30
Children: Welcome Dogs: Welcome
Licences: ♦♦♦ Parking: Off-street and monitored
Directions: From M40 junction 15, follow A46 towards
Coventry, second exit A452, turn right towards
Leamington, follow signs NAC Stoneleigh Park.

Mobile traffic information

Just dial 1740* from any mobile
phone to get up-to-the-minute
RAC traffic information on
motorways and major A roads.
Try it now! *Calls to 1740 cost up to 59p
per minute. Check with your network.

Campanile Hotel Grille

Travel Accommodation
4 Wigston Road, Walsgrave, West Midlands, CV2 2SD
Tel: 02476 622311 Fax: 02476 602362

Typical Campanile bedroom

Campanile hotels offer comfortable and convenient
budget accommodation and a traditional French-style
Bistro providing freshly-cooked food for breakfast,
lunch and dinner. All rooms ensuite with tea/coffee-
making facilities, DDT and TV with Sky channels.
Rooms: 47 all ensuite
Pricing: Sgl £43.50–47.90 Dbl £49.45–53.85
Dinner from £6.50 CC: Accepted
Room facilities: 🖵 ☎ 🖳 📠 Access: ♿
Conference: 1 meeting room (Thtr 30 max),
24hr-delegate from £68, day-delegate rate from £19.50
Children: Welcome Dogs: Welcome
Licences: ♦♦♦ Parking: Off-street and monitored
Directions: The hotel is off M6 Junction 2. Take the
A4600 for ³/₄ mile and turn right on second roundabout.

West Midlands

Droitwich, Worcestershire

The Old Farmhouse

◆◆◆◆◆

Hadley Heath, Ombersley, near Droitwich,
Worcestershire, WR9 0AR
Tel: 01905 620837 Fax: 01905621722
Email: judylambe@ombersley.demon.co.uk
Web: www.the-old-farmhouse.com
Rooms: 5 (3 ensuite) ⊛ Room facilities: ▢ ☕
Children: Welcome ⊭ Dogs: Welcome
Leisure: Tennis Parking: Off-street and monitored
Directions: Exit J6 M5, A449 towards Kidderminster;
turn right to Hadley; third house 1 mile on right. From
J5, take A38, A4133 for 1 mile, then left to end of lane.

Travelodge Droitwich

Travel Accommodation
A38, Rashwood Hill, Droitwich,
Worcestershire, WR9 8DA
Web: www.travelodge.co.uk
Rooms: 32 all ensuite ⊛
Pricing: Sgl £59.40 Dbl £63.85
CC: Accepted Room facilities: ▢ ☕ Access: ⅊

Dudley, West Midlands

Copthorne Hotel Merry Hill Dudley

★★★★

The Waterfront, Level Street, Brierley Hill, Dudley,
West Midlands, DY5 1UR
Tel: 01384 482882 Fax: 01384 482773
Email: sales.mhdudley@mill-cop.com
Web: www.millenniumhotels.com

Modern 138-bedroom hotel in an attractive waterfront
setting in the heart of the Midlands. Faradays bar &
restaurant offers a wide range of Mediterranean dishes.
Rooms: 138 all ensuite ⊛
Pricing: Sgl £40–140 Dbl £50–140
Dinner from £14 CC: Accepted
Room facilities: ▢ ☎ ☕ 🍷 Access: ⊔⊔ ⅊
Conference: 8 meeting rooms (Thtr 600 max),
24hr-delegate from £175, day-delegate rate from £65
Children: Welcome ⊭ Dogs: Guide dogs only
Licences: ⅏⅏⅏ Leisure: Indoor pool, Gym,
Beauty salon Parking: Off-street and monitored
Directions: Leave M5 at Junction 2. Follow A4123 for
Dudley. After 2½ miles follow signs for A461 to
Stourbridge/Merry Hill Centre.

Eccleshall, Staffordshire

Glenwood

◆◆◆

Croxton, Stafford, Staffordshire, ST21 6PF
Tel: 01630 620238
Rooms: 3 (1 ensuite) ⊛
Pricing: Sgl £20–23 Dbl £38–42
Room facilities: ☕ Children: Welcome ⊭
Dogs: Welcome Parking: Off-street
Directions: Leave M6 at Junction 14. Travel to
Eccleshall. Take B5026 to Loggerheads. After 3 miles,
enter the village of Croxton. The Cottage is on right.

Evesham, Worcestershire

Evesham Hotel

★★★★ ⍨

Cooper's Lane, off Waterside, Evesham,
Worcestershire, WR11 1DA
Tel: 01386 765566 Fax: 01386 765443
Email: reception@eveshamhotel.com
Web: www.eveshamhotel.com
Rooms: 40 all ensuite ⍩ ⊛
Pricing: Sgl £71–83 Dbl £108–113
Dinner from £21 CC: Accepted
Room facilities: ▢ ☎ ☕ Access: ⅊
Conference: 1 meeting room (Thtr 12 max)
Children: Welcome ⊭ ⅊ Dogs: Welcome
Licences: ⅏⅏⅏ Leisure: Indoor pool, Games room
Parking: Off-street
Directions: Cooper's Lane runs off Waterside, the road
that runs along the River Avon.

Northwick Hotel

★★★

Waterside, Evesham, Worcestershire, WR11 1BT
Tel: 01386 40322 Fax: 01386 41070
Email: enquiries@northwickhotel.co.uk
Web: www.northwickhotel.co.uk
Rooms: 31 all ensuite ⍩ ⍣ ⊛
Pricing: Sgl £66–66 Dbl £95–120
Dinner from £22.50 CC: Accepted
Room facilities: ▢ ☎ ☕ 🍷 Access: ⅊
Conference: 3 meeting rooms (Thtr 160 max),
24hr-delegate from £105, day-delegate rate from £30
Children: Welcome ⊭ Dogs: Welcome
Licences: ⟁ ⅏⅏⅏ Parking: Off-street and monitored
Directions: M5 J9, follow signposts to Evesham for 11
miles, then follow road signposted to town centre. Turn
right at bridge and follow signs for Northwick Hotel.
Hotel is ½ mile on right.

Mobile traffic information

Just dial 1740* from any mobile
phone to get up-to-the-minute
RAC traffic information on
motorways and major A roads.
Try it now! *Calls to 1740 cost up to 59p
per minute. Check with your network.

Mill at Harvington

★★ 🎀 🎀 *Blue Ribbon Winner*

Anchor Lane, Harvington, Evesham,
Worcestershire, WR11 8PA
Tel: 01386 870688 Fax: 01386 870688
Email: millatharvington@aol.com

Tastefully converted beautiful Georgian house and
former baking mill, set in acres of parkland on the
banks of the River Avon, ½ mile from the main road.
Rooms: 21 all ensuite
Pricing: Sgl £65–89 Dbl £89–129 Dinner from £12
CC: Accepted Room facilities: 🖵 ☎ 🍵
Conference: 1 meeting room (Thtr 12 max),
24hr-delegate from £105, day-delegate rate from £35
Children: Welcome, 10yrs min age ❡
Dogs: Guide dogs only Licences: ♦♦♦
Leisure: Outdoor pool, Tennis, Fishing,
Parking: Off-street and monitored
Directions: Turn south off the Norton/Bidford Road
opposite Harvington Village, 4 miles northeast of
Evesham. Hotel 600 yards on left.

Falfield, Gloucestershire

Pipers Lodge

Bristol Road, Falfield, South Gloucestershire,
GL12 8DF
Tel: 01454 260485 Fax: 01454 260812
Seasonal closure: Christmas
Rooms: 4 all ensuite 🍵
Pricing: Sgl £30–35 Dbl £45–50 CC: Accepted
Room facilities: 🖵 🍵 Children: Welcome ♰
Dogs: Welcome Parking: Off-street and monitored
Directions: J14 M5, Falfield Village on A38, last house in
village on right-hand side going south towards Bristol.

Fownhope, Herefordshire

Green Man Inn

★★

Fownhope, Herefordshire, HR1 4PE
Tel: 01432 860243 Fax: 01432 860207
Email: enquries@thegreenmaninn.fsnet.co.uk
Web: www.smoothhound.co.uk/hotels/greenman.html
Rooms: 20 all ensuite 🍵 🛏
Pricing: Sgl £39.50–40.50 Dbl £67.50–69.50
Dinner from £10.95 CC: Accepted

Room facilities: 🖵 ☎ 🍵 Access: ♿
Children: Welcome ♰ ❡ Dogs: Welcome
Licences: ♦♦♦
Leisure: Indoor pool, Gym, Health spa,
Beauty salon
Parking: Off-street and monitored
Directions: From M50 take Ledbury Road (A449). After
2 miles, turn left onto B4224 Fownhope for 5 miles.
Green Man is in centre of village on left.

Gloucester, Gloucestershire

Kings Head Inn

♦♦♦ ✁

Birdwood, Huntley, Gloucestershire, GL19 3EF
Tel: 01452 750348 Fax: 01452 750348
Rooms: 6 all ensuite 🍵
Pricing: Sgl £30 Dbl £40 Dinner from £4.50
CC: Accepted Room facilities: 🖵 🍵
Conference: 2 meeting rooms (Thtr 50 max)
Children: Welcome ♰
Licences: ♦♦♦
Leisure: Beauty salon, Games room, Snooker/billiards
Parking: Off-street and monitored
Directions: Take A40 from Gloucester to Ross-on-Wye.
We are about 6 miles from Gloucester on left-hand side
with row of flag poles on front of large car park.

West Midlands

The Little Thatch

◆ ◆ ◆

141 Bristol Road, Quedgeley, Gloucester,
Gloucestershire, GL2 4PQ
Tel: 01452 720687 Fax: 01452 724141
Email: info@thelittlethatch.co.uk
Web: www.thelittlethatch.co.uk
Rooms: 22 all ensuite 🍽 🚫 Pricing: Sgl £43 Dbl £48
Dinner from £20CC: Accepted
Room facilities: 🖵 ☎ 🍵 Children: Welcome � ☕
Dogs: Guide dogs only Licences: 🜲 ♟
Parking: Off-street
Directions: Exit M5 junction 12, follow directions to
Severn Vale shopping centre, B4008 to Quedgeley.
Just past Tesco roundabout on the right.
See advert on previous page

Great Malvern, Worcestershire

Thornbury House Hotel

★ ★

16 Avenue Road, Great Malvern,
Worcestershire, WR14 3AR
Tel: 01684 572273 Fax: 01684 577042
Email: thornburyhousehotel@compuserve.com
Rooms: 17 all ensuite 🍽 📠 🚫
Pricing: Dinner from £5 (2002 rate) CC: Accepted
Room facilities: 🖵 🍵 Children: Welcome ♟
Dogs: Welcome Licences: ♟ Parking: Off-street
Directions: Follow signs for Great Malvern Railway
Station. Hotel is situated just above the station.

Hampton in Arden, West Midlands

Cottage Guest House

◆ ◆ ◆

Kenilworth Road, Hampton in Arden,
West Midlands, B92 0LW
Tel: 01675 442323 Fax: 01675 443323
Web: www.smoothhound.co.uk/cottage.html
Rooms: 9 all ensuite 🚫
Pricing: Sgl £30–35 Dbl £46–56
Room facilities: 🖵 🍵 Access: ♿ Children: Welcome ♟
Dogs: Welcome Parking: Off-street and monitored
Directions: 3 miles from J6 M42; 4 miles J4 M6; NEC 3
miles, Birmingham Airport 3 ½ miles, National
Motorcycle Museum 3 miles. Telephone and we send
you a map.

Hartlebury, Worcestershire

Yew Tree House

◆ ◆ ◆ ◆ ✒

Norchard, Crossway Green, Hartlebury,
Worcestershire, DY13 9SN
Tel: 01299 250921 Fax: 01299 253472
Email: paul@knightp.swinternet.co.uk
Web: www.yewtreeworcester.co.uk

Elegant Georgian farmhouse and cider house cottage,
both with a wealth of beams and shrouded in history.
Warm welcome, splendid breakfast, 10 minutes from
M5, excellent eating establishments close by.
Rooms: 4 all ensuite 🍽 🚫
Pricing: Sgl £30–35 Dbl £50–55 Dinner from £15
Room facilities: 🖵 🍵 Children: Welcome
Dogs: Welcome Leisure: Tennis Parking: Off-street
Directions: Take Norchard sign at Crossway Green
roundabout on A449, down lane, round sharp left
bend; Yew Tree House is 150 yards on the left.

Henley-in-Arden, Warwickshire

Lapworth Lodge

◆ ◆ ◆

Bushwood Lane, Lapworth, Henley-in-Arden,
Warwickshire, B94 5PJ
Tel: 01564 783038 Fax: 01564 783635

Hereford, Herefordshire

Belmont Lodge & Golf

★ ★ ★

Belmont, Hereford, HR2 9SA
Tel: 01432 352666 Fax: 01432 358090
Email: info@belmont-hereford.co.uk
Web: www.belmont-hereford.co.uk

Belmont Lodge has 30 ensuite bedrooms, 26 twin
rooms and 4 superior rooms with splendid views over
both the golf course and River Wye.
Rooms: 30 all ensuite 🍽 🚫
Pricing: Sgl £47.40–57.40 Dbl £54.25–64.85
Dinner from £14.95 CC: Accepted
Room facilities: 🖵 ☎ 🍵 🔌 Access: ♿
Conference: 2 meeting rooms (Thtr 50 max),
24hr-delegate from £64.50, day-delegate rate from £21
Children: Welcome ♟ Dogs: Guide dogs only
Licences: ♟ Leisure: Tennis, Golf, Fishing
Parking: Off-street and monitored
Directions: Situated southwest of Hereford on the A456
Hereford to Abergavenny Road, 1 ½ miles from
Hereford city centre.

THE MOST ELEGANT HOTEL IN HEREFORD

Sited in Castle Street, formerly the historic crossroads of Norman Hereford, Castle House is a gracious and hospitable town house with just fifteen rooms where guests can enjoy unashamed luxury and unrivalled personal attention.

The award-winning restaurant 'La Rive' promises to be an exquisite experience with impeccable service and outstanding cuisine.
For guests staying on business, there is a fully equipped office for their exclusive use and Castle House is accessible for guests with walking difficulties.

With quiet garden views over the tranquil moat, and barely a hundred metres stroll from the Cathedral with its world famous Chained Library and Mappa Mundi, Castle House is centrally located in the heart of rural Herefordshire.

Castle
HOUSE

Castle House, Castle Street, Hereford, England, HR1 2NW
Tel: +44(0)1432 356321 Fax: +44(0)1432 365909 Email: info@castlehse.co.uk www.castlehse.co.uk

Castle House

Gold Ribbon Winner

★★★★ R R R R R

Castle Street, Hereford, Herefordshire, HR1 2NW
Tel: 01432 356321 Fax: 01432 365909
Email: info@castlehse.co.uk
Web: www.castlehse.co.uk
Rooms: 15 all ensuite 🛏 ⊛
Pricing: Sgl £90 Dbl £155
Dinner from £25 CC: Accepted
Room facilities: 🖵 ☎ 🌣 ❄ Access: ⫼ ♿
Children: Welcome ⋔ Dogs: Welcome
Licences: 🔔 ⅲ Parking: Off-street and monitored
Directions: Follow signs for city centre, then city centre
east. At the end of St Owen Street, right into Ethelbert
Street, then right into Castle Street.
See advert on previous page

Green Dragon

★★★

Broad Street, Hereford, Herefordshire, HR4 9BG
Tel: 0870 400 8113 Fax: 01432 352 139
Web: www.macdonaldhotels.co.uk
Rooms: 83 all ensuite ⇌ 🛏 ⊛
Pricing: Sgl £54 Dbl £108
Dinner from £15 CC: Accepted
Room facilities: 🖵 ☎ 🍵 Access: ⫼
Conference: 7 meeting rooms (Thtr 120 max)
Children: Welcome ⋔ Dogs: Welcome
Licences: 🔔 ⅲ Parking: Off-street and monitored

Three Counties Hotel

★★★

Belmont Road, Hereford, Herefordshire, HR2 7BP
Tel: 01432 299955 Fax: 01432 275114
Email: enquiries@threecountieshotel.co.uk
Web: www.threecountieshotel.co.uk

Modern hotel with a relaxing atmosphere and beautiful
scenery on the outskirts of the city. Bedrooms set by a
quiet garden.
Rooms: 60 all ensuite ⇌ ⊛
Pricing: Sgl £39.50–64 Dbl £60–83
Dinner from £17.50 CC: Accepted
Room facilities: 🖵 ☎ 🍵 🌣 Access: ♿
Conference: 5 meeting rooms (Thtr 350 max),
24hr-delegate from £89, day-delegate rate from £27
Children: Welcome ⋔ ⅈℂ Dogs: Welcome
Licences: 🔔 ⅲ Parking: Off-street
Directions: 1½ miles outside Hereford city on A465 —
the main road to Abergavenny.

Kenilworth, Warwickshire

Peacock Hotel

★★★★ R R

149 Warwick Road, Kenilworth,
Warwickshire, CV8 1HY
Tel: 01926 851156 Fax: 01926 864644
Email: reservations@peacockhotel.com
Web: www.peacockhotel.com

Luxuriously furnished hotel, themed in a vibrant and
colourful decor, offers attractive accommodation
facilities, award-winning cuisine and outstanding
service. Easily accessible from all major routes and is
within minutes of NEC and Birmingham Airport. Close
to Stratford upon Avon and Warwick Castle, it makes
an ideal venue for short breaks.
Rooms: 22 all ensuite ⇌ ⊛
Pricing: Sgl £39–100 Dbl £49–120
Dinner from £9.75 CC: Accepted
Room facilities: 🖵 ☎ 🍵 🌣 Access: ♿
Conference: 5 meeting rooms (Thtr 60 max),
24hr-delegate from £90, day-delegate rate from £34
Children: Welcome ⋔ ⅈℂ Licences: 🔔 ⅲ
Parking: Off-street and monitored
Directions: M40 exit junction 15, A46 north towards
Coventry. Left at A452 signposted Kenilworth and
Leamington, turn at first roundabout to Kenilworth
town centre. Hotel is 200 yds ahead on Warwick Road.

Kidderminster, Worcestershire

Stone Manor Hotel

★★★★ R

Nr Kidderminster, Stone, Worcestershire, DY10 4PJ
Tel: 01562 777555 Fax: 01562 777834
Email: enquiries@stonemanorhotel.co.uk
Web: www.stonemanorhotel.co.uk
Rooms: 57 all ensuite 🛏 ⊛
Pricing: Sgl £96.25–148.75 Dbl £102.50–154.50
Dinner from £22 CC: Accepted
Room facilities: 🖵 ☎ 🍵
Conference: 6 meeting rooms (Thtr 150 max)
Children: Welcome ⅈℂ Dogs: Welcome
Licences: 🔔 ⅲ
Leisure: Outdoor pool, Tennis, Games room
Parking: Off-street and monitored
Directions: From south M40/M42 J1 to A38 and A448
to Kidderminster. From south M5 J6 onto A449, A450
and A448. From north M5 J3, A456 to A450 and A448.

Redfern Hotel

★★★

Lower Street, Cleobury Mortimer,
Shropshire, DY14 8AA
Tel: 01299 270395 Fax: 01299 271011
Email: redfernhotel@btconnect.com
Web: www.redfern-hotel.co.uk
Rooms: 11 all ensuite
Pricing: Sgl £55–75 Dbl £80–130 Dinner from £15
CC: Accepted Room facilities: ☐ ☎ ☐
Conference: 2 meeting rooms (Thtr 30 max),
24hr-delegate from £90, day-delegate rate from £35
Children: Welcome Dogs: Welcome
Licences: Parking: Off-street
Directions: Midway between Ludlow and Kidderminster
(11 miles) on A4117.

Travelodge Hartlebury

Travel Accommodation
A449 Southbound, Shorthill Nurseries, Hartlebury,
Kidderminster, Worchestershire, DY13 9SH
Web: www.travelodge.co.uk
Rooms: 32 all ensuite
Pricing: Sgl £47.40–54.40 Dbl £51.85–58.85
CC: Accepted Room facilities: ☐ ☐ Access: ♿

Kington, Herefordshire

Burton Hotel

★★

Mill Street, Kington, Herefordshire, HR5 3BQ
Tel: 01544 230323 Fax: 01544 230323
Email: burton@hotelherefordshire.co.uk
Web: www.hotelherefordshire.co.uk
Rooms: 15 all ensuite
Pricing: Sgl £42–49 Dbl £64–69 Dinner from £17
CC: Accepted Room facilities: ☐ ☎ ☐
Conference: 3 meeting rooms (Thtr 150 max),
24hr-delegate from £75, day-delegate rate from £28.50
Children: Welcome Dogs: Welcome
Licences: Leisure: Games room
Parking: Off-street and monitored
Directions: 14 miles from Leominster on the A44,
driving due west. Three miles from the Welsh border.

Traffic news

Sign up now for one month's free
trial of RAC Route Minder for
personalised traffic information.
Visit **www.rac.co.uk/routeminder**

Navigation with a difference

ⓘ Smartnav-In-Car satellite navigation
with live traffic information and much
more at a fraction of the cost of
traditional satellite navigation.
Call 0800 096 1740

Leamington Spa, Warwickshire

Angel Hotel

★★★

Regent Street, Leamington Spa,
Warwickshire, CV32 4NZ
Tel: 01926 881296 Fax: 01926 881296
Email: angelhotel143@hotmail.com
Web: www.the-angel-hotel.co.uk
Rooms: 50 all ensuite
Pricing: Sgl £45–75 Dbl £60–85 Dinner from £16.50
CC: Accepted Room facilities: ☐ ☎ ☐ Access: ♿
Conference: 3 meeting rooms (Thtr 40 max),
24hr-delegate from £85, day-delegate rate from £20
Children: Welcome Dogs: Welcome
Licences: Parking: Off-street and monitored
Directions: Leamington Spa junction from M40, head
for town centre. Turn off main parade opposite
Barclay's Bank, up Holly Walk to Archway car park.

Abbacourt Hotel

★★★

40 Kenilworth Road, Leamington Spa, Warwickshire,
CV32 6JF
Tel: 01926 451755 Fax: 01926 886339
Email: abbacourt@maganto.freeserve.co.uk
Web: www.abbacourthotel.com
Rooms: 23 all ensuite
Pricing: Sgl £55–65 Dbl £55–80 Dinner from £10
CC: Accepted Room facilities: ☐ ☎ ☐
Conference: 2 meeting rooms (Thtr 60 max),
24hr-delegate from £86, day-delegate rate from £30
Children: Welcome Dogs: Welcome
Licences: Parking: Off-street
Directions: Heading into Leamington Spa on the A452,
500m after the residential homes begin we are on left.

Adams Hotel

★★

22 Avenue Road, Leamington Spa, Warwickshire,
CV31 3PQ
Tel: 01926 450742 Fax: 01926 313110
Email: bookings@adams-hotel.co.uk
Web: www.adams-hotel.co.uk
Rooms: 12 all ensuite
Pricing: Sgl £58–72 Dbl £72–76 Dinner from £22
CC: Accepted Room facilities: ☐ ☎
Children: Welcome Licences: Parking: Off-street
Directions: Situated on A452/A425 near Victoria Park,
five minutes walk from railway station.

Travelodge Leamington Spa

The Regent Hotel, The Parade, Leamington Spa,
Warwickshire, CV32
Web: www.travelodge.co.uk
Room facilities: ☐ ☐ CC: Accepted
Opens 2003

Ledbury, Herefordshire

Wall Hills Country Guest house

Hereford Road, Ledbury, Herefordshire, HR8 2PR
Tel: 01531 632833 Fax: 01531 632833
Seasonal closure: Christmas and New Year

This Georgian house overlooking Ledbury offers outstanding views, peace and quiet. Excellent wine list. Short breaks available. "Jennifer's warm welcome ushers in David's stupendous dinners" (Country Living magazine).
Rooms: 3 all ensuite
Pricing: Sgl £40–50 Dbl £50–65
Dinner from £16.75 CC: Accepted
Room facilities:
Children: Welcome Licences:
Parking: Off-street
Directions: Leave Ledbury on A438, Hereford Road entrance to drive is within 200 yards on left after roundabout.

Leominster, Herefordshire

Talbot Hotel

★★★

West Street, Leominster, Herefordshire, HR6 8EP
Tel: 01568 616347 Fax: 01568 614880
Email: talbot@bestwestern.co.uk
Rooms: 20 all ensuite
Pricing: Dinner from £13 (2002 rate)
CC: Accepted
Room facilities: Children: Welcome
Dogs: Welcome Licences: P
arking: Off-street
Directions: Talbot Hotel is in the centre of Leominster, found when following the one-way traffic system.

One click does it all

For the latest special offers and online booking, plus detailed information on over 3,000 RAC inspected properties, visit www.rac.co.uk/hotels

Lichfield, Staffordshire

Swinfen Hall Hotel

★★★★★

Swinfen, Near Lichfield, Lichfield, Staffordshire, WS14 9RE
Tel: 01543 481494 Fax: 01543 480341
Email: info@swinfenhallhotel.co.uk
Web: www.swinfenhallhotel.co.uk

Set in picturesque gardens amid rolling Staffordshire farmland, this 18th century manor house, lovingly restored, is now an independent hotel, offering contemporary facilities in a relaxed yet professional atmosphere.
Rooms: 17 all ensuite
Pricing: Sgl £125–175 Dbl £140–195
Dinner from £35
CC: Accepted Room facilities:
Conference: 5 meeting rooms (Thtr 180 max), 24hr-delegate from £160, day-delegate rate from £55
Children: Welcome
Dogs: Guide dogs only
Licences: Leisure: Tennis
Parking: Off-street and monitored
Directions: From London/Birmingham take A38 towards Lichfield after crossing as Swinfen Hall Hotel is clearly marked on the right-hand side.

Angel Croft Hotel

★★

Beacon Street, Lichfield, Staffordshire, WS13 1AA
Tel: 01543 258737 Fax: 01543 415605

Coppers End Guest House

Walsall Road, Muckley Corner, Lichfield, Staffordshire, WS14 0BG
Tel: 01543 372910 Fax: 01543 360423
Rooms: 6 (4 ensuite)
Pricing: Sgl £31–34 Dbl £41–50
CC: Accepted Room facilities:
Children: Welcome Dogs: Guide dogs only
Licences: Parking: Off-street

Lower Slaughter, Gloucestershire

Lower Slaughter Manor　　Gold Ribbon Winner
★★★ ♕ ♕ ♕
Lower Slaughter, Gloucestershire, GL54 2HP
Tel: 01451 820456 Fax: 01451 822150
Email: lowsmanor@aol.com
Web: www.lowerslaughter.co.uk
Rooms: 16 all ensuite 📺 Room facilities: 🖥 ☎
Conference: 1 meeting room (Thtr 20 max),
24hr-delegate from £225, day-delegate rate from £85
Children: Welcome, 12yrs min age
Dogs: Guide dogs only Licences: 🍾
Leisure: Indoor pool, Tennis
Parking: Off-street and monitored
Directions: From A429 Cirencester to Stow-on-the-Wold Road, just 2 miles from Stow, follow signs to The Slaughters just past an Esso garage. Entering the village, the Manor is on the right.

Ludlow, Shropshire

Dinham Hall
★★★★ ♕ ♕
Dinham, Ludlow, Shropshire, SY8 1EJ
Tel: 01584 876464 Fax: 01584 876019
Email: info@dinhamhall.co.uk
Web: www.dinhamhall.co.uk

Centrally located just off the main square yet in a quiet residential street, Dinham is perfectly placed for exploring the town and the ideal base for anyone visiting Ludlow/Shropshire.
Rooms: 14 all ensuite 📺
Pricing: Sgl £75–105 Dbl £130–180 Dinner from £30.50
CC: Accepted Room facilities: 🖥 ☎ 🍵
Conference: 2 meeting rooms (Thtr 43 max),
24hr-delegate from £125, day-delegate rate from £25
Children: Welcome Dogs: Welcome
Licences: ⟁ 🍾 Parking: Off-street
Directions: Turn left at Ludlow Castle: Dinham Hall is 50 metres on left.

Traffic news

Sign up now for one month's free trial of RAC Route Minder for personalised traffic information.
Visit www.rac.co.uk/routeminder

The Feathers Hotel
★★★★ ♕ ♕
The Bull Ring, Ludlow, Shropshire, SY8 !AA
Tel: 01584 875261 Fax: 01584 876030
Email: feathers.ludlow@btconnect.com
Rooms: 40 all ensuite 🍴 📺 🖥
Pricing: Sgl £70–81.75 Dbl £90–113.50
Dinner from £21.95 CC: Accepted
Room facilities: 🖥 ☎ 🍵 🔌 Access: ⛰ ♿
Conference: 3 meeting rooms (Thtr 108 max)
Children: Welcome, 13yrs min age
Dogs: Guide dogs only
Licences: ⟁ 🍾
Parking: Off-street and monitored
Directions: Birmingham to Ludlow M6 M54 then A49 from Shrewsbury, from London M40 M5 then A49 from Hereford.
See advert on this page

Number Twenty Eight　　Little Gem
◆ ◆ ◆ ◆ ◆ ⚡ ♟
28 Lower Broad Street, Ludlow, Shropshire, SY8 1PQ
Tel: 01584 876996 Fax: 01584 876860
Email: ross@no28.co.uk Web: www.no28.co.uk
Rooms: 9 all ensuite 🍵
Pricing: Dbl £80–95 CC: Accepted
Room facilities: 🖥 ☎ 🍵 Children: Welcome
Dogs: Welcome Licences: 🍾
Directions: From South, A49 fork left (B4361) through lights, 20m on right. From North, A49 fork left (B4361) through town to lights, right, 20m on right.

Chadstone Guest House

Aston Munslow, Craven Arms,
Shropshire, SY7 9ER
Tel: 01584 841675 Fax: 01584 841620
Email: chadstone.lee@btinternet.com
Web: www.chadstonebandb.co.uk

Friendly personal service, luxurious
accommodation, tastefully furnished with
well-equipped bedrooms. Spacious
lounge and attractive dining room
with panoramic views of the Shropshire
countryside.

RAC ◆◆◆◆

Chadstone Guest House

◆◆◆◆

Aston Munslow, Craven Arms, Shropshire, SY7 9ER
Tel: 01584 841675 Fax: 01584 841620
Email: chadstone.lee@btinternet.com
Web: www.chadstonebandb.co.uk
Rooms: 3 all ensuite ⊛
Pricing: Sgl £24–28 Dbl £48–56 Dinner from £17
Room facilities: ▢ ⊚
Children: Welcome, 12yrs min age
Licences: ⁙ Parking: Off-street
Directions: Turn east off A49 onto B4368 in Craven
Arms. In Aston Munslow, pass the Swan Inn;
Chadstone is 100 metres on right
See advert on this page

The Hoopits

◆◆◆◆

Greete, Ludlow, Shropshire, SY8 3BS
Tel: 01584 879187
Email: thehoopits@talk21.com
Seasonal closure: 14 December to 14 January
Rooms: 2 (1 ensuite) ⊛
Pricing: Sgl £25 Dbl £50
Dinner from £15
Room facilities: ▢ ⊚
Children: Welcome
Parking: Off-street and monitored
Directions: A49 turn at sign for Clee Hill and
Caynham. In Caynham turn right at sign, property is
1 mile on left.

The Church Inn

◆◆◆

Buttercross, Ludlow, Shropshire, SY8 1AW
Tel: 01584 872174 Fax: 01584 877146
Email: reception@thechurchinn.com
Web: www.thechurchinn.com

700-year-old traditional inn on the corner of the
church green. The only free house within the town
walls offering many real ales, good wines and home
cooked food.
Rooms: 9 all ensuite ⏬
Pricing: Sgl £30–60 Dbl £50–60 Dinner from £4
CC: Accepted Room facilities: ▢ ☎ ⊚ ⏳
Children: Welcome Dogs: Welcome Licences: ⁙
Directions: From A49 Shrewsbury–Hereford Road,
signs for town centre. Inn is behind the Buttercross in
the town centre.

Travelodge Ludlow

Travel Accommodation
A49, Station Road, Woofferton, Ludlow, Shropshire,
SY8 4AL
Web: www.travelodge.co.uk
Rooms: 32 all ensuite ⊛
Pricing: Sgl £49.40 Dbl £53.85 CC: Accepted
Room facilities: ▢ ⊚ Access: ♿

Lydney, Gloucestershire

George Inn

 ♦ ♦ ♦

High Street, St Briavels, Lydney,
Gloucestershire, GL15 6TA
Tel: 01594 530228 Fax: 01594 530260
Email: mail@ithegeorge.fsnet.co.uk
Web: www.thegeorgeinn.info

The George is an unspoilt 16th century freehouse
overlooking the castle in a quiet village above the Wye
Valley. We specialise in home-cooked food, real ales
and real fires.
Rooms: 4 all ensuite ⊛
Pricing: Sgl £35–35 Dbl £50–60 CC: Accepted
Room facilities: ▢ ⊆ Children: Welcome
Licences: ⁙ Parking: Off-street
Directions: 6 miles from Chepstow on the Lydney Road.

Malvern, Worcestershire

Malvern Hills Hotel

 ★ ★

Wynds Point, Malvern, Worcestershire, WR13 6DW
Tel: 01684 540690 Fax: 01684 540327
Email: malhilhotl@aol.com
Web: www.malvernhillshotel.co.uk

A character bedroomed country house hotel set amidst
the tranquillity of the Malvern Hills, with direct access for
walking. Excellent cuisine and real ales. Pets welcome.
Rooms: 14 all ensuite 🛏 ⊛
Pricing: Sgl £35–50 Dbl £80–90
Dinner from £20 CC: Accepted
Room facilities: ▢ ☎ ⊆ ⌁ Access: ♿
Conference: 1 meeting rooms (Thtr 40 max),
24hr-delegate from £65, day-delegate rate from £20
Children: Welcome ⅋ Dogs: Welcome Licences: ⁙
Leisure: Games room Parking: Off-street and monitored
Directions: On A449 Malvern to Ledbury Road at
junction with B4232 (opposite car park for British
Camp Iron Age hill fort).

Holdfast Cottage Hotel

 ❖

Marbank Road, Little Malvern, Malvern,
Worcestershire, WR13 6NA
Tel: 01684 310288 Fax: 01684 311117

Moreton-in-Marsh, Gloucestershire

Crown Inn & Hotel

★ ★ ★

High Street, Blockley, Gloucestershire, GL56 9EX
Tel: 01386 700245 Fax: 01386 700247
Email: info@crown-inn-blockley.co.uk
Web: www.crown-inn-blockley.co.uk
Rooms: 24 all ensuite ⊛ ⛎ Pricing: Sgl £60–80
Dbl £90–120 Dinner from £20 CC: Accepted
Room facilities: ▢ ☎ ⊆ Conference: 1 meeting room
(Thtr 25 max), 24hr-delegate from £115, day-delegate
rate from £35 Children: Welcome ⅋ ⁙ Dogs: Welcome
Licences: ⁙ Parking: Off-street
Directions: Follow tourist board signs after Bourton-on-
the-Hill.

Farriers Cottage

 ♦ ♦ ♦ ✕

44 Todenham, Moreton-in-Marsh,
Gloucestershire, GL56 9PF
Tel: 01608 652664 Fax: 01608 652668
Email: susanannwoolston@aol.com
Web: www.thefarrierscottage.co.uk
Rooms: 1 ensuite ⊛ Pricing: Dbl £45–55
Room facilities: ▢ ⊆
Directions: Leave Moreton northbound on A429. Take
first right after railway bridge to Todenham. Cottage
opposite church and pub, after 3 miles.

Newcastle-under-Lyme, Staffordshire

Borough Arms Hotel

★ ★

King Street, Newcastle-under-Lyme,
Staffordshire, ST5 1HX
Tel: 01782 629421 Fax: 01782 712388

Comfort Inn Newcastle-under-Lyme

 ★ ★

Liverpool Road, Cross Heath, Newcastle-under-Lyme,
Staffordshire, ST5 9DX
Tel: 01782 717000 Fax: 01782 713669
Email: admin@gb617.u-net.com
Web: www.choicehotels.com
Rooms: 68 all ensuite ⊛ ⊛ Pricing: Sgl £68.25–78.25
Dbl £77–97 Dinner from £11.75 CC: Accepted
Room facilities: ▢ ☎ ⊆ Conference: 3 meeting rooms
(Thtr 200 max), 24hr-delegate from £85, day-delegate
rate from £26.50 Children: Welcome ⅋ Dogs: Welcome
Licences: ⬠ ⁙ Leisure: Gym, Snooker/billiards
Parking: Off-street and monitored
Directions: From the M6, take Junction 16 and pick up
A500 for Newcastle-under-Lyme, then the A34.

Newent, Gloucestershire

Three Choirs Vineyards   Little Gem

◆ ◆ ◆ ◆ ◆ ♫ ♫ ✳ ☜

Newent, Gloucestershire, GL18 1LS
Tel: 01531 890223 Fax: 01531 890877
Email: info@threechoirs.com
Web: www.threechoirs.com

Set in 100 acres of rolling Gloucestershire countryside,
we offer peace and tranquillity in which to enjoy our
fine wines and excellent food. All rooms have lovely
views over the vineyards.
Rooms: 8 all ensuite ⊗
Pricing: Sgl £55–85 Dbl £65–95
Dinner from £20 CC: Accepted
Room facilities: ▢ ☎ ☕ ⚲ Access: ♿
Conference: 2 meeting rooms (Thtr 20 max)
Children: Welcome ⊢ ⫯ Licences: ♨
Parking: Off-street
Directions: Follow brown tourist signs from Newent or
Dymock. On B4215, 2 miles north of Newent

Newland, Gloucestershire

Cherry Orchard Farm

◆ ◆ ☜

Newland, Coleford, Gloucestershire, GL16 8NP
Tel: 01594 832212 Fax: 01594 832212

Working dairy farm with warm welcome guaranteed.
Only half a mile from Offas Dyke footpath, centrally
situated for Forest of Dean, beautiful Wye valley and
for exploring mountains of South Wales.
Rooms: 3 ⚲ ⊗
Pricing: Sgl £24 Dbl £48
Room facilities: ☕
Children: Welcome ⊢ ⫯
Dogs: Guide dogs only
Parking: Off-street
Directions: 1½ miles east of Redbrook, 3 miles south
of Monmouth off A466, ¼ mile north of Newland on
the B4231.

Nuneaton, Warwickshire

Travelodge Bedworth (Nuneaton) (SA)

Travel Accommodation
A444, Bedworth By Pass, Nuneaton,
Warwickshire, CV10 7TF
Web: www.travelodge.co.uk
Rooms: 40 all ensuite ⊗
Pricing: Sgl £47.40 Dbl £51.85 CC: Accepted
Room facilities: ▢ ☕ Access: ♿

Travelodge Nuneaton (SA)

Travel Accommodation
A47, St Nicholas Park Drive, Nuneaton,
Warwickshire, CV11 6EN
Web: www.travelodge.co.uk
Rooms: 28 all ensuite ⊗
Pricing: Sgl £47.40 Dbl £51.85 CC: Accepted
Room facilities: ▢ ☕ Access: ♿ :

Oakamoor, Staffordshire

Ribden Farm

◆ ◆ ◆ ◆ ✳

Oakamoor, Stoke-on-Trent, Staffordshire, ST10 3BW
Tel: 01538 702830 Fax: 01538 702830
Email: ribdenfarm@aol.com
Web: www.ribden.fsnet.co.uk
Rooms: 5 all ensuite ⚲ ⚿ ⊗
Room facilities: ▢ ☕
Children: Welcome ⊢
Parking: Off-street and monitored
Directions: Situated on the B5417 Cheadle to Wardlow
Road, on the right, ½ mile before junction with A52.
Ribden Farm is second farm down drive.

Oswestry, Shropshire

Travelodge Oswestry

Travel Accommodation
A5/A483, Mile End Services, Oswestry,
Shropshire, SY11 4JA
Web: www.travelodge.co.uk
Rooms: 40 all ensuite ⊗
Pricing: Sgl £54.40 Dbl £58.85 CC: Accepted
Room facilities: ▢ ☕ Access: ♿

Painswick, Gloucestershire

Painswick Hotel

★★★★ ℞ ℞ ℞

Kemps Lane, Painswick, Gloucestershire, GL6 6YB
Tel: 01452 812160 Fax: 01452 814059
Email: reservations@painswickhotel.com
Web: www.painswickhotel.com

Set in an enchanting Cotswold village, the hotel offers individually designed bedrooms with ravishing views of the countryside. The light and delicious food is the reason our restaurant is so highly rated.
Rooms: 19 all ensuite ✇ 🍽
Pricing: Sgl £80–150 Dbl £125–195
Dinner from £27.50
CC: Accepted Room facilities: 📺 ☎
Conference: 2 meeting rooms (Thtr 50 max),
24hr-delegate from £150, day-delegate rate from £45
Children: Welcome ♫ ℃ Dogs: Welcome
Licences: ◈ ♦♦♦
Parking: Off-street and monitored
Directions: Follow A46 to Painswick, turning into St Mary's Street next to the church. Follow the road around and turn right at The March Hare. Hotel 200 yards on right.

Hambutts Mynd

◆ ◆ ◆

Edge Road, Painswick, Gloucestershire, GL6 6UP
Tel: 01452 812352 Fax: 01452 813862
Email: e.warland@aol.com
Web: www.accommodation.uk.net/painswick.htm
Seasonal closure: January
Rooms: 3 all ensuite ✇
Pricing: Sgl £27–36 Dbl £48–50
CC: Accepted Room facilities: 📺 ☺
Children: Welcome, 10yrs min age
Dogs: Welcome Parking: Off-street and monitored
Directions: Entering Painswick from Cheltenham, turn right at end of church wall. From Stroud, take first left after car park.

Redditch, Worcestershire

Quality Hotel Redditch

★ ★ ★

Pool Bank, Southcrest, Redditch,
Worcestershire, B97 4JS
Tel: 01527 541511 Fax: 01527 402600
Email: admin@gb646.u-net.com
Web: www.choicehotels.com
Rooms: 73 all ensuite ✇ 🍽
Pricing: Sgl £95 Dinner from £12.95
CC: Accepted Room facilities: 📺 ☎ ☺
Conference: 5 meeting rooms (Thtr 100 max),
24hr-delegate from £125, day-delegate rate from £35
Children: Welcome ♫ ℃ Dogs: Welcome
Licences: ◈ ♦♦♦ Parking: Off-street and monitored

Campanile

Travel Accommodation
Far Moor Lane, Winyates Green, Redditch,
Worcestershire, B98 0SD
Tel: 01527 510710 Fax: 01527 517269
Web: www.campanile.fr

Typical Campanile bistro

Rooms: 45 all ensuite ✇
Pricing: Sgl £43.95–46.90 Dbl £49.90–55.85
Dinner from £11.55 CC: Accepted
Room facilities: 📺 ☎ ☺ ✎ Access: ♿
Conference: 1 meeting room, 24hr-delegate from £68,
day-delegate rate from £19.50
Children: Welcome ♫ Dogs: Welcome
Licences: ♦♦♦ Parking: Off-street and monitored
Directions: Exit M42 J3 and head for Redditch along the A435, then take the first exit for Redditch.

Plan your route

Visit www.rac.co.uk for RAC's interactive route planner, including up to the minute traffic reports.

Navigation with a difference

Smartnav-In-Car satellite navigation with live traffic information and much more at a fraction of the cost of traditional satellite navigation.
Call 0800 096 1740

Ross-on-Wye, Herefordshire

Chase Hotel

★★★

Gloucester Road, Ross-on-Wye,
Herefordshire, HR9 5LH
Tel: 01989 763161 Fax: 01989 768330
Email: info@chasehotel.co.uk
Web: www.chasehotel.co.uk

Georgian country house set in 11 acres of grounds.
Award-winning cuisine, relaxed and informal
surroundings. Conference and events for up to 300
guests.
Rooms: 36 all ensuite ☺
Pricing: Sgl £70–110 Dbl £85–175 Dinner from £2
CC: Accepted Room facilities: ☐ ☎ ☺
Conference: 5 meeting rooms (Thtr 300 max),
24hr-delegate from £130, day-delegate rate from £35
Children: Welcome � Licences: ⚔ ♦♦♦
Leisure: Gym Parking: Off-street and monitored
Directions: From M50 Junction 4, turn left for Ross-on-
Wye. Take A40 Gloucester at second roundabout and
right for town centre at third roundabout. Hotel on left.

Chasedale Hotel

★★

Walford Road, Ross-on-Wye, Herefordshire, HR9 5PQ
Tel: 01989 562423 Fax: 01989 567900
Email: chasedale@supanet.com
Web: www.chasedale.co.uk
Rooms: 10 all ensuite ☺
Pricing: Sgl £32.50–36.50 Dbl £65–73 Dinner from £15
CC: Accepted Room facilities: ☐ ☎ ☺
Conference: 2 meeting rooms (Thtr 50 max)
Children: Welcome � ☜ Dogs: Welcome
Licences: ♦♦♦ Parking: Off-street
Directions: Half a mile south of Ross-on-Wye, on
B4234 Ross-to-Coleford Road on left.

Old Court Hotel

★

Symonds Yat West, Ross-on-Wye,
Herefordshire, HR9 6DA
Tel: 01600 890367 Fax: 01600 890964
Email: oldcourt@aol.com Web: www.oldcourthotel.com
Rooms: 18 (15 ensuite) ☑ Pricing: Sgl £46.50–55
Dbl £73–90 Dinner from £23 CC: Accepted
Room facilities: ☐ ☎ ☺ ↙ Dogs: Welcome
Licences: ⚔ ♦♦♦ Leisure: Outdoor pool
Parking: Off-street and monitored
Directions: Follow sign for Symonds Yat West from
A40, midway between Ross-on-Wye and Monmouth.

Rosswyn Hotel

★

High Street, Ross-on-Wye, Herefordshire, HR9 5BZ
Tel: 01989 562733 Fax: 01989 567115
Email: rosswynhotel@talk21.com
Rooms: 8 (7 ensuite) ☑
Pricing: Dinner from £12 (2002 rate) CC: Accepted
Room facilities: ☐ ☎ ☺ Children: Welcome �
Dogs: Welcome Parking: Off-street

Garth Cottage Hotel

♦♦♦♦

Symonds Yat East, Herefordshire, HR9 6JL
Tel: 01600 890364 Fax: 01600 890364
Email: bertie@yateast.fsnet.co.uk
Seasonal closure: November to March
Rooms: 4 all ensuite ☺ Pricing: Sgl £25–45 Dbl £50
Dinner from £16.50 Room facilities: ☺
Children: Welcome, 12yrs min age Licences: ♦♦♦
Parking: Off-street
Directions: From A40, leave at Little Chef Whitchurch.
Follow signs for Symonds Yat East on B4229.

The Whitehouse

♦♦♦

Wye Street, Ross-on-Wye, Herefordshire, HR9 7BX
Tel: 01989 763572 Fax: 01989 763572
Rooms: 7 all ensuite ☺ Pricing: Sgl £38 Dbl £58–65
CC: Accepted Room facilities: ☐ ☺
Children: Welcome, 11yrs min age � Licences: ♦♦♦
Directions: Halfway down Wye street from Tourist
Office, adjacent to river.

Rugby, Warwickshire

The Olde Coach House Inn

♦♦♦

Main Street, Ashby St Ledgers, near Rugby,
Warwickshire, CV23 8DN
Tel: 01788 890349 Fax: 01788 891922
Email: oldecoachhouse@traditionalfreehouses.com
Rooms: 6 all ensuite ☺ ☑ ☺ Pricing: Sgl £51
Dbl £65 Dinner from £7.95 CC: Accepted
Room facilities: ☐ ☎ ☺ Conference: 1 meeting room
(Thtr 20 max) Children: Welcome �
Dogs: Guide dogs only Licences: ♦♦♦ Parking: Off-street

Travelodge Rugby

Travel Accommodation
A45, London Church, Dunchurch, Thurlaston,
Nr. Rugby, Warwickshire, CV23 9LG
Web: www.travelodge.co.uk
Rooms: 40 all ensuite
Pricing: Sgl £47.40–54.40 Dbl £51.85–58.85
CC: Accepted Room facilities: ☐ ☕ Access: ♿

Rugeley, Staffordshire

Travelodge Rugeley

Travel Accommodation
A51/B5013, Western Springs Road, Rugeley,
Staffordshire, WS15 2AS
Web: www.travelodge.co.uk
Rooms: 32 all ensuite)
Pricing: Sgl £49.40 Dbl £53.85 CC: Accepted
Room facilities: ☐ ☕ Access: ♿

Shrewsbury, Shropshire

Prince Rupert Hotel
★★★★ ☕ ☕
Butcher Row, Shrewsbury, Shropshire, SY1 1UQ
Tel: 01743 499955 Fax: 01743 357306
Email: post@prince-rupert-hotel.co.uk
Web: www.prince-rupert-hotel.co.uk
Rooms: 70 all ensuite ☕ ☕
Pricing: Sgl £75 Dbl £95–160 Dinner from £14
CC: Accepted Room facilities: ☐ ☎ ☕ ☕ Access: ♿
Conference: 3 meeting rooms (Thtr 120 max),
24hr-delegate from £105, day-delegate rate from £30
Children: Welcome ☂ ☕ Dogs: Welcome Licences: ♣
Leisure: Gym, Health spa, Beauty salon,
Snooker/billiards
Parking: Off-street and monitored
Directions: From the M54, follow signs for town centre.
Travel over English Bridge and up the Wyle Cop. Turn
sharp right into Fish Street. Hotel is 200m ahead.

Travelodge Shrewsbury

Travel Accommodation
A5/A49, Bayston Hill Services, Shrewsbury, Shropshire,
SY3 0DA
Web: www.travelodge.co.uk
Rooms: 40 all ensuite
Pricing: Sgl £54.40 Dbl £58.85 CC: Accepted
Room facilities: ☐ ☕ Access: ♿

Need help booking?

RAC Hotel Reservations will find
the accommodation that's right
for you – and book it too.
Call today on 0870 603 9109
and quote 'Guide 2003'

Solihull, West Midlands

Renaissance Solihull Hotel Birmingham
★★★★★ ☕ ☕
651 Warwick Road, Solihull, West Midlands, B91 1AT
Tel: 0121 7113000 Fax: 0121 7113963
Email: reservations.solihull@whitbread.com
Web: www.whitbread.com
Rooms: 179 all ensuite ☕ ☕
Pricing: Sgl £58–133 Dbl £78–169
Dinner from £22.50 CC: Accepted
Room facilities: ☐ ☎ ☕ ☕ Access: ♿ ♿
Conference: 11 meeting rooms (Thtr 700 max),
24hr-delegate from £175, day-delegate rate from £59
Children: Welcome ☂ ☕
Dogs: Welcome Licences: ♣ ♣
Leisure: Indoor pool, Gym, Health spa,
Beauty salon Parking: Off-street and monitored
Directions: Leave Junction 5 of M42. Take B4025 to
Solihull town centre. Drive through centre, over
roundabout, hotel on right.

The Arden Hotel & Leisure Club
★★★
Coventry Road, Bickenhill, Solihull,
West Midlands, B92 0EH
Tel: 01675 443221 Fax: 01675 445604
Email: enquiries@ardenhotel.co.uk
Web: www.ardenhotel.co.uk
Rooms: 216 all ensuite ☕ ☕
Pricing: Sgl £65–109.75 Dbl £75–149.50
Dinner from £15.95 CC: Accepted
Room facilities: ☐ ☎ ☕ ☕ Access: ♿ ♿
Conference: 16 meeting rooms (Thtr 180 max),
24hr-delegate from £145, day-delegate rate from £35
Children: Welcome ☕
Dogs: Welcome Licences: ♣ ♣
Leisure: Indoor pool, Gym, Health spa, Games room,
Snooker/billiards
Parking: Off-street and monitored
Directions: M42 junction 6, A4 to B'ham, stay left and
at roundabout 180 degrees to A45 Coventry, slip-road
after petrol station.
See advert on following page

Flemings Hotel
★★
141 Warwick Road, Olton, Solihull,
West Midlands, B92 7HW
Tel: 0121 706 0371 Fax: 0121 706 4494
Email: reservations@flemingshotel.co.uk
Web: www.flemingshotel.co.uk
Rooms: 70 all ensuite ☕ ☕
Pricing: Sgl £32–56 Dbl £40–56 Dinner from £7
CC: Accepted Room facilities: ☐ ☎ ☕ ☕
Access: ♿
Conference: 3 meeting rooms (Thtr 45 max)
Children: Welcome ☂ Dogs: Welcome
Licences: ♣ Leisure: Games room, Snooker/billiards
Parking: Off-street and monitored
Directions: M42 J5 onto A41 Seven Stars Road turn
right 100 yards past fourth set of traffic lights.

The Arden Hotel
& Leisure Club

The Arden Hotel
is the perfect location in the
Heart of England (within one mile of the
NEC and Birmingham International
Airport) with easy access from the M42.
All 216 bedrooms have private facilities,
many rooms overlooking landscaped
gardens.
Residents have complementary use
of the well-equipped Leisure Club
including the swimming pool.
All tastes are catered for from the table
d'hôte menu to the à la carte in the
Burgundy Restaurant.
Conference and Exhibition facilities are
available for meetings for
2 to 200 delegates with easy access and
free car parking.
The Arden Hotel prides itself with tailor-
made Civil Weddings & Wedding
Receptions.
Being one of the largest privately owned
and run hotels in the Midlands, The
Arden Hotel offers
the perfect location for everyone.

Coventry Road, Bickenhill, Solihull, West Midlands B92 0EH
Tel: 01675 443221 Fax: 01675 445604
Web: www.ardenhotel.co.uk
Email: enquiries@ardenhotel.co.uk

Stafford, Staffordshire

Quality Hotel Stafford

★ ★ ★

Pinfold Lane, Penkridge, Stafford,
Staffordshire, ST19 5QP
Tel: 01785 712459 Fax: 01785 715532
Email: admin@gb067.u-net.com
Web: www.choicehotels.com
Rooms: 47 all ensuite Pricing: Sgl £50–79
Dbl £70–99 Dinner from £13.95 CC: Accepted
Room facilities: 🖵 ☎ 🛗 🐾
Conference: 7 meeting rooms (Thtr 300 max)
Children: Welcome 🍴 ℅
Dogs: Guide dogs only Licences: ⚲ ♦♦♦
Leisure: Indoor pool, Gym, Snooker/billiards
Parking: Off-street
Directions: Exit at either Junction 12 or 13 of the M6
motorway. After approximately 2 miles, at George and
Fox pub turn into Pinfold Lane. Hotel on left-hand side.

Abbey Hotel

★ ★

65–68 Lichfield Road, Stafford, Staffordshire, ST17 4LW
Tel: 01785 258531 Fax: 01785 246875
Seasonal closure: Christmas and New Year
Rooms: 17 all ensuite Pricing: Sgl £40–50 Dbl £55–65
Dinner from £12 CC: Accepted
Room facilities: 🖵 ☎ 🛗 🐾 Children: Welcome ℅
Dogs: Guide dogs only Licences: ♦♦♦
Parking: Off-street

Directions: Leave M6 at Junction 13, head towards
Stafford. Turn right at Esso garage to roundabout,
follow Silkmore Lane. At second roundabout take
second exit. Hotel ¼ mile on right.

Albridge Hotel

★

72 Wolverhampton Road, Stafford, ST17 4AW
Tel: 01785 254100 Fax: 01785 223895
Rooms: 9 (7 ensuite) 🐾
Pricing: Sgl £29–35 Dbl £38.95–45 CC: Accepted
Room facilities: 🖵 ☎ 🛗 Children: Welcome 🍴 ℅
Dogs: Welcome Licences: ♦♦♦
Leisure: Games room Parking: Off-street
Directions: Leave M6 at Junction 13. Follow signs for
Stafford, the town is 2¾ miles on A449. Hotel is on left
after Telegraph Inn, opposite Victoria Wine.

Leonards Croft Hotel

◆ ◆ ◆

80 Lichfield Road, Stafford, Staffordshire, ST17 4LP
Tel: 01785 223676
Seasonal closure: Christmas
Rooms: 9 all ensuite 🐾 🛗
Pricing: Dinner from £5 CC: Accepted
Room facilities: 🖵 🛗 Children: Welcome
Dogs: Welcome Licences: ♦♦♦ Parking: Off-street
Directions: Leave M6 at Junction 13. Take A449 and
turn right at the Esso garage to roundabout. Hotel is
on A34 over bridge on right.

Offley Grove Farm

 ◆ ◆ ◆ ☕

Adbaston, nr Eccleshall, Stafford,
Staffordshire, ST20 0QB
Tel: 01785 280205 Fax: 01785 280205
Email: accom@offleygrovefarm.freeserve.co.uk
Web: www.offleygrovefarm.co.uk
Rooms: 2 all ensuite 🛇
Pricing: Sgl £25 Dbl £44 CC: Accepted
Room facilities: 🛇 Children: Welcome
Dogs: Guide dogs only Parking: Off-street
Directions: From North; Exit J15 M6 onto A519; follow
signs for Eccleshall, then Woodseaves, Shebdon and
Adbaston. From south; J10A M6, M54, A41, A519 and
first left, travel a further 3¹/₂ miles.

Staunton-on-Wye, Herefordshire

The Portway Inn

 ◆ ◆ ◆

The Brecon Road, Staunton-on-Wye,
Herefordshire, HR4 7NH
Tel: 01981 500474 Fax: 01981 500151
Rooms: 4 all ensuite 🛇 Pricing: Sgl £35 Dbl £50
CC: Accepted Room facilities: 🛇 🛇
Children: Welcome ⋔ Licences: ⋔⋔⋔ Leisure: Games
room, Snooker/billiards Parking: Off-street

Stoke-on-Trent, Staffordshire

George Hotel

 ★ ★ ★ 🛇 🛇

Swan Square, Burslem, Stoke-on-Trent,
Staffordshire, ST6 2AE
Tel: 01782 577544 Fax: 01782 837496
Email: georgestoke@btinternet.com
Web: www.georgehotelstock.cwc.net
Rooms: 39 all ensuite Pricing: Dinner from £16.95
(2002 rate) CC: Accepted Room facilities: 🛇 ☎ 🛇 🛇
Access: ⬆ Dogs: Guide dogs only
Licences: ⋔⋔⋔ Parking: Off-street and monitored
Directions: From M6, take Junctions 15 or 16 onto
A500. Turn left onto A53. At A50 junction turn left.
Burslem is 1 mile further.

North Stafford Hotel

★ ★ ★

Station Road, Winton Square, Stoke-on-Trent,
Staffordshire, ST4 2AE
Tel: 01782 744477 Fax: 01782 744580
Email: stuart.mcmanus@northstaffordhotel.co.uk
Web: www.northstaffordhotel.co.uk
Rooms: 80 (67 ensuite) 🛇
Room facilities: 🛇 ☎ 🛇 🛇 ❄ Access: ⬆ ♿
Conference: 9 meeting rooms (Thtr 450 max),
24hr-delegate from £95, day-delegate rate from £25
Children: Welcome ⋔ Dogs: Welcome
Licences: ⬧ ⋔⋔⋔ Leisure: Games room
Parking: Off-street and monitored
Directions: M6 at Junction 15. Join A555 after ²/₃ mile.
Follow signs for railway station, hotel directly opposite.

Corrie Guest House

  ◆ ◆ ◆ ◆ ⌖ ☕

13-15 Newton Street, Basford, Stoke-on-Trent,
Staffordshire, ST4 6JN
Tel: 01782 614838 Fax: 01782 625465
Email: the.corrie@talk21.com
Web: www.thecorrie.com

A warm and friendly welcome awaits you at this fine
Victorian house, ideally situated for shopping, Alton
Towers, theatres, universities and hospitals. In a quiet
location between Newcastle and Hanley.
Rooms: 8 (4 ensuite) 🛇
Pricing: Sgl £23–33 Dbl £40–46
CC: Accepted
Room facilities: 🛇 🛇
Children: Welcome Parking: Off-street and monitored
Directions: From M6 take Junction 15 or 16 onto A500
towards Stoke. Take the A53 exit towards Newcastle-
under-Lyme. Take the third left turn.

Rhodes Hotel

 ◆ ◆ ◆

42 Leek Road, Stoke-on-Trent, Staffordshire, ST4 2AR
Tel: 01782 416320 Fax: 01782 416323
Email: rhodeshot42@aol.com
Rooms: 7 (4 ensuite) 🛇
Pricing: Dbl £35–42 CC: Accepted
Room facilities: 🛇 🛇
Children: Welcome Dogs: Welcome
Directions: Ten minutes drive from M6 Junctions 15/16.
Close to Stoke-on-Trent station, on A52 Stoke to Leek
Road.

Wheatsheaf Hotel

 ◆ ◆ ◆

Sheaf street, Shelton, Stoke-on-Trent,
Staffordshire, ST1 4LN
Tel: 01782 212384 Fax: 01782 861874
Rooms: 11 (8 ensuite) 🗒
Pricing: Sgl £26–30 Dbl £39–50
Dinner from £4.95
CC: Accepted Room facilities: 🛇 🛇
Conference: 1 meeting room (Thtr 24 max)
Children: Welcome
Dogs: Guide dogs only
Parking: Monitored
Directions: M6 A500 follow signs to city centre, turn
into Saint Marks Street.

L. Beez Guest House

46 Leek Road, Stoke-on-Trent, Staffordshire, ST4 2AR
Tel: 01782 846727 Fax: 01782 846727
Rooms: 5 (1 ensuite) ♨ ⊗
Pricing: Sgl £20 Dbl £35–42
Room facilities: ▢ ☕ Access: ♿
Children: Welcome ⅂ Dogs: Welcome
Parking: Monitored
Directions: On A52 Stoke to Leek, 10 minutes from
M6/J15, 250 yards Stoke railway station. Opposite
Post Office enquiry office.

Travelodge Stoke

Travel Accommodation
A34/A500, Newcastle Road, Talke, Stoke on Trent,
Staffordshire, ST7 1UP
Web: www.travelodge.co.uk
Rooms: 62 ensuite ⊗
Pricing: Sgl £54.40 Dbl £58.85 CC: Accepted
Room facilities: ▢ ☕ Access: ♿

Stone, Staffordshire

Travelodge Stafford (MOTO)

Travel Accommodation
M6 Moto Service Area, Eccleshall Road, Stone,
Staffordshire, ST15 0EU
Web: www.travelodge.co.uk
Rooms: 49 all ensuite ⊗
Pricing: Sgl £54.40–57.40 Dbl £58.85–61.85
CC: Accepted Room facilities: ▢ ☕ Access: ♿

Stow-on-the-Wold, Gloucestershire

Fosse Manor Hotel

★★★★ 👥 👥
Stow-on-the-Wold, Cheltenham,
Gloucestershire, GL54 1JX
Tel: 01451 830354 Fax: 01451 832486
Email: fossemanor@bestwestern.co.uk
Web: www.bestwesternhotels.co.uk
Seasonal closure: 21–29 December

Rooms: 22 all ensuite ♨ 🛏 ⊗
Pricing: Sgl £65–85 Dbl £80–170 Dinner from £26
CC: Accepted Room facilities: ▢ ☎ ☕ 🍸
Conference: 2 meeting rooms (Thtr 40 max),

24hr-delegate from £130, day-delegate rate from £30
Children: Welcome ⅂ ⅄ Dogs: Welcome
Licences: 🍷 🕯 Leisure: Beauty salon
Parking: Off-street
Directions: 1 mile south of Stow-on-the-Wold on the
A429 Warwick to Cirencester Road.

Stow Lodge Hotel

★★★
The Square, Stow-on-the-Wold, Gloucs, GL54 1AB
Tel: 01451 830485 Fax: 01451 831671
Email: chris@stowlodge.com
Web: www.stowlodge.com
Seasonal closure: Christmas and early January
Rooms: 21 all ensuite 🛏 ⊗
Pricing: Sgl £60–130 Dbl £70–140 Dinner from £19.50
CC: Accepted Room facilities: ▢ ☎ ☕
Children: Welcome, 5yrs min age
Licences: 🕯 Parking: Off-street
Directions: The hotel has entrances off the main market
square and also the A429 in Stow-on-the-Wold

Grapevine Hotel

♦
Sheep Street, Stow-on-the-Wold,
Gloucestershire, GL54 1AU
Tel: 01451 830344 Fax: 01451 832278
Web: www.vines.co.uk

Aston House

♦♦♦♦ 🌙 🕯
Broadwell, Moreton-in-Marsh,
Gloucestershire, GL56 0TJ
Tel: 01451 830475 Email: fja@netcomuk.co.uk
Web: www.netcomuk.co.uk/~nmfa/aston_house.html
Seasonal closure: December and January

Quiet village location 1½ miles from Stow-on-the-
Wold, central for touring Cotswolds, non-smoking.
Comfortable accommodation with bed time drinks and
biscuits, electric blankets for those colder nights and
good English breakfast.
Rooms: 3 (2 ensuite) ⊗ Pricing: Dbl £48–52
Room facilities: ▢ ☕ Children: Welcome, 10yrs min age
Parking: Off-street and monitored
Directions: A429 from Stow-on-the-Wold towards
Moreton. After 1 mile turn right at Broadwell/
Donnington crossroads. First house on left after ½ mile.

Limes

◆ ◆ ◆

Tewkesbury Road, Stow-on-the-Wold,
Gloucestershire, GL54 1EN
Tel: 01451 830034 Fax: 01451 830034
Seasonal closure: Christmas
Rooms: 5 all ensuite 🛏 🖃 🚭
Pricing: Sgl £29.50–31 Dbl £44–45
Room facilities: 🖵 🍵 Access: 🚹
Children: Welcome Dogs: Welcome
Parking: Off-street and monitored
Directions: Off A429 towards Evesham & Broadway
Road (A424). 300 yards on left.

Stratford-upon-Avon, Warwickshire

Stratford Manor

★ ★ ★ ★ 🕾 🕾

Warwick Road, Stratford-upon-Avon,
Warwickshire, CV37 0PY
Tel: 01789 731173 Fax: 01789 731131
Email: stratfordmanor@marstonhotels.com
Web: www.marstonhotels.com

Modern hotel in countryside setting, minutes from
centre of Stratford-upon-Avon. Leisure facilities
including heated indoor pool, sauna, gym, steam, spa,
plunge pool and two all-weather tennis courts. Superb
food.
Rooms: 104 all ensuite 🛏 🚭
Pricing: Sgl £115 Dbl £149
Dinner from £28 CC: Accepted
Room facilities: 🖵 🕾 🍵 🖳 Access: 👖 🚹
Conference: 22 meeting rooms (Thtr 350 max), 24hr-
delegate from £170, day-delegate rate from £52.50
Children: Welcome 🍴 ⁍
Dogs: Guide dogs only Licences: 🍷 👯
Leisure: Indoor pool, Gym, Health spa,
Beauty salon, Tennis
Parking: Off-street and monitored
Directions: Leave M40 at Junction 15, follow A46
towards Stratford. Take A439 signposted Stratford
town centre. Hotel 1 mile on left.

Stratford Victoria

★ ★ ★ ★ 🕾

Arden Street, Stratford-upon-Avon,
Warwickshire, CV37 6QQ
Tel: 01789 271000 Fax: 01789 271001
Email: stratfordvictoria@marstonhotels.com
Web: www.marstonhotels.com

Modern hotel in centre of Stratford-upon-Avon,
executive rooms and four-poster suites available.
Leisure facilities on site include a mini-gym and
whirlpool spa, superb food and friendly service.
Rooms: 102 all ensuite 🛏 🖃 🚭
Pricing: Sgl £105 Dbl £139
Dinner from £24 CC: Accepted
Room facilities: 🖵 🕾 🍵 🖳
Access: 👖 🚹
Conference: 9 meeting rooms (Thtr 140 max), 24hr-
delegate from £140, day-delegate rate from £45
Children: Welcome 🍴 ⁍ Dogs: Guide dogs only
Licences: 🍷 👯
Leisure: Gym, Beauty salon
Parking: Off-street and monitored
Directions: Exit M40 Junction 15, take A46 then A3400.
Turn right at traffic light, into Arden Street; hotel is 150
yards on right.

The Alveston Manor

★ ★ ★ ★ 🕾

Clopton Bridge, Stratford-upon-Avon,
Warwickshire, CV37 7HP
Tel: 0870 400 8181 Fax: 01789 413333
Email: sales.alvestonmanor@heritage-hotels.co.uk
Web: www.macdonaldhotels.co.uk
Rooms: 113 all ensuite 🖃 🚭
Pricing: Sgl £65 Dbl £130
Dinner from £23
CC: Accepted Room facilities: 🖵 🕾 🍵 🖳
Access: 🚹 Children: Welcome 🍴
Dogs: Welcome Licences: 🍷 👯
Parking: Off-street and monitored
Directions: M40 Junction 15. A46 then A439 into
Stratford. Follow one-way system towards Banbury
and Oxford. Hotel just over bridge.

The Shakespeare

★★★★★

Chapel Street, Stratford-upon-Avon,
Warwickshire, CV37 6ER
Tel: 0870 400 8182 Fax: 01789 415411
Email: shakespeare@heritage-hotels.co.uk
Web: www.macdonaldhotels.co.uk
Rooms: 70 all ensuite
Pricing: Sgl £72.50 Dbl £145 Dinner from £25
CC: Accepted Room facilities:
Access: & Children: Welcome
Dogs: Welcome Licences:
Parking: Off-street and monitored

Salford Hall

★★★★

Abbots Salford, Warwickshire, WR11 5UT
Tel: 01386 871300 Fax: 01386 871301
Email: reception@salfordhall.co.uk
Web: www.salfordhall.co.uk
Seasonal closure: Christmas
Rooms: 33 all ensuite Room facilities:
Children: Welcome Licences:
Leisure: Tennis, Snooker/billiards Parking: Off-street
Directions: From M40 Junction 15, take A46 towards
Stratford. After 12 miles, take road signposted "Salford
Priors, Abbots Salford". Follow for 1½ miles and
Salford Hall is on left.

The Swan's Nest

★★★

Bridgefoot, Stratford-upon-Avon,
Warwickshire, CV37 7LT
Tel: 0870 400 8183 Fax: 01789 414 547
Email: swansnest@heritage-hotels.co.uk
Web: www.macdonaldhotels.co.uk
Rooms: 68
Pricing: Sgl £57 Dbl £114 Dinner from £20
CC: Accepted Room facilities:
Access: & Children: Welcome
Dogs: Welcome Licences:
Parking: Off-street and monitored

Ambleside Guest House

◆◆◆◆

41 Grove Road, Stratford-upon-Avon,
Warwickshire, CV37 6PB
Tel: 01789 297239 Fax: 01789 295670
Email: peter@amblesideguesthouse.com
Web: www.amblesideguesthouse.com
Rooms: 8 (4 ensuite)
Pricing: Sgl £20–28 Dbl £40–56 CC: Accepted
Room facilities: Access: &
Children: Welcome Parking: Off-street
Directions: Opposite Firs Park, five minutes' walk from
railway station and town centre, ten minutes' walk from
river and coach station.

Avon View Hotel

◆◆◆◆

121 Shipston Road, Stratford-upon-Avon,
Warwickshire, CV37 9QL
Tel: 01789 297542 Fax: 01789 292936
Email: avon-view@lineone.net
Rooms: 10 all ensuite
Pricing: Dinner from £13 (2002 rate) CC: Accepted
Room facilities: Access: &
Children: Welcome Licences:
Parking: Off-street and monitored
Directions: South of river on A3400, or walk from river
bridge along old tramway walk.

Eastnor House

◆◆◆◆

33 Shipston Road, Stratford-upon-Avon, Warwickshire,
CV37 7LN
Tel: 01789 268115 Fax: 01789 551133
Email: enquiries@eastnorhouse.com
Web: www.eastnorhouse,com
Rooms: 10 all ensuite
Pricing: Sgl £45–59 Dbl £69–80 CC: Accepted
Room facilities:
Children: Welcome
Parking: Off-street and monitored
Directions: Located just south of the river on the
Shipston Road (A3400) close to the centre of Stratford.

Hampton Lodge Guest House

◆◆◆◆

38 Shipston Road, Stratford-upon-Avon,
Warwickshire, CV37 7LP
Tel: 01789 299374 Fax: 01789 299374
Email: hamptonlodgeinfo@aol.com
Web: www.hamptonlodge.co.uk
Rooms: 6 all ensuite
Pricing: Sgl £35–58 Dbl £58–64 CC: Accepted
Room facilities: Children: Welcome
Parking: Off-street
Directions: M40 J15, take A46 then A439 to Stratford.
Follow A3400 over River Avon. Turn right into Shipston
Road; Hampton Lodge on left.

Mayfield House

◆◆◆◆

7 Mayfield Avenue, Stratford-upon-Avon,
Warwickshire, CV37 6XB
Tel: 01789 299731/07971 489449 Fax: 01789 299731
Seasonal closure: Christmas/New Year/Easter
Rooms: 3 (1 ensuite)
Pricing: Sgl £35 Dbl £50–65
Room facilities:
Parking: Off-street and monitored
Directions: From A439 at northern edge of town turn
by church into St Gregory's Road. Crossroad 500
yards ahead, Mayfield Avenue straight over.

Penryn Guest House

126 Alcester Road, Stratford-upon-Avon,
Warwickshire, CV37 9DP
Tel: 01789 293718 Fax: 01789 266077
Email: penrynhouse@btinternet.com
Web: www.penrynguesthouse.co.uk
Seasonal closure: 1–31 January
Rooms: 7 (5 ensuite) 🛏 🚭 Pricing: Sgl £25–30
Dbl £45–55 CC: Accepted Room facilities: ☐ ☕
Access: ♿ Children: Welcome 🍴 Dogs: Guide dogs only
Parking: Off-street
Directions: From M40 Junction 15, follow signs to
Stratford on A46. At third roundabout (8 miles from
motorway), left onto A422 to Stratford. Penryn 1 mile
on left, 800 yards from rail station. Do not turn onto
A439 or A3400.

Sequoia House Hotel

51-53 Shipston Road, Stratford-upon-Avon,
Warwickshire, CV37 7LN
Tel: 01789 268852 Fax: 01789 414559
Email: info@sequoiahotel.co.uk
Web: www.sequoiahotel.co.uk
Rooms: 23 all ensuite 🚭
Pricing: Sgl £49–59 Dbl £65–95 CC: Accepted
Room facilities: ☐ ☎ ☕ Children: Welcome, 5yrs min
age 🍼 Licences: 🍴 Parking: Off-street
Directions: On A3400 100 metres from Clopton bridge.
From south, hotel on left. From north, enter Stratford
and follow signs for Shipston A3400. Cross river,
continue on A3400 and hotel is on right.

Victoria Spa Lodge

Bishopton Lane, Bishopton, Stratford-upon-Avon,
Warwickshire, CV37 9QY
Tel: 01789 267985 Fax: 01789 204728
Email: ptozer@victoriaspalodge.demon.co.uk
Web: www.stratford-upon-avon.co.uk/victoriaspa.htm

Explore the wonderful Cotswolds from this Grade II
listed lodge. Seven beautifully appointed ensuite
bedrooms, with all modern facilities. Ample parking.
Completely non-smoking.
Rooms: 7 all ensuite 🛏 🚭 Pricing: Dbl £60–65
CC: Accepted Room facilities: ☐ ☕
Children: Welcome 🍴 Parking: Off-street

Directions: Take A3400 north from Stratford town about
1½ miles where it intersects with A46. First exit,
Bishopton Lane, first house on right-hand side

Cymbeline House

24 Evesham Place, Stratford-upon-Avon,
Warwickshire, CV37 6HT
Tel: 01789 292958 Fax: 01789 292958
Email: cymbelinebb@btopenworld.com
Seasonal closure: Christmas
Rooms: 6 all ensuite 📺 🚭 Pricing: Sgl £20–30
Dbl £40–60 Room facilities: ☐ ☕ Children: Welcome
Dogs: Welcome Parking: Off-street and monitored

Ingon Bank Farm B&B

Ingon Bank Farm, Warwick Road, Stratford-upon-Avon,
Warwickshire, CV37 0NY
Tel: 01789 292642 Fax: 01789 292642
Rooms: 3 all ensuite 🚭
Pricing: Sgl £25–30 Dbl £40–44
Room facilities: ☐ ☕ Children: Welcome 🍴
Dogs: Welcome Parking: Off-street
Directions: From Stratford, take A439 north towards
Warwick for 2 miles. Hotel is signposted on left, 350
yards north of the Snitterfield turning.

Stroud, Gloucestershire

The Crown Inn

Frampton Mansell, Stroud, Gloucestershire, GL6 8JG
Tel: 01285 760601 Fax: 01285 760681
Email: crowninn.framptonmansell@eldridge-pope.co.uk
Rooms: 12 all ensuite 🛏 🚭
Pricing: Sgl £44 Dbl £69 Dinner from £6.95
CC: Accepted Room facilities: ☐ ☎ ☕ 🍼
Access: ♿ Children: Welcome 🍴
Dogs: Welcome Licences: 🍴 Parking: Off-street
Directions: Take the A419 from Stroud to Cirencester,
come through Stroud and head towards Cirencester up
a windy steep hill (with an airfield on right at top), 150
yards on left turning Frampton Mansell.

Downfield Hotel

134 Cainscross Road, Stroud,
Gloucestershire, GL5 4HN
Tel: 01453 764496 Fax: 01453 753150
Email: info@downfieldhotel.co.uk
Web: www.downfieldhotel.co.uk
Rooms: 21 (11 ensuite) 🛏
Pricing: Sgl £28–42 Dbl £45–60 Dinner from £12
CC: Accepted Room facilities: ☐ ☕
Children: Welcome 🍴 Dogs: Welcome
Licences: 🍴 Parking: Monitored
Directions: M5 exit 13 to A419; hotel 4½ miles on left.
M4 exit 15 to A419; hotel on right just after Stroud
ring road.

Travelodge Stonehouse

Travel Accommodation
A419, Eastington, Stonehouse, Nr. Stroud,
Gloucestershire, GL10 3SQ
Web: www.travelodge.co.uk
Rooms: 40 all ensuite ⊗
Pricing: Sgl £57.40 Dbl £61.85
CC: Accepted Room facilities: ▢ ☕ Access: ♿

Sutton Coldfield, West Midlands

New Hall Country House   Gold Ribbon Winner

★★★★★ ☕ ☕ ☕

Walmley Road, Walmley, Sutton Coldfield, B76 1QX
Tel: 0121 378 2442 Fax: 0121 378 4637
Email: newhall@thistle.co.uk
Web: www.newhallhotel.net

Rooms: 60 all ensuite ☕ 🖨 ⊗
Pricing: Dinner from £29.50 CC: Accepted
Room facilities: ▢ ☎ ☕ 🔌 Access: ♿
Conference: 4 meeting rooms (Thtr 80 max),
24hr-delegate from £255, day-delegate rate from £75
Children: Welcome, 8yrs min age
Dogs: Guide dogs only Licences: ⚓ ♟
Leisure: Indoor pool, Gym, Health spa,
Beauty salon, Tennis, Golf
Parking: Off-street and monitored

Moor Hall Hotel

★★★★ ☕

Moor Hall Drive, Four Oaks, Sutton Coldfield,
West Midlands, B75 6LN
Tel: 0121 308 3751 Fax: 0121 308 8974
Email: mail@moorhallhotel.co.uk
Web: www.moorhallhotel.co.uk
Rooms: 82 all ensuite ☕ 🖨 ⊗
Pricing: Sgl £59–121 Dbl £78–126
Dinner from £20 CC: Accepted
Room facilities: ▢ ☎ ☕ 🔌 Access: ⏫ ♿
Conference: 8 meeting rooms (Thtr 250 max),

24hr-delegate from £145, day-delegate rate from £45
Children: Welcome ♙ Licences: ⚓ ♟
Leisure: Indoor pool, Gym
Parking: Off-street and monitored
Directions: Leave M42 at Junction 9. Take A446 to
Lichfield, A453 to Sutton Coldfield, turn right at traffic
lights into Weeford Road and Moor Hall is on the left.

Reindeer Park Lodge

♦ ♦ ♦ ♦ ✳

Kingsbury Road, Leamarston, Sutton Coldfield,
West Midlands, B76 0DE
Tel: 01675 470811 Fax: 01675 470710
Email: beck@reindeerpark.co.uk
Web: www.reindeerpark.co.uk
Rooms: 6 all ensuite ☕ ⊗ Pricing: Sgl £37.50–39.50
Dbl £47.50–57.50 Room facilities: ▢ ☕ 🔌 Access: ♿
Conference: 2 meeting rooms (Thtr 20 max),
24hr-delegate from £39.50
Children: Welcome ♙ ♟ Dogs: Welcome
Parking: Off-street and monitored

Travelodge Sutton Coldfield (SA)

Travel Accommodation
A452, Boldmere Road, Sutton Coldfield,
West Midlands, B73 5UP
Web: www.travelodge.co.uk
Rooms: 32 all ensuite ⊗
Pricing: Sgl £47.40–54.40 Dbl £51.85–58.85
CC: Accepted Room facilities: ▢ ☕ Access: ♿

Symonds Yat, Herefordshire

Saracens Head Inn

★★

Symonds Yat, Symonds Yat, Herefordshire, HR9 6JL
Tel: 01600 890435 Fax: 01600 890034
Email: bookings@saracenshead.com
Web: www.saracenshead.com
Seasonal closure: December to January
Rooms: 9 all ensuite ☕
Room facilities: ☎ ☕
Children: Welcome, 9yrs min age ♙ ♟
Licences: ♟ Leisure: Fishing, Games room
Parking: Off-street and monitored
Directions: Leave A40 between Ross-on-Wye and
Monmouth at the Little Chef restaurant. Follow signs to
Symonds Yat East for 3 miles.
See advert on next page

Tamworth, Staffordshire

Travelodge Tamworth (MOTO)

Travel Accommodation
M42 Moto Service Area, Green Lane, Tamworth,
Staffordshire, B77 5PS
Web: www.travelodge.co.uk
Rooms: 62 ensuite ⊗ Pricing: Sgl £54.40–57.40
Dbl £58.85–61.85 CC: Accepted Room facilities: ▢ ☕
Access: ♿

Telford, Shropshire

Clarion, Madeley Court

Castlefields Way, Madeley Court, Telford,
Shropshire, TF7 5DW
Tel: 01952 680068 Fax: 01952 684275
Email: admin@gb068.u-net.com
Web: www.choicehotels.com
Rooms: 47 all ensuite 😋 📠 ⊗
Pricing: Sgl £57.50–75 Dbl £85–135
Dinner from £23 CC: Accepted
Room facilities: ☐ ☎ 🖥 📞 Access: ♿
Conference: 6 meeting rooms (Thtr 175 max)
Children: Welcome ♯ ℅ Dogs: Welcome
Licences: ⚱ 🏮 Parking: Off-street and monitored
Directions: Leave M54 at Exit 4. Take A442 towards
Kidderminster to Castlefields roundabout. Hotel is
situated as you exit first left.

White House Hotel

Wellington Road, Muxton, Telford,
Shropshire, TF2 8NG
Tel: 01952 604276 Fax: 01952 670336
Email: james@whhotel.co.uk
Web: www.whhotel.co.uk
Rooms: 32 all ensuite 😋 📠 ⊗
Pricing: Sgl £50–62.50 Dbl £65–75
Dinner from £13.50 CC: Accepted
Room facilities: ☐ ☎ 🖥 Conference: 1 meeting room
Children: Welcome ♯ ℅ Dogs: Welcome
Licences: 🏮
Directions: Leave M54 junction 4, follow B5060
towards Newport, then follow signs for Muxton. White
House is ¼ mile on the right.

Travelodge Telford (SA)

Travel Accommodation
A5233, Whitchurch Drive, Shawbirch, Telford,
Shropshire, TF1 3QA
Web: www.travelodge.co.uk
Rooms: 40 all ensuite ⊗
Pricing: Sgl £54.40 Dbl £58.85 CC: Accepted
Room facilities: ☐ 🖥 Access: ♿

Making a booking?

Don't forget to mention RAC
Hotels and Bed & Breakfast 2003.

Are you covered?

For competitively priced travel
insurance, buy online at
www.rac.co.uk or call RAC Travel
Sales on 0800 55 00 55. Quote GUI3

The Saracens Head Inn

16th Century Riverside Inn situated on the
bank of the scenic River Wye at
Symonds Yat East.
Ideal for outdoor activities such as walking,
canoeing and fishing.
Good bar and restaurant food, real ales.
Bar open all day (February–November),
relaxed atmosphere, all rooms ensuite.

**Symonds Yat East, Ross-on-Wye,
Herefordshire HR9 6JL**
Tel: 01600 890435 Fax: 01600 890034
Email: bookings@saracenshead.com
Web: www.saracenshead.com

Tetbury, Gloucestershire

Calcot Manor

Gold Ribbon Winner

Near Tetbury, Gloucestershire, GL8 8YJ
Tel: 01666 890391 Fax: 01666 890394
Email: reception@calcotmanor.co.uk
Web: www.calcotmanor.co.uk

Charming Cotswold stone manor house originally
dating back to the 15th century.
Rooms: 28 all ensuite 😋 📠 Pricing: Sgl £130–145
Dbl £145–160 Dinner from £30 CC: Accepted
Room facilities: ☐ ☎ 🖥 📞 Access: ♿
Conference: 3 meeting rooms (Thtr 100 max),
24hr-delegate from £180, day-delegate rate from £45
Children: Welcome ♯ 🐴 ℅ Licences: ⚱ 🏮
Leisure: Outdoor pool, Tennis
Parking: Off-street and monitored
Directions: 3 miles outside Tetbury, on the crossroads
of the A4135 and A46.

West Midlands

The Snooty Fox

The Snooty Fox has all the traditional friendliness and charm of an old coaching inn, whilst offering present day comforts and the best standards of food and service.

This carefully restored 16th Century mellow stone building occupies a prime site in the historic market town of 'Royal' Tetbury, in the heart of the Cotswold Hills. With a wealth of original brick, stone and timber features, the hotel offers a welcoming and timeless atmostphere.

Market Place, Tetbury, Gloucestershire. GL8 8DD
Tel: 01666 502436 Fax: 01666 503479
res@snooty-fox.co.uk
www.snooty-fox.co.uk

Ye Olde Dog & Partridge

One of England's oldest and finest coaching inns, situated in the historic village of Tutbury. This warm and friendly hotel offers luxury accommodation and excellent dining facilities in both the famous Carvery and Brasserie Restaurants. All 29 bedrooms have been individually designed and furnished to the highest standards. Mini-weekend breaks available all year.

High Street, Tutbury, Staffordshire DE13 9LS
Tel: 01283 813030 Fax: 01283 813178
Email: info@dogandpartridge.net
Website: www.dogandpartridge.net

The Snooty Fox

★★★

Market Place, Tetbury, Gloucestershire, GL8 8DD
Tel: 01666 502436 Fax: 01666 503479
Email: res@snooty-fox.co.uk
Web: www.snooty-fox.co.uk
Rooms: 12 all ensuite
Pricing: Sgl £75 Dbl £110
Dinner from £10.95
CC: Accepted Room facilities:
Conference: 1 meeting room (Thtr 20 max)
Children: Welcome
Dogs: Guide dogs only
Licences:
Directions: At the centre of the market town of Tetbury overlooking the covered market place.
See advert on this page

Tutbury, Staffordshire

Ye Olde Dog & Partridge Hotel

★★★

High Street, Tutbury, near Burton-upon-Trent, Staffordshire, DE13 9LS
Tel: 01283 813030 Fax: 01283 813178
Email: info@dogandpartridge.net
Web: www.dogandpartridge.net
Rooms: 20 all ensuite
Pricing: Sgl £68–85 Dbl £85–120
Dinner from £12.25 CC: Accepted
Room facilities:
Children: WelcomeDogs: Welcome
Licences:
Parking: Off-street
Directions: From Junction 24 off M1, take A50 to Stoke-on-Trent. Take A511 toward Burton-on-Trent (Scrofton, Foston, Hatton) and follow signs for Tutbury.
See advert on this page

Upper Slaughter, Gloucestershire

Lords Of The Manor

★★★ ♕ ♕ ♕   Gold Ribbon Winner

Upper Slaughter, Gloucestershire, GL54 2JD
Tel: 01451 820243 Fax: 01451 820696
Email: lordsofthemanor@btinternet.com
Web: www.lordsofthemanor.com

A 17th-century former rectory set amidst eight acres of gardens. Comfortable surroundings and fine cuisine make it an ideal base to explore the Cotswolds.
Rooms: 27 all ensuite 🖼
Pricing: Sgl £99 Dbl £149–299 CC: Accepted
Room facilities: 🖳 ☎ 🍵 Access: ♿
Conference: 2 meeting rooms (Thtr 20 max),
24hr-delegate from £170, day-delegate rate from £55
Children: Welcome, 7yrs min age
Licences: 🍷 🏛 Parking: Off-street
Directions: From M5, take A40 heading for Oxford, turn left on A429, take "The Slaughters" turning on left. From M25, M40 heading for Oxford, A40 at junction 8, right onto A429, "The Slaughters" turning on the left.

Upton St Leonards, Gloucestershire

Hatton Court Hotel

★★★★ ♕ ♕

Upton Hill, Upton St Leonards, Gloucester,
Gloucestershire, GL4 8DE
Tel: 01452 617412 Fax: 01452 612945
Email: res@hatton-court.co.uk
Web: www.hatton-court.co.uk
Rooms: 45 all ensuite 🖼 ⊗
Pricing: Dinner from £27.50 (2002 rate) CC: Accepted
Room facilities: 🖳 ☎ 🍵 📠
Children: Welcome 🍴 🐾 Dogs: Guide dogs only
Licences: 🍷 🏛 Leisure: Gym, Health spa
Parking: Off-street and monitored

Upton-upon-Severn, Worcestershire

White Lion Hotel

★★★★ ♕ ♕

High Street, Nr Malvern, Worcestershire, WR8 0HJ
Tel: 01684 592551 Fax: 01684 593333
Email: info@whitelionhotel.demon.co.uk
Web: www.whitelionhotel.demon.co.uk
Rooms: 12 all ensuite 🍴 🖼 ⊗
Pricing: Sgl £53–58 Dbl £82.50–110
Dinner from £10 CC: Accepted

Room facilities: 🖳 ☎ 🍵 📠 Access: ♿
Children: Welcome 🍴 Dogs: Welcome
Licences: 🏛 Parking: Off-street
Directions: From Worcester, junction 7 and Tewkesbury, junction 8 off M5. Take A38 for B4104 signposted Upton, over the bridge and turn left.

Uttoxeter, Staffordshire

Oldroyd Guest House & Hotel

◆ ◆ ◆

18–22 Bridge Street, Uttoxeter,
Staffordshire, ST14 8AP
Tel: 01889 562763 Fax: 01889 568916

Travelodge Uttoxeter

Travel Accommodation
A40/B5030, Ashbourne Road, Uttoxeter,
Staffordshire, ST14 5AA
Web: www.travelodge.co.uk
Rooms: 32 all ensuite ⊗
Pricing: Sgl £57.40 Dbl £61.85 CC: Accepted
Room facilities: 🖳 🍵 Access: ♿

Walsall, West Midlands

Quality Hotel and Suites Walsall

★★★

20 Wolverhampton Road West, Bentley, Walsall,
West Midlands, WS2 0BS
Tel: 01922 724444 Fax: 01922 723148
Email: admin@gb622.u-net.com
Web: www.choicehotels.com
Rooms: 154 all ensuite 🍴 🖼 ⊗
Pricing: Sgl £35–95 Dbl £50–135
Dinner from £14.50 CC: Accepted
Room facilities: 🖳 ☎ 🍵 📠 Access: ♿
Conference: 13 meeting rooms (Thtr 180 max), 24hr-delegate from £140, day-delegate rate from £38
Children: Welcome 🍴 Dogs: Guide dogs only
Licences: 🍷 🏛 Leisure: Indoor pool, Gym
Parking: Off-street and monitored
Directions: Located at Junction 10 of M6.

Quality Hotel M6 J7

★★★

Birmingham Road, Walsall, West Midlands, WS5 3AB
Tel: 01922 633609 Fax: 01922 635727
Email: info@boundaryhotel.com
Web: www.qualityhotelM6J7.com
Rooms: 94 all ensuite 🍴 ⊗ Pricing: Sgl £55–95
Dbl £65–95 Dinner from £10 CC: Accepted
Room facilities: 🖳 ☎ 🍵 📠 Access: �
Conference: 9 meeting rooms (Thtr 50 max), 24hr-delegate from £110, day-delegate rate from £34
Children: Welcome 🍴 🐾 Dogs: Welcome
Licences: 🍷 🏛 Leisure: Tennis
Parking: Off-street and monitored
Directions: Exit J7 M6; follow A34 for Walsall. Just over 1 mile on left.

Royal Hotel

 ★★

Ablewell Street, Walsall, West Midlands, WS1 2EL
Tel: 01922 621561 Fax: 01922 630028
Rooms: 28 all ensuite
Room facilities: ☐ ☎ ⊙ Access: ↿↾ ⚲
Children: Welcome � Dogs: Welcome
Leisure: Games room, Snooker/billiards
Parking: Off-street and monitored

Warley, West Midlands

Travelodge Oldbury

Travel Accommodation
A4123, Wolverhampton Road, Oldbury, Warley,
West Midlands, B69 2BH
Web: www.travelodge.co.uk
Rooms: 33 all ensuite ⊗
Pricing: Sgl £47.40 Dbl £51.85 CC: Accepted
Room facilities: ☐ ⊙ Access: ⚲ :

Warwick, Warwickshire

Le Meridien Warwick

 ★★★★★ ℞

Chesford Bridge, Kenilworth,
Warwickshire, CV8 2LD
Tel: 0800 028 2840 Fax: 01926 859 075
Email: sales.chesford@btinternet.com
Web: www.lemeridien.com
Rooms: 219 all ensuite ⏣ ⊗
Room facilities: ☐ ☎ ⊙ ☍ Access: ↿↾ ⚲
Conference: 12 meeting rooms (Thtr 860 max),
24hr-delegate from £190, day-delegate rate from £65
Children: Welcome � Dogs: Welcome
Licences: ⚘ ⅲ
Leisure: Indoor pool, Gym, Health spa, Beauty salon
Parking: Off-street and monitored
Directions: Exit M40 at Junction 15. Take A46 toward
Coventry and A452 slip road to Leamington. Right at
roundabout to Leamington; hotel is 250 yards on right.

Glebe Hotel

★★★★ ℞ ℞

Church Street, Barford, Warwick,
Warwickshire, CV35 8BS
Tel: 01926 624218 Fax: 01926 624625
Web: www.glebehotel.co.uk
Rooms: 39 all ensuite ⬚
Pricing: Sgl £98 Dbl £118
Dinner from £22.50 CC: Accepted
Room facilities: ☐ ☎ ⊙ Access: ↿↾
Conference: 6 meeting rooms (Thtr 120 max),
24hr-delegate from £149, day-delegate rate from £45
Children: Welcome ⚮ ⌇ Dogs: Welcome
Licences: ⅲ
Leisure: Indoor pool, Gym, Health spa, Beauty salon
Parking: Off-street
Directions: Excellent location only 1½ miles from
junction 15 of the M40. Follow A429 (Cirencester), turn
left at roundabout.

Warwick Arms Hotel

 ★★

17 High Street, Warwick, Warwickshire, CV34 4AT
Tel: 01926 492759 Fax: 01926 410587
Rooms: 35
Pricing: Sgl £55 Dbl £65
Dinner from £4.95
CC: Accepted Room facilities: ☐ ☎ ⊙
Conference: 3 meeting rooms (Thtr 100 max),
24hr-delegate from £95, day-delegate rate from £25
Children: Welcome ⚮ Licences: ⅲ
Parking: Off-street and monitored
Directions: Junction 15 off the M40, continue into High
Street, turn right down back lane, car park is first left.

Croft Guest House

 ◆◆◆◆ ⚼

Haseley Knob, Warwick, Warwickshire, CV35 7NL
Tel: 01926 484447 Fax: 01926 484447
Email: david@croftguesthouse.co.uk
Web: www.croftguesthouse.co.uk
Rooms: 9 all ensuite ⊗
Pricing: Sgl £35–40 Dbl £48–55 CC: Accepted
Room facilities: ☐ ⊙
Children: Welcome ⚮
Dogs: Welcome Parking: Off-street
Directions: From A46 follow A4177 for 4 miles to
second roundabout. Turn right (still A4177). After ½
mile turn right to Haseley Knob Village.

Chesterfield Guest House

◆◆◆

Chesterfield, 84 Emscote Road, Warwick,
Warwickshire, CV34 5QJ
Tel: 01926 774844
Email: jchampman@chesterfield.freeserve.co.uk
Web: www.tithe.pwp.blueyonder.co.uk/chesterfields
Seasonal closure: 24–27 December
Rooms: 7 (1 ensuite) ⏣ ⊗
Pricing: Sgl £19–25 Dbl £35–45
Room facilities: ☐ ⊙
Children: Welcome ⚮ Dogs: Guide dogs only
Parking: Off-street and monitored
Directions: M40 J15 A429 Warwick, through town
centre, A445 Leamington Coten End leading to Emscote
Road, under railway bridge, 150 yards on right.

King's Head Inn

 ◆◆◆ ℘

39 Saltisford, Warwick, Warwickshire, CV34 4TD
Tel: 01926 775177 Fax: 01926 775166
Email: thekingsheadwarwick@hotmail.com
Web: www.thekingsheadwarwick.co.uk
Rooms: 9 all ensuite ⏣ ⊗
Pricing: Dinner from £11 (2002 rate)
CC: Accepted
Room facilities: ☐ ⊙ Children: Welcome ⚮ ⌇
Dogs: Welcome Licences: ⅲ
Parking: Off-street and monitored
Directions: M40 J15 A429 Warwick, left at Bowling
Green Street, left at roundabout. We are on the left.

The Rose and Crown

30 Marketplace, Warwick, Warwickshire, CV34 45H
Tel: 01926 411117 Fax: 01926 492117
Rooms: 5 all ensuite
Pricing: Dbl £65–120 Dinner from £15 CC: Accepted
Room facilities:
Conference: 1 meeting room (Thtr 22 max)
Children: Welcome Dogs: Guide dogs only
Licences:
Directions: M40 to Warwick Castle to town centre, in
the market square by the museum.

Weobly, Herefordshire

Ye Olde Salutation Inn

Market Pitch, Weobly, Herefordshire, HR4 8SJ
Tel: 01544 318443 Fax: 01544 318216

Westonbirt, Gloucestershire

Hare and Hounds

★★★

Westonbirt, Tetbury, Gloucestershire, GL8 8QL
Tel: 01666 880233 Fax: 01666 880241
Email: hareandhoundswbt@aol.com
Web: www.hareandhoundshotel.co.uk

Spacious, comfortable hotel in extensive gardens next
to Westonbirt Arboretum, within easy reach of M4 and
M5. Quality dining in the restaurant or bar. Conference
and banquetting suite. Tennis and squash.
Rooms: 31 all ensuite
Pricing: Sgl £77–110 Dbl £96–110
Dinner from £20 CC: Accepted
Room facilities: Access:
Conference: 4 meeting rooms (Thtr 150 max),
24hr-delegate from £99, day-delegate rate from £30
Children: Welcome Dogs: Welcome
Licences:
Leisure: Tennis, Games room, Snooker/billiards
Parking: Off-street
Directions: Exit J17 M4 to Tetbury via Malmesbury;
A433 for 2 miles to Westonbirt. Exit J13 M5, Stroud
and A46 to Westonbirt turning.

Whitchurch, Shropshire

Dukes

◆ ◆ ◆ ◆

Halghton, Whitchurch, Shropshire, SY13 3DU
Tel: 01948 830269
Email: gilberts@thedukes.fsbusiness.co.uk
Web: www.smoothhound.co.uk/hotels/dukes.html
Rooms: 3 all ensuite
Pricing: Sgl £30 Dbl £27
Room facilities: Children: Welcome
Leisure: Tennis Parking: Off-street and monitored
Directions: At Whitchurch, A525 for Wrexham. After 6
miles, turn left for Horseman's Green. Past houses,
turn right for Halghton. Hotel is on right after ¹/₂ mile.

Whittington, Shropshire

Ye Olde Boot Inn

★★

Castle Street, Whittington, Shropshire, SY11 4DF
Tel: 01691 662250 Fax: 01691 662250
Rooms: 6 all ensuite
Pricing: Sgl £32.50 Dbl £45 Dinner from £5
CC: Accepted Room facilities:
Children: Welcome Licences:
Leisure: Games room Parking: Off-street

Wolverhampton, West Midlands

Connaught Hotel

★★★

Tettenhall Road, Wolverhampton,
West Midlands, WV1 4SW
Tel: 01902 424433 Fax: 01902 710353
Email: conhotel@wolverhampton.co.uk

Wolverhampton's leading 3-star independent hotel
excellent venue for weddings and parties. Civil licence
for weddings. Situated outside Wolverhampton on the
A41 Tettenhall Road to Whitchurch. Telephone 01902
424433.
Rooms: 60 all ensuite
Pricing:6080 Dinner from £14.50 CC: Accepted
Room facilities: Access:
Conference: 5 meeting rooms (Thtr 200 max),
24hr-delegate from £60, day-delegate rate from £20
Children: Welcome Dogs: Welcome
Licences:

Quality Hotel Wolverhampton

★★★★

Penn Road, Wolverhampton, WV3 0ER
Tel: 01902 429216 Fax: 01902 710419
Email: admin@gb069.u-net.com
Web: www.choicehotels.com
Rooms: 92 all ensuite 🖨 ⊛
Pricing: Sgl £47–115 Dbl £64–115
Dinner from £16.95 CC: Accepted
Room facilities: 📺 ☎ 🍵 ⛷
Conference: 6 meeting rooms (Thtr 140 max),
24hr-delegate from £130, day-delegate rate from £35
Children: Welcome 🏄 🦌 Dogs: Welcome
Licences: ⟁ ⛄
Leisure: Indoor pool, Gym, Games room
Parking: Off-street and monitored
Directions: M6 Junction 10, take A454 to
Wolverhampton. On approach to town centre, follow
A449 Kidderminster signs. Hotel is ¼ mile on right.

Barons Court Hotel

★★

142 Goldthorn Hill, Wolverhampton, West Midlands,
WV2 3JE
Tel: 01902 341751 Fax: 01902 340033
Email: info@baronscourthotel.com
Web: www.baronscourthotel.com

This country house hotel situated near the centre of
town retains its Edwardian charm and character.
Original oak floors and beams. Graceful dining rooms,
innovative menu.
Rooms: 13 all ensuite ⊛
Pricing: Sgl £45–50 Dbl £60–70
Dinner from £12.50 CC: Accepted
Room facilities: 📺 ☎ 🍵 Access: ♿
Children: Welcome, 10yrs min age
Dogs: Guide dogs only Licences: ⛄
Parking: Off-street
Directions: Take A449 Kidderminster Road from
Wolverhampton ring road. At third set of traffic lights (1
mile), turn left into Goldthorn Hill.

Making a booking?

 Don't forget to mention RAC
Hotels and Bed & Breakfast 2003.

Fox Hotel

◆◆◆

118 School Street, Wolverhampton, WV3 0NR
Tel: 01902 421680 Fax: 01902 711654
Email: sales@foxhotel.co.uk
Web: www.foxhotel.co.uk
Rooms: 33 all ensuite 🖨 ⊛
Pricing: Sgl £35–39 Dbl £55–59
Dinner from £8 CC: Accepted
Room facilities: 📺 ☎ 🍵
Conference: 1 meeting room (Thtr 80 max)
Children: Welcome 🏄 🦌 🦌 Licences: ⛄
Leisure: Games room
Parking: Off-street and monitored
Directions: Situated on city centre ring road, clockwise
on the right, anticlockwise on your left.

Worcester, Worcestershire

The Giffard

★★★

High Street, Worcester, Worcestershire, WR1 2QR
Tel: 0870 400 8133 Fax: 01905 723458
Web: www.macdonaldhotels.co.uk
Rooms: 102 all ensuite 🍴
Pricing: Sgl £48 Dbl £96 Dinner from £16.95
CC: Accepted Room facilities: 📺 ☎ 🍵
Access: |↕|
Conference: 8 meeting rooms (Thtr 150 max)
Children: Welcome 🏄 🦌 Dogs: Welcome
Licences: ⟁ ⛄ Parking: Monitored

Manor Arms Country Inn & Hotel

◆◆◆

Abberley Village, Worcestershire, WR6 6BN
Tel: 01299 896507 Fax: 01299 896723
Email: themanorarms@btconnect.com
Web: www.themanorarms.co.uk
Rooms: 9 all ensuite
Pricing: Sgl £40 Dbl £54 Dinner from £10
CC: Accepted Room facilities: 📺 ☎ 🍵
Licences: ⛄ Parking: Off-street
Directions: Leave A443 at Abberley follow brown
tourist signs "Manor Arms Inn & Hotel".

Wotton-under-Edge, Gloucestershire

Burrows Court

◆◆◆

Nibley Green, North Nibley, Gloucestershire, GL11 6AZ
Tel: 01453 546230 Fax: 01453 546230
Email: p.f.rackley@tesco.net
Web: www.burrowscourt.co.uk
Seasonal closure: January to February
Rooms: 6 all ensuite
Pricing: Sgl £31–37 Dbl £44–56 CC: Accepted
Room facilities: 📺 🍵 Children: Welcome
Dogs: Welcome Licences: ⛄ Parking: Off-street
Directions: From the A38 Bristol to Gloucester Road,
turn off at sign to Blanchworth, North Nibley,
Stinchcombe. Hotel opposite North Nibley village sign.

St Abb's Head

Cockburnspath
Eyemouth
Ayton
Duns
Berwick-upon-Tweed
Greenlaw
Holy Island
Coldstream
Cornhill-on-Tweed
Waren Mill
Bamburgh
Belford
Seahouses
Kelso
St Boswells
don &
eaderfoot
Wooler
B6348
Hawick
Jedburgh
Alnwick
Lesbury
NORTHUMBERLAND
Warkworth
Amble
Newton-on-the-Moor
Rothbury
Felton
NORTHUMBERLAND
Longhorsley
Otterburn
Falstone
Kielder
Water
Ashington
Bellingham
Newbiggin-by-the-Sea
R. North Tyne
Morpeth
Canonbie
Bedlington
Blyth
Ponteland
Seaton Burn
Newcastl
Whitley Bay
Chollerford
Gosforth
Newcastle
Tynemouth
Upper Denton
Haydon
Bridge
upon Tyne
South Shields
Haltwhistle
Bardon
Mill
Corbridge
Blaydon
Jarrow
Boldon
Langley
Hexham
Prudhoe
Gateshead
Brampton
Allendale
Town
Slaley
Wardley
Sunderland
Stanley
Washington
Houghton le Spring
Blanchland
Consett
Chester-le-Street
Hetton-le-Hole
Seaham
Alston
Tow Law
Easington
Horden
Stanhope
Durham
Pittington
Peterlee
Shincliffe
Blackhall
North
Pennines
R.
Wear
Crook
Fir Tree
DURHAM
Bishop Auckland
Spennymoor
Sedgefield
Ha
Rushyford
Middleton in
Teesdale
Newton Aycliffe
Billingham
TEESS
Appleby-in-
Westmorland
Romaldkirk
Redworth
Walworth
Stockton-on-Tees
Mid
Brough
Barnard
Castle
Darlington
Eaglescliffe
Thornaby-on-Tees
Esto
Orton
Yarm
Crathorn
Kirkby
Stephen
Scotch
Corner
Ravenstonedale
Richmond
Catterick Br.
Sedbergh
Catterick
Leeming
Bar
Northallerton
Hawes
Leyburn
Arrathorne
Bedale
West
Witton
YORKSHIRE
Thirsk
Helm

n-by-the-Sea
Loftus
Easington
Whitby
A174
A171
R Esk
A169
Robin Hood's
Bay
ORK
Goathland
A171
Rosedale Abbey
Cloughton
Hackness
Scalby
Cropton
bymoorside
Middleton
Scarborough
70
East Ayton
Pickering
Filey

Note:
Dark blue dots
represent the
location of
RAC-inspected
accommodation

Northeast

Note:
Dark blue dots represent the location of RAC-inspected accommodation

rn-by-the-Sea
Loftus
Easington
gh
A174
Whitby
A171
R Esk
A169
Robin Hood's
YORK
Bay
Goathland
A171
S
Rosedale Abbey
Cloughton
Cropton
Hackness
Scalby
kbymoorside
Middleton
Scarborough
A170
A170
East Ayton
Pickering
Filey
B1257
A64
A1039
Malton
Norton
B1253
Flamborough Head
B1248
B1249
Kilham
A614
Bridlington
ford
Fridaythorpe
ge
A166
Bridlington
A166
Driffield
Bay
EAST RIDING OF YORKSHIRE
Pocklington
Hornsea
A1079
Market
Cherry
A1035
Weighton
Burton
B1244
A1079
Tickton
Northlands
Beverley
North
B1230
Cave
South
Kingston
Cave
Willerby
upon Hull
M62
A63
Withernsea
Hedon
A1033
den
Humber Br.
Patrington
Easington
Goole
Winterton
A1077
Barton-upon-
Humber
NORTH LINCOLNSHIRE
A160
Immingham
Spurn Head
horne
Crowle
Scunthorpe
B1206
Grimsby
M180
Broughton
Humberside
Cleethorpes
NE LINCOLNSHIRE
Belton
Brigg
Caistor
Kirton in
Lindsey
North Somercotes
try
Lincolnshire
B1206
Wolds
Gainsborough
Market
Louth
Rasen
B1200
Retford

Northeast

Gold Ribbon Award

Devonshire Arms	★★★	402
Middlethorpe Hall Hotel, York	★★★	447

Blue Ribbon Award

Crathorne Hall Hotel, Crathorne	★★★★	445
Feversham Arms Hotel, Halmsley	★★★	413
Grange Hotel, York	★★★	447
Hob Green, Harrogate	★★★	411
Judges Country Hall Hotel, Yarm	★★★	446
Redworth Hall Hotel, Newton Aycliffe	★★★★	427
Rose & Crown Hotel, Romaldkirk	★★	428
Seaham Hall Hotel, Seaham	★★★★	437
Vermont Hotel, Newcastle	★★★★	424

Little Gem

Clow Beck House, Darlington	♦♦♦♦♦	406
The Moorlands, Pickering	♦♦♦♦♦	426

Alnwick, Northumberland

Hawkhill Farmhouse

◆ ◆ ◆ ◆

Lesbury, Alnwick, Northumberland, NE66 3PG
Tel: 01665 830380 Fax: 01665 830093
Email: stay@hawkhillfarmhouse.com
Web: www.hawkhillfarmhouse.com
Seasonal closure: Christmas
Rooms: 3 all ensuite ⊛ Pricing: Dbl £48–50
Room facilities: ▢ ⬀
Children: Welcome 10yrs min age Parking: Off-street
Directions: Leave A1 for Alnwick. Take A1068
Alnmouth. After 2 miles at second farm turn right up
tree-lined drive.

Austwick, North Yorkshire

The Austwick Country House Hotel

◆ ◆ ◆ ◆ ⬀ ⬈

Austwick, Nr Settle, Via Lancaster,
North Yorkshire, LA2 8BY
Tel: 01524 251224 Fax: 01524 251796
Email: austwickh@aol.com
Web: www.austwickhotel.co.uk
Rooms: 12 (11 ensuite) ⬈ ⊛
Pricing: Sgl £45 Dbl £90–100 Dinner from £15
CC: Accepted Room facilities: ▢ ☎ ⬀
Children: Welcome ⬈ Dogs: Welcome Licences: ▮▮▮
Leisure: Tennis, Golf, Fishing, Riding
Parking: Off-street and monitored
Directions: Follow A65 from Skipton to Kendal. Three
miles past Settle turn right at the Cross Street Pub into the
National Park. ¾ mile over bridge, hotel is on the left.

Bamburgh, Northumberland

Waren House Hotel

★ ★ ★ ⬀

Waren Mill, Belford, Northumberland, NE70 7EE
Tel: 01668 214581 Fax: 01668 214484
Email: enquiries@warenhousehotel.co.uk
Web: www.warenhousehotel.co.uk

Traditional Country House Hotel in 6-acre grounds on
edge of Budle Bay and 2 miles from Bamburgh Castle.
Superb accommodation, excellent food, extensive
reasonably priced wine list. ⬀ ⊛
Rooms: 11 all en-suite ⬀ ⊛
Pricing: Sgl £90–110 Dbl £120–195 Dinner from £22
CC: Accepted Room facilities: ▢ ☎ ⬀

Conference: 1 meeting room (Thtr 20 max),
24hr-delegate from £120, day-delegate rate from £30
Children: Welcome 14yrs min age Dogs: Welcome
Licences: ▮▮▮ Parking: Off-street
Directions: 14 miles south of Berwick-upon-Tweed.
Take B1342, off the A1, to Waren Mill. Hotel on
southwest corner of Budle Bay.

Lord Crewe Arms

★ ★ ⬀

Front Street, Bamburgh, Northumberland, NE69 7BL
Tel: 01668 214243 Fax: 01668 214273
Email: lca@tinyonline.co.uk
Web: www.lordcrewe.com
Seasonal closure: 1 December to 1 March
Rooms: 18 (17 ensuite) ⬀
Pricing: Sgl £35–42 Dbl £70–104 Dinner from £18
CC: Accepted Room facilities: ▢ ☎ ⬀
Children: Welcome 5yrs min age � Dogs: Welcome
Licences: ▮▮▮ Parking: Off-street

Barnard Castle, Co. Durham

Number 34

◆ ◆ ◆ ◆

34 The Bank, Barnard Castle, Durham, DL12 8PN
Tel: 01833 631304 Fax: 01833 631304
Rooms: 2 all ensuite ⊛ Pricing: Sgl £35 Dbl £50
Room facilities: ▢ ⬀
Conference: 2 meeting rooms (Thtr 12 max)
Children: Welcome 12yrs min age Parking: Off-street
Directions: Situated in the centre of Barnard castle in
the antique quarter beyond the Market Cross and next
to Blagraves restaurant.

Old Well Inn

◆ ◆ ◆ ◆

21 The Bank, Barnard Castle, County Durham,
DL12 8PH
Tel: 01833 690130 Fax: 01833 690140
Email: reservations@oldwellinn.co.uk
Web: www.oldwellinn.co.uk
Rooms: 10 all ensuite ⬀ ⊛ Pricing: Dinner from £8
CC: Accepted Room facilities: ▢ ☎ ⬀ Access: ♿
Children: Welcome � Dogs: Welcome Licences: ▮▮▮
Directions: Situated in the centre of Barnard Castle
below the Market Cross, in the antique quarter.

Northeast

Barnsley, South Yorkshire

Tankersley Manor

★★★★ ℞

Church Lane, Tankersley, Barnsley,
South Yorkshire, S75 3DQ
Tel: 01226 744700 Fax: 01226 744505
Email: tankersley@marstonhotels.com
Web: www.marstonhotels.com

Now awarded four stars, Tankersley Manor is a mellow
stone building high on the moors overlooking
surrounding countryside. Enjoy fine food in the oak
beamed restaurant and a warm welcome.
Rooms: 69 all ensuite 🐾 🗗 ⊗
Pricing: Sgl £105 Dbl £139 Dinner from £25
CC: Accepted Room facilities: ▢ ☎ ⊙ ☏ Access: ♿
Conference: 16 meeting rooms (Thtr 375 max),
24hr-delegate from £140, day-delegate rate from £45
Children: Welcome ♀ Dogs: Guide dogs only
Licences: ⚓ ♟ Parking: Off-street and monitored
Directions: Leave M1 at junction 36 and follow A61
towards Sheffield. Hotel is half a mile on the left.

The Fountain Inn & Rooms

◆◆◆◆

Wellthorne Lane, Ingbirchworth, Sheffield,
South Yorkshire, S36 7QJ
Tel: 01226 763125 Fax: 01226 761336
Email: reservations@fountain-inn.co.uk
Web: www.mortal-man-inns.co.uk/fountaininn
Seasonal closure: Christmas day
Pricing: Sgl £48.50–68.50 Dbl £58.50–78.50
CC: Accepted Room facilities: ▢ ☎ ⊙ Access: ♿
Conference: 2 meeting rooms (Thtr 200 max),
24hr-delegate from £70, day-delegate rate from £12.95
Children: Welcome ♀ Dogs: Guide dogs only
Licences: ♟ Parking: Off-street
Directions: J37 from M1 and head for the A629
Huddersfield road – continue through to village of
Ingbirchworth.

Travelodge Barnsley

Travel Accommodation
A633/A635, School Street, Stairfoot, Barnsley,
Yorkshire, S70 3PT
Web: www.travelodge.co.uk
Rooms: 32 all ensuite ⊗
Pricing: Sgl £47.40 Dbl £51.85 CC: Accepted
Room facilities: ▢ ⊙ Access: ♿

Bedale, North Yorkshire

Elmfield Country House

◆◆◆◆◆ ✖

Arrathorne, Bedale, North Yorkshire, DL8 1NE
Tel: 01677 450558 Fax: 01677 450557
Email: stay@elmfieldhouse.freeserve.co.uk
Web: www.elmfieldhouse.co.uk

Situated in own grounds between Bedale and
Richmond, this award-winning house offers a superb
setting at the start of the Yorkshire Dales, an ideal
place for the holiday and business traveller.
Rooms: 9 all ensuite 🐾 🗗
Pricing: Sgl £37–40 Dbl £55–65 Dinner from £15
CC: Accepted Room facilities: ▢ ☎ ⊙ ☏ Access: ♿
Children: Welcome ♀ Dogs: Guide dogs only
Licences: ♟ Leisure: Fishing, Games room
Parking: Off-street and monitored
Directions: From A1, take A684 into Bedale. Follow
A684 towards Leyburn after village of Patrick
Brompton. Turn right at crossroads towards Richmond.
Elmfield is 1½ miles on right.

Little Holtby

◆◆◆◆

Little Holtby, Leeming Bar, Northallerton,
North Yorkshire, DL7 9LH
Tel: 01609 748762 Fax: 01609 748822
Email: littleholtby@yahoo.co.uk
Web: www.littleholtby.co.uk
Rooms: 3 (1 ensuite) 🗗 ⊗
Pricing: Sgl £30 Dbl £50–55 Dinner from £12.50 CC:
Accepted Room facilities: ▢ ⊙ Parking: Off-street
Directions: 50 yards from A1 northbound, 2 miles from
junction of A684 Northallerton/Bedale.

Southfield

 ◆ ◆ ◆

96 South End, Bedale, North Yorkshire, DL8 2DS
Tel: 01677 423510
Rooms: 4 (2 ensuite) ⊛
Pricing: Sgl £22–28 Dbl £44 Room facilities: 🗗
Children: Welcome ♒ ⋇€ Dogs: Guide dogs only
Parking: Off-street and monitored
Directions: Take A1 to Bedale. Turn left at 'White Bear'.
Hotel 400yds on right, with privet hedge and white
stone front.

Belford, Northumberland

Blue Bell

 ★ ★ ★ ⓡ

Market Square, Belford, Northumberland, NE70 7NE
Tel: 01668 213543 Fax: 01668 213787
Email: bluebell@globalnet.co.uk
Web: www.bluebellhotel.com
Rooms: 17 all ensuite ⬤ 🗗
Pricing: Sgl £34–48 Dbl £80–104 Dinner from £23
CC: Accepted Room facilities: 🖵 ☎ 🗗
Conference: 2 meeting rooms (Thtr 80 max)
Children: Welcome ♒ ⋇€ Dogs: Welcome Licences: ⫯⫯
Leisure: Games room Parking: Off-street
See advert on this page

Bellingham, Northumberland

Riverdale Hall Hotel

★ ★ ⓡ

Bellingham, Northumberland, NE48 2JT
Tel: 01434 220254 Fax: 01434 220457
Email: iben@riverdalehall.demon.co.uk
Web: www.riverdalehall.demon.co.uk

A stone-built 19th-century mansion with a modern
wing set in five acres of grounds alongside the North
Tyne River.
Rooms: 20 all ensuite ⬤ 🗗
Pricing: Sgl £46–52 Dbl £70–88 Dinner from £19.95
CC: Accepted Room facilities: 🖵 ☎ 🗗
Conference: 2 meeting rooms (Thtr 40 max),
24hr-delegate from £69, day-delegate rate from £25
Children: Welcome ♒ ⋇€ Dogs: Welcome Licences: ⫯⫯
Leisure: Indoor pool, Fishing Parking: Off-street
Directions: Turn off B6320 after bridge onto C200.
Hotel is 150yds on left.

Bentley, Yorkshire

Eastfarm B&B

 ✦

Eastfarm Owston Lane, Owston, Bentley,
Yorkshire, DN5 0LP
Tel: 01302 338300 Fax: 01302 726224

Berwick-upon-Tweed, Northumberland

Kings Arms Hotel

 ★ ★ ★ ⓡ

Hide Hill, Berwick-upon-Tweed,
Northumberland, TD15 1EJ
Tel: 01289 307454 Fax: 01289 308867
Email: kingsarmshotel@virgin.co.uk
Web: www.kings-arms-hotel.com
Rooms: 36 all ensuite ⬤ 🗗
Pricing: Sgl £59 Dbl £89 Dinner from £12.50
CC: Accepted Room facilities: 🖵 ☎ 🗗
Conference: 4 meeting rooms (Thtr 200 max),
24hr-delegate from £90, day-delegate rate from £35
Children: Welcome ♒ ⋇€ Dogs: Welcome
Licences: ⬤ ⫯⫯
Directions: Leave A1 from north or south into town
centre, then right at Guildhall and first right into Hyde Hill.
See advert on following page

Northeast

Queen's Head Hotel

 ★

Sandgate, Berwick-upon-Tweed, Northumberland, TD15 1EP
Tel: 01289 307852 Fax: 01289 307858
Email: queensheadhotel@berwickontweed.fsbusiness.co.uk
Rooms: 6 all ensuite 🐾 ⊗
Pricing: Sgl £40–45 Dbl £60–65 Dinner from £15
CC: Accepted
Room facilities: ▢ ☎ ▨ 📞 Children: Welcome ⊼
Dogs: Welcome Licences: ⋔ Parking: Off-street
Directions: In town centre pass by town hall, turn right into Hide Hill, hotel at bottom of hill.

Number 40 Ravensdowne

 ◆ ◆ ◆ ◆ ⌀

40 Ravensdowne, Berwick-upon-Tweed, Northumberland, TD15 1DQ
Tel: 01289 306992 Fax: 01289 331606
Email: petedot@dmuckle.freeserve.co.uk
Web: www.secretkingdom.com/40/ravensdowne.html
Seasonal closure: Christmas, New Year
Rooms: 3 all ensuite ⊗ Pricing: Dbl £45–55
Room facilities: ▢ ▨ Children: Welcome ⊼
Dogs: Guide dogs only
Directions: Down main street past Town Hall clock into Woolmarket; turn left, and the house is on the right.

Beverley, East Yorkshire

Tickton Grange

 ★ ★ ★ ★ ℞ ℞

Tickton, Beverley, East Yorkshire, HU17 9SH
Tel: 01964 543666 Fax: 01964 542556
Email: maggy@tickton-grange.demon.co.uk
Web: www.ticktongrange.co.uk

A very warm welcome awaits you at the independently owned Tickton Grange. Enjoy every detail, from elegant bedrooms with ensuite power shower bathrooms to our award-winning restaurant.
Rooms: 17 all ensuite 🐾 📠
Pricing: Sgl £79.50 Dbl £99 Dinner from £25
CC: Accepted Room facilities: ▢ ☎ ▨
Conference: 3 meeting rooms (Thtr 200 max)
Children: Welcome ⊼ Licences: ⊲ ⋔
Parking: Off-street
Directions: 3 miles from Beverley on the A1035.

The Manor House

★ ★ ☖ ☖ ☖

Northlands, Walkington, Nr Beverley, East Yorkshire, HU17 8RU
Tel: 01482 881645 Fax: 01482 866501
Web: www.the-manor-house.co.uk
Rooms: 7 all ensuite ⬥ ⬥
Pricing: Sgl £80–86 Dbl £96–108 Dinner from £15
CC: Accepted Room facilities: ⬜ ☎ ⬥ Access: ⬥
Conference: 2 meeting rooms (Thtr 20 max)
Children: Welcome 12yrs min age ⬥
Dogs: Guide dogs only Licences: ⬥ ⬥
Parking: Off-street and monitored
Directions: Located between Bishop Burton and Walkington on the Newbald road.

Burton Mount Country House

◆ ◆ ◆ ◆ ◆ ⬥

Burton Mount, Malton Road, Cerry Burton, Beverley, East Yorkshire, HU17 7RA
Tel: 01964 550541 Fax: 01964 551955
Email: pg@burtonmount.co.uk
Web: www.burtonmount.co.uk

A charming country house just 2 miles from Beverley, set in extensive gardens and offering luxurious accommodation everywhere. Pauline Greenwood is renowned locally for her focused customer care, culinary skills and warm hospitality.
Rooms: 3 all ensuite
Pricing: Sgl £40–95 Dbl £105–140 Dinner from £16
Room facilities: ⬜ ⬥ ⬥ Access: ⬥
Conference: 2 meeting rooms (Thtr 25 max),
24hr-delegate from £125, day-delegate rate from £50
Children: Welcome 10yrs min age
Dogs: Guide dogs only Leisure: Games room
Parking: Monitored
Directions: M62 to South Cave onwards to B1230 T-junction, right Walkington onwards to traffic lights. Turn left onto roundabout and take B1248 to Malton, at next crossroad turn right.

Rudstone Walk Country Accommodation

◆ ◆ ◆ ◆

South Cave, near Beverley, East Yorkshire, HU15 2AH
Tel: 01430 422230 Fax: 01430 424552
Email: office@rudstone-walk.co.uk
Web: www.rudstone-walk.co.uk
Rooms: 14 all ensuite ⬥ ⬥
Pricing: Sgl £40–47 Dbl £55–59 Dinner from £18
CC: Accepted Room facilities: ⬜ ☎ ⬥ ⬥ Access: ⬥
Conference: 3 meeting rooms (Thtr 50 max),
24hr-delegate from £89, day-delegate rate from £19.95
Children: Welcome ⬥ Dogs: Welcome
Licences: ⬥ ⬥ Parking: Off-street and monitored
Directions: Exit J38 M62; through South Cave to B1230 and turn right to Beverley. House sign is on the corner.

Eastgate Guest House

◆ ◆ ◆ ⬥

7 Eastgate, Beverley, HU17 0DR
Tel: 01482 868464 Fax: 01482 871899

Rooms: 16 (7 ensuite) ⬥ ⬥
Pricing: Sgl £15–38 Dbl £20–50 Room facilities: ⬜ ⬥
Children: Welcome Dogs: Welcome
Directions: Very close to train and bus stations, within sight of Beverley Minster.

Mobile traffic information

Just dial 1740* from any mobile phone to get up-to-the-minute RAC traffic information on motorways and major A roads. Try it now! *Calls to 1740 cost up to 59p per minute. Check with your network.

Need help booking?

RAC Hotel Reservations will find the accommodation that's right for you – and book it too. Call today on 0870 603 9109 and quote 'Guide 2003'

Plan your route

Visit www.rac.co.uk for RAC's interactive route planner, including up to the minute traffic reports.

Northeast

Bingley, West Yorkshire

Five Rise Locks Hotel and Restaurant

◆ ◆ ◆ ◆ ® ✕

Beck Lane, off Park Road, Bingley,
West Yorkshire, BD16 4DD
Tel: 01274 565296 Fax: 01274 568828
Email: info@five-rise-locks.co.uk
Web: www.five-rise-locks.co.uk

Formerly a wealthy Victorian mill owner's house, now in
the rural setting of the canal conservation area. Each
bedroom is individually designed and tastefully
furnished. Enjoy freshly-prepared food complemented
by an imaginative wine list in elegant, yet relaxing
surroundings.
Rooms: 9 all ensuite ⊛
Pricing: Sgl £40–57 Dbl £55–70 Dinner from £10
CC: Accepted Room facilities: ▢ ☎ ⊗ ✎ Access: ⅄
Conference: 1 meeting room (Thtr 16 max),
day-delegate rate from £25
Children: Welcome ⅋℃ Dogs: Welcome Licences: ⅄⅄⅄
Parking: Off-street and monitored
Directions: From Bingley, turn onto Park Road.
Continue for ¼ of a mile. At crossroads sign turn left.
Hotel on left.

Bishop Auckland, Co. Durham

Greenhead Country House Hotel

◆ ◆ ◆ ◆ ✕ ®

Fir Tree, Crook, Bishop Auckland,
County Durham, DL15 8BL
Tel: 01388 763143 Fax: 01388 763143
Email: info@thegreenheadhotel.co.uk
Web: www.thegreenheadhotel.co.uk

Offers clean, comfortable accommodation set in acres
of open countryside. Great hospitality ensuring guests'
comfort. 'Richly deserves the Warm Welcome and
Sparkling Diamond awards' – RAC report, 2002.
Rooms: 7 all ensuite ▱ ⊛
Pricing: Sgl £45–55 Dbl £65–75 CC: Accepted
Room facilities: ▢ ⊗ Licences: ⅄⅄⅄
Parking: Off-street and monitored
Directions: A1 to A68 into Fir Tree. Turn right at pub.
Hotel 500 yards on the left.

Blanchland, Northumberland

Lord Crewe Arms Hotel

★ ★ ★ ®

Nr Consett, Blanchland, Co. Durham, DH8 9SP
Tel: 01434 675251 Fax: 01434 675337
Email: lord@crewearms.freeserve.co.uk
Web: www.lordcrewehotel.com
Rooms: 19 all ensuite ⊛ ▱
Pricing: Sgl £80 Dbl £120 Dinner from £28
CC: Accepted Access: ⅄
Conference: 2 meeting rooms (Thtr 18 max),
24hr-delegate from £29, day-delegate rate from £17.50
Children: Welcome ⅋ ℃ Dogs: Welcome Licences: ⅄ ⅄⅄⅄
Directions: 10 miles south of Hexham on B 6306.

Bolton Abbey, North Yorkshire

Devonshire Arms   Gold Ribbon Winner

★ ★ ★ ★ ® ® ®

Bolton Abbey, near Skipton, North Yorkshire, BD23 6AJ
Tel: 01756 718111 Fax: 01756 710564
Email: reservations@thedevonshirearms.co.uk
Web: www.thedevonshirearms.co.uk

Owned by the Duke and Duchess of Devonshire, The
Devonshire Arms Country House Hotel offers
individually-designed bedrooms, award-winning
restaurants and a fully-equipped leisure club, all in
beautiful surroundings
Rooms: 41 all ensuite ▱ ⊛ Pricing: Sgl £145–345
Dbl £195–345 Dinner from £45 CC: Accepted
Room facilities: ▢ ☎ ⊗ ✲ Access: ⅄
Children: Welcome ⅋ ℃ Dogs: Welcome Licences: ⅄ ⅄⅄⅄
Leisure: Indoor pool, Gym, Health spa, Beauty salon,
Tennis, Fishing Parking: Off-street and monitored
Directions: The Devonshire Arms is situated 5 miles
east of Skipton on the B6160, just 250 yards north of
the junction with the A59.

Boroughbridge, North Yorkshire

Crown Hotel

★★★★

Horsefair, Boroughbridge, North Yorkshire, YO51 9LB
Tel: 01423 322328 Fax: 01423 324512
Email: sales@crownboroughbridge.co.uk
Web: www.crownboroughbridge.co.uk

Former coaching inn with 37 bedrooms, all ensuite.
Leisure facilities include pool, gym and beauty
therapist. Large secure private car park. Excellent
conference facilities, bars and restaurant.
Rooms: 37 all ensuite 🐾 🖨 ⊗
Pricing: Sgl £75 Dbl £90–110 CC: Accepted
Room facilities: 📺 ☎ ⏾ Access: |↓↑
Conference: 3 meeting rooms (Thtr 150 max)
Children: Welcome ⼍ ℃ Licences: ⚓ ⚜
Leisure: Indoor pool, Gym, Beauty salon
Parking: Off-street and monitored
Directions: Leave A1(M) at Junction 48 and take road
into Boroughbridge. Follow signs into town; hotel is
located on the T-junction. Car park is at rear.

Rose Manor

★★★

Horsefair, Boroughbridge, North Yorkshire, YO51 9LL
Tel: 01423 322245 Fax: 01423 324920
Email: rosemanorhotel@ukf.net
Web: www.rosemanorhotel.co.uk
Rooms: 20 all ensuite 🐾 🖨 ⊗
Pricing: Sgl £85 Dbl £118–124 Dinner from £18
CC: Accepted Room facilities: 📺 ☎ ⏾ ✆
Conference: 5 meeting rooms (Thtr 200 max),
24hr-delegate from £105, day-delegate rate from
£31.50
Children: Welcome ⼍ Licences: ⚜ Parking: Off-street
Directions: Within 1 mile of exit 48 on A1(M) –
signposted Boroughbridge.

The Crown Inn

◆ ◆ ◆

Roecliffe, Boroughbridge, North Yorkshire, YO51 9LY
Tel: 01423 322578 Fax: 01423 324060
Rooms: 9 all ensuite 🖨 ⊗
Pricing: Sgl £35 Dbl £50–80 Dinner from £2.95
CC: Accepted Room facilities: 📺 ☎ ⏾ Access: ♿
Children: Welcome ⼍ Dogs: Welcome Licences: ⚓ ⚜
Leisure: Games room Parking: Off-street
Directions: A1(M) J48, follow signs for Bar Lane and
Roecliffe. The Crown is on the right at the end of the
village.

Bradford, West Yorkshire

Hanover International Hotel & Club Bradford

★★★★

Mayo Avenue, off Rooley Lane, Bradford, West
Yorkshire, BD5 8HZ
Tel: 0870 240 2957 Fax: 01274 406600
Email: crso@hanover-international.com
Web: www.hanover-international.com

HANOVER INTERNATIONAL
HOTELS & CLUBS

Rooms: 131 all ensuite 🖨 ⊗
Pricing: Sgl £78–120 Dbl £88–130 Dinner from £17.95
CC: Accepted Room facilities: 📺 ☎ ⏾ ✆
Access: |↓↑ ♿ Children: Welcome ⼍ ℃
Dogs: Welcome Licences: ⚓ ⚜
Leisure: Indoor pool, Gym, Health spa, Beauty salon,
Games room Parking: Off-street and monitored
Directions: Leave M62 at Junction 26. Take M606 to
Bradford. Take third exit A6177 Mayo Avenue off
roundabout at end of M606. Take first sharp right.

Northeast

Midland Hotel

★★★

Forster Square, Bradford, West Yorkshire, BD1 4HU
Tel: 01274 735735 Fax: 01274 720003
Email: info@midland-hotel-bradford.com
Web: www.midland-hotel-bradford.com

90 standard and executive bedrooms, magnificent
public areas, grill room, 2 elegant ballrooms, 2 bars, 9
conference/training rooms, ISDN lines and air
conditioning and free on-site car parking right in the
heart of Bradford.
Rooms: 90 all ensuite
Pricing: Sgl £85–95 Dbl £95–120 Dinner from £10
CC: Accepted Room facilities: ☐ ☎ ☕ ✆ Access: |↕|
Conference: 11 meeting rooms (Thtr 440 max),
24-hr delegate from £125, day-delegate rate from £38
Children: Welcome ⼍ 🐴 ⅊ Dogs: Welcome
Licences: ⬙ ⅲ Parking: Off-street and monitored
Directions: Head towards Bradford city centre,
following signs for Forster Square Station. Hotel
located 50 yards from station.

Quality Hotel Bradford

★★★

Bridge Street, Bradford, BD1 1JX
Tel: 01274 728706 Fax: 01274 736358
Email: admin@gb654.u-net.com
Web: www.choicehotels.com
Rooms: 57 all ensuite ☢
Pricing: Dinner from £16.50 (2002 rate) CC: Accepted
Room facilities: ☐ ☎ ☕ ✆ Access: |↕| ♿
Children: Welcome ⼍ ⅊ Dogs: Welcome Licences: ⅲ
Leisure: Gym, Games room
Parking: Off-street and monitored
Directions: From all directions, follow signs for city
centre and Bradford Interchange. The hotel is situated
directly opposite the Interchange.

Travelodge Bradford (SA)

Travel Accommodation
1 Mid-Point, Dick Lane, Pudsely, Thornbury,
Bradford, BD3 8QD
Web: www.travelodge.co.uk Rooms: 48 all ensuite ☢
Pricing: Sgl £49.40 Dbl £53.85
CC: Accepted Room facilities: ☐ ☕ Access: ♿

Bridlington, East Yorkshire

Expanse Hotel

★★★

North Marine Drive, Bridlington, YO15 2LS
Tel: 01262 675347 Fax: 01262 604928
Email: expanse@brid.demon.co.uk
Web: www.expanse.co.uk
Rooms: 48 all ensuite
Pricing: Dinner from £17 CC: Accepted
Room facilities: ☐ ☎ ☕ Access: |↕|
Conference: 4 meeting rooms (Thtr 200 max)
Children: Welcome ⼍ ⅊ Dogs: Guide dogs only
Licences: ⬙ ⅲ Parking: Off-street and monitored
Directions: At A165/A614 roundabout take Bridlington
North, at mini roundabout take sign to Sewerby, follow
North Bead parking signs.

Revelstoke Hotel

★★★

1–3 Flamborough Road, Bridlington, YO15 2HU
Tel: 01262 672362 Fax: 01262 409700
Email: info@revelstokehotel.co.uk
Web: www.revelstokehotel.co.uk
Rooms: 26 (25 ensuite)
Pricing: Sgl £43.25–60 Dbl £71.50–96.50
Dinner from £12.95 CC: Accepted
Room facilities: ☐ ☎ ☕ ✆
Conference: 50 meeting rooms (Thtr 250 max)
Children: Welcome ⼍ ⅊ Dogs: Guide dogs only
Licences: ⅲ Leisure: Games room
Parking: Off-street
Directions: From town centre head north to
Flamborough, the Revelstoke is approx 400m from the
centre on the left of Flamborough road.

Abbey Court Hotel

◆◆◆

31, Horsforth Avenue, Bridlington,
East Yorkshire, YO15 3DG
Tel: 01262 401402
Email: abbeycourthotel@btconnet.com
Web: www.smoothhound.co.uk/abbeycourthotel
Rooms: 10 (7 ensuite) ☢ ☢
Pricing: Sgl £15–19 Dbl £30–38 Room facilities: ☐ ☕
Children: Welcome ⼍ ⅊ Dogs: Guide dogs only
Licences: ⅲ
Directions: Follow signs for the Spa theatre, take the
turning for Horsforth Avenue, off roundabout. Hotel is
situated 200 yards on the right.

Marina Guest House

◆ ◆ ◆

8 Summerfield Road, Bridlington,
East Yorkshire, YO15 3LF
Tel: 01262 677138
Rooms: 7 (5 ensuite)
Pricing: Sgl £24.50 Dbl £39–43
Dinner from £7.50 CC: Accepted Room facilities:
Children: Welcome Dogs: Welcome Licences:
Directions: From the Spa Theatre complex heading
south along South Marine Drive, Summerfield Road is
the second turning on the right.

Sunflower Lodge

◆ ◆ ◆

24 Flamborough Road, Bridlington,
East Riding of Yorkshire, YO15 2HX
Tel: 01262 400447
A relaxing oasis, caring hosts, kettle always boiling,
pretty ensuite bedrooms, thoughtful exterior,
exceptional housekeeping, delicious meals. Families,
couples, especially welcome, "more than you expect,
all that you desire".
Rooms: 7 (5 ensuite)
Pricing: Sgl £24–29 Dbl £36–46 Dinner from £5.50
Room facilities: Children: Welcome
Dogs: Welcome

The Ivanhoe Hotel

◆ ◆ ◆

63 Cardigan Road, Bridlington,
East Yorkshire, YO15 3JS
Tel: 01262 675983
Email: ivanhoe-hotel@yahoo.co.uk
Web: www.bridlington-hotel.co.uk
Rooms: 8 all ensuite
Pricing: Sgl £23–26 Dbl £38–44 Dinner from £7
CC: Accepted Room facilities:
Children: Welcome Dogs: Guide dogs only
Licences: Parking: Off-street
Directions: 200m from Spa theatre at junction of
Cardigan Road and Horsforth Avenue, opposite church.

The Victoria Hotel

◆ ◆ ◆

25-27 Victoria Road, Bridlington,
East Yorkshire, YO15 2AT
Tel: 01262 673871 Fax: 01262 609431

Park View Hotel

◆ ◆

9–11 Tennyson Avenue, Bridlington,
East Yorkshire, YO15 2EU
Tel: 01262 672140 Fax: 01262 672140
Rooms: 16 (4 ensuite) Room facilities:
Children: Welcome Dogs: Welcome Licences:
Parking: Off-street

Cleethorpes, Lincolnshire

Kingsway Hotel

★ ★ ★

Kingsway, Cleethorpes, N. E. Lincolnshire, DN35 0AE
Tel: 01472 601122 Fax: 01472 601381
Web: www.kingsway-hotel.com
Seasonal closure: 25/26th Dec
Rooms: 49 all ensuite Pricing: Sgl £49–65 Dbl £84–90
Dinner from £15.95 CC: Accepted
Room facilities: Access:
Conference: 1 meeting room (Thtr 22 max)
Children: Welcome 5yrs min age Dogs: Guide dogs only
Licences: Parking: Off-street and monitored

Mallow View

◆ ◆

9/11 Albert Road, Cleethorpes, Lincolnshire, DN35 8LX
Tel: 01472 691297 Fax: 01472 691297
Rooms: 15 (5 ensuite) Room facilities:
Access: Children: Welcome Dogs: Welcome
Licences: Leisure: Games room, Snooker/billiards
Directions: Just off seafront, centre.

Cornhill-on-Tweed, Northumberland

Collingwood Arms Hotel

★ ★

Cornhill-on-Tweed, Northumberland, TD12 4UH
Tel: 01890 882424 Fax: 01890 883644

The Collingwood Arms hotel is a family-owned
Georgian coaching inn situated adjacent to the river
Tweed, famous for Salmon fishing. It is ideal for touring
the beautiful border country.
Rooms: 10 all ensuite
Pricing: Sgl £39.50 Dbl £65 CC: Accepted
Room facilities: Dogs: Welcome Licences:
Parking: Off-street

Darlington, Co. Durham

Walworth Castle Hotel

★ ★ ★ ★

Walworth, Darlington, Co. Durham, DL2 2LY
Tel: 01325 485470 Fax: 01325 462257

Clow Beck House

Little Gem

◆◆◆◆◆ ℞ ℞ ✕ ✆

Monk End Farm, Croft-on-Tees, Darlington,
Durham, DL2 2SW
Tel: 01325 721075 Fax: 01325 720419
Email: david@clowbeckhouse.co.uk
Web: www.clowbeckhouse.co.uk
Seasonal closure: Christmas to New Year

One of Yorkshire's best kept secrets, our award
winning home nestles in 2 acres of garden. Thirteen
luxurious individually themed rooms, an extensive
menu, great wines and great hospitality awaits every
guest.
Rooms: 13 all ensuite ⊛ 🖨
Pricing: Sgl £55 Dbl £85 Dinner from £10
CC: Accepted Room facilities: ☐ ☎ 🖥 📞 Access: ⅙
Children: Welcome ⧘ Licences: ⁂
Parking: Off-street and monitored
Directions: Follow brown tourist signs that are on all
roads leading to Croft-on-Tees.

Doncaster, South Yorkshire

Regent Hotel

★★★

Regent Square, Doncaster, South Yorkshire, DN1 2DS
Tel: 01302 364180 Fax: 01302 322331
Email: admin@theregenthotel.co.uk
Web: www.theregenthotel.co.uk

A charming Victorian building overlooking a secluded
Regency park. The hotel is ideally situated within easy
reach of Doncaster's vibrant town centre and only
minutes away from the historic racecourse.
Rooms: 50 all ensuite ⊛ 🖨 ⊗
Pricing: Sgl £75–80 Dbl £90–100 Dinner from £12.50
CC: Accepted Room facilities: ☐ ☎ 🖥 Access: ⅙
Conference: 3 meeting rooms (Thtr 100 max),

24hr-delegate from £99.50, day-delegate rate from £25
Children: Welcome ⧘ ⅙ Dogs: Welcome Licences: ⁂
Parking: Off-street and monitored
Directions: Follow brown signs to racecourse. Turn into
Bennetthorpe Road. After 1/2 mile, hotel is on right.

Wentbridge House Hotel

★★★ ℞

Wentbridge, near Pontefract, West Yorkshire, WF8 3JJ
Tel: 01977 620444 Fax: 01977 620148
Email: info@wentbridgehouse.co.uk
Web: www.wentbridgehouse.co.uk
Rooms: 18 all ensuite 🖨
Pricing: Dinner from £25 (2002 rate) CC: Accepted
Room facilities: ☐ ☎ 🖥 📞 Access: ⅙
Children: Welcome ⧘ ⅙ Licences: ⚘ ⁂
Parking: Off-street
Directions: Wentbridge House is 1/2 mile off the A1 and
4 miles south of the A1/A162 interchange.

Canda Lodge

◆◆◆◆ ✕

Hampole Balk Lane, Skellow, Doncaster,
South Yorkshire, DN6 8LF
Tel: 01302 724028 Fax: 01302 727999
Rooms: 4 all ensuite ⊛ ⊗
Pricing: Sgl £35 Dbl £40 CC: Accepted
Room facilities: ☐ ☎ 🖥 📞
Parking: Off-street and monitored
Directions: On A1 south take Skellow exit, or
northbound take Pontefract exit (A639), then take A1
south.

Campanile

Travel Accommodation
Bawtry Road, Doncaster Leisure Park,
South Yorkshire, DN4 7PD
Tel: 01302 370770 Fax: 01302 370813

Typical Campanile bistro

A lodge-style hotel situated close to the town centre.
Ideal for all people, from business and leisure to
conferences. Restaurant open to non-residents.
Rooms: 50 all ensuite ⊗
Pricing: Sgl £40.95–47.90 Dbl £46.90–53.85
Dinner from £6.50 CC: Accepted
Room facilities: ☐ ☎ 🖥 📞 Access: ⅙
Conference: 1 meeting room (Thtr 25 max),
24hr-delegate from £68, day-delegate rate from £13.50

Children: Welcome ⊬ Dogs: Welcome
Licences: ⋔ Parking: Off-street and monitored
Directions: Leave the M18 at Junction 3. Follow tourist
signs for Racecourse and Leisure Park. Hotel is
situated behind the Dome Leisure Park.

Travelodge Doncaster

Travel Accommodation
A1, Great North Road, Carcroft, Nr. Doncaster,
South Yorkshire, DN6 9LF
Web: www.travelodge.co.uk
Pricing: Sgl £47.40 Dbl £51.85 CC: Accepted
Room facilities: ▢ ☕

Travelodge Doncaster North (MOTO)

Travel Accommodation
M18/M180 Jct 5 Moto Service Area, Hatfield,
Doncaster, DN8 5GS
Web: www.travelodge.co.uk
Rooms: 41 all ensuite ⊗
Pricing: Sgl £47.40 Dbl £51.85 CC: Accepted
Room facilities: ▢ ☕ Access: ♿

Driffield, East Yorkshire

Blacksmiths Country Cottage Guest House

◆ ◆ ◆ ℰ

Driffield Road, Kilham, near Driffield,
East Yorkshire, YO25 4SN
Tel: 01262 420624
Email: maxatblacksmiths@ukonline.co.uk
Web: www.blacksmiths-cottage.co.uk
Seasonal closure: Christmas and New Year
Rooms: 4 all ensuite ❤
Pricing: Sgl £34 Dbl £40–48 Dinner from £10
Room facilities: ▢ ☕ Children: Welcome
Dogs: Welcome Licences: ⋔ Parking: Off-street
Directions: A164 from Bridlington, next right after
Burton Agnes from Driffield, first left after Nafferton
roundabout, we are situated in the middle of Kilham.

Mobile traffic information

Just dial 1740* from any mobile
phone to get up-to-the-minute
RAC traffic information on
motorways and major A roads.
Try it now! *Calls to 1740 cost up to 59p
per minute. Check with your network.

Travelling abroad by car?

European Motoring Assistance can
help you out of a sticky situation
abroad. Buy online at www.rac.co.uk
or call RAC Travel Sales
on 0800 55 00 55. Quote GUI3

Durham, Co Durham

Hardwick Hall Hotel

★★★
Sedgefield, Co. Durham, TS21 2EH
Tel: 01740 620253 Fax: 01740 622771
Email: hardwickhallsedgefield@virgin.net
Web: www.hardwickhall.co.uk

Rooms: 52 all ensuite ▦ ⊗
Pricing: Sgl £75–120 Dbl £90–140 Dinner from £25
CC: Accepted Room facilities: ▢ ☎ ☕ ☍
Access: ⇞ ♿
Conference: 7 meeting rooms (Thtr 600 max)
Children: Welcome Dogs: Guide dogs only
Licences: ◮ ⋔ Parking: Monitored
Directions: Turn off junction 60 on A1(M), head for
Sedgefield 2 miles left at Harwick country park brown
sign.

Helme Park Hall Hotel

★★★
Near Fir Tree, Tow Law, Bishop Auckland,
Co Durham, DL13 4NW
Tel: 01388 730970 Fax: 01388 731799
Email: post@helmeparkhotel.co.uk
Web: www.helmeparkhotel.co.uk
A country hotel with a reputation for service and
plentiful quality of food set in 2-arces of grounds with
tremendous views of the countryside near Durham well
worth a visit.
Rooms: 13 all ensuite ❤ ▦ ⊗
Pricing: Sgl £49 Dbl £79 Dinner from £13.75 CC:
Accepted Room facilities: ▢ ☎ ☕
Conference: 3 meeting rooms (Thtr 220 max),
24hr-delegate from £58, day-delegate rate from £12.95
Children: Welcome ⊬ Dogs: Welcome Licences: ◮ ⋔
Parking: Off-street and monitored
Directions: Located on the A68 1½ miles north of the
intersection with the A689.

Plan your route

Visit www.rac.co.uk for RAC's
interactive route planner, including
up to the minute traffic reports.

Swallow Eden Arms Hotel

★★★ ®

Rushyford, County Durham, DL17 0LL
Tel: 01388 720541 Fax: 01388 721871
Email: edenarms.swallow@whitbread.com
Web: www.swallow-hotels.com

SWALLOW
HOTELS

Rooms: 45 all ensuite 🛏 🚭
Pricing: Sgl £68–88 Dbl £95–105 Dinner from £20
CC: Accepted Room facilities: 🖥 ☎ 🕮 🍵
Conference: 3 meeting rooms, 24hr-delegate from
£105, day-delegate rate from £30
Children: Welcome 🍴 Dogs: Welcome Licences: ⚓ ⛊
Leisure: Indoor pool, Gym, Health spa
Parking: Off-street and monitored
Directions: Located 2 miles from A1(M), leaving at J60
onto A689 to Bishop Auckland.

Swallow Three Tuns Hotel

★★★★ ®

New Elvet, Durham City, County Durham, DH1 3AQ
Tel: 0191 375 1504 Fax: 0191 384 2093
Email: threetuns.reservations@btinternet.com
Web: www.swallow-hotels.com

SWALLOW
HOTELS

Rooms: 50 all ensuite 🛏 🚭
Pricing: Dinner from £22.50 CC: Accepted
Room facilities: 🖥 ☎ 🕮 🍵
Conference: 5 meeting rooms (Thtr 300 max),
24hr-delegate from £135, day-delegate rate from £30
Children: Welcome 🍴 🍼 Dogs: Welcome
Licences: ⛊ Parking: Off-street and monitored
Directions: From A1 take A690 for two miles, straight
ahead at first roundabout, left at second roundabout,
over bridge past lights.

Hallgarth Manor Hotel

★★★ ®

Pittington, Durham, County Durham, DH6 1AB
Tel: 0191 372 1188 Fax: 0191 372 1249
Email: sales@hallgarthmanorhotel.com
Web: www.hallgarthmanorhotel.com
Rooms: 23 all ensuite 🛏 🚭
Pricing: Dinner from £17.95 CC: Accepted
Room facilities: 🖥 ☎ 🕮
Conference: 3 meeting rooms (Thtr 250 max),
24hr-delegate from £90, day-delegate rate from £28
Children: Welcome 🍴 🍼 Dogs: Welcome
Licences: ⛊ Parking: Off-street and monitored
Directions: A1(M) Junction 62, A690 Sunderland. After
¹/₂ mile turn right. Half mile to crossroads – straight
over. After 1 mile turn left.
See advert on facing page

Travelodge Durham

Travel Accommodation
Station Lane, Gilesgate, Durham, Tyneside, DH1 1LJ
Web: www.travelodge.co.uk
Rooms: 57 all ensuite 🚭
Pricing: Sgl £54.40–59.40 Dbl £58.85–63.85
CC: Accepted Room facilities: 🖥 🕮 Access: ♿

Easington, Cleveland

Grinkle Park Hotel

★★★ ®

Grinkle Lane, Easington, Saltburn-by-the-Sea,
Cleveland, TS13 4UB
Tel: 01287 640515 Fax: 01287 641278
Email: grinkle.parkhotel@sixcretail.com
Web: www.grinklepark.co.uk

Refurbished 19th century house. Set in 35 acres of
parkland. Drive lined with Rhododendrons and Azaleas.
Perfect location to get away from it all.
Rooms: 20 all ensuite 🛏 🛏
Pricing: Sgl £86 Dbl £105 Dinner from £22
CC: Accepted Room facilities: 🖥 ☎ 🕮
Conference: 2 meeting rooms (Thtr 60 max)
Children: Welcome 🍼 Dogs: Welcome Licences: ⛊
Leisure: Tennis, Snooker/billiards
Parking: Off-street and monitored
Directions: Situated 9 miles from Guisborough, signed
left off the main A171 Guisborough to Whitby road.

Filey, North Yorkshire

Seafield Hotel

♦ ♦ ♦

9-11 Rutland Street, Filey, North Yorkshire, YO14 9JA
Tel: 01723 513715
Rooms: 14 all ensuite
Pricing: Sgl £19–20 Dbl £38–42 Dinner from £6
CC: Accepted Room facilities: Access:
Children: Welcome Licences: Parking: Off-street
Directions: Follow signpost to Filey from A64. At
crossroads in town centre turn right. Take second left
into Rutland Street.

Gateshead, Tyne & Wear

Travelodge Newcastle East

Travel Accommodation
A194, Wardley, Whitemare Pool, Nr. Gateshead,
Tyne & Wear, NE10 8YB
Web: www.travelodge.co.uk
Rooms: 71 all ensuite
Pricing: Sgl £54.40 Dbl £58.85 CC: Accepted
Room facilities: Access:

Goathland, North Yorkshire

Heatherdene

♦ ♦ ♦ ♦

The Common, Goathland, near Whitby,
North Yorkshire, YO22 5AN
Tel: 01947 896334
Email: info@heatherdenehotel.co.uk
Web: www.heatherdenehotel.co.uk
Rooms: 6 all ensuite
Pricing: Sgl £35 Dbl £60–90 Dinner from £13
CC: Accepted Room facilities:
Children: Welcome Licences: Parking: Off-street

Grimsby, Lincolnshire

Travelodge Grimsby (Opens 2003)

Travel Accommodation
A180
Web: www.travelodge.co.uk
Room facilities:

Need help booking?

 RAC Hotel Reservations will find
the accommodation that's right
for you – and book it too.
Call today on 0870 603 9109
and quote 'Guide 2003'

Hallgarth Manor Hotel

**Relax in this tastefully
converted Country
Manor House set
in four acres of
its own grounds.**

**Dine in Victorian
elegance in the
Glemore Restaurant.
Superb bar meals
also available.**

**Three and a half miles
from the historic
Durham City.**

**Friendly,
personal service and a
warm welcome awaits.**

Pittington, Durham City
DH6 1AB
Tel: 0191 372 1188
Fax: 0191 372 1249
Email:
sales@hallgarthmanorhotel.com
Web:
www.hallgarthmanorhotel.com

RAC
★★

Northeast

Halifax, West Yorkshire

The Rock Inn Hotel

★★★

Holywell Green, Halifax, West Yorkshire, HX4 9BS
Tel: 01422 379721 Fax: 01422 379110
Email: reservations@rockinnhotel.com
Web: www.rockinnhotel.com
Rooms: 30 all ensuite 🛏 🖨 ⊗
Pricing: Sgl £55–120 Dbl £58–120 Dinner from £15
CC: Accepted Room facilities: 🖵 ☎ 🗄 📞 Access: ♿
Conference: 4 meeting rooms (Thtr 200 max),
24hr-delegate from £99, day-delegate rate from £29
Children: Welcome 🍴 🍼 Dogs: Welcome
Licences: ⬦ ♦♦♦ Leisure: Games room
Parking: Off-street and monitored
Directions: 1½ miles from Junction 24 of M62 towards
Blackley.

Shibden Mill Inn

♦ ♦ ♦ ♦ ♦ 🍷 ⚜

Shibden Mill Fold, Shibden, Halifax,
West Yorkshire, HX3 7UL
Tel: 01422 365840 Fax: 01422 362971
Email: shibdenmillinn@zoom.co.uk
Web: www.shibdenmillinn.com

Shibden Mill Inn nestles in the fold of the Shibden
valley overlooking Red Beck. The 17th century inn is
steeped in history and has been sympathetically
renovated by present owners.
Rooms: 12 all ensuite 🖨 ⊗
Pricing: Sgl £60 Dbl £72 CC: Accepted
Room facilities: 🖵 ☎ 🗄 📞 Children: Welcome 🍴
Licences: ⬦ ♦♦♦ Parking: Off-street
Directions: Leave M62 at junction 26, follow A58
Halifax for 5½ miles, turn left onto Kell Lane, follow
Shibden Mill Inn signs.

The Fleece Inn

♦ ♦ ♦

Ripponden Bank, Barkisland, Halifax,
West Yorkshire, HX4 0DJ
Tel: 01422 822598 Fax: 01422 822598
Rooms: 4 all ensuite 🛏 ⊗ Pricing: Dinner from £5
CC: Accepted Room facilities: 🖵 🗄
Children: Welcome 5yrs min age 🍴
Dogs: Welcome Licences: ♦♦♦ Parking: Off-street
Directions: M62 J22, A672 to Halifax. At traffic lights in
Ripponden take first right onto B6113 to Elland.

Harrogate, North Yorkshire

Cedar Court Hotel

★★★★

Queen Building, Park Parade, Harrogate,
North Yorkshire, HG1 5AH
Tel: 01423 858585 Fax: 01423 504950
Email: cedarcourt@karoo.co.uk
Web: www.cedarcourthotels.co.uk
Rooms: 100 all ensuite 🛏 🖨 ⊗
Pricing: Sgl £65–125 Dbl £80–140 Dinner from £19.50
CC: Accepted
Room facilities: 🖵 ☎ 🗄 📞
Access: ⬆ ♿
Conference: 10 meeting rooms (Thtr 323 max),
24hr-delegate from £30, day-delegate rate from £34
Children: Welcome 🍴
Dogs: Guide dogs only
Licences: ⬦ ♦♦♦ Leisure: Gym
Parking: Off-street and monitored
Directions: A1 to Wetherlay, A661 to Harrogate. M1 or
M62 to Leeds, then A61 to Harrogate or via M1/A1
Link.

The Majestic Hotel

★★★★

Ripon Road, Harrogate, North Yorkshire, HG1 2HU
Tel: 01423 700300 Fax: 01423 502283
Email: majestic@paramount-hotels.co.uk
Web: www.paramount-hotels.co.uk
Rooms: 156 all ensuite 🛏 ⊗
Pricing: Sgl £117.25–347.25 Dbl £164.50–354.50
Dinner from £20 CC: Accepted
Room facilities: 🖵 ☎ 🗄 Access: ⬆ ♿
Conference: 10 meeting rooms (Thtr 500 max),
24hr-delegate from £190, day-delegate rate from £65
Children: Welcome 🍴 Dogs: Welcome Licences: ⬦ ♦♦♦
Leisure: Indoor pool, Gym, Health spa, Beauty salon,
Tennis, Snooker/billiards
Parking: Off-street and monitored
Directions: From M1, leave at Leeds and take A61 to
Harrogate. The hotel is on Ripon Road which lead from
the town centre.

Boar's Head Hotel

★★★ 🍴 🍴 🍴

Ripley, Harrogate, North Yorkshire, HG3 3AY
Tel: 01423 771888 Fax: 01423 771509
Email: reservations@boarsheadripley.co.uk
Web: www.boarsheadripley.co.uk

PARAMOUNT
GROUP OF HOTELS

Elegantly restored coaching inn provides outstanding food, fine wines, friendly attentive service with comfortable and relaxing surroundings. In historic village location and beautiful Dales countryside.
Rooms: 25 all ensuite 🅢
Pricing: Sgl £99–120 Dbl £120–140 Dinner from £21.50
CC: Accepted
Room facilities: 💻 ☎ 🗐 Access: ♿
Conference: 7 meeting rooms, 24hr-delegate from £145, day-delegate rate from £45
Children: Welcome 🍴 🎠 Dogs: Welcome
Licences: ◇ � Leisure: Tennis, Fishing
Parking: Off-street
Directions: The Boar's Head is 3 miles north of Harrogate on the A61, 10 minutes from the A1.

Grants Hotel & Chimney Pots Bistro

★★★ 🍴

3–13 Swan Road, Harrogate,
North Yorkshire, HG1 2SS
Tel: 0800 371 343 Fax: 01423 502550
Email: enquiries@grantshotel-harrogate.com
Web: www.grantshotel-harrogate.com
Rooms: 42 all ensuite ◈ 🗐
Pricing: Sgl £110–118.50 Dbl £110 CC: Accepted
Room facilities: 💻 ☎ 🗐 🔧
Access: ↕ ♿
Conference: 3 meeting rooms (Thtr 70 max),
24hr-delegate from £110, day-delegate rate from £32
Children: Welcome 🍴 🎠
Dogs: Welcome
Licences: �
Parking: Off-street
Directions: From south, take A61 past Betty's tea room on left, down hill to traffic lights, and straight across then 1st left into Swan Road.
See advert on this page

Hob Green Hotel

★★★★ 🍴 🍴

Markington, Harrogate, North Yorkshire, HG3 3PJ
Tel: 01423 770031 Fax: 01423 771589
Email: info@hobgreen.com
Web: www.hobgreen.com

Set in 800 acres of beautiful rolling countryside, a charming and elegant hotel known locally for its excellent restaurant. The main rooms, furnished with antiques, enjoy a stunning view of the valley below.
Rooms: 12 all ensuite 🗐
Pricing: Sgl £80–85 Dbl £100–125 Dinner from £23.50
CC: Accepted Room facilities: 💻 ☎ 🗐 🔧
Children: Welcome 🍴 🎠 Dogs: Welcome Licences: ◇ �
Parking: Off-street and monitored
Directions: Between Harrogate and Ripon on A61 turn towards Markington at Wormald Green, following brown information road signs.
See advert on next page

Imperial Hotel

★★★

Prospect Place, Harrogate, North Yorkshire, HG1 1LA
Tel: 01423 565071 Fax: 01423 500082
Email: imperial@british-trust-hotels.com
Web: www.british-trust-hotels.com

Centre of famous spa town of Harrogate, Victorian hotel with modern comforts – charm and style all of its own. Ideal for exploring North Yorkshire (Bronte country, historic houses and other attractions).
Rooms: 83 all ensuite 🛏 Ⓢ
Pricing: Sgl £75–85 Dbl £100–125 Dinner from £18
CC: Accepted Room facilities: 🖥 ☎ ⊙ 🔧 Access: ⬆ ♿
Conference: 4 meeting rooms (Thtr 200 max), 24hr-delegate from £110, day-delegate rate from £38
Children: Welcome ♀ ⌾ Dogs: Welcome
Licences: ◈ ⛊ Parking: Off-street
Directions: Follow signs for the town centre, the Imperial hotel is opposite Betty's tearooms just before the Cenotaph.

Swallow St George

★★★

1 Ripon Road, Harrogate,
North Yorkshire, HG1 2SY
Tel: 01423 561431 Fax: 01423 530037
Email: harrogate.swallow@whitbread.co.uk
Web: www.swallowhotels.com

SWALLOW
HOTELS

Rooms: 90 all ensuite 🛏 ⛱ Ⓢ
Pricing: Sgl £45–105 Dbl £90–130
Dinner from £19.95 CC: Accepted
Room facilities: 🖥 ☎ ⊙ 🔧
Access: ⬆ ♿
Conference: 5 meeting rooms (Thtr 200 max), 24hr-delegate from £125, day-delegate rate from £39
Children: Welcome ♀ Dogs: Guide dogs only
Licences: ◈ ⛊
Leisure: Indoor pool, Gym, Health spa, Beauty salon
Parking: Off-street and monitored
Directions: From A1 exit at Weatherby follow signs through Harrogate for Ripon A61. Other directions follow signs for Harrogate Conference Centre.

Ascot House Hotel

★★ 🏆

53 Kings Road, Harrogate, North Yorkshire, HG1 5HJ
Tel: 01423 531005 Fax: 01423 503523
Email: admin@ascothouse.com
Web: www.ascothouse.com
Seasonal closure: New Year

Delightful, refurbished Hotel with lovely Victorian features – easy walk to conference centre, shops or gardens. Comfortable lounge bar, quality cuisine and great value wines. Well equipped ensuite bedrooms, lots of local attraction brochures.
Rooms: 19 all ensuite 🛏 🖥
Pricing: Sgl £55–65 Dbl £80–90 Dinner from £16.50
CC: Accepted Room facilities: 🖥 ☎ ☕ 📞
Conference: 3 meeting rooms (Thtr 80 max), 24hr-delegate from £95, day-delegate rate from £22.50
Children: Welcome ♫ ℃ Dogs: Welcome
Licences: 🔔 ♦♦♦ Parking: Off-street
Directions: Follow signs for town centre and conference/exhibition centre. Hotel is on left as you drive up Kings Road, about 500 yards from conference centre.

Alexa House Hotel

26 Ripon Road, Harrogate, North Yorkshire, HG1 2JJ
Tel: 01423 501988 Fax: 01423 504086
Email: alexahouse@msn.com
Web: www.alexa-house.co.uk
Rooms: 13 all ensuite 🖥 🚭 Pricing: Sgl £45–55
Dbl £65–85 Dinner from £15 CC: Accepted
Room facilities: 🖥 ☎ ☕ Children: Welcome ♫ ℃
Dogs: Welcome Licences: ♦♦♦ Parking: Off-street
Directions: ½ mile from crossroads of A59 and A61, towards Harrogate town centre.

Ashley House Hotel

36–40 Franklin Road, Harrogate,
North Yorkshire, HG1 5EE
Tel: 01423 507474 Fax: 01423 560858
Email: ron@ashleyhousehotel.com
Web: www.ashleyhousehotel.com
Rooms: 18 all ensuite 🚭 Room facilities: 🖥 ☎ ☕
Children: Welcome ℃ Dogs: Guide dogs only
Licences: ♦♦♦ Parking: Off-street

Shannon Court Hotel

65 Dragon Avenue, Harrogate,
North Yorkshire, HG1 5DS
Tel: 01423 509858 Fax: 01423 530606
Email: shannon@courthotel.freeserve.co.uk
Web: www.harrogate.com/shannon

A short walk from Harrogate centre and ideally located for exploring Yorkshire's attractions. We offer a warm welcome, together with comfortable accommodation and residents lounge bar, contact Kath or Bob.
Rooms: 8 all ensuite 🛏 🚭
Pricing: Sgl £30–38 Dbl £50–60 CC: Accepted
Room facilities: 🖥 ☕ Children: Welcome 5yrs min age
Dogs: Guide dogs only Licences: ♦♦♦ Parking: Off-street
Directions: Five minutes from town centre in High Harrogate, off the Skipton Road (A59).

Helmsley, North Yorkshire

Feversham Arms Hotel

★★★★ 🅡 🅡
1 High Street, Helmsley, York, YO62 5AG
Tel: 01439 770766 Fax: 01439 770346
Email: info@fevershamarms.com
Web: www.feversham.com

This historic country inn in Helmsley offers outstanding hospitality and comfort in relaxing surroundings with fabulous food and wines. 17 ensuite rooms, traditional dining room and contemporary "Brasserie at the Fev", comfortable lounges, garden terrace, outdoor heated pool, tennis court and gym.
Rooms: 17 all ensuite 🛏 🚭
Pricing: Sgl £70–90 Dbl £90–110 Dinner from £20
CC: Accepted Room facilities: 🖥 ☎ ☕ Access: ♿
Conference: 1 meeting room, 24hr-delegate from £125, day-delegate rate from £35
Children: Welcome ♫ ℃ Dogs: Welcome Licences: ♦♦♦
Leisure: Outdoor pool, Gym, Tennis
Parking: Off-street
Directions: From A1, take A168 dual carriageway to Thirsk, then A170. Or, at A1 junction with A64, take A64 to York North bypass, then B1363.
See advert on next page

Northeast

Pheasant Hotel

★★★

Harome, Helmsley, North Yorkshire, YO62 5JG
Tel: 01439 771241 Fax: 01439 771744
Seasonal closure: December–February
Rooms: 12 all ensuite
Pricing: Sgl £40–50 Dbl £80–100 Dinner from £22
CC: Accepted
Room facilities: Access: &
Children: Welcome 5yrs min age Dogs: Welcome
Licences: ﬁﬁﬁ
Leisure: Indoor pool
Parking: Off-street and monitored
Directions: Leave Helmsley on A170 in direction of
Scarborough, after ¼ of a mile, turn right for Harome,
hotel near church.

The Black Swan

★★★★ ⬡ ⬡

Market Place, Helmsley, North Yorkshire, YO62 5BJ
Tel: 0870 400 8112 Fax: 01439 770 174
Email: blackswan@heritage-hotels.co.uk
Web: www.macdonaldhotels.co.uk
Rooms: 45 all ensuite ⊛
Pricing: Sgl £79 Dbl £158 Dinner from £26.50
CC: Accepted Room facilities:
Conference: 3 meeting rooms (Thtr 40 max)
Children: Welcome ﬂ ⅌ Dogs: Welcome Licences: ﬁﬁﬁ
Parking: Off-street
Directions: Entering Helmsley on the A170, the hotel is
at the top of the Market Square

Crown Hotel

★★

Market Place, Helmsley, North Yorkshire, YO62 5BJ
Tel: 01439 770297 Fax: 01439 771595
Rooms: 12 all ensuite
Pricing: Sgl £30–36 Dbl £60–72 Dinner from £16.25
CC: Accepted Room facilities:
Children: Welcome ﬂ Dogs: Welcome Licences: ﬁﬁﬁ
Parking: Off-street
Directions: In the market square in the centre of
Helmsley.

The Feathers

★★

Market Place, Helmsley, North Yorkshire, YO6 5BH
Tel: 01439 770275 Fax: 01439 771101
Email: feathershotel@aol.com
Web: www.feathershotel.com
Rooms: 14 all ensuite
Pricing: Dinner from £10 (2002 rate) CC: Accepted
Room facilities: ⬚ ☎ ⬚ Children: Welcome ﬂ
Dogs: Welcome Licences: ﬁﬁﬁ Parking: Off-street
Directions: On the A170 Thirsk to Scarborough road
directly facing the Market Square.

Hexham, Northumberland

Langley Castle Hotel

★★★★

Langley-on-Tyne, Hexham, Northumberland, NE47 5LU
Tel: 01434 688888 Fax: 01434 684019
Email: manager@langleycastle.com
Web: www.langleycastle.com
Rooms: 18 all ensuite
Pricing: Sgl £94.50–144.50 Dbl £104.50–200
Dinner from £29.50 CC: Accepted
Room facilities: Access:
Conference: 2 meeting rooms (Thtr 100 max),
24hr-delegate from £145, day-delegate rate from £35
Children: Welcome Dogs: Welcome
Licences:
Parking: Off-street
Directions: By car, follow A69 to Hagdon Bridge, then
2 miles south on A686 to Langley Castle.
See advert on this page

Swallow George Hotel

★★★

Chollerford, Hexham, Northumberland, NE46 4EW
Tel: 01434 681611 Fax: 01434 681727
Email: chollerford.swallow@whitbread.com
Web: www.georgehotel-chollerford.com

This delightful country hotel on the banks of the river
North Tyne offers comfortable accommodation (many
with river view), excellent food and full leisure facilities.
Rooms: 47 all ensuite
Pricing: Sgl £70–110 Dbl £95–145 Dinner from £22.50
CC: Accepted Room facilities: Access:
Conference: 4 meeting rooms (Thtr 70 max),
24hr-delegate from £125, day-delegate rate from £30
Children: Welcome 15yrs min age
Dogs: Welcome Licences:
Leisure: Indoor pool, Gym, Health spa, Fishing
Parking: Off-street and monitored
Directions: From the A1 at Newcastle, turn onto A69
(Hexham). Pass Hexham, take A6079 to Chollerford.

Plan your route

Visit www.rac.co.uk for RAC's
interactive route planner, including
up to the minute traffic reports.

Montcoffer B&B

◆◆◆◆◆

Bardon Mill Village, Hexham,
Northumberland, NE47 7HZ
Tel: 01434 344 138 Fax: 01434 344 730
Email: john-dehlia@talk21.com
Web: www.montcoffer.co.uk
Rooms: 2 both ensuite Pricing: Sgl £28–32
Dbl £52–58 Room facilities: Access:
Children: Welcome Parking: Off-street
Directions: 4 miles west of Haydon bridge off the A69,
100 yards from Bardon pottery, map reference 778645.

Rose & Crown Inn

◆◆◆

Main Street, Slaley, Hexham,
Northumberland, NE47 0AA
Tel: 01434 673263 Fax: 01434 673305
Email: rosecrowninn@supanet.com
Web: www.smoothhound.co.uk/hotels/rosecrowninn
Rooms: 3 all ensuite
Pricing: Sgl £29.50–35 Dbl £45–50 Dinner from £11.95
CC: Accepted Room facilities:
Children: Welcome Dogs: Guide dogs only
Licences: Parking: Off-street
Directions: From A68, take B6306. Rose & Crown Inn
on left after approximately 4 miles.

Northeast

Huddersfield, West Yorkshire

Bagden Hall

★★★

Wakefield Road, Scissett, Huddersfield,
West Yorkshire, HD8 9LE
Tel: 01484 865330 Fax: 01484 861001
Email: info@bagdenhall.demon.co.uk
Web: www.bagdenhall.demon.co.uk

Traditional country house hotel, set in 40 acres of
beautiful parkland and boasting a superb 9-hole golf
course.
Rooms: 17 all ensuite
Pricing: Sgl £60–65 Dbl £80–100 Dinner from £18.95
CC: Accepted Room facilities: Access:
Conference: 3 meeting rooms (Thtr 90 max),
24hr-delegate from £105, day-delegate rate from £30
Children: Welcome Dogs: Guide dogs only
Licences: Leisure: Golf Parking: Off-street
Directions: On A636 between Scissett and Denby Dale.
Only 10 minutes drive from J38 and J39 on the M1.

George Hotel

★★★★

St George Square, Huddersfield,
West Yorkshire, HD1 1JA
Tel: 01484 515444 Fax: 01484 435056
Email: accounts@georgehotel.fsnet.co.uk
Web: www.brook-hotels.co.uk
Rooms: 60 all ensuite
Pricing: Sgl £45–85 Dbl £60–95 Dinner from £14.95
CC: Accepted Room facilities: Access:
Conference: 7 meeting rooms (Thtr 180 max),
24hr-delegate from £95, day-delegate rate from £28
Children: Welcome Dogs: Welcome
Licences: Parking: Off-street
Directions: From M62, exit Junction 24 and follow
signs for Huddersfield town centre. Hotel is adjacent to
train station.

Hanover International Huddersfield

★★★

Penistone Road, Kirkburton, Huddersfield, West
Yorkshire, HD8 0PE
Tel: 01484 607783 Fax: 01484 607961
Web: www.hanover-international.com
Rooms: 47 all ensuite

HANOVER INTERNATIONAL
HOTELS & CLUBS

Room facilities:
Children: Welcome
Dogs: Welcome Licences:
Parking: Off-street and monitored

Huddersfield Hotel

★★★

33–47 Kirkgate, Huddersfield,
West Yorkshire, HD1 1QT
Tel: 01484 512111 Fax: 01484 435262
Email: enquiries@huddersfieldhotel.com
Web: www.huddersfieldhotel.com
Rooms: 60 all ensuite
Pricing: Sgl £40–55 Dbl £50–75 Dinner from £12
CC: Accepted Room facilities: Access:
Children: Welcome Dogs: Welcome Licences:
Leisure: Games room Parking: Off-street and monitored
Directions: From the town centre ring road, we are 50
metres from the Kirkgate exit, off Southgate, opposite
the Sports Centre.

Dalton Bed & Breakfast

◆◆◆

2 Crossley Lane, Dalton, Huddersfield,
West Yorkshire, HD5 9SX
Tel: 01484 540091 Fax: 01484 540091
Email: jackie-vivion@ntlworld.com
Rooms: 3 Pricing: Sgl £20 Dbl £40
Room facilities: Children: Welcome
Dogs: Welcome Parking: Off-street and monitored
Directions: Hotel is situated 2 miles south-east of town
centre, 3 miles from M62 Junction 25, 13 miles from
Junction 38 of M1.

Hull, East Yorkshire

Portland Hotel

★★★

Paragon Street, Hull, Humberside, HU1 3JP
Tel: 01482 326462 Fax: 01482 213460
Email: info@portland-hotel.co.uk
Web: www.portland-hull.com

Located next to the City Hall and within a short walk to the station, the main retail and entertainment areas, the cobbled streets of the Old Town and "The Deep".
Rooms: 126 all ensuite 🐾 🚭
Pricing: Sgl £55–110 Dbl £70–125 Dinner from £16.95
CC: Accepted Room facilities: ▯ ☎ 🍵 🍸
Access: ⬆ ♿
Conference: 6 meeting rooms (Thtr 220 max),
24hr-delegate from £129, day-delegate rate from £28.50
Children: Welcome ⟊ 🍴 Dogs: Welcome Licences: ♦♦♦
Parking: Off-street and monitored
Directions: M62 onto A63 leading to city centre, sign posted Paragon street area, five minutes from railway station.

Quality Hotel, Kingston-upon-Hull

★★★

Ferensway, Hull, East Yorkshire, HU1 3UF
Tel: 01482 325087 Fax: 01482 323172
Email: admin@gb611.u-net.com
Web: www.choicehotels.com
Rooms: 155 all ensuite 🐾 🚭
Pricing: Sgl £65–100 Dbl £35–120 Dinner from £16.95
CC: Accepted Room facilities: ▯ ☎ 🍵 🍸
Access: ⬆ ♿ Children: Welcome ⟊ 🍴
Dogs: Welcome Licences: 🔱 ♦♦♦
Leisure: Indoor pool, Gym, Health spa
Parking: Off-street and monitored
Directions: M62 onto A63, onto Clive Sullivan Way. Turn left at roundabout (A1079). Follow signs for railway station. Hotel 200yds on left.

Willerby Manor

★★★★ ⓡ

Well Lane, Willerby, Hull, East Yorkshire, HU10 6ER
Tel: 01482 652616 Fax: 01482 653901
Email: info@willerbymanor.co.uk
Web: www.willerbymanor.co.uk
Seasonal closure: Christmas
Rooms: 51 all ensuite 🐾 🚭 🚭
Pricing: Sgl £80–90 Dbl £93–103 Dinner from £15
CC: Accepted Room facilities: ▯ ☎ 🍵 🍸
Conference: 14 meeting rooms (Thtr 500 max),
24hr-delegate from £95, day-delegate rate from £24
Children: Welcome ⟊ Dogs: Guide dogs only
Licences: 🔱 ♦♦♦
Leisure: Indoor pool, Gym, Beauty salon
Parking: Off-street and monitored
Directions: M62 runs into A63. Take exit to Beverley and Humber Bridge. Follow until you reach Willerby. At roundabout take third exit, hotel signposted from next roundabout.

Comfort Inn Hull

★★

11 Anlaby Road, Hull, East Yorkshire, HU1 2PJ
Tel: 01482 323299 Fax: 01482 214730
Email: admin@gb631.u-net.com
Web: www.choicehotels.com
Rooms: 59 all ensuite 🐾 🚭 🚭
Pricing: Dinner from £12 CC: Accepted
Room facilities: ▯ ☎ 🍵 🍸 Access: ⬆
Children: Welcome ⟊ 🍴 Dogs: Welcome
Licences: ♦♦♦
Leisure: Indoor pool, Gym, Games room
Parking: Off-street and monitored
Directions: Follow the signs to Hull railway station, we are located on the left, 250 yards before the station.

Earlsmere

♦♦♦

76–78 Sunny Bank, Spring Bank West, Hull, East Yorkshire, HU3 1LQ
Tel: 01482 341977 Fax: 01482 473714
Email: su@earlsmerehotel.karoo.co.uk
Web: www.earlsmerehotel.karoo.net
Rooms: 9 (7 ensuite) 🚭
Room facilities: ▯ 🍵 Access: ♿
Children: Welcome ⟊ 🍴 Dogs: Welcome
Licences: ♦♦♦
Directions: Located only 1 mile from the city centre, ½ mile from motorway (Infermany exit).

Northeast

Campanile Hotel

Travel Accommodation
Beverley Road, Freetown Way, Hull, East Yorkshire,
HU2 9AN
Tel: 01482 325530 Fax: 01482 587538
Email: hull@envergare.co.uk

Typical Campanile bedroom

The hotel is situated in the city centre of Hull. Facilities
include a French bistro restaurant and conference
facilities. Good access for the disabled.
Rooms: 47 all ensuite ⊗
Pricing: Sgl £47.90 Dbl £53.85 Dinner from £5.95
CC: Accepted Room facilities: ▢ ☎ ◔ ☏
Access: ♿
Conference: 1 meeting room (Thtr 35 max)
Children: Welcome ⋔ Dogs: Welcome
Licences: ⛊
Parking: Off-street and monitored
Directions: From M62, A63 into Hull, passing Humber
Bridge. Pass on a flyover, follow signs for city centre
and train station – at junction of Freetown Way and
Beverley Road, straight across lights and turn right.

Ilkley, West Yorkshire

Rombalds Hotel & Restaurant

★★★★ ℞ ℞
West View, Wells Road, Ilkley, West Yorkshire, LS29
9JG
Tel: 01943 603201 Fax: 01943 816586
Email: reception@rombalds.demon.co.uk
Web: www.rombalds.co.uk

Standing between the town and the moors, this
elegantly-furnished hotel provides comfortable
lounges, well-equipped bedrooms and an attractive
restaurant service with award-winning cuisine.

Rooms: 15 all ensuite ⛼ ⊟ ⊗
Pricing: Sgl £55–99 Dbl £80–119 Dinner from £10.95
CC: Accepted Room facilities: ▢ ☎ ◔ ☏
Conference: 2 meeting rooms (Thtr 70 max),
24hr-delegate from £115, day-delegate rate from £32.50
Children: Welcome ⋔ ⍟ Dogs: Welcome
Licences: ⚓ ⛊ Parking: Off-street
Directions: On Leeds/Skipton A65, left at second main
lights, follow signs for Ilkley Moor. Hotel 600 yards on
left.

Ingleton, North Yorkshire

Springfield Country House Hotel

◆ ◆ ◆ ✕
Main Street, Ingleton, North Yorkshire, LA6 3HJ
Tel: 01524 241280 Fax: 01524 241280
Seasonal closure: Christmas

Detached Victorian villa, large garden. Patio down to
River Greta, with home-grown vegetables in season.
Home cooking. Private fishing, car park. Pets
welcome.
Rooms: 5 all ensuite ⛼
Pricing: Dinner from £11 CC: Accepted
Room facilities: ▢ ◔ Children: Welcome
Dogs: Welcome Licences: ⛊ Parking: Off-street
Directions: On A65(T), 11 miles north-west of Settle.
Springfield is 100 yards from A65(T).

Keighley, West Yorkshire

Dalesgate Hotel

★★
406 Skipton Road, Utley, Keighley,
West Yorkshire, BD20 6HP
Tel: 01535 664930 Fax: 01535 611253
Email: stephen.e.atha@btinternet.com
Web: www.dalesgate.co.uk
Rooms: 20 all ensuite
Pricing: Dinner from £13.95 CC: Accepted
Room facilities: ▢ ☎ ◔ Access: ♿
Children: Welcome ⋔ Dogs: Welcome
Licences: ⛊ Parking: Off-street
Directions: From Keighley town centre follow the signs
for Skipton. At roundabout go straight across. The
hotel is in the village of Utley, 1½ miles on right on
Skipton Road.

Kielder Water, Northumberland

Blackcock Inn

♦ ♦ ♦

Falstone, Kielder Water, Northumberland, NE48 1AA
Tel: 01434 240200 Fax: 01434 240200
Email: blackcock@falstone.fsbusiness.co.uk
Web: www.smoothhound.co.uk/hotels/black.html
Rooms: 4 all ensuite
Pricing: Sgl £28 Dbl £50 Dinner from £5.95
CC: Accepted Room facilities:
Conference: 1 meeting room
Children: Welcome Dogs: Welcome Licences:
Leisure: Games room Parking: Off-street
Directions: Falstone can be accessed off the C200
road from Bellingham which can be accessed off the
A68 or the B6320.

Knaresborough, North Yorkshire

Abbey Garth

♦ ♦ ♦ ♦

28 Abbey Road, Knaresborough,
North Yorkshire, HG5 8HX
Tel: 01423 862043 and 07811 615947
Email: abbeygarth@talk21.com
Web: www.gocities.com/abbey_garth
Rooms: 2 (1 ensuite)
Pricing: Sgl £35–40 Dbl £50–55
Room facilities: Children: Welcome
Parking: Off-street and monitored
Directions: From A1(M), A59 to Knaresborough. At third
traffic lights turn left to River Bridge, then left at Half
Moon pub.

Newton House Hotel

♦ ♦ ♦ ♦

5–7 York Place, Knaresborough,
North Yorkshire, HG5 0AD
Tel: 01423 863539 Fax: 01423 869748
Email: newtonhouse@btinternet.com
Web: www.newtonhousehotel.com
Rooms: 12 all ensuite
Pricing: Sgl £40–65 Dbl £60–80 Dinner from £19.50
CC: Accepted Room facilities: Access:
Children: Welcome Dogs: Welcome Licences:
Parking: Off-street and monitored
Directions: Take A59 turn-off to A1(M), follow signs to
Knaresborough. Hotel on right just before third set of
traffic lights.

Yorkshire Lass

♦ ♦ ♦

High Bridge, Harrogate Road, Knaresborough,
North Yorkshire, HG5 8DA
Tel: 01423 862962 Fax: 01423 869091
Email: yorkshirelass@knaresborough.co.uk
Web: www.knaresborough.co.uk/yorkshirelass
Rooms: 6 all ensuite
Pricing: Dinner from £12.50 (2002 rate) CC: Accepted
Room facilities:

Children: Welcome Licences: Parking: Off-street
Directions: Situated on A59 between Knaresborough
and Harrogate, opposite Mother Shipton's Cave.

Knottingley, West Yorkshire

Travelodge Pontefract, Ferrybridge (MOTO)

Travel Accommodation
A1/M62 Moto Service Area, Ferrybridge, Knottingley,
West Yorkshire, WF11 0AF
Web: www.travelodge.co.uk
Rooms: 36 all ensuite
Pricing: Sgl £49.40–54.40 Dbl £53.85–58.85
CC: Accepted Room facilities: Access:

Leeds, West Yorkshire

42 The Calls

★ ★ ★ ★ ★ Townhouse
Leeds, Yorkshire, LS2 7EW
Tel: 01132 440099 Fax: 01132 344100
Email: hotel@42thecalls.co.uk
Web: www.42thecalls.co.uk
Seasonal closure: Christmas
Rooms: 41 all ensuite
Room facilities: Access:
Conference: 6 meeting rooms (Thtr 70 max),
24hr-delegate from £186.50, day-delegate rate from £45
Children: Welcome Dogs: Welcome Licences:
Parking: Off-street and monitored
Directions: Follow city centre signs onto the city centre
loop. Turn left at junction 15. Number 42 is then
immediately on your right.

Le Meridien Metropole

★ ★ ★ ★

King Street, Leeds, West Yorkshire, LS1 2HQ
Tel: 0800 028 2840 Fax: 01132 425156
Web: www.lemeridien.com
Rooms: 118 all ensuite
Pricing: Dinner from £19.50 CC: Accepted
Room facilities: Access:
Conference: 8 meeting rooms (Thtr 250 max),
24hr-delegate from £150, day-delegate rate from £45
Children: Welcome Dogs: Guide dogs only
Licences: Parking: Off-street and monitored
Directions: From M1 and M621 follow city centre signs,
follow road into Wellington Street. At 1st traffic island
take right into King Street. Hotel on right.

Ask the experts

To book a Hotel or Guest
Accommodation, or for help
and advice, call RAC Hotel
Reservations on 0870 603 9109
and quote 'Guide 2003'

Northeast

Le Méridien Queens

★★★★

City Square, Leeds, LS1 1PL
Tel: 0800 028 2840 Fax: 0113 242 5154
Email: queens.reservations@lemeridien.com
Web: www.lemeridien.com
Rooms: 199 all ensuite 🅢
Pricing: Dinner from £19.50 CC: Accepted
Room facilities: 🖵 ☎ 🛇 ☕ Access: ⦀ 🚺
Conference: 13 meeting rooms (Thtr 600 max),
24hr-delegate from £160, day-delegate rate from £55
Children: Welcome 🍴 Dogs: Welcome Licences: 🍸 🎎
Parking: Off-street and monitored
Directions: Follow signs for city centre, hotel adjacent
to railway station in city centre.

Thorpe Park Hotel & Spa

★★★★ 🍷

1150 Century Way, Thorpe Park, Leeds, LS15 8SB
Tel: 0113 264 1000 Fax: 0113 264 1010
Email: thorpepark@shirehotels.co.uk
Web: www.shirehotels.co.uk
Rooms: 123 all ensuite 🛏 🅢
Pricing:£140 Dbl £120–160 CC: Accepted
Room facilities: 🖵 ☎ 🛇 ☕ ❄
Access: ⦀ 🚺
Conference: 14 meeting rooms (Thtr 200 max),
24hr-delegate from £175, day-delegate rate from £59
Children: Welcome 🍴 🌡 Dogs: Guide dogs only
Licences: 🍸 🎎
Leisure: Indoor pool, Gym, Health spa, Beauty salon
Parking: Off-street and monitored
Directions: Exit J46 of M1, 6 miles east of Leeds city
centre.

Chevin Lodge Country Park Hotel

★★★

Yorkgate, Otley, West Yorkshire, LS21 3NU
Tel: 01943 467818 Fax: 01943 850335
Email: reception@chevinlodge.co.uk
Web: www.chevinlodge.co.uk
Rooms: 49 all ensuite 🍷 🅢
Pricing: Sgl £65–110 Dbl £110–125 Dinner from £21.50
CC: Accepted Room facilities: 🖵 ☎ 🛇 ☕ Access: 🚺
Conference: 3 meeting rooms (Thtr 150 max)
Children: Welcome 🍴 Dogs: Welcome Licences: 🍸 🎎
Leisure: Indoor pool, Gym, Health spa, Tennis, Fishing,
Games room
Parking: Off-street and monitored
Directions: On a quiet rural road just off the A658
Leeds/Bradford airport to Harrogate road, 2 miles north
of airport.
See advert on facing page

Golden Lion Hotel

★★★

2 Lower Briggate, Leeds,
West Yorkshire, LS1 4AE
Tel: 0113 243 6454 Fax: 0113 242 9327
Email: info@goldenlionhotel-leeds.com

89 standard and executive bedrooms, Brasserie, bar
and lounge, 3 purpose-built ground floor conference
rooms with air conditioning and daylight. Car parking
overnight free 100m away. Superb city centre location.
Rooms: 89 all ensuite 🅢
Pricing: Sgl £99–110 Dbl £109–125 CC: Accepted
Room facilities: 🖵 ☎ 🛇 ☕ Access: ⦀
Conference: 3 meeting rooms (Thtr 120 max),
24hr-delegate from £130, day-delegate rate from £40
Children: Welcome 🍴 🌡 Dogs: Welcome Licences: 🎎
Parking: Off-street and monitored
Directions: Half mile from Junction 3 of M621, towards
city centre. On loop road Junction 16. Five minutes
walk from station.

Milford Hotel

★★★

A1 Great North Road, Peckfield, Leeds, LS25 5LQ
Tel: 01977 681800 Fax: 01977 681245
Email: enquiries@mlh.co.uk
Web: www.mlh.co.uk
Rooms: 47 all ensuite 🍷 🅢
Pricing: Dinner from £12.95 CC: Accepted
Room facilities: 🖵 ☎ 🛇 ☕ ❄ Access: 🚺
Conference: 3 meeting rooms (Thtr 70 max),
24hr-delegate from £95, day-delegate rate from £27
Children: Welcome 🍴 Dogs: Welcome Licences: 🎎
Parking: Off-street and monitored
Directions: Situated on southbound carriageway of A1
where A63 from Leeds joins A1, and 6 miles north of
A1/M62 intersection.

Pinewood Hotel

78 Potternewton Lane, Leeds,
West Yorkshire, LS7 3LW
Tel: 0113 2622561 Fax: 0113 2622561
Seasonal closure: Christmas and New Year

Rooms: 10 all ensuite
Pricing: Sgl £39 Dbl £50 Dinner from £12.95 CC:
Accepted
Room facilities: ▢ ☕
Children: Welcome Licences: ▮▮▮
Directions: Leave town centre on A61 towards
Harrogate. After 2 miles, at the first roundabout turn
right. Hotel is 600yds on left.

Travelodge Leeds Central (SA)

Travel Accommodation
Blayds Court, Blayds Yard, Swinegate, Leeds, LS1 4AD
Web: www.travelodge.co.uk
Rooms: 100 all ensuite ⊗
Pricing: Sgl £59.40 Dbl £63.85 CC: Accepted
Room facilities: ▢ ☕ Access: ♿

Travelodge Leeds East

Travel Accommodation
A63, Selby Road, Styal Hill Way, Colton, Leeds,
Web: www.travelodge.co.uk
Pricing: Sgl £54.40 Dbl £58.85 CC: Accepted
Room facilities: ▢ ☕

Leeming Bar, North Yorkshire

White Rose Hotel

★★
Bedale Road, Leeming Bar, Northallerton,
North Yorkshire, DL7 9AY
Tel: 01677 422707 Fax: 01677 425123
Email: royston@whiterosehotel.co.uk
Web: www.whiterosehotel.co.uk
Rooms: 18 all ensuite ⊛ ⊗
Pricing: Sgl £42–45 Dbl £56–60 Dinner from £5.95
CC: Accepted Room facilities: ▢ ☎ ☕ 📞 ❄
Children: Welcome 🐾 Dogs: Welcome Licences: ▮▮▮
Leisure: Games room Parking: Off-street and monitored
Directions: 12 miles south of Scotch Corner, take A684
turning right for Northallerton. We are half a mile along
on left.

The Lodge at Leeming Bar

Travel Accommodation
The Great North road, Bedale, Leeming Bar,
North Yorkshire, DL8 1DT
Tel: 01677 422122 Fax: 01677 424507
Email: thelodgeatleemingbar@btinternet.com
Web: www.leemingbar.com
Rooms: 39 all ensuite ⊛ 🖨 ⊗
Pricing: Sgl £45–65 Dbl £60–80 Dinner from £10
CC: Accepted Room facilities: ▢ ☎ ☕ Access: ♿
Conference: 3 meeting rooms (Thtr 150 max),
24hr-delegate from £20, day-delegate rate from £80
Children: Welcome 🐾 🐾 Dogs: Welcome Licences: ▮▮▮
Parking: Off-street and monitored
Directions: Just off the A1 at the Bedale/Northallerton
junction 10 miles south of Scotch Corner.

Leyburn, North Yorkshire

Golden Lion Hotel

★
Market Square, Leyburn, North Yorkshire, DL8 5AS
Tel: 01969 622161 Fax: 01969 623836
Email: annegoldenlion@aol.com
Web: www.thegoldenlion.co.uk
Seasonal closure: 25th–26th Dec Rooms: 15 all ensuite ⊛
Pricing: Sgl £26–34 Dbl £52–68 Dinner from £6.50
CC: Accepted Room facilities: ▢ ☎ ☕ Access: ▮▮ ♿
Children: Welcome 🐾 🐾 Dogs: Welcome Licences: ▮▮▮
Parking: Off-street
Directions: 8 miles from either Leeming or Scotch
Corner exits from A1, centrally located in town centre.

Northeast

Liversedge, West Yorkshire

Healds Hall Hotel

★★

Leeds Road, Liversedge, West Yorkshire, WF15 6JA
Tel: 01924 409112 Fax: 01924 401895
Email: enquire@healdshall.co.uk
Web: www.healdshall.co.uk
Rooms: 24 all ensuite 🛏️ 🚭
Pricing: Sgl £35–60 Dbl £60–75 Dinner from £6.95
CC: Accepted Room facilities: 🖥️ ☎️ 🍵 🛎️ Access: ♿
Conference: 2 meeting rooms (Thtr 80 max),
24hr-delegate from £20, day-delegate rate from £40
Children: Welcome Dogs: Welcome Licences: 👤👤👤
Parking: Off-street and monitored
Directions: On A62 between Leeds and Huddersfield.
Near M1 Junction 40 and M62 Junction 26/27.

Malham, North Yorkshire

Buck Inn

★★

Malham, Skipton, North Yorkshire, BD23 4DA
Tel: 01729 830317 Fax: 01729 830670
Email: thebuckinn@uk.online.co.uk
Rooms: 10 all ensuite 📺
Pricing: Sgl £35–45 Dbl £65–90 CC: Accepted
Room facilities: 🖥️ ☎️ 🍵 Children: Welcome
Dogs: Guide dogs only Licences: 👤👤👤
Leisure: Games room Parking: Off-street
Directions: Take A65 Skipton–Settle. Turn right in
Gargrove, signposted Malham. Follow this main road
for seven miles to Malham. The Buck Inn is in the
village centre.

Malton, North Yorkshire

Green Man Hotel

★★★

15 Market Street, Malton, North Yorkshire, YO17 7LY
Tel: 01653 600370 Fax: 01653 696006
Email: greenman@englishrosehotels.co.uk
Web: www.englishrosehotels.co.uk
Rooms: 24 all ensuite 🛏️
Pricing: Sgl £60 Dbl £90 Dinner from £15.50
CC: Accepted
Room facilities: 🖥️ ☎️
Conference: 2 meeting rooms (Thtr 150 max),
24hr-delegate from £85, day-delegate rate from £25
Children: Welcome 🎎 ☕ Licences: 👤👤👤
Leisure: Games room Parking: Off-street
Directions: Follow A64 from A1/M1.
Leave at exit for Malton at start of
bypass. Turn first left after passing
Talbot Hotel.

It's easier online

For all your motoring and travel
needs, www.rac.co.uk

Talbot Hotel

★★

Yorkersgate, Malton, North Yorkshire, YO17 7AJ
Tel: 01653 694031 Fax: 01653 693355
Email: talbothotel@englishrosehotels.co.uk
Web: www.englishrosehotels.co.uk

A classic and comfortable inn, close to local
attractions, which include Castle Howard and Eden
Camp. A warm welcome awaits at this hotel with its
ample free parking.
Rooms: 31 all ensuite 🛏️ 📺
Pricing: Sgl £49.50 Dbl £90 Dinner from £16.95
CC: Accepted Room facilities: 🖥️ ☎️ 🍵
Conference: 5 meeting rooms (Thtr 70 max),
24hr-delegate from £85, day-delegate rate from £25
Children: Welcome 🎎 ☕ Licences: 👤👤👤 Parking: Off-street
Directions: From A64 follow road into Malton: the hotel
is on right.

Mirfield, West Yorkshire

Travelodge Huddersfield, Mirfield

Travel Accommodation
A62, Leeds Road, Mirfield, West Yorkshire, WF14 0BY
Web: www.travelodge.co.uk
Rooms: 27 all ensuite 🚭
Pricing: Sgl £47.40–54.40 Dbl £51.85–58.85
CC: Accepted Room facilities: 🖥️ 🍵 Access: ♿

Monk Fryston, North Yorkshire

Monk Fryston Hall Hotel

★★★

Monk Fryston, nr Leeds, North Yorkshire, LS25 5DU
Tel: 01977 682369 Fax: 01977 683544
Email: reception@monkfryston-hotel.com
Web: www.monkfryston-hotel.com
Rooms: 30 all ensuite 📺 🚭
Pricing: Sgl £89 Dbl £109–155 Dinner from £26
CC: Accepted Room facilities: 🖥️ ☎️ 🍵 🛎️ Access: ♿
Conference: 3 meeting rooms (Thtr 35 max),
24hr-delegate from £130, day-delegate rate from £36.50
Children: Welcome 🎎 ☕ Dogs: Welcome
Licences: 🍷 👤👤👤 Parking: Off-street and monitored
Directions: Travelling from A1 take turning to Selby, A63, continue
straight on for 3 miles into Monk Fryston village. Hotel on left.

Morpeth, Northumberland

Linden Hall

★★★★ ♚ ♚

Longhorsley, Morpeth, Northumberland, NE65 8XF
Tel: 01670 500000 Fax: 01670 500001
Email: stay@lindenhall.co.uk
Web: www.lindenhall.co.uk

A magnificent grade II listed Georgian country house set in 450 acres of park and woodland, perfectly situated in beautiful Northumberland. Facilities include a fully-equipped health centre and an award-winning golf course.
Rooms: 50 all ensuite ♨ 🛏
Pricing: Sgl £74.50–84.50 Dbl £108–128
Dinner from £24.50 CC: Accepted
Room facilities: ☐ ☎ 🍵 ☏ Access: ⇪ ₲
Conference: 6 meeting rooms (Thtr 300 max),
24hr-delegate from £140, day-delegate rate from £35
Children: Welcome � 🐾 Dogs: Welcome
Licences: ◈ ♟♟♟
Leisure: Indoor pool, Gym, Health spa, Beauty salon, Tennis, Golf, Snooker/billiards
Parking: Off-street and monitored
Directions: Linden Hall is located off the A697 between the villages of Longhorsley and Longframlington.

The Cook and Barker Inn

◆◆◆◆ ♚ ♚

Newton-on-the-Moor, Felton, Morpeth,
Northumberland, NE65 9JY
Tel: 01665 575234 Fax: 01665 575234
Rooms: 5 all ensuite 🛏 ☏
Pricing: Sgl £37.50 Dbl £70 Dinner from £20 CC:
Accepted Room facilities: ☐ 🍵
Children: Welcome ♂ Dogs: Guide dogs only
Licences: ♟♟♟ Parking: Off-street
Directions: Heading north on the A1 from Morpeth, travel about 9 miles. The A1 merges back into dual carriageway; look for signs for Newton-on-the-Moor.

Newcastle, Gateshead

Swallow Hotel

★★★

High West Street, Gateshead, Tyne & Wear, NE8 1PE
Tel: 0191 477 1105 Fax: 0191 478 1638
Email: swallowgateshead@btconnect.com
Web: www.swallowhotels.com

SWALLOW
HOTELS

Rooms: 103 all ensuite ♨ ☏
Pricing: Sgl £60–85 Dbl £70–115 Dinner from £19.75
CC: Accepted Room facilities: ☐ ☎ 🍵 ☏
Access: ⇪ ₲
Conference: 10 meeting rooms (Thtr 350 max),
24hr-delegate from £110, day-delegate rate from £30
Children: Welcome ♂ ⅛ Dogs: Welcome Licences: ♟♟♟
Leisure: Indoor pool, Gym, Health spa, Beauty salon
Parking: Off-street and monitored
Directions: From A1(M) take A184 to Gateshead. At Jet garage roundabout turn right, cross next two roundabouts and follow hotel signs.

Northeast

Newcastle upon Tyne, Tyne & Wear

Copthorne Hotel Newcastle

★★★★ ⛄ ⛄

The Close, Quayside, Newcastle upon Tyne,
Tyne & Wear, NE1 3RT
Tel: 0191 222 0333 Fax: 0191 230 1111
Email: sales.newcastle@mill-cop.com
Web: www.millenniumhotels.com

HANOVER INTERNATIONAL
HOTELS & CLUBS

Situated on the Quayside, the hotel has clear views
across the River Tyne where you can take walk down
to the Gateshead Millennium Bridge. Weekend rates
are also available.
Rooms: 156 all ensuite ⊗
Pricing: Dinner from £18 CC: Accepted
Room facilities: ⬜ ☎ ⊠ ☎ ✳ Access: ↕ ♿
Conference: 7 meeting rooms (Thtr 200 max),
24hr-delegate from £175, day-delegate rate from £44
Children: Welcome ♀ Dogs: Welcome Licences: ◁ ⅲ
Leisure: Indoor pool, Gym, Beauty salon
Parking: Off-street and monitored
Directions: From A1, follow signs for city centre (A184
and A189). Over the bridge, sharp left, left at mini
roundabout, then B1600. Situated on the banks of the
Tyne.

The Vermont
Blue Ribbon Winner

★★★★★ ⛄ ⛄

Castle Garth, Newcastle, NE1 1RQ
Tel: 0191 233 1010 Fax: 0191 233 1234
Email: info@vermont-hotel.co.uk
Web: www.vermont-hotel.com

With an unrivalled setting next to the castle and unique
views of the Tyne and it's famous bridges. Only a short
walk to the main shopping area including Fenwicks,
Eldon Square, the station and entertainment areas,
including direct access to the quayside.
Rooms: 101 all ensuite 🖥 ⊗
Pricing: Sgl £110–155 Dbl £130–175 CC: Accepted
Room facilities: ⬜ ☎ ⊠ ☎ Access: ↕ ♿
Conference: 12 meeting rooms (Thtr 200 max),
24hr-delegate from £165, day-delegate rate from £40
Children: Welcome ♀ Dogs: Welcome Licences: ⅲ
Leisure: Gym Parking: Off-street and monitored
Directions: City Centre location by the high level bridge
and the castle.

Swallow Imperial Newcastle

★★★

Jesmond Road, Jesmond, Newcastle upon Tyne,
Tyne & Wear, NE2 1PR
Tel: 0191 231 5511 Fax: 0191 212 1069
Email: newcastleimperial@whitbread.com

SWALLOW
HOTELS

Close to Jesmond metro station and 5 mins from the city centre. Good meeting rooms, leisure club and ample free parking.
Rooms: 122 all ensuite
Pricing: Sgl £85–99 Dbl £120–135 Dinner from £19.50
CC: Accepted Room facilities:
Access:
Conference: 7 meeting rooms (Thtr 150 max), 24hr-delegate from £140, day-delegate rate from £32
Children: Welcome Dogs: Welcome Licences:
Leisure: Indoor pool, Gym, Health spa
Parking: Off-street and monitored
Directions: Just off A167. Follow signs for coast A1058.

The Caledonian

★ ★ ★
Osborne Road, Jesmond, Newcastle upon Tyne, Tyne & Wear, NE2 2AT
Tel: 0191 281 7881 Fax: 0191 281 6241
Email: caledonian.hotel@lineone.net
Web: www.peelhotel.com
Rooms: 89 all ensuite
Pricing: Sgl £50–80 Dbl £80–120 Dinner from £15
CC: Accepted Room facilities: Access:
Children: Welcome Dogs: Guide dogs only
Licences: Parking: Off-street and monitored
Directions: From A1 follow Jesmond signs. Turn left into Osborne Road, OR from Tyne Tunnel follow Newcastle signs – A1058. Turn right into Osborne Road.

Cairn Hotel

★ ★
97 Osborne Road, Jesmond, Newcastle upon Tyne, Tyne & Wear, NE2 2TA
Tel: 0191 281 1358 Fax: 0191 281 9031
Email: cairn-hotel@hotmail.com
Web: www.cairnhotelgroup.com
Rooms: 50 all ensuite
Pricing: Sgl £49–59 Dbl £69–79 Dinner from £12.50
CC: Accepted Room facilities:
Conference: meeting rooms, 24hr-delegate from £90, day-delegate rate from £25
Children: Welcome Dogs: Welcome Licences:
Parking: Off-street and monitored
Directions: Situated ½ mile from the city centre, in the area of Jesmond, minutes from a metro station.
See advert on this page

Travelodge Newcastle Central (SA)

Travel Accommodation
City Road, 4 Forster Street, Nr. Quayside, Newcastle, Tyne & Wear, NE1 2NH
Web: www.travelodge.co.uk
Rooms: 120 all ensuite
Pricing: Sgl £64.40 Dbl £68.85 CC: Accepted
Room facilities: Access:

Otterburn, Northumberland

Butterchurn Guest House

◆ ◆ ◆ ◆
Main Street, Otterburn, Northumberland, NE19 1NP
Tel: 01830 520585 Fax: 01830 520874
Email: keith@butterchurn.freeserve.co.uk
Web: www.butterchurn.freeserve.co.uk
Rooms: 7 all ensuite
Room facilities: Access:
Children: Welcome Dogs: Welcome Parking: Off-street
Directions: The Butterchurn is in the middle of Otterburn village, opposite the church, on the A696.

Pateley Bridge, North Yorkshire

Roslyn Hotel

◆ ◆ ◆
King Street, Pateley Bridge, North Yorkshire, HG3 5AT
Tel: 01423 711374 Fax: 01423 711374
Email: enquires@roslynhotel.co.uk
Web: www.roslynhotel.co.uk
Rooms: 6 all ensuite
Pricing: Sgl £30–40 Dbl £40–52 Dinner from £11
CC: Accepted Room facilities:
Children: Welcome Licences: Parking: Off-street
Directions: Turn right off Main Street. Hotel 250yds on left-hand side of King Street.

Northeast

Peterlee, Co. Durham

Hardwicke Hall Manor Hotel

★★

Heslenden Road, Blackhall, Peterlee,
County Durham, TS27 4PA
Tel: 01429 836326 Fax: 01429 837676
Rooms: 15 all ensuite ✒ 🖋
Pricing: Dinner from £18.95 CC: Accepted
Room facilities: ☐ ☎ 🗒
Children: Welcome ❄ Dogs: Welcome Licences: ◇ ⅲ
Parking: Off-street and monitored
Directions: Leave A19 at Castle Eden A181 and B1281.
Follow B1281 for 2 miles; hotel is on the left-hand side.

Pickering, North Yorkshire

Blacksmith's Country Inn

★★★★ ®® ®

Hartoft End, Rosedale Abbey, Pickering,
North Yorkshire, YO18 8EN
Tel: 01751 417331 Fax: 01751 417167
Email: blacksmiths.rosedale@virgin.net
Web: www.blacksmithsinn-rosedale.co.uk
Rooms: 19 all ensuite ✒ ⊛
Pricing: Sgl £47.50–83.50 Dbl £75–87 Dinner from £15
CC: Accepted Room facilities: ☐ ☎ 🗒 Access: ♿
Children: Welcome ❄ Dogs: Welcome
Licences: ◇ ⅲ Parking: Off-street
Directions: From Pickering A170 for Helmsley, right at
Wrelton, Hartoft sign posted.
See advert on this page

Blacksmiths Country Inn

Lovely 16th-century hostelry, fully refurbished
but retaining all the ambience of years past.
Cosy lounges, superb food and wine in
wonderful surroundings. Quality ensuites,
some ground floor, panoramic views, ideal
walking base.

Hartoft End, Rosedale Abbey,
Pickering, North Yorkshire YO18 8EN
Tel: 01751 417331 Fax: 01751 417167
Email: blacksmiths.rosedale@virgin.net
Website: www.blacksmithsinn-
rosedale.co.uk

Cottage Leas Country Hotel

★★★ ®

Nova Lane, Middleton, Pickering, N. Yorks, YO18 8PN
Tel: 01751 472129 Fax: 01751 474930
Email: cottageleas@aol.com
Rooms: 11 all ensuite ✒ 🖋 ⊛
Pricing: Sgl £35–46.50 Dbl £60–83 Dinner from £10.50
CC: Accepted Room facilities: ☐ ☎ 🗒 Access: ⅲ ♿
Conference: 2 meeting rooms (Thtr 75 max),
24hr-delegate from £95, day-delegate rate from £35
Children: Welcome ❄ ❄ Dogs: Welcome
Licences: ◇ ⅲ Parking: Off-street and monitored
Directions: From Pickering take the A170 signposted
Thursk, at Middleton turn right at church and continue
for 1½ miles.

Moorlands Country House Hotel
Little Gem

◆◆◆◆◆ ❄ ☕

Pickering, Levisham, North Yorkshire, YO18 7NL
Tel: 01751 460229 Fax: 01751 460470
Email: ronaldoleonardo@aol.com
Web: www.moorlandslevisham.co.uk
Seasonal closure: December to March

A beautifully-restored Victorian country house in four
acres of wooded gardens with stunning views across
the valley. Ideal base for walking, cycling or touring the
beautiful North York Moors.
Rooms: 7 all ensuite 🖋 ⊛
Pricing: Sgl £35–45 Dbl £70–90 Dinner from £18
CC: Accepted Room facilities: ☐ 🗒
Children: Welcome 15yrs min age Licences: ⅲ
Parking: Off-street and monitored
Directions: A169 from Pickering, turn left. Go through
Lockton into Levisham. First house on the right.
See advert on facing page

Rose Cottage Farm

◆◆◆◆ ☕

Cropton, Pickering, North Yorkshire, YO18 8HL
Tel: 01751 417302
Web: www.smoothhound.co.uk
Rooms: 2 all ensuite ⊛
Pricing: Dbl £44 Dinner from £12
Room facilities: ☐ 🗒 Parking: Off-street
Directions: Leave A170 at Wrelton; follow signs to
Cropton. At the New Inn take first right; Rose Cottage
in centre of village.

Pontefract, West Yorkshire

Rogerthorpe Manor

★★★

Thorpe Lane, Badsworth, Pontefract,
West Yorkshire, WF9 1AB
Tel: 01977 643839 Fax: 01977 645704
Email: ops@rogerthorpemanor.co.uk
Web: www.rogerthorpemanor.co.uk

Rooms: 24 all ensuite 🛏 ⊗
Pricing: Sgl £55–120 Dbl £75–120 Dinner from £14.95
CC: Accepted Room facilities: 🖵 ☎ 🖲 📞 ❄
Conference: 6 meeting rooms (Thtr 400 max),
24hr-delegate from £24.95, day-delegate rate from
£124.50
Children: Welcome ⱴ Licences: ⟁ ⅲ Parking: Off-street

Travelodge Pontefract, Barnsdale Bar

Travel Accommodation
A1 Southbound, Barnsdale Bar, Wentbridge,
nr. Pontefract, West Yorkshire, WF8 3QQ
Web: www.travelodge.co.uk
Rooms: 36 all ensuite ⊗
Pricing: Sgl £47.40 Dbl £51.85
CC: Accepted
Room facilities: 🖵 🖲 Access: ♿

Redworth, Co. Durham

Redworth Hall Hotel

★★★★ Blue Ribbon Winner

Redworth, Newton Aycliffe, County Durham, DL5 6NL
Tel: 01388 770600 Fax: 01388 770654
Email: redworthhall@paramount-hotels.co.uk
Web: www.paramount-hotels.co.uk

Redworth Hall is a beautiful Georgian manor house set
in 26 acres of private grounds with 100 bedrooms, two
restaurants and a superb leisure club with beauty and
hair salons.
Rooms: 100 all ensuite 🛏 🛏 ⊗
Pricing: Sgl £115–145 Dbl £130–190
Dinner from £23.50 CC: Accepted
Room facilities: 🖵 ☎ 🖲 📞 Access: ⅼↄ ♿
Conference: 14 meeting rooms (Thtr 300 max),
24hr-delegate from £150, day-delegate rate from £47
Children: Welcome ⱴ Dogs: Welcome
Licences: ⟁ ⅲ
Leisure: Indoor pool, Gym, Health spa,
Beauty salon, Tennis
Parking: Off-street and monitored
Directions: Leave A1M at Junction 58. Take A68 to
Bishop Auckland roundabout. Proceed straight on,
hotel ¼ mile on left.

Northeast

Richmond, North Yorkshire

Quality Hotel Scotch Corner

★★★

Junction A1/A66, Scotch Corner, Richmond,
North Yorkshire, DL10 6NR
Tel: 01748 850900 Fax: 01748 825417
Email: admin@gb609.u-net.com
Web: www.choicehotels.com
Rooms: 90 all ensuite
Pricing: Sgl £50–94.95 Dbl £60–114.90
Dinner from £17.95 CC: Accepted
Room facilities: 🖥 ☎ ☕ 🍵 Access: ⬆ ♿
Children: Welcome �📕 ☕ Dogs: Welcome
Licences: 🔱 👫
Leisure: Indoor pool, Gym, Health spa, Beauty salon
Parking: Off-street and monitored
Directions: Situated off Scotch Corner roundabout on
the A1/A66 junction on the northbound side of the A1.

The Kings Head Hotel

★★★★ 🍴

Market Place, Richmond,
North Yorkshire, DL10 4HS
Tel: 01748 850220 Fax: 01748 850635
Email: res@kingsheadrichmond.co.uk
Web: www.kingsheadrichmond.co.uk
Rooms: 30 all ensuite 📼 ⊗
Pricing: Sgl £67 Dbl £92–120 Dinner from £45.95
CC: Accepted
Room facilities: 🖥 ☎ ☕
Conference: 2 meeting rooms (Thtr 160 max),
24hr-delegate from £80, day-delegate rate from £29.50
Children: Welcome �📕 ☕ Dogs: Welcome
Licences: 👫 Parking: Off-street
Directions: Leave the A1 or A66 at Scotch Corner, take
A6108 to Richmond, follow signs to hotel located in
the town centre.

Bridge House Hotel

★★

Catterick Bridge, Richmond, North Yorkshire, DL10 7PE
Tel: 01748 818331 Fax: 01748 818331
Email: bridgehousehotel@hotmail.com
Rooms: 15 all ensuite
Pricing: Dinner from £15 (2002 rate) CC: Accepted
Room facilities: 🖥 ☎ ☕ Children: Welcome �📕
Dogs: Welcome Licences: 👫
Leisure: Fishing, Games room Parking: Off-street
Directions: Take Catterick exit off the A1.
Approximately 4 miles south of Scotch Corner, hotel
opposite Catterick racecourse.

Travelodge Skeeby, Scotch Corner

Travel Accommodation
A1 North, Scotch Corner, Skeeby, Nr. Richmond,
North Yorkshire, DL10 5EQ
Web: www.travelodge.co.uk
Rooms: 40 all ensuite ⊗
Pricing: Sgl £54.40 Dbl £58.85
CC: Accepted Room facilities: 🖥 ☕ Access: ♿

Ripon, North Yorkshire

Unicorn Hotel

★★

Market Place, Ripon, North Yorkshire, HG4 1BP
Tel: 01765 602202 Fax: 01765 690734
Email: admin@unicorn-hotel.co.uk
Web: www.unicorn-hotel.co.uk
Seasonal closure: Christmas
Rooms: 33 all ensuite 🍵 Pricing: Sgl £48–54
Dbl £68–75 Dinner from £14.95 CC: Accepted
Room facilities: 🖥 ☎ ☕ Conference: 1 meeting room
(Thtr 50 max), 24hr-delegate from £93.50, day-delegate
rate from £30.50 Children: Welcome �📕 ☕
Dogs: Welcome Licences: 👫 Parking: Off-street
Directions: 4 miles from A1 on A61. Located in market
place, city centre.

Box Tree Cottages

◆ ◆ ◆

Coltsgate Hill, Ripon, North Yorkshire, HG4 2AB
Tel: 01765 698006 Fax: 01765 698015
Email: riponbandb@aol.com
Web: www.boxtreecottages.com
Rooms: 6 (4 ensuite) 🍵 ⊗ Pricing: Sgl £35 Dbl £50–65
Room facilities: 🖥 ☕ Children: Welcome
Dogs: Guide dogs only Parking: Off-street
Directions: From Market Place take North Street and
Coltsgate Hill will be found 300 yards on the left.

Romaldkirk, Co. Durham

Rose & Crown

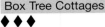

★★★★ 🍴🍴🍴

Blue Ribbon Winner

Romaldkirk, Barnard Castle,
County Durham, DL12 9EB
Tel: 01833 650213 Fax: 01833 650828
Email: hotel@rose-and-crown.co.uk
Web: www.rose-and-crown.co.uk
Seasonal closure: Christmas

An award-winning 18th century coaching inn offering
very comfortable accommodation, the best of English
food and friendly attentive service.
Rooms: 12 all ensuite 🍵
Pricing: Sgl £65 Dbl £90–110 Dinner from £25
CC: Accepted Room facilities: 🖥 ☎ ☕ 🍵 Access: ♿
Children: Welcome �📕 ☕ Dogs: Welcome Licences: 👫
Parking: Off-street
Directions: Six miles north-west of Barnard Castle on B6277

Rotherham, South Yorkshire

Hellaby Hall

★★★★

Old Hellaby Lane, Hellaby, Rotherham,
South Yorkshire, S66 8SN
Tel: 01709 702701 Fax: 01709 700979
Web: www.hellabyhallhotel.co.uk
Rooms: 52 all ensuite
Pricing: Sgl £45–105 Dbl £79–165 Dinner from £21.95
CC: Accepted Room facilities:
Access:
Conference: 7 meeting rooms (Thtr 140 max),
24hr-delegate from £140, day-delegate rate from £45
Children: Welcome Dogs: Welcome
Licences:
Leisure: Indoor pool, Gym, Health spa, Beauty salon
Parking: Off-street and monitored
Directions: Exit J32 M1, then J1 M18. Follow signs for A631 to Dawtry. On the left after traffic lights.
See advert on this page

Best Western Consort Hotel

★★★

Brampton Road, Thurcroft, Rotherham,
South Yorkshire, S66 9JA
Tel: 01709 530022 Fax: 01709 531529
Email: info@consorthotel.com
Web: www.consorthotel.com
Rooms: 27 all ensuite
Pricing: Sgl £72–90 Dbl £82–90 Dinner from £17.95
CC: Accepted Room facilities:
Access:
Conference: 3 meeting rooms (Thtr 300 max),
24hr-delegate from £96, day-delegate rate from £28
Children: Welcome Dogs: Guide dogs only
Licences: Parking: Off-street and monitored
Directions: Take M18 Jct 1, turn right after 50 yards, right for 2 miles to T-junction, hotel on right.

Best Western Elton Hotel

★★★

Main Street, Bramley, Rotherham,
South Yorkshire, S66 2SF
Tel: 01709 545681 Fax: 01709 549100
Email: bestwestern.eltonhotel@btinternet.com
Web: www.bestwestern.co.uk
Rooms: 29 all ensuite
Pricing: Dinner from £20 CC: Accepted
Room facilities: Access:
Children: Welcome Dogs: Welcome
Licences: Parking: Monitored
Directions: 1/4 mile from M18 Junction 1. Follow A631 Rotherham. Turn right into Ravenfield. Hotel at end of Bramley village.

It's easier online

For all your motoring and travel needs, www.rac.co.uk

Courtyard by Marriott Rotherham

★★★

West Bawtry Road, Rotherham,
South Yorkshire, S60 4NA
Tel: 01709 830630 Fax: 01709 830549
Rooms: 100 all ensuite
Room facilities: Access:
Children: Welcome Licences:
Leisure: Indoor pool, Gym, Beauty salon
Parking: Off-street and monitored
Directions: Leave M1 at Junction 33 and follow signs for Rotherham A630. Turn left at next roundabout, hotel visible on right.

Brecon Hotel

★★

Moorgate Road, Rotherham, South Yorkshire, S60 2AY
Tel: 01709 828811 Fax: 01709 513030
Web: www.breconhotel.co.uk
Rooms: 21 all ensuite
Pricing: Sgl £35–48.50 Dbl £49–57 Dinner from £16.75
CC: Accepted Room facilities: Access:
Children: Welcome Dogs: Welcome Licences:
Parking: Off-street
Directions: Junction 33 of M1, follow signs to Bawtry (A631). After 1/2 mile turn left at traffic lights for A618. Hotel 1 mile on right.
See advert on following page

Hellaby Hall

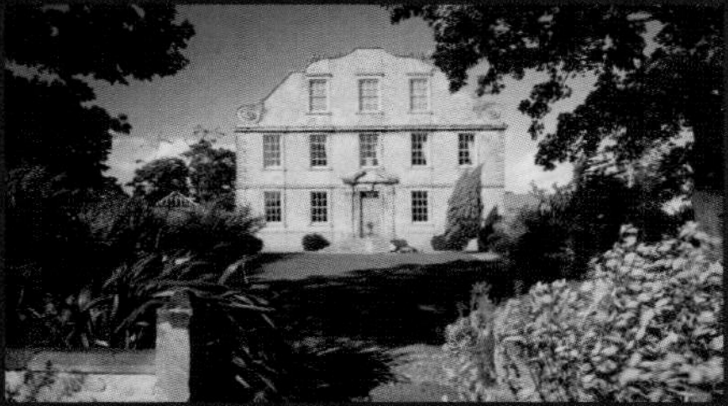

Behind the original Dutch Colonial frontage, many features have been retained or restored and Hellaby is a fine example of the marriage between period charm and modern convenience. Our comfortable and tastefully decorated bedrooms reflect our basic philosophy of no compromise on quality and are equipped to the highest standard.
Enjoy full use of Bodyscene Health & Leisure Club, including: swimming pool, gymnasium, hair and beauty salons.From arrival and throughout your visit, our caring friendly staff will do all they can to make your stay as comfortable and as pleasurable as possible

Old Hellaby Lane, Hellaby, Rotherham,
South Yorkshire S66 8SN
Tel: 01709 702701 Fax: 01709 700979
www.hellabyhallhotel.co.uk

Campanile

Travel Accommodation
Lowton Way off Denby Way, Hellaby Industrial Estate,
Rotherham, South Yorkshire, S66 8RY
Tel: 01709 700255 Fax: 01709 545169
Email: rotherham@envergure.co.uk

The Campanile offers its nationwide tradition of a
relaxed atmosphere in the Bistro Restaurant, with
comfortable rooms. Conference, business or weekend
stays all catered for.
Rooms: 52 all ensuite ⊛
Pricing: Sgl £30.95 Dbl £36.90 Dinner from £6.95
CC: Accepted Room facilities: ☐ ☎ ◑ ⌇ Access: ♿
Conference: 1 meeting room (Thtr 30 max),
24hr-delegate from £68, day-delegate rate from £19.50
Children: Welcome ⴷ Dogs: Welcome Licences: ♦♦♦
Parking: Off-street and monitored
Directions: Leave M1 at Junction 32, leave M18 at

Junction 1, at roundabout take third exit, for Bawtry,
left at lights, then second left.

Roxby, Lincolnshire

The Fox Inn

◆ ◆

Roxby, Lincolnshire, TS13 5EB
Tel: 01947 840548
Rooms: 2 both ensuite ⊛ Room facilities: ☐ ◑
Children: Welcome ⴷ Dogs: Welcome Licences: ♦♦♦
Parking: Off-street

Scarborough, North Yorkshire

Ambassador Leisure Hotel

★★★

Centre of The Esplanade, South Cliff, Scarborough,
North Yorkshire, YO11 2AY
Tel: 01723 362841 Fax: 01723 366166
Email: ambassador@chariethotels.co.uk
Web: www.chariethotels.co.uk
Rooms: 59 all ensuite ⊛ ⊞ ⊛
Pricing: Sgl £24–50 Dbl £45–90 Dinner from £18.95
CC: Accepted Room facilities: ☐ ☎ ◑ ⌇
Access: ⬆ ♿
Conference: 2 meeting rooms (Thtr 140 max)
Children: Welcome ⴷ ⊰ Dogs: Welcome Licences: ♦♦♦
Leisure: Indoor pool Parking: Off-street
Directions: On A64, turn right at roundabout opposite
B&Q, turn right at next roundabout, then immediately
left down Avenue Victoria to the cliff top.
See advert on facing page top

Clifton Hotel

★★★

Queens Parade, Scarborough, North Yorkshire, YO12
7HX
Tel: 01723 875691 Fax: 01723 364203
Email: cliftonhotel@englishrosehotels.co.uk
Web: www.englishrosehotels.co.uk

Overlooking the North Bay and close to Sea Life
Centre, Atlantic Water Park and Kinderland. Ensuite
bedrooms with direct-dial phone, TV and a welcome
refreshment tray. The hotel offers ample free car
parking.

Typical Campanile bistro

Rooms: 69 all ensuite 🛏 📠 ⊗
Pricing: Sgl £55 Dbl £90 Dinner from £16.50
CC: Accepted Room facilities: ☐ ☎ ☕ Access: ⫞ ♿
Conference: 3 meeting rooms (Thtr 120 max),
24hr-delegate from £85, day-delegate rate from £25
Children: Welcome ⅋ ☷ Licences: ⦙⦙⦙
Parking: Off-street
Directions: Follow A64 from A1/M1. Turn left at
Scarborough rail station and right at Peasholm Park.
Hotel is opposite Alexandra Bowls Centre.

Crown Hotel
★★★
Esplanade, Scarborough, North Yorkshire, YO11 2AG
Tel: 01723 357450 Fax: 01723 362271
Email: crown@chariethotels.co.uk
Web: www.chariethotels.co.uk
Rooms: 83 all ensuite 🛏 📠 ⊗
Pricing: Sgl £24–55 Dbl £48–100 Dinner from £18.95
CC: Accepted Room facilities: ☐ ☎ ☕ ☏
Access: ⫞ ♿
Conference: 7 meeting rooms (Thtr 200 max)
Children: Welcome ⅋ Dogs: Welcome Licences: ⟁ ⦙⦙⦙
Leisure: Indoor pool, Gym, Health spa, Games room,
Snooker/billiards
Parking: Off-street and monitored
Directions: At south end of Valley Bridge (A165), turn
east across Valley Bridge Parade onto Belmont Road.
Continue to cliff top, hotel on right.
See advert on this page

East Ayton Lodge Country Hotel
★★★
Moor Lane, East Ayton, Scarborough,
North Yorkshire, YO13 9EW
Tel: 01723 864227 Fax: 01723 862681
Email: ealodgentl@cix.co.uk
Web: www.eastlaytonlodgehotel.com
Seasonal closure: 2 Jan to 10 Feb
Rooms: 30 all ensuite 🛏 📠
Pricing: Sgl £40–50 Dbl £60–90 Dinner from £4.95
CC: Accepted Room facilities: ☐ ☎ ☕ Access: ♿
Conference: 2 meeting rooms (Thtr 80 max),
24hr-delegate from £75, day-delegate rate from £25
Children: Welcome ⅋ Dogs: Welcome Licences: ⦙⦙⦙
Parking: Off-street
Directions: 400 yards off the A170 Scarborough/Thirsk
road in the village of East Ayton, 3¹/₂ miles from
Scarborough.

The Royal Hotel Scarborough

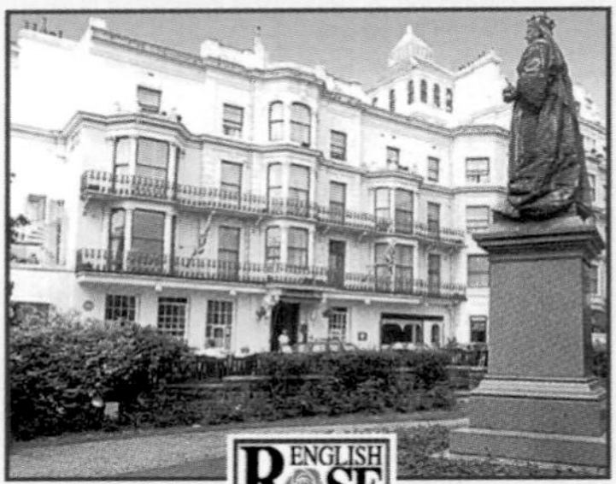

ENGLISH ROSE HOTELS

This famous and historic hotel overlooks the beautiful South Bay and is close to the town's attractions. Being restored to its Regency splendour and offering all the facilities of a modern hotel which include a leisure club with pool and gym. This is the obvious choice for the discerning traveller.

St Nicholas Street, Scarborough,
North Yorkshire YO11 2HE
Tel: 01723 364333 Fax: 01723 500618
royalhotel@englishrosehotels.co.uk
www.englishrosehotels.co.uk

Hackness Grange

★★★

North Yorkshire Moors National Park, Hackness,
North Yorkshire, YO13 0JW
Tel: 01723 882345 Fax: 01723 882391
Email: hacknessgrange@englishrosehotels.co.uk
Web: www.englishrosehotels.co.uk

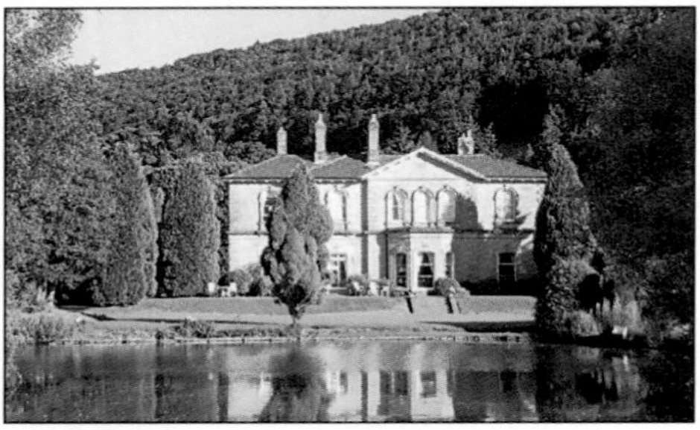

ENGLISH ROSE HOTELS

A Georgian country house hotel with facilities that include an indoor pool, tennis and pitch and putt golf. There are delightful walks and the hotel enjoys an excellent reputation for cuisine.
Rooms: 33 all ensuite
Pricing: Sgl £77.50 Dbl £135 Dinner from £25
CC: Accepted Room facilities:
Conference: 1 meeting room (Thtr 15 max), 24hr-delegate from £95, day-delegate rate from £28.50
Children: Welcome Licences:
Leisure: Indoor pool, Tennis
Parking: Off-street and monitored
Directions: From A1/M1 take A64. On entering Scarborough follow B1261 and follow Hackness sign on right. Entering Hackness village, turn left for hotel.

Hotel St Nicholas

★★★

St Nicholas Cliff, Scarborough,
North Yorkshire, YO11 2EU
Tel: 01723 364101 Fax: 01723 500538
Email: stnicholas@british-trust-hotels.com
Web: www.british-trust-hotels.com

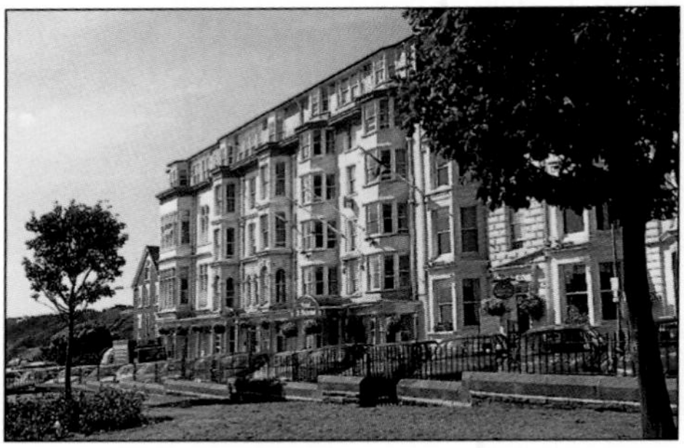

An ideal location for business or leisure. RAC 3-star hotel, which offers a range of superb conference rooms, leisure club with indoor swimming pool, security car parking and a choice of excellent cuisine complemented by the finest wines.
Rooms: 139 all ensuite
Pricing: Sgl £55–75 Dbl £85–125
Dinner from £16.95 CC: Accepted
Room facilities: Access:
Conference: 5 meeting rooms (Thtr 400 max), 24hr-delegate from £85, day-delegate rate from £27.50
Children: Welcome Dogs: Guide dogs only
Licences: Leisure: Indoor pool, Gym, Beauty salon, Games room, Snooker/billiards
Parking: Off-street and monitored
Directions: Take the A64 into town centre, turn right at railway station then first left through roundabout, finally turn first left again.

Palm Court Hotel

★★★

St Nicholas Cliff, Scarborough,
North Yorkshire, YO11 2ES
Tel: 01723 368161 Fax: 01723 371547
Rooms: 46 all ensuite
Pricing: Sgl £42–47 Dbl £78–88 Dinner from £13.50
CC: Accepted Room facilities: Access:
Conference: 4 meeting rooms (Thtr 200 max), 24hr-delegate from £20, day-delegate rate from £65
Children: Welcome Dogs: Guide dogs only
Licences: Leisure: Indoor pool
Parking: Off-street and monitored
Directions: Follow the signs for the town centre, then the town hall. The hotel is en-route.

The Royal Hotel

St Nicholas Street, Scarborough,
North Yorkshire, YO11 2HE
Tel: 01723 364333 Fax: 01723 500618
Email: royalhotel@englishrosehotels.co.uk
Web: www.englishrosehotels.co.uk

Rooms: 137 all ensuite
Pricing: Sgl £57.50 Dbl £105 Dinner from £18.50
CC: Accepted Room facilities: Access:
Conference: 7 meeting rooms (Thtr 200 max),
24hr-delegate from £105, day-delegate rate from £33
Children: Welcome Licences:
Leisure: Indoor pool, Gym, Health spa,
Snooker/billiards
See advert on facing page

Wrea Head Country Hotel

Off Barmoor Lane, Scalby, Scarborough,
North Yorkshire, YO13 0PB
Tel: 01723 378211 Fax: 01723 355936
Email: wreaheadhotel@englishrosehotels.co.uk
Web: www.englishrosehotels.co.uk

Peace and tranquillity, in landscaped woodlands on the
edge of the North York Moors National Park describe
this beautifully-decorated English country house,
where fine wines and quality cuisine combine to create
the perfect retreat.
Rooms: 20 all ensuite
Pricing: Dinner from £25 CC: Accepted
Room facilities: Access:
Conference: 2 meeting rooms (Thtr 30 max),
24hr-delegate from £95, day-delegate rate from £28.50
Children: Welcome Licences:
Parking: Off-street and monitored
Directions: Take A64 from A1/M1. On entering
Scarborough, take A171 (Whitby Road). Pass Scalby
and turn left. Hotel drive on left, after pond.

Bradley Court Hotel

7–9 Filey Road, Scarborough,
North Yorkshire, YO11 2SE

Tel: 01723 360476 Fax: 01723 376661
Email: info@bradleycourthotel.co.uk
Web: www.bradleycourthotel.co.uk
Rooms: 40 all ensuite Room facilities:
Access: Children: Welcome Licences:
Leisure: Games room, Parking: Off-street
Directions: Follow A64 into Scarborough. Turn right at
mini roundabout after B&Q. Follow road to next mini
roundabout, turn left, hotel 50yds further on.

Brooklands Hotel

Esplanade Gardens, South Cliff, Scarborough,
North Yorkshire, YO11 2AW
Tel: 01723 376576 Fax: 01723 376576
Email: stay@brooklands-hotel.co.uk
Web: www.brooklands-hotel.co.uk
Seasonal closure: January
Rooms: 62 (61 ensuite)
Pricing: Sgl £20–35 Dbl £40–70 Dinner from £10
CC: Accepted Room facilities:
Access:
Conference: 1 meeting room (Thtr 80 max),
24hr-delegate from £45, day-delegate rate from £25
Children: Welcome Dogs: Guide dogs only
Licences: Leisure: Riding, Games room
Parking: Off-street
Directions: From York A64, turn right at mini-roundabout
after B&Q, right at next mini-roundabout, left at Victoria
Avenue, left at Esplanade, then second left.
See advert on this page

Crescent Hotel

★★★

The Crescent, Scarborough,
North Yorkshire, YO11 2PP
Tel: 01723 360929 Fax: 01723 354126
Email: reception@crescent-hotel.co.uk
Web: www.crescent-hotel.co.uk
Rooms: 20 all ensuite 🛏 ⊛
Pricing: Sgl £46.50 Dbl £85 Dinner from £17.50
CC: Accepted Room facilities: 🖵 ☎ ⊚ ☏
Access: ⎸↥ Children: Welcome 6yrs min age
Licences: ♦♦♦
Directions: On arrival in Scarborough town centre,
follow signs to Brunswick Centre, Museum & Art
Gallery. At Brunswick Centre, turn right into The
Crescent.

Red Lea Hotel

★★

Prince of Wales Terrace, South Cliff, Scarborough,
North Yorkshire, YO11 2AJ
Tel: 01723 362431 Fax: 01723 371230
Email: redlea@globalnet.co.uk
Web: www.redleahotel.co.uk

Whatever the weather a warm welcome is guaranteed
at the Red Lea. Situated on the south cliff with views
over gardens to the sea. Facilities include an indoor
swimming pool.
Rooms: 67 all ensuite
Pricing: Sgl £28–38 Dbl £56–76 Dinner from £18.50
CC: Accepted Room facilities: 🖵 ☎ ⊚ Access: ⎸↥ ⅙
Conference: 1 meeting room (Thtr 30 max)
Children: Welcome ♁ Dogs: Guide dogs only
Licences: ♦♦♦
Leisure: Indoor pool, Gym, Games room,
Directions: Follow signs for South Cliff. Hotel is located
off the Esplanade near the cliff lift.

Ryndle Court Hotel

★★

47 Northstead Manor Drive, Scarborough,
North Yorkshire, YO12 6AF
Tel: 01723 375188 Fax: 01723 375188
Email: enquiries@ryndlecourt.co.uk
Web: www.ryndlecourt.co.uk
Seasonal closure: November and January
Rooms: 14 all ensuite ⚄ ⊛
Pricing: Sgl £30–38 Dbl £58–64 Dinner from £10

CC: Accepted Room facilities: 🖵 ⊚
Children: Welcome ♁ Licences: ♦♦♦ Parking: Off-street
Directions: Follow signs marked 'North Bay and
Leisure Parks' to Northstead Manor Drive.
See advert on facing page

Sunningdale Hotel

★★

105 Peasholm Drive, Scarborough,
North Yorkshire, YO12 7NB
Tel: 01723 372041
Email: sunningdale@barclays.net
Web: www.sunningdale-scarborough.co.uk
Rooms: 11 all ensuite
Pricing: Dinner from £9 CC: Accepted
Room facilities: 🖵 ⊚
Children: Welcome ♁ Licences: ♦♦♦
Directions: Drive into Scarborough and turn left at the
rail station onto Northway. Follow this road down
Columbus Ravine to Peasholm Park. Hotel is on left.

The New Southlands

★★

15 West Street, Scarborough,
North Yorkshire, YO11 2QW
Tel: 01723 361461 Fax: 01723 376035
Email: tony@slands.fsnet.co.uk
Web: www.epworth.co.uk
Rooms: 58 all ensuite
Room facilities: 🖵 ☎ ⊚ Access: ⎸↥
Children: Welcome ♁ Dogs: Welcome Licences: ♦♦♦
Parking: Off-street

Ganton Greyhound

♦♦♦♦

Main Road, Ganton, near Scarborough, North
Yorkshire, YO12 4NX
Tel: 01944 710116 Fax: 01944 712705
Email: gantongreyhound@supanet.com
Web: www.gantongreyhound.com
Rooms: 18 (16 ensuite) ⚄ 🛏
Pricing: Dinner from £7 (2002 rate) CC: Accepted
Room facilities: 🖵 ☎ ⊚ ☏ Access: ⅙
Children: Welcome ♁ ⽸ Licences: ♦♦♦
Leisure: Games room Parking: Off-street and monitored
Directions: Alongside the A64 at Ganton, 9 miles from
Scarborough, 35 miles from York.

Olivers

♦♦♦♦

34 West Street, South Cliff, Scarborough,
North Yorkshire, YO11 2QP
Tel: 01723 368717
Email: olivers@scarborough.co.uk
Rooms: 6 all ensuite ⊛
Pricing: Sgl £25–26 Dbl £40–42 Dinner from £8.50
CC: Accepted Room facilities: 🖵 ⊚
Directions: Turn left off the Filey road A165 into
Granville Road, and Olivers is at the end at 34 West
Street.

Ashcroft Hotel

102 Columbus Ravine, Scarborough,
North Yorkshire, YO12 7QZ
Tel: 01723 375092
Rooms: 7 all ensuite
Room facilities: 🖵 ☕ Children: Welcome Ħ
Licences: ♙ Parking: Off-street
Directions: Hotel is situated in North Bay area, 500 yards up Columbus Ravine from Peasholm Park.

Blacksmiths Arms

High Street, Cloughton, Scarborough,
North Yorkshire, YO13 0AE
Tel: 01723 870244
Rooms: 11 all ensuite
Room facilities: 🖵 ☕ Licences: ♙ Parking: Off-street

Casablanca hotel

20 Ryndleside, Scarborough, Yorkshire, YO12 6AD
Tel: 01723 362288 Fax: 01723 362288
Web: www.hotel-scarborough.co.uk
Seasonal closure: Christmas & New Year
Rooms: 13 all ensuite 🍴 ⓢ
Pricing: Sgl £25–28 Dbl £50–60 Dinner from £10
Room facilities: 🖵 ☕ Children: Welcome Ħ
Dogs: Welcome Licences: ♙ Parking: Off-street
Directions: Follow signs for north bay leisure parks to Peasholm park, Ryndleside is part of circular road round the park.

Clarence Gardens

4–5 Blenheim Terrace, Scarborough,
North Yorkshire, YO12 7HF
Tel: 01723 374884 Fax: 01723 374884
Seasonal closure: November-March
Rooms: 24 (12 ensuite) 🍴 ⓢ
Pricing: Sgl £18–21 Dbl £41–48 Dinner from £9.50
Room facilities: 🖵 ☕ Children: Welcome Ħ
Dogs: Guide dogs only Licences: ♙
Leisure: Games room Parking: Off-street
Directions: From the top of the North Bay we are approximately 700 yards from the castle facing the sea.

Granby Hotel

1-2 Granby Place, Queen Street, Scarborough,
North Yorkshire, YO11 1HL
Tel: 01723 373031 Fax: 01723 373031
Seasonal closure: March – October
Rooms: 25 all ensuite 🍴
Pricing: Sgl £26.50 Dbl £45–47 Dinner from £8
Room facilities: 🖵 ☕
Children: Welcome 16yrs min age Ħ Licences: ♙
Parking: Off-street
Directions: Follow signs for town centre/castle. Queen street is right after mini roundabout on Castle road.

Hotel Levante

118 Columbus Ravine, Scarborough,
North Yorkshire, YO12 7QZ
Tel: 01723 372366
Rooms: 7 all ensuite 🍴 ⓢ
Pricing: Sgl £18–22 Dbl £36–44 Dinner from £24
Room facilities: 🖵 ☕ Children: Welcome Ħ
Licences: ♙
Parking: Off-street
Directions: From station turn onto Northway which runs into Columbus Ravine. On the left 100m before Peasholm Park.

Kenways Guest House

9 Victoria Park Avenue, Scarboough,
North Yorkshire, YO12 7TR
Tel: 01723 365757 Fax: 01723 365757
Web: www.kenwaysguesthouse.cjb.net
Rooms: 7 all ensuite 🖨 ⓢ
Pricing: Sgl £17.50–18 Dbl £35–36 Dinner from £5.50
Room facilities: 🖵 ☕
Children: Welcome 🍼
Dogs: Welcome
Directions: North Bay seafront to roundabout, past Atlantis, first left up to Peasholm Park Hotel. Victoria Park Avenue is to the side.

Ryndle Court Hotel

Delightfully situated overlooking Peasholm Park near the sea and North Bay leisure parks. One mile to the town centre, harbour and castle. All bedrooms ensuite and comfortably furnished to a high standard with TV, radio and tea/coffee facilities. Traditional style menu with choice. Guests' car park.

47 Northstead Manor Drive,
Scarborough, N. Yorkshire YO12 6AF
Tel: 01723 375188   Fax: 01723 375188
Email: enquiries@ryndlecourt.co.uk
Website: www.ryndlecourt.co.uk

Northeast

Lincoln Hotel

112 Columbus Ravine, North Bay, Scarborough,
North Yorkshire, YO12 7QZ
Tel: 01723 500897 Fax: 01723 500897
Email: sandra@lincolnhotel.fsnet.co.uk
Web: www.lincolnhotel.fsnet.co.uk
Rooms: 8 all ensuite
Room facilities: ☐ ☕ Children: Welcome ⍟ ⍟
Dogs: Guide dogs only Licences: ⍟ Parking: Off-street
Directions: Follow tourist attraction signs for North
Bay; at Peasholm roundabout last exit Columbus
Ravine; hotel is approx 400 yards on right–hand side.

Lynton Private Hotel

104 Columbus Ravine, Scarborough,
North Yorkshire, YO12 7QZ
Tel: 01723 374240
Email: watson@paul-cherryl.fsnet.co.uk
Rooms: 8 all ensuite ☕ ☕
Pricing: Sgl £18–21 Dbl £36–42 Dinner from £5
CC: Accepted Room facilities: ☐ ☕
Children: Welcome ⍟ Licences: ⍟ Parking: Off-street
Directions: From the railway station take Northway. Go
straight on through two roundabouts. The Lynton Hotel
is on the left.

Outlook Hotel

18 Ryndleside, Scarborough, North Yorkshire, YO12 6AD
Tel: 01723 364900
Email: info@outlookhotel.co.uk
Web: www.outlookhotel.co.uk
Rooms: 10 all ensuite ☕
Pricing: Sgl £20–30 Dbl £40–50 Dinner from £7
Room facilities: ☐ ☕
Children: Welcome 6yrs min age ⍟
Dogs: Guide dogs only Licences: ⍟ Parking: Off-street
Directions: Follow signs for North Bay; at Peasholm
Park proceed up hill on Northstead Manor Drive;
Ryndleside is first on left.

Sefton Hotel

18 Prince of Wales Terrace, South Cliff, Scarborough,
North Yorkshire, YO11 2AL
Tel: 01723 372310
Seasonal closure: November to February
Rooms: 14 (12 ensuite) ☕
Pricing: Sgl £23–24 Dbl £46–48 Dinner from £8
Access: ⍟ Dogs: Guide dogs only Licences: ⍟
Parking: Off-street

Tudor House Hotel

164/166 North Marine Road, Scarborough,
North Yorkshire, YO12 7HZ
Tel: 01723 361270

Tudor House is a family-run hotel ideally situated close
to Scarboroughs' beautiful North bay with all it's family
amenities, yet only a short distance to town, theatre
and night clubs.
Rooms: 15 (7 ensuite) ☕
Pricing: Sgl £17–23 Dbl £17–23 Dinner from £8
Room facilities: ☐ ☕
Conference: 1 meeting room (Thtr 12 max)
Children: Welcome ⍟ Dogs: Welcome Licences: ⍟

West Lodge Hotel

38 West Street, Scarborough,
North Yorkshire, YO11 2QP
Tel: 01723 500754
Rooms: 7 (4 ensuite) ☕
Pricing: Sgl £19–21 Dbl £38–42 Dinner from £7
CC: Accepted Room facilities: ☐ ☕
Children: Welcome ⍟ Dogs: Welcome Licences: ⍟
Directions: From Railway Station, follow sign for Filey
over bridge. Church on the right. West Street is opposite.

Wheatcroft Lodge

156-158 Filey Road, Scarborough,
North Yorkshire, YO11 3AA
Tel: 01723 374613
Email: wheatcroftlodge@bushinternet.com
Web: www.wheatcroft.scarborough.co.uk
Seasonal closure: Christmas
Rooms: 7 all ensuite ☕
Pricing: Sgl £25 Dbl £47–50 CC: Accepted
Room facilities: ☐ ☎ ☕ Parking: Off-street
Directions: On the A165 Scarborough to Bridlington
Road 2 miles south of Scarborough centre, near South
Cliff Golf Club.

Willow Dene Hotel

110 Columbus Ravine, North Bay, Scarborough,
North Yorkshire, YO12 7QZ
Tel: 01723 365173
Seasonal closure: November to February
Rooms: 10 all ensuite
Room facilities: 🖥 ☕
Children: Welcome 3yrs min age ⊓ Parking: Off-street
Directions: A64 to Falsgrave lights; right to railway
station, left through lights; two roundabouts on, left
past church before Peasholm Park.

Newlands Hotel

80 Columbus Ravine, Scarborough,
North Yorkshire, YO12 7QU
Tel: 01723 367261
Seasonal closure: 24 Dec to 1 Jan
Rooms: 5 (2 ensuite) ⬤ ⊗
Pricing: Dbl £32–40
Room facilities: 🖥 ☕ Children: Welcome ⊓ Licences: ⵜ
Directions: A64 from Leeds to Scarborough, north bay
end in between Peasholm Park and town centre.

Scotch Corner, North Yorkshire

Vintage Hotel

Scotch Corner, North Yorkshire, DL10 6NP
Tel: 01758 824424 Fax: 01758 826272
Seasonal closure: Christmas to New Year

Family-run roadside hotel overlooking open
countryside. Open plan rustic style bar and restaurant.
Ideal overnight stop or base for visiting Yorkshire
Dales/Moors.
Rooms: 8 (5 ensuite)
Pricing: Sgl £27.50–42.50 Dbl £44–55.50
Dinner from £18 CC: Accepted
Room facilities: 🖥 ☎ ☕
Conference: 2 meeting rooms (Thtr 50 max)
Children: Welcome ⊓ Dogs: Guide dogs only
Licences: ⵜ Parking: Off-street
Directions: Leave A1 at Scotch Corner. Take A66
towards Penrith, Vintage Hotel 200 yards on left.

Seaham, Co. Durham

Seaham Hall Hotel and Oriental Spa

★★★★★ 🏵 🏵 🏵

Lord Byron's Walk, Seaham, Co. Durham, SR7 7AG
Tel: 0191 516 1400 Fax: 0191 516 1410
Email: reservations@seaham-hall.com
Web: www.seaham-hall.com

An innovative and stylish hotel combining historical
elegance and modern luxury. Set in 30 acres of
landscaped cliff top grounds, Seaham Hall is ideally
located for visiting Durham, Newcastle and
Sunderland.
Rooms: 19 all ensuite ⊗
Pricing: Sgl £185–600 Dbl £195–600 Dinner from £34
CC: Accepted Room facilities: 🖥 ☎ ☏ ❄
Access: ⇅ ♿
Conference: 4 meeting rooms (Thtr 120 max),
24hr-delegate from £235, day-delegate rate from £70
Children: Welcome ⊓ 🚼 ⍟ Dogs: Guide dogs only
Licences: ⬧ ⵜ
Leisure: Indoor pool, Gym, Health spa, Beauty salon
Parking: Off-street and monitored
Directions: Exit A1 J62. A19 south to Seaham. B1410
into Seaham, straight over at lights.
See advert on following page

Seahouses, Northumberland

Bamburgh Castle Hotel

★★

Seahouses, Northumberland, NE68 7SQ
Tel: 01665 720283 Fax: 01665 720848
Email: bamburghcastlehotel@talk21.com
Web: www.bamburghcastlehotel.co.uk
Seasonal closure: mid-January, 2 weeks
Rooms: 20 all ensuite ⬤ 📷 ⊗
Pricing: Sgl £39.95–46.95 Dbl £75.90–95.00
Dinner from £15.50
Room facilities: 🖥 ☎ ☕
Children: Welcome ⊓
Dogs: Welcome Licences: ⵜ
Parking: Off-street and monitored
Directions: Follow signs for seahouses from A1 hotel,
car park entrance is on mini roundabout opposite
Barclays Bank.

Seaham Hall Hotel & Oriental Spa

An innovative and stylish hotel combining historical elegance and modern luxury. Set in 30 acres of landscaped clifftop grounds, Seaham Hall is ideally located for visiting Durham, Newcastle and Sunderland. The Oriental Spa is unique in Europe for its combination of Oriental and Western treatments.

Lord Byron's Walk, Seaham, Co.Durham. SR7 7AG
Tel: 0191 516 1400 Fax: 0191 516 1410
Email: reservations@seaham-hall.com
Website: www.seaham-hall.com

Olde Ship Hotel
★ ★
9 Main Street, Seahouses, Northumberland, NE68 7RD
Tel: 01665 720200 Fax: 01665 721383
Email: theoldeship@seahouses.co.uk
Web: www.seahouses.co.uk
Seasonal closure: December to January

A stone's throw from the harbour, this friendly family-run hotel has tremendous character, with its cosy public areas and corridors adorned with nautical and period memorabilia.
Rooms: 18 all ensuite
Pricing: Dinner from £17.50 CC: Accepted
Room facilities: 🖵 ☎ 🍵 Children: Welcome 10yrs min age
Licences: ⚄ Parking: Monitored
Directions: 5 miles north of Alnwick on A1. Take B1340 to Seahouses. The hotel is perched at the harbour top.

Seaton Burns, Newcastle

Travelodge Newcastle North
Travel Accommodation
A1, Gosforth, Front Street, Seaton Burns, Newcastle, NE13 6ED
Web: www.travelodge.co.uk
Rooms: 40 all ensuite
Pricing: Sgl £54.40 Dbl £58.85 CC: Accepted
Room facilities: 🖵 🍵 Access: ♿

Sedgefield, Co. Durham

Dun Cow Inn and Restaurant
♦ ♦ ♦
43 Front Street, Sedgefield, Durham, TS21 3AT
Tel: 01740 620894 Fax: 01740 622163
Email: duncowinn@grayner.fsnet.co.uk
Web: www.mortal-man-inns.co.uk/duncow/
Rooms: 6 all ensuite
Pricing: Sgl £49.50 Dbl £65 Dinner from £7.50
CC: Accepted Room facilities: 🖵 ☎ 🍵
Children: Welcome Dogs: Welcome Licences: ⚄ ⚄
Parking: Off-street and monitored
Directions: A19/A1M turn off A689 (Hartlepool), follow signs for Sedgefield, right onto front street.

Selby, North Yorkshire

The Royal Oak Inn-Hotel
♦ ♦ ♦
Main Street, Hirst Courtney, Selby, North Yorkshire, YO8 8QT
Tel: 01757 270633 Fax: 01757 270333

Settle, North Yorkshire

Plough Inn
★ ★ ★ ⓡ
Wigglesworth, North Yorkshire, BD23 4RJ
Tel: 01729 840243 Fax: 01729 840243
Email: sue@ploughinn-info
Web: www.ploughinn.info

Lovely 18th century country inn with spectacular views. Beautifully positioned between the Yorkshire Dales and Forest of Bowland. Perfect combination of homemade food, wines, real ales and warm, friendly welcome.

Rooms: 12 all ensuite
Room facilities: 🖵 ☎ 🍵 Access: ♿
Children: Welcome ♀ ⟨♔ Dogs: Guide dogs only
Licences: ♦♦♦ Parking: Off-street
Directions: Take the B6478 of the A65 at Long Preston and follow signs to Wigglesworth.

Golden Lion Hotel

♦ ♦ ♦ ♦

Duke Street, Settle, North Yorkshire, BD24 9DU
Tel: 01729 822203 Fax: 01729 824103
Email: bookings@goldenlion.yorks.net
Web: www.yorkshirenet.co.uk/stayat/goldenlion
Rooms: 12 (10 ensuite)
Pricing: Sgl £25.50–33 Dbl £50–62 Dinner from £9.25
CC: Accepted Room facilities: 🖵 🍵
Conference: 1 meeting room (Thtr 12 max)
Children: Welcome ♀ Dogs: Welcome Licences: ♦♦♦
Leisure: Games room Parking: Off-street
Directions: As you enter Settle town centre from south, hotel is on right-hand side of road, just before the market square.

Sheffield, South Yorkshire

Holiday Inn Royal Victoria – Sheffield

★ ★ ★ ★ ⍟

Victoria Station Road, Sheffield,
South Yorkshire, S4 7YE
Tel: 0114 276 8822 Fax: 0114 252 6526
Web: www.holiday-inn.com/sheffielduk
Rooms: 100 all ensuite
Pricing: Dinner from £19.95 (2002 rate) CC: Accepted
Room facilities: 🖵 ☎ 🍵 ✆ Access: |↓↑
Children: Welcome ♀ Dogs: Welcome Licences: ⚘ ♦♦♦
Leisure: Gym Parking: Off-street and monitored
Directions: Exit J33 M1 to Sheffield. At Park Square roundabout take A61N. At first set of lights turn right.

Charnwood Hotel

★ ★ ★

10 Sharrow Lane, Sheffield, South Yorkshire, S11 8AA
Tel: 0114 2589411 Fax: 0114 2555107
Email: king@charnwood.force9.co.uk
Web: www.charnwoodsheffield.co.uk
Seasonal closure: Christmas to New Year

This charming Georgian residence has elegant public

areas and conference facilities, charming bedrooms and two excellent restaurants. Situated 1¹/₂ miles south-west of the city centre and only 10 minutes by car from Derbyshire's Peak District National Park.
Rooms: 22 all ensuite
Pricing: Sgl £69–93 Dbl £83–110 Dinner from £15.25
CC: Accepted Room facilities: 🖵 ☎ 🍵 Access: |↓↑ ♿
Conference: 7 meeting rooms (Thtr 100 max),
24hr-delegate from £113.50, day-delegate rate from £29.50
Children: Welcome ♀ ⟨♔ Licences: ⚘ ♦♦♦
Parking: Off-street and monitored

The Briary

♦ ♦ ♦ ♦

12 Moncrieffe Road, Nether Edge, Sheffield,
South Yorkshire, S7 1HR
Tel: 0114 255 1951 Fax: 0114 249 4745
Email: briaryguesthouse@hotmail.com
Web: www.thebriary.co.uk
Rooms: 10 all ensuite
Pricing: Sgl £40 Dbl £52 CC: Accepted Room facilities:
🖵 🍵
Children: Welcome Dogs: Welcome
Parking: Off-street and monitored
Directions: Turn right off A621 from Abbeydale Road at Yorkshire Bank traffic lights, up Sheldon Road to next lights, turn right onto Moncrieffe Road.

Andrews Park Hotel

♦ ♦ ♦

48 Kenwood Road, Nether Edge, Sheffield,
South Yorkshire, S7 1NQ
Tel: 0114 2500111 Fax: 0114 2555423
Email: andrewsparkhotel@talk21.com
Rooms: 13 (9 ensuite)
Pricing: Sgl £39–48 Dbl £54–62 Dinner from £14.50
CC: Accepted Room facilities: 🖵 ☎ 🍵 Access: ♿
Conference: 3 meeting rooms (Thtr 20 max),
24hr-delegate from £65, day-delegate rate from £14
Children: Welcome ♀ Dogs: Welcome Licences: ♦♦♦
Parking: Off-street and monitored
Directions: One mile from city centre. Take A625 inner ring road. Hotel is located by Ecclesall Road.

Etruria House Hotel

♦ ♦ ♦

91 Crookes Road, Broomhill, Sheffield,
South Yorkshire, S10 5BD
Tel: 01142 662241 Fax: 01142 670853
Email: etruria@waitrose.com
Rooms: 10 (6 ensuite)
Pricing: Sgl £32–40 Dbl £46–54 CC: Accepted
Room facilities: 🖵 🍵 Children: Welcome
Dogs: Guide dogs only Parking: Off-street
Directions: Leave M1 at Junction 33. Follow A57 towards Glossop for 2 miles. At traffic lights in Broomhill, turn right. Hotel 200 yards on left.

Hunter House Hotel

♦ ♦ ♦

685–691 Ecclesall Road, Sheffield,
South Yorkshire, S11 8TG
Tel: 0114 2662709 Fax: 0114 2686370
Email: ma@hhh.freeserve.co.uk
Web: www.hunterhousehotel.co.uk
Rooms: 24 (11 ensuite) 🛏 🖥 🚭
Pricing: Sgl £32–50 Dbl £50–75 CC: Accepted
Room facilities: 🖥 ☎ 🍵
Conference: 1 meeting room (Thtr 30 max)
Children: Welcome Dogs: Welcome Licences: ♦♦♦
Parking: Off-street
Directions: From Sheffield town centre take A624 to
Bakewell. Hotel is on Ecclesall Road at Hunters Bar
roundabout.

Lindrick Hotel

♦ ♦ ♦

226 Chippinghouse Road, Sheffield,
South Yorkshire, S7 1DR
Tel: 0114 258 5041 Fax: 0114 255 4758
Email: reception@thelindrick.co.uk
Web: www.thelindrick.co.uk
Rooms: 21 (13 ensuite)
Pricing: Sgl £30–44 Dbl £50–60 Dinner from £5.50
CC: Accepted Room facilities: 🖥 ☎ 🍵
Children: Welcome Dogs: Welcome Licences: ♦♦♦
Directions: 1½ miles south of the city centre,
Chippinghouse road is a right turning off the A621
Bakewell road.

Travelodge Sheffield

Travel Accommodation
A630 Ring Road, 340 Prince of Wales Road, Sheffield,
South Yorkshire, S2 1FF
Web: www.travelodge.co.uk
Rooms: 67 all ensuite 🚭
Pricing: Sgl £54.40 Dbl £58.85 CC: Accepted
Room facilities: 🖥 🍵 Access: ♿

Shincliffe, Co. Durham

The Seven Stars Inn

♦ ♦ ♦ 🍴

High Street North, Shincliffe Village, Durham, DH1 2NU
Tel: 0191 384 8454 Fax: 0191 386 0640
Email: enquiries@sevenstarsinn.co.uk
Web: www.sevenstarsin.co.uk
Rooms: 8 all ensuite
Pricing: Sgl £40 Dbl £55 CC: Accepted
Room facilities: 🖥 🍵 Children: Welcome 🍴
Dogs: Guide dogs only Licences: ♦♦♦
Parking: Off-street and monitored
Directions: Take junction 61 off the A1 (M) onto A177,
signposted Durham, travel for 2 miles and turn left into
Shincliffe village.

Skipton, North Yorkshire

Hanover International Hotel & Club Skipton

★ ★ ★

Keighley Road, Skipton, North Yorkshire, BD23 2TA
Tel: 0870 241 7084 Fax: 01756 700107
Email: crso@hanover-international.com
Web: www.hanover-international.com
Seasonal closure: Christmas

HANOVER INTERNATIONAL
HOTELS & CLUBS

Offers stunning views of the Yorkshire Dales, with a
state-registered nursery and extensive leisure club.
Brasserie H2O has an enviable reputation for mouth-
watering cuisine.
Rooms: 75 all ensuite 🛏 🖥 🚭
Pricing: Sgl £90 Dbl £100 Dinner from £16.95
CC: Accepted Room facilities: 🖥 ☎ 🍵 Access: ⅲ ♿
Conference: 12 meeting rooms (Thtr 350 max),
24hr-delegate from £115, day-delegate rate from £30
Children: Welcome 🍴 🐴 Dogs: Welcome
Licences: 🍷 ♦♦♦
Leisure: Indoor pool, Gym, Beauty salon
Parking: Off-street
Directions: Approach Skipton from A629. Follow signs
for town centre. Hotel is on right-hand side on entering
Skipton.

Skipton Park Guest'otel

♦ ♦ ♦

2 Salisbury Street, Skipton, North Yorkshire, BD23 1NQ
Tel: 01756 700640 Fax: 01756 700641
Email: derekchurch@skiptonpark.freeserve.co.uk
Web: www.milford.co.uk/go/skiptonpark.html
Rooms: 7 all ensuite 🚭
Pricing: £35-48 Room facilities: 🖥 🍵 Parking: Off-
street

Travelodge Skipton

Travel Accommodation
A65/A59, Gargrave Road, Skipton,
North Yorkshire, BD23 1UD
Web: www.travelodge.co.uk
Rooms: 32 all ensuite 🚭
Pricing: Sgl £54.40 Dbl £58.85 CC: Accepted
Room facilities: 🖥 🍵 Access: ♿

South Cave, Humberside

Travelodge Hull, South Cave East

Travel Accommodation
A63 East, Beacon Service Area, South Cave,
Humberside, HU15 1RZ
Web: www.travelodge.co.uk
Rooms: 40 all ensuite ⊛ Pricing: Sgl £47.40
Dbl £51.85 CC: Accepted Room facilities: ▢ ☐
Access: ⅊

Stockton-on-Tees, Co. Durham

Swallow Hotel

★★★★ ⚲
10 John Walker Square, Stockton-on-Tees,
County Durham, TS18 1AQ
Tel: 01642 679721 Fax: 01642 601714
Email: info@swallowhotelstockton.co.uk
Web: www.swallowhotelstockton.co.uk

SWALLOW
HOTELS

Rooms: 125 all ensuite ⊛
Pricing: Sgl £60–100 Dbl £70–116 Dinner from £19.95
CC: Accepted Room facilities: ▢ ☎ ☐ ✆ Access: |↑↑
Conference: 7 meeting rooms (Thtr 300 max),
24hr-delegate from £100, day-delegate rate from £30
Children: Welcome ⱨ Dogs: Welcome Licences: ◬ ⅲ
Leisure: Indoor pool, Gym, Health spa,
Parking: Off-street and monitored
Directions: Follow A19 northbound to A66 Stockton
turning, onto A1130. Over three roundabouts, turning
right to Castlegate car park.

Claireville

★★
519 Yarm Road, Eaglescliffe,
County Durham, TS16 9BG
Tel: 01642 780378 Fax: 01642 784109
Email: reception@clairev.demon.co.uk
Web: www.clairev.demon.co.uk
Rooms: 18 all ensuite ⧉ ⊛ Room facilities: ▢ ☎ ☐
Children: Welcome ⱨ Dogs: Welcome Licences: ⅲ
Parking: Off-street and monitored
Directions: On the A135 between the A66 (Stockton-
on-Tees) and the A19 at Yarm. Adjacent to Eaglescliffe
Golf Course.

Sunnyside Hotel

★★
580–582 Yarm Road, Eaglescliffe, Cleveland, TS16 0DF
Tel: 01642 780075 Fax: 01642 783789
Email: info@sunnysidehotel.co.uk
Web: www.sunnysidehotel.co.uk
Rooms: 23 (21 ensuite) ⊛
Pricing: Sgl £30–45 Dbl £50–57 Dinner from £10
CC: Accepted Room facilities: ▢ ☎ ☐
Children: Welcome ⱨ ⓒ Dogs: Welcome Licences: ⅲ
Parking: Off-street and monitored
Directions: Hotel located on A135 between Stockton-
on-Tees and Yarm. A135 can be accessed from A19
and A66.

Travelodge Sedgefield

Travel Accommodation
A177/A689 roundabout, Sedgefield,
Stockton-on-Tees, Co. Durham, TS21 2JX
Web: www.travelodge.co.uk
Rooms: 40 all ensuite ⊛
Pricing: Sgl £49.40 Dbl £53.85 CC: Accepted
Room facilities: ▢ ☐ Access: ⅊

Sunderland, Tyne & Wear

Quality Hotel Sunderland

★★★
Boldon Business Park, Boldon,
near Sunderland, NE35 9PE
Tel: 0191 519 1999 Fax: 0191 519 0655
Email: admin@gb621.u-net.com
Web: www.choicehotels.com
Rooms: 82 all ensuite ⧉ ⊛
Pricing: Sgl £100.75–110.75 Dbl £110.75–120.75
Dinner from £11.95 CC: Accepted
Room facilities: ▢ ☎ ☐ ✆ Access: ⅊
Children: Welcome 14yrs min age ⱨ ⓒ
Dogs: Welcome Licences: ◬ ⅲ
Leisure: Indoor pool
Parking: Off-street and monitored
Directions: Hotel is situated on the junction between
A19 and A184, 7 miles from Newcastle train station.

Travelodge Sunderland

❖
Web: www.travelodge.co.uk
Room facilities: ▢ ☐

Northeast

Tadcaster, North Yorkshire

Hazlewood Castle

★★★★

Paradise Lane, Hazlewood, Tadcaster,
North Yorkshire, LS24 9NJ
Tel: 01937 535353 Fax: 01937 530630
Email: info@hazlewoodcastle.co.uk
Web: www.hazlewoodcastle.co.uk

This former Monastery has been sensitively restored
and converted into a cookery school, conference
centre, banqueting suites and private dining rooms,
along with bistro, 'restaurant 1086' and luxury
accommodation.
Rooms: 21 all ensuite
Pricing: Sgl £110–180 Dbl £135–200
Dinner from £10.86 CC: Accepted
Room facilities:
Conference: 4 meeting rooms (Thtr 160 max),
24hr-delegate from £170, day-delegate rate from £44
Children: Welcome Dogs: Guide dogs only
Licences: Parking: Off-street and monitored
Directions: Off A1M at A64 junction (Leeds/York). Take
A64 towards York. First left (A659) towards Tadcaster,
signs to Hazlewood castle.

Travelodge York East

Travel Accommodation
A64 East Bound, Bilbrough, Steeton, Nr. Tadcaster,
North Yorkshire, LS24 8EG
Web: www.travelodge.co.uk
Rooms: 62 all ensuite
Pricing: Sgl £64.40 Dbl £68.85 CC: Accepted
Room facilities: Access:

Thirsk, North Yorkshire

Angel Inn

★★

Long Street, Topcliffe, Thirsk,
North Yorkshire, YO7 3RW
Tel: 01845 577237 Fax: 01845 578000
Web: www.angelinn.co.uk
Rooms: 15 all ensuite
Pricing: Sgl £44.50 Dbl £60 Dinner from £14.95
CC: Accepted Room facilities:
Children: Welcome Licences:
Parking: Off-street
Directions: Situated just off the A168, 3 miles from
Junction 49 A1M. 3 miles from A19.

Tynemouth, Tyne & Wear

Grand Hotel

★★★

Grand Parade, Tynemouth, Tyne & Wear, NE30 4ER
Tel: 0191 293 6666 Fax: 0191 293 6665
Email: info@grandhotel-uk.com
Web: www.grandhotel-uk.com
Rooms: 45 all ensuite
Pricing: Sgl £55–95 Dbl £60–180 Dinner from £20
CC: Accepted Room facilities: Access:
Conference: 3 meeting rooms (Thtr 130 max),
24hr-delegate from £115, day-delegate rate from £29
Children: Welcome Dogs: Guide dogs only
Licences: Parking: Off-street
Directions: From A1 take A19 and then A1058. Follow
the signs for Tynemouth. At the seafront, turn right.
Grand Hotel is approx ½ mile.

Wakefield, West Yorkshire

Cedar Court Hotel

★★★★

Denby Dale Road, Wakefield, West Yorkshire, WF4 3QZ
Tel: 01924 276310 Fax: 01924 280221
Email: sales@cedarcourthotels.co.uk
Web: www.cedarcourthotels.co.uk
Rooms: 151 all ensuite
Pricing: Sgl £55–119 Dbl £60–129 Dinner from £19.95
CC: Accepted Room facilities:
Access: Children: Welcome
Dogs: Welcome Licences:
Leisure: Indoor pool, Gym, Health spa, Beauty salon,
Snooker/billiards
Parking: Off-street and monitored
Directions: Off Junction 39 of M1, located adjacent to
roundabout under motorway.

Hotel St Pierre

★★★ ®

Barnsley Road, Newmillerdam, Wakefield,
West Yorkshire, WF2 6QG
Tel: 01924 255596 Fax: 01924 252746
Email: res@hotelstpierre.co.uk
Web: www.hotelstpierre.co.uk
Rooms: 54 all ensuite ❤ 🖨 ⊗
Pricing: Sgl £54.50–84.50 Dbl £65–104 Dinner from
£16.95 CC: Accepted
Room facilities: ☐ ☎ 🖥 💺 Access: ⅃↕ 🕭
Conference: 6 meeting rooms (Thtr 120 max),
24hr-delegate from £99, day-delegate rate from £29
Children: Welcome ⼁ Dogs: Welcome
Licences: ⟁ ⅲ Leisure: Gym, Parking: Off-street

Campanile

Travel Accommodation
Monckton Road, Wakefield, West Yorkshire, WF2 7AL
Tel: 01924 201054 Fax: 01924 201055

Typical Campanile bedroom

Campanile hotels offer comfortable and convenient
budget accommodation and a traditional French-style
Bistro providing freshly-cooked food for breakfast,
lunch and dinner. All rooms ensuite with tea/coffee-
making facilities, DDT and TV with Sky channels.
Rooms: 77 all ensuite ⊗
Pricing: Sgl £36.95–47.90 Dbl £41.85–53.85
Dinner from £11.95 CC: Accepted
Room facilities: ☐ ☎ 🖥 💺 Access: 🕭
Conference: 1 meeting room (Thtr 35 max),
24hr-delegate from £68, day-delegate rate from £19.50
Children: Welcome ⼁ Dogs: Welcome Licences: ⅲ
Parking: Off-street
Directions: Take Junction 39 M1. Towards Wakefield
Centre on A636, hotel is 1 mile from motorway on the
left side, on Monkton Road Industrial Estate.

Travelodge Wakefield. Woolley Edge South (MOTO)

Travel Accommodation
M1 Moto Service Area, Woolley Edge, West Bretton,
Wakefield, West Yorkshire, WF4 4LQ
Web: www.travelodge.co.uk
Rooms: 41 all ensuite ⊗
Pricing: Sgl £54.40 Dbl £58.85 CC: Accepted
Room facilities: ☐ 🖥 Access: 🕭

Warkworth, Northumberland

Warkworth House Hotel

★★ ®

16 Bridge Street, Warkworth,
Northumberland, NE65 0XB
Tel: 01665 711276 Fax: 01665 713323
Email: welcome@warkworthhousehotel.co.uk
Web: www.warkworthhousehotel.co.uk
Rooms: 15 all ensuite 🖨 ⊗
Pricing: Sgl £55–58 Dbl £90–95 Dinner from £17.95
CC: Accepted Room facilities: ☐ ☎ 🖥 Access: 🕭
Dogs: Welcome Licences: ⅲ
Parking: Off-street and monitored
Directions: From the A1, take the B6345 and follow
signs for Warkworth Castle. Hotel is situated on the
B1068 near the bridge.

Washington, Tyne & Wear

Campanile Hotel Washington

Travel Accommodation
Emerson Road, District 5, Washington,
Tyne & Wear, NE37 1LE
Tel: 0191 416 5010 Fax: 0191 416 5023
Web: www.envergure.fr

Typical Campanile bistro

Campanile hotels offer comfortable and convenient
budget accommodation and a traditional French-style
Bistro providing freshly-cooked food for breakfast,
lunch and dinner. All rooms ensuite with tea/coffee-
making facilities, DDT and TV with Sky channels.
Rooms: 78 all ensuite ⊗
Pricing: Sgl £40.95–48.90 Dbl £46.90–54.85
Dinner from £5.95 CC: Accepted
Room facilities: ☐ ☎ 🖥 💺 Access: 🕭
Children: Welcome ⼁ Dogs: Welcome Licences: ⅲ
Parking: Off-street and monitored
Directions: From north or south take A1M, J64 to
Birtley Services. Follow Emerson Road to arrive at
hotel.

Ask the experts

To book a Hotel or Guest
Accommodation, or for help
and advice, call RAC Hotel
Reservations on 0870 603 9109
and quote 'Guide 2003'

West Bretton, West Yorkshire

Travelodge Wakefield, Woolley Edge North (MOTO)

Travel Accommodation
M1 Moto Service Area, Woolley Edge, West Bretton, West Yorkshire, WF4 4LQ
Web: www.travelodge.co.uk
Rooms: 32 all ensuite
Pricing: Sgl £54.40 Dbl £58.85 CC: Accepted
Room facilities: Access:

West Witton, Wensleydale

Wensleydale Heifer

★★
West Witton, Wensleydale, North Yorkshire, DL8 4LS
Tel: 01969 622322 Fax: 01969 624183
Email: heifer@westwitton.fsnet.co.uk
Rooms: 9 all ensuite
Pricing: Sgl £60 Dbl £80–98 Dinner from £7.95
CC: Accepted Room facilities:
Children: Welcome Dogs: Welcome Licences:
Parking: Off-street
Directions: The inn is on the A684 trans-Pennine road from Leyburn to Hawes.

One click does it all

Book RAC inspected hotels and B&Bs at www.rac.co.uk/hotels

Crathorne Hall Hotel

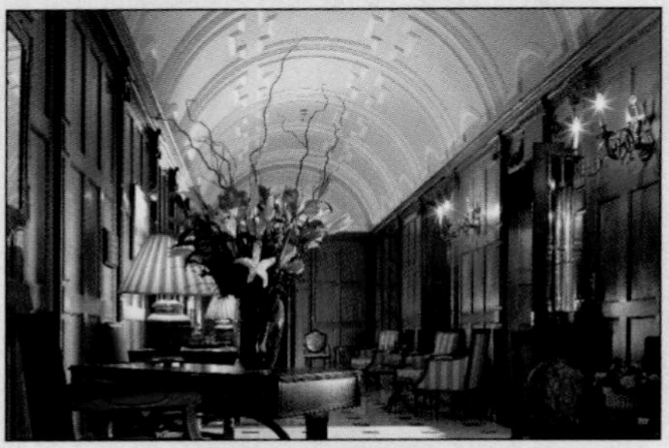

Crathorne Hall is one of the finest hotels in the Northeast of England and an outstanding example of Edwardian architecture and design.
From the magnificent lobby and quietly sumptuous drawing room to the 37 spacious bedrooms and suites, Crathorne Hall exudes the comfort and style of the quintessential English country residence.

Crathorne, N. Yorkshire TS15 0AR
Tel: 01642 700398
Email: enquiries@arcadianhotels.co.uk
Web: www.crathornehall.com

Whitby, North Yorkshire

Saxonville Hotel

★★★
Ladysmith Avenue, Whitby, North Yorkshire, YO21 3HX
Tel: 01947 602631 Fax: 01947 820250
Email: newtons@saxonville.co.uk
Web: www.saxonville.co.uk
Seasonal closure: December to February
Rooms: 22 all ensuite
Pricing: Sgl £47.50–52.50 Dbl £95–105
Dinner from £21 CC: Accepted Room facilities:
Conference: 3 meeting rooms (Thtr 120 max), 24hr-delegate from £70, day-delegate rate from £20
Children: Welcome Dogs: Guide dogs only
Licences: Parking: Off-street
Directions: Follow signs for Whitby/Westcliff. At large four towered building turn inland into Argyle road. Saxonville first turning on right.

Old West Cliff Hotel

★★
42 Crescent Avenue, Whitby, North Yorkshire, YO21 3EQ
Tel: 01947 603292 Fax: 01947 821716
Email: oldwestcliff@telinco.co.uk
Web: www.oldwestcliff.telinco.co.uk
Seasonal closure: January
Rooms: 12 all ensuite
Pricing: Sgl £35 Dbl £56 CC: Accepted
Room facilities: Children: Welcome
Dogs: Guide dogs only Licences:
Directions: On approaching Whitby, follow signs for West Cliff. Hotel off the central exit of Crescent Gardens, opposite Spa and Pavillion complex.

White House Hotel

★★
Upgang Lane, Whitby, North Yorkshire, YO21 3JJ
Tel: 01947 600469 Fax: 01947 821600
Web: www.s-h-systems.co.uk/hotels/whitehse.html
Rooms: 10 all ensuite
Pricing: Sgl £30–37 Dbl £60–74 Dinner from £13
CC: Accepted Room facilities:
Children: Welcome Dogs: Welcome Parking: Off-street
Directions: Follow signs for Westcliff/Sandsend. Hotel located off A174 adjacent to golf course.

Glendale Guest House

♦♦♦♦
16 Crescent Avenue, Whitby, North Yorkshire, YO21 3ED
Tel: 01947 604242
Pricing: Dinner from £11
Room facilities: Children: Welcome
Dogs: Welcome Licences: Parking: Off-street
Directions: At railway station turn into Bagdale, proceed to roundabout at Chubb hill, turn right to roundabout, take second exit and first right into Crescent Avenue.

Seacliffe Hotel

◆ ◆ ◆ ◆

North Promenade, West Cliff, Whitby, North Yorkshire,
YO21 3JX
Tel: 01947 603139 Fax: 01947 603139
Email: julie@seacliffe.fsnet.co.uk
Web: seacliffehotel.co.uk

Whitbys' premier family hotel, overlooking the sea. All
rooms are ensuite, wine and dine in our candlelit à la
carte restaurant. Local seafood a speciality, succulent
steaks and vegetarian dishes.
Rooms: 20 all ensuite 🐾 🚭
Pricing: Sgl £42.50–49.50 Dbl £69–73 Dinner from £15
CC: Accepted
Room facilities: 🖵 ☎ 🍵
Children: Welcome 🍴 🍼 Dogs: Welcome Licences: 🏳
Leisure: Games room Parking: Off-street
Directions: Follow signs for West Cliff and West Cliff
car park. Hotel located on seafront.

Arundel House Hotel

◆ ◆ ◆

Bagdale, Whitby, N. Yorks, YO21 1QJ
Tel: 01947 603645 Fax: 01947 603645
Email: arundel_house@hotmail.com
Web: www.arundelhousehotel.co.uk
Rooms: 11 all ensuite 🐾 📺 🚭
Pricing: Sgl £30–35 Dbl £54 CC: Accepted
Room facilities: 🖵 🍵 Access: ♿
Children: Welcome 🍴 🍼 Dogs: Welcome
Licences: 🏳 Parking: Off-street
Directions: We are situated 500 yards from the Town
Centre and station on the A171 in the direction of
Scarborough.

Sandbeck Hotel

◆ ◆ ◆

2 Crescent Terrace, West Cliff, Whitby,
North Yorkshire, YO21 3EL
Tel: 01947 604012 Fax: 01947 606402
Email: dysonsandbeck@tesco.net
Seasonal closure: December
Rooms: 15 all ensuite 🐾 📺 🚭
Pricing: Dbl £21–32.50 CC: Accepted
Room facilities: 🖵 🍵
Children: Welcome 🍴 Dogs: Welcome Licences: 🏳
Directions: Take A169/A171 and follow signs for West
Cliff.

Windsor Hotel

★ ★ ★ ☕

South Parade, Whitley Bay, Tyne & Wear, NE26 2RF
Tel: 0191 251 8888 Fax: 0191 297 0272
Email: info@windsorhotel-uk.com
Web: www.windsorhotel-uk.com
Rooms: 70 all ensuite 🐾
Pricing: Sgl £49–65 Dbl £60–70 Dinner from £14.75
CC: Accepted
Room facilities: 🖵 ☎ 🍵 Access: ⬆
Conference: 1 meeting room (Thtr 80 max),
day-delegate rate from £25
Children: Welcome 🍴 Licences: 🏳
Parking: Off-street and monitored
Directions: From A1, join A19. Follow signs for A1058.
Once on seafront turn left. Travel approximately
2 miles.

Yarm, North Yorkshire

Crathorne Hall Hotel

Blue Ribbon Winner

★ ★ ★ ★ ☕ ☕ ☕

Crathorne, North Yorkshire, TS15 0AR
Tel: 01642 700398 Fax: 01642 700456
Email: enquiries@arcadianhotels.co.uk
Web: www.crathornehall.com

Impressive Edwardian mansion in classical style with
oak-panelled rooms and fine antiques. Set in 15 acres
of wooded grounds.
Rooms: 37 all ensuite 📺
Pricing: Sgl £90–135 Dbl £140–295 Dinner from £30
CC: Accepted Room facilities: 🖵 ☎ 🍵
Conference: 6 meeting rooms (Thtr 100 max),
24hr-delegate from £176.25, day-delegate rate from
£58.75
Children: Welcome 🍴 Dogs: Welcome Licences: 🏳
Parking: Off-street and monitored
Directions: From A1 north, take A19 Teesside exit.
Crathorne is signposted off A19 at Yarm/Teesside
airport exit, and is 1 mile from slip road.
See advert on facing page

Judges Country House Hotel

The hotel's 21 guestrooms, gourmet restaurant and private dining room sit on top of its own 22 acres of immaculate gardens. Award winning 'Head Chef' Colin Woodward and his team of twelve chefs take much time and trouble to source the very best in fresh local produce with game, fish and prime cuts of meats featuring on our menus.
Judges has become a favoured destination for the discerning traveller. Besides the comfort of comtemporary amenities in a setting rich with Victorian charm, guests have come to depend on the hotel's gracious hospitality and superior, unobtrusive service.

Kirklevington Hall, Kirklevington, Yarm, Cleveland TS15 9LW
Tel: 01642 789000 Fax: 01642 782878 Email: enquiries@judgeshotel.co.uk Web: www.judgeshotel.co.uk

Judges Country House Hotel

★★★★ 🏅🏅🏅 Blue Ribbon Winner

Kirklevington Hall, Kirklevington, Yarm, Cleveland, TS15 9LW
Tel: 01642 789000 Fax: 01642 782878
Email: enquires@judgeshotel.co.uk
Web: www.judgeshotel.co.uk
Rooms: 21 all ensuite 😋 🖨 😊
Pricing: Sgl £123–165 Dbl £138–225 Dinner from £32
CC: Accepted Room facilities: ⬜ ☎ ☕ 🧺 Access: ♿
Conference: 7 meeting rooms (Thtr 350 max), 24hr-delegate from £165, day-delegate rate from £39
Children: Welcome 🍴 ☕ Dogs: Welcome
Licences: 🍷 👫 Leisure: Gym, Tennis, Fishing, Games room Parking: Off-street and monitored
Directions: From the A19 take the A67 heading to Yarm and we are 1 mile on the left-hand side.
See advert on this page

York, North Yorkshire

Le Meridien York

★★★★

Station Road, York, North Yorkshire, YO24 1AA
Tel: 0800 028 2840 Fax: 01904 623003
Email: julia.bodmer@lemeridien.com
Web: www.lemeridien.com
Rooms: 165 all ensuite 😋
Pricing: Dinner from £24.50 CC: Accepted
Room facilities: ⬜ ☎ ☕ 🧺 Access: ⬆ ♿

Conference: 13 meeting rooms (Thtr 410 max), 24hr-delegate from £175, day-delegate rate from £60
Children: Welcome 🍴 ☕
Dogs: Guide dogs only
Licences: 🍷 👫
Leisure: Indoor pool, Gym, Health spa
Parking: Off-street and monitored
Directions: From M1 take Junction 32 and M18 then Junction 2 onto A1 (north). From A1, take A64 to York then A1036 to York City Centre.

Aldwark Manor Hotel

★★★★ 🏅🏅

Aldwark, Nr Alne, York, North Yorkshire, YO61 1UF
Tel: 01347 838146 Fax: 01347 838867
Email: aldwark@marstonhotels.com
Web: www.marstonhotels.com

Victorian Manor House set in beautiful Yorkshire countryside. rosette awarded restaurant, indoor pool,

spa, sauna, solarium, gym and a challenging
18-hole golf course.
Rooms: 60 all ensuite
Pricing: Sgl £75 Dbl £125 Dinner from £29.95
CC: Accepted Room facilities: Access:
Conference: 5 meeting rooms (Thtr 250 max),
24hr-delegate from £140, day-delegate rate from £39
Children: Welcome Dogs: Guide dogs only
Licences:
Leisure: Indoor pool, Gym, Health spa, Beauty salon,
Golf Parking: Monitored
Directions: Leave A1(M) onto A59 for York; turn left at
Green Hammerton and follow the brown tourist signs.

Dean Court Hotel

★★★
Duncombe Place, York, North Yorkshire, YO1 7EF
Tel: 01904 625082 Fax: 01904 620305
Email: info@deancourt-york.co.uk
Web: www.deancourt-york.co.uk
Rooms: 39 all ensuite
Pricing: Dinner from £19.75 (2002 rate) CC: Accepted
Room facilities: Access:
Children: Welcome Licences:
Parking: Off-street and monitored
Directions: From outer ring road, take A64 York North,
then A1237 A19 Thirsk, then Clifton (inner ring road) to
city centre and Minster.

Grange Hotel

★★★ Blue Ribbon Winner
1 Clifton, York, North Yorkshire, YO30 6AA
Tel: 01904 644744 Fax: 01904 612453
Email: info@grangehotel.co.uk
Web: www.grangehotel.co.uk

Exclusive Regency townhouse just minutes from the
Minster and city centre. Luxurious accommodation,
three superb restaurants and award-winning food.
Excellent conference facilities. Private car park.
Rooms: 30 all ensuite
Pricing: Sgl £105–170 Dbl £125–230 Dinner from £28
CC: Accepted Room facilities: Access:
Conference: 2 meeting rooms (Thtr 50 max)
24hr-delegate from £149, day-delegate rate from £41
Children: Welcome Dogs: Welcome Licences:
Parking: Off-street and monitored
Directions: On A19 York to Thirsk road, 500 yards from
city centre.

Kilima

★★★
129 Holgate Road, York, North Yorkshire, YO24 4AZ
Tel: 01904 625787 Fax: 01904 612083
Email: sales@kilima.co.uk
Web: www.kilima.co.uk
Rooms: 26 all ensuite
Pricing: Sgl £65–70 Dbl £90–110 Dinner from £21.95
CC: Accepted Room facilities: Access:
Conference: 1 meeting room (Thtr 14 max),
24hr-delegate from £110, day-delegate rate from £32.50
Children: Welcome Dogs: Guide dogs only
Licences:
Leisure: Indoor pool, Gym, Health spa
Parking: Off-street and monitored
Directions: Located on west side of city, on A59
Harrogate road.

Middlethorpe Hall

★★★★ Gold Ribbon Winner
Bishopthorpe Road, York, North Yorkshire, YO23 2GB
Tel: 01904 641241 Fax: 01904 620176
Email: info@middlethorpe.com
Web: www.middlethorpe.com

Five minutes from central York, grade II listed building,
combined with every modern comfort. Spa with pool
and treatment rooms, rosette restaurant combining
traditional and contemporary, ample free and secure
parking.
Rooms: 30 all ensuite
Pricing: Sgl £123.50–154.50 Dbl £189–369
Dinner from £36 CC: Accepted Room facilities:
Access:
Conference: 2 meeting rooms (Thtr 56 max)
24hr-delegate from £170.38, day-delegate rate from £58.75
Children: Welcome 8yrs min age Licences:
Leisure: Indoor pool, Gym, Health spa, Beauty salon
Parking: Off-street and monitored
Directions: Leave the A64 to join the A1036 sign
posted York/Racecourse. Then follow smaller signs to
Bishopthorpe and Middlethorpe.

Making a booking?

Don't forget to mention RAC
Hotels and Bed & Breakfast 2003.

Monkbar Hotel

★★★

Monkbar, York, North Yorkshire, YO31 7JA
Tel: 01904 638086 Fax: 01904 629195
Email: sales@monkbar-hotel.co.uk
Web: www.monkbar-hotel.co.uk

The Monkbar Hotel is at the heart of the city and offers free parking for residents. Great training facilities and investors in people award indicates the care we offer.
Rooms: 99 all ensuite 🛏 🖥 🚫
Pricing: Sgl £90–110 Dbl £130–150 Dinner from £18.50
CC: Accepted Room facilities: ⬜ ☎ 🖳 Access: ⛓
Children: Welcome ♀ ☕ Dogs: Welcome
Licences: ⬩ ♦♦♦ Parking: Off-street and monitored
Directions: From A64 take A1079 Hull/York. Left to city centre; right at city walls. Large traffic lights straight ahead. Hotel on the right.

Parsonage Country House Hotel

★★★★ ⚬⚬

Escrick, York, North Yorkshire, YO19 6LF
Tel: 01904 728111 Fax: 01904 728151
Email: sales@parsonagehotel.co.uk
Web: www.parsonagehotel.co.uk

Set in 6½ acres of landscaped gardens only minutes from York city centre. Weekend breaks from £49.50 per person per night. 2 AA rosettes for restaurant, 4 poster, non-smoking rooms available.
Rooms: 46 all ensuite 🖥 🚫
Pricing: Sgl £75–95 Dbl £90–140 Dinner from £19.75
CC: Accepted Room facilities: ⬜ ☎ 🖳 📞
Access: ⛓ ♿
Conference: 6 meeting rooms (Thtr 160 max), 24hr-delegate from £130, day-delegate rate from £40
Children: Welcome ♀ ☕ Dogs: Guide dogs only
Licences: ⬩ ♦♦♦ Parking: Off-street and monitored
Directions: The Parsonage Hotel is situated in the village of Escrick on the A19 between York and Selby.

Abbots Mews Hotel

★★

Marygate Lane, Bootham, York,
North Yorkshire, YO30 7DE
Tel: 01904 634866 Fax: 01904 612848
Rooms: 47 all ensuite
Pricing: Sgl £40–45 Dbl £70–80 Dinner from £15
CC: Accepted Room facilities: ⬜ ☎ 🖳
Children: Welcome ♀ Licences: ♦♦♦
Parking: Off-street and monitored
Directions: Follow A19 into York. Just before Bootham Bar and traffic lights at Exhibition Square, turn right into Marygate. At end of Marygate, turn right and right again. Hotel overlooking car park.

Beechwood Close Hotel

★★

19 Shipton Road, York, North Yorkshire, YO30 5RE
Tel: 01904 658378 Fax: 01904 647124
Email: bch@selcom.co.uk
Web: www.beechwood-close.co.uk

A warm welcome is assured from Beverley & Graham and their staff. Set in its own grounds, the hotel is ideal for visiting the city and surrounding countryside.
Rooms: 14 all ensuite 🛏
Pricing: Sgl £45–49 Dbl £65–80 Dinner from £14
CC: Accepted Room facilities: ⬜ ☎ 🖳
Conference: 2 meeting rooms (Thtr 30 max), 24hr-delegate from £71.50, day-delegate rate from £18
Children: Welcome ♀ Licences: ♦♦♦
Parking: Off-street and monitored
Directions: From Outer Ring Road (A1237), turn to city centre at A19 Thirsk roundabout. Hotel is 1 mile on right, just inside 30mph zone.

Cottage Hotel

★★

3 Clifton Green, York, North Yorkshire, YO3 6LH
Tel: 01904 643711 Fax: 01904 611230
Rooms: 25 all ensuite 🛏 🖥 🚫
Pricing: Sgl £35–55 Dbl £55–80 Dinner from £11
CC: Accepted Room facilities: ⬜ ☎ 🖳
Children: Welcome ♀ Licences: ♦♦♦
Parking: Off-street and monitored
Directions: On A1237 follow signs to York north A19 Thirsk until sign for Rawcliffe, turn right for Clifton and carry straight on.

Heworth Court Hotel

★★

Heworth Green, York, North Yorkshire, YO31 7TQ
Tel: 01904 425156 Fax: 01904 415290
Email: hotel@heworth.co.uk
Web: www.visityork.com

A traditional English hotel within one mile of York
Minster with ensuite hotel accommodation, four-
posters, whisky bar, candlelit restaurant and ample
parking. Special 'short breaks' available all year.
Rooms: 28 all ensuite
Pricing: Sgl £50–86 Dbl £60–111 Dinner from £12.95
CC: Accepted Room facilities: 🖵 ☎ 🍵 ⌁
Conference: 1 meeting room (Thtr 50 max)
Children: Welcome ♁ Licences: ⚱ ⚱⚱
Parking: Off-street and monitored
Directions: Use outer ring road (York bypass) and turn
into York from Scarborough roundabout. Hotel is
12 minutes walk from Minster

Judges Lodging

★★

9 Lendal, York, North Yorkshire, YO1 8AQ
Tel: 01904 638733 Fax: 01904 679947
Email: judgeshotel@aol.com
Web: www.judges-lodging.co.uk

Charming Georgian townhouse of historic importance,
the most centrally located hotel in city centre. Some
rooms with four posters and spa baths. Excellent
restaurant and beer garden, car parking available.
Rooms: 14 all ensuite ⚓ ⌁ ⊗
Pricing: Sgl £75 Dbl £100–150 Dinner from £30
CC: Accepted Room facilities: 🖵 ☎ 🌀
Conference: 3 meeting rooms (Thtr 20 max)
Children: Welcome ♁ Dogs: Welcome Licences: ⚱⚱⚱
Parking: Off-street and monitored

Knavesmire Manor Hotel

★★

302 Tadcaster Road, York, North Yorkshire, YO24 1HE
Tel: 01904 702941 Fax: 01904 709274
Email: enquire@knavesmire.co.uk
Web: www.knavesmire.co.uk
Rooms: 20 all ensuite ⚓ ⌁
Pricing: Dinner from £15.95 CC: Accepted
Room facilities: 🖵 ☎ 🌀 Access: ⑊
Conference: 20 meeting rooms (Thtr 30 max),
day-delegate rate from £23.95
Children: Welcome ♁ ⅋ Dogs: Welcome
Licences: ⚱ ⚱⚱
Leisure: Indoor pool, Health spa
Parking: Off-street and monitored
Directions: Take the A64 off the A1, near Tadcaster.
Follow signs to York West, then signs to Bishopthorpe
or Racecourse. Hotel opposite the Knavesmire
racecourse.
See advert on this page

Northeast

Minster Hotel

★ ★

60 Bootham, York, North Yorkshire, YO30 7BZ
Tel: 01904 621267 Fax: 01904 654719
Email: res@minsterhotel.co.uk
Web: www.minsterhotel.co.uk

Hotel 5 minutes from York Minster and city centre, refurbished rooms with sky TV, trouser presses and hospitality trays. Car parking, restaurant and bar, conference and meeting rooms.
Rooms: 31 all ensuite
Pricing: Dinner from £9.95 CC: Accepted
Room facilities:
Conference: 2 meeting rooms (Thtr 60 max)
24hr-delegate from £110, day-delegate rate from £35
Children: Welcome 5yrs min age Licences:
Parking: Monitored

Arndale Hotel

♦ ♦ ♦ ♦

290 Tadcaster Road, York, North Yorkshire, YO24 1ET
Tel: 01904 702424 Fax: 01904 709800
Rooms: 12 all ensuite
Room facilities:
Children: Welcome Licences:
Parking: Off-street and monitored
Directions: From A64 take the York West 1036 road. Follow the city centre signs. Hotel situated approximately 1 mile from A64 on left-hand side overlooking racecourse.

Ascot House

♦ ♦ ♦ ♦

80 East Parade, York, North Yorkshire, YO31 7YH
Tel: 01904 426826 Fax: 01904 431077
Email: j+k@ascot-house-york.demon.co.uk
Web: www.ascothouseyork.com

A family-run Victorian villa 15 minutes' walk from city centre, Castle Museum or York Minster with rooms of character and many four-poster or canopy beds. Traditional English breakfasts. Residential licence, sauna, private enclosed car park.
Rooms: 15 (12 ensuite)
Pricing: Sgl £22–50 Dbl £44–60 CC: Accepted
Room facilities: Children: Welcome
Dogs: Welcome Licences:
Parking: Off-street and monitored
Directions: From northeast, junction A1237 and A64 (ring road) take A1036. Turn left for Heworth after 30mph sign, then right at traffic lights into East Parade.

Ashbourne House

♦ ♦ ♦ ♦

139 Fulford Road, York, North Yorkshire, YO10 4HG
Tel: 01904 639912 Fax: 01904 631332
Email: ashbourneh@aol.com
Web: www.ashbourne-house.com

Family-run Victorian house; ensuite rooms are furnished in a contemporary style and fully equipped. Licenced with a small honesty bar in a comfortable guest lounge. Car parking. Non-smoking.
Rooms: 7 (6 ensuite)
Pricing: Sgl £35–45 Dbl £40–60 CC: Accepted
Room facilities: Children: Welcome
Licences: Parking: Off-street
Directions: On the A19 road south (York to Selby), one mile from the city centre.

Bloomsbury Hotel

♦♦♦♦

127 Clifton, York, North Yorkshire, YO30 6BL
Tel: 01904 634031 Fax: 01904 634855
Email: bloomsburyhotel@btinternet.com
Web: www.bloomsburyhotel.co.uk
Rooms: 9 all ensuite ♨ ⊗
Pricing: Sgl £40–60 Dbl £50–80 CC: Accepted
Room facilities: ▢ 🌣 Children: Welcome
Dogs: Welcome Parking: Off-street
Directions: From A1237 north York bypass take A19
York turn at roundabout. We are approximately one
mile along A19 opposite the church.

Curzon Lodge & Stable Cottages

♦♦♦♦

23 Tadcaster Road, Dringhouses, York, North
Yorkshire, YO24 1QG
Tel: 01904 703157 Fax: 01904 703157
Web: www.smoothhound.co.uk/hotels/curzon.html
Seasonal closure: Christmas

Relax and unwind in a unique atmosphere at this
charming 17th-century former farmhouse and stables
overlooking York racecourse. Close to centre. Parking
in grounds. Personal service.
Rooms: 10 all ensuite ♨ 🛏 ⊗
Pricing: Sgl £39–49 Dbl £59–70 CC: Accepted
Room facilities: ▢ 🌣
Children: Welcome 7yrs min age Parking: Off-street
Directions: From A64 take A1036 towards city centre;
hotel is 2 miles on right between York Holiday Inn and
York Marriott Hotels.

Plan your route

Visit www.rac.co.uk for RAC's
interactive route planner, including
up to the minute traffic reports.

Need help booking?

RAC Hotel Reservations will find
the accommodation that's right
for you – and book it too.
Call today on 0870 603 9109
and quote 'Guide 2003'

Holly Lodge

♦♦♦♦ ✎

204–206 Fulford Road, York, North Yorkshire, YO1 4DD
Tel: 01904 646005
Web: www.thehollylodge.co.uk

Beautifully appointed Grade II listed building, 10
minutes' stroll to centre. Convenient for all York's
attractions. On-site parking. All rooms ensuite
overlooking garden or terrace. Booking recommended.
1½ miles from A64/A19 intersection.
Rooms: 5 all ensuite ♨ ⊗
Pricing: Sgl £58–78 Dbl £68–78 CC: Accepted
Room facilities: ▢ 🌣
Children: Welcome 7yrs min age
Parking: Off-street and monitored
Directions: On corner of Fulford road and Wenlock,
1½ miles towards centre from A19/A64 intersection.
10 minutes' walk along A19 south from centre.

Holmwood House Hotel

♦♦♦♦

114 Holgate Road, York, North Yorkshire, YO24 4BB
Tel: 01904 626183 Fax: 01904 670899
Email: holmwood.house@dial.pipex.com
Web: www.holmwoodhousehotel.co.uk

Elegant Victorian house.
Rooms: 14 all ensuite ♨ 🛏 ⊗
Pricing: Sgl £45–70 Dbl £65–105 CC: Accepted
Room facilities: ▢ ☎ 🌣
Conference: 1 meeting room (Thtr 12 max)
Children: Welcome 8yrs min age
Dogs: Guide dogs only Licences: ⛏
Parking: Off-street and monitored
Directions: 400m past the Fox pub on the left of A59
Harrogate to York road, in built-up York.

The Hazelwood

◆◆◆◆ ✻

24–25 Portland Street, York, YO31 7EH
Tel: 01904 626548 Fax: 01904 628032
Email: admin@thehazelwoodyork.com
Web: www.thehazelwoodyork.com

Situated in the very heart of York yet in an extremely
quiet location, an award-winning Victorian town house
with private car park. Wide breakfast menu including
vegetarian. Non-smoking.
Rooms: 14 all ensuite 🖵 🛇
Pricing: Sgl £35–95 Dbl £75–105 CC: Accepted
Room facilities: 🖵 🛇 Children: Welcome 8yrs min age
Licences: 👬 Parking: Off-street
Directions: Situated just 400 yards from York Minster in
residential side street, just off inner ring road (Gillygate).
See advert on this page

Blue Bridge Hotel

◆◆◆

Fishergate, York, North Yorkshire, YO10 4AP
Tel: 01904 621193 Fax: 01904 671571
Email: info@bluebridgehotel.co.uk
Web: www.bluebridgehotel.co.uk
Rooms: 18 (16 ensuite) 🛇
Pricing: Sgl £45–50 Dbl £55–90 Dinner from £12
CC: Accepted
Room facilities: 🖵 ☎ 🛇
Conference: 2 meeting rooms (Thtr 20 max),
24hr-delegate from £90, day-delegate rate from £25
Children: Welcome 🏳 🍴 Dogs: Welcome
Licences: 👬
Parking: Off-street and monitored
Directions: On A19 York to Selby road, 2 miles from
outer ring road on right hand side. Five minutes' walk
from city centre.

Ivy House Farm

 ◆◆◆

Hull Road, Kexby, York, North Yorkshire, YO41 5LQ
Tel: 01904 489368
Email: kevin-jayne-daniel@supanet.com

Situated on the A1079 east of York, with easy access to the Yorkshire wolds, dales, moors and east coast. Comfortable accommodation with lounge, dining room and gardens, with TV and hot and cold water in all rooms.
Rooms: 4 (2 ensuite) ☕
Pricing: Sgl £20–22 Dbl £32–36
Room facilities: ☐ ☕ Children: Welcome ⌐
Parking: Off-street
Directions: Leaving York on the A1079 Hull Road, about 5 miles from town centre, Ivy House Farm is on right-hand side of the road.

Linden Lodge Hotel

◆◆◆

6 Nunthorpe Avenue, Scarcroft Road,
York, North Yorkshire, YO23 1PF
Tel: 01904 620107 Fax: 01904 620985
Email: bookings@lindenlodge.yorks.net
Web: www.yorkshirenet.co.uk/stayat/lindenlodge
Rooms: 13 (10 ensuite) ⊗
Pricing: Sgl £24–27.50 Dbl £46–52
CC: Accepted
Room facilities: ☐ ☕ Children: Welcome
Licences: ⦚
Directions: Linden Lodge is 10 minutes' walk from the city centre, rail station and racecourse. With a mix of doubles, singles and family rooms, all with tea- and coffee-making facilities and colour television.

Priory Hotel & Garth Restaurant

◆◆◆

126–128 Fulford Road, York, North Yorkshire, YO10 4BE
Tel: 01904 625280
Email: reservations@priory-hotelyork.co.uk
Web: www.priory-hotelyork.co.uk
Rooms: 16 all ensuite ☕
Pricing: Sgl £50–80 Dbl £70–90 Dinner from £9.95
CC: Accepted Room facilities: ☐ ☎ ☕
Children: Welcome ⌐ Dogs: Welcome Licences: ⦚
Parking: Off-street
Directions: Situated on the A19 road to Selby on south side of city. No.9 bus or 1½ miles from station.

St Denys Hotel

◆◆◆

St Denys Road, York, North Yorkshire, YO1 1QD
Tel: 01904 622207 Fax: 01904 624800
Email: info@stdenyshotel.co.uk
Web: www.stdenyshotel.co.uk
Rooms: 13 all ensuite ☞ ⊗
Pricing: Sgl £40–50 Dbl £55–80 CC: Accepted
Room facilities: ☐ ☎ ☕ Access: ♿
Children: Welcome ☡ Dogs: Welcome Licences: ⦚
Parking: Off-street
Directions: Take A1079 for York/Hull, 2½ miles from outer ring road, through Walmgate Bar. After ½ a mile turn left into one-way system. Hotel is on left, 2 minutes' walk from city centre.

St Georges Hotel

◆◆◆

6 St Georges Place, York, North Yorkshire, YO24 1DR
Tel: 01904 625056 Fax: 01904 625009
Email: sixstgeorg@aol.com
Web: www.members.aol.com/sixstgeorg
Rooms: 10 all ensuite ☕ ☞
Pricing: Sgl £30–40 Dbl £48–57 Dinner from £7
CC: Accepted Room facilities: ☐ ☕ Access: ♿
Children: Welcome ⌐ Dogs: Welcome Licences: ⦚
Parking: Off-street and monitored
Directions: From south, take A1036. Turn left as racecourse ends on right. From north, on A59 turn right after iron bridge. Turn right again and second right.

Winston House

◆◆◆

4 Nunthorpe Drive, York, North Yorkshire, YO23 1DY
Tel: 01904 653171
Rooms: 2 all ensuite
Pricing: Dbl £23–25 Room facilities: ☐ ☕ ❄
Children: Welcome 10yrs min age ⌐
Parking: Off-street and monitored
Directions: From A64 Leeds to York onto Racecourse Road, onto Scarcroft Road, turn right onto Bishopthorpe road, second right onto Nunthorpe Drive

Barrington House

♟

15, Nunthorpe Avenue, Scarcroft Road, York YO23 1PF
Tel: 01904 634539
Email: alan.bell@btinternet.com
Rooms: 7 all ensuite ☕ ⊗
Room facilities: ☐ ☕ Children: Welcome
Directions: Turn off A64 onto A1036 to city centre. After ½ mile, turn right into Scarcroft Road.

Travelodge York Central (SA)

Travel Accommodation
90 Piccadilly, York, Yorkshire, YO1 9NX
Web: www.travelodge.co.uk
Rooms: 90 all ensuite ⊗
Pricing: Sgl £64.40 Dbl £68.85 CC: Accepted
Room facilities: ☐ ☕ Access: ♿

Northeast

Northwest

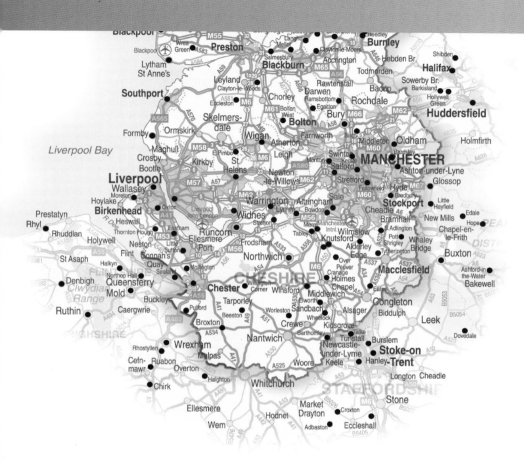

Blackpool · Wrea Green · Langho Heedley · Burnley · Shibden
Blackpool ✈ · Preston · Mellor · Clayton-le-Moors · Hebden Br. · Halifax
Lytham St Anne's · Salmesbury · Accrington · Todmorden · Sowerby Br. · Barkisland
Southport · Leyland · Blackburn · Rawtenstall · Rochdale · Hollywell Green · Huddersfield
Eccleston · Clayton-le-Woods · Chorley · Darwen · Ramsbottom · Bacup · Holmfirth
Skelmers-dale · Bolton West · Bolton · Bury
Formby · Ormskirk · Wigan · Atherton · Farnworth · Middleton · Oldham
Liverpool Bay · Maghull · Leigh · Swinton · MANCHESTER · Glossop
Crosby · Kirkby · St Helens · Newton-le-Willows · Salford · Ashton-under-Lyne
Bootle · Warrington · Stretford · Hyde
Liverpool · Wallasey · Altrincham · Sale · Stockport · New Mills · Edale
Hoylake · Birkenhead · Widnes · Lymm · Bowdon · Cheadle · Bramhall · Hope
Prestatyn · Heswall · Stretton · Mere · Wilmslow · Chapel-en-le-Frith
Rhyl · Rhuddlan · Thornton Hough · Eastham · Runcorn · Knutsford · Alderley Edge · Whaley Bridge · Buxton
Holywell · Neston · Ellesmere Port · Frodsham · Over · Macclesfield · Ashford-in-the-Water
St Asaph · Flint · Connah's Quay · Northwich · Cranage · Holmes · Bakewell
Denbigh · Halkyn · Northop Hall · Sealand · CHESHIRE · Chester · Congleton · Leek · Dovedale
Mold · Buckley · Winsford · Middlewich · Biddulph
Ruthin · Caergwrie · Pulford · Tarporley · Sandbach · Alsager
Broxton · Beeston · Wheelock · Kidsgrove · Burslem
Rhostyllen · Wrexham · Nantwich · Crewe · Barthomley · Talke · Tunstall · Stoke-on-Trent
Cefn-mawr · Ruabon · Malpas · Newcastle-under-Lyme · Hanley
Chirk · Overton · Haughton · Woore · Keele · Longton · Cheadle
Whitchurch · STAFFORDSHIRE · Stone
Ellesmere · Hodnet · Market Drayton · Croxton
Wern · Adbaston · Eccleshall

Glasgow · · Edinburgh
· Newcastle
Belfast ·
Dublin · · Manchester
Birmingham ·
Cardiff · · London

Note:
Dark blue dots
represent the
location of
RAC-inspected
accommodation

Northwest

Northwest

Gold Ribbon Award

Gilpin Lodge Country House, Windermere	★★★	510
Holbeck Ghyll Country House Hotel, Windermere	★★★	511
Miller Howe Hotel, Windermere	★★	514
Sharrow Bay Hotel, Penrith	★★★	482

Blue Ribbon Award

Broadoaks Country House, Windermere	★★	513
Chester Crabwell Manor Hotel, Chester	★★★★	472
Chester Grosvenor, Chester	★★★★★	471
Leeming House - Macdonald Hotel, Ullswater	★★★★	507
Lindeth Fell Country House Hotel, Bowness-on-Windermere	★★	514
Linthwaite House Hotel, Bowness-on-Windermere	★★★	512
Rookery Hall Hotel, Nantwich	★★★	474
Swinside Lodge, Keswick	★	485
The Samling, Windermere	★★★	458

Little Gem

Hazel Bank, Country House, Keswick	♦♦♦♦♦	468
Coniston Lodge Private Hotel, Coniston	♦♦♦♦♦	477
Rowanfield Country Hotel, Ambleside	♦♦♦♦♦	459
The Old Coach House, Blackpool	♦♦♦♦♦	464

Alderley Edge, Cheshire

The Alderley Edge Hotel
★★★★ ☒ ☒ ☒
Macclesfield Road, Alderley Edge, Cheshire, SK9 7BJ
Tel: 01625 583033 Fax: 01625 586343
Email: sales@alderley-edge-hotel.co.uk
Web: www.alderleyedge-hotel.co.uk
Rooms: 52 all ensuite
Pricing: Sgl £45–119.50 Dbl £90–140
Dinner from £25.50 CC: Accepted
Room facilities: ☐ ☎ ☕ ☏ Access: ♿
Conference: 3 meeting rooms (Thtr 90 max), 24hr-
delegate from £145, day-delegate rate from £45
Children: Welcome ☖
Licences: ◁ ♟
Parking: Off-street and monitored
Directions: Located on B5087, just 400 yards from
Alderley Edge village.

Alston, Cumbria

Lowbyer Manor
★★ ☒
Alston, Cumbria, CA9 3JX
Tel: 01434 381230 Fax: 01434 381427
Email: stay@lowbyer.com
Web: www.lowbyer.com
Rooms: 11 all ensuite ☐ ☒
Pricing: Sgl £38–53 Dbl £76–96 Dinner from £18
CC: Accepted Room facilities: ☐ ☕
Conference: 2 meeting rooms (Thtr 30 max), 24hr-
delegate from £90, day-delegate rate from £38
Children: Welcome
Dogs: Welcome
Licences: ♟
Parking: Off-street
Directions: From Junction 40 on M6, join A686. Hotel
in wooded location, out of Alston on A686 towards
Heaham.

Altrincham, Cheshire

Cresta Court
★★★
Church Street, Altrincham, Cheshire, WA14 4DP
Tel: 0161 927 7272 Fax: 0161 929 6548
Email: info@cresta-court.co.uk
Web: www.cresta-court.co.uk
Rooms: 136 all ensuite ☒ ☒ ☒
Pricing: Sgl £68–90 Dbl £78–100 Dinner from £15.95
CC: Accepted
Room facilities: ☐ ☎ ☕ ☏ Access: ♿ ♿
Conference: 7 meeting rooms (Thtr 220 max)
Children: Welcome ☖
Dogs: Welcome
Licences: ◁ ♟
Leisure: Gym, Beauty salon,
Parking: Off-street and monitored
Directions: Situated in Altrincham town centre on A56.
From J19 M6, take A556 towards Manchester. The
hotel is on the right.

Quality Hotel Altrincham
★★★★ ☒ ☒
Langham Road, Bowdon, Altrincham,
Cheshire, WA14 2HT
Tel: 0161 928 7121 Fax: 0161 927 7560
Email: admin@gb064.u-net.com
Web: www.choicehotels.com
Rooms: 91 all ensuite ☒ ☒ ☒
Pricing: Sgl £105.75–135.75 Dbl £131.50–146.50
Dinner from £17.95 CC: Accepted
Room facilities: ☐ ☎ ☕ ☏
Conference: 5 meeting rooms (Thtr 150 max), 24hr-
delegate from £135, day-delegate rate from £34
Children: Welcome ☖
Dogs: Welcome Licences: ◁ ♟
Leisure: Indoor pool, Gym, Health spa, Beauty salon,
Parking: Off-street
Directions: Exit M6 at Junction 19. Follow A556
towards Manchester onto A56. Turn left onto B5161.
Hotel one mile on right.

Ambleside, Cumbria

Ambleside Salutation Hotel
★★★ ☒
Lake Road, Ambleside, Cumbria, LA22 9BX
Tel: 01539 432244 Fax: 01539 434157
Email: enquiries@hotelambleside.uk.com
Web: www.hotelambleside.uk.com
Rooms: 42 all ensuite ☒ ☒
Pricing: Sgl £43–56 Dbl £82–112 Dinner from £20
CC: Accepted
Room facilities: ☐ ☎ ☕ ☏
Conference: 2 meeting rooms (Thtr 60 max), 24hr-
delegate from £74, day-delegate rate from £28
Children: Welcome ☖ ☕
Dogs: Welcome Licences: ♟
Leisure: Gym, Health spa
Parking: Off-street and monitored
Directions: M6 Junction 36, A591 into Ambleside one-
way system. Right lane at traffic lights. Hotel on brow
of hill on left corner.

Langdale Hotel & Country Club
★★★
Langdale Estate, Great Langdale, Ambleside,
Cumbria, LA22 9JD
Tel: 015394 37302 Fax: 015394 37130
Email: info@langdale.co.uk
Web: www.langdale.co.uk
Rooms: 65 all ensuite ☒ ☒
Pricing: Sgl £120–130 Dbl £190–210 Dinner from £20
CC: Accepted
Room facilities: ☐ ☎ ☕
Children: Welcome ☖ Licences: ♟
Leisure: Indoor pool, Gym, Health spa, Beauty salon,
Tennis, Fishing, Games room, Snooker/billiards,
Parking: Off-street
Directions: Leave M6 at Junction 36 and take A591
through Windermere to Ambleside. Turn left onto B593.
At Skelwith Bridge turn right onto B5343, signposted
Langdale.

Rothay Manor

★ ★ ★ ⓡ ⓡ

Rothay Bridge, Ambleside, Cumbria, LA22 0EH
Tel: 01539 433605 Fax: 01539 433607
Email: hotel@rothaymanor.co.uk
Web: www.rothaymanor.co.uk
Seasonal closure: 3 January to 8 February

Enjoy comfortable, relaxed hospitality with excellent
food and wine in beautiful surroundings. Families and
disabled guests welcome. Free use of nearby Leisure
centre, short breaks and specialised holidays available.
Rooms: 17 all ensuite
Pricing: Sgl £75–80 Dbl £120–130 Dinner from £29
CC: Accepted Room facilities: ☐ ☎ ☺ Access: ♿
Conference: 1 meeting room (Thtr 22 max), 24hr-
delegate from £130, day-delegate rate from £38
Children: Welcome ♯ ℃ Licences: ♦♦♦ Parking: Off-street
Directions: Exit J36 M6; follow A591 to Ambleside.
Follow signs to Coniston by turning left at traffic lights,
and again ¼ mile later.

The Samling

★ ★ ★ ⓡ ⓡ ⓡ

Blue Ribbon Winner

Ambleside Road, Windermere, Cumbria, LA23 1LR
Tel: 015394 31922 Fax: 015394 30400
Email: info@thesamling.com
Web: www.@thesamling.com

The Samling has superb views overlooking Lake
Windermere and ten spacious guest suites. The
experience is the perfect prescription for relaxation
combined with privacy and pure indulgence.
Rooms: 10 all ensuite ♿
Pricing: Dinner from £40 CC: Accepted
Room facilities: ☐ ☎ Children: Welcome ♯ ℃
Dogs: Guide dogs only Licences: ⚐ ♦♦♦
Parking: Off-street and monitored
Directions: A591 to Windemere, then on towards
Ambleside. Hotel is in a drive on the right.

Queens Hotel

★ ★

Market Place, Ambleside, Cumbria, LA22 9BU
Tel: 01539 432206 Fax: 01539 432721
Email: queenshotel.ambleside@btinternet.com
Web: www.smoothhound.co.uk/hotels/quecum
Rooms: 26 all ensuite ♿ ☐
Pricing: Sgl £30–41 Dbl £60–82 CC: Accepted
Room facilities: ☐ ☎ ☺
Children: Welcome ♯ ℃ Licences: ♦♦♦
Leisure: Games room, Parking: Off-street
Directions: From south, leave M6 at Junction 36. Take
A591 to Windermere and Ambleside. The hotel is in the
town centre.

The Waterhead Hotel

★ ★ ★ ⓡ

Lake Road, Ambleside, Cumbria, LA22 0ER
Tel: 015394 32566 Fax: 015394 31255
Email: waterhead@elhmail.co.uk
Web: www.elh.co.uk
Rooms: 27 all ensuite ♿ ♿
Pricing: Sgl £45 Dbl £90 Dinner from £10.95
CC: Accepted Room facilities: ☐ ☎ ☺
Access: ♿
Conference: 2 meeting rooms (Thtr 35 max), 24hr-
delegate from £88.12, day-delegate rate from £25
Children: Welcome ♯ ℃
Dogs: Welcome Licences: ♦♦♦
Parking: Off-street and monitored
Directions: From north J40 M6, from south J36; A591
to Windemere, then to Ambleside. Hotel at Waterhead
Bay opposite pier.
See advert on this page

Rowanfield Country House
Little Gem

◆ ◆ ◆ ◆ ◆

Kirkstone Road, Ambleside, Cumbria, LA22 9ET
Tel: 01539 433686 Fax: 01539 431569
Email: email@rowanfield.com
Web: www.rowanfield.com
Seasonal closure: January to February

Idyllic, quiet countryside setting with breathtaking lake and mountain views. Superb central Lakeland location. Beautiful period house decorated in Laura Ashley style. Award-winning breakfasts, excellent restaurants locally. Non-smoking.
Rooms: 8 all ensuite ⊗
Pricing: Dbl £67–100 CC: Accepted
Room facilities: ▢ ☕
Children: Welcome 8yrs min age Parking: Off-street
Directions: Exit A591 north of Ambleside at Button roundabout, signposted Kirkstone 3 miles. Rowanfield is ³/₄ mile on the right.

Elder Grove

◆ ◆ ◆ ◆

Lake Road, Ambleside, Cumbria, LA22 0DB
Tel: 01539 432504 Fax: 01539 432251
Email: info@eldergrove.co.uk
Web: www.eldergrove.co.uk
Seasonal closure: Christmas
Rooms: 10 all ensuite ▨ ⊗
Pricing: Sgl £25.50–33 Dbl £51–69 CC: Accepted
Room facilities: ▢ ☕
Children: Welcome ⼓ ⽤ Dogs: Welcome
Licences: ⼭⼭⼭ Parking: Off-street
Directions: On the south of Ambleside, A591/Lake Road, opposite BP petrol station at the start/end of the one-way system.

Meadowbank

◆ ◆ ◆

Rydal Road, Ambleside, Cumbria, LA22 9BA
Tel: 015394 32710
Email: enquires@meadowbank.org.uk
Web: meadowbank.org.uk
Rooms: 7 (5 ensuite) ⊗
Pricing: Sgl £20–32 Dbl £40–64 CC: Accepted
Room facilities: ▢ ☕ Children: Welcome ⼓
Dogs: Welcome Parking: Off-street
Directions: On A591 last house on left on northern edge of Ambleside.

Appleby-in-Westmorland, Cumbria

Appleby Manor Country House Hotel

★ ★ ★ ℞ ℞

Roman Road, Appleby-in-Westmorland,
Cumbria, CA16 6JB
Tel: 01768 351571 Fax: 01768 352888
Email: reception@applebymanor.co.uk
Web: www.applebymanor.co.uk

Relaxing and friendly country house hotel with magnificent views over the Eden valley. Enjoy great food and leisurely days in our leisure centre or stride out on the Lakeland fells.
Rooms: 30 all ensuite ⊗ ▨ ⊗
Pricing: Sgl £75–83 Dbl £110–146
Dinner from £17
CC: Accepted
Room facilities: ▢ ☎ ☕ ⚒
Access: ♿
Conference: 3 meeting rooms (Thtr 25 max), 24hr-delegate from £119, day-delegate rate from £38.50
Children: Welcome ⼓ ⽤
Dogs: Welcome Licences: ⼭⼭⼭
Leisure: Indoor pool, Games room, Snooker/billiards
Parking: Off-street and monitored
Directions: Situated half a mile from the town centre on the hill towards A66, Appleby Manor overlooks the castle.

Northwest

Royal Oak Inn

★★

45 Bondgate, Appleby-in-Westmorland,
Cumbria, CA16 6UN
Tel: 01768 351463 Fax: 01768 352300
Email: royaloakinn@mortalmaninns.fsnet.co.uk
Web: www.mortal-man-inns.co.uk/royaloak

A lovely genuine old inn, the Royal Oak in Appleby stands out for its good food and drink, and above all its atmosphere.
Rooms: 9 (7 ensuite)
Pricing: Sgl £39 Dbl £78–90 Dinner from £7.95
CC: Accepted
Room facilities:
Children: Welcome Dogs: Welcome
Licences:
Parking: Off-street
Directions: From south follow B6260 through Appleby turn right at river follow B6542 for 2 miles, from A66 north follow B6542 for 1 mile.

Old Hall Farmhouse

♦♦♦♦

Bongate, Appleby-In-Westmorland,
Cumbria, CA16 6HW
Tel: 017683 51773/ 0800 035 0422 Fax: 017683 51773
Email: old.hall.farmhouse@lineone.net
Web: www.oldhallfarmhouses.co.uk
Rooms: 3 all ensuite
Pricing: Sgl £29 Dbl £48 Room facilities:
Dogs: Guide dogs only
Parking: Off-street
Directions: 200 yds east of Royal Oak Hotel on B6542 at top of hill.

Courtfield Hotel

♦♦♦

Bongate, Appleby-in-Westmorland,
Cumbria, CA16 6UP
Tel: 017683 51394 Fax: 017683 51394
Rooms: 11 (4 ensuite)
Pricing: Dinner from £15.50
Room facilities: Dogs: Welcome
Parking: Monitored
Directions: You will find the Courtfield Hotel a real home-from-home. Set in 3 acres of lawns and gardens, a relaxing place to stay, and ideal for those wishing to enjoy the Eden valley and explore the Lake District.

Ashton-under-Lyne, Lancashire

York House Hotel

★★

York Place, Ashton-under-Lyne, Lancashire, OL6 7TT
Tel: 0161 330 5899 Fax: 0161 343 1613
Email: enquiries@yorkhouse-hotel.co.uk
Web: www.yorkhouse-hotel.co.uk
Seasonal closure: Boxing day
Rooms: 34 all ensuite
Pricing: Sgl £52–65 Dbl £80 Dinner from £16
CC: Accepted
Room facilities: Access:
Conference: 3 meeting rooms (Thtr 50 max), 24hr-delegate from £82, day-delegate rate from £22
Children: Welcome
Dogs: Welcome Licences:
Parking: Off-street and monitored
Directions: The hotel is situated 2 mins drive from the motorway network, 15 mins from Manchester Airport, and a short distance from Manchester city centre.

Welbeck House Hotel

♦♦♦

324 Katharine Street, Ashton-under-Lyne,
Lancashire, OL6 7BD
Tel: 0161 344 0751 Fax: 0161 343 4278
Email: welbeck5000@breathemail.net
Web: www.smoothhound.co.uk/hotels/welbeck.html
Rooms: 8 all ensuite
Pricing: Sgl £35 Dbl £48 Dinner from £8 CC: Accepted
Room facilities:
Access: Children: Welcome
Dogs: Welcome Licences:
Leisure: Games room, Snooker/billiards,
Parking: Off-street and monitored
Directions: Junction 23 on M60 to Ashton-under-Lyne.

Barrow-in-Furness, Cumbria

Abbey House Hotel

★★★

Abbey Road, Barrow-in-Furness, Cumbria, LA13 0PA
Tel: 01229 838282 Fax: 01229 820403
Email: enquiries@abbeyhousehotel.com
Web: www.abbeyhousehotel.com
Rooms: 57 all ensuite
Pricing: Sgl £70–106 Dbl £80–130 CC: Accepted
Room facilities:
Access:
Conference: 5 meeting rooms (Thtr 300 max), 24hr-delegate from £105, day-delegate rate from £27.50
Children: Welcome
Dogs: Welcome Licences:
Parking: Off-street and monitored

King Alfred Hotel

Ocean Road, Walney Island, Barrow-in-Furness,
Cumbria, LA14 3DU
Tel: 01229 474717 Fax: 01229 474717

Bassenthwaite, Cumbria

Lakeside Guest House

◆ ◆ ◆ ◆

Dubwath, Bassenthwaite, Cumbria, CA13 9YD
Tel: 01768 776358 Fax: 01768 776163

Rooms: 8 (7 ensuite) 🐾 🚭
Room facilities: 🖵 🍵
Children: Welcome �🏮
Dogs: Guide dogs only
Licences: ⛏⛏⛏
Parking: Off-street and monitored
Directions: From J-40 M6, take A66 west to the
northern end of Bassenthwaite lake. 400m after dual
carriageway turn right at the sign to Castle Inn. Hotel
400m on left.

Beeston, Cheshire

The Wild Boar Hotel & Restaurant

★ ★ ★ ★ ☕ ☕

Whitchurch Road, Beeston, near Tarporley,
Cheshire, CW6 9NW
Tel: 01829 260309 Fax: 01829 261081

Birkenhead, Merseyside

Leasowe Castle Hotel

★ ★ ★

Leasowe Road, Moreton, Wirral, Merseyside, CH46 3RF
Tel: 0151 606 9191 Fax: 0151 678 5551
Email: reservations@leasowecastle.com
Web: www.leasowecastle.com

Built in 1593 and set in 5 acres of grounds. Many
bedrooms have sea views. Hotel has good quality
resturant and public bar. Leisure club planned to open
early 2003.
Rooms: 50 all ensuite 🖨
Pricing: Sgl £70–85 Dbl £80–100 Dinner from £19.50
CC: Accepted
Room facilities: 🖵 ☎ 🍵
Access: ⛏⛏ ♿
Conference: 6 meeting rooms (Thtr 400 max), 24hr-
delegate from £120, day-delegate rate from £35
Children: Welcome �🏮
Dogs: Guide dogs only
Licences: 🔷 ⛏⛏⛏
Parking: Off-street and monitored
Directions: Junction 1 M53 follow Moreton signs (Max
Spielmann Photography on right) take next left onto
dual carriageway. Hotel 1 mile on right.

Birtley, Co.Durham

Travelodge Washington (MOTO) North

Travel Accommodation
A1(M) Moto Service Area, Portobello, Birtley, Co.
Durham, DH3 2SJ
Web: www.travelodge.co.uk
Rooms: 31 all ensuite 🚭
Pricing: Sgl £49.40 Dbl £53.85 CC: Accepted
Room facilities: 🖵 🍵 Access: ♿

Travelodge Washington (MOTO) South

Travel Accommodation
A1(M) Moto Service Area, Portobello, Birtley,
Co. Durham, DH3 2SJ
Web: www.travelodge.co.uk
Rooms: 36 all ensuite 🚭
Pricing: Sgl £49.40 Dbl £53.85 CC: Accepted
Room facilities: 🖵 🍵 Access: ♿

Blackburn, Lancashire

Clarion Hotel & Suites Foxfields, Blackburn

★★★★

Whalley Road, Billington, Clitheroe,
Lancashire, BB7 9HY
Tel: 01254 822556 Fax: 01254 824613
Email: admin@gb065.u-net.com
Web: www.choicehotels.com
Rooms: 44 all ensuite 🛏 🚭
Pricing: Sgl £94–110 Dbl £110–125 Dinner from £19.50
CC: Accepted Room facilities: 🖵 ☎ 🍵 🐾 Access: ♿
Conference: 5 meeting rooms (Thtr 150 max), 24hr-delegate from £120, day-delegate rate from £35
Children: Welcome ⌖ ⅔𝄐 Dogs: Welcome
Licences: ⚓ ♦♦♦
Leisure: Indoor pool, Gym, Parking: Off-street
Directions: M6 Junction 31, follow signs to Blackburn (A677). Take A59 to Clitheroe. Straight over next roundabout, through traffic lights, second exit next roundabout, hotel ½ mile on right.

Dunkenhalgh Hotel

★★★★

Blackburn Road, Clayton-le-Moors, Accrington,
near Blackburn, Lancashire, BB5 5JP
Tel: 01254 398021 Fax: 01254 872230
Email: dunkenhalgh@macdonald-hotels.co.uk
Web: www.macdonald-hotels.co.uk
Rooms: 122 all ensuite 🚲 🛏 🚭
Pricing: Dinner from £15.50 CC: Accepted
Room facilities: 🖵 ☎ 🍵 Access: ⦀ ♿
Children: Welcome ⌖ Dogs: Guide dogs only
Licences: ⚓ ♦♦♦ Leisure: Indoor pool, Gym, Health spa, Beauty salon Parking: Off-street and monitored
Directions: Leave M6 at Junction 29, onto M65 towards Blackburn. Exit Junction 7, turn left at mini-roundabout, left at lights, and left into hotel drive.

Mytton Fold Hotel & Golf Complex

★★★

Langho, near Blackburn,
Lancashire, BB6 8AB
Tel: 01254 240662 Fax: 01254 248119
Email: enquiries@myttonfold.co.uk
Web: www.myttonfoldhotel.co.uk
Rooms: 28 all ensuite 🚲 🛏 🚭
Pricing: Dinner from £11 (2002 rate) CC: Accepted
Room facilities: 🖵 ☎ 🍵 🐾 Access: ♿
Children: Welcome Licences: ⚓ ♦♦♦
Leisure: Golf, Games room Parking: Off-street
Directions: Leave the M6 at Junction 31. Follow A59 signposted Whalley and Clitheroe for 10 miles. At second roundabout follow Whalley sign (minor road). Gateway is about 500 yards on right.

Millstone Hotel

★★

Church Lane, Mellor, Blackburn, Lancashire, BB2 7JR
Tel: 01254 813333 Fax: 01254 812628
Email: millstone@shirehotels.co.uk
Web: www.shirehotels.co.uk
Rooms: 24 all ensuite 🚲 🚭
Pricing: Sgl £98 Dbl £156 Dinner from £11.95
CC: Accepted Room facilities: 🖵 ☎ 🍵 🐾 Access: ♿
Conference: 1 meeting room (Thtr 20 max)
Children: Welcome ⌖ ⅔𝄐 Dogs: Guide dogs only
Licences: ♦♦♦ Parking: Off-street
Directions: Exit J31 M6. Follow A59 towards Clitheroe. Turn right at Mellor sign, then take 2nd left at roundabout up Mellor Lane.

Travelodge Blackburn

Travel Accommodation
M65
Web: www.travelodge.co.uk
Room facilities: 🖵 🍵

Blackpool, Lancashire

Imperial Hotel

★★★★

North Promenade, Blackpool, Lancashire, FY1 2HB
Tel: 01253 623971 Fax: 01253 751784
Email: imperial-blackpool@paramount-hotels.co.uk
Web: www.paramount-hotels.co.uk

PARAMOUNT
GROUP OF HOTELS

Rooms: 181 all ensuite 🚲 🚭
Pricing: Sgl £120 Dbl £175 Dinner from £20.50
CC: Accepted Room facilities: 🖵 ☎ 🍵 🐾
Access: ⦀ ♿
Conference: 13 meeting rooms (Thtr 600 max), 24hr-delegate from £160, day-delegate rate from £43
Children: Welcome ⌖
Dogs: Welcome Licences: ⚓ ♦♦♦
Leisure: Indoor pool, Gym, Health spa, Beauty salon

Parking: Off-street and monitored
Directions: Exit J4 M55, take A583 North Shore, follow signs to North Promanade. The hotel is on the seafront, north of the tower.

Manor House Hotel

★★★

Ribby Hall Village, Ribby Road, Wrea Green, near Blackpool, Lancashire, PR4 2PR
Tel: 01772 688000 Fax: 01772 688036
Email: themanorhousehotel@ribbyhall.co.uk
Web: www.mhhotel.co.uk

29 sumptous one and two bedroom suites in an imposing setting, in the heart of the Fylde countryside. Extensive sport, leisure and entertainment facilities all at walking distance within village.
Rooms: 29 all ensuite 🍴 🚭
Pricing: Dinner from £15.95 CC: Accepted
Room facilities: 📺 ☎ 🍵 🔌
Access: ↕ ♿
Children: Welcome 🍴
Dogs: Guide dogs only Licences: ◈ ♟
Leisure: Indoor pool, Gym, Health spa, Beauty salon, Tennis, Golf, Fishing, Riding, Games room, Snooker/billiards
Parking: Off-street and monitored
Directions: 2 miles from J3 M55. Follow signs to Wrea Green on A585. Cross the A583, and Ribby is 200 yards on the left.

Brabyns Hotel

★★

Shaftesbury Avenue, North Shore, Blackpool, Lancashire, FY2 9QQ
Tel: 01253 354263 Fax: 01253 352915
Web: www.brabyns-hotel.co.uk
Rooms: 22 all ensuite
Pricing: Sgl £30–45 Dbl £60–80 Dinner from £12.50
CC: Accepted
Room facilities: 📺 ☎ 🍵
Dogs: Welcome Licences: ♟
Parking: Off-street
Directions: M55 at Junction 4, Preston New Road to box junction. Turn right into Whitegate Drive, then onto Devonshire Road. Third left after island. Hotel on left.

Chequers Hotel

★★

24 Queens, Blackpool, Lancashire, FY2 9RN
Tel: 01253 356431 Fax: 01253 500076

Gables Balmoral Hotel

★★

Balmoral Road, Blackpool, Lancashire, FY4 1HR
Tel: 01253 345432 Fax: 01253 406058
Web: www.gables-balmoral.co.uk
Rooms: 60 all ensuite 🍴 🚭 Room facilities: 📺 ☎ 🍵
Access: ↕ Conference: 1 meeting room (Thtr 50 max)
Children: Welcome Dogs: Welcome Licences: ♟
Leisure: Indoor pool, Games room
Directions: Follow signs off M55 for Blackpool pleasure beach: hotel is directly opposite the Sandcastle Grosvenor Casino and main entrance to the Pleasure beach.
See advert on this page

Northwest

Headlands

★★

611–613 New South Promenade, Blackpool,
Lancashire, FY4 1NJ
Tel: 01253 341179 Fax: 01253 342047
Email: headlands@blackpool.net
Web: www.theheadlands.blackpool.net
Seasonal closure: 2–16 January
Rooms: 42 all ensuite
Pricing: Dinner from £14.50 CC: Accepted
Room facilities: Access:
Children: Welcome Dogs: Welcome
Licences: Leisure: Snooker/billiards
Parking: Off-street and monitored
Directions: Take M6 to M55, turn left at first
roundabout, right at second roundabout (to
Promenade), turn right at Promenade. The Headlands
is half a mile along Promenade.

Revill's Hotel

★★

190–194 North Promenade, Blackpool,
Lancashire, FY1 1RJ
Tel: 01253 625768 Fax: 01253 624736
Email: revillshotel@blackpool.net
Web: www.blackpool.net/www/revills
Rooms: 45 all ensuite
Pricing: Sgl £20–35 Dbl £40–70 Dinner from £8.50
CC: Accepted
Room facilities:
Access: Children: Welcome
Dogs: Guide dogs only
Licences:
Leisure: Snooker/billiards Parking: Off-street
Directions: 3 minutes' walk along north promenade,
northwards from Blackpool Tower. Almost opposite
north pier.

Stretton Hotel

★★

206–214 North Promenade, Blackpool,
Lancashire, FY1 1RU
Tel: 01253 625688 Fax: 01253 752534
Email: strettonhotel@btconnect.com
Web: www.strettonhotel.co.uk
Rooms: 50 all ensuite
Pricing: Dinner from £7.95 CC: Accepted
Room facilities:
Access:
Children: Welcome Dogs: Welcome
Licences:
Parking: Off-street
Directions: Take the M55 into Blackpool. Turn right
onto promenade. Hotel is 100m past north pier.

Plan your route

Visit www.rac.co.uk for RAC's
interactive route planner, including
up to the minute traffic reports.

Warwick

★★

603 New South Promenade, Blackpool,
Lancashire, FY4 1NG
Tel: 01253 342192 Fax: 01253 405776
Seasonal closure: January
Rooms: 51 all ensuite
Pricing: Sgl £25–37 Dbl £50–74 Dinner from £12.50
CC: Accepted Room facilities: Access:
Conference: 2 meeting rooms (Thtr 35 max)
Children: Welcome Dogs: Welcome Licences:
Leisure: Indoor pool Parking: Off-street
Directions: From the end of the M55 follow the A5230
to South Shore. Turn right at promenade. Hotel is ½ a
mile on right.

The Old Coach House   Little Gem

♦♦♦♦♦

50 Dean Street, Blackpool, Lancashire, FY4 1BP
Tel: 01253 349195 Fax: 01253 344330
Email: blackpool@theoldcoachhouse.freeserve.co.uk
Web: www.theoldcoachhouse.freeserve.co.uk

Rooms: 11 all ensuite
Pricing: Sgl £50–70 Dbl £40–90 Dinner from £19.95
CC: Accepted Room facilities:
Access: Children: Welcome
Licences: Leisure: Health spa
Parking: Off-street
Directions: M6 Junction 32, M55 to large roundabout.
Straight over, take next right, left at lights, left at next
lights, second right before car showroom, hotel on right.

Sunray

♦♦♦♦

42 Knowle Avenue, North Shore, Blackpool,
Lancashire, FY2 9TQ
Tel: 01253 351937 Fax: 01253 593307
Email: sun.ray@cwcom.net
Web: sunray_hotel@yahoo.co.uk
Seasonal closure: December to March
Rooms: 9 all ensuite
Pricing: Sgl £24–30 Dbl £48–60 Dinner from £13
CC: Accepted
Room facilities: Children: Welcome
Dogs: Welcome Parking: Off-street
Directions: 1¾ miles north of Tower along Promenade.
Turn right at Uncle Tom's Cabin. Sunray is 300 yards
on left.

The Windsor Hotel

◆◆◆◆

21 King Edward Ave, North Shore, Blackpool,
Lancashire, FY2 9TA
Tel: 01253 353735 Fax: 01253 353546
Rooms: 9 all ensuite 🍴 🚭
Pricing: Sgl £20–22 Dbl £40–44 Dinner from £7.50
CC: Accepted
Room facilities: 🖥 ☎ 🍵 Children: Welcome ⍩
Dogs: Welcome Licences: 👫👫
Parking: Off-street and monitored
Directions: About 200 yds off the Queens Promenade,
take the second turning right by the Cliffs hotel into
King Edward Avenue.

Beaucliffe Hotel

◆◆◆

20–22 Holmfield Road, North Shore, Blackpool,
Lancashire, FY2 9TB
Tel: 01253 351663
Email: don.siddall@talk21.com
Web: members.netscapeonline.co.uk/beaucliffe
Rooms: 13 all ensuite 🍴 Pricing: Sgl £22–40
Dbl £40–65 Dinner from £7 Room facilities: 🖥 🍵
Access: ♿ Children: Welcome ⍩ Dogs: Welcome
Licences: 👫👫 Parking: Off-street
Directions: Proceed north along promenade to Gynn
square roundabout onto Queen's promenade, 3rd on
the right King Edward Avenue, 50 yards on right hand
corner King Edward Ave/Holmfield Road.

Hotel Pilatus

◆◆◆

10 Willshaw Road, Gynn Square, North Shore,
Blackpool, Lancashire, FY2 9SH
Tel: 01253 352470 Fax: 01253 352470
Email: cynthia@pilatushotel.co.uk
Web: www.pilatus.co.uk
Seasonal closure: Dec-Jan closed

Small licenced private hotel overlooking the sea and
Gynn gardens. Close to all the entertainment venues
Blackpool has to offer yet far enough away to ensure a
quiet relayed stay.
Rooms: 9 all ensuite 🚭
Pricing: Sgl £24–26 Dbl £38–42 Dinner from £6
CC: Accepted Room facilities: 🖥 🍵

Children: Welcome ⍩ Dogs: Guide dogs only
Licences: 👫👫 Parking: Off-street and monitored
Directions: From Blackpool Tower Promenade travel
past North Pier to Gynn gardens roundabout. Turn
opposite Savoy hotel, Pilatus fourth hotel down.

Knowlsley Hotel

◆◆◆

68 Dean Street, Blackpool, Lancashire, FY4 1BP
Tel: 01253 343414
Rooms: 11 all ensuite Room facilities: 🖥 ☎ 🍵
Children: Welcome ⍩ Licences: 👫👫
Parking: Off-street
Directions: Dean Street is situated opposite South Pier.
Knowlsley is 400 metres ahead on the left.

Langwood Hotel

◆◆◆

250 Queens Promenade, Bispham, Blackpool,
Lancashire, FY2 9HA
Tel: 01253 351370
Seasonal closure: January to March
Rooms: 24 all ensuite 🍴
Pricing: Sgl £25–30 Dbl £50–60 Dinner from £10
Room facilities: ☎ 🍵 Access: 🛗 Children: Welcome ⍩
Dogs: Guide dogs only Licences: 🦢 Parking: Off-street

Maxime Hotel

◆◆◆

416-418 North Promenade, Gynn Square, Blackpool,
Lancashire, FY1 2LB
Tel: 01253 351215 Fax: 01253 354670
Email: maxime@amserve.net
Web: www.blackpooltourism.com
Seasonal closure: Jan/Feb

Rooms: 30 all ensuite 🍴
Pricing: Sgl £19.65–36.50 Dbl £39.28–73
Dinner from £15 CC: Accepted Room facilities: 🖥 ☎ 🍵
Access: 🛗 Children: Welcome ⍩
Dogs: Guide dogs only Licences: 👫👫
Leisure: Indoor pool, Health spa
Directions: At M55 roundabout follow sign to north
shore then to Gynn Square roundabout.

Northwest

Sunny Cliff Hotel

♦ ♦ ♦

98 Queens Promenade, Blackpool, Lancashire, FY2 9NS
Tel: 01253 351155
Seasonal closure: November to March
Rooms: 9 all ensuite ⊗
Pricing: Sgl £22–24 Dbl £44–48 Dinner from £8
Room facilities: ▢ ☕ Children: Welcome
Dogs: Guide dogs only Licences: ⦙⦙⦙
Parking: Off-street
Directions: 1½ miles from North Pier on A584, towards Bispham.

The Kelvin Private

♦ ♦ ♦

98 Reads Avenue, Blackpool, Lancashire, FY1 4JJ
Tel: 01253 620293 Fax: 01253 620293

Villa Private Hotel

♦ ♦ ♦

9-11 Withnell Road, Blackpool, Lancashire, FY4 1HF
Tel: 01253 343314

Westdean Hotel

♦ ♦ ♦

59 Dean Street, Blackpool, Lancashire, FY4 1BP
Tel: 01253 342904 Fax: 01253 342926
Email: mikeball@westdeanhotel.freeserve.co.uk
Web: www.westdeanhotel.freeserve.com
Rooms: 11 all ensuite 🛏 Pricing: Sgl £21–27
Dbl £42–54 CC: Accepted Room facilities: ▢ ☕
Children: Welcome ⦙ Licences: ⦙⦙⦙ Leisure: Games
room, Snooker/billiards Parking: Off-street
Directions: Along Promenade from Pleasure Beach
towards Blackpool Tower. Take first right after South Pier.

Wilmar

♦ ♦ ♦

42 Osborne Road, Blackpool, Lancashire, FY4 1HQ
Tel: 01253 346229
Rooms: 7 all ensuite
Pricing: Sgl £23–28 Dbl £46–56 Dinner from £5.50
Room facilities: ▢ ☕ Children: Welcome 5yrs min age
Directions: On Promenade, pass South Pier towards
Pleasure Beach. Turn left immediately after pedestrian
lights. Wilmar is approximately 150m on left.

Bolton by Bowland, Lancashire

Middle Flass Lodge

♦ ♦ ♦ ♦

Settle Road, Bolton by Bowland, Clitheroe,
Lancashire, BB7 4NY
Tel: 01200 447259 Fax: 01200 447300
Email: info@middleflasslodge.fsnet.co.uk
Web: www.middleflasslodge.co.uk

Tasteful barn conversion, unrivalled views across
countryside in Forest of Bowland, peaceful location.
Always personal and professional attention. Chef
prepared cuisine in restaurant, table licence. Lounge
with store. Gardens.
Rooms: 7 all ensuite 🛏 ⊗
Pricing: Sgl £36–40 Dbl £48–64 Dinner from £21.50
CC: Accepted Room facilities: ▢ ☕
Children: Welcome ⦙ Licences: ⦙⦙⦙ Parking: Off-street
Directions: A59 Skipton–Clitheroe by-pass turn for
Sawley, follow sign Bolton-by-Bowland. At Copynook
2nd left signed H.F.L. 2 miles right.

Bolton, Greater Manchester

Egerton House Hotel

★ ★ ★ 🛏 🛏

Blackburn Road, Egerton, Bolton, Manchester, BL7 9PL
Tel: 01204 307171 Fax: 01204 593030
Email: egerton@macdonald-hotels.co.uk
Web: www.macdonaldhotels.co.uk
Rooms: 32 all ensuite 🛏 ⊗ Pricing: Sgl £61–81
Dbl £65–85 Dinner from £20 CC: Accepted
Room facilities: ▢ ☎ ☕ Access: ♿
Conference: 4 meeting rooms (Thtr 150 max), 24hr-
delegate from £120, day-delegate rate from £35
Children: Welcome ⦙ Dogs: Welcome Licences: ⚜
Parking: Off-street
Directions: From North exit J29 onto M6, then onto
M65. Exit J4 onto A666, through Darwen to Egerton.
From South exit J3 on M61, onto A666. Egerton House
is 3 miles north of town centre.

Travelodge Bolton West

Travel Accommodation
M61, Bolton, BL6 5UZ
Web: www.travelodge.co.uk
Rooms: 32 all ensuite ⊗ Pricing: Sgl £49.40
Dbl £53.85 CC: Accepted Room facilities: ▢ ☕
Access: ♿

Mobile traffic information

Just dial 1740* from any mobile
phone to get up-to-the-minute
RAC traffic information on
motorways and major A roads.
Try it now! *Calls to 1740 cost up to 59p
per minute. Check with your network.

Borrowdale, Cumbria

Borrowdale Gates Country House Hotel

★★★★ ⍨ ⍨

Grange-in-Borrowdale, Keswick, Cumbria, CA12 5UQ
Tel: 01768 777204 Fax: 01768 777254
Email: hotel@borrowdale-gates.com
Web: www.borrowdale-gates.com
Seasonal closure: January

Delightful and charming lakeland house, nestling in peaceful wooded gardens amid the breathtaking scenery of the Borrowdale valley. Charming and unpretentious hotel with fine food and service. Hotel proprietor-managed.
Rooms: 29 all ensuite
Pricing: Sgl £47.50–70
Dbl £90–130 Dinner from £32.50 CC: Accepted
Room facilities: ▢ ☎ ◴
Access: ♿
Children: Welcome ⍤ ☕
Licences: ⍨⍨⍨
Parking: Off-street and monitored
Directions: From Keswick follow B5289 to Grange. Turn right over the double hump-backed bridge into Grange village. Hotel is through village on right.

Borrowdale Hotel

★★★★ ⍨ ⍨

Borrowdale Road, Borrowdale, Keswick,
Cumbria, CA12 5UV
Tel: 01768 777224 Fax: 01768 777338
Email: theborrowdalehotel@yahoo.com
Rooms: 33 all ensuite ⍨ ⍨
Pricing: Dinner from £22.25 (2002 rate)
CC: Accepted
Room facilities: ▢ ☎ ◴ ☏
Children: Welcome ⍤ ☕
Dogs: Welcome
Licences: ⍨⍨⍨
Parking: Off-street
Directions: 3 miles from the market town of Keswick at the head of Lake Derwent Water.

The Leathes Head

★★★★ ⍨

Borrowdale, Keswick, Cumbria, CA12 5UY
Tel: 017687 77247 Fax: 017687 77363
Email: email@leatheshead.co.uk
Web: www.leatheshead.co.uk

Set in three acres of grounds in the beautiful Borrowdale Valley. Award-winning cuisine, tranquil surroundings and stunning views. A small, welcoming hotel offering high quality service and accommodation.
Rooms: 11 all ensuite ⊗
Pricing: Sgl £39.95–54.95 Dbl £69.90–109.90
Dinner from £21.50 CC: Accepted
Room facilities: ▢ ☎ ◴ Access: ♿
Children: Welcome 7yrs min age ⍤
Dogs: Guide dogs only Licences: ⍨⍨⍨
Parking: Off-street
Directions: Follow the B5289 Borrowdale road out of Keswick for 3³/₄ miles; we are on the left after the Borrowdale Hotel.

Scafell Hotel

★★★ ⍨

Rosthwaite, Borrowdale, Cumbria, CA12 5XB
Tel: 01768 777208 Fax: 01768 777280
Email: info@scafell.co.uk
Web: www.scafell.co.uk
Rooms: 24 all ensuite
Pricing: Sgl £26.25–43.50 Dbl £52.50–89
Dinner from £23 CC: Accepted
Room facilities: ▢ ☎ ◴ Access: ♿
Children: Welcome ⍤ ☕ Dogs: Welcome
Licences: ⍉ ⍨⍨⍨
Parking: Off-street
Directions: 6¹/₂ miles south of Keswick on B5289
See advert on following page

Northwest

Scafell Hotel

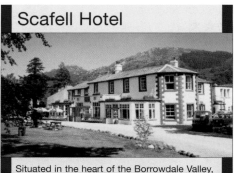

Situated in the heart of the Borrowdale Valley, the Scafell Hotel was formerly a coaching inn frequented by travellers making the journey over Honister Pass from Keswick to Cockermouth. Tastefully modernised with 24 ensuite bedrooms, it still retains its old charm and character. The restaurant (open to non-residents) is renowned for its fine food and wines; 5-course table d'hôte & Late Supper menu. Fully licensed, with Cocktail and Riverside Bar selling real ale, both well noted for bar lunches.

Rosthwaite, Borrowdale,
Cumbria CA12 5XB

Tel: 01768 777208   Fax: 01768 777280
Email: info@scafell.co.uk
Website: www.scafell.co.uk

Hazel Bank Country House   Little Gem

◆◆◆◆◆ ☙ ☙ ✲ ☙
Rosthwaite, Borrowdale, Keswick, Cumbria, CA12 5XB
Tel: 017687 77248 Fax: 017687 77373
Email: enquires@hazelbankhotel.co.uk
Web: www.hazelbankhotel.co.uk
Seasonal closure: Christmas

Award-winning Hazel Bank stands in 4-acre grounds amid the Lakeland peaks. Luxuriously appointed ensuite bedrooms, award-winning food and excellent wines. Attentive service and warm hospitality ensures guests return year after year.
Rooms: 8 all ensuite ▨ ⊛
Pricing: Sgl £52.50–77.50 Dbl £105–155

Dinner from £22.95 CC: Accepted
Room facilities: ▢ ☕
Children: Welcome 10yrs min age
Dogs: Guide dogs only
Licences: ♦♦♦
Parking: Off-street and monitored
Directions: From Keswick follow B5289 signposted Borrowdale for 6 miles to Rosthwaite. On approaching village turn left over humped-back bridge.

Greenbank Country House Hotel

◆◆◆◆ ✲ ☙ ☙
Borrowdale, Keswick, Cumbria, CA12 5UY
Tel: 01768 777215
Email: jeanwwood@lineone.net
Web: www.greenbankcountryhousehotel.co.uk
Seasonal closure: Christmas and January

Small friendly hotel with log fires and excellent cuisine set in glorious scenic countryside. The perfect setting for a peaceful holiday with excellent walking adjacent. Also 2 self-catering cottages.
Rooms: 10 all ensuite ☙ ⊛
Pricing: Sgl £30–35 Dbl £60–70 Dinner from £17
CC: Accepted Room facilities: ☕
Children: Welcome 2yrs min age
Licences: ♦♦♦ Parking: Off-street
Directions: Take A66 to Keswick. Follow signs to Borrowdale on B5289 for approximately 3½ miles.

Brampton, Cumbria

Bush Nook Guest House

◆◆◆◆ ☙ ✲
Upper Denton, Gilsland, Brampton, Cumbria, CA8 7AF
Tel: 01697 747194 Fax: 01697 747790
Email: info@bushnook.co.uk
Web: www.bushnook.co.uk
Rooms: 4 (2 ensuite)
Pricing: Sgl £20–26 Dbl £46–52 Dinner from £12.50
CC: Accepted
Room facilities: ▢ ☕
Children: Welcome
Dogs: Welcome
Licences: ♦♦♦
Parking: Off-street
Directions: Easy access from A1 or M6. Half mile off A69 between Brampton and Haltwhistle, signposted Birdoswald, Spadeadam and Bush Nook.

Broxton, Cheshire

Broxton Hall

★★★

Whitchurch Road, Broxton, Cheshire, CH3 9JS
Tel: 01829 782321 Fax: 01829 782330
Email: reservations@broxtonhall.co.uk
Web: www.broxtonhall.co.uk
Rooms: 10 all ensuite
Pricing: Dbl £75–125 CC: Accepted
Room facilities: 🖵 ☎ ☕
Children: Welcome 12yrs min age
Dogs: Welcome
Licences: ♦♦♦
Parking: Off-street
Directions: 9 miles south of Chester on A41 towards Whitchurch.
See advert on this page

Burnley, Lancashire

Higher Trapp Country House Hotel

★★★

Trapp Lane, Simonstone, near Burnley, Lancashire, BB12 7QW
Tel: 01282 772781 Fax: 01282 772782
Email: reception@highertrapphotel.co.uk
Web: www.highertrapphotel.co.uk
Rooms: 30 all ensuite
Pricing: Sgl £49–57 Dbl £84–70 CC: Accepted
Room facilities: 🖵 ☎ ☕
Access: ♿
Children: Welcome
Licences: ♦ ♦♦♦
Parking: Off-street and monitored
Directions: Leave M65 at Junction 8 and take A678, following signs for Clitheroe, through one set of traffic lights to next. Turn left following signs to Whailey. Take A671 for Clitheroe. Turn right onto School Lane (this becomes Trapp Lane). Higher Trapp is 1 mile on left.

Oaks Hotel

★★★

Colne Road, Reedley, Burnley, Lancashire, BB10 2LF
Tel: 01282 414141 Fax: 01282 433401
Email: oaks@shirehotels.co.uk
Web: www.shirehotels.co.uk
Rooms: 50 all ensuite
Pricing: Sgl £99 Dbl £192 Dinner from £22
CC: Accepted
Room facilities: 🖵 ☎ ☕ 📠
Conference: 10 meeting rooms (Thtr 120 max)
Children: Welcome Dogs: Guide dogs only
Licences: ♦ ♦♦♦ Leisure: Indoor pool, Gym
Parking: Off-street and monitored
Directions: Leave the M65 at junction 12. Follow signs for Burnley at next three roundabouts. The Oaks is on A682/A56 after about 1 mile.

Travelodge Burnley

Travel Accommodation
A671/A679, Cavalry Barracks, Barracks Road, Burnley, Lancashire, BB11 4AS
Web: www.travelodge.co.uk
Rooms: 32 all ensuite
Pricing: Sgl £47.40 Dbl £51.85 CC: Accepted
Room facilities: 🖵 ☕ Access: ♿

Bury, Lancashire

The Bolholt Country Park (Best Western)

★★★

Walshaw Road, Bury, Lancs, BL8 1PU
Tel: 0161 762 4000
Email: enquiries@bolholt.co.uk
Web: www.bolholt.co.uk
Rooms: 64 all ensuite
Pricing: Sgl £74–84 Dbl £73–89 Dinner from £15
CC: Accepted Room facilities: 🖵 ☎ ☕ 📠
Access: ♿
Conference: 7 meeting rooms (Thtr 350 max), 24hr-delegate from £99, day-delegate rate from £25
Children: Welcome Dogs: Welcome Licences: ♦ ♦♦♦
Leisure: Indoor pool, Gym, Health spa, Beauty salon, Fishing, Games room
Parking: Off-street and monitored
Directions: From Jct 17 M60 follow signs for Bury and signs for Walshaw and Tottington, situated one mile on right of Walshaw road.

Buttermere, Cumbria

Bridge Hotel

★★

Buttermere, Lake District, Cumbria, CA13 9UZ
Tel: 01768 770252 Fax: 01768 770215
Email: enquiries@bridge-hotel.com
Web: www.bridge-hotel.com
Rooms: 21 (20 ensuite)
Pricing: Sgl £39–52 Dbl £78–104 Dinner from £21.50
CC: Accepted Room facilities: ☎
Children: Welcome
Dogs: Welcome Licences: ♦♦♦ Parking: Off-street
Directions: Take A66 around Keswick. Turn off at
Braithwaite. Head over "Newlands Pass". This brings
you down into Buttermere and the hotel.

Carlisle, Cumbria

Central Plaza Hotel

★★★

Victoria Viaduct, Carlisle, Cumbria, CA3 8AL
Tel: 01228 520256 Fax: 01228 514657
Email: info@centralplazahotel.co.uk
Web: www.centralplazahotel.co.uk
Rooms: 84 all ensuite
Pricing: Dinner from £14.95 (2002 rate) CC: Accepted
Room facilities: ☐ ☎ 🖫 Access: |↓↑
Children: Welcome Dogs: Welcome Licences: ♦♦♦
Directions: The Central Plaza Hotel is situated in the
heart of Carlisle.

Cumbria Park

★★★

32 Scotland Road, Carlisle, CA3 9DG
Tel: 01228 522887 Fax: 01228 514796
Email: enquiries@cumbriaparkhotel.co.uk
Web: www.cumbriaparkhotel.co.uk
Seasonal closure: Christmas
Rooms: 53 all ensuite Pricing: Sgl £74–90
Dbl £95–125 Dinner from £15.95 CC: Accepted
Room facilities: ☐ ☎ 🖫 Access: |↓↑ ♿
Conference: 6 meeting rooms (Thtr 120 max),
24hr-delegate from £105, day-delegate rate from £25
Children: Welcome Dogs: Guide dogs only
Licences: ♦♦♦ Leisure: Gym, Health spa
Parking: Off-street and monitored
Directions: Leave M6 at Junction 44. Hotel is 1½ miles
down main road into Carlisle on left-hand side.

Swallow Hilltop Hotel

★★★

London Road, Carlisle, Cumbria, CA1 2PQ
Tel: 01228 529255 Fax: 01228 525238
Email: carlisle.swallow@whitbread.com
Web: www.swallowhotels.com

SWALLOW
HOTELS

Rooms: 92 all ensuite
Pricing: Sgl £60–75 Dbl £75–95 Dinner from £18.50
CC: Accepted Room facilities: ☐ ☎ 🖫 Access: |↓↑
Conference: 6 meeting rooms (Thtr 400 max), 24hr-
delegate from £105, day-delegate rate from £34
Children: Welcome
Dogs: Welcome Licences: ♦♦♦
Leisure: Indoor pool, Gym, Beauty salon, Games room
Parking: Off-street and monitored
Directions: Leave the M6 at Junction 42. Follow signs
for Carlisle on A6. Swallow Hilltop Hotel 2 miles on left,
up a hill.

Graham Arms Hotel

★★

English Street, Longtown, near Carlisle,
The Borders, CA6 5SE
Tel: 01228 791213 Fax: 01228 791213
Email: office@grahamarms.com
Web: www.grahamarms.com
Rooms: 15 all ensuite
Pricing: Sgl £32–34 Dbl £56 Dinner from £9.95
CC: Accepted Room facilities: ☐ 🖫
Conference: 2 meeting rooms (Thtr 40 max)
Children: Welcome Dogs: Welcome Licences: ♦♦♦
Parking: Off-street and monitored
Directions: Just 6 miles from Junction 44 of M6. Follow
signposts to Galashiels/The Borders Tourist Route. The
Graham Arms is about 400m on the right as you enter
this small town.

Pinegrove Hotel

★★

262 London Road, Carlisle, Cumbria, CA1 2QS
Tel: 01228 524828 Fax: 01228 810941
Email: info@pinegrovehotel.co.uk
Web: www.pinegrovehotel.co.uk
Seasonal closure: Christmas Day
Rooms: 31
Pricing: Sgl £40–48 Dbl £50–60
Dinner from £6.75 CC: Accepted
Room facilities: ☐ ☎ 🖫 Access: ♿
Conference: 2 meeting rooms (Thtr 120 max)
Children: Welcome Dogs: Welcome
Licences: ♦♦♦ Leisure: Games room
Parking: Off-street and monitored
Directions: Leave M6 at Junction 42, onto A6. Carlisle
Hotel is situated 1½ miles along this road on left-hand
side.

Vallum House Garden Hotel

◆ ◆ ◆

Burgh Road, Carlisle, Cumbria, CA2 7NB
Tel: 01228 521860
Rooms: 9 (5 ensuite)
Pricing: Sgl £25–35 Dbl £50–60 Dinner from £10
CC: Accepted
Room facilities: ▢ ☎ ⊜
Children: Welcome ⊓ Dogs: Welcome
Licences: ◁ ▥ Parking: Off-street
Directions: On west side of city, 1½ miles from town centre.

Travelodge Carlisle Southwaite (MOTO)

Travel Accommodation
M6 Moto Service Area, Broadfield Site, Carlisle, Cumbria, CA4 0NT
Web: www.travelodge.co.uk
Rooms: 38 all ensuite ⊛
Pricing: Sgl £64.40 Dbl £68.85 CC: Accepted
Room facilities: ▢ ⊜ Access: ♿

Carnforth, Lancashire

Royal Station Hotel

★★

Market Street, Carnforth, Lancashire, LA5 9BT
Tel: 01524 732033 Fax: 01524 720267
Email: royalstation@mitchellshotels.co.uk
Web: www.mitchellshotels.co.uk

Rooms: 13 all ensuite ⊛ ⊠
Pricing: Sgl £40 Dbl £54 Dinner from £4.75
CC: Accepted Room facilities: ▢ ☎ ⊜
Conference: 2 meeting rooms (Thtr 180 max)
Children: Welcome ⊓
Dogs: Guide dogs only Licences: ▥
Leisure: Games room
Directions: Leave M6 at J35. Follow signs for Carnforth. At crossroads turn right into Market Street. We are on the right.

The Country Hotel

★★

Lancaster Road, Carnforth, Lancs, LA3 9LD
Tel: 01524 732469 Fax: 01524 720142
Email: county@mitchellshotels.co.uk
Web: www.mitchellshotels.co.uk

Rooms: 12 all ensuite ⊛ ⊛
Pricing: Dbl £47.95 CC: Accepted
Room facilities: ▢ ☎ ⊜ Access: ♿
Conference: 2 meeting rooms (Thtr 160 max)

Children: Welcome ⊓ Dogs: Welcome
Licences: ▥
Parking: Off-street and monitored
Directions: Take J35 from the M6 and follow directions to Carnforth. Situated at the traffic lights on the left hand side.

Travelodge Burton in Kendal (MOTO)

Travel Accommodation
M6 Moto Service Area, Burton, Carnforth, Lancashire, LA6 1JF
Web: www.travelodge.co.uk
Rooms: 47 all ensuite ⊛
Pricing: Sgl £59.40 Dbl £63.85 CC: Accepted
Room facilities: ▢ ⊜ Access: ♿

Chester, Cheshire

The Chester Grosvenor — Blue Ribbon Winner

★ ★ ★ ★ ★ ⊛ ⊛ ⊛
Eastgate, Chester, CH1 1LT
Tel: 01244 324024 Fax: 01244 313246
Email: chesgrov@chestergrosvenor.co.uk
Web: www.chestergrosvenor.co.uk
Seasonal closure: 24th, 25th & 26th December 2003

This deluxe property is set in the heart of historic Chester. The hotel has 83 individually designed bedrooms and suites, with two award-winning restaurants, a leisure suite and car parking.
Rooms: 83 all ensuite ⊛ ⊠ ⊛
Pricing: Sgl £214.25–631.37
Dbl £228.75–645.87 Dinner from £50 CC: Accepted
Room facilities: ▢ ☎ ⊠ ❄
Access: ▥ ♿
Conference: 5 meeting rooms (Thtr 200 max)
Children: Welcome ⊓ ⊜
Dogs: Guide dogs only
Licences: ◁ ▥
Leisure: Gym
Parking: Off-street and monitored
Directions: Turn off M56 for M53 at Junction 15; turn off M53 at Junction 12 for A56. Follow signs for Chester and city centre hotels.

Chester Crabwall Manor ★★★★★ 🇷 🇷 🇷 Blue Ribbon Winner

Parkgate Road, Mollington, Chester, Cheshire, CH1 6NE
Tel: 01244 851666 Fax: 01244 851000/400
Email: crabwallmanor@marstonhotels.com
Web: www.marstonhotels.com

Splendid grade II listed country house hotel set in 11 acres of mature gardens, 4 miles from the centre of Chester, 5 minutes from the M5, 2 AA rosette restaurants.
Rooms: 48 all ensuite 🛏 🛋 🚭
Pricing: Sgl £136 Dbl £167 Dinner from £35
CC: Accepted
Room facilities: 🖥 ☎ 🛏 Access: 🚹
Conference: 17 meeting rooms (Thtr 100 max), 24hr-delegate from £170, day-delegate rate from £52.50
Children: Welcome 🍴
Dogs: Guide dogs only Licences: 🍷 ♦♦♦
Leisure: Indoor pool, Gym, Health spa, Beauty salon, Golf, Snooker/billiards
Parking: Off-street and monitored
Directions: At the end of the M56, follow signs for Queensferry/North Wales for approximately ½ a mile, turn left at the roundabout. Crabwall Manor is 1³/₄ miles down this road, on the left.

The Queen Hotel ★★★★ 🇷

City Road, Chester, Cheshire, CH1 3AH
Tel: (44) 1244 305000 Fax: (44) 1244 318483
Email: reservations.queen@principalhotels.co.uk
Web: www.principalhotels.co.uk
Rooms: 128 all ensuite 🚭
Pricing: Dinner from £25 CC: Accepted
Room facilities: 🖥 ☎ 🛏
Access: ↕ 🚹
Conference: 8 meeting rooms (Thtr 330 max), 24hr-delegate from £110, day-delegate rate from £30
Children: Welcome 🍴 ♨
Dogs: Welcome
Licences: 🍷 ♦♦♦
Parking: Off-street
Directions: From M53 take junction 12 and follow signs for Chester and Chester Railway station.

Gateway To Wales ★★★★ 🇷

Welsh Road, Sealand, near Chester, Cheshire, CH5 2HX
Tel: 01244 830332 Fax: 01244 836190
Email: mikesudbury@bt.connect.co.uk
Web: www.gatewaytowaleshotel.co.uk
Rooms: 40 all ensuite 🚭
Pricing: Sgl £55–65 Dbl £65–75 Dinner from £17.95
CC: Accepted
Room facilities: 🖥 ☎ 🛏 Access: ↕ 🚹
Conference: 2 meeting rooms (Thtr 150 max), 24hr-delegate from £95, day-delegate rate from £28
Children: Welcome 🍴
Licences: ♦♦♦
Leisure: Indoor pool, Gym
Parking: Off-street and monitored
Directions: From the A55 take the A494. Four miles from Chester.

Green Bough Hotel ★★★ 🇷 🇷 🇷

60 Hoole Road, Hoole, Chester, Cheshire, CH2 3NL
Tel: 01244 326241 Fax: 01244 326265
Email: luxury@greenbough.co.uk
Web: www.smoothhound.co.uk/hotels/greenbo.html
Rooms: 16 all ensuite 🛋 🚭
Pricing: Dinner from £22.50 CC: Accepted
Room facilities: 🖥 ☎ 🛏 Access: 🚹
Conference: 2 meeting rooms (Thtr 20 max), day-delegate rate from £35
Children: Welcome 11yrs min age
Dogs: Guide dogs only
Licences: ♦♦♦
Parking: Off-street and monitored
Directions: Take M53 to Chester. Leave at Junction 12 and take A56 to Chester city. Hotel is 1 mile from motorway.
See advert on next page

Grosvenor Pulford Hotel ★★★

Wrexham Road, Pulford, Chester, Cheshire, CH4 9DG
Tel: 01244 570560 Fax: 01244 570809
Email: enquiries@grosvenorpulfordhotel.co.uk
Web: www.grosvenorpulfordhotel.co.uk
Rooms: 76 all ensuite 🛏 🛋 🚭
Pricing: Sgl £70–100 Dbl £90–130 Dinner from £20
CC: Accepted
Room facilities: 🖥 ☎ 🛏 ♨ Access: 🚹
Conference: 5 meeting rooms (Thtr 250 max), 24hr-delegate from £28, day-delegate rate from £118
Children: Welcome 🍴
Dogs: Welcome
Licences: 🍷 ♦♦♦
Leisure: Indoor pool, Gym, Health spa, Beauty salon, Snooker/billiards
Parking: Off-street and monitored
Directions: Leave M53/A55 at junction signposted A483 Chester, Wrexham & North Wales. Turn onto B5445, hotel is 2 miles on right.
See advert on next page

Llyndir Hall Hotel

★★★

Llyndir Lane, Rossett, Clwyd, LL12 0AY
Tel: 01244 571648 Fax: 01244 571258
Email: llyndirhall@pageant.co.uk
Web: www.pageant.co.uk
Rooms: 38 all ensuite 🛏 ⊗
Room facilities: 🖵 ☎ 🗇 🔧 Access: 👤
Children: Welcome 🍴 🐎 🟦 Dogs: Welcome
Licences: ◁ Leisure: Indoor pool, Gym, Health spa
Parking: Off-street

Mill Hotel

★★★

Milton Street, Chester, Cheshire, CH1 3NF
Tel: 01244 350035 Fax: 01244 345635
Email: reservations@millhotel.com
Web: www.millhotel.com
Rooms: 129 all ensuite 🛏 🖥 ⊗ Pricing: Sgl £60–80
Dbl £78–95 Dinner from £19.50 CC: Accepted
Room facilities: 🖵 ☎ 🗇 🔧 Access: ⚹ 👤
Conference: 5 meeting rooms (Thtr 60 max), 24hr-
delegate from £90, day-delegate rate from £30
Children: Welcome 🍴 🟦 Dogs: Guide dogs only
Licences: ⦀ Leisure: Indoor pool, Gym, Health spa,
Beauty salon Parking: Off-street and monitored
Directions: J12 M53 to A56 to city centre, left at
second roundabout (A5268), first left Sellar Street,
second left Milton Street.
See advert on following page

Northop Hall Country House Hotel

★★★

Northop Hall Village, near Mold, Flintshire, CH7 6HJ
Tel: 01244 816181 Fax: 01244 814661
Email: northop@hotel-chester.com
Web: www.hotel-chester.com

Dating from 1872, steeped in history and set in acres
of tranquil gardens and woodland, offering the modern
comfort and service you would expect from a lovely
country house hotel.
Rooms: 38 all en-suite 🛏 🖥 ⊗
Pricing: Sgl £68–73 Dbl £87–123 Dinner from £21.95
CC: Accepted Room facilities: 🖵 ☎ 🗇 🔧 Access: 👤
Conference: 4 meeting rooms (Thtr 26 max), 24hr-
delegate from £89.50, day-delegate rate from £25
Children: Welcome 🍴 🟦 Dogs: Guide dogs only
Licences: ◁ ⦀ Parking: Off-street and monitored
Directions: A55 Queensferry, take first exit for Buckley;
at roundabout take first exit, then immediate right to
Northop Hall/Ewloe Castle. After 2 miles bear left, hotel
is 200 yards on left.

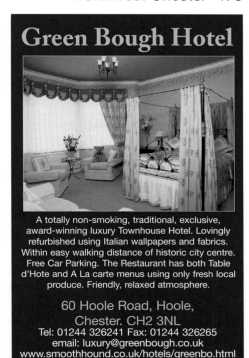
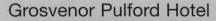

Northwest

MILL HOTEL

10. Good reasons to discover Chester's Little Venice

1. City centre 130 Bedroom Hotel with parking.
2. 4 classes of rooms. Standard, Business, Premier, and Club (pictured).
3. Chester's waterside "Restaurant Canaletto".
   Friday & Saturday nights' Dine & Dance.
4. Broad Beam 50 seater Restaurant Cruiser.
5. Health Club with 60ft Swimming Pool, Spa Bath, Steam Room, Sauna, Aerobics, Technogym gymnasium.
6. A Beauty Spa using Pevonia Botonica.
   Complete treatments for Men & Women.
7. "Venezia" Cafe Bar.
8. Public Bar serving 15 Traditional Cask Ales.
9. Deli-Bar.
10. Conference Rooms.

*** Discover Chester's most innovative Hotel ***

Mill Hotel, Milton Street, Chester, Cheshire CH1 3NF   Tel: 01244 350035 Fax: 01244 345635
Email: reservations@millhotel.com   RAC ★★★   www.millhotel.com

Rookery Hall Hotel & Restaurant

★★★★ ⍟ ⍟ ⍟   *Blue Ribbon Winner*

Main Road, Worleston, Nantwich,
nr Chester, Cheshire, CW5 6DQ
Tel: 01270 610016 Fax: 01270 626027
Email: rookery@arcadianhotels.co.uk
Web: www.arcadianhotels.com

Award-winning country house hotel set in 38 acres of peaceful countryside, offering 45 luxuriously-appointed bedrooms. Several elegant lounges and a fine dining restaurant.
Rooms: 45 all ensuite 🛏 🚭
Pricing: Sgl £80–112.50 Dbl £110–125 Dinner from £32
CC: Accepted
Room facilities: 🖥 ☎ 🍵 Access: ⥮ ♿
Conference: 6 meeting rooms (Thtr 90 max), 24hr-delegate from £150, day-delegate rate from £50

Children: Welcome 🧒
Dogs: Welcome Licences: 🍷 🍸
Leisure: Tennis Parking: Off-street and monitored
Directions: M6 north take Junction 18, A54 Middlewich, A530 Crewe/Nantwich, A51 Chester, B5074 Winsford. Hotel 1½ miles on right. M6 south jct 16, A500 Nantwich, A51 Chester, B5074.

The Blossoms

★★★
St John's Street, Chester, Cheshire, CH1 1HL
Tel: 0870 400 8108 Fax: 01244 346433
Email: blossoms@heritage-hotels.co.uk
Web: www.macdonaldhotels.co.uk
Rooms: 59 all ensuite 🛏 🚭
Pricing: Sgl £60 Dbl £120 Dinner from £18
CC: Accepted Room facilities: 🖥 ☎ 🍵 🍷
Access: ⥮
Conference: 3 meeting rooms (Thtr 80 max)
Children: Welcome 🧒 Dogs: Guide dogs only
Licences: 🍷 🍸
Directions: Leave M53 at Junction 12. Follow signs for city centre. St John Street is off Eastgate Street at centre of shopping area.

Willington Hall Hotel

★★★★

Willington, Nr Tarporley, Cheshire, CW6 0NB
Tel: 01829 752321 Fax: 01829 752596
Email: enquiries@willingtonhall.co.uk
Web: www.willingtonhall.co.uk
Seasonal closure: 25, 26, 27 December
Rooms: 10 all ensuite
Pricing: Sgl £70 Dbl £110 Dinner from £21.50
CC: Accepted Room facilities:
Conference: 3 meeting rooms (Thtr 120 max), 24hr-delegate from £115, day-delegate rate from £26
Children: Welcome
Dogs: Welcome Licences:
Parking: Off-street
Directions: 2 miles southeast of Tarporley on A51 turn at Bulls Head Inn signed Willington Hall, 2 miles down Willington lane on left.

Brookside Hotel

★★

Brooklane, Chester, Cheshire, CH3 9PA
Tel: 01244 381943 Fax: 01244 379701
Email: info@brookside-hotel.co.uk
Web: www.brookside-hotel.co.uk
Rooms: 26 all ensuite
Pricing: Sgl £35–45 Dbl £55–65 Dinner from £9.95
CC: Accepted Room facilities: Access:
Conference: 1 meeting room (Thtr 12 max), 24hr-delegate from £50, day-delegate rate from £20
Children: Welcome
Dogs: Guide dogs only Licences:
Parking: Off-street
Directions: From city centre on A5116 Liverpool road turn right into Brook lane hotel 300 yds on left car park at rear.

Chester Court Hotel

★★

48 Hoole Road, Chester, Cheshire, CH2 3NL
Tel: 01244 320779 Fax: 01244 344795
Email: info@chestercourthotel.com
Web: www.chestercourthotel.com
Rooms: 20 all ensuite
Pricing: Sgl £45–50 Dbl £65–70 Dinner from £16
CC: Accepted
Room facilities: Access:
Children: Welcome
Licences: Parking: Off-street and monitored
Directions: From M53 Junction 12, take A56 into Chester. Proceed along Hoole Road (A56), and find Chester Court Hotel on right opposite All Saints Church.

Dene Hotel

★★

95 Hoole Road, Chester, Cheshire, CH2 3ND
Tel: 01244 321165 Fax: 01244 350277
Email: info@denehotel.com
Web: www.denehotel.com
Rooms: 52 all ensuite
Pricing: Sgl £44–55 Dbl £65–85 Dinner from £7.95
CC: Accepted
Room facilities:
Children: Welcome
Dogs: Welcome Licences:
Leisure: Games room
Parking: Off-street
Directions: Take Junction 12 of the M53. Follow signs for A56 Hoole Road. The Dene Hotel is about 500 yards on left.

Redland Hotel

◆◆◆◆◆

64 Hough Green, Chester, Cheshire, CH4 8JY
Tel: 01244 671024 Fax: 01244 681309
Rooms: 13 all ensuite
Room facilities:
Licences:
Parking: Off-street

The Guesthouse at Old Hall Country Club

◆◆◆◆◆

Aldford Road, Chester, Cheshire, CH3 6EA
Tel: 01244 317273 Fax: 01244 313785
Email: info@oldhallcountryclub.com
Web: www.oldhallcountryclub.com
Rooms: 6 all ensuite
Pricing: Sgl £60–90 Dbl £107–120 Dinner from £7.50
CC: Accepted Room facilities:
Dogs: Welcome Licences:
Leisure: Indoor pool, Outdoor pool, Gym, Health spa, Beauty salon, Tennis
Parking: Off-street and monitored
Directions: Call reception on 01244 311593 for detailed directions, or use website.
See advert on following page

Stone Villa

◆◆◆◆

3 Stone Place, Chester, Cheshire, CH2 3NR
Tel: 01244 345014 Fax: 01244 345015
Email: stonevilla@freeserve.co.uk
Web: www.smoothhound.co.uk
Rooms: 9 all ensuite
Pricing: Sgl £28–30 Dbl £30–35 CC: Accepted
Room facilities:
Children: Welcome
Parking: Off-street and monitored
Directions: From M5, M6, M53, take A56. Follow past church on left. Pass through traffic lights, take second left into Stone Place. Proceed to bottom of cul-de-sac and through entrance into car park.

Northwest

The Guesthouse at Old Hall Country Club

Award-winning, independently-run Health Club and Spa. Six stylish guest rooms overlooking Cheshire countryside but only minutes from historic Chester. Swimming, tennis and lounge bar serving modern healthy food. Conference/meeting facilities.

Aldford Road, Chester CH3 6EA
Tel: 01244 317273   Fax: 01244 313785
info@oldhallcountryclub.com
www.oldhallcountryclub.com

Ba Ba Guest House

 ◆ ◆ ◆ ✕

65 Hoole Road, Hoole, Chester, Cheshire, CH2 3NJ
Tel: 01244 315047 Fax: 01244 315046
Email: reservations@babaguesthouse.co.uk
Web: www.babaguesthouse.co.uk
Rooms: 5 all ensuite ⊗ Pricing: Sgl £30–35
Dbl £52–60 CC: Accepted Room facilities: ⬜ ♨
Children: Welcome ♭ Parking: Off-street
Directions: Exit J12 M53 onto A56, signs for Chester. The guest house is situated 1 mile from the motorway on the left hand side.

Chorley, Lancashire

Pines Hotel

★ ★ ★ ⦿

Preston Road, Clayton-le-Woods, Lancashire, PR6 7ED
Tel: 01772 338551 Fax: 01772 629002
Email: mail@thepines-hotel
Web: www.thepines-hotel.co.uk

A warm and friendly welcome awaits at this privately owned hotel. The Pines offers every modern comfort and luxury, yet still retains much of the ambience of a bygone era, a perfect setting for any occasion.
Rooms: 36 all ensuite ⊛ ⊟ ⊗
Room facilities: ⬜ ☎ ♨ ⬝ Access: ♿
Conference: 5 meeting rooms (Thtr 200 max)
Children: Welcome ♭ Dogs: Guide dogs only
Licences: ⬥ ♦♦♦ Parking: Monitored
Directions: M6 Junction 29 to Preston south. Right at roundabout. Follow A6. After fourth mini roundabout, hotel is immediately on left.

Parr Hall Farm

◆ ◆ ◆ ◆ ✕

Parr Lane, Eccleston, Chorley, Lancashire, PR7 5SL
Tel: 01257 451917 Fax: 01257 453749
Email: parrhall@talk21.com
Rooms: 4 all ensuite ⊛ ⊗ Pricing: Sgl £30–35
Dbl £50–60 CC: Accepted Room facilities: ⬜ ♨
Children: Welcome ♭ Parking: Off-street
Directions: M6 J27, A5209 for Parbold; immediately right on B5250 for Eccleston. After 5 miles Parr Lane on right, property first left.

Travelodge Preston, Chorley (SA)

Travel Accommodation
A6, Preston Road, Clayton Le Woods, Chorley, Lancaster, PR6 7JB
Web: www.travelodge.co.uk Rooms: 40 all ensuite ⊗
Pricing: Sgl £47.40 Dbl £51.85 CC: Accepted
Room facilities: ⬜ ♨ Access: ♿

Clitheroe, Lancashire

Brooklyn Guest House

◆ ◆ ◆ ◆ ✕

32 Pimlico Road, Clitheroe, Lancashire, BB7 2AH
Tel: 01200 428268
Email: rg@classicfm.net
Rooms: 4 all ensuite ⊗ Pricing: Sgl £25–27
Dbl £40–43 Dinner from £10 CC: Accepted
Room facilities: ⬜ ♨ Children: Welcome ♭ Licences: ♦♦♦
Directions: North of town centre. Close to roundabout with BP garage: take Waddington Road, 200 yards. Turn right at smaller roundabout.

Congleton, Cheshire

The Plough At Eaton

◆ ◆ ◆ ◆ ✕

Macclesfield Road, Eaton, Congleton, Cheshire, CW12 2NR
Tel: 01260 280207 Fax: 01260 298377
Rooms: 8 all ensuite Pricing: Sgl £50 Dbl £60
Dinner from £7 CC: Accepted Room facilities: ⬜ ☎ ♨
Conference: 1 meeting room (Thtr 40 max)
Children: Welcome ♭ Dogs: Guide dogs only
Licences: ⬥ ♦♦♦ Parking: Off-street
Directions: Situated north of Congleton in the village of Eton on the main Macclesfield road.

Coniston, Cumbria

Coniston Lodge

Little Gem

Station Road, Coniston, Cumbria, LA21 8HH
Tel: 01539 441201 Fax: 01539 441201
Email: info@coniston-lodge.com
Web: www.coniston-lodge.com
Seasonal closure: January

An RAC Little Gem winner. Beautiful scenery, peaceful surroundings, fine home cooking and a very warm welcome.
Rooms: 6 all ensuite
Pricing: Sgl £42.50–52 Dbl £75–90 Dinner from £21.50
CC: Accepted Room facilities:
Children: Welcome 10yrs min age
Dogs: Guide dogs only Licences:
Parking: Off-street
Directions: Leave A593 at the crossroads close to filling station. Turn up the hill (Station Road). Hotel is 100m on left. Park under the building.

The Crown

♦♦♦♦

Tilferthwaite Avenue, Coniston, Cumbria, LA21 8EA
Tel: 01539 441243 Fax: 01539 441804
Email: info@crown-hotel-coniston.com
Web: www.crown-hotel-coniston.com

All the bedrooms at the Crown are ensuite and all are centrally heated, each has colour television, direct dial telephone, plus hair dryer and tea/coffee making facilities.
Rooms: 12 all ensuite
Pricing: Sgl £40–60 Dbl £70–90 Dinner from £15
CC: Accepted Room facilities:

Children: Welcome Dogs: Guide dogs only
Licences: Leisure: Games room
Parking: Off-street
Directions: Leave the M6 at J36 onto A591 towards Windermere, continue to Amblescole, when in Amblescole take the A593 to Coniston.

Crewe Cheshire

Travelodge Crewe

Travel Accommodation
M6/A500 Jct 16, Alsager Road, Barthomley, Crewe, Cheshire, CW2 5PT
Web: www.travelodge.co.uk
Rooms: 42 all ensuite
Pricing: Sgl £57.40 Dbl £61.85 CC: Accepted
Room facilities: Access:

Dalston, Cumbria

Dalston Hall Hotel

★★★★

Dalston, Cumbria, CA5 7JX
Tel: 01228 710271 Fax: 01228 711273
Email: info@dalston-hall-hotel.co.uk
Web: www.dalston-hall-hotel.co.uk
Rooms: 12 all ensuite
Pricing: Sgl £80 Dbl £130 Dinner from £25
CC: Accepted Room facilities:
Conference: 3 meeting rooms (Thtr 80 max), 24hr-delegate from £115, day-delegate rate from £25
Children: Welcome
Dogs: Welcome Licences:
Leisure: Health spa, Golf, Fishing
Parking: Off-street
Directions: 5 miles from junction 42 on M6 follow signs for Dalston 3 miles from Carlisle city centre on B5299.

Dalton-on-Furness

Clarence House Hotel

Skelgate, Dalton-in-Furness, Barrow-in-Furness, Cumbria, LA15 8BQ
Tel: 01229 462508 Fax: 01229 467177
Email: clarencehsehotel@aol.com
Web: www.clarencehousehotel.co.uk
Seasonal closure: Christmas and Boxing day
Rooms: 18 all ensuite
Pricing: £75 Dbl £95–195 Dinner from £12.95
CC: Accepted
Room facilities: Access:
Conference: 3 meeting rooms (Thtr 50 max), 24hr-delegate from £120, day-delegate rate from £30
Children: Welcome Dogs: Welcome
Licences:
Parking: Off-street and monitored
Directions: M6 exit J36, follow A590 to Barrow through Lindal village, 2nd roundabout, 1st left to Dalton, hotel on right, 1/2 mile.
See advert on following page

Northwest

Clarence House is a beautiful mid-Victorian mansion, set in over 3 acres of landscaped tranquil gardens overlooking St Thomas' Valley. With an enviable reputation as being one of the best hotels in the area offering excellent accommodation, fine dining and a warm and friendly atmosphere.

Situated on the Furness Peninsula we are surrounded by beaches and open countryside, with the dramatic ruins of one of the largest Cistercian abbeys in England a brisk walk away.

Clarence House

Country Hotel & Restaurant
Skelgate,
Dalton-in-Furness,
Cumbria.

Telephone: 01229 462508
Facsimile: 01229 467177

Ellesmere Port, Cheshire

Quality Hotel Chester

★★★

Berwick Road, off Welsh Road, Little Sutton, Ellesmere Port, Cheshire, CH66 4PS
Tel: 0151 339 5121 Fax: 0151 339 3214
Email: admin@gb066.u-net.com
Web: www.choicehotels.com
Rooms: 53 all ensuite
Pricing: Sgl £95–105 Dbl £110–130 Dinner from £18.50
CC: Accepted Room facilities: 🖥 ☎ ⌖ 📞 Access: ♿
Conference: 6 meeting rooms (Thtr 200 max), 24hr-delegate from £110, day-delegate rate from £30
Children: Welcome ⅋ ⅌ Dogs: Welcome
Licences: ◈ ⅲ Leisure: Indoor pool, Gym, Health spa Parking: Off-street
Directions: Junction five M53 follow Queensferry, at second set of traffic lights turn right onto A550, the hotel is one mile on left.

Eskdale, Cumbria

Brook House Inn

◆ ◆ ◆ ◆ ⓡ

Boot, Eskdale, Cumbria, CA19 1TG
Tel: 01946 723288 Fax: 01946 723160
Email: stay@brookhouseinn.co.uk
Web: www.brookhouseinn.co.uk
Rooms: 8 all ensuite 🐾 ⓢ
Pricing: Dinner from £18.50 CC: Accepted
Room facilities: 🖥 ⌖ Children: Welcome ⅋
Licences: ⅲ Leisure: Games room Parking: Off-street
Directions: Located in Boot on the Ambleside-Eskdale road. Please post/fax/e-mail for directions.

Forton, Lancashire

Travelodge Lancaster Forton (MOTO)

Travel Accommodation
M6 Moto Service Area, White Carr Lane, Bay Horse, Lancashire, LA2 9DU
Web: www.travelodge.co.uk
Rooms: 52 all ensuite ⓢ
Pricing: Sgl £57.40 Dbl £61.85 CC: Accepted
Room facilities: 🖥 ⌖ Access: ♿

Garstang, Lancashire

Crofters Hotel

★★★★ ⓡ

A6 Cabus, Garstang, Lancashire, PR3 1PH
Tel: 01995 604128 Fax: 01995 601646
Email: crofters@mitchellshotels.co.uk
Web: www.mitchellshotels.co.uk

Rooms: 19 all ensuite
Pricing: Sgl £46 Dbl £64 Dinner from £16.10
CC: Accepted Room facilities: 🖥 ☎ ⌖
Children: Welcome ⅋ Dogs: Welcome
Licences: ◈ ⅲ Leisure: Games room
Parking: Off-street
Directions: Situated midway between Preston and Lancaster, on the A6 trunk road, near the market town of Garstang.

Grange-over-Sands, Cumbria

Graythwaite Manor Hotel

★★★★ ⓡ

Fernhill Road, Grange-over-Sands, Cumbria, LA11 7JE
Tel: 01539 532001 Fax: 01539 535549
Email: graythwaitemanor@aol.com
Web: www.graythwaitemanor.co.uk

Fine country house hotel owned by the Auchlochan Trust, ten acres of award winning gardens. Fine dining and extensive wine list, a place full of history and nostalgia.
Rooms: 22 all ensuite 🐾 ⓢ
Pricing: Sgl £62.50–85 Dbl £55–85 Dinner from £22.50
CC: Accepted Room facilities: 🖥 ☎ ⌖ 📞 Access: ⅲ ♿
Conference: 2 meeting rooms (Thtr 40 max)
Children: Welcome ⅌ Dogs: Guide dogs only
Licences: ◈ ⅲ Leisure: Tennis
Parking: Off-street and monitored
Directions: Follow B5277 through Grange. Turn right opposite fire station into Fernhill Road.

Netherwood

★★★★ ⓡ

Lindale Road, Grange-over-Sands, Cumbria, LA11 6ET
Tel: 01539 532552 Fax: 01539 534121
Email: blawith@aol.com
Web: www.netherwood-hotel.co.uk
Rooms: 28 all ensuite 🐾 ⓢ
Pricing: Sgl £65–75 Dbl £130–150 Dinner from £26
CC: Accepted Room facilities: 🖥 ☎ ⌖ 📞
Access: ⅲ ♿
Conference: 4 meeting rooms (Thtr 150 max), 24hr-delegate from £115, day-delegate rate from £30
Children: Welcome ⅋ ⅌ Dogs: Welcome
Licences: ◈ ⅲ Leisure: Indoor pool, Gym, Health spa, Beauty salon Parking: Off-street and monitored
Directions: Leave M6 at Junction 36. Take A590 for Barrow-in-Furness. Follow for Holker Hall on B5277. Netherwood is on right just before rail station.

Elton Hotel

◆◆◆◆

Windermere Road, Grange-over-Sands,
Cumbria, LA11 6EQ
Tel: 01539 532838 Fax: 01539 532838
Email: chris.crane@btclick.com
Seasonal closure: January to February
Rooms: 7 all ensuite 🐾 ⊗
Pricing: Sgl £25–30 Dbl £40–50
Room facilities: ▢ ☕ Access: ♿
Children: Welcome ⑂ Dogs: Welcome Licences: ⧫⧫⧫
Directions: 50m after Railway Station, take right exit at mini roundabout. Hotel 200m on left.

The Crown Inn

◆◆◆◆

High Newton, Newton in Cartmel, Grange over Sands,
Cumbria, LA11 6JH
Tel: 015395 31793 Fax: 015395 30012
Email: reception@thecrowninn-lakeland.com
Web: www.thecrowninn-lakeland.com
Rooms: 5 all ensuite 🐾 Pricing: Sgl £40 Dbl £50
Dinner from £14 CC: Accepted Room facilities: ▢ ☕
Children: Welcome ⑂ Licences: ⧫⧫⧫
Leisure: Games room Parking: Off-street
Directions: Exit 36 M6 west on A590 to High Newton, three possible turnings to right converge outside Inn.

Grasmere, Cumbria

Wordsworth Hotel

★★★★★ ⓡ ⓡ

Grasmere, Cumbria, LA22 9SW
Tel: 01539 435592 Fax: 01539 435765
Email: enquiry@wordsworth-grasmere.co.uk
Web: www.grasmere-hotels.co.uk

Set in the heart of Lakeland, in magnificent surroundings, the Wordsworth Hotel has a reputation for the high quality of its food, accommodation and hospitality.
Rooms: 37 all ensuite 🐾 🖨
Pricing: Sgl £90 Dbl £150 Dinner from £38.50
CC: Accepted Room facilities: ▢ ☎ ☕ Access: ⧉ ♿
Conference: 3 meeting rooms (Thtr 100 max), 24hr-delegate from £137.50, day-delegate rate from £37.50
Children: Welcome ⑂ 🍼 🎮 Dogs: Guide dogs only
Licences: ⟁ ⧫⧫⧫ Leisure: Indoor pool, Gym
Parking: Off-street
Directions: From north M6 J40 for Keswick, A591 for Grasmere; from south, J36 M6 A590, then A591 as above.

Grasmere Red Lion Hotel

★★★

Red Lion Square, Grasmere, Cumbria, LA22 9SS
Tel: 01539 435456 Fax: 01539 435579
Email: enquiries@hotelgrasmere.uk.com
Web: www.hotelgrasmere.uk.com
Rooms: 47 all ensuite 🐾 ⊗
Pricing: Sgl £43–57.50 Dbl £86–115 Dinner from £15
CC: Accepted
Room facilities: ▢ ☎ ☕ 🔌 Access: ⧉ ♿
Conference: 5 meeting rooms (Thtr 60 max), 24hr-delegate from £91, day-delegate rate from £28
Children: Welcome ⑂ 🎮
Dogs: Welcome
Licences: ⧫⧫⧫
Leisure: Gym, Health spa, Beauty salon, Games room
Parking: Off-street and monitored
Directions: From South, M6 Junction 36. Take A591 to Grasmere. From North, M6 J40 and take A66 towards Keswick. Turn left (signposted Windermere). A591 to Grasmere.

The Gold Rill Hotel

★★★

Red Bank Road, Grasmere, Ambleside,
Cumbria, LA22 9PU
Tel: 015394 35486 Fax: 015394 35486
Email: enquires@gold-rill.com
Web: www.gold-rill.com
Rooms: 31 all ensuite 🐾 ⊗
Pricing: Sgl £45–70 Dbl £45–70 Dinner from £22
CC: Accepted Room facilities: ▢ ☎ ☕ ☕
Access: ♿ Children: Welcome ⑂ 🎮
Dogs: Guide dogs only
Licences: ⧫⧫⧫
Leisure: Outdoor pool
Parking: Off-street and monitored

The Swan

★★★

Keswick Road, Grasmere, Cumbria, LA22 9RF
Tel: 0870 400 8132 Fax: 01539 435741
Email: swangrasmere@heritage-hotels.co.uk
Web: www.macdonaldhotels.co.uk
Rooms: 38 all ensuite 🐾 🖨 ⊗
Pricing: Sgl £69 Dbl £138 Dinner from £23
CC: Accepted
Room facilities: ▢ ☎ ☕ 🔌
Children: Welcome ⑂ 🎮 Dogs: Welcome
Licences: ⧫⧫⧫
Parking: Off-street
Directions: From M6 Jct 36 A591 to Windermere, then through Ambleside to Grasmere. Hotel on Keswick Road on outskirts of Grasmere village.

Grasmere Hotel

 ★ ★

Broadgate, Grasmere, Cumbria, LA22 9TA
Tel: 01539 435277 Fax: 01539 435277
Email: enquiries@grasmerehotel.co.uk
Web: www.grasmerehotel.co.uk
Seasonal closure: 2 January to 13 February
Rooms: 13 all ensuite 🖥 🚭
Pricing: Sgl £40–100 Dbl £60–120 Dinner from £22.50
CC: Accepted Room facilities: 🖵 ☎ 🍵
Access: ♿ Children: Welcome 10yrs min age
Dogs: Welcome Licences: ♙
Parking: Off-street and monitored
Directions: From the M6 take exit 36 to South Lakes, follow A591 to Grasmere. Take 2nd entrance into village (opposite The Swan).

Moss Grove Hotel

 ★ ★

Grasmere, Cumbria, LA22 9SW
Tel: 01539 435251 Fax: 01539 435691
Email: martinw@globalnet.co.uk
Web: www.grasmereccomodation.co.uk
Seasonal closure: December and January
Rooms: 13 all ensuite 🖥 🚭
Pricing: Sgl £30–50 Dbl £60–115 Dinner from £13
CC: Accepted
Room facilities: 🖵 ☎ 🍵 Children: Welcome ♙ 🌡
Licences: ♙ Parking: Off-street
Directions: From South, M6 Junction 36, then A591 and left to village. Hotel on right just past church. From North, M6 J40, A66 Keswick, A591 Grasmere and right into village. On left opposite church.

Halifax, West Yorkshire

Travelodge Halifax Central (SA)

Travel Accommodation
Gate 9, Dean Clough Ind Park, Halifax,
West Yorkshire, HX3 5AY
Web: www.travelodge.co.uk
Pricing: Sgl £49.40 Dbl £53.85 CC: Accepted
Room facilities: 🖵 🍵

Hampson Green, Lancashire

Hampson House Hotel

★ ★

Galgate, Hampson Green, Lancashire, LA2 0JB
Tel: 01524 751158 Fax: 01524 751779

Hawkshead, Cumbria

Highfield House Country Hotel

 ★ ★

Hawkshead Hill, Hawkshead, Cumbria, LA22 0PN
Tel: 01539 436344 Fax: 01539 436793
Email: rooms@highfield-hawkshead.com
Web: www.highfield-hawkshead.com
Seasonal closure: January

Award-winning family-owned-and-run country house hotel with the best panoramic mountain views in the Lake District. Superb hospitality, service and location. 3 acres of gardens, wonderful food.
Rooms: 11 all ensuite 🐾 🚭
Pricing: Sgl £27.50–57.50 Dbl £55–130 CC: Accepted
Room facilities: 🖵 ☎ 🍵
Conference: 1 meeting room (Thtr 25 max)
Children: Welcome ♙ 🌡 Dogs: Welcome
Parking: Off-street
Directions: Exit J36 M6. Follow signs for Hawkshead. Just outside Hawkshead on B5285.

Sawrey House Country Hotel

 ◆ ◆ ◆ ◆ ◆ 🚮 🚮 🚮

Near Sawrey, Hawkshead, Cumbria, LA22 0LF
Tel: 01539 436387 Fax: 01539 436010
Email: shirley@sawreyhouse.com
Web: www.sawreyhouse.com
Seasonal closure: Early Dec and Jan, open Christmas and New Year.

Overlooking Esthwaite Waters, in the heart of Beatrix Potter village. Quality comfortable family-run hotel. Excellent food, tranquil setting; a haven for wildlife. Centrally situated. Totally non-smoking.
Rooms: 11 all ensuite 🚭
Pricing: Sgl £70 Dbl £140–170 Dinner from £35
CC: Accepted
Room facilities: 🖵 ☎ 🍵
Access: ♿
Conference: 2 meeting rooms (Thtr 35 max)
Children: Welcome 10yrs min age
Dogs: WelcomeLicences: ♙
Parking: Off-street
Directions: On B5285 from Hawkshead towards Windermere car ferry.

Ivy House

◆◆◆◆

Ambleside, Hawkshead, Cumbria, LA22 0NS
Tel: 01539 436204 Fax: 01539 436171
Email: david@ivyhousehotel.com
Web: www.ivyhousehotel.com
Rooms: 11 all ensuite
Pricing: Sgl £33–35 Dbl £66–70 CC: Accepted
Room facilities:
Children: Welcome
Dogs: Welcome
Licences:
Parking: Off-street and monitored
Directions: M6 J36 or J37, signs for Kendall,
Windemere, Ambleside, Coniston and then
Hawkshead.

Heywood, Lancashire

Travelodge Manchester North Eastbound (MOTO)

Travel Accommodation
M62, Moto Service Area, Birch, Heywood,
Lancashire, OL10 2HQ
Web: www.travelodge.co.uk
Rooms: 55 all ensuite
Pricing: Sgl £47.40 Dbl £51.85 CC: Accepted
Room facilities: Access:

Travelodge Manchester North Westbound (MOTO)

Travel Accommodation
M62, Moto Service Area, Birch, Heywood,
Lancashire, OL10 2HQ
Web: www.travelodge.co.uk
Rooms: 35 all ensuite
Pricing: Sgl £47.40 Dbl £51.85 CC: Accepted
Room facilities: Access:

Holmes Chapel, Cheshire

Old Vicarage Hotel

★★★★ ℞ ℞

Knutsford Road, Cranage, Holmes Chapel,
Cheshire, CW4 8EF
Tel: 01477 532041 Fax: 01477 535728
Email: oldvichotel@aol.com
Rooms: 29 all ensuite
Pricing: Sgl £45–80 Dbl £60–90 Dinner from £17.50
CC: Accepted
Room facilities:
Access:
Conference: 2 meeting rooms (Thtr 60 max)
Children: Welcome
Dogs: Guide dogs only
Licences:
Directions: Situated on the A50 only 1 mile from
Junction 18 of the M6.

Holmrook, Cumbria

Lutwidge Arms Hotel

★★

Holmrook, Cumbria, CA19 1UH
Tel: 01946 724230 Fax: 01946 724100
Email: ian@lutwidgewestcumbria.co.uk
Web: www.lutwidgewestcumbria.co.uk
Rooms: 18 all ensuite
Pricing: Sgl £33–41.50 Dbl £48–114 Dinner from £12
CC: Accepted
Room facilities:
Access: Children: Welcome
Dogs: WelcomeLicences:
Leisure: Gym, Games room
Parking: Off-street
Directions: On A595 at Holmrook, three miles south of
Gosforth.

Howtown, Cumbria

Sharrow Bay Hotel Gold Ribbon Winner

★★★ ℞ ℞ ℞ ℞

Lake Ullswater, Penrith, Cumbria, CA10 2LZ
Tel: 01768 486301 Fax: 01768 486349
Email: enquiries@ sharrow-bay.com
Web: www.sharrow-bay.com
Seasonal closure: early December to early March

Nestling on the shores of Ullswater, enjoying one of the
most breathtaking views in the country. Providing a
haven for rest and relaxation with internationally-
renowned cuisine within idyllic surroundings.
Rooms: 26 (24 ensuite)
Pricing: Sgl £112–145 Dbl £240–420 Dinner from £49
CC: Accepted
Room facilities:
Access:
Conference: 2 meeting rooms (Thtr 24 max), 24hr-
delegate from £200, day-delegate rate from £50
Children: Welcome 13yrs min age Licences:
Parking: Off-street and monitored
Directions: M6 exit 40 A66 west A592, Pooley Bridge,
turn right after the church towards Howtown.

Kendal, Cumbria

Heaves Hotel

 ★★

Heaves, nr Kendal, Cumbria, LA8 8EF
Tel: 01539 560396 Fax: 01539 560269
Email: hotel@heaves.freeserve.co.uk
Web: www.heaveshotel.co.uk

Spacious Georgian mansion in 10 acres of formal
gardens and woodland. Four miles from Exit 36 of M6
and Kendal. Family owned and run. Library and billiard
room.
Rooms: 13 all ensuite 🛏 🖼
Pricing: Sgl £34 Dbl £58–70 Dinner from £15
CC: Accepted
Room facilities: 📺 ☎ 🍵
Conference: 3 meeting rooms (Thtr 60 max)
Children: Welcome ☍
Dogs: Welcome Licences: ⚜ 🎎
Leisure: Snooker/billiards Parking: Off-street
Directions: M6 Junction 36, A590 Barrow & South
Lakes. After 3 miles follow A590 to roundabout, again
take A590. Second junction on right (Sizergh), signs on
left after turn.

Blaven Homestay

 ◆◆◆◆◆♚ ♚ ⚜ ✦

Middleshaw, Old Hutton, Kendal, Cumbria, LA8 0LZ
Tel: 01539 734894 Fax: 01539 727447
Email: enquiries@blavenhomestay.co.uk
Web: www.blavenhomestay.co.uk

Luxury Lakeland house, quiet streamside location,
lovely garden. Excellent base for M6, Lakes and Dales.
Amiable hosts Janet and Barry offer gourmet meals,
fine wine and every comfort to guests.

Rooms: 2 all ensuite ⊛
Pricing: Sgl £39.50–46 Dbl £59.90–72 CC: Accepted
Room facilities: 📺 🍵 Dogs: Guide dogs only
Parking: Off-street and monitored
Directions: From Oxenholme station take B6254 Kirkby
Lonsdale road for approx. 1¹/₂ miles. Turn left to
Ewebank. Blaven 200m on right.

Garnett House Farm

◆◆◆◆

Burneside, Kendal, Cumbria, LA9 5SF
Tel: 01539 724542 Fax: 01539 724542
Email: info@garnetthousefarm.co.uk
Web: www.garnetthousefarm.co.uk
Seasonal closure: Christmas to New Year
Rooms: 5 all ensuite 🛏 ⊛
Room facilities: 📺 🍵
Children: Welcome ☍ ⫶₵ Parking: Off-street
Directions: Leave M6 J36, left for 10 miles at
roundabout, 2nd left to Windermere. Turn right on dual
carriageway signed Burneside.

Keswick, Cumbria

Derwentwater Hotel

★★★★ 🍴

Portinscale, Keswick, Cumbria, CA12 5RE
Tel: 01768 772538 Fax: 01768 771002
Email: info@derwentwater-hotel.co.uk
Web: www.derwentwater-hotel.co.uk
Rooms: 48 all ensuite 🖼 ⊛
Pricing: Dinner from £22.50 CC: Accepted
Room facilities: 📺 ☎ 🍵
Access: ⊞ ♿
Conference: 2 meeting rooms (Thtr 20 max), 24hr-
delegate from £80, day-delegate rate from £30
Children: Welcome ☍ ⫶₵
Dogs: Welcome Licences: 🎎
Leisure: Fishing, Games room Parking: Off-street
Directions: Exit J40 M6 west on A66. 150 yards past
third Keswick junction, left into Portinscale, then left as
road bears right.
See advert on following page

Keswick Country House Hotel

★★★

Station Road, Keswick, Cumbria, CA12 4NQ
Tel: 01768 772020 Fax: 01768 771300
Web: www.thekeswickcountryhousehotel.co.uk
Rooms: 74 all ensuite 🛏 🖼 ⊛
Pricing: Dinner from £18.50 CC: Accepted
Room facilities: 📺 ☎ 🍵
Access: ⊞ ♿
Conference: 3 meeting rooms (Thtr 70 max), 24hr-
delegate from £120, day-delegate rate from £30
Children: Welcome ☍ ⫶₵ Dogs: Guide dogs only
Licences: ⚜ 🎎 Leisure: Snooker/billiards
Parking: Off-street
Directions: Exit J40 M6; A66 to Keswick; follow signs
for leisure pool and museum; turn left into Station
Road.

Derwentwater Hotel

Set in 16 acres of conservation grounds on the shores of Derwentwater. Providing high standards of accommodation. Award winning hospitality, pets welcome, entry to leisure club, the perfect Lakeland retreat.

Portinscale, Keswick, Cumbria CA12 5RE
Tel: 017687 72538   Fax: 017687 71002
Email: info@derwentwater-hotel.co.uk
Website: www.derwentwater-hotel.co.uk

RaC ★★★
RAC Dining Award
Best Western

Chaucer House Hotel
★★

Derwentwater Place, opposite St John's Church, Keswick, Cumbria, CA12 4DR
Tel: 01768 772318/773223 Fax: 01768 775551
Email: info@chaucer-house.co.uk
Web: www.chaucer-house.co.uk
Seasonal closure: December to January

Lakeland hospitality at its best, quiet setting, surrounded by spectacular mountains. Close to theatre, market place, lake. Renowned for a relaxed informal atmosphere and excellent freshly prepared food. Drying room, cycle shed and lift.
Rooms: 34 all ensuite
Pricing: Sgl £41–42 Dbl £80–95
Dinner from £21.50 CC: Accepted
Room facilities: Access:

Conference: 1 meeting room (Thtr 15 max), 24hr-delegate from £65, day-delegate rate from £21
Children: Welcome   Dogs: Welcome
Licences:
Parking: Off-street
Directions: From A591 turn into Manor Brow. The road is signed Keswick via Manor Brow. Hotel is opposite church of St John's at the bottom of the road.

Crow Park Hotel
★★

The Heads, Keswick, Cumbria, CA12 5ER
Tel: 01768 772208 Fax: 01768 774776
Email: enquires@crowpark.co.uk
Web: www.crowpark.co.uk
Rooms: 28
Room facilities:
Children: Welcome
Dogs: Welcome
Parking: Off-street
Directions: Approximately 200 metres from town centre, overlooking park and lake.

Highfield Hotel
★★

The Heads, Keswick, Cumbria, CA12 5ER
Tel: 01768 772508 Fax: 01768 780634
Email: info@highfieldkeswick.co.uk
Web: www.highfieldkeswick.co.uk
Seasonal closure: January
Rooms: 18 all ensuite
Pricing: Sgl £55–60 Dbl £92–120 Dinner from £20
CC: Accepted
Room facilities:
Children: Welcome 8yrs min age
Licences:
Parking: Off-street
Directions: From A66 take 2nd exit at roundabout. Turn left and follow to T-junction. Turn left again then right at mini roundabout. The Heads is fourth turning on right.

Lyzzick Hall

 ★ ★

Underskiddaw, Keswick, Cumbria, CA12 4PY
Tel: 01768 772277 Fax: 01768 772278
Email: lyzzickhall@btconnect.com
Web: www.lyzzickhall.co.uk
Seasonal closure: mid-January to mid-February

Lyzzick has an idyllic position in glorious nothern
Lakeland and easy access to the whole of "this most
beautiful corner of England". We have stupendous
mountain views and the opportunity to get off the
beaten track and leave the crowds behind. Being
family run the highest standards are zealously guarded.
Rooms: 29 all ensuite
Pricing: Sgl £47–49 Dbl £94–98 Dinner from £24
CC: Accepted Room facilities:
Children: Welcome Licences:
Leisure: Indoor pool Parking: Off-street
Directions: 2 miles north of Keswick on the A591, 19
miles west from Junction 40 (Penrith exit) on the M6.

Middle Ruddings Hotel

 ★ ★

Braithwaite, Keswick, Cumbria, CA12 5RY
Tel: 01768 778436 Fax: 01768 778436
Email: middleruddings@aol.com
Web: www.middleruddings.com
Rooms: 11 all ensuite
Pricing: Dinner from £5.95 (2002 rate) CC: Accepted
Room facilities: Access:
Children: Welcome Dogs: Welcome
Licences: Parking: Off-street
Directions: J40 M6, Penrith A66, follow past Keswick.
Pass the turn for Braithwaite, then turn left after 150
yards – hotel faces you.

Morrel's Restaurant & Rooms

 ★ ★

34 Lake Road, Keswick, Cumbria, CA12 5DQ
Tel: 01768 772666
Email: info@morrels.co.uk
Web: www.morrels.co.uk
Rooms: 14 all ensuite Pricing: Sgl £25–35 Dbl £50–70
Dinner from £15 CC: Accepted
Room facilities: Children: Welcome
Dogs: Welcome Licences: Parking: Off-street
Directions: Leave M6 at Junction 40. Follow A66
Keswick then take signs to the lake. Morrel's is on left
by roundabout.

Thwaite Howe Hotel

 ★ ★

Thornthwaite, nr Keswick, Cumbria, CA12 5SA
Tel: 01768 778281 Fax: 01768 778529
Email: info@thwaitehowe.co.uk
Web: www.thwaitehowe.co.uk
Seasonal closure: Mid November-1st February

Exquisite small country house hotel set against
Thornthwaite Forest and overlooking Derwent valley
across to Skiddaw, Dodd and Latrigg and mountains.
Quite, peaceful retreat offering good food and wines,
comfortable and well furnished rooms and wonderful
walks in the immediate vicinity.
Rooms: 8 all ensuite
Pricing: Sgl £45–65 Dbl £90–110 Dinner from £19.50
CC: Accepted Room facilities:
Children: Welcome 12yrs min age Dogs: Welcome
Licences: Parking: Off-street
Directions: A66 past Keswick. Left at Thornthwaite. After
Thornthwaite Gallery car park fork right, hotel at top of hill.

Swinside Lodge Hotel

Blue Ribbon Winner

 ★

Grange Road, Newlands, Keswick, Cumbria, CA12 5UE
Tel: 01768 772948 Fax: 01768 772948
Email: info@swinsidelodge-hotel.co.uk
Web: www.swinsidelodge-hotel.co.uk
Rooms: 7 all ensuite Pricing: Dinner from £25
CC: Accepted Room facilities:
Children: Welcome 10yrs min age
Dogs: Guide dogs only Licences:
Parking: Off-street and monitored
Directions: Leave Keswick on the A66 to Cockermouth.
Turn left signposted Portinscale. Continue on this road
for 2 miles, signposted Grange, not Swinside.
See advert on following page

Cottage in the Wood

Whinlatter Pass , Braithwaite, Keswick,
Cumbria, CA12 5TW
Tel: 017687 78409 Fax: 017687 78064
Email: cottage@whinlatter.fsnet.co.uk
Web: www.lake-district.net/cottage
Rooms: 10 all en-suite
Pricing: Sgl £20–50 Dbl £71–84 Dinner from £18.50
CC: accepted Room facilities: Access:
Children: Welcome 2yrs min age Dogs: Welcome
Licenses: Parking: Off-street and monitored
Directions: Exit the A66 after Keswick for Braithwaite.
Follow signs for Whinlatter Visitors Centre. Hotel is 400
yards before Visitors Centre.

Northwest

Acorn House Hotel

◆ ◆ ◆ ◆ ✳

Ambleside Road, Keswick, Cumbria, CA12 4DL
Tel: 01768 772553 Fax: 01768 775332
Email: info@acornhousehotel.co.uk
Web: www.acornhousehotel.co.uk
Seasonal closure: November to February
Rooms: 10 all ensuite ♨ ✍ ⊗
Pricing: Sgl £35.50–50 Dbl £57–65 CC: Accepted
Room facilities: ☐ ☕
Children: Welcome 8yrs min age
Licences: ⚲
Parking: Off-street
Directions: 400m from town centre, opposite St John's Church on Ambleside Road.

Dalegarth House Country Hotel

◆ ◆ ◆ ◆ ✳

Portinscale, Keswick, Cumbria, CA12 5RQ
Tel: 01768 772817 Fax: 01768 772817
Email: john@dalegarth-house.co.uk
Web: www.dalegarth-house.co.uk
Rooms: 10 all ensuite ♨ ⊗
Pricing: Sgl £32–34 Dbl £64–68 Dinner from £20
CC: Accepted
Room facilities: ☐ ☕
Children: Welcome 5yrs min age
Licences: ⚲ Parking: Off-street
Directions: Approach Portinscale from A66. Enter village, pass Farmers Arms. Dalegarth approx 100 yards on left, behind Dorothy Well.

Honister House

◆ ◆ ◆ ◆ ✳ ⚘

1 Borrowdale Road, Keswick, Cumbria, CA12 5DD
Tel: 017687 73181 Fax: 0870 1202948
Email: philandsueh@aol.com
Web: www.honisterhouse.co.uk

A warm welcome awaits you at our 18th-century home. We are centrally located close to all local amenities. We especially cater for walkers, cyclists and families. Drying room and cycle storage. Special breaks and brochure available.
Rooms: 3 all ensuite ♨ ⊗
Pricing: Sgl £25–45 Dbl £45–65 CC: Accepted
Room facilities: ☐ ☕
Children: Welcome ☕ Parking: Off-street
Directions: From Tourist Information office we are 400 yards along lake road, on left-hand side, opposite 'George Fisher's'.

Parkfield No Smoking Guest House

The Heads, Keswick, Cumbria, CA12 5ES
Tel: 01768 772328 Fax: 01768 771396
Email: enquires@parkfieldkeswick.com
Web: www.parkfieldkeswick.com
Rooms: 8 all ensuite ⊗
Pricing: Sgl £32–35 Dbl £52–54 CC: Accepted
Room facilities: ▢ ☺ Children: Welcome 16yrs min age
Parking: Off-street and monitored
Directions: From A66 or A591, follow road through town and turn left at mini-roundabout. After 500m, turn right onto 'The Heads'. Parkfield is on left.

Rickerby Grange

Portinscale, near Keswick, Cumbria, CA12 5RH
Tel: 01768 772344 Fax: 01768 775588
Email: val@ricor.demon.co.uk
Web: www.ricor.demon.co.uk
Rooms: 12 (11 ensuite) ✥ ⊗
Pricing: Sgl £32–34 Dbl £64–68 Dinner from £13
CC: Accepted
Room facilities: ▢ ☎ ☺
Access: ♿ Children: Welcome 5yrs min age
Dogs: Welcome Licences: ◭ ♣
Parking: Off-street
Directions: Bypass Keswick on A66 Cockermouth road. Turn left at Portinscale sign. Pass Farmers Arms Inn on left, and turn down second lane to the right.

Shemara Guest House

27 Bank Street, Keswick, Cumbria, CA12 5JZ
Tel: 01768 773936 Fax: 01768 780785
Email: info@shemara.uk.com
Web: www.shemara.uk.com
Seasonal closure: Christmas
Rooms: 7 all ensuite ✥ ⊗
Pricing: Sgl £25 Dbl £39–50 CC: Accepted
Room facilities: ▢ ☺
Children: Welcome 2yrs min age
Dogs: Welcome Parking: Off-street
Directions: From A66, go into Keswick, over pedestrian crossing. Pass car park on left; guest house is on right.

Sunnyside Guest House

♦♦♦♦ ⋇

25 Southey Street, Keswick, Cumbria, CA12 4EF
Tel: 01768 772446
Email: mbrownandco@alo.com
Web: www.survey.u-net.com
Seasonal closure: 18–28 December
Rooms: 7 (5 ensuite) ✥ ⊗
Pricing: Sgl £25 Dbl £40–50 CC: Accepted
Room facilities: ▢ ☺
Children: Welcome Dogs: Guide dogs only
Parking: Off-street
Directions: From M6 take A66 west, turn off for Keswick, right at T-junction, left at war memorial. Sunnyside 100 yards on left.

Tarn Hows

3/5 Eskin Street, Keswick, Cumbria, CA12 4DH
Tel: 01768 773217 Fax: 01768 773217
Email: info@tarnhows.co.uk
Web: www.tarnhows.co.uk
Rooms: 8 (6 ensuite) ⊗
Pricing: Sgl £22–26 Dbl £44–52 Dinner from £13
CC: Accepted
Room facilities: ▢ ☺
Children: Welcome 6yrs min age Dogs: Welcome
Licences: ♣ Parking: Off-street
Directions: From Penrith or Grasmere follow Keswick Town Centre. After Conservative Club turn left into Greta Street and continue into Eskin Street.

The Paddock Guest House

Wordsworth Street, Keswick, Cumbria, CA12 4HU
Tel: 017687 72510 Fax: 017687 72510
Email: val@keswickonderwentwater.fsnet.co.uk
Web: www.keswickguesthouse.com
Rooms: 6 all ensuite ✥
Pricing: Dbl £38–48 CC: Accepted
Room facilities: ▢ ☺
Children: Welcome 5yrs min age ⵏ
Licences: ♣ Parking: Off-street
Directions: A591 to town centre, pass the Dogs Inn, under bridge, third left into Wordsworth Street. Paddock is on the right.

Pitcairn House

7 Blencathra Street, Keswick, Cumbria, CA12 4HW
Tel: 017687 72453 Fax: 017687 73887
Email: enquiries@pitcairnhouse.co.uk
Web: www.pitcairnhouse.co.uk
Rooms: 8 (5 ensuite) ⊗
Pricing: Sgl £18.50–36 Dbl £32–44
Room facilities: ▢ ☺
Children: Welcome Dogs: Welcome
Parking: Off-street
Directions: From Penrith Road turn left into Station Street and immediately left again into Southey Street, Blencathra Street is second left.

Swiss Court Guest House

25 Bank Street, Keswick, Cumbria, CA12 5JZ
Tel: 01768 772637 Fax: 01768 780146
Email: info@swisscourt.co.uk
Web: www.swisscourt.co.uk
Rooms: 7 all ensuite ✥ ⊗
Pricing: Sgl £20–22.50 Dbl £40–45 CC: Accepted
Room facilities: ▢ ☺
Children: Welcome 8yrs min age ⵏ
Dogs: Welcome
Parking: Off-street
Directions: Swiss Court is located on the main through road in Keswick, opposite Bell Close car park and the police station.

Kirkby Lonsdale, Cumbria

The Snooty Fox Tavern

Main Street, Kirkby Lonsdale, Cumbria, LA6 2AH
Tel: 015242 71308 Fax: 015242 72642
Web: www.mortal-man-inns.co.uk
Rooms: 9 all ensuite
Pricing: Sgl £36 Dbl £56 Dinner from £10
CC: Accepted
Room facilities: ☐ ☕
Children: Welcome ♇ Dogs: Welcome
Licences: ▟▟▟ Parking: Off-street and monitored
Directions: M6 J36, A65 (Skipton road), approx 7 miles,
turn left into Kirkby Lonsdale (signposted). Snooty fox
situated on the main street just off main square,
parking at the rear.

Kirkby Stephen, Cumbria

Black Swan Hotel

Ravenstonedale, Kirkby Stephen, Cumbria, CA17 4NG
Tel: 01539 623204 Fax: 01539 623604

Knutsford, Cheshire

Cottons Hotel & Spa

Manchester Road, Knutsford, Cheshire, WA16 0SU
Tel: 01565 650333 Fax: 01565 755351
Email: cottons@shirehotels.co.uk
Web: www.shirehotels.co.uk
Rooms: 109 all ensuite 🖨 Ⓢ
Pricing: Sgl £145 Dbl £165 CC: Accepted
Room facilities: ☐ ☎ ☕ ✎
Access: ↥↥ ♿
Conference: 14 meeting rooms (Thtr 200 max)
Children: Welcome ♇ ▒Ⓒ Dogs: Guide dogs only
Licences: ◬ ▟▟▟
Leisure: Indoor pool, Gym, Health spa, Beauty salon,
Tennis Parking: Off-street and monitored
Directions: Just 1 mile from Junction 19 of M6, on the
A50 Knutsford to Warrington road.

Mere Court Hotel

Warrington Road, Mere, Knutsford,
Cheshire, WA16 0RW
Tel: 01565 831000 Fax: 01565 831001
Email: sales@merecourt.co.uk
Web: www.merecourt.co.uk
Rooms: 34 all ensuite 🍴 🖨 Ⓢ
Pricing: Sgl £80–130 Dbl £90–150 Dinner from £24.95
CC: Accepted Room facilities: ☐ ☎ ☕ ✎
Access: ↥↥ ♿
Conference: 11 meeting rooms (Thtr 200 max), 24hr-
delegate from £149, day-delegate rate from £49
Children: Welcome ♇ ▒Ⓒ Dogs: Guide dogs only
Licences: ◬ ▟▟▟ Parking: Off-street and monitored
See advert on next page

Longview Hotel

Manchester Road, Knutsford, Cheshire, WA16 0LX
Tel: 01565 632119 Fax: 01565 652402
Email: enquiries@longviewhotel.com
Web: www.longviewhotel.com
Rooms: 26 all ensuite 🖨 Ⓢ
Pricing: Sgl £52.50–72.50 Dbl £72.50–135.50
Dinner from £7.95 CC: Accepted
Room facilities: ☐ ☎ ☕ ✎
Children: Welcome ♇ ▒Ⓒ Dogs: Welcome
Licences: ▟▟▟ Parking: Off-street
Directions: Leave M6 at Junction 19 and take A556
towards Chester. After 1 mile turn left at lights. After
1³/₄ miles, turn left at roundabout and hotel is 150
yards on right.

Dog Inn

Well Bank Lane, Over Peover, Knutsford,
Cheshire, WA16 8UP
Tel: 01625 861421 Fax: 01625 864800
Web: www.cheshireinns.co.uk
Rooms: 6 all ensuite
Room facilities: ☐ ☎ ☕ ✎ Children: Welcome
Licences: ▟▟▟ Leisure: Games room
Parking: Off-street
Directions: From Knutsford, follow A50 Holmes Chapel
Road. Turn left at "Whipping Stocks". Proceed for 2
miles.

Travelodge Knutsford

Travel Accommodation
A556, Chester Road, Tabley, Knutsford,
Cheshire, WA16 0PP
Web: www.travelodge.co.uk
Rooms: 32 all ensuite Ⓢ
Pricing: Sgl £54.40 Dbl £58.85 CC: Accepted
Room facilities: ☐ ☕ Access: ♿

Travelodge Knutsford, M6

Travel Accommodation
M6, Junction 18-19, Moto Service Area,
Off Northwich Road, Knutsford, Cheshire, WA1 0TL
Web: www.travelodge.co.uk
Rooms: 54 all ensuite Ⓢ
Pricing: Sgl £54.40 Dbl £58.85 CC: Accepted
Room facilities: ☐ ☕ Access: ♿

Lancaster, Lancashire

Lancaster House Hotel

★★★★

Green Lane, Ellel, Lancaster, LA1 4GJ
Tel: 01524 844822 Fax: 01524 844766
Email: lancaster@elhmail.co.uk
Web: www.elh.co.uk
Rooms: 80 all ensuite 🛏 🚭
Pricing: Sgl £91.45–138.45 Dbl £100.90–147.90
CC: Accepted
Room facilities: 🖥 ☎ 🍵 🎚
Access: ♿
Conference: 14 meeting rooms (Thtr 180 max), 24hr-delegate from £89, day-delegate rate from £33.50
Children: Welcome 🍴 ♨
Dogs: Welcome
Licences: ⚖ 🎭
Leisure: Indoor pool, Gym, Beauty salon
Parking: Off-street and monitored
Directions: From Junction 33 on the M6, turn right at roundabout, and travel approx. 2 miles, where it is sign posted on right.
See advert on this page

The Castle Hotel

★★

49 Main street, Hornby, near Lancaster,
Lancashire, LA2 8ST
Tel: 015242 21204 Fax: 015242 22258

Family-run hotel with facilities for conferences and weddings. Games room and children's room. Excellent bar food and also an exclusive restaurant are available, all set in the Lune valley.
Rooms: 8 all ensuite 🛏 🚭
Pricing: Dinner from £15 CC: Accepted
Room facilities: 🖥 ☎ 🍵
Children: Welcome 🍴
Dogs: Guide dogs only
Licences: 🎭
Leisure: Games room, Snooker/billiards
Parking: Off-street and monitored
Directions: J34 M6, follow A683 to Kirkby Lonsdale. Hotel is situated on the A683 in Hornby.

The Greaves Hotel

★ ★

Greaves Road, Lancaster, Lancaster,
Lancastershire, LA1 4UP
Tel: 01524 63943 Fax: 01524 382679
Email: greaves@mitchellshotels.co.uk
Web: www.mitchelllshotels.co.uk

Rooms: 16 all ensuite 🛏 Room facilities: 📺 ☎ 🍵
Conference: 2 meeting rooms (Thtr 80 max)
Children: Welcome Dogs: Guide dogs only
Parking: Off-street
Directions: From J33 follow the A6 to Lancaster. The
Greaves is situated on the left handside ½ a mile
before the city centre.

Liverpool, Merseyside

The Gladstone Hotel

★ ★ ★

Lord Nelson Street, Liverpool, Merseyside, L3 5QB
Tel: 0151 471 0054 Fax: 0151 707 0352
Email: reservations@gladstone-hotel.co.uk
Rooms: 154 all ensuite 🍴 🚭
Pricing: Dinner from £8.95 CC: Accepted
Room facilities: 📺 ☎ 🍵
Access: ⬆ ♿
Conference: 13 meeting rooms (Thtr 500 max), 24hr-
delegate from £75, day-delegate rate from £28
Children: Welcome ⴕ Dogs: Guide dogs only
Licences: ⵊⵊⵊ Parking: Off-street and monitored

Aachen Hotel

♦ ♦ ♦ ⸙

91 Mount Pleasant, Liverpool, Merseyside, L3 5TB
Tel: 0151 709 3477 Fax: 0151 709 1126/3633
Email: enquirysaachenhotel.co.uk
Web: www.merseyword.com/aachen
Seasonal closure: Christmas to New Year
Rooms: 18 (11 ensuite) 🍴 🚭
Pricing: Sgl £30–40 Dbl £46–54 Dinner from £12.75
CC: Accepted Room facilities: 📺 ☎ 🍵
Access: ♿ Children: Welcome ⴕ ⸙
Licences: ⵊⵊⵊ Leisure: Snooker/billiards
Parking: Off-street and monitored
Directions: Follow signs city centre to Mount Pleasant
car park.

Campanile Hotel

Travel Accommodation
Wapping & Chaloner Street, Queens Dock,
Liverpool, L3 4AJ
Tel: 0151 709 8104 Fax: 0151 709 8725
Email: liverpool@envergure.co.uk
Web: www.envergure.fr

Campanile hotels offer comfortable and convenient
budget accommodation and a traditional French-style
Bistro providing freshly-cooked food for breakfast,
lunch and dinner. All rooms ensuite with tea/coffee-
making facilities, DDT and TV with Satelite channels.
Rooms: 100 all ensuite 🚭
Pricing: Sgl £49.90 Dbl £55.85 Dinner from £11.55
CC: Accepted
Room facilities: 📺 ☎ 🍵 🔌 Access: ♿
Conference: meeting rooms (Thtr 30 max), day-
delegate rate from £19.50
Children: Welcome ⴕ Dogs: Welcome
Licences: ⵊⵊⵊ Parking: Off-street
Directions: Follow brown tourist signs for the Albert
Dock. The Campanile Hotel is next to Queens Dock.

Travelodge Liverpool Central

Travel Accommodation
25 Haymarket, Liverpool, L1
Web: www.travelodge.co.uk
Rooms: 142 all ensuite 🚭
Pricing: Sgl £57.40 Dbl £61.85 CC: Accepted
Room facilities: 📺 🍵 Access: ♿

Travelodge Liverpool South

❖

Brunswick Dock, Sefton Street, Liverpool, L3 4BN
Web: www.travelodge.co.uk
Rooms: 87 all ensuite 🚭
Room facilities: 📺 🍵 Access: ♿

Loweswater, Cumbria

Grange Country House Hotel

★ ★

Loweswater, near Cockermouth, Cumbria, CA13 0SU
Tel: 01946 861211
Web: thegrange-loweswater.co.uk
Rooms: 8 all ensuite 🍴 🛏 🚭
Pricing: Sgl £30–40 Dbl £30–37 Dinner from £16
Room facilities: 📺 🍵
Children: Welcome ⴕ ⸙ Dogs: Welcome
Licences: ⵊⵊⵊ Parking: Off-street
Directions: A66 to Keswick and Cockermouth; left onto
A5086 Lamplugh/Egremont; travel 4 miles, take left
turn for Mockerkin village. Left for Loweswater; hotel at
bottom of hill.

Lymm, Cheshire

Travelodge Lymm (MOTO)

Travel Accommodation
Lymm Services, Poplar 2000, Cliffe Lane, Lymm,
Cheshire, WA13 0SP
Web: www.travelodge.co.uk
Rooms: 61 all ensuite
Pricing: Sgl £47.40 Dbl £51.85 CC: Accepted
Room facilities: ▢ ☕ Access: ♿

Lytham St Annes, Lancashire

Clifton Arms Hotel

★★★★ ⌂
West Beach, Lytham St Annes, Lancashire, FY8 5QJ
Tel: 01253 739898 Fax: 01253 730657
Email: welcome@cliftonarms.com
Web: www.cliftonarms.com
Rooms: 48 all ensuite ✇ ▥ ⊗
Pricing: Sgl £93–103 Dbl £117–130 Dinner from £21.50
CC: Accepted Room facilities: ▢ ☎ ☕ ☏
Access: ⥮ ♿
Conference: 6 meeting rooms (Thtr 200 max), 24hr-
delegate from £35, day-delegate rate from £155
Children: Welcome ♜ ⅀ Dogs: Welcome
Licences: ◈ ⅲ Parking: Off-street and monitored
Directions: From M55 Junction 4, follow signs for
A584. Hotel is situated on the seafront at Lytham.

Chadwick Hotel

★★★
South Promenade, Lytham St Annes,
Lancashire, FY8 1NP
Tel: 01253 720061 Fax: 01253 714455
Email: sales@thechadwickhotel.com
Web: www.thechadwickhotel.com

Seafront family-run award-winning hotel and leisure
complex renowned for good food service and comfort.
See our website and brochure for our special breaks
and holidays.
Rooms: 75 all ensuite ✇ ▥ ⊗
Pricing: Sgl £46–48 Dbl £64–69 Dinner from £16
CC: Accepted Room facilities: ▢ ☎ ☕
Access: ⥮ ♿
Conference: 3 meeting rooms (Thtr 70 max), 24hr-
delegate from £68, day-delegate rate from £24
Children: Welcome ♜ ⅀ Dogs: Guide dogs only
Licences: ⅲ Leisure: Indoor pool, Gym, Health spa,
Games room

Parking: Monitored
Directions: From M6 to M55, then follow signs to Lytham
St Annes. Hotel is on the Promenade at St Annes.

Fernlea Hotel

★★★
11–17 South Promenade, Lytham St Annes,
Lancashire, FY8 1LU
Tel: 01253 726726 Fax: 01253 721561
Email: enquiries@thefernleahotel.co.uk
Web: www.thefernleahotel.co.uk
Rooms: 110 all ensuite ✇ ▥ ⊗
Pricing: Sgl £40–60 Dbl £80–120 Dinner from £15.50
CC: Accepted Room facilities: ▢ ☎ ☕ ☏
Access: ⥮ ♿
Conference: 10 meeting rooms (Thtr 300 max), 24hr-
delegate rate from £70, day-delegate rate from £27.50
Children: Welcome ♜ ⅀ Dogs: Welcome
Licences: ◈ ⅲ Leisure: Indoor pool, Gym, Health spa,
Beauty salon, Games room, Snooker/billiards
Parking: Off-street
Directions: From M6 take M55 to Blackpool, follow
signs to St Annes. Property is 100 yards south of St
Annes pier on the promenade.

Lindum

★★
63–67 South Promenade, Lytham St Annes,
Lancashire, FY8 1LZ
Tel: 01253 721534 Fax: 01253 721364
Email: info@lindumhotel.co.uk
Web: www.lindumhotel.co.uk

Holiday or business in St Annes? You will find exactly
what you are looking for at our popular seafront hotel,
renowned for its excellent food and warm welcome
Rooms: 78 all ensuite ✇ ⊗
Pricing: Sgl £30–35 Dbl £50–75 Dinner from £16
CC: Accepted Room facilities: ▢ ☎ ☕ Access: ⥮
Conference: 4 meeting rooms (Thtr 75 max), 24hr-
delegate from £60, day-delegate rate from £17.50
Children: Welcome ♜ ⅀ Dogs: Welcome
Licences: ⅲ Leisure: Games room
Parking: Off-street
Directions: Situated on the main promenade (A584) at
St Annes.

Endsleigh Hotel

◆ ◆ ◆

315 Clifton Drive South, Lytham St Annes,
Lancashire, FY8 1HN
Tel: 01253 725622 Fax: 01253 720072
Rooms: 15 all ensuite 🐾 ⊛
Pricing: Sgl £23 Dbl £46 Dinner from £9
Room facilities: ▢ 🖫 Children: Welcome �
Dogs: Guide dogs only Licences: 🛉
Parking: Off-street
Directions: 2 miles east of of Blackpool on the A584.
First hotel east of St Anne's Square shopping centre.

Strathmore Hotel

◆ ◆ ◆

305 Clifton Drive South, Lytham St Annes,
Lancashire, FY8 1HN
Tel: 01253 725478
Rooms: 8 (5 ensuite)
Pricing: Sgl £18–24 Dbl £36–48 Dinner from £5
Room facilities: ▢ 🖫
Children: Welcome 9yrs min age � Licences: 🛉
Parking: Off-street
Directions: Follow signs to St Annes off M55.
Strathmore Hotel after 200 yards on main Blackpool to
Preston road.

Macclesfield, Cheshire

Shrigley Hall Hotel

★ ★ ★ ★ ★ 🛏

Shrigley Park, Pott Shrigley, Macclesfield,
Cheshire, SK10 5SB
Tel: 01625 575757 Fax: 01625 573323
Email: shrigleyhall@paramount-hotels.co.uk
Web: www.paramount-hotels.co.uk

PARAMOUNT
GROUP OF HOTELS

Set in 262 acres of rolling Cheshire countryside looking
out over the Cheshire Plain. 18th century building
boasts history and character. On edge of Peak District.
Rooms: 143 all en-suite 🐾 🚗 ⊛
Pricing: Sgl £125–340 Dbl £155–340
CC: accepted
Room facilities: ▢ ☎ 🖫 Access: |↟↟
Conference: 12 meeting rooms (Thtr 250 max), 24hr-
delegate from £177, day-delegate rate from £56
Children: Welcome �

Dogs: Welcome
Licenses: 🜹 🛉
Leisure: Indoor pool, Gym, Health spa, Beauty salon,
Tennis, Golf Parking: Off-street and monitored
Directions: 12 miles from Manchester Airport. Through
Macclesfield into Bollington. Follow signs for Pott
Shrigley.

Moorhayes House Hotel

◆ ◆ ◆

27 Manchester Road, Tytherington, Macclesfield,
Cheshire, SK10 2JJ
Tel: 01625 433228 Fax: 01625 429878
Email: helen@moorhayes.co.uk
Web: www.smoothhound.co.uk/hotels/moorhaye
Rooms: 8 all ensuite ⊛
Pricing: Sgl £35 Dbl £55 CC: Accepted
Room facilities: ▢ ☎ 🖫 ☏
Children: Welcome �
Dogs: Welcome
Parking: Off-street
Directions: From Macclesfield, take the A538
northbound, signposted Tytherington. Moorhayes is on
left, half a mile from town.

Travelodge Macclesfield

Travel Accommodation
A523, London Road, South Adlington, Macclesfield,
Cheshire, SK12 4NA
Web: www.travelodge.co.uk
Rooms: 32 all ensuite ⊛
Pricing: Sgl £54.40 Dbl £58.85 CC: Accepted
Room facilities: ▢ ☕ 🖫 Access: ♿

Manchester

The Lowry Hotel

★ ★ ★ ★ ★ 🛏 🛏 🛏

50 Dearmans Place, Chapel Wharf, Salford,
Manchester, M3 5LH
Tel: 0161 827 4000 Fax: 0161 827 4001
Email: enquiries@thelowryhotel.com
Web: www.roccofortehotels.com
Rooms: 165 all ensuite ⊛
Pricing: Sgl £215 Dbl £260 Dinner from £18
CC: Accepted
Room facilities: ▢ ☎ 🖫 ☏ ❄ Access: |↟↟ ♿
Conference: 12 meeting rooms (Thtr 350 max), 24hr-
delegate from £220, day-delegate rate from £65
Children: Welcome �
Dogs: Welcome
Licences: 🜹 🛉
Leisure: Gym, Health spa, Beauty salon
Parking: Off-street and monitored
Directions: Take the M602 to Salford and Manchester
until you see the Grosvenor casino. Turn left at the
traffic light on to Water Street and past Granada
studios. At the end turn on to New Quay street/Trinity
way. At the first major set of traffic lights turn right on
to Chapel street, then right into Dearmans place.
See advert on next page

THE LOWRY HOTEL
MANCHESTER

The *Lowry Hotel*
MANCHESTER'S MOST FASHIONABLE VENUE

A stylish and vibrant venue in the heart of the city, with friendly service, contemporary design, space, modern comforts, hi-tech facilities, attention to detail and renowned cuisine in the award-winning River Room Marco Pierre White restaurant. All rooms are flooded with natural light and are equipped with the latest in-room facilities and comforts. Complement your stay with a visit to our holistic spa and fitness centre or relax in our library lounge. For business meetings we have a separate self-contained floor of banqueting suites.

ROCCO FORTE
HOTELS

The Lowry Hotel 50 Dearmans Place Chapel Wharf Salford Manchester M3 5LH
Telephone +44 (0)161 827 4000 Facsimile +44 (0)161 827 4001
E-mail enquiries@thelowryhotel.com Website www.roccofortehotels.com

Copthorne Hotel Manchester

★★★★ ♖

Clippers Quay, Salford Quays, Salford,
Manchester, M50 3SN
Tel: 0161 873 7321 Fax: 0161 877 8110
Email: manchester@mill-cop.com
Web: millenniumhotels.com

At this four-star property guests enjoy spacious
comfort within a peaceful location overlooking the
waterfront. Ideally situated minutes from the motorway
with complementary car parking.
Rooms: 166 all ensuite ♨ ⊗
Pricing: Sgl £145–170 Dbl £145–170 Dinner from £21
CC: Accepted Room facilities: ⬜ ☎ ⊜ ☎
Access: ⒧⒧ ♿
Conference: 8 meeting rooms (Thtr 150 max), 24hr-
delegate from £165, day-delegate rate from £45
Children: Welcome ♔ Dogs: Guide dogs only
Licences: ♦♦♦ Leisure: Indoor pool, Gym, Health spa
Parking: Off-street and monitored
Directions: From M602 follow A57/A5063 to Salford.
A5063 Salford Quays onto Trafford Road. Turn right
into Clippers Quay, hotel on right.

Le Meridien Palace

★★★★

Oxford Street, Manchester, M60 7HA
Tel: 0800 028 2840 Fax: 0161 288 2222
Email: linda.hefferon@lemeridien.com
Web: www.lemeridien.com
Rooms: 252 all ensuite ⊗
Room facilities: ⬜ ☎ ⊜ ☎ Access: ⒧⒧ ♿
Conference: 12 meeting rooms (Thtr 1000 max), 24hr-
delegate from £165, day-delegate rate from £49
Children: Welcome ♔ Dogs: Guide dogs only
Licences: ♦♦ ♦♦♦ Parking: Off-street and monitored
Directions: Follow signs for Manchester city centre;
pick up signs for aquatic centre. Hotel is two minutes'
drive on the same side.

Le Méridien Victoria & Albert

★★★★★ ♖ ♖

Water Street, Manchester, M3 4JQ
Tel: 0800 028 2840 Fax: 0161 834 2484
Email: rm1452@lemeridien.com
Web: www.lemeridien.com
Rooms: 158 all ensuite ⊗
Pricing: Sgl £150–180 Dbl £150–180 Dinner from £15

CC: Accepted Room facilities: ⬜ ☎ ⊜ ☎ ❄
Access: ⒧⒧ ♿
Conference: 5 meeting rooms (Thtr 250 max), 24hr-
delegate from £179, day-delegate rate from £55
Children: Welcome ᗺ⒞ Dogs: Guide dogs only
Licences: ♦♦ ♦♦♦ Parking: Off-street and monitored
Directions: M6, M62, M602 Manchester. Exit M602 for
A57 Manchester, continue through lights, at 2nd lights
turn left onto Water Street.

Marriott Worsley Park Hotel & Country Club

★★★★ ♖ ♖

Worsley Park, Manchester, M28 2QT
Tel: 0161 975 2000 Fax: 0161 799 6341
Web: www.marriotthotels.com/mangs
Rooms: 158 all ensuite ♨ ⊗
Room facilities: ⬜ ☎ ⊜ ☎
Access: ⒧⒧ ♿
Children: Welcome ♔ ♘ Dogs: Guide dogs only
Licences: ♦♦ ♦♦♦
Leisure: Indoor pool, Gym, Health spa, Beauty salon,
Golf Parking: Off-street and monitored
Directions: Exit J13 M60, follow signs for A575
Worsley; hotel is 1/2 mile on left. From A580 follow A575
for Worsley.

Bredbury Hall Hotel and Country Club

★★★ ♖

Dark Lane, Goyt Valley, Bredbury, Stockport,
Cheshire, SK6 2DH
Tel: 0161 430 7421 Fax: 0161 430 5079
Email: reservations@bredburyhallhotel.co.uk
Web: www.bredburyhallhotel.co.uk

Family-run hotel, one mile M60, 7 miles Manchester
Airport. 150 ensuite bedrooms, corner baths, showers,
satellite TV, conference facilities for up to 150 people.
Country Club weekends. Leisure 2003.
Rooms: 150 all ensuite ♨ 🖼
Pricing: Sgl £57.50–77.50 Dbl £80.50–95.50
Dinner from £16.50 CC: Accepted
Room facilities: ⬜ ☎ ⊜ ☎
Conference: 8 meeting rooms (Thtr 150 max)
Children: Welcome ᗺ⒞ Licences: ♦♦ ♦♦♦
Leisure: Snooker/billiards
Parking: Off-street and monitored
Directions: Leave M60 at Junction 25. Follow the
Bredbury Hall signs. Turn right at traffic lights, then
turn left after 400 yards into Osbourne Street.

Jurys Inn Manchester
★★★
56 Great Bridgewater Street, Manchester, M1 5LE
Tel: +353(0)1 6070000 Fax: +353(0)1 6316999
Email: bookings@jurysdoyle.com
Web: www.jurysdoyle.com

JURYS DOYLE
H O T E L S

Rooms: 265 all ensuite 🐾 ⊗
Pricing: Sgl £65–71 Dbl £65–71 Dinner from £18
CC: Accepted
Room facilities: 🖵 ☎ ☕ 📞 ❄ Access: ⊥⊥ ⅃
Children: Welcome ☍
Dogs: Guide dogs only
Licences: ⅲ
Directions: Located 9 miles/14 km from Manchester
Airport. Piccadilly Station 1 mile. G-mex Metrolink
Station two minutes walk.

Stanneylands Hotel
★★★★ 🔔 🔔 🔔
Stanneylands Road, Wilmslow, Cheshire, SK9 4EY
Tel: 01625 525225 Fax: 01625 537282
Email: enquiries@stanneylandshotel.co.uk
Web: www.stanneylandshotel.co.uk
Rooms: 32 all ensuite 🗇 ⊗
Pricing: Sgl £69–128 Dbl £102–138 Dinner from £25
CC: Accepted
Room facilities: 🖵 ☎ ☕ 📞
Access: ⅃
Conference: 6 meeting rooms (Thtr 120 max), 24hr-
delegate from £140, day-delegate rate from £40
Children: Welcome ☍ ⅋
Licences: ⟁ ⅲ
Parking: Off-street and monitored
Directions: Leave M56 at Junction 5, follow signs to
Styal. Follow B5166 and then B5358, hotel signposted
on right-hand side.
See advert on this page

Willow Bank Hotel
★★★
Wilmslow Road, Fallowfield, Manchester, M14 6AF
Tel: 0161 224 0461 Fax: 0161 257 2561
Email: willowbankhotel@feathers.uk.com
Web: www.feathers.uk.com
Rooms: 120 all ensuite 🐾 🗇 ⊗
Pricing: Sgl £54–69 Dbl £74–125 Dinner from £10.95
CC: Accepted
Room facilities: 🖵 ☎ ☕ 📞
Conference: 4 meeting rooms (Thtr 120 max), 24hr-
delegate from £99, day-delegate rate from £30
Children: Welcome ☍ ⅋
Dogs: Guide dogs only
Licences: ⟁ ⅲ
Parking: Off-street and monitored
Directions: M6 M56 Manchester Airport go to end
A5103 dual carriageway; fifth set of lights turn right;
turn second left at lights into Wilmslow Road; hotel
500 yards on left.

Stanneylands Hotel
 RAC ★★★   RAC Dining Award 🔔🔔🔔

Stanneylands Hotel is a strikingly handsome
house set in beautiful gardens. Dine in
elegance in our award-winning, oak-panelled
dining room, which serves outstanding
cuisine and fine wines.

Stanneylands Road, Wilmslow, Cheshire, SK9 4EY
Tel: 01625 525225   Fax: 01625 537282
enquiries@stanneylandshotel.co.uk
Web: www.stanneylandshotel.co.uk

Comfort Inn, Manchester
★★
Hyde Road, Birch Street, West Gorton,
Manchester, M12 5NT
Tel: 0161 220 8700 Fax: 0161 220 8848
Email: admin@gb615.u-net.com
Web: www.choicehotels.com
Rooms: 90 all ensuite 🐾 ⊗
Pricing: Sgl £40–61.25 Dbl £50–70 Dinner from £12.75
CC: Accepted
Room facilities: 🖵 ☎ ☕
Access: ⅃
Children: Welcome ☍ ⅋
Dogs: Welcome
Licences: ⅲ
Leisure: Games room
Parking: Off-street and monitored
Directions: Leave M60 at junction 24 taking the A57
towards Manchester. Situated just off the A57, 2¹/₂
miles southeast of city.

Northwest

Monton House Hotel - Venture Hotels

★★

116–118 Monton Road, Monton, Eccles, Manchester,
Greater Manchester, M30 9HG
Tel: 0161 789 7811 Fax: 0161 787 7609
Email: hotel@montonhousehotel.co.uk
Web: www.montonhousehotel.co.uk

VENTURE HOTELS

Superbly located hotel with 62 ensuite bedrooms. 4
miles to Manchester city centre, minutes from M602,
M60, M62. Offering excellent restaurants, bar and
conference facilities at value for money prices.
Rooms: 62 all ensuite
Pricing: Sgl £52.50–55 Dbl £62.50–65 Dinner from £10
CC: Accepted Room facilities:
Access:
Conference: 3 meeting rooms (Thtr 150 max), 24hr-
delegate from £90, day-delegate rate from £27.50
Children: Welcome Dogs: Welcome
Licences: Parking: Off-street and monitored
Directions: Exit M602 at J2 turn to Pendleton and take
second left onto Half Edge Lane. Hotel 1 mile on right.

Highbury Hotel

◆◆◆◆ ✍

113 Monton Road, Monton, Manchester, M30 9HQ
Tel: 0161 787 8545 Fax: 0161 787 9023
Email: enquiries@highbury-hotel.co.uk
Web: www.highbury-hotel.co.uk
Rooms: 16 all ensuite
Pricing: Sgl £30–38 Dbl £42–49.50 CC: Accepted
Room facilities:
Access:
Children: Welcome
Dogs: Welcome
Licences:
Parking: Off-street and monitored
Directions: M60 Junction 12, then M602 Junction 2.
Left for A576 Guilder Brook, second left Half Edge
Lane into Monton Road. Hotel ½ mile on left.

See advert on next page

Ascott Hotel

◆◆◆ ✍

6 Half Edgr Lane, Eccles, Manchester, M30 9GJ
Tel: 0161 950 2453 Fax: 0161 661 7063
Rooms: 10 (9 ensuite)
Pricing: Sgl £35 Dbl £45 Dinner from £8 CC: Accepted
Room facilities:
Children: Welcome
Dogs: Guide dogs only
Parking: Off-street
Directions: M60 onto M602 exit 2 follow Pendreton
signs through first lights turn left 2nd lights we are ¼
mile on left , No.6 blue sign.

Imperial Hotel

◆◆◆

157 Hathersage Road, Manchester, M13 0HY
Tel: 0161 225 6500 Fax: 0161 225 6500
Email: www.imphotel1@aol.com
Web: www.hotelimperialmanchester.co.uk
Seasonal closure: Christmas to New Year
Rooms: 27 (21 ensuite)
Pricing: Sgl £35–45 Dbl £48 Dinner from £8
CC: Accepted
Room facilities:
Access:
Children: Welcome
Licences:
Parking: Off-street
Directions: 1¼ miles south of city centre. By
Manchester Royal Infirmary and Manchester University.

Victoria Park Hotel

◆◆◆

4 Park Crescent, Victoria Park, Manchester, M14 5RE
Tel: 0161 224 1399 Fax: 0161 225 4949
Email: vph.manchester@claranet.co.uk
Web: www.victoriapark-hotel.co.uk
Rooms: 19 (18 ensuite)
Pricing: Sgl £38–40 Dbl £48–52 CC: Accepted
Room facilities:
Children: Welcome
Leisure: Snooker/billiards
Parking: Monitored
Directions: 1 mile from city centre. Follow signs for
Manchester University on Oxford Road, continue until
Oxford Road becomes Wilmslow Road, and we are off
this on Park Crescent.

Campanile

Travel Accommodation
55 Ordsall Lane, Regent Road, Salford,
Manchester, M5 4RS
Tel: 0161 833 1845 Fax: 0161 833 1847
Web: www.campanile.fr

Campanile hotels offer comfortable and convenient
budget accommodation and a traditional French-style
Bistro providing freshly-cooked food for breakfast,
lunch and dinner. All rooms ensuite with tea/coffee-
making facilities, DDT and TV with Sky channels.
Rooms: 104 all ensuite
Pricing: Sgl £45.45–49.90 Dbl £50.40–55.95
Dinner from £11.55 CC: Accepted
Room facilities: Access:
Conference: 2 meeting rooms (Thtr 50 max), 24hr-
delegate from £68, day-delegate rate from £19.50
Children: Welcome Dogs: Welcome Licences:
Parking: Off-street and monitored

Directions: Leave M6 Junction 21a onto M62 to
Manchester, then M602 Salford. Continue over roundabout onto Regent Road. Hotel on right, after Sainsbury's.

Travelodge Manchester Central (SA)

Travel Accommodation
Blackfriars Street, Manchester, M3 5AB
Web: www.travelodge.co.uk
Rooms: 181 all ensuite
Pricing: Sgl £54.40 Dbl £58.85 CC: Accepted
Room facilities: Access:

Travelodge Manchester South

Travel Accommodation
A34, Kingsway, Didsbury, Manchester
Web: www.travelodge.co.uk
Rooms: 50 all ensuite
Pricing: Sgl £54.40 Dbl £58.85 CC: Accepted
Room facilities: Access:

Middlewich, Cheshire

Travelodge Middlewich

Travel Accommodation
A54, Holmes Chapel Road, Middlewich,
Cheshire, CW10 0JB
Web: www.travelodge.co.uk
Rooms: 32 all ensuite
Pricing: Sgl £54.40 Dbl £58.85 CC: Accepted
Room facilities: Access:

Millom, Cumbria

Duddon Pilot Hotel

◆ ◆ ◆ ◆

Devonshire Road, Millom, Cumbria, LA18 4JT
Tel: 01229 774116 Fax: 01229 774116
Rooms: 6 all ensuite
Pricing: Sgl £25–30 Dbl £50–60 Dinner from £15
Room facilities:
Children: Welcome ⋔ Dogs: Guide dogs only
Licences: ⦙⦙⦙ Parking: Off-street
Directions: Exit M6 at Junction 36. Take the A590 to
Greenodd, followed by A5092 and A595 to Millom.
Railway station turn left 1 mile down the road hotel on
the left.

Morecambe, Lancashire

Clarendon Hotel

★★★

Marine Road West, Morecambe, Lancashire, LA4 4EP
Tel: 01524 410180 Fax: 01524 421616
Email: clarendon@mitchellshotels.co.uk
Web: www.mitchellshotels.co.uk

Rooms: 29 all ensuite
Pricing: Sgl £50 Dbl £70 CC: Accepted
Room facilities: Access: ⦙⦙⦙
Conference: 4 meeting rooms, 24hr-delegate from £68,
day-delegate rate from £20
Children: Welcome Dogs: Welcome
Licences: ⦙⦙⦙ Parking: Off-street and monitored
Directions: M6 J34 Morecambe, take last roundabout
by Shrimp pub, 1st exit follow road to promenade, turn
right. Clarendon on 3rd block.

The Elms Hotel

★★★

Bare Village, Morecambe, Lancashire, LA4 6DD
Tel: 01524 411501 Fax: 01524 831979
Email: elms@mitchellshotels.co.uk
Web: www.mitchellshotels.co.uk

Rooms: 40 all ensuite
Pricing: Sgl £61 Dbl £90 Dinner from £16.95
CC: Accepted Room facilities:
Access: ⦙⦙⦙ Children: Welcome ⋔
Dogs: Welcome Licences: ⦙⦙⦙
Parking: Off-street and monitored
Directions: M6 Junction 34. Follow signs for
Morecambe until you reach large roundabout. Take
fourth exit onto Hall Drive which adjoins Bare Lane.
Follow road, hotel on right.

Midland Grand Hotel

Marine Road, Morecambe, Lancashire, LA4 4BG
Tel: 01524 417180 Fax: 01524 832827

Beach Mount Hotel

◆ ◆ ◆

395/6 Marine Road East, Morecambe, Lancs, LA4 5AN
Tel: 01524 420753 Fax: 01524 420753
Seasonal closure: November to March
Rooms: 20 all ensuite
Pricing: Sgl £24.25–26 Dbl £45.50–49 CC: Accepted
Room facilities:
Children: Welcome ⋔
Dogs: Welcome
Licences: ⦙⦙⦙
Parking: Off-street
Directions: Situated on the East Promenade.

Hotel Prospect

◆ ◆ ◆

363 Marine Road East, Morecambe,
Lancashire, LA4 5AQ
Tel: 01524 417819 Fax: 01524 417819
Email: peter@hotelprospect.fsnet.co.uk
Rooms: 14 all ensuite
Pricing: Sgl £16–18 Dbl £32–36 Dinner from £8
CC: Accepted
Room facilities:
Access: ⦵
Children: Welcome ⋔
Dogs: Welcome
Licences: ⦙⦙⦙
Parking: Off-street and monitored
Directions: Exit M6 Junction 34/35. Follow signs to
Lancaster/Morecambe. At Morecambe, follow signs to
East Promenade. Turn left at Promenade. Hotel on left.

Channings Hotel

◆ ◆

455 Marine Road East, Bare, Morecambe,
Lancashire, LA4 6AD
Tel: 01524 417925 Fax: 01524 411794
Email: channings.hotel@ukgateway.net
Web: www.channingshotel.co.uk
Rooms: 19 (17 ensuite)
Room facilities:
Children: Welcome ⋔
Dogs: Welcome
Licences: ⦵ ⦙⦙⦙
Parking: Monitored
Directions: From the south, leave M6 at Junction 34.
After 3½ miles, the hotel is situated on the promenade
directly opposite Bare Pool and close to Happy Mount
Park.

Newby Bridge, Cumbria

Whitewater Hotel

★★★

The Lakeland Village, Ulverston, Newby Bridge,
Cumbria, LA12 8PX
Tel: 01539 531133 Fax: 01539 531881
Email: enquiries@whitewater-hotel.co.uk
Web: www.whitewater-hotel.co.uk

In a fantastic location in south Lakeland on the river,
between Windermere and Ulverston, the Whitewater
offers a friendly welcome and superb leisure facilities,
including pool, gym, and beauty spa.
Rooms: 35 all ensuite
Pricing: Sgl £80–95 Dbl £100–160 Dinner from £22.50
CC: Accepted Room facilities: 📺 ☎ 🛏 Access: ♿ ♿
Conference: 3 meeting rooms (Thtr 80 max), 24hr-
delegate from £30, day-delegate rate from £120
Children: Welcome 🍴 🌡 Dogs: Guide dogs only
Licences: 🍷 🕴 Leisure: Indoor pool, Gym,
Health spa, Beauty salon, Tennis, Games room
Parking: Off-street and monitored
Directions: Exit M6, J36 follow A590 towards Barrow for
16 miles. Hotel is one mile past Newby Bridge on right.

Lyndhurst Country House

◆◆◆◆ 🌂 🍸

Newby Bridge, Cumbria, LA12 8ND
Tel: 01539 531245
Rooms: 3 all ensuite 🌡
Pricing: Sgl £30 Dbl £50 CC: Accepted
Room facilities: 📺 🛏 Children: Welcome
Parking: Off-street
Directions: Lyndhurst is situated on A590 at its junction
with the A592.

The Knoll Country House

◆◆◆◆ 🌂 🍸

Lakeside, Newby Bridge, near Ulverston,
Cumbria, LA12 8AU
Tel: 015395 31347 Fax: 015395 30850
Email: info@theknoll-lakeside.co.uk
Web: www.theknoll-lakeside.co.uk
Rooms: 8 all ensuite 📠 🌡
Pricing: Sgl £36–45 Dbl £60–90 Dinner from £15
CC: Accepted Room facilities: 📺 ☎ 🛏
Dogs: Guide dogs only Licences: 🕴
Parking: Off-street
Directions: A590 to Newby Bridge. Turn right opposite
Newby Bridge Hotel to Lakeside. 300m past the
Lakeside Hotel on left.

Northwich, Cheshire

Quality Hotel Northwich

★★★

London Road, Northwich, Cheshire, CW9 5HD
Tel: 01606 44443 Fax: 01606 42596
Email: admin@gb618.u-net.com
Web: www.choicehotels.com
Rooms: 60 all ensuite 🌡 📠 🌡
Pricing: Sgl £38–80 Dbl £76–111.25
Dinner from £15.50 CC: Accepted
Room facilities: 📺 ☎ 🛏 🍵 Access: ♿ ♿
Conference: 4 meeting rooms (Thtr 100 max), 24hr-
delegate from £85, day-delegate rate from £30
Children: Welcome 🍴 🌡 Dogs: Welcome
Licences: 🍷 🕴 Parking: Off-street and monitored
Directions: M6 at Junction 19 and take A556 to
Northwich. Northwich join A533 (London Road) to hotel.

Oldham, Lancashire

Hotel Smokies Park

★★★★ 📖

Ashton Road, Bardsley, Oldham, Lancashire, OL8 3HX
Tel: 0161 785 5000 Fax: 0161 785 5010
Email: sales@smokies.co.uk
Web: www.smokies.co.uk
Stylish hotel offering comfortable well equipped
bedrooms/suites. Extensive range of Italian and English
dishes offered in award-winning restaurants. Nightclub
onsite with live music at weekends. Small well
equipped fitness centre.
Rooms: 73 all ensuite 🌡 🌡
Pricing: Sgl £55–90 Dbl £55–100 Dinner from £18.95
CC: Accepted Room facilities: 📺 ☎ 🛏 🍵
Access: ♿ ♿
Conference: 5 meeting rooms (Thtr 150 max), 24hr-
delegate from £120, day-delegate rate from £29
Children: Welcome 🍴 🌡 Dogs: Guide dogs only
Licences: 🕴 Leisure: Gym
Parking: Off-street and monitored
Directions: On the A627 midpoint between Oldham and
Ashton-under-Lyne.

High Point Hotel

★★

Napier Street East, Oldham, Lancashire, OL8 1TR
Tel: 0161 624 4130 Fax: 0161 627 2757
Email: info@highpointhotel.co.uk
Web: highpointhotel.co.uk
Rooms: 19 all ensuite 🌡 📠 🌡
Pricing: Sgl £35–42 Dbl £45–53 Dinner from £12.95
CC: Accepted Room facilities: 📺 ☎ 🛏 Access: ♿
Conference: 1 meeting room (Thtr 25 max), 24hr-
delegate from £64, day-delegate rate from £19
Children: Welcome 🍴 Dogs: Guide dogs only
Licences: 🕴 Parking: Off-street and monitored
Directions: Leave M62 at Junction 20. Follow signs for
Oldham and Ashton on A627M. Take A62 to
Manchester. Turn right off Manchester Street
roundabout. Take first left then right at top and right
again.

Travelodge Oldham

Travel Accommodation
A663, 432 Broadway, Oldham, OL9 8AU
Web: www.travelodge.co.uk
Rooms: 50 all ensuite 🛇
Pricing: Sgl £54.40 Dbl £58.85 CC: Accepted
Room facilities: ⬚ ☕ Access: ♿

Penrith, Cumbria

North Lakes Hotel

★★★★
Ullswater Road, Penrith,
Cumbria, CA11 8QT
Tel: 01768 868111 Fax: 01768 868291
Email: nlakes@shirehotels.co.uk
Web: www.shirehotels.co.uk
Rooms: 84 🛏 🗔 🛇
Pricing: Sgl £105 Dbl £110 CC: Accepted
Room facilities: ⬚ ☎ ☕ ⚲
Access: ⌊⌊ ♿
Children: Welcome ⱨ ⫶
Dogs: Guide dogs only Licences: ⚶ ⫼
Leisure: Indoor pool, Gym, Health spa, Beauty salon
Parking: Off-street and monitored
Directions: Leave M6 at Junction 40 and follow signs
for Penrith.

Westmorland Hotel

★★★
Orton, Penrith, Cumbria, CA10 3SB
Tel: 015396 24351 Fax: 015396 24354
Email: westmorlandhotel@aol.com
Web: www.westmorlandhotel.com

Situated in the heart of the Cumbrian Mountains, with
breathtaking views over the moors. Indulge yourself in
the award-winning Bretherdale Restaurant. An ideal
location to relax or explore the Lakes.
Rooms: 50 all ensuite 🛏 🛇
Pricing: Sgl £59–84 Dbl £73–100 CC: Accepted
Room facilities: ⬚ ☎ ☕ ⚲
Access: ⌊⌊ ♿
Conference: 6 meeting rooms (Thtr 80 max)
Children: Welcome ⱨ ⫶
Dogs: Welcome
Licences: ⚶ ⫼
Directions: The hotel is reched via Westmorland motor-
way services between junctions 38 and 39 of the M6

Brooklands Guest House

◆ ◆ ◆ ◆ ※⌖
2 Portland Place, Penrith, Cumbria, CA11 7QN
Tel: 01768 863395 Fax: 01768 864895
Email: enquiries@brooklandsguesthouse.com
Web: www.brooklandsguesthouse.com
Rooms: 6 (4 ensuite) 🛏 🗔 🛇
Pricing: Sgl £25–40 Dbl £40–55 CC: Accepted
Room facilities: ⬚ ☕
Children: Welcome ⱨ Dogs: Guide dogs only
Parking: Off-street
Directions: Exit J40 M6 follow tourist information signs,
turn left at town hall into Portland Place, Brooklands
50m on the left.

Elm House

◆ ◆ ◆ ◆ ※⌖ ⫝
Pooley Bridge, Penrith, Cumbria, CA10 2NH
Tel: 01768 486334 Fax: 01768 486851
Email: b&b@elmhouse.demon.co.uk
Web: www.elmhouse.demon.co.uk
Rooms: 5 (4 ensuite) 🛇
Pricing: Dbl £38–49 CC: Accepted
Room facilities: ⬚ ☕ Children: Welcome 12yrs min age
Parking: Off-street
Directions: From M6 (junction 40) A66 Keswick, ½ mile
onto A592 to B5320, left into Pooley Bridge, Elm
House last on right.

Norcroft Guest House

◆ ◆ ◆ ◆ ※⌖
Graham Street, Penrith, Cumbria, CA11 9LQ
Tel: 01768 862365 Fax: 01768 862365
Email: info@norcroft-guesthouse.co.uk
Web: www.norcroft-guesthouse.co.uk
Seasonal closure: Christmas and New Year

Conveniently situated for M6 yet 5 minutes walk from
town centre. Norcroft guesthouse offers a warm
welcome, spacious and comfortable ensuite rooms
with secure off-street parking.
Rooms: 9 all ensuite 🛏 🛇
Pricing: Sgl £23–26 Dbl £42–46 CC: Accepted
Room facilities: ⬚ ☕ Children: Welcome
Dogs: Guide dogs only Licences: ⫼
Parking: Off-street and monitored
Directions: From M6 follow one-way system to town
centre, left at town hall, left into Drovers lane, Norcroft
400 yards.

Tymparon Hall

◆ ◆ ◆ ◆ ✳

Newbiggin, Stainton, Penrith, Cumbria, CA11 0HS
Tel: 017684 83236 Fax: 017684 83236
Email: margaret@tymparon.freeserve.co.uk
Web: www.tymparon.freeserve.co.uk
Seasonal closure: December & January

Close to Lake Ullswater and M6 Junction 40. A warm
welcome, hearty breakfasts and traditional dinners
served. Peaceful rural setting on village fringe.
Rooms: 3 all ensuite ◔ ⊛
Pricing: Sgl £25–35 Dbl £46–50 Dinner from £12
Room facilities: ⊛ Children: Welcome ⍫ ⍕
Dogs: Welcome Parking: Off-street
Directions: Leave M6 at Junction 40. Take A66 to
Keswick. Turn right at sign for Newbiggin. Hotel at
extreme end of village on right.

Travelodge Penrith

Travel Accommodation
A66, Redhills, Penrith, Cumbria, CA11 0DT
Web: www.travelodge.co.uk
Rooms: 54 all ensuite ⊛
Pricing: Sgl £54.40 Dbl £58.85 CC: Accepted
Room facilities: ⊡ ⊛ Access: ⅋

Preston, Lancashire

Swallow Hotel

★ ★ ★ ⍦

Preston New Road, Samlesbury, Preston,
Lancashire, PR5 0UL
Tel: 01772 877351 Fax: 01772 877424
Email: preston.swallow@wwtbread.com
Web: www.swallowhotels.com

Rooms: 78 all ensuite ⊛
Pricing: Sgl £60–78 Dbl £65–91 Dinner from £17
CC: Accepted Room facilities: ⊡ ☎ ⊛ ⍩ Access: ⅋⅋
Conference: 8 meeting rooms (Thtr 250 max), 24hr-
delegate from £118, day-delegate rate from £32
Children: Welcome ⍫ Dogs: Welcome Licences: ⍦⍦⍦
Leisure: Indoor pool, Gym, Games room
Parking: Off-street and monitored
Directions: Exit Junction 31 of M6, go 1 mile towards
Blackburn, situated at the junction of the A677 and A59.

The Villa Hotel

★ ★ ★

Moss Side Lane, Wrea Green, Kirkham, Preston,
Lancashire, PR4 2PE
Tel: 01772 684347 Fax: 01772 687647
Rooms: 25 all ensuite ⍭ ⊛
Pricing: Sgl £55–75 Dbl £55–90 Dinner from £10
CC: Accepted
Room facilities: ⊡ ☎ ⊛ ⍩ ✳
Access: ⅋⅋ ⅋
Conference: 30 meeting rooms (Thtr 30 max)
Children: Welcome ⍫
Dogs: Guide dogs only
Licences: ⍦⍦⍦
Parking: Off-street
Directions: Junction 3 M55 follow signs to Kirkham, at
Wrea Green follow signs to Lytham
See advert on following page

Brook House Hotel

★ ★

662 Preston Road, nr. Chorley, Clayton-Le-Woods,
Lancashire, PR6 7EH
Tel: 01772 336403 Fax: 01772 337369
Email: enquiries@hotel-preston-chorley.co.uk
Web: www.hotel-preston-chorley.co.uk
Rooms: 20 all ensuite ⍭ ⊛
Pricing: Sgl £40–55 Dbl £50–65 Dinner from £10
CC: Accepted
Room facilities: ⊡ ☎ ⊛
Conference: 3 meeting rooms (Thtr 70 max), 24hr-
delegate from £71.95, day-delegate rate from £16.95
Children: Welcome ⍫
Dogs: Guide dogs only
Licences: ⍦⍦⍦
Parking: Off-street and monitored
Directions: Brook House is situated on the A6 half a
mile from Junction 29 M6, Junction 9 M61 and
Junction 2 M65.

It's easier online

For all your motoring and travel
needs, www.rac.co.uk

THE VILLA

DINING ROOMS BAR AND BEDROOMS

To the Manor Born

It's rare to find a distinctive hotel in an idyllic setting, and even rarer to discover one that offers a fine dining experience to match... Yet that's exactly what's in store for visitors to The Villa, an elegant former 19th century gentleman's residence, set amidst rolling parkland and situated in the picture perfect Lancashire village of Wrea Green.

A Warm Welcome

Many visitors come to The Villa for its historic charm, air of quiet elegance and splendid location, yet often return again and again to experience the warm hospitality and excellent

personal service.

The hotel rooms are spacious and luxuriously appointed, offering stylish, comfortable accommodation. All twenty five air-conditioned rooms feature superb en-suite facilities and have been tastefully designed and furnished to create the ideal atmosphere for a relaxing visit.

Dining in Style

Residents and non-residents alike can sample the culinary delights of The Villa's superb bistro-style menu created with considerable flair by our in-house chef. The uniquely designed restaurant comprises a series of interlinked dining areas and lends itself perfectly to elegant informal entertaining, be it a relaxed lunch with friends or a romantic dinner for two.

Our mouth-watering, freshly cooked meals are complemented by a good selection of quality wines from our well stocked cellars. We set a great deal of sore by the reputation of our restaurant, why not join us and enjoy a first class dining experience at The Villa.

Ramsbottom, Lancashire

Old Mill

★★★

Springwood Street, Ramsbottom, Lancashire, BL0 9DS
Tel: 01706 822991 Fax: 01706 822291
Email: oldmill@ccsconnect.com
Web: www.oldmillhotel.co.uk
Rooms: 28 all ensuite
Pricing: Sgl £51–59 Dbl £67–74 Dinner from £14.95
CC: Accepted
Room facilities:
Conference: 2 meeting rooms
Children: Welcome
Licences:
Leisure: Indoor pool, Gym
Parking: Off-street and monitored
Directions: Close to Junction 1 on M66, 5 miles from
Bury, 15 miles from Manchester city centre.

Ravenglass, Cumbria

Muncaster Country Guest House

◆ ◆ ◆

Muncaster, Ravenglass, Cumbria, CA18 1RD
Tel: 01229 717693 Fax: 01229 717693
Email: cford7777@aol.com
Rooms: 8 (2 ensuite)
Room facilities:
Access:
Children: Welcome
Licences:
Parking: Off-street and monitored
Directions: Situated on the A595 1 mile east of
Ravenglass, opposite main entrance to Muncaster
Castle.

Richmond, North Yorkshire

Travelodge Scotch Corner (MOTO)

Travel Accommodation
A1/A66 Moto Service Area, Middleton Tyas Lane, Scotch
Corner, Nr. Richmond, North Yorkshire, DL10 6PQ
Web: www.travelodge.co.uk
Rooms: 50 all ensuite
Pricing: Sgl £54.40 Dbl £58.85 CC: Accepted
Room facilities: Access:

Runcorn, Cheshire

Campanile Hotel

Travel Accommodation
Lowlands Road, Runcorn, Cheshire, WA7 5TP
Tel: 01928 581771 Fax: 01928 581730
Email: runcorn@envergure.co.uk
Web: www.campanile.fr

Campanile hotels offer comfortable and convenient
budget accommodation and a traditional French-style
Bistro providing freshly-cooked food for breakfast,
lunch and dinner. All rooms ensuite with tea/coffee-
making facilities, DDT and TV with Sky channels.
Rooms: 53 all ensuite
Pricing: Sgl £40.95–47.90 Dbl £46.90–52.85
Dinner from £6.35 CC: Accepted
Room facilities: Access:
Conference: 1 meeting room (Thtr 30 max), 24hr-
delegate from £68, day-delegate rate from £19.50
Children: Welcome
Dogs: Welcome Licences: Parking: Off-street
Directions: Exit M56 at Junction 12, joining A557
towards Runcorn. Follow signs for Runcorn railway
station.

Rydal, Cumbria

Rydal Lodge Hotel

◆ ◆ ◆

Rydal, Cumbria, LA22 9LR
Tel: 01539 433208
Seasonal closure: January
Rooms: 2 both ensuite
Pricing: Dinner from £16.50 (2002 rate) CC: Accepted
Room facilities:
Children: Welcome
Dogs: Welcome Licences:
Parking: Off-street
Directions: Situated on A591 in Rydal, 1½ miles from
Ambleside, 3 miles from Grasmere.

Salford, Manchester

Hazeldean Hotel

◆ ◆ ◆

467 Bury New Road, Kersal, Salford,
Manchester, M7 3NE
Tel: 0161 792 6667 Fax: 0161 792 6668
Seasonal closure: Christmas
Rooms: 21 (19 ensuite)
Pricing: Sgl £42 Dbl £53 Dinner from £10
CC: Accepted
Room facilities: Access:
Children: Welcome
Licences:
Parking: Off-street and monitored

Sandbach, Cheshire

Grove House Hotel & Restaurant

★★★ ⍟ ⍟ ⍟

Mill Lane, Wheelock, Sandbach, Cheshire, CW11 4RD
Tel: 01270 762582 Fax: 01270 759465
Email: grovehousehotel@supanet.com
Seasonal closure: Christmas

Restaurant with rooms, family-owned and run.
Relaxing ambience, individually-styled rooms. Excellent
restaurant offering ambitious modern cooking by chef-
proprietor. Two miles from Jct 17 on M6.
Rooms: 8 all ensuite ⍟ ⍟
Pricing: Sgl £30–47.50 Dbl £60–85 Dinner from £11
CC: Accepted
Room facilities: ⌨ ☎ ⍟
Conference: 1 meeting room (Thtr 24 max)
Children: Welcome ⍟ ⍟ Dogs: Welcome
Licences: ⍟⍟⍟ Parking: Off-street
Directions: Junction 17 M6, then A534. Through the
traffic lights, go left at roundabout. Follow Wheelock
signs.

Poplar Mount Guest House

◆ ◆ ◆

2 Station Road, Elworth, Sandbach,
Cheshire, CW11 3JG
Tel: 01270 761268 Fax: 01270 761268
Email: popmntgh@aol.co.uk
Rooms: 4 all ensuite ⍟
Pricing: Sgl £22–32 Dbl £42–46 Dinner from £9
CC: Accepted
Room facilities: ⌨ ⍟
Children: Welcome
Parking: Off-street
Directions: 3 miles from M6 Junction 17, off A533
Middlewich Road, on B5079. Opposite Sandbach
Railway Station.

Sawrey, Cumbria

Sawrey Hotel

★★

Far Sawrey, Ambleside, Cumbria, LA22 0LQ
Tel: 01539 443425 Fax: 01539 443425
Seasonal closure: Christmas

An attractive two-storey, 18th-century inn built in
traditional Lake District style. Former stables converted
into a bar.
Rooms: 18 all ensuite ⍟
Pricing: Sgl £31.50 Dbl £63 Dinner from £17.50
CC: Accepted
Room facilities: ⌨ ☎ ⍟ Access: ⍟
Children: Welcome ⍟ ⍟
Dogs: Welcome
Licences: ⍟⍟⍟
Parking: Off-street
Directions: One mile from Windermere (Bowness) car
ferry on B5285 Hawkshead Road.

West Vale Country Guest House

◆ ◆ ◆ ◆ ⍟

Far Sawrey, Ambleside, Sawrey, Cumbria, LA22 0LQ
Tel: 01539 442817 Fax: 01539 445302
Email: enquiries@westvalecountryhouse.co.uk
Web: www.westvalecountryhouse.co.uk
Rooms: 7 (6 ensuite) ⍟
Pricing: Sgl £40–50 Dbl £56–76 Dinner from £20
CC: Accepted Room facilities: ⌨ ⍟
Children: Welcome 7yrs min age ⍟
Licences: ⍟⍟⍟
Parking: Off-street
Directions: West Vale is on the B5285 between
Hawkshead and the Ferry at Windermere.

High Green Gate Guest House

◆ ◆ ◆ ⍟ ⍟

near Sawrey, Ambleside, Cumbria, LA22 0LF
Tel: 01539 436296
Email: highgreengate@amserve.net
Seasonal closure: November to March
Rooms: 5 (4 ensuite) ⍟ ⍟
Pricing: Sgl £28–31 Dbl £50–56 Dinner from £11
Room facilities: ⍟
Children: Welcome ⍟ ⍟
Dogs: Welcome
Parking: Off-street
Directions: On B5285 between Hawkshead and
Bowness via Ferry.

Shap, Cumbria

Shap Wells Hotel

★★★

Shap, Penrith, Cumbria, CA10 3QU
Tel: 01931 716628 Fax: 01931 716377
Email: manager@shapwells.com
Web: www.shapwells.com
Seasonal closure: January to mid-February
Rooms: 98 all ensuite
Pricing: Sgl £53–60 Dbl £86–90 Dinner from £16
CC: Accepted Room facilities: 💻 ☎ ☕
Access: ⏫ ♿
Conference: 7 meeting rooms (Thtr 170 max), 24hr-delegate from £95, day-delegate rate from £25
Children: Welcome ⼑ Dogs: Welcome
Licences: ⚓ ⅲ
Leisure: Tennis, Games room, Snooker/billiards
Parking: Off-street
Directions: Exit J39 M6, then A6 for Kendall. After 1½–2 miles, hotel drive (1 mile long) on left.

Silloth, Cumbria

Golf Hotel

★★

Criffel Street, Silloth, Cumbria, CA5 4AB
Tel: 016973 31438 Fax: 016973 32582

Skelmersdale, Lancashire

Quality Hotel Skelmersdale

★★★

Prescott Road, East Pimbo, Skelmersdale,
Lancs, WN8 9PU
Tel: 01695 720401 Fax: 01695 50953
Email: admin@gb656.u-net.com
Web: www.choicehotels.com
Rooms: 55 all ensuite 🍽 🚭
Pricing: Dinner from £17.75 CC: Accepted
Room facilities: 💻 ☎ ☕ 🔌 Access: ♿
Children: Welcome ⼑ ⼂ Dogs: Welcome
Licences: ⚓ ⅲ Parking: Off-street and monitored
Directions: M6 Junction 26, M58 Junction 5. Down to roundabout, turn left, 100 yards further turn left again. Hotel 300 yards on right.

Southport, Merseyside

Scarisbrick Hotel

★★★

Lord Street, Southport, Merseyside, PR8 1NZ
Tel: 01704 543000 Fax: 01704 533335
Email: scarisbrickhotel@talk21.com
Web: www.scarisbrickhotel.com
Rooms: 90 all ensuite 🍽 🚭
Pricing: Sgl £30–80 Dbl £60–110 Dinner from £12
CC: Accepted Room facilities: 💻 ☎ ☕ 🔌
Access: ⏫ ♿
Conference: 8 meeting rooms (Thtr 200 max), 24hr-delegate from £110, day-delegate rate from £30

Children: Welcome ⼑ ⼂ Dogs: Welcome
Licences: ⚓ ⅲ
Leisure: Indoor pool, Gym, Health spa, Beauty salon,
Games room Parking: Off-street and monitored
Directions: From South, leave M6 at Junction 26, and take M58 to Ormskirk, then A570. From North, take M6 to Junction 31, then A59 through Preston to A565.

Tree Tops Country House Restaurant and Hotel

★★★★ ☈ ☈

Southport Old Road, Formby, Southport,
Merseyside, L37 0AB
Tel: 01704 572430 Fax: 01704 572430
Web: www.treetopsformby.fsnet

Ideal for business or pleasure, situated in five acres of wooded grounds offering top class dining in our elegant restaurant. Within easy reach of coast and championship golf courses.
Rooms: 11 all ensuite
Pricing: Sgl £57–77 Dbl £95–110 Dinner from £16.95
CC: Accepted Room facilities: 💻 ☎ ☕ 🔌 Access: ♿
Conference: 2 meeting rooms (Thtr 200 max)
Children: Welcome Dogs: Guide dogs only
Licences: ⚓ ⅲ Leisure: Outdoor pool
Parking: Off-street
Directions: Follow A565 from Southport to Formby, turn left onto Southport Old road at Woodvale, hotel 100 yards on left.

Balmoral Lodge Hotel

★★

41 Queens Road, Southport, Merseyside, PR9 9EX
Tel: 01704 544298 Fax: 01704 501224

Metropole

★★

Portland Street, Southport, Merseyside, PR8 1LL
Tel: 01704 536836 Fax: 01704 549041
Email: metropole.southport@btinternet.com
Web: www.btinternet.com/~metropole.southport
Rooms: 23 all ensuite 🚭
Pricing: Sgl £25–38.50 Dbl £50–66 Dinner from £12
CC: Accepted Room facilities: 💻 ☎ ☕
Children: Welcome ⼑ ⼂ Dogs: Welcome
Licences: ⅲ Leisure: Snooker/billiards
Parking: Off-street and monitored
Directions: 100m from Southport's Lord Street –
a 4-minute walk from the railway station.

Northwest

Ambassador

13 Bath Street, Southport, Merseyside, PR9 0DP
Tel: 01704 543998
Email: ambassador.walton@virgin.net
Web: www.ambassadorprivatehotel.co.uk
Seasonal closure: 23 December to 2 January
Rooms: 8 all ensuite ⓢ Pricing: Sgl £28–38 Dbl £30
Dinner from £10 CC: Accepted Room facilities: ⌑ ☕
Access: ♿ Children: Welcome Dogs: Guide dogs only
Licences: ⅲ Parking: Off-street
Directions: Along Lord Street to Cenotaph, turn into
Neville Street; take second right into Bath Street; hotel
is on left.

Rosedale Hotel

11 Talbot Street, Southport, Merseyside, PR8 1HP
Tel: 01704 530604 Fax: 01704 530604
Email: info@rosedalehotelsouthport.co.uk
Web: www.rosedale-hotel.co.uk
Seasonal closure: late December to early January
Rooms: 9 (8 ensuite)
Pricing: Sgl £26–30 Dbl £50–56 CC: Accepted
Room facilities: ⌑ ☕ Children: Welcome ⅓
Licences: ⅲ Parking: Off-street
Directions: Entering the town via A570, follow signs to
town centre into Eastbank Street. Talbot Street is on left.

Whitworth Falls Hotel

16 Lathom Road, Southport, Merseyside, PR9 0JH
Tel: 01704 530074
Email: whitworthfalls@rapid.co.uk
Web: www.whitworthfallshotel.co.uk
Rooms: 12 all ensuite ⚲ ⓢ
Pricing: Sgl £20–30 Dbl £40–60 Dinner from £8.50
Room facilities: ⌑ ☎ ☕ ⚑ Children: Welcome ⅓ ⅈ
Dogs: Welcome Licences: ⅲ
Parking: Off-street and monitored
Directions: From Southport town centre, Lord Street,
head north to fire station over roundabout. Take second
left (Alexandra Road), and fourth right (Lathom Road).

White Lodge

12 Talbot Street, Southport, Merseyside, PR8 1HP
Tel: 01704 536320 Fax: 01704 536320
Rooms: 7 (6 ensuite) ⓢ
Pricing: Sgl £25–28 Dbl £50–55 Dinner from £10
Room facilities: ⌑ ☕ Children: Welcome ⅓
Licences: ⅲ Parking: Off-street
Directions: From town centre Tourist Information office,
proceed along Eastbank Street. Talbot Street is fourth
on the right. First hotel on the right.

St Bees, Cumbria

Manor House Hotel & Coast to Coast Bar

12 Main Street, St Bees, Cumbria, CA27 0DE
Tel: 01946 822425 Fax: 01946 824949
Email: manorhousehotel@aol.com
Rooms: 8 all ensuite ⓢ
Pricing: Sgl £25–35 Dbl £40–50 Dinner from £5
CC: Accepted Room facilities: ⌑ ☕
Conference: 1 meeting room (Thtr 30 max)
Children: Welcome ⅓ Dogs: Welcome
Leisure: Games room Parking: Off-street
Directions: From A595 Whitehaven follow signs for St
Bees, take first left after the railway crossing then 2nd
right into the Crofts, car park is signposted on right.

St Helens, Merseyside

Travelodge Haydock, St Helens

Travel Accommodation
A580, Piele Road, Haydock, St Helens,
Merseyside, WA11 0JZ
Web: www.travelodge.co.uk
Rooms: 62 all ensuite ⓢ
Pricing: Sgl £47.40 Dbl £51.85 CC: Accepted
Room facilities: ⌑ ☕ Access: ♿

Thornton Hough, Merseyside

Thornton Hall & Country Health Club

Neston Road, Thornton Hough, Merseyside, CH63 1JF
Tel: 0151 336 3938 Fax: 0151 336 7864
Email: thorntonhallhotel@btinternet.com
Web: www.thorntonhallhotel.com

Rooms: 63 all ensuite ⚏ ⓢ
Pricing: Dinner from £24 CC: Accepted
Room facilities: ⌑ ☎ ☕ ⚑ Access: ♿
Conference: 6 meeting rooms (Thtr 170 max), 24-hr
delegate from £135, day-delegate rate from £37.50
Children: Welcome ⅓
Dogs: Welcome Licences: ⟡ ⅲ
Leisure: Indoor pool, Gym, Health spa,
Beauty salon, Tennis
Parking: Off-street
Directions: M53 junction 4 take A5151 to Clatterbridge
then B5136 to Neston. Thornton Hall is after Thornton
Hough village on the left

Todhills, Cumbria

Travelodge Carlisle North, Todhills

Travel Accommodation
A74 Southbound, Todhills, Cumbria, CA6 4HA
Web: www.travelodge.co.uk
Pricing: Sgl £57.40 Dbl £61.85 CC: Accepted
Room facilities: Access: &

Troutbeck, Windermere

Mortal Man Inn

★★ ®
Troutbeck, Windermere, Cumbria, LA23 1PL
Tel: 015394 33193 Fax: 015394 31261
Email: the-mortalman@btinternet.com
Web: www.mortal-man-inns.co.uk

The Mortal Man Inn boast 13 ensuite bedrooms,
delicious fresh food and fine ales. Surrounded by
stunning landscapes, excellent reputation for standards
of service and hospitality, superb traditional values.
Rooms: 13 all ensuite
Pricing: Sgl £40–45 Dbl £60–90 Dinner from £6.95
CC: Accepted
Room facilities: ☐ ☎ ☕
Conference: 1 meeting room (Thtr 30 max)
Children: Welcome 5yrs min age ⅋
Dogs: Welcome
Licences: ♣♣♣
Leisure: Games room
Parking: Off-street
Directions: Junction 36 off the M6 take A591 to
Windermere, turn right onto A592, after 2½ miles turn
left at Troutbeck sign, right at T-junction, the inn is 800
yards on the right.

Ullswater, Cumbria

Leeming House

 Blue Ribbon Winner

★★★★★ ® ®
Watermillock, nr. Penrith, Ullswater, Cumbria, CA11 0JJ
Tel: 0870 400 8131 Fax: 01768 486443
Email: leeminghouse@heritage-house.co.uk
Web: www.macdonaldhotels.co.uk
Rooms: 40 all ensuite ☜ ⊗
Pricing: Sgl £89 Dbl £178 Dinner from £25
CC: Accepted
Room facilities: ☐ ☎ ☕ ☏ Access: &
Conference: 2 meeting rooms (Thtr 40 max)
Children: Welcome ⅋ ⫶
Dogs: Welcome Licences: ♦ ♣♣♣
Parking: Off-street
Directions: From M6 J40 follow signs for Ullswater. At
lakeside take right fork for Windermere. Hotel is 2½
miles further on left.

Patterdale Hotel

★★
Patterdale, Penrith, Cumbria, CA11 0NN
Tel: 0845 458 4333 Fax: 01253 754222
Email: reservations@choice-hotels.co.uk
Web: www.patterdalehotel.co.uk
Seasonal closure: December to February
Rooms: 61 all ensuite ☜
Pricing: Sgl £32–47 Dbl £64–99 Dinner from £15
CC: Accepted
Room facilities: ☐ ☎ ☕
Access: ⫼ &
Conference: 2 meeting rooms, 24hr-delegate from £86,
day-delegate rate from £21
Children: Welcome ⅋ ⫶
Dogs: Guide dogs only Licences: ♣♣♣
Leisure: Tennis, Fishing
Parking: Off-street
Directions: From M6 Junction 40, take A66 towards
Keswick, at roundabout take first exit, signposted
Ullswater (A592). Turn right at T-junction. Continue
through Glenridding to Patterdale.

Wallasey, Merseyside

Grove House Hotel

★★★★ ® ®
Grove Road, Wallasey, Merseyside, CH43 3HF
Tel: 0151 639 3947 Fax: 0151 639 0028
Web: www.thegrovehouse.co.uk
Rooms: 14 all ensuite ☜
Pricing: Sgl £63.45 Dbl £73.65 Dinner from £17.95
CC: Accepted
Room facilities: ☐ ☎ ☕
Conference: 2 meeting rooms (Thtr 50 max), 24hr-
delegate from £95, day-delegate rate from £24.50
Children: Welcome ⅋
Dogs: Welcome Licences: ♦ ♣♣♣
Parking: Off-street and monitored
Directions: Junction 1 M53, A554 Wallasey New
Brighton; right after church onto Harrison drive, left after
Windsors garage onto Grove road.

Warrington, Cheshire

Hanover International Hotel & Club Warrington

★★★★★ ⬛ ⬛

Stretton Road, Stretton, Warrington, Cheshire, WA4 4NS
Tel: 0870 2417085 Fax: 01925 730740
Email: crso@hanover-international.com
Web: www.hanover-international.com

HANOVER INTERNATIONAL
HOTELS & CLUBS

Award-winning hotel, set in the heart of Cheshire. With deluxe bedrooms, an AA rosette restaurant, conference and banquetting facilities for 400 guests and a super health and leisure spa with beauty suites.
Rooms: 142 all ensuite 🛁 🚭
Pricing: Sgl £130.50–200.50 Dbl £140.50–210.50
Dinner from £19.95 CC: Accepted
Room facilities: 🖵 ☎ 🍵 📠 Access: ↟ ♿
Conference: 16 meeting rooms (Thtr 400 max), 24hr-delegate from £154, day-delegate rate from £45
Children: Welcome ⼌ ℃ Dogs: Guide dogs only
Licences: ◬ ♂♀♂
Leisure: Indoor pool, Gym, Health spa, Beauty salon, Tennis Parking: Off-street and monitored
Directions: Leave M56 at J10 and follow A49 towards Warrington. At first set of traffic lights turn right. The hotel is 200 yards on right.

Paddington House Hotel – Venture Hotels

★★

514 Manchester Road, Warrington, Cheshire, WA1 3TZ
Tel: 01925 816767 Fax: 01925 816651
Email: hotel@paddingtonhouse.co.uk
Web: www.paddingtonhouse.co.uk

VENTURE HOTELS

Friendly, family-run Georgian house situated in its own grounds. Conveniently located close to junction 21 M6 and 2 miles from Warrington town centre. Antique-themed bar and restaurant.
Rooms: 37 all ensuite 🛁 📠 🚭
Pricing: Sgl £59.50–62.50 Dbl £70–75
Dinner from £14.95 CC: Accepted
Room facilities: 🖵 ☎ 🍵 📠 Access: ↟ ♿
Conference: 4 meeting rooms (Thtr 180 max), 24hr-delegate from £99, day-delegate rate from £30
Children: Welcome ⼌ ℃
Dogs: Welcome
Licences: ◬ ♂♀♂
Parking: Off-street and monitored
Directions: Exit M6 J-21. Follow signs for Warrington (A57). Continue along A57 for approximately 1 mile, hotel is on the right hand side.

Travelodge Warrington (SA)

Travel Accommodation
A57, Kendrick/Leigh Street, Warrington, Cheshire, WA1 1UZ
Web: www.travelodge.co.uk
Rooms: 63 all ensuite 🚭
Pricing: Sgl £49.40 Dbl £53.85 CC: Accepted
Room facilities: 🖵 🍵 Access: ♿

Wasdale, Cumbria

Wasdale Head Inn

◆◆◆◆ ⬛ ✕

Wasdale, near Gosforth, Cumbria, CA20 1EX
Tel: 01946 726229 Fax: 01946 726334
Email: wasdaleheadinn@msn.com
Web: www.wasdale.com
Rooms: 13 all ensuite 📠 🚭
Pricing: Sgl £40–49 Dbl £80–98 Dinner from 22
CC: Accepted
Room facilities: ☎ 🍵
Children: Welcome
Dogs: Welcome
Licences: ♂♀♂
Parking: Off-street and monitored
Directions: From M6, proceed to West Cumbria. From A595, turn into Gosforth village and take left fork for Wasdale. After 1 mile bear right to climb steep hill. Inn is another 9 miles along single track road.

Widnes, Cheshire

Travelodge Widnes

Travel Accommodation
A562, Fiddlers Ferry Road, A562 Widnes, Cheshire, WA8 2NR
Web: www.travelodge.co.uk
Rooms: 32 all ensuite 🚭
Pricing: Sgl £47.40 Dbl £51.85 CC: Accepted
Room facilities: 🖵 🍵 Access: ♿

Wigan, Lancashire

Quality Hotel Wigan

★★★

River Way, Wigan, Greater Manchester, WN1 3SS
Tel: 01942 826888 Fax: 01942 825800
Email: admin@gb058.u-net.com
Web: www.choicehotels.com
Rooms: 88 all ensuite ⊛
Pricing: Sgl £45–85 Dbl £55–95 Dinner from £15.95
CC: Accepted
Room facilities: 🖵 ☎ 🗂 ⅃ Access: ⅃⅃ &
Conference: 7 meeting rooms (Thtr 200 max), 24hr-delegate from £85, day-delegate rate from £27.50
Children: Welcome ℍ
Dogs: Welcome
Licences: ⚘ ᛉᛉᛉ Parking: Off-street and monitored
Directions: M6 northbound take junction 25 or from M6 southbound take junction 27, follow signs for Wigan on A577.

Bel Air

★★

236 Wigan Lane, Wigan, Lancashire, WN1 2NU
Tel: 01942 241410 Fax: 01942 243967
Email: belair@hotelwigan.freeserve.co.uk
Web: www.belairhotel.co.uk
Rooms: 11 all ensuite ⊛ 🗂
Pricing: Sgl £35–39.50 Dbl £45–49.50
Dinner from £6.95 CC: Accepted
Room facilities: 🖵 ☎ 🗂 ⅃
Children: Welcome ℍ
Dogs: Welcome
Licences: ⚘ ᛉᛉᛉ
Parking: Off-street
Directions: 2 miles from Junction 27 of M6. Follow A49 towards Wigan. Bel Air is on right before large roundabout and Cherry Gardens public house.

Wigton, Cumbria

Wheyrigg Hall Hotel

◆ ◆ ◆

Abbeytown, Wigton, near Carlisle, Cumbria, CA7 0DH
Tel: 01697 361242 Fax: 01697 361020

Farmhouse hotel close to Solway coast, Lake district to the south, Carlisle and Border country to the north. Excellent homemade food with wine to complement friendly local bar, good flexible service, easy going.
Rooms: 12 all ensuite ⊛
Pricing: Sgl £30–45 Dbl £50–52 Dinner from £10
CC: Accepted
Room facilities: 🖵 ☎ 🗂
Conference: 2 meeting rooms (Thtr 100 max), 24hr-delegate from £65, day-delegate rate from £15
Children: Welcome ℍ
Dogs: Guide dogs only
Licences: ⚘ ᛉᛉᛉ
Leisure: Games room Parking: Off-street
Directions: From south M6 J41 to Wigton B5305. From Scotland J44 to Wigton A595/596, B5302 Wigton to Silloth

Windermere, Cumbria

Lakeside Hotel

★★★★★ ℛ ℛ

Lakeside, Newby Bridge, Cumbria, LA12 8AT
Tel: 01539 530001 Fax: 01539 531699
Email: sales@lakesidehotel.co.uk
Web: www.lakesidehotel.co.uk

Overlooking nothing but the lake… Lakeside Hotel is in the perfect location right on the shores of Lake Windemere. Lake cruisers depart from directly outside the hotel.
Rooms: 75 all ensuite ⊛ 🗂 ⊛
Pricing: Sgl £120–250 Dbl £150–260 Dinner from £30
CC: Accepted
Room facilities: 🖵 ☎ 🗂
Access: ⅃⅃ &
Conference: 8 meeting rooms (Thtr 100 max), 24hr-delegate from £140, day-delegate rate from £45
Children: Welcome ℍ ❅
Dogs: Welcome Licences: ⚘ ᛉᛉᛉ
Leisure: Indoor pool, Gym, Health spa, Beauty salon
Parking: Off-street
Directions: Leave M6 at Junction 36 and follow A590 to Newby Bridge or follow signs for Lakeside Steamers.

Making a booking?

Don't forget to mention RAC Hotels and Bed & Breakfast 2003.

Northwest

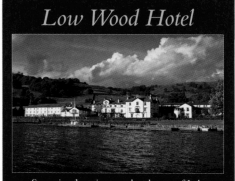

Low Wood Hotel

Stunning location on the shores of Lake Windermere with Magnificent views of the Langdale Pikes, with a choice of two restaurants and three bars. Extensive leisure facilities including indoor pool, sauna, solarium, hairdressing, beauty salon, gymnasium, squash court, watersports and activity centre, making this the North's premier resort hotel.

Windermere, Cumbria LA23 1LP
Tel: *01539 433338* Fax: *01539 434072*
Email: *lowwood@elhmail.co.uk*
www.elh.co.uk

Low Wood Hotel
★★★★ ♜
Windermere, Cumbria, LA23 1LP
Tel: 01539 433338 Fax: 01539 434072
Email: lowwood@elhmail.co.uk
Web: www.elh.co.uk
Rooms: 110 all ensuite 🍴 📺 ⊗ Pricing: Sgl £93–98
Dbl £146–156 Dinner from £21.50 CC: Accepted
Room facilities: 🖥 ☎ 🍵 Access: ⬆ ♿
Conference: 11 meeting rooms (Thtr 340 max), 24hr-delegate from £105, day-delegate rate from £34
Children: Welcome ♿ ▒ Dogs: Welcome
Licences: ⚓ ♙ Leisure: Indoor pool, Gym, Health spa, Beauty salon, Games room, Snooker/billiards
Parking: Off-street and monitored
Directions: Take J36 of M6 then A591 to Windermere. Continue for 2 miles. Hotel situated on right on lake shore.
See advert on this page

Beech Hill Hotel
★★★★ ♜ ♜
Newby Bridge Road, Bowness-on-Windermere, Windermere, Cumbria, LA23 3LR
Tel: 01539 442137 Fax: 01539 443745
Email: beechhill@richardsonhotels.co.uk
Web: www.richardsonhotels.co.uk
Rooms: 58 all ensuite 🍴 📺
Pricing: Dinner from £27.50 (2002 rate)
CC: Accepted
Room facilities: 🖥 ☎ 🍵
Access: ♿

Children: Welcome ♿ ▒ Dogs: Welcome
Licences: ⚓ ♙ Leisure: Indoor pool
Parking: Off-street
Directions: Leave M6 at Junction 36, take A591 to Windermere. Turn left onto A592 towards Newby Bridge.

Craig Manor Hotel
★★★ ♜
Lake Road, Windermere, Cumbria, LA23 3HR
Tel: 015394 88877 Fax: 015394 88878

Gilpin Lodge Country House Hotel
Gold Ribbon Winner
★★★★ ♜ ♜ ♜
Crook Road, Windermere, Cumbria, LA23 3NE
Tel: 01539 488818 Fax: 01539 488058
Email: hotel@gilpin-lodge.co.uk
Web: www.gilpin-lodge.co.uk

Unwind by roaring fires, forage into Sybaritic menus and wine lists in cosy, elegant dinning rooms, retreat to luxurious tranquility in the bedrooms. Sumptuous pampering at this friendly award-winning family run hotel.
Rooms: 14 all ensuite 📺 ⊗
Pricing: Sgl £105 Dbl £110–210 Dinner from £35
CC: Accepted Room facilities: 🖥 ☎ 🍵 Access: ♿
Children: Welcome 7yrs min age Licences: ♙
Parking: Off-street and monitored
Directions: Leave M6 at Junction 36. Take A590/A591 to roundabout north of Kendal, then B5284 for 5 miles.
See advert on next page

Hillthwaite House
★★★
Thornbarrow Road, Windermere, Cumbria, LA23 2DF
Tel: 01539 443636 Fax: 01539 488660
Email: reception@hillthwaite.com
Web: www.hillthwaite.com
Rooms: 29 all ensuite 🍴 📺
Pricing: Dinner from £17.50 (2002 rate) CC: Accepted
Room facilities: 🖥 ☎ 🍵
Access: ♿ Children: Welcome ♿ ▒ Dogs: Welcome
Licences: ♙ Leisure: Indoor pool
Parking: Off-street
Directions: Halfway between Windermere and Bowness, turn left into Thornbarrow Road. Hillthwaite House Hotel can be seen on skyline.

Holbeck Ghyll Country House Hotel
Gold Ribbon Winner

★★★ ®® ®® ®®

Holbeck Lane, Windermere, Cumbria, LA23 1LU
Tel: 01539 432375 Fax: 01539 434743
Email: stay@holbeckghyll.com
Web: www.holbeckghyll.com

19th-century hunting lodge in 8 acres with breathtaking views of Lake Windemere. Art Nouveau features with log fires, Michelin-star food and exclusive health spa. Central touring location, special breaks.
Rooms: 20 all ensuite 🛏 🖥 🚭
Pricing: Sgl £95–220 Dbl £160–260 Dinner from £42.50
CC: Accepted
Room facilities: 📺 ☎

Access: ♿
Conference: 3 meeting rooms (Thtr 50 max), 24hr-delegate from £150, day-delegate rate from £45
Children: Welcome ⛹ ⚞
Dogs: Welcome
Licences: 🍸 ⅲⅲ
Leisure: Gym, Health spa, Beauty salon, Tennis
Parking: Off-street and monitored
Directions: Leave M6 at Junction 36. Take A591 to Windermere. Head towards Ambleside, turn right after Brockhole (Holbeck Lane, signposted Troutbeck). Hotel is half a mile on left.

Langdale Chase Hotel

★★★★ ®®

Windermere, Cumbria, LA23 1LW
Tel: 01539 432201 Fax: 01539 432604
Email: sales@langdalechase.co.uk
Web: www.langdalechase.co.uk
Rooms: 27 all ensuite 🛏 🖥
Pricing: Dinner from £30 CC: Accepted
Room facilities: 📺 ☎ 🖥 🎱
Access: ♿
Children: Welcome ⛹ 🐎 ⚞
Dogs: Welcome
Licences: 🍸 ⅲⅲ
Parking: Off-street and monitored
Directions: Leave M6 at Junction 36. Follow signs to Windermere on A591, then sign for Ambleside. Hotel is ¼ of a mile past Brockhole on left.

Northwest

Lindeth Howe Country House

★★★ ⓇⓇ

Lindeth Drive, Longtail Hill, Windermere,
Cumbria, LA23 3JF
Tel: 01539 445759 Fax: 01539 446368
Email: hotel@lindeth-howe.co.uk
Web: www.lindeth-howe.co.uk

Traditional Lakeland Country House, formerly owned
by Beatrix Potter. Comfy rooms, awarding-winning
restaurant, private gardens, superb lake and fell views.
Indoor pool and leisure facilities, the perfect place to
relax.
Rooms: 36 all ensuite ⓈⓈ 🖥 ⓈⓈ
Pricing: Sgl £52–95 Dbl £80–150 Dinner from £29.95
CC: Accepted Room facilities: 🖵 ☎ 🖳 📞 Access: ♿
Conference: 2 meeting rooms (Thtr 20 max), 24hr-
delegate from £125, day-delegate rate from £30
Children: Welcome ♭ 🐾 Dogs: Guide dogs only
Licences: 🎗 Leisure: Indoor pool, Gym
Parking: Off-street
Directions: From Junction 36 of the M6, take
A590/A591 at roundabout, then first left onto B5284.
Travel 6 miles, drive straight over crossroads to
Longtail Hill. Hotel 200 yards on left (first drive).

Linthwaite House Hotel and Restaurant
Blue Ribbon Winner

★★★★ ⓇⓇⓇ

Crook Road, Windermere, The Lake District,
Cumbria, LA23 3JA
Tel: 01539 488600 Fax: 01539 488601
Email: admin@linthwaite.com
Web: www.linthwaite.com

Sublime peaceful location, stunning lake and fell views,
14 acres, log fires, personally run, independently
owned, 'unstuffy' staff, good food and eclectic wine list.

Rooms: 26 all ensuite ⓈⓈ 🖥 ⓈⓈ
Pricing: Sgl £95–200 Dbl £95–215 Dinner from £40
CC: Accepted Room facilities: 🖵 ☎ 🖳 📞
Access: ♿ Children: Welcome ♭
Licences: 🍷 🎗 Parking: Off-street and monitored
Directions: Exit M6 J-36. A591 towards Windermere,
then B5284 through Crook. Linthwaite is 6 miles on
left, up private drive.

The Famous Wild Boar

★★★★ ⓇⓇ

Crook Road, Crook, near Windermere,
Cumbria, LA23 3NF
Tel: 015394 45225 Fax: 015394 42498
Email: wildboar@elhmail.co.uk
Web: www.elh.co.uk
Rooms: 36 all ensuite ⓈⓈ 🖥 ⓈⓈ
Pricing: Sgl £57.50–80 Dbl £57.50–115
Dinner from £22.95 CC: Accepted
Room facilities: 🖵 ☎ 🖳
Conference: 1 meeting room (Thtr 40 max), 24hr-
delegate from £90, day-delegate rate from £27
Children: Welcome ♭ 🐾 Dogs: Welcome
Licences: 🎗 Parking: Off-street
Directions: M6 exit 36 signed A5090/A591 to
Windermere. Join B5284 to Crook. Hotel 2 miles
beyond the village of Crook.
See advert on next page

The Old England

★★★

Bowness-on-Windermere, Cumbria, LA23 3DF
Tel: 0870 400 8130 Fax: 01539 443432
Email: oldengland@heritage-hotels.co.uk
Web: www.macdonaldhotels.co.uk
Rooms: 72 all ensuite ⓈⓈ 🖥 ⓈⓈ
Pricing: Sgl £69 Dbl £138 Dinner from £27.50
CC: Accepted
Room facilities: 🖵 ☎ 🖳 📞 Access: ⇕ ♿
Conference: 7 meeting rooms (Thtr 120 max)
Children: Welcome ♭ 🐾 Dogs: Welcome
Licences: 🍷 🎗
Leisure: Outdoor pool, Snooker/billiards
Parking: Off-street
Directions: Leave M6 at Junction 36. Take A592 to
Windermere. Hotel is on right, next to the lake, 18
miles from junction.

Broadoaks Country House

Blue Ribbon Winner

★★

Bridge Lane, Troutbeck, Windermere,
Cumbria, LA23 1LA
Tel: 015394 45566 Fax: 015394 88766
Email: trev@broadoaksf9.co.uk
Web: www.broadoaks-lake-district.co.uk

Award-winning country house set in own grounds. Superb views, luxury bedrooms with four-posters and jacuzzis. Exceptional cuisine in our Victorian dining room. Simply somewhere special.

Rooms: 14 all ensuite
Pricing: Sgl £69.50–165 Dbl £110–210
Dinner from £42.50 CC: Accepted
Room facilities:
Access:
Conference: 3 meeting rooms (Thtr 50 max), 24hr-delegate from £140, day-delegate rate from £60
Children: Welcome 5yrs min age
Dogs: Welcome
Licences:
Parking: Off-street and monitored
Directions: M6 J36 A590/591 to Windemere, over small roundabout to Ambleside, through Troutbeck, bridge right, into Bridge Lane. Property is 1/2 mile on right

Cedar Manor Hotel

★★

Ambleside Road, Windermere, Cumbria, LA23 1AX
Tel: 01539 443192 Fax: 01539 445970
Email: cedarmanor@fsbdial.co.uk
Web: www.cedarmanor.co.uk
Rooms: 12 all ensuite
Pricing: Sgl £30–57 Dbl £60–100 Dinner from £19.50
CC: Accepted
Room facilities:
Children: Welcome
Dogs: Welcome
Licences:
Parking: Off-street and monitored
Directions: 1/4 mile north of Windermere on A591. Nearest motorway, Junction 36 on M6. Follow signs for South Lakes.

Hideaway Hotel

★ ★

Phoenix Way, Windermere, Cumbria, LA23 1DB
Tel: 01539 443070 Fax: 01539 448664
Email: enquiries@hideaway-hotel.co.uk
Web: www.hideaway-hotel.co.uk
Seasonal closure: January
Rooms: 15 all ensuite
Pricing: Dinner from £11.50 CC: Accepted
Room facilities:
Children: Welcome
Dogs: Welcome
Licences:
Parking: Off-street
Directions: Take A591 into Windermere; turn off into
Phoenix Way. The hotel is 100m on the right down
the hill.
See advert on previous page

Lindeth Fell Country House Hotel

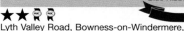
Blue Ribbon Winner

★ ★

Lyth Valley Road, Bowness-on-Windermere,
Cumbria, LA23 3JP
Tel: 01539 443286 Fax: 01539 447455
Email: kennedy@lindethfell.co.uk
Web: www.lindethfell.co.uk

Above Lake Windermere in magnificent gardens
Lindeth Fell is beautifully situated, and offers a warm
and friendly atmosphere, superior accommodation and
superb modern English cooking, at outstanding value.
Rooms: 14 all ensuite
Pricing: Sgl £55–75 Dbl £110–139 Dinner from £25
CC: Accepted
Room facilities:
Access:
Conference: 1 meeting room (Thtr 12 max), 24hr-
delegate from £90
Children: Welcome
Dogs: Guide dogs only
Licences:
Parking: Off-street and monitored
Directions: Lindeth Fell is situated one mile south of
Bowness on the Kendal/Lyth valley Lancaster road,
which is the A5074 road, leave M6 at junction 36.
See advert on next page

Miller Howe Hotel

Gold Ribbon Winner

★ ★

Rayrigg Road, Windermere, Cumbria, LA23 1EY
Tel: 015394 42536 Fax: 015394 45664
Email: lakeview@millerhowe.com
Web: www.millerhowe.com

Stunning views from this elegant Edwardian hotel with
gourmet restaurant, warm welcoming and friendly
service. Miller Howe feels like a home. Now with three
luxury suites in the Miller Howe cottage.
Rooms: 15 all ensuite
Pricing: Sgl £95–175 Dbl £120–270 Dinner from £39.50
CC: Accepted Room facilities:
Children: Welcome 8yrs min age Dogs: Welcome
Licences: Parking: Off-street and monitored
Directions: On A592 between Windemere and
Bowness. Ring for detailed location map or visit
website.

Newstead Guest House

♦ ♦ ♦ ♦ ♦

New Road, Windermere, Cumbria, LA23 2EE
Tel: 01539 444485
Rooms: 7 all ensuite
Pricing: Dbl £55 (2002 rate)
Room facilities:
Children: Welcome 7yrs min age
Parking: Off-street and monitored
Directions: Leave M6 at Junction 36. Follow
A590/A591 to Windermere village. Newstead is ¼ mile
on left.

The Beaumont

♦ ♦ ♦ ♦ ♦

Holly Road, Windermere, Cumbria, LA23 2AF
Tel: 01539 447075 Fax: 01539 447075
Email: thebeaumonthotel@btinternet.com
Web: www.lakesbeaumont.co.uk
Rooms: 10 all ensuite
Pricing: Sgl £35–45 Dbl £65–120 CC: Accepted
Room facilities:
Children: Welcome 10yrs min age
Dogs: Guide dogs only Licences:
Parking: Off-street
Directions: Follow town centre signs through one-way
system, then take second left into Ellerthwaite Road
and then first left into Holly Road.
See advert on next page

Blenheim Lodge Hotel

◆ ◆ ◆ ◆

Brantfell Road, Bowness-on-Windermere, Windermere,
Cumbria, LA23 3AE
Tel: 01539 443440 Fax: 01539 443440
Email: blenheimlodge@supanet.com
Web: www.blenheim-lodge.com
Rooms: 11 all ensuite
Pricing: Sgl £37–42 Dbl £60–90 CC: Accepted
Room facilities:
Children: Welcome 6yrs min age
Licences:
Parking: Off-street
Directions: Leave M6 at Juncion 36. Take A591 to
Windermere. Turn left to Bowness Cross mini
roundabout, take first left and first left again.

Fairfield

Brantfell Road, Bowness-on-Windermere, Cumbria,
LA23 3AE
Tel: 01539 446565 Fax: 01539 446565
Email: Ray&barb@the-fairfield.co.uk
Web: www.the-fairfield.co.uk
Seasonal closure: December to January

An attractive 200-year-old house set in a quiet,
secluded, well-matured garden. Close to the village,
lake, fells & Dales Way. Superb value.
Rooms: 9 (8 ensuite)
Pricing: Sgl £27–34 Dbl £54–68 CC: Accepted
Room facilities:
Children: Welcome
Licences:
Parking: Off-street
Directions: From mini roundabout in the centre of
Bowness village, take road towards lake, turn left, then
left again into Brantfell Road.

Northwest

Royal Hotel

Located in the heart of Bowness village only a minutes walk from the lake and surrounded by an excellent choice of restaurants, shops and attractions. Two lively theme bars, with a McGinty's Irish fun pub and Circuit Sports bar and also allows it's guests full use of the Low Wood leisure facilities

Queens Square, Bowness, Windermere, Cumbria, LA23 3DB
Tel: 01539 443045 Fax: 01539 444990
Web: www.elh.co.uk

Royal Hotel

◆ ◆ ◆
Royal Square, Bowness, Windermere, Cumbria, LA23 3DB
Tel: 01539 443045 Fax: 01539 444990
Web: www.elh.co.uk
Seasonal closure: 24–25 December
Rooms: 29 all ensuite 🦽 🛗
Pricing: Sgl £29.95–35 Dbl £59.90–84 CC: Accepted
Room facilities: 🖳 ☎ 🍵 Children: Welcome � ⚙
Dogs: Welcome Licences: ⛲
Parking: Off-street and monitored
Directions: Exit J36 M6, follow signs for Windemere. A591 in to Bowness. In centre of village.
See advert on this page

Wirral, Merseyside

Riverhill Hotel

★★★★ 🏵
Talbot Road, Oxton, Wirral, Cheshire, L43 2HJ
Tel: 0151 653 3773 Fax: 0151 653 7162
Email: reception@theriverhill.co.uk
Web: www.theriverhill.co.uk
Rooms: 14 all ensuite 🦽 🛗
Pricing: Sgl £56.50 Dbl £59.75 Dinner from £9.99
CC: AcceptedRoom facilities: 🖳 ☎ 🍵
Conference: 50 meeting rooms (Thtr 50 max)
Children: Welcome � ⚙
Licences: ⬧ ⛲
Parking: Off-street

Travelodge Wirral, Bebington

Travel Accommodation
A41 Northbound, 1408 New Chester Rod, Eastham, Wirral, Merseyside, CH62 9AQ
Web: www.travelodge.co.uk
Rooms: 31 all ensuite 🚭
Pricing: Sgl £47.40 Dbl £51.85 CC: Accepted
Room facilities: 🖳 🍵 Access: ♿

Workington, Cumbria

Cumberland Hotel

★★★
Station Road, Workington, Cumbria, CA14 2XQ
Tel: 01900 64401 Fax: 01900 872400
Email: cumberlandhotel@aol.com
Web: www.smoothhound.co.uk/hotels/cumberland
Rooms: 29 all ensuite 🦽 🛗 🚭
Pricing: Sgl £45–52 Dbl £60–72 Dinner from £12
CC: Accepted
Room facilities: 🖳 ☎ 🍵 📞
Access: ⇞ ♿
Conference: 3 meeting rooms (Thtr 200 max)
Children: Welcome �
Dogs: Welcome
Licences: ⛲
Parking: Off-street and monitored
Directions: Opposite Workington railway station, close to town centre. At junction of A66(M6), A595/A596, follow signs for station.

Drive in to a warm welcome at Swallow Hotels:

3 or 4 star hotels with a high standard of facilities and en-suite accommodation

FREE access to leisure club and indoor heated pool at every hotel

Superb dining with many hotels holding RAC dining awards

Ideal for a great value relaxing break

A.	**Glasgow Swallow**	0141 427 3146
B.	**Dundee Swallow**	01382 631 200
C.	**Carlisle Swallow Hilltop**	01228 529 255
D.	**Preston Swallow**	01772 877 351
E.	**Newcastle Swallow Imperial**	0191 281 5511
F.	**Newcastle Gateshead Swallow**	0191 477 1105
G.	**Rushyford** nr. Durham **Swallow Eden Arms**	01388 720 541
H.	**Chollerford** nr. Hexham **Swallow George**	01434 681 611
I.	**Durham Swallow Three Tuns**	0191 386 4326
J.	**Stockton on Tees Swallow**	01642 679 721
K.	**Harrogate Swallow St. George**	01423 561 431
L.	**Old Harlow Swallow Churchgate**	01279 420 246
M.	**Ipswich Swallow Belstead Brook**	01473 684 241

For a brochure or to book call Central Reservations on 0845 600 4 666

Wales

Liverpool Bay

Crosby
Bootle
Kirkby
Liverpool
Wallasey
Moreton
Hoylake
Birkenhead
Oxton
Widnes
restatyn
Heswall
Rhuddlan
Thornton Hough
Eastham
Runcorn
Ellesmere
Port
Frodsham
Holywell
Neston
Little
Sutton
St Asaph
Flint
Connah's
Quay
Halkyn
Mollington
Northop Hall
Sealand
Denbigh
Queensferry
Mold
Chester
Clwydian
Range
Buckley
Ruthin
Caergwrle
Pulford
Broxton
Nantwich
DENBIGHSHIRE
Wrexham
Rhostyllen
Malpas
Corwen
Cefn-
mawr
Ruabon
Overton
A525
Llangollen
Chirk
Haighton
Whitchurch
Llanarmon
Dyffryn Ceiriog
Ellesmere
Hodnet
Oswestry
Whittington
Wem
Llanfyllin
Mile End
Nesscliffe
Criggion
Shrewsbury
Welshpool
Llanfair
Caereinion
Bayston
Hill
Montgomery
Church
Stretton
SHROPSHIRE
Newtown
Lydham
Upper
Affcot
Bishops
Castle
Aston
Munslow
Clun
Craven Arms
Bromfield
Ludlow
Llanbister
Knighton
Greete
Woofferton
POWYS
Cross Gates
Penybont
Presteigne
Tenbury
Wells
Llandrindod
Wells
New Radnor
Leominster
Builth
Wells
Kington
Weobly
Eardisley
HEREFORD
Staunton-
on-Wye
Hereford
Hay-
on-Wye
Llyswen
Belmont
Talgarth
Portrilas
Ross-
on-Wye
Brecon
Llanhamlach
BEACONS
Symonds Yat
Mitcheldean
Talybont on Usk
Merthyr
Brynmawr
Abergavenny
Monmouth
Cinderford

Note:
Dark blue dots
represent the
location of
RAC-inspected
accommodation

Wales

Wales

Wales

Wales

Gold Ribbon Award

Bodysgallen Hall Hotel, Llandudno ★★★ 539

Fairyhill, Swansea ★★ 551

St Tudno Hotel, Llandudno ★★ 541

The Lake Country House,
Llangammarch Wells ★★★ 542

The Old Rectory Country
House Hotel, Conwy ★★ 534

Ynyshir Hall Hotel, Machynlleth ★★★ 544

Blue Ribbon Award

Celtic Manor Resort, Newport ★★★★★ 546

Hotel Portmeirion, Portmeirion ★★★ 548

The St Davids Hotel & Spa,
Cardiff Bay ★★★★★ 529

Little Gem

Sychnant Pass House, Conwy ◆◆◆◆◆ 535

Abercraf, West Glamorgan

The Abercrave Inn

★★

145 Heol Tawe, Abercraf, Swansea,
West Glamorgan, SA9 1XS
Tel: 01639 731002 Fax: 01639 730796
Email: abercraveinn@netscapeonline.co.uk
Web: www.abercraveinn.co.uk
Rooms: 12 all ensuite
Pricing: Sgl £30 Dbl £50 Room facilities: 🖵 🍵
Children: Welcome ♯ Dogs: Guide dogs only
Parking: Off-street and monitored

Aberdovey, Gwynedd

Trefeddian Hotel

★★★★ ℞ ℞

Aberdovey, Gwynedd, LL35 0SB
Tel: 01654 767213 Fax: 01654 767777
Email: tref@saqnet.co.uk
Web: www.trefwales.com
Rooms: 59 all ensuite 🍴 🚗 🚭
Pricing: Sgl £40–50 Dbl £80–100 Dinner from £22.25
CC: Accepted Room facilities: 🖵 ☎ 🍵
Access: ⇂↑↓ ㋕
Children: Welcome ♯ ⁑℃ Dogs: Welcome
Licences: ♦♦♦
Leisure: Indoor pool, Beauty salon, Tennis,
Games room, Snooker/billiards
Parking: Off-street and monitored
Directions: ¹⁄₂ mile north of Aberdovey village off A493,
overlooking golf links and Cardigan Bay.
See advert on following page

Abergavenny, Monmouthshire

Llansantffraed Court Hotel

★★★★ ℞ ℞

Llanvihangel Gobion, near Abergavenny,
Monmouthshire, NP7 9BA
Tel: 01873 840678 Fax: 01873 840674
Email: mikemorgan@llch.co.uk
Web: www.llch.co.uk
Rooms: 21 all ensuite 🍴 🚗 🚭
Room facilities: 🖵 ☎ 🍵 Access: ⇂↑↓ ㋕
Children: Welcome ♯ 🐴 ⁑℃ Dogs: Welcome
Licences: ◭ ♦♦♦
Leisure: Tennis, Fishing
Parking: Off-street and monitored
Directions: From convergence of A465 and A40 at
Abergavenny, take B4598 to Usk. Hotel gates are on
left after 4¹⁄₂ miles.

Abergele, Conwy

Kinmel Manor

★★★

St George's Road, Abergele, Conwy, LL22 9AS
Tel: 01745 832014 Fax: 01745 832014
Rooms: 51 all ensuite 🍴 🚭
Pricing: Dinner from £17 (2002 rate) CC: Accepted
Room facilities: 🖵 ☎ 🍵 Access: ㋕
Children: Welcome ♯ ⁑℃ Dogs: Welcome
Licences: ◭ ♦♦♦
Leisure: Indoor pool, Gym, Health spa
Parking: Off-street and monitored
Directions: Travelling west, take Abergele turn-off to
roundabout entrance. Travelling east A55, take Rhuddlan
turn-off to roundabout entrance. We are on the roundabout.

Aberporth, Cardigan

Hotel Penrallt

★★★★ ℞

Aberporth, Cardigan, SA43 2BS
Tel: 01239 810227 Fax: 01239 811375
Email: info@hotelpenrallt.co.uk
Web: www.hotelpenrallt.co.uk
Rooms: 16 all ensuite 🍴 🚭
Pricing: Dinner from £20 (2002 rate) CC: Accepted
Room facilities: 🖵 ☎ 🍵
Children: Welcome ♯ ⁑℃ Dogs: Welcome
Licences: ♦♦♦
Leisure: Indoor pool, Outdoor pool,
Gym, Tennis, Games room
Parking: Off-street and monitored
Directions: On A487 5 miles north of Cardigan Town, take
B4333 signed Aberporth. Hotel Penrallt 1 mile on right.

Aberystwyth, Ceredigion

Belle Vue Royal Hotel

★★★★ ℞

Marine Terrace, Aberystwyth, Ceredigion, SY23 2BA
Tel: 01970 617558 Fax: 01970 612190
Email: reception@bellevueroyalhotel.fsnet.co.uk
Web: www.bellevueroyal.co.uk
Rooms: 36 all ensuite 🍴 🚭
Pricing: Dinner from £22 (2002 rate) CC: Accepted
Room facilities: 🖵 ☎ 🍵 Children: Welcome ♯ ⁑℃
Licences: ♦♦♦
Parking: Off-street and monitored
Directions: Situated on promenade overlooking
Cardigan Bay.

Plan your route

Visit www.rac.co.uk for RAC's
interactive route planner, including
up to the minute traffic reports.

Ask the experts

To book a Hotel or Guest
Accommodation, or for help
and advice, call RAC Hotel
Reservations on 0870 603 9109
and quote 'Guide 2003'

Trefeddian Hotel

Standing prominently overlooking golf links, sand dunes and Cardigan Bay, 1½ miles north of Aberdyfi (Aberdovey) village, Trefeddian is set in its own grounds and suitable for all the family. Trefeddian is renowned for friendly attentive service, excellent meals, an extensive wine list, and spacious lounges, affording relaxing holidays.

The hotel has an indoor swimming pool, tennis court,

9-hole pitch/putt, snooker room, children's indoor/outdoor play areas, sun terraces, and lift.

Trefeddian Hotel
Aberdovey,
Gwynedd LL35 0SB
Tel: 01654 767213
Fax: 01654 767777
Email: tref@saqnet.co.uk

Conrah Country House Hotel

★★★

Chancery, Aberystwyth, Ceredigion, SY23 4DF
Tel: 01970 617941 Fax: 01970 624546
Email: enquiries@conrah.co.uk
Web: www.conrah.co.uk
Seasonal closure: Christmas
Rooms: 17 all ensuite
Pricing: Sgl £75–100 Dbl £110–145 Dinner from £25
CC: Accepted Room facilities: Access:
Conference: 2 meeting rooms (Thtr 60 max),
24hr-delegate from £125, day-delegate rate from £25
Children: Welcome 5yrs min age
Dogs: Guide dogs only Licences:
Leisure: Indoor pool, Games room
Parking: Off-street and monitored
Directions: 3¹/₂ miles south of Aberystwyth on A487.

George Borrow Hotel

★★

Ponterwyd, Aberystwyth, Ceredigion, SY23 3AD
Tel: 01970 890230 Fax: 01970 890587
Email: georgeborrow@clara.net
Web: www.george-borrow.co.uk
Rooms: 9 all ensuite
Pricing: Dinner from £11.95 (2002 rate) CC: Accepted
Room facilities: Children: Welcome
Dogs: Welcome Licences: Leisure: Games room
Parking: Off-street
Directions: Alongside A44, Aberystwyth side of village
of Ponterwyd, 15 mins from Aberystwyth.

Glyn-Garth Guest House

◆◆◆◆

South Road, Aberystwyth, Ceredigion, SY23 1JS
Tel: 01970 615050 Fax: 01970 636835
Email: glyngarth@aol.com
Web: glyngarthgh.cjb.net
Seasonal closure: Christmas to New Year
Rooms: 10 (6 ensuite)
Pricing: Sgl £21–22 Dbl £42–56
Room facilities:
Children: Welcome, 7yrs min age Parking: Off-street
Directions: Close to town centre, near harbour and
castle grounds. Adjacent to South Promenade.

Amlwch, Anglesey

Trecastell Hotel

★★

Bull Bay, Amlwch, Isle of Anglesey, LL68 9SA
Tel: 01407 830651 Fax: 01407 832114
Email: trecastellhotel@aol.com
Rooms: 15 (2 ensuite)
Pricing: Sgl £35 Dbl £55 CC: Accepted
Room facilities:
Conference: 1 meeting room (Thtr 30 max)
Children: Welcome Licences:
Directions: A55 to Britannia Bridge, over bridge take
A5025 to Amlwch, then drive through hotel on left just
beyond Golf club.

Bala, Gwynedd

Plas Coch Hotel

★★

High Street, Bala, Gwynedd, LL23 7AB
Tel: 01678 520309 Fax: 01678 521135

Bangor, Gwynedd

The Menai Court Hotel

◆◆◆

Craig Y Don Road, Bangor,
Gwynedd, LLS7 2BG
Tel: 01248 354 200 Fax: 01248 354 512
Email: info@themenai33.freeserve.co.uk
Rooms: 9 all ensuite
Pricing: Sgl £35–51 Dbl £50–69 Dinner from £7.25
CC: Accepted
Room facilities:
Conference: 1 meeting room (Thtr 25 max),
day-delegate rate from £50
Children: Welcome Dogs: Welcome Licences:
Leisure: Games room Parking: Off-street
Directions: Exit A55 junction 11 into Bangor, at station,
turn right after roundabout take third right then first left.

Travelodge Bangor

Travel Accommodation
A5/A55, Llys-Y-Gwynt, Bangor, Gwynedd, LL57 4BG
Web: www.travelodge.co.uk
Rooms: 62 all ensuite
Pricing: Sgl £54.40 Dbl £58.85 CC: Accepted
Room facilities: Access:

Barmouth, Gwynedd

Bontddu Hall Hotel

★★★

Bontddu, Dolgellau, Gwynedd, LL40 2UF
Tel: 01341 430661 Fax: 01341 430284
Email: reservations@bontdduhall.co.uk
Web: www.bontdduhall.co.uk
Rooms: 20 all ensuite
Pricing: Sgl £55–85 Dbl £90–150 Dinner from £30
CC: Accepted
Room facilities: Access:
Conference: 2 meeting rooms (Thtr 100 max),
24hr-delegate from £125, day-delegate rate from £25
Dogs: Welcome Licences:
Parking: Off-street and monitored
Directions: Turn off A470 north of Dolgellau onto A496
towards Barmouth. 3 miles to Bontddu — hotel is on
right-hand side.

Beddgelert, Gwynedd

Royal Goat Hotel

★★★★ 🖥

Beddgelert, Gwynedd, LL55 4YE
Tel: 01766 890224 Fax: 01766 890422
Email: info@royalgoathotel.co.uk
Web: www.royalgoathotel.co.uk
Rooms: 32 all ensuite 🍴 📺 🚭
Pricing: Sgl £46.50–53.50 Dbl £82–96
Dinner from £19.50 CC: Accepted
Room facilities: 📺 ☎ 🗑 Access: ♿
Children: Welcome 🍴 Dogs: Welcome Licences: ♙
Leisure: Fishing, Games room Parking: Off-street
Directions: Situated in the centre of the village.
See advert on this page

Tanronnen Hotel

★★ 🖥

Beddgelert, Gwynedd, LL55 4YB
Tel: 01766 890347 Fax: 01766 890606
Email: brewery@frederic-robinson.co.uk
Web: www.frederic-robinson.co.uk
Rooms: 7 all ensuite 🚭
Pricing: Dinner from £9.90 CC: Accepted
Room facilities: 📺 ☎ 🗑
Children: Welcome 🍴
Dogs: Guide dogs only
Licences: ♙ Parking: Off-street
Directions: Situated in village centre.

Betws-y-Coed, Conwy

Royal Oak Hotel

★★★★ 🖥

Betws-y-Coed, Conwy, LL24 0AY
Tel: 01690 710219 Fax: 01690 710603
Email: glenn.evans@btinternet.com
Web: www.royaloak@betwsycoed.co.uk/
 acc/royal-oak/default/html
Rooms: 26 all ensuite 🍴 🚭
Pricing: Dinner from £16 CC: Accepted
Room facilities: 📺 ☎ 🗑 Children: Welcome 🍴
Licences: ♦ ♙ Leisure: Golf
Parking: Off-street and monitored
Directions: The hotel is situated on the main A5
London to Holyhead route, at the village centre.

Park Hill Hotel

★★

Llanrwst Road, Betws-y-Coed, Conwy, LL24 0HD
Tel: 01690 710540 Fax: 01690 710540
Email: parkhill.hotel@virgin.net
Web: www.betws-y-coed.co.uk/acc/parkhill
Rooms: 9 all ensuite 📺
Pricing: Dinner from £16.50 CC: Accepted
Room facilities: 📺 🗑
Children: Welcome, 6yrs min age 🍴 Licences: ♙
Leisure: Indoor pool Parking: Off-street and monitored
Directions: On elevated position on A470 northbound
from Betws-y-Coed, 1/2 mile from crossing with
A5/Waterloo Bridge.

Fron Heulog Country House

◆◆◆◆

Betws-y-Coed, Conwy, LL24 0BL
Tel: 01690 710736 Fax: 01690 710920
Email: jean&peter@fronheulog.co.uk
Web: www.fronheulog.co.uk
Rooms: 3 all ensuite
Pricing: Dbl £44–56
Room facilities:
Dogs: Guide dogs only Parking: Off-street
Directions: From A5 road in Betwys-y-Coed take
B5106 road over picturesque Pont-y-Pair bridge,
immediately turn left along riverbank. Fron Heulog is
150 yards up ahead.

Brecon, Powys

Peterstone Court

★★★

Llanhamlach, Brecon, Powys, LD3 7YB
Tel: 01874 665387 Fax: 01874 665376
Email: info@peterstone-court.com
Web: www.peterstone-court.com
Seasonal closure: 26–31 December
Rooms: 12 all ensuite
Pricing: Sgl £98.70 Dbl £109.75 Dinner from £15.25
CC: Accepted
Room facilities:
Conference: 3 meeting rooms (Thtr 130 max),
24hr-delegate from £120, day-delegate rate from £31
Children: Welcome Dogs: Welcome Licences:
Leisure: Outdoor pool, Gym, Health spa,
Beauty salon, Games room
Parking: Off-street
Directions: We are 3 miles from Brecon on the A40,
Brecon to Abergavenny road.
See advert on facing page

Usk Inn

◆◆◆◆

Station Road, Talybont on Usk, Brecon,
Powys, LD3 7JE
Tel: 01874 676251 Fax: 01874 676392
Email: stay@uskinn.co.uk
Web: www.uskinn.co.uk
Seasonal closure: Christmas

Whether walking, mountain bike riding or touring in a
classic car, good food, wine, beer and above all
rooms combine in an Inn that continues to exceed

guests' expectations.
Rooms: 11 all ensuite
Pricing: Sgl £35–50 Dbl £70–100 Dinner from £17.95
CC: Accepted
Room facilities: Children: Welcome
Licences: Parking: Off-street
Directions: From A40, we are 6 miles east of Brecon.
Turn into Talybont on Usk. The Inn is 250 yards from
the river bridge.

Beacons

◆◆◆

16 Bridge Street, Brecon, Powys, LD3 8AH
Tel: 01874 623339 Fax: 01874 623339
Email: beacons@brecon.co.uk
Web: www.beacons.brecon.co.uk

This recently-restored listed Georgian house offers
beautifully appointed bedrooms. The candle-lit
restaurant has fine food and wines. Cosy cellar bar,
elegant lounge and private parking.
Rooms: 14 (11 ensuite)
Pricing: Sgl £30–35 Dbl £19–30 Dinner from £9.95
CC: Accepted
Room facilities: Access:
Children: Welcome Dogs: Welcome
Licences: Parking: Off-street and monitored
Directions: Following the A40 west through town
centre, turn left. Go downhill at traffic lights, over
bridge, then hotel is 100 yards on right.

Wales

Cherrypicker House

♦ ♦ ♦

9 Orchard Street, Brecon, Powys, LD3 8AN
Tel: 01874 624665
Email: info@cherrypickerhouse.co.uk
Web: www.cherrypickerhouse.co.uk
Rooms: 3 (1 ensuite) ⊗
Pricing: Sgl £25 Dbl £36–50
Room facilities: ☐ ☕ Children: Welcome ħ
Dogs: Guide dogs only Parking: Off-street
Directions: From junction of A40/A470 follow signs to
Brecon House is half a mile on left.

Maeswalter

♦ ♦ ♦

Heol Senni, near Brecon, Powys, LD3 8SU
Tel: 01874 636629
Email: maeswalter@talk21.com
Web: www.smoothhound.co.uk/hotels/maeswalter.html

A 300-year-old farmhouse situated in Brecon Beacons
National Park with magnificent views against a Senni
Valley. Tastefully decorated and comfortable ensuite
bedrooms with tea/coffee-making facilities and TV in
each room.
Rooms: 4 (2 ensuite) ⊗
Pricing: Sgl £20–25 Dbl £40–55 Dinner from £12
Room facilities: ☐ ☕ Children: Welcome 10yrs min age ħ ⊰
Dogs: Welcome Parking: Off-street
Directions: Take A470 (Brecon to Merthyr). Turn right onto
A4215. After 2 miles turn left for Heol Senni. Maeswalter
is 1¹/₂ miles on right.

Bridgend, Glamorgan

Bryngarw House

♦ ♦ ♦ ♦

Bryngarw Country Park, Brynmenyn, near Bridgend,
Glamorgan, CF32 8UU
Tel: 01656 729009 Fax: 01656 729007
Web: www.bridgend.gov.uk
Rooms: 19 all ensuite ♨ ⊗
Pricing: Sgl £55–60 Dbl £75–95 Dinner from £21
CC: Accepted Room facilities: ☐ ☎ ☕ Access: ᪥
Conference: 4 meeting rooms (Thtr 80 max)
Children: Welcome ħ Dogs: Guide dogs only
Licences: ⟁ ⁂ Parking: Off-street and monitored
Directions: Exit M4 J36 and follow Country Park signs for
2¹/₂ miles.

Travelodge Pencoed (SA)

Travel Accommodation
The Old Mill, Felindre Road, Pencoed, Nr. Bridgend,
Glamorgan, CF35 5HU
Web: www.travelodge.co.uk
Rooms: 40 all ensuite ⊗
Pricing: Sgl £47.40 Dbl £51.85 CC: Accepted
Room facilities: ☐ ☕ Access: ᪥

Burry Port, Carmarthenshire

George Hotel

♦ ♦ ♦ ♦

Stepney Road, Burry Port, Carmarthenshire, SA16 0BH
Tel: 01554 832211
Rooms: 5 all ensuite ♨
Pricing: Sgl £25–37 Dbl £42–48 Dinner from £5.95
Room facilities: ☐ ☕
Children: Welcome, 7yrs min age ħ
Licences: ⁂
Directions: M4 J48, A484 to Burry Port. Turn at pelican
crossing into town centre along Stepney Road.

Caernarfon, Gwynedd

Celtic Royal Hotel

★ ★ ★ ★

Bangor Street, Caernarfon, Gwynedd, LL55 1AY
Tel: 01286 674477 Fax: 01286 674139
Email: admin@celtic-royal.co.uk
Web: www.celtic-royal.co.uk
Rooms: 110 all ensuite ♨ ⊠ ⊗
Pricing: Dinner from £15 (2002 rate) CC: Accepted
Room facilities: ☐ ☎ ☕ Access: ⟙ ᪥
Children: Welcome ħ Dogs: Guide dogs only
Licences: ⟁ ⁂
Leisure: Indoor pool, Gym, Health spa
Parking: Off-street and monitored

Seiont Manor

★ ★ ★ ★

Llanrug, Caernarfon, Gwynedd, LL55 2AQ
Tel: 01286 673366 Fax: 01286 672840
Web: www.arcadianhotels.co.uk
Rooms: 28 all ensuite ♨ ⊠ ⊗
Pricing: Dinner from £25 (2002 rate) CC: Accepted
Room facilities: ☐ ☎ ☕
Children: Welcome ħ ⊰ Dogs: Guide dogs only
Licences: ⟁ ⁂
Leisure: Indoor pool, Gym, Fishing
Parking: Off-street
Directions: Follow A55 to Caernarfon. Hotel situated 3
miles outside Caernarfon on A4086.

Pengwern

Saron, Llanwnda, Caernarfon, Gwynedd, LL54 5UH
Tel: 01286 831500 Fax: 01286 830741
Email: pengwern@talk21.com
Seasonal closure: December and January

Charming spacious farm house of character, beautifully situated between mountains and sea, unobstructed views of Snowdonia, well-appointed bedrooms all with ensuite facilities, Jane has Cookery diploma and provides excellent meals using local produce.
Rooms: 3 all ensuite
Pricing: Sgl £35–38 Dbl £48–56 Dinner from £17.50
CC: Accepted
Room facilities:
Children: Welcome
Parking: Off-street
Directions: From Caernarfon south on A487, pass supermarket over bridge, turn right for Saron, 2 miles through Saron and over crossroads, first farm drive on right.

Cardiff

The St David's Hotel & Spa

★★★★★
Blue Ribbon Winner

Havannah Street, Cardiff Bay,
Cardiff, CF10 5SD
Tel: 029 2045 4045 Fax: 029 2048 7056
Email: reservations@thestdavidshotel.com
Web: www.thestdavidshotel.com
Rooms: 132 all ensuite
Pricing: Sgl £204.50 Dbl £219 Dinner from £30
CC: Accepted
Room facilities:
Access:
Conference: 7 meeting rooms (Thtr 270 max),
24hr-delegate from £195, day-delegate rate from £55
Children: Welcome Dogs: Guide dogs only
Licences:
Leisure: Indoor pool, Gym, Health spa, Beauty salon
Parking: Off-street and monitored
Directions: Follow signs for Cardiff Bay, the hotel is adjacent to the Techniquest science centre, close to mermaid quay.
See advert on following page

Angel

★★★★

Castle Street, Cardiff, CF10 1SZ
Tel: 029 2064 9200 Fax: 029 2022 5980
Email: angel@paramount-hotels.co.uk
Web: www.paramount-hotels.co.uk
Rooms: 102 all ensuite
Pricing: Sgl £130.50–190.50 Dbl £161–201
Dinner from £19.50 CC: Accepted
Room facilities:
Access:
Conference: 7 meeting rooms (Thtr 300 max),
24hr-delegate from £140, day-delegate rate from £34
Children: Welcome Dogs: Welcome
Licences:
Parking: Off-street and monitored
Directions: Exit J29 or J32 M4.
Situated in Cardiff city centre,
opposite Cardiff Castle.

PARAMOUNT
GROUP OF HOTELS

Copthorne Hotel Cardiff Caerdydd

★★★★

Copthorne Way, Culverhouse Cross, Cardiff, CF5 6DH
Tel: 029 2059 9100 Fax: 029 2059 9080
Email: sales.cardiff@mill-cop.com
Web: www.millenniumhotels.com

In a picturesque setting just four miles from the city centre, this luxurious modern lakeside hotel offers you a warm welcome to Wales.
Rooms: 135 all ensuite
Pricing: Sgl £75–140 Dbl £75–150 Dinner from £21.95
CC: Accepted
Room facilities: Access:
Conference: 8 meeting rooms (Thtr 300 max),
24hr-delegate from £145, day-delegate rate from £40
Children: Welcome Dogs: Welcome
Licences:
Leisure: Indoor pool, Gym
Parking: Off-street and monitored
Directions: J33 M4 take A4232 for 3 miles. Take first exit signposted for A48. Fourth exit off roundabout. Hotel on the left.

Making a booking?

Don't forget to mention RAC Hotels and Bed & Breakfast 2003.

THE ST DAVID'S HOTEL & SPA
CARDIFF

The *St David's Hotel & Spa*
THE JEWEL OF CARDIFF BAY

Contemporary design, the latest facilities and comforts, breathtaking views
- reasons enough to visit Rocco Forte's St David's Hotel & Spa, a striking
landmark on the waterfront of Cardiff Bay. All bedrooms are stylishly decorated
with private balconies overlooking the bay. Indulge in our extensive spa, marine
hydropools and treatment rooms and enjoy a wide range of delicious Welsh
cuisine in Tides Marco Pierre White Restaurant. If visiting on business, all of
our conference suites enjoy natural light and are equipped with the latest
audio-visual technology.

ROCCO FORTE
HOTELS

The St David's Hotel & Spa Havannah Street Cardiff Bay Cardiff CF10 5SD Wales
Telephone +44 (0)29 2045 4045 Facsimile +44 (0)29 2048 7056
E-mail reservations@thestdavidshotel.com Website www.roccofortehotels.com

Hanover International Hotel & Club Cardiff

★★★★

Schooner Way, Atlantic Wharf, Cardiff, CF10 4RT
Tel: 0870 241 7107 Fax: 029 2048 1491
Email: crso@hanover-international.com
Web: www.hanover-international.com

HANOVER INTERNATIONAL
HOTELS & CLUBS

Imaginative design with a maritime theme throughout, this hotel provides quality accommodation and an exceptional leisure club. Close to the scenic Brecon Beacons.
Rooms: 156 all ensuite 🚭
Pricing: Sgl £60–107 Dbl £90–140 Dinner from £18
CC: Accepted Room facilities: 🖳 ☎ 🍵 📞
Access: ⬆ ♿
Conference: 10 meeting rooms (Thtr 200 max)
Children: Welcome ⍢ ⧂ Dogs: Guide dogs only
Licences: ⬥ ♜ Leisure: Indoor pool, Gym, Health spa, Games room, Snooker/billiards
Parking: Off-street and monitored
Directions: M4 J29, take M48, then A48(M). Follow signs to Cardiff Bay; or, M4 J33, A4232 to Cardiff Bay.

Jurys Cardiff Hotel

★★★★

Mary Ann Street, Cardiff, CF10 2JH
Tel: +353(0)1 6070000 Fax: +353(0)1 6316999
Email: bookings@jurysdoyle.com
Web: www.jurysdoyle.com

🐾 JURYS DOYLE
HOTELS

Rooms: 146 all ensuite 🐾 🚭
Pricing: Sgl £121–151 Dbl £132–152
Dinner from £18.95 CC: Accepted
Room facilities: 🖳 ☎ 🍵 📞 Access: ⬆ ♿
Children: Welcome, 12yrs min age ⍢
Dogs: Guide dogs only Licences: ♜
Parking: Off-street and monitored

Directions: Located 14 miles from Cardiff Int'l Airport. Central Station only 5 mins walk. Hotel is adjacent to Cardiff International Arena.

Manor Parc Country Hotel & Restaurant

★★★ ☙ ☙ ☙

Thornhill Road, Thornhill, Cardiff, CF14 9UA
Tel: 029 2069 3723 Fax: 029 2061 4624

Small select hotel with private parking set in mature gardens with large patios overlooking Cardiff. Conference, banqueting and restaurant facilities offering excellent English and Continental cuisine for the discerning guest.
Rooms: 12 all ensuite 🚿 Room facilities: 🖳 ☎ 🍵
Children: Welcome Licences: ⬥ ♜
Leisure: Tennis Parking: Off-street
Directions: Situated on A469 on outskirts of the city of Cardiff, going towards Caerphilly. Manor Parc on left.

Quality Hotel & Suites, Cardiff

★★★

Junction 32/M4 Merthyr Road, Tongwynlais, Cardiff, CF15 7LD
Tel: 029 2052 9988 Fax: 029 2052 9977
Email: admin@gb629@u-net.com
Web: www.choicehotels.com
Rooms: 95 all ensuite 🐾 🚭
Pricing: Sgl £36.50–105.95 Dbl £73–126.90
Dinner from £15.95 CC: Accepted
Room facilities: 🖳 ☎ 🍵 📞 Access: ⬆ ♿
Conference: 6 meeting rooms (Thtr 180 max), 24hr-delegate from £130, day-delegate rate from £34
Children: Welcome ⍢ Dogs: Welcome
Licences: ⬥ ♜
Leisure: Indoor pool, Gym, Health spa
Parking: Off-street and monitored
Directions: Take Junction 32 off the M4. Follow roundabout through and take the A4054 exit for Tongwynlais. Hotel is located on right.

Wales

St Mellons Hotel & Country Club

★★★

Castleton, Cardiff, CF3 2XR
Tel: 01633 680355 Fax: 01633 680399
Email: stmellons@bestwestern.co.uk
Web: www.stmellonshotel.com
Rooms: 41 all ensuite
Pricing: Dinner from £18 CC: Accepted
Room facilities: ▢ ☎ ☕ ☏
Conference: 1 meeting room (Thtr 250 max)
Children: Welcome ♀ ⚘ Dogs: Welcome
Licences: ⬧ ♦♦♦
Leisure: Indoor pool, Gym, Beauty salon, Tennis
Parking: Monitored
Directions: Leave M4 at Junction 28. Follow signs to
A48 Cardiff. After Castleton village, hotel is signposted
on left-hand side.

Sandringham Hotel

★★

21 St Mary Street, Cardiff, CF10 1PL
Tel: 029 2023 2161 Fax: 029 2038 3998
Email: mm@sandringham-hotel.com
Web: www.sandringham-hotel.com
Rooms: 28 all ensuite
Pricing: Sgl £35–100 Dbl £45–120 Dinner from £6
CC: Accepted Room facilities: ▢ ☎ ☕
Conference: 2 meeting rooms (Thtr 80 max),
24hr-delegate from £65, day-delegate rate from £15
Children: Welcome ♀ ☼ Dogs: Guide dogs only
Licences: ♦♦♦ Parking: Off-street and monitored
Directions: Exit 29 from M4, follow signs for city centre,
turn left opposite Cardiff castle high street and St Mary
Street.

Marlborough Guest House

◆ ◆ ◆ ◆ ✗

98 Newport Road, Cardiff, CF2 1DG
Tel: 029 2049 2385

Campanile

Travel Accommodation
Caxton Place, Pentwyn, Cardiff, CF23 8HA
Tel: 029 2054 9044 Fax: 029 2054 9900
Email: cardiff@envergure.co.uk
Web: www.campanile.fr / www.envergure.fr

Typical Campanile bistro

A comfortable hotel with 47 ensuite rooms, colour TV
and satellite channels, telephone and welcome tray.
With a friendly restaurant, bar and free parking for our
guests.
Rooms: 47 all ensuite
Pricing: Sgl £40.95–47.90 Dbl £46.90–53.85 Dinner
from £6.25 CC: Accepted
Room facilities: ▢ ☎ ☕ ☏ Access: ♿
Conference: 1 meeting room (Thtr 30 max),
24hr-delegate from £68, day-delegate rate from £19.50
Children: Welcome ♀ Dogs: Welcome Licences: ♦♦♦
Parking: Off-street and monitored
Directions: Exit J30 M4. Follow signs for city centre.

Travelodge Cardiff Central (SA)

Travel Accommodation
St Mary's Street, Imperial Gate, Cardiff, CF10 1FA
Web: www.travelodge.co.uk
Rooms: 100 all ensuite ⊗
Pricing: Sgl £54.40 Dbl £58.85 CC: Accepted
Room facilities: ▢ ☕ Access: ♿

Travelodge Cardiff East (SA)

Travel Accommodation
A48, Circle Way East, Llanderyrn, Cardiff,
South Wales, CF23 9PD
Web: www.travelodge.co.uk
Pricing: Sgl £47.40 Dbl £51.85 CC: Accepted
Room facilities: ▢ ☕

Travelodge Cardiff West (MOTO)

Travel Accommodation
M4 Moto Service Area, Pontyclun,
Nr. Cardiff, CF72 8SA
Web: www.travelodge.co.uk
Rooms: 50 all ensuite ⊗
Pricing: Sgl £54.40 Dbl £58.85 CC: Accepted
Room facilities: ▢ ☕ Access: ♿

Cardigan, Ceredigion

Castell Malgwyn

★★

Llechryd, Cardigan, Ceredigion, SA43 2QA
Tel: 01239 682382 Fax: 01239 682644
Email: reception@malgwyn.co.uk
Web: www.castellmalgwyn.co.uk
Rooms: 20 all ensuite ⛱ ⊗
Pricing: Sgl £40–90 Dbl £70–110 Dinner from £18
CC: Accepted
Room facilities: ▢ ☎ ☕ ☏
Conference: 4 meeting rooms (Thtr 200 max),
24hr-delegate from £85, day-delegate rate from £25
Children: Welcome ♀ ☼
Dogs: Welcome
Licences: ⬧ ♦♦♦
Leisure: Beauty salon, Fishing
Parking: Off-street and monitored
Directions: In Llechryd village, drive over River Teifi
Bridge to hotel entrance.

Penbontbren

★★

Glynarthen, Cardigan, Ceredigion, SA44 6PE
Tel: 01239 810248 Fax: 01239 811129
Email: welcome@penbontbern.com
Web: www.penbontbern.com
Seasonal closure: 22–28 December
Rooms: 10 all ensuite
Pricing: Sgl £42–49 Dbl £74–86 Dinner from £20
CC: Accepted Room facilities: 🖵 ☎ 🍵 Access: ♿
Conference: 1 meeting room (Thtr 25 max)
Children: Welcome ⴹ 🎦 Dogs: Welcome Licences: ♦♦♦
Parking: Off-street and monitored
Directions: Travelling south from Aberystwyth on A487,
take first left after Sarnau. Travelling north on A487
from Cardigan take second right about 1 mile after
Tan-y-groes (signposted Penbontbren).

The Pembrokeshire Retreat

◆ ◆ ◆ ◆

Rhos-y-Gilwen Mansion, Rhos-y-Gilwen Hill, Cardigan,
Ceredigion, SA43 2TW
Tel: 01239 841387 Fax: 01239 841387
Email: enquiries@retreat.co.uk
Web: www.retreat.co.uk
Rooms: 3 all ensuite
Pricing: Dinner from £15 (2002 rate) CC: Accepted
Room facilities: 🖵 🍵 Children: Welcome ⴹ
Licences: ⟁ ♦♦♦ Leisure: Tennis Parking: Off-street

Brynhyfryd Guest House

◆ ◆ ◆

Gwbert Road, Cardigan, Ceredigion, SA43 1AE
Tel: 01239 612861 Fax: 01239 612861
Email: g.arcus@btinternet.com
Rooms: 7 (3 ensuite)
Pricing: Sgl £18–25 Dbl £36–40 Dinner from £7
Room facilities: 🖵 🍵 Children: Welcome 10yrs min age ⴹ
Directions: From town centre drive through main street.
Spar shop on right — turn left after it. The guest house
is opposite tennis courts.

Carmarthen, Carmarthenshire

Capel Dewi Uchaf Country House

◆ ◆ ◆ ◆

Capel Dewi, Carmarthen, Carmarthenshire, SA32 8AY
Tel: 01267 290799 Fax: 01267 290003
Email: uchaffarm@aol.com
Web: www.walescottageholidays.uk.com

Rooms: 3 all ensuite
Pricing: Sgl £40 Dbl £60 Dinner from £25
CC: Accepted Room facilities: 🖵 🍵
Children: Welcome ⴹ 🎦 Licences: ♦♦♦ Parking: Off-street
Directions: Leave M4 at Junction 4. Take A48 until exit
for National Botanic Garden. Take B4310 to junction with
B4300. Turn left. Capel Dewi is ³/₄ mile on right.

Travelodge St Clears, Carmathen

Travel Accommodation

A477, Tenby Road, St Clears, Carmathen,
Carmarthenshire, SA33 4JN
Web: www.travelodge.co.uk
Rooms: 32 all ensuite
Pricing: Sgl £57.40 Dbl £61.85 CC: Accepted
Room facilities: 🖵 🍵 Access: ♿

Chepstow, Monmouthshire

Beaufort Hotel Chepstow

★★

Beaufort Square, Chepstow,
Monmouthshire, NP16 5EP
Tel: 01291 622497 Fax: 01291 627389
Email: info@beauforthotel.co.uk
Web: www.beauforthotelchepstow.com
Rooms: 22 all ensuite
Pricing: Sgl £44.50–52 Dbl £67–75 Dinner from £14.95
CC: Accepted Room facilities: 🖵 ☎ 🍵 Access: ♿
Conference: 3 meeting rooms (Thtr 150 max),
24hr-delegate from £75, day-delegate rate from £25
Children: Welcome ⴹ Dogs: Welcome
Licences: ⟁ ♦♦♦ Parking: Off-street
Directions: From M48, signs to Chepstow. Stay on
A48. Take second left at lights by church. Hotel car
park on Nelson Street.

Colwyn Bay, Conwy

Hopeside Hotel

★★★

63 Princes Drive, Colwyn Bay, Conwy, LL29 8PW
Tel: 01492 533244 Fax: 01492 532850
Email: hopesidejd@aol.com
Rooms: 14 all ensuite
Pricing: Dinner from £9.95 (2002 rate) CC: Accepted
Room facilities: 🖵 ☎ 🍵
Children: Welcome ⴹ Dogs: Welcome Licences: ♦♦♦
Leisure: Gym Parking: Off-street
Directions: From direction of Chester on A55 — take
B5115, turn off for Rhos-on-Sea — turn left; hotel 100
yards on right.

Wales

Norfolk House Hotel

★★★

Princes Drive, Colwyn Bay, Conwy, LL29 9PF
Tel: 01492 531757 Fax: 01492 533781
Rooms: 22 all ensuite
Pricing: Sgl £47.50 Dbl £62 Dinner from £17
CC: Accepted Room facilities: ☐ ☎ ☕ Access: ⬆
Conference: 2 meeting rooms (Thtr 35 max)
Children: Welcome ⍗ Dogs: Welcome Licences: ♦♦♦
Leisure: Snooker/billiards Parking: Off-street
Directions: Colwyn Bay exit off A55 — turn right,
500 meters on the left.

Quality Hotel Colwyn Bay

★★

Penmaenhead, Old Colwyn, Colwyn Bay,
Conwy, LL29 9LD
Tel: 01492 516555 Fax: 01492 515565
Email: colwynbayhotel@cwcom.net
Rooms: 43 all ensuite ✍ ⊗
Room facilities: ☐ ☎ ☕ ⌕ Children: Welcome ⍗ ℃
Dogs: Welcome Licences: ⬧ ♦♦♦ Parking: Off-street
Directions: Hotel stands beside the A547 on cliffs
above A55. Leave A55 at Llandulas exit, follow A547
towards Old Colwyn.

Northwood Hotel

♦♦♦ ⌦

47 Rhos Road, Rhos-on-Sea, Colwyn Bay,
Conwy, LL28 4RS
Tel: 01492 549931 Fax: 01492 549931
Email: mail@northwoodhotel.co.uk
Web: www.northwoodhotel.co.uk
Rooms: 12 (10 ensuite)
Pricing: Sgl £25–26 Dbl £50 Dinner from £10
CC: Accepted
Room facilities: ☐ ☕ ☕
Access: ♿
Children: Welcome ⍗
Dogs: Welcome
Licences: ♦♦♦
Parking: Off-street
Directions: Opposite Tourist Information Centre, 150
yards up Rhos Road.

Rosehill Manor

♦♦♦ ⌦ ⍾

Queens Avenue, Colwyn Bay, Conwy, LL29 7BE
Tel: 01492 532993
Email: lawrence_ford@hotmail.com
Web: www.rosehillmanor.co.uk
Rooms: 6 (2 ensuite) ⊗
Pricing: Sgl £40–43 Dbl £80–86
Room facilities: ☐ ☕ Access: ♿
Conference: 1 meeting room (Thtr 25 max)
Children: Welcome, 12yrs min age
Dogs: Welcome
Parking: Off-street
Directions: Situated in the west end of Colwyn Bay
immediately to the rear of Rydal School.

Conwy

Old Rectory Country House

Gold Ribbon Winner

★★ ℞ ℞ ℞ ℞

Llanwrst Road, Llansanffraid Glan Conwy,
Conwy, LL28 5LF
Tel: 01492 580611 Fax: 01492 584555
Email: info@oldrectorycountryhouse.co.uk
Web: www.oldrectorycountryhouse.co.uk
Seasonal closure: Dec/Jan, weekends only Nov/Feb

Idyllically situated, beautiful terraced gardens overlook
Conwy Castle, estuary and Snowdonia beyond.
Charming, tastefully decorated, antiques and paintings
abound. Appealing innovative 'Masterchef' cuisine.
Award-winning wine cellar. A relaxing friendly
atmosphere. 4 miles Boonant Gardens, Llandudno.
Rooms: 6 all ensuite ✍ ⊗
Pricing: Sgl £99–129 Dbl £129–169 Dinner from £34.90
CC: Accepted Room facilities: ☐ ☎ ☕
Children: Welcome, 5yrs min age Dogs: Welcome
Licences: ♦♦♦ Parking: Off-street
Directions: Situated on A470, half mile south of its
junction with A55. Gates on left-hand side just before
30mph sign.

Tir-y-Coed Country House Hotel

★★ ℞

Rowen, Conwy, Conway, LL32 8TP
Tel: 01492 650219 Fax: 01492 650219
Email: tirycoed@btinternet.com
Web: www.tirycoedhotel.co.uk
Seasonal closure: November to February

Surrounded by magnificent scenery in the peaceful
rural setting of a delightful Snowdonia National Park
village. Mountains, coast, castles, stately homes and
gardens nearby. Well-appointed ensuite bedrooms.
Spectacular views.

Rooms: 8 all ensuite 🦢
Pricing: Sgl £29.50–33.50 Dbl £55–62.50
Dinner from £15 CC: Accepted Room facilities: 📺 ☕
Children: Welcome ⁇ Dogs: Welcome Licences: ⁇⁇
Parking: Off-street and monitored
Directions: From B5106, take signposted turning to
Rowen (unclassified road). Hotel is on fringe of village,
about 60 yards north of post office.

Sychnant Pass House   Little Gem

Sychnant Pass Road, Conwy, LL32 8BJ
Tel: 01492 596868 Fax: 01492 596868
Email: bresykes@sychnant-pass-house.co.uk
Web: www.sychnant-pass-house.co.uk

Our country home is set in 2½ acres of natural garden,
surrounded by National Park land. Large sitting rooms
with log fires and comfy sofas. See you soon!
Rooms: 10 all ensuite 🦢 📺 ⊗
Pricing: Sgl £50–90 Dbl £70–110 Dinner from £17.95
CC: Accepted Room facilities: 📺 ☕ Access: ♿
Children: Welcome ⁇ Dogs: Welcome
Licences: ⚓ ⁇⁇
Parking: Off-street and monitored
Directions: Go around Conwy system past Visitors'
Centre. Take 2nd turn on left into Upper Gate Street:
proceed up hill for 2 miles.

Cowbridge, Glamorgan

Bear Hotel
★★★ ⁇ ⁇
High Street, Cowbridge, Vale of Glamorgan, CF71 7AF
Tel: 01446 774814 Fax: 01446 775425
Email: enquires@bearhotel.com
Web: www.bearhotel.com
Rooms: 34 all ensuite 🦢 📺
Pricing: Sgl £49.50–60 Dbl £75–95 CC: Accepted
Room facilities: 📺 ☎ ☕ Access: ♿
Conference: 3 meeting rooms (Thtr 100 max)
Children: Welcome ⁇ Dogs: Welcome
Licences: ⚓ ⁇⁇
Parking: Off-street and monitored
Directions: Situated just off the A48, 7 miles from
Cardiff city centre and close to motorway links.

Criccieth, Gwynedd

Bron Eifion Country House Hotel
★★★ ⁇
Criccieth, Gwynedd, LL52 0SA
Tel: 01766 522385 Fax: 01766 522003
Email: broneifion@criccieth.co.uk
Web: www.broneifion.co.uk

A magnificent baronial mansion set in five acres of
glorious gardens and woodlands. Close to the rugged
mountains of Snowdonia. Friendly service, fresh
cuisine and a well-stocked wine cellar.
Rooms: 19 all ensuite 📺
Pricing: Sgl £78–81 Dbl £120–150 Dinner from £24
CC: Accepted Room facilities: 📺 ☎ ☕
Conference: 1 meeting room (Thtr 35 max)
Children: Welcome ⁇ Licences: ⁇⁇
Directions: On A487 from Porthmadog go through
Criccieth. We are ½ mile outside Criccieth on
right-hand side.

Lion Hotel
★★
Y Maes, Criccieth, Gwynedd, LL52 0AA
Tel: 01766 522460 Fax: 01766 523075
Email: info@lionhotelcriccieth.co.uk
Web: www.lionhotelcriccieth.co.uk
Rooms: 46 all ensuite 🦢
Pricing: Sgl £33.50–38.50 Dbl £60.50–66.50
Dinner from £17.50 CC: Accepted
Room facilities: 📺 ☎ ☕ Access: ⁇ ♿
Children: Welcome ⁇ ⁇ Dogs: Welcome Licences: ⁇⁇
Leisure: Games room Parking: Off-street
Directions: The Lion is situated just off the A497 or
B4411 in the centre of Criccieth on Upper Village Green.

Glyn-y-Coed Hotel
◆◆◆ ⁇ ⁇
Portmadoc Road, Criccieth, Gwynedd, LL52 0HL
Tel: 01766 522870 Fax: 01766 523341
Email: glyn-y-coedhotel@amserve.net
Seasonal closure: Only 25/26 December
Rooms: 10 all ensuite 🦢 📺 ⊗
Pricing: Sgl £25–35 Dbl £42–56 Dinner from £15
CC: Accepted Room facilities: 📺 ☎ ☕ Access: ♿
Children: Welcome Dogs: Guide dogs only
Licences: ⁇⁇ Parking: Off-street
Directions: On main A497 Portmadoc to Pwhelli Road. On
right-hand side facing sea, nearest hotel to shops/village.

Min-y-Gaer Hotel

 ◆ ◆ ◆ ◆

Porthmadog Road, Criccieth, Gwynedd, LL52 0HP
Tel: 01766 522151 Fax: 01766 523540
Email: info@minygaer.co.uk
Web: www.minygaer.co.uk
Seasonal closure: November to February
Rooms: 10 all ensuite ⌖ ⊗ Room facilities: ☐ ♨
Children: Welcome ⍋ Dogs: Guide dogs only
Licences: ⍟ Parking: Off-street
Directions: Close to Criccieth centre on A497 Porthadog
to Pwllheli road, 300 yards east of junction with B4411.

Deganwy, Conwy

Deganwy Castle Hotel

 ★ ★

Station Road, Deganwy, Conwy, LL31 9DA
Tel: 01492 583555 Fax: 01492 583555
Email: deganwycastlehtl@yahoo.co.uk
Web: www.geocities.com/deganwycastlehtl
Rooms: 31 all ensuite ⌖ ⊠ ⊗
Pricing: Sgl £34–38 Dbl £68–76 Dinner from £6.95
CC: Accepted Room facilities: ☐ ☎ ♨
Conference: 2 meeting rooms (Thtr 110 max),
24hr-delegate from £62, day-delegate rate from £25
Children: Welcome ⍋ Dogs: Welcome Licences: ⍛ ⍟
Leisure: Indoor pool, Gym, Beauty salon
Parking: Off-street
Directions: From Chester, exit the A55, at
Deganwy/Conwy. Take the A546 passing Tesco to the
centre of Deganwy village.

Denbigh, Denbighshire

Cayo Guest House

 ◆ ◆ ◆

74 Vale Street, Denbigh, Denbighshire, LL16 3BW
Tel: 01745 812686
Rooms: 6 (4 ensuite) ⊗
Room facilities: ☐ ♨ Children: Welcome
Dogs: Welcome Licences: ⍟
Directions: On A525, follow signs to Denbigh. At the
traffic lights turn up the hill into town. Look for
supermarket on right. Hotel is a little way up on left.

Devil's Bridge, Ceredigion

Hafod Arms Hotel

 ★ ★

Devil's Bridge, Aberystwyth, Ceredigion, SY23 3JL
Tel: 01970 890232 Fax: 01970 890394
Email: enquiries@hafodarms.co.uk
Web: www.hafodarms.co.uk
Seasonal closure: 15 December to 15 January
Rooms: 15 all ensuite ⌖ ⊠
Pricing: Dinner from £15 (2002 rate) CC: Accepted
Room facilities: ☐ ♨
Children: Welcome, 10yrs min age Licences: ⍟
Parking: Off-street and monitored
Directions: From Aberystwyth take A4120 for 11 miles.
From Llangurig travel along A44. Turn off left at
Ponterwyd onto the A4120. Hotel 5 miles.

Dolgellau, Gwynedd

Fronoleu Farm Hotel

 ★ ★

Tabor, Dolgellau, Gwynedd, LL40 2PS
Tel: 01341 422361 Fax: 01341 422023
Rooms: 11 all ensuite ⌖ ⊠ ⊗
Room facilities: ☐ ♨ Children: Welcome ⍋ ⍨
Dogs: Welcome Licences: ⍛ ⍟
Leisure: Games room Parking: Off-street
Directions: From Dolgellau town centre, follow road
past hospital. Proceed up hill. Follow restaurant sign.

George III Hotel

 ★ ★

Penmaenpool, Dolgellau, Gwynedd, LL40 1YD
Tel: 01341 422525 Fax: 01341 423565
Email: reception@george-3rd.co.uk
Web: www.george-3rd.co.uk
Rooms: 11 all ensuite
Pricing: Sgl £45–58 Dbl £80–98 Dinner from £25
CC: Accepted
Room facilities: ☐ ☎ ♨ Access: ⌖
Children: Welcome ⍋ Dogs: Welcome Licences: ⍟
Leisure: Golf, Fishing, Riding
Parking: Off-street
Directions: Turn left off A470 signposted Tywyn, after
approximately 2 miles turn right for toll bridge then first
left for hotel.

Royal Ship Hotel

 ★

Queen's Square, Dolgellau, Gwynedd, LL40 1AR
Tel: 01341 422209 Fax: 01341 421027
Email: brewery@frederic-robinson.co.uk
Web: www.frederic-robinson.co.uk
Rooms: 24 (18 ensuite) ⌖ ⊗
Pricing: Dinner from £9.95 CC: Accepted
Room facilities: ☐ ♨ Children: Welcome ⍋
Dogs: Guide dogs only Licences: ⍟
Leisure: Games room Parking: Off-street
Directions: Situated in town centre.

Fishguard, Pembrokeshire

Abergwaun Hotel

 ★ ★

Market Square, Fishguard, Pembrokeshire, SA65 9HA
Tel: 01348 872077 Fax: 01348 875412
Web: via smoothhound
Rooms: 10 all ensuite ⌖ ⊠
Pricing: Sgl £39.50 Dbl £58
Dinner from £6 CC: Accepted
Room facilities: ☐ ♨
Conference: 1 meeting room
Children: Welcome ⍋ ⍨ Dogs: Welcome
Licences: ⍟ Parking: Off-street and monitored
Directions: The hotel is situated in the centre of
Fishguard on the A40/A487.

Halkyn, Clwyd

Travelodge Halkyn, North Wales

Travel Accommodation
A55, Halkyn, Flintshire, Clwyd, CH8 8RF
Web: www.travelodge.co.uk
Rooms: 31 all ensuite
Pricing: Sgl £54.40 Dbl £58.85 CC: Accepted
Room facilities: Access:

Harlech, Gwynedd

Castle Cottage

Y Llech, Harlech, Gwynedd, LL46 2YL
Tel: 01766 780479 Fax: 01766 781251
Email: glyn@castlecottageharlech.co.uk
Web: www.castlecottageharlech.co.uk
Seasonal closure: February
Rooms: 6 (4 ensuite)
Pricing: Sgl £31–45 Dbl £67 Dinner from £24
CC: Accepted Room facilities:
Children: Welcome Licences:
Directions: Just off Harlech High St, behind the Castle.

Haverfordwest, Pembrokeshire

Hotel Mariners
★★

Mariner's Square, Haverfordwest,
Pembrokeshire, SA61 2DU
Tel: 01437 763353 Fax: 01437 764258
Seasonal closure: Few days over Christmas
Rooms: 28 all ensuite
Pricing: Sgl £54.50 Dbl £74.50 Dinner from £19
CC: Accepted Room facilities:
Conference: 2 meeting rooms (Thtr 50 max)
Children: Welcome Dogs: Welcome Licences:
Parking: Off-street
Directions: Follow signs to town centre and up High St.
First turn on right, Dark St, leads to Mariner's Square.

Wolf's Castle Country Hotel
★★★

Wolf's Castle, Haverfordwest, Pembrokeshire, SA62 5LZ
Tel: 01437 741225 Fax: 01437 741383
Email: enquiries@wolfscastle.com
Web: www.wolfscastle.com
Seasonal closure: Christmas

In village of Wolf's Castle, equidistant from Fishguard
and Haverfordwest. Ideal location for exploring
Pembrokeshire National Park and beaches. Conference
facilities and 20 ensuite bedrooms.
Rooms: 20 all ensuite
Pricing: Dinner from £16 CC: Accepted
Room facilities: Children: Welcome
Dogs: Welcome Licences: Parking: Off-street
Directions: Situated in village of Wolf's Castle, 6 miles
north of Haverfordwest on A40.

Highland Grange Guest House
♦ ♦ ♦

Robeston Wathen, Narberth, Pembrokeshire, SA67 8EP
Tel: 01834 860952 Fax: 01834 860952
Email: info@highlandgrange.co.uk
Web: www.highlandgrange.co.uk
Rooms: 4 (2 ensuite)
Pricing: Sgl £22–28 Dbl £42–49 Dinner from £9
CC: Accepted Room facilities: Access:
Children: Welcome Licences:
Parking: Off-street and monitored
Directions: Take A40 22 miles west of Carmarthen to
Robeston. Petrol station on left, property last on right
before Bush Inn. 7 miles east of Haverfordwest in small
village.
See advert on this page

Wales

Holyhead, Anglesey

Bull Hotel

★★

London Road, Valley, Holyhead,
Isle of Anglesey, LL65 3DP
Tel: 01407 740351 Fax: 01407 742328
Email: valleyhotel@tinyworld.co.uk
Web: www.valley-hotel-anglesey.co.uk

Superior ensuite bedrooms with TVs, telephone, tea/coffee-makers etc. Our Tudor-style lounges serve food and drinks all day. Restaurant open every evening and Sunday lunchtime. Excellent beer garden.
Rooms: 14 all ensuite
Pricing: Sgl £37.50–37.50 Dbl £49.50–49.50
Dinner from £7.95 CC: Accepted
Room facilities: Access:
Conference: 1 meeting room (Thtr 75 max)
Children: Welcome Dogs: Welcome
Licences: Leisure: Games room Parking: Off-street
Directions: Situated at valley (Y Fali) on A5, take exit 3 from A55 expressway, only 4 miles from ferries.

Valley Hotel

♦♦♦

London Road, Valley, Holyhead,
Isle of Anglesey, LL65 3DU
Tel: 01407 740203 Fax: 01407 740686
Email: valleyhotel@tinyworld.co.uk
Web: www.valley-hotel-anglesey.co.uk

Ensuite bedrooms with TVs, telephones, tea/coffee makers, hairdryers etc. Our light, airy bar lounges serve food and drink all day. Excellent party rooms, gardens with play equipment and snooker room.
Rooms: 20 (18 ensuite)
Pricing: Sgl £39.50 Dbl £54.50
Dinner from £7.50 CC: Accepted
Room facilities:
Conference: 3 meeting rooms (Thtr 120 max)
Children: Welcome Dogs: Welcome
Licences:
Leisure: Games room, Snooker/billiards
Parking: Off-street
Directions: Situated at valley (Y Fali) on A5. Take exit 3 from A55 expressway, only 4 miles from ferry port.

Knighton, Powys

Knighton Hotel

★★★

Broad Street, Knighton, Powys, LD7 1BL
Tel: 01547 520530 Fax: 01547 520529
Email: knightonhotel@freeuk.com
Rooms: 15 all ensuite
Pricing: Sgl £45–65 Dbl £68–90
Dinner from £16.50 CC: Accepted
Room facilities:
Access:
Conference: 3 meeting rooms (Thtr 150 max), 24hr-delegate from £65, day-delegate rate from £17
Children: Welcome, 12yrs min age
Dogs: Welcome
Licences:
Leisure: Games room
Parking: Off-street
Directions: Take A4113 off A49 at Ludlow on the A388 or Shrewsbury-Llandrindod Wells road.

Lampeter, Ceredigion

Falcondale Country House Hotel

★★★

Falcondale Drive, Lampeter, Ceredigion, SA43 7RX
Tel: 01570 422910 Fax: 01570 423559
Web: www.falcondalehotel.com
Seasonal closure: late January
Rooms: 21 all ensuite
Pricing: Dinner from £21 (2002 rate) CC: Accepted
Room facilities: Access:
Children: Welcome Dogs: Welcome
Licences: Leisure: Tennis
Parking: Off-street and monitored
Directions: The hotel is 500 yards west of Lampeter centre on the A475 or 1 mile north-west of Lampeter on the A482.

Llanbedr, Gwynedd

Ty Mawr Hotel

★★

Llanbedr, Gwynedd, LL45 2NH
Tel: 01341 241440 Fax: 01341 241440
Email: tymawrhotel@netscapeonline.co.uk
Web: www.tymawrhotel.org.uk
Rooms: 10 all ensuite
Pricing: Sgl £40–45 Dbl £30–35 Dinner from £10
CC: Accepted Room facilities:
Children: Welcome Dogs: Welcome Licences:
Leisure: Games room Parking: Off-street
Directions: Llanbedr is situated on A496 between Barmouth and Harlech. Approaching from Barmouth, turn right after bridge. Ty-Mawr is 100 yards up on left.

Victoria Inn

◆◆◆◆

Llanbedr, Gwynedd, LL45 2LD
Tel: 01341 241213 Fax: 01341 241644
Email: brewery@frederic-robinson.co.uk
Web: www.frederic-robinson.com
Rooms: 5 all ensuite
Pricing: Dinner from £6 CC: Accepted
Room facilities: ☐ ☕ Children: Welcome ħ
Dogs: Welcome Licences: ♦♦♦ Parking: Off-street
Directions: The Victoria stands in the centre of village
of Llanbedr on the A496 coast road.

Llandrindod Wells, Powys

Severn Arms Hotel

★★

Penybont, Llandrindod Wells, Powys, LD1 5UA
Tel: 01597 851224 Fax: 01597 851693
Rooms: 10 all ensuite
Room facilities: ☐ ☎ ☕ Children: Welcome ħ
Dogs: Welcome Licences: ♦♦♦
Leisure: Fishing, Games room
Parking: Off-street
Directions: Located on the junction of A488 and A44 in
the village of Penybont, east of Llandrindod Wells.

Guidfa House

◆◆◆◆

Cross Gates, Llandrindod Wells, Powys, LD1 6RF
Tel: 01597 851241 Fax: 01597 851875
Email: guidfa@globalnet.co.uk
Web: www.guidfa-house.co.uk

Stylish Georgian house with an enviable reputation for
its comfort, good food and service. Set in the very
heart of Wales, offering an excellent base for touring
both Wales and the Borders.
Rooms: 6 all ensuite
Pricing: Sgl £33.50–39.50 Dbl £55–60
Dinner from £18.50 CC: Accepted
Room facilities: ☐ ☕ Children: Welcome 10yrs min age
Dogs: Guide dogs only Licences: ♦♦♦ Parking: Off-street
Directions: In the centre of village of Cross Gates,
where A44 Kington to Rhayader Road crosses A483
Builth Wells to Newtown Road.

Llandudno, Conwy

Bodysgallen Hall

★★★ ⓡ ⓡ ⓡ ⓡ   Gold Ribbon Winner

Llandudno, Conwy, LL30 1RS
Tel: 01492 584466 Fax: 01492 582519
Email: info@bodysgallen.com
Web: www.bodysgallen.com

Bodysgallen Hall stands in 220 acres of its own gardens
and parkland, and is only 45 minutes from Chester.
With 19 rooms in the main house, 16 cottage suites
and its own superb spa, Bodysgallen provides all that
is best in country house hospitality.
Rooms: 35 all ensuite
Pricing: Sgl £123.50–154.50 Dbl £174–289
Dinner from £34.90 CC: Accepted
Room facilities: ☐ ☎ Access: ♿
Conference: 3 meeting rooms (Thtr 50 max),
24hr-delegate from £140, day-delegate rate from £45
Children: Welcome, 8yrs min age
Dogs: Guide dogs only Licences: ♦♦♦
Leisure: Indoor pool, Gym, Health spa,
Beauty salon, Tennis
Parking: Off-street and monitored
Directions: Take A55 to its intersection with A470.
Follow A470 towards Llandudno. The hotel is 2 miles
on the right.

Dunoon Hotel

★★★ ⓡ

Gloddaeth Street, Llandudno, Conwy, LL30 2DW
Tel: 01492 860787 Fax: 01492 860031
Email: reservations@dunoonhotel.co.uk
Web: www.dunoonhotel.co.uk
Rooms: 50 all ensuite
Pricing: Sgl £44–48 Dbl £60–96 Dinner from £14.50
CC: Accepted
Room facilities: ☐ ☎ ☕ Access: ♿ ♿
Children: Welcome ħ Dogs: Welcome
Licences: ♦♦♦ Leisure: Games room,
Parking: Off-street
Directions: Turn off promenade by War Memorial near
pier onto wide ave 200 yards from promenade on right.

St. Tudno Hotel & Restaurant

Charming seafront hotel with outstanding reputation for fine food and wine. Elegantly and lovingly furnished offering the best in service and hospitality. Host of awards for excellence. Lift, car park, indoor heated pool.

Promenade, Llandudno, Conwy, LL30 2LP
Tel: 01492 874411 Fax: 01492 860407
Email: sttudnohotel@btinternet.com
Web: www.st-tudno.co.uk

Imperial Hotel

★★★★

Vaughan Street, Llandudno, Conwy, LL30 1AP
Tel: 01492 877466 Fax: 01492 878043
Email: imphotel@btinternet.com
Web: www.theimperial.co.uk

Elegant Hotel, sea front location overlooking Llandudno Bay, comfortable bedrooms, awards winning restaurant, leisure facilities, licensed for civil weddings conference facilities and friendly staff.
Rooms: ⌕ ⊗ Pricing: Dinner from £25 CC: Accepted
Room facilities: ▢ ☎ ⑤ Access: ⑴⑴
Conference: 9 meeting rooms (Thtr 150 max), 24hr-delegate from £99, day-delegate rate from £26
Children: Welcome ⋔ Dogs: Guide dogs only
Licences: ◁ Leisure: Indoor pool, Gym, Health spa, Beauty salon Parking: Off-street
Directions: Take A55 to A470, follow signs for Llandudno. Hotel is situated on the Promenade.

Ambassador Hotel

★★

Grand Promenade, Llandudno, Conwy, LL30 2NR
Tel: 01492 876886 Fax: 01492 876347
Email: reception@ambasshotel.demon.co.uk

Family-run hotel in superb Promenade corner position , 57 rooms, three lifts, two sun verandas, all day coffee shop, entertainment in season, out of season special added value breaks.
Rooms: 57 all ensuite ⌕
Pricing: Sgl £32–45 Dbl £60–96 Dinner from £14
CC: Accepted
Room facilities: ▢ ⑤ Access: ⑴⑴ ⑹
Children: Welcome ⋔ Dogs: Guide dogs only
Licences: ⅰⅰⅰ Parking: Off-street and monitored
Directions: From A55 road to A470. Turn to Promenade. Turn left at Promenade junction. Hotel approx 300 yards from pier.

Epperstone Hotel

★★

15 Abbey Road, Llandudno, Conwy, LL30 2EE
Tel: 01492 878746 Fax: 01492 871223
Rooms: 8 all ensuite ⌕ ⑤ ⊗
Pricing: Dinner from £16 (2002 rate) CC: Accepted
Room facilities: ▢ ☎ ⑤ Access: ⑹
Children: Welcome ⋔ ⅈⅇ Dogs: Welcome
Licences: ⅰⅰⅰ Parking: Off-street
Directions: From A55 follow sign for A470 to Llandudno (Mostyn Street), turn left at roundabout, fourth right into York Road. Hotel on apex of York Road and Abbey Road.

Esplanade Hotel

★★

Central Promenade, Llandudno, Conwy, LL30 2LL
Tel: 0800 318 688 Fax: 01492 860418
Email: info@esplanadehotel.co.uk
Web: www.esplanadehotel.co.uk
Rooms: 59 all ensuite ⌕
Pricing: Sgl £15–68 Dbl £30–96 Dinner from £12.50
CC: Accepted Room facilities: ▢ ☎ ⑤ Access: ⑴⑴
Conference: 5 meeting rooms (Thtr 80 max), 24hr-delegate from £47.50, day-delegate rate from £22.50
Children: Welcome Dogs: Guide dogs only
Licences: ⅰⅰⅰ Parking: Off-street
Directions: In Llandudno follow brown tourist signs for beach: turn towards Great Orme and pier.

Headlands Hotel
 ★★

Hill Terrace, Llandudno, Conwy, LL30 2LS
Tel: 01492 877485
Seasonal closure: January to February
Rooms: 17 (15 ensuite) 🍵 🛏
Room facilities: ☐ ☎ 🍵 Children: Welcome, 5yrs min age Dogs: Welcome Parking: Off-street

Royal Hotel
 ★★

Church Walks, Llandudno, Conwy, LL30 2HW
Tel: 01492 876476 Fax: 01492 870210

Sandringham Hotel
 ★★

West Parade, West Shore, Llandudno, Conwy, LL30 2BD
Tel: 01492 876513 Fax: 01492 872753
Email: enquiries@thesandringhamhotel.co.uk
Web: www.sandringhamhotel.co.uk
Rooms: 18 all ensuite 🍵 Pricing: Sgl £28.50–31
Dbl £57–62 Dinner from £14 CC: Accepted
Room facilities: ☐ ☎ 🍵 Conference: 3 meeting rooms
(Thtr 60 max) Children: Welcome ⻖ Licences: ⚱⚱⚱
Parking: Off-street and monitored
Directions: Follow A470 to Llandudno town centre.
Turn left at roundabout by Woolworths. Proceed
approx ½ mile; hotel on left-hand corner.

Somerset Hotel
 ★★

Central Promenade, Llandudno, Conwy, LL30 2LF
Tel: 01492 876540 Fax: 01492 863700
Email: favroy@somerset.freeserve.co.uk
Seasonal closure: January to February
Rooms: 37 all ensuite 🍵
Pricing: Dinner from £17.50 (2002 rate) CC: Accepted
Room facilities: ☐ ☎ 🍵 Access: |↕
Children: Welcome ⻖ Dogs: Welcome Licences: ⚱⚱⚱
Leisure: Games room, Snooker/billiards
Parking: Off-street and monitored

St Tudno Hotel & Restaurant
Gold Ribbon Winner
 ★★★ 🦋 🦋 🦋

Promenade, Llandudno, Conwy, LL30 2LP
Tel: 01492 874411 Fax: 01492 860407
Email: sttudnohotel@btinternet.com
Web: www.st-tudno.co.uk

Charming seafront hotel with outstanding reputation for fine food and wine. Elegantly and lovingly furnished, offering the best in service and hospitality. Host of awards for excellence. Lift, car park, indoor heated pool.
Rooms: 19 all ensuite 🍵 🛏 ⊗
Pricing: Sgl £70–80 Dbl £85 CC: Accepted
Room facilities: ☐ ☎ 🍵 🔥 Access: |↕
Children: Welcome ⻖ ⅋ Dogs: Welcome
Licences: ⚱⚱⚱ Leisure: Indoor pool
Parking: Off-street and monitored
Directions: Directly opposite pier on Llandudno's promenade.
See advert on previous page

Min-y-don Hotel
 ★

North Parade, Llandudno, Conwy, LL30 2LP
Tel: 01492 876511 Fax: 01492 878169
Seasonal closure: November to February
Rooms: 28 (22 ensuite) 🍵
Pricing: Sgl £28–30 Dbl £52–50 CC: Accepted
Room facilities: ☐ 🍵 Access: ⚹
Children: Welcome Licences: ⚱⚱⚱
Parking: Off-street
Directions: From Chester follow A55 to Conwy and exit at Llandudno junction, taking A470. Drive through Martyn Street onto Promenade. Hotel is on North Parade opposite the pier entrance.

Warwick Hotel
 ★

56 Church Walks, Llandudno, Conwy, LL30 2HL
Tel: 01492 876823
Seasonal closure: 1 January to 1 March
Rooms: 🍵
Pricing: Sgl £30–38 Dbl £50–56 Dinner from £11.50
Room facilities: ☐ 🍵 Children: Welcome ⻖
Dogs: Welcome Licences: ⚱⚱⚱
Parking: Off-street

Carmel Private Hotel
 ◆◆◆◆ 🦋 ⅋

17 Craig-Y-Don Parade, Promenade, Llandudno, Conwy, LL30 1BG
Tel: 01492 877643
Rooms: 9 (6 ensuite) ⊗
Pricing: Sgl £22–31 Dbl £36–42
Room facilities: ☐ 🍵
Children: Welcome, 4yrs min age
Parking: Off-street and monitored
Directions: Take A470 into Llandudno. By Links Hotel turn right at roundabout towards north. At second roundabout turn right. Hotel is on right-hand side.

St Hilary Hotel

Craig-Y-Don Parade, Promenade, Llandudno,
Conwy, LL30 1BG
Tel: 01492 875551 Fax: 01492 877538
Email: info@sthilaryhotel.co.uk
Web: www.sthilaryhotel.co.uk
Seasonal closure: December to January
Rooms: 11 (9 ensuite) ⊛
Pricing: Sgl £22.50–27.50 Dbl £37–52 CC: Accepted
Room facilities: 🖵 🍵 Children: Welcome Licences: ♦♦♦
Directions: Situated on the Promenade, just 500 yards
from the North Wales Theatre, towards the Little Orme.

Minion Hotel

♦♦♦

21–23 Carmen Sylva, Llandudno,
Conwy, LL30 1EQ
Tel: 01492 877740
Seasonal closure: November to March
Rooms: 10 all ensuite Pricing: Sgl £17–18.50 Dbl £34–37
Room facilities: 🍵 Children: Welcome, 3yrs min age
Dogs: Welcome Licences: ♦♦♦ Parking: Off-street
Directions: Exit A55 onto A470 proceed to Promenade,
turn right then right at Carmen Sylva Road, Minion
situated 150 yards on right.

Rosedene Private Hotel

10 Arvon Avenue, Llandudno, Conwy, LL30 2DY
Tel: 01492 876491 Fax: 01492 872150
Email: janet@hodgett97.freeserve.co.uk

Janet and Bill welcome you to our friendly hotel.
Promenade and amenities within few minutes walk.
Midweek bookings taken. Comfortable TV lounge,
attractive dining room with separate tables and choice of
menu. Ensuite bedrooms with colour TV and tea/coffee
facilities. Also ground floor bedroom. Reduction for
pensioners. Highly recommended. Brochure available.
Rooms: 9 all ensuite ⊛
Pricing: £19 Dbl £38 Dinner from £9.50
Room facilities: 🖵 🍵 Children: Welcome

Karden House Hotel

♦

16 Charlton Street, Llandudno, Conwy, LL30 2AN
Tel: 01492 879347 Fax: 01492 879347
Rooms: 10 (6 ensuite) ⊛ ⊛
Pricing: Sgl £15–16.50 Dbl £30–35
Room facilities: 🖵 🍵
Children: Welcome ♦ ☕ Licences: ♦♦♦
Directions: From Llandudno Railway Station head for
sea front, turn left after 300 yards onto Charlton Street.
Karden House on left.

Llanelli, Carmarthenshire

Hotel Miramar

★★

158 Station Road, Llanelli, Carmarthenshire, SA15 1YH
Tel: 01554 773607 Fax: 01554 772454
Email: hotelmiramar1@aol.com
Web: www.smoothhound.co.uk/hotels/hotelmir.html
Rooms: 10 all ensuite ⊛
Pricing: Dinner from £8.50 CC: Accepted
Room facilities: 🖵 ☎ 🍵 🧺
Children: Welcome ♦ Licences: ♦♦♦
Parking: Off-street and monitored
Directions: M4 Junction 48 to Llanelli. When in Llanelli
look for railway station. The Miramar is adjacent to
Llanelli Railway Station.

Travelodge Llanelli, Cross Hands

Travel Accommodation
A48, Cross Hands, Llanelli,
Carmarthenshire, SA14 6NW
Web: www.travelodge.co.uk
Room facilities: 🖵 🍵

Llangammarch Wells, Powys

Lake Country House Hotel

Gold Ribbon Winner

★★★★ ℞℞℞

Llangammarch Wells, Powys, LD4 4BS
Tel: 01591 620202 Fax: 01591 620457
Email: info@lakecountryhouse.co.uk
Web: www.lakecountryhouse.co.uk

This award-winning hotel is calm and comfort
epitomised; the richly furnished sitting rooms with fine

antiques, paintings and sumptuous sofas beside log fires combine to make visitors feel like guests in a Welsh country home.
Rooms: 19 all ensuite
Pricing: Sgl £95–135 Dbl £160–230
Dinner from £35 CC: Accepted
Room facilities: 🖵 ☎ Access: ♿
Conference: 2 meeting rooms (Thtr 60 max), 24hr-delegate from £115, day-delegate rate from £35
Children: Welcome ♀ ℃ Dogs: Welcome
Licences: 🔱 ♟
Leisure: Tennis, Golf, Fishing, Games room, Snooker/billiards
Parking: Off-street
Directions: From Builth Wells, head west on the A483 for 6 miles to Garth Village. Hotel is clearly signposted from here.

Llangefni, Anglesey

Tre-Ysgawen Hall Hotel
❖

Capel Coch, Llangefni, Anglesey, LL77 7UR
Tel: 01248 750 750 Fax: 01248 750 035
Email: enquires@treysgawen-hall.co.uk
Web: www.treysgawen-hall.co.uk
Rooms: 29 🖵 📺 ⊗
Pricing: Sgl £90 Dbl £140 Dinner from £25
CC: Accepted Room facilities: 🖵 ☎ 🖥 Access: ♿
Conference: 4 meeting rooms (Thtr 160 max)
Children: Welcome ♀ Dogs: Guide dogs only
Licences: 🔱 Leisure: Indoor pool, Gym, Health spa
Parking: Monitored
Directions: From the A5 follow signs for Llangefni.

Llangollen, Denbighshire

Bryn Howel Hotel
★★★★ ♖ ♖

Llangollen, Denbighshire, LL20 7UW
Tel: 01978 860331 Fax: 01978 860119
Email: hotel@brynhowel.co.uk
Web: www.brynhowel.co.uk
Rooms: 36 all ensuite 🖵 📺 ⊗
Pricing: Sgl £47.50–84 Dbl £95–113
Dinner from £24.50 CC: Accepted
Room facilities: 🖵 ☎ 🖥 📞 Access: ⊥↑ ♿
Conference: 3 meeting rooms (Thtr 250 max), 24hr-delegate from £99.70, day-delegate from £27.90
Children: Welcome ♀ ℃ Dogs: Guide dogs only
Licences: 🔱 ♟ Leisure: Fishing, Games room
Parking: Off-street and monitored
Directions: Take A539 exit off A483 to Llangollen, through Acrefair and Trevor. 2 miles after Trevor, Bryn Howell is signposted on the left.

The Hand Hotel, Llanarmon D.C.
★★

The Hand Hotel, Llanarmon-Dyffryn-Ceiriog, Ceiriog Valley, Clwyd, LL20 7LD
Tel: 01691 600 666 Fax: 01691 600 262
Email: handllandc6@btopenworld.com
Web: www.handhotelllanarmondc.co.uk

This 17th century inn offers cosy log fires, ensuite bedrooms, excellent food in bar and restaurant 7 days a week, lunchtimes and evenings. Special breaks available, relax and enjoy!
Rooms: 13 all ensuite 🖵 ⊗
Pricing: Sgl £28–42.50 Dbl £40–85 Dinner from £17.50
CC: Accepted Room facilities: 🖵 ☎ 🖥 📞 Access: ♿
Conference: 1 meeting room (Thtr 12 max)
Children: Welcome ♀ Dogs: Welcome Licences: ♟
Leisure: Beauty salon, Games room, Snooker/billiards
Parking: Off-street
Directions: From A483 follow signs to Chirk, at centre of Chirk follow B4500 to Ceiriog Valley, Llanarmon DC approx 12 miles on.

Tyn-y-Wern Hotel
★★

Maes Mawr Road, Llangollen, Denbighshire, LL20 7PH
Tel: 01978 860252 Fax: 01978 860252
Rooms: 11 all ensuite 🖵
Pricing: Sgl £32 Dbl £48 Dinner from £3.50
CC: Accepted
Room facilities: 🖵 ☎ 🖥 Access: ♿
Children: Welcome ♀ ℃ Dogs: Welcome
Licences: ♟ Parking: Off-street
Directions: On main A5 approximately half a mile east of town centre.

West Arms Hotel

★★ ® ®

Llanarmon-Dyffryn-Ceiriog, Llangollen,
LL20 7LD
Tel: 01691 600665 Fax: 01691 600622
Email: gowestarms@aol.com
Web: www.thewestarms.co.uk

A hotel since 1670, the West Arms is a hidden gem
waiting to be discovered in the stunning Ceiriog Valley,
not far from Llangollen. Ancient beams and inglenooks,
superb cooking and accommodation to match.
Rooms: 15 all ensuite ♋
Pricing: Sgl £56.50–74 Dbl £99–138
Dinner from £21.75 CC: Accepted
Room facilities: ▢ ☎ ▣
Access: ⴕ Children: Welcome Ħ ⅏
Dogs: Welcome
Licences: ⟁ ♐
Parking: Off-street
Directions: Follow B4500 from Chirk through Ceiriog
Valley or via Shrewsbury to Oswestry. Follow signs for
Llansilin but bear right before village.

Llannerch-Y-Medd, Anglesey

Drws-Y-Coed

◆◆◆◆ ⌦ ꝗ

Drws-Y-Coed, Llannerch-Y-Medd, Anglesey, LL71 8AD
Tel: 01248 470473
Web: www.smoothhound.co.uk/hotels/drwsycoed.html
Rooms: 3 all ensuite ⊗
Pricing: Sgl £27.50–30 Dbl £50–50 CC: Accepted
Room facilities: ▢ ▣
Children: Welcome
Dogs: Guide dogs only
Leisure: Fishing, Games room
Parking: Off-street
Directions: A55 to junction 6, A5114 to Llangefni, B5111
to Llannerch-Y-Medd outskirts. On left bend turn right
for Benllech, 1/3 mile on left is Drws-Y-Coed sign.

Llanwrtyd Wells, Powys

Neuadd Arms Hotel

★

The Square, Llanwrtyd Wells, Powys, LD5 4RB
Tel: 01591 610236 Fax: 01591 610610

Web: www.neuaddarmshotel.co.uk
Seasonal closure: Christmas
Rooms: 23 (18 ensuite) ⊗
Pricing: Sgl £26–37 Dbl £52–74 Dinner from £12.50
CC: Accepted Room facilities: ▢ ▣
Children: Welcome Ħ ⅏ Dogs: Welcome
Licences: ♐ Leisure: Games room
Parking: Off-street
Directions: Centre of town on main A483, between Builth
Wells and Llandovery, and on heart of Wales railway.

Machynlleth, Powys

Ynyshir Hall Hotel   Gold Ribbon Winner

★★★★ ® ® ® ®

Eglwysfach, Machynlleth, Powys, SY20 8TA
Tel: 01654 781209 Fax: 01654 781366
Email: info@ynyshir-hall.co.uk
Web: www.ynyshir-hall.co.uk

A small luxury Georgian mansion set in idyllic
surroundings betwixt sea and mountains. The perfect
place to unwind with award-winning cuisine, a warm
welcome and pampered service.
Rooms: 9 all ensuite ⌕ ⊗
Pricing: Sgl £95–180 Dbl £125–275 Dinner from £42
CC: Accepted Room facilities: ▢ ☎ Access: ⴕ
Conference: 1 meeting room (Thtr 15 max),
24hr-delegate from £150, day-delegate rate from £45
Children: Welcome, 9yrs min age Dogs: Welcome
Licences: ⟁ ♐ Parking: Off-street
Directions: 6 miles from Machynlleth and 11 miles from
Aberystwyth on the A487.

The Wynnstay

★★ ®

Maengwyn Street, Machynlleth, Powys, SY20 8AE
Tel: 01654 702941 Fax: 01654 703884
Email: info@wynnstay-hotel.com
Web: www.wynnstay-hotel.com
Rooms: 23 all ensuite ♋ ⌕ ⊗
Pricing: Sgl £45–55 Dbl £70–100 Dinner from £21
CC: Accepted Room facilities: ▢ ☎ ▣ ꝗ
Conference: 2 meeting rooms (Thtr 60 max),
24hr-delegate from £75, day-delegate rate from £20
Children: Welcome Ħ Dogs: Welcome Licences: ♐
Leisure: Games room, Parking: Off-street
Directions: The Wynnstay hotel is right in the centre of
town, in the street opposite the clock tower, hotel car
park via Bank Street.

Magor, Monmouthshire

Travelodge Magor

M4, Magor, Monmouthshire, NP26 3YL
Web: www.travelodge.co.uk
Rooms: 43 all ensuite
Pricing: Sgl £54.40 Dbl £58.85 CC: Accepted
Room facilities: ☐ ☕ Access: ♿

Manorbier, Dyfed

Castlemead Hotel

Manorbier, Dyfed, SA70 7TA
Tel: 01834 871358 Fax: 01834 871358
Email: castlemeadhot@aol.com
Web: www.castlemeadhotel.co.uk
Seasonal closure: November to February
Rooms: 8 all ensuite Pricing: Dinner from £13 (2002 rate)
CC: Accepted Room facilities: ☐ ☕ Children: Welcome
Dogs: Welcome Licences: ♦♦♦
Parking: Off-street and monitored
Directions: Situated at bottom of village, above beach. Car park on left.

Merthyr Tydfil, Glamorgan

Castle Hotel

Castle Street, Merthyr Tydfil, Glamorgan, CF47 8BG
Tel: 01685 377825 Fax: 01685 383898
Email: enquiries@castlehotelwales.com
Web: www.castlehotelwales.com
Rooms: 44 all ensuite 📺 🐾
Pricing: Sgl £59–79 Dbl £65–95 Dinner from £8.95
CC: Accepted Room facilities: ☐ ☎ ☕ ♨ Access: ♿ ♿
Conference: 2 meeting rooms (Thtr 130 max)
Children: Welcome Dogs: Welcome Licences: ♦♦♦
Parking: Off-street and monitored
Directions: Leave A470 at Merthyr junction. Proceed to town centre. Hotel is adjacent to Civic Centre and Law Courts — a prominent five-storey building.

The Baverstock Hotel

The Heads of the Valleys Road, Aberdare, near Merthyr Tydfil, Mid Glamorgan, CF44 0LX
Tel: 01685 386221 Fax: 01685 723670
Email: baverstockhotel@btinternet.com
Web: www.baverstock-hotel.co.uk
Rooms: 50 all ensuite 🐾 🐾
Pricing: Sgl £55 Dbl £80–120 Dinner from £5.95
CC: Accepted Room facilities: ☐ ☎ ☕ Access: ♿
Conference: 5 meeting rooms (Thtr 400 max),
24hr-delegate from £49.50 Children: Welcome ♨ ❄
Dogs: Welcome Licences: ⚜ ♦♦♦
Parking: Off-street and monitored
Directions: Heads of the Valleys road (A465) between Merthyr Tydfil and Aberdare, M4, M5 and M50 motorways easily accessible to hotel.

Tredegar Arms Hotel

66 High Street, Dowlais Top, Merthyr Tydfil, Glamorgan, CF48 3PW
Tel: 01685 377467 Fax: 01685 376540
Rooms: 8 all ensuite 🐾 Pricing: Sgl £30–30
Dbl £34–40 Dinner from £5 CC: Accepted
Room facilities: ☐ ☕ Children: Welcome ♨
Directions: A465 to Merthyr Tydfil off A5 Asda/BP petrol station — Dowlais — 100 yards down hill on left.

Milford Haven, Pembrokeshire

Belhaven House Hotel

29 Hamilton Terrace (A5076), Milford Haven, Pembrokeshire, SA73 3JJ
Tel: 01646 695983 Fax: 01646 690787
Email: hbruceh@aol.com
Web: www.westwaleshotels.com
Seasonal closure: 22–29 December
Rooms: 9 (7 ensuite) 🐾 Pricing: Dinner from £5 (2002 rate) CC: Accepted Room facilities: ☐ ☕ Access: ♿
Children: Welcome ♨ Dogs: Welcome Licences: ♦♦♦
Parking: Off-street
Directions: Opposite the Cenotaph on the A4076 300 yards from town hall above the marina and waterway.

Mold, Flintshire

Bryn Awel Hotel

Denbigh Road, Mold, Flintshire, CH7 1BL
Tel: 01352 758622 Fax: 01352 758625
Email: bryn@awel.fsbusiness.co.uk
Web: bryn-awel.fsnet.co.uk
Rooms: 18 all ensuite 🐾 📺 Pricing: Sgl £40–48
Dbl £55–65 Dinner from £8.50 CC: Accepted
Room facilities: ☐ ☎ ☕ ♨ Conference: 1 meeting room (Thtr 30 max), 24hr-delegate from £69, day-delegate rate from £19 Children: Welcome ♨
Dogs: Guide dogs only Licences: ♦♦♦

Travelodge Northop Hall

Travel Accommodation
A55 East Bound Expressway, Northop Hall, Mold, Flintshire, CH7 6HB
Web: www.travelodge.co.uk
Rooms: 40 all ensuite 🐾 Pricing: Sgl £54.40
Dbl £58.85 CC: Accepted Room facilities: ☐ ☕
Access: ♿

Monmouth, Gwent

Travelodge Monmouth (MOTO)

Travel Accommodation
A40 North bound, Nr. Monmouth, Gwent, NP5 4BG
Web: www.travelodge.co.uk
Rooms: 43 all ensuite 🐾
Pricing: Sgl £54.40 Dbl £58.85 CC: Accepted
Room facilities: ☐ ☕ Access: ♿

Morfa Nefyn, Gwynedd

Woodlands Hall

★★

Edern, Morfa Nefyn, Gwynedd, LL53 6JB
Tel: 01758 720425

Neath, Glamorgan

Castle Hotel

★★

The Parade, Neath, Glamorgan, SA11 1RB
Tel: 01639 641119 Fax: 01639 641624
Email: info@castlehotelneath.co.uk
Web: www.castlehotelneath.co.uk
Rooms: 29 all ensuite
Pricing: Sgl £45–55 Dbl £55–75 Dinner from £6.50
CC: Accepted Room facilities: 🖵 ☎ 🍵
Conference: 3 meeting rooms (Thtr 160 max)
Children: Welcome ⅋ Licences: ⅋⅋⅋
Parking: Off-street and monitored
Directions: Leave M4 at J43. Follow signs for Neath, hotel 200 yards past railway station on right. Car park 20 yards further on left.

New Quay, Ceredigion

Brynarfor Hotel

◆ ◆ ◆

New Road, New Quay, Ceredigion, SA45 9SB
Tel: 01545 560358 Fax: 01545 561204
Email: enquiries@brynarfor.co.uk
Web: www.brynarfor.co.uk
Seasonal closure: November to February
Rooms: 7 all ensuite 🍷 ⊗
Pricing: Dinner from £8.50 CC: Accepted
Room facilities: 🖵 🍵 Children: Welcome ⅋
Licences: ⅋⅋⅋ Leisure: Games room Parking: Off-street
Directions: A487 to Llanarth, B4342 New Quay. Hotel left overlooking sea, before town.

Newport

The Celtic Manor Resort   Blue Ribbon Winner

★ ★ ★ ★ ★ ⊗ ⊗ ⊗

Coldra Woods, Newport, Gwent, NP18 1HQ
Tel: 01633 413000 Fax: 01633 412910
Email: postbox@celtic-manor.com
Web: www.celtic-manor.com
Rooms: 400 all ensuite
Pricing: Sgl £204.85 Dbl £219.35 Dinner from £24.50
CC: Accepted Room facilities: 🖵 ☎ 🍵 ⌇ Access: ⅂↥ ৬
Conference: 40 meeting rooms (Thtr 1500 max),
24hr-delegate from £200, day-delegate rate from £68
Children: Welcome ⅋ ⅋ Dogs: Guide dogs only
Licences: ⟐ ⅋⅋⅋
Leisure: Indoor pool, Gym, Health spa, Beauty salon, Tennis, Golf, Snooker/billiards Parking: Off-street
Directions: Exit M4 at Junction 24. At roundabout exit A48 towards Newport. Follow brown signs turning right to the resort after 100 yards.

Parkway Hotel

★★★★

Cwmbran Drive, Cwmbran, Newport,
Torfaen, NP44 3UW
Tel: 01633 871199 Fax: 01633 869160
Email: hotel.enquires@parkwayhotel.co.uk
Web: www.bestwestern.com
Rooms: 70 all ensuite 🍷 📠 ⊗
Pricing: Sgl £85.45–102.95 Dbl £106.40–123.90
Dinner from £16.95 CC: Accepted
Room facilities: 🖵 ☎ 🍵 ⌇ Access: ৬
Conference: 6 meeting rooms (Thtr 500 max),
24hr-delegate from £79, day-delegate rate from £27
Children: Welcome ⅋ ⅋ Dogs: Welcome
Licences: ⟐ ⅋⅋⅋
Leisure: Indoor pool, Gym, Health spa
Parking: Off-street and monitored
Directions: From M4 take J25A (west). J26 (East) then A4042/ A4051 towards Cwmbran. At mini roundabout take third exit, then first right.

Kings Hotel

★★★

7-8 High Street, Newport, NP20 1QU
Tel: 01633 842020 Fax: 01633 244667
Email: kingshotel.wales@netscapeonline.co.uk
Rooms: 61 all ensuite 🍷 ⊗
Pricing: Sgl £62–90 Dbl £78–90 CC: Accepted
Room facilities: 🖵 ☎ 🍵 ⌇ Access: ⅂↥
Conference: 4 meeting rooms (Thtr 440 max),
24hr-delegate from £80, day-delegate rate from £26
Children: Welcome ⅋
Dogs: Guide dogs only
Licences: ⟐ ⅋⅋⅋
Parking: Off-street and monitored
Directions: From Junction 26 of M4, drive towards city centre (A4051). At main roundabout take third exit to the hotel.

Hotel@Walkabout

✦

19 Bridge Street, Gwent, Newport, NP20 4AN
Tel: 01633 235 990 Fax: 01633 235 991
Email: walkaboutnewport.regentinns.plc.com
Web: www.walkabout.eu.uk
Seasonal closure: Christmas 23-27

Experience the awesome spirit of Australian Hospitality! Only a three-minute walk from train station,

Hotel@Walkabout offers 29 spacious ensuite rooms, TV, telephones and tea and coffee making facilities.
Rooms: 29 all ensuite ⊛
Pricing: Sgl £44.85 Dbl £64.75
CC: Accepted Room facilities: ☐ ☎ ☕ ☏ Access: ⌊⌊⌋
Conference: 1 meeting room (Thtr 110 max),
24hr-delegate from £120, day-delegate rate from £120
Dogs: Guide dogs only Licences: ⅲ
Directions: M4 to junction A4042 follow to town centre, pass train station on the Queensway, next roundabout turn left, located on Bridge Street.

The Inn At The Elm Tree

St Brides, Wentlooge, Newport, NP10 8SQ
Tel: 01633 680225 Fax: 01633 681035
Email: inn@the-elm-tree.co.uk
Web: www.the-elm-tree.co.uk

Wales' only five diamond Inn, 2 miles M4 Junction 28, peaceful village location, four-posters, spa jacuzzi, enviable reputation for excellent cuisine. Ideal for short breaks, sightseeing, country pursuits, relaxing and romancing.
Rooms: 10 all ensuite ▱
Pricing: Sgl £70–100 Dbl £80–120
Dinner from £12.50 CC: Accepted
Room facilities: ☐ ☎ ☕ ☏ Access: ⌖
Conference: 2 meeting rooms (Thtr 20 max),
24hr-delegate from £125, day-delegate rate from £38
Children: Welcome, 10yrs min age Dogs: Welcome
Licences: ⅲ Parking: Off-street and monitored
Directions: Exit M4 at Junction 28. Take A48 to B4239 2 miles along country lane. We are on S-bend in St Brides village on left.

Newtown, Powys

Elephant & Castle Hotel
★★
Broad Street, Newtown, Powys, SY16 2BQ
Tel: 01686 626271 Fax: 01686 622123
Email: info@theelephant.prestel.co.uk
Web: www.elephanthotel.co.uk
Seasonal closure: Christmas
Rooms: 38 (35 ensuite) ⊜ ⊛
Room facilities: ☐ ☎ ☕ Children: Welcome ♨
Licences: ◔ ⅲ Leisure: Gym Parking: Off-street
Directions: Turn for town centre at traffic lights by church to reach main street. The hotel is opposite the junction next to the river bridge.

Pembroke, Pembrokeshire

Cleddau Bridge Hotel
★★★
Essex Road, Pembroke Dock,
Pembrokeshire, SA72 6EG
Tel: 01646 685961 Fax: 01646 685746
Email: information@cleddaubridgehotel.co.uk
Web: www.cleddaubridgehotel.co.uk
Rooms: 24 all ensuite ⊜ ⊛
Pricing: Sgl £50–63 Dbl £70–79
Dinner from £15.30 CC: Accepted
Room facilities: ☐ ☎ ☕ ☏ Access: ⌖
Conference: 3 meeting rooms (Thtr 160 max),
24hr-delegate from £75, day-delegate rate from £25
Children: Welcome ♨ Dogs: Welcome
Licences: ◔
Parking: Off-street
Directions: M4 to Pont Abraham, A48 to Carmarthen, A477 to Pembroke Dock, follow signs to toll bridge and turn left.

Lamphey Court Hotel
★★★★ ⓐ
Lamphey, Pembroke, Pembrokeshire, SA71 5NT
Tel: 01646 672273 Fax: 01646 672480
Email: info@lampheycourt.co.uk
Web: www.lampheycourt.co.uk

This elegant Georgian mansion, now a deluxe hotel with superb leisure centre, is set in quiet grounds. Ideally situated for the local business area and exploring Pembrokeshire's National Park coast with beautiful beaches.
Rooms: 38 all ensuite ⊜
Pricing: Sgl £74–85 Dbl £100–150 Dinner from £20
CC: Accepted Room facilities: ☐ ☎ ☕ ☏
Conference: 4 meeting rooms (Thtr 80 max),
24hr-delegate from £125, day-delegate rate from £27
Children: Welcome ♨ ※ Dogs: Guide dogs only
Licences: ◔ ⅲ
Leisure: Indoor pool, Gym, Beauty salon, Tennis
Parking: Off-street
Directions: M4 to Carmarthen and A477 to Pembroke. Left at Milton Village. In Lamphey, turn at roadside hotel sign: entrance next to Bishop's Palace.

Wales

Wheeler's Old King's Arms Hotel

★ ★

Main Street, Pembroke, Pembrokeshire, SA71 4JS
Tel: 01646 683611 Fax: 01646 682335
Email: reception@oldkingsarmshotel.freeserve.co.uk
Web: www.oldkingsarmshotel.co.uk
Rooms: 16 all ensuite
Pricing: Sgl £33–40 Dbl £50 Dinner from £15.95 CC:
Accepted Room facilities:
Children: Welcome Dogs: Welcome
Licences: Parking: Off-street
Directions: M4 to Carmarthen, A477 to Pembroke. Turn
left for Pembroke. At roundabout, follow town centre
sign. Turn right onto the Parade. Car park is
signposted.

Penarth, Glamorgan

Glendale Hotel

♦ ♦ ♦

10 Plymouth Road, Penarth, Glamorgan, CF64 3DH
Tel: 029 20706701 Fax: 029 20709269
Web: www.infotel.co.uk
Rooms: 22 (17 ensuite)
Pricing: Sgl £23.50 Dbl £36 Dinner from £14.75
CC: Accepted Room facilities: Access:
Children: Welcome Licences:
Parking: Off-street and monitored
Directions: Penarth town centre, 4 miles west of Cardiff
(approach via M4 junction).

Port Talbot, Glamorgan

Aberavon Beach Hotel

★ ★ ★

Neath Port Talbot, Swansea Bay, Neath Port Talbot,
Glamorgan, SA12 6QP
Tel: 01639 884949 Fax: 01639 897885
Email: sales@aberavonbeach.com
Web: www.aberavonbeach.com

Modern hotel close to M4 and 7 miles from centre of
Swansea. Seafront location with views across Swansea
bay. Comfortable bedrooms, elegant restaurant with
fine food, conference facilities and friendly staff.
Rooms: 52 all ensuite
Pricing: Sgl £62–75 Dbl £72–85 Dinner from £15
CC: Accepted Room facilities: Access:
Conference: 6 meeting rooms (Thtr 400 max),
24hr-delegate from £95, day-delegate rate from £31

Children: Welcome Dogs: Welcome
Licences:
Leisure: Indoor pool, Health spa Parking: Off-street
Directions: Leave M4 at Junction 41, take A48 and
follow signs for Aberavon and Hollywood Park.

Portmeirion, Gwynedd

Hotel Portmeirion
Blue Ribbon Winner

★ ★ ★ ★

Portmeirion, Gwynedd, LL48 6ET
Tel: 01766 770000 Fax: 01766 771331
Email: hotel@portmeirion-village.com
Web: www.portmeirion-village.com

Portmeirion is situated on a private peninsula in
Snowdonia. It has 51 rooms, two restaurants, seven
shops, beauty salon and outdoor pool. See website for
full details and special offers.
Rooms: 51 all ensuite
Pricing: Sgl £116–161 Dbl £147–207 Dinner from £35
CC: Accepted
Room facilities: Access:
Conference: 4 meeting rooms (Thtr 100 max)
Children: Welcome Dogs: Guide dogs only
Licences:
Leisure: Outdoor pool, Beauty salon, Golf
Parking: Off-street and monitored
Directions: Off the A487 at Minffordd between
Penrhyndeudraeth and Porthmadog.

Rhos-on-Sea, Conwy

Plas Rhos Hotel

♦ ♦ ♦ ♦ ♦

53 Cayley Promenade, Rhos-on-Sea, Colwyn Bay,
Conwy, LL28 4EP
Tel: 01492 543698 Fax: 01492 540088
Email: enquiries@destination.wales.co.uk
Web: www.destination-wales.co.uk
Rooms: 9 all ensuite
Pricing: Sgl £26.50–33.50 Dbl £53–67
Dinner from £9.50 CC: Accepted
Room facilities: Children: Welcome
Dogs: Guide dogs only Licences:
Parking: Off-street
Directions: Come off A55 at Rhos-on-Sea, turn right to
roundabout, take 4th turning, follow road to seafront,
hotels on left.

Rhyl, Denbighshire

Barratts Restaurant At Ty'n Rhyl

♦ ♦ ♦ ♦

167 Vale Road, Rhyl, Denbighshire, LL18 2PH
Tel: 01745 344138 Fax: 01745 344138

Ruabon, Clwyd

Wynnstay Arms Hotel

★ ★

High Street, Ruabon, Nr. Wrexham, Clwyd, LL14 6BL
Tel: 01978 822187 Fax: 01978 820093
Rooms: 6 all ensuite
Pricing: Sgl £32.50 Dbl £47.50 Dinner from £8
CC: Accepted
Room facilities: 📺 ☎ ♨ Licences: 🍴
Parking: Off-street and monitored

Ruthin, Denbighshire

Ruthin Castle

★ ★ ★

Corwen Road, Ruthin, Denbighshire, LL15 2NU
Tel: 01824 702664 Fax: 01824 705978
Email: reservations@ruthincastle.co.uk
Web: www.ruthincastle.co.uk
Rooms: 58 all ensuite
Pricing: Dinner from £19.95 (2002 rate) CC: Accepted
Room facilities: 📺 ☎ ♨ Access: |↥↥
Children: Welcome 🍴 ♨ Licences: 🍷 🍴
Leisure: Fishing, Snooker/billiards
Parking: Off-street
Directions: A494 to Ruthin; castle at end of Castle
Street, just off town square

Saundersfoot, Pembrokeshire

St Bride's Hotel

★ ★ ★ ★

St Bride's Hill, Saundersfoot,
Pembrokeshire, SA69 9NH
Tel: 01834 812304 Fax: 01834 811766
Email: andrew.evans9@virgin.net
Rooms:
Children: Welcome 🍴
Licences: 🍴
Leisure: Outdoor pool
Directions: Travel west along M4 to Carmarthen. Follow
A477 towards Tenby. Saundersfoot is 4 miles before
Tenby. Enter village: hotel overlooks harbour on a
clifftop.

It's easier online

For all your motoring and travel
needs, www.rac.co.uk

Merlewood Hotel

★ ★

St Bride's Hill, Saundersfoot,
Pembrokeshire, SA69 9NP
Tel: 01834 812421 Fax: 01834 814886
Web: www.merlewood.co.uk
Seasonal closure: November to February
Rooms: 28 all ensuite
Pricing: Sgl £32–35 Dbl £54–60 Dinner from £13.50
CC: Accepted Room facilities: 📺 ♨ Access: ♿
Children: Welcome 🍴 Licences: 🍴
Leisure: Outdoor pool, Games room
Parking: Off-street
Directions: From Carmarthen, travel west towards
Tenby. At Begelly roundabout take turning for
Saundersfoot. Hotel just out of Saundersfoot centre,
on right as you reach top of St Bride's Hill

Rhodewood House Hotel

★ ★

St Bride's Hill, Saundersfoot, Pembrokeshire, SA69 9NU
Tel: 01834 812200 Fax: 01834 815005
Email: relax@rhodewood.co.uk
Web: www.rhodewood.co.uk
Seasonal closure: January
Rooms: 45 all ensuite
Pricing: Sgl £38–58 Dbl £56–96 Dinner from £13.95
CC: Accepted Room facilities: 📺 ☎ ♨ Access: ♿
Children: Welcome 🍴 ♨ Dogs: Guide dogs only
Licences: 🍴 Leisure: Games room Parking: Off-street
Directions: From Carmarthen take A40 to Kilgetty, A477
to B4316. Turn left. Hotel on left half a mile further on.

Woodlands Hotel

♦ ♦ ♦

St Bride's Hill, Saundersfoot, Pembrokeshire, SA69 9NP
Tel: 01834 813338 Fax: 01834 811480
Email: woodlands.hotel@virgin.net
Web: www.woodlands-hotel.net
Seasonal closure: November to March
Rooms: 10 all ensuite
Pricing: Sgl £29.50–34 Dbl £47.50–57.95
Dinner from £13.50 CC: Accepted Room facilities: 📺 ♨
Children: Welcome 🍴 ♨ Licences: 🍴
Parking: Off-street and monitored
Directions: From centre of village, take road to Tenby.
500 yards up hill, hotel is on right.

Bay View Hotel

♦ ♦

Pleasant Valley, Stepaside, Saundersfoot,
Pembrokeshire, SA67 8LR
Tel: 01834 813417
Seasonal closure: October to March
Rooms: 11 (8 ensuite)
Room facilities: ♨ Children: Welcome
Licences: 🍴 Leisure: Outdoor pool
Parking: Off-street
Directions: Turn off A477 to Stepaside. Proceed
downhill to flats. Turn left. After 50 yards turn left. 1/2 mile
on, turn left round chapel.

Lochmeyler Farm
Guest House

Located on a 220 acre working dairy farm, the tastefully renovated 16th century house provides all the modern facilities for a memorable holiday. Quiet country location, three miles from the coastal footpath, six miles from St Davids. Bedrooms, non-smoking, have central heating, TV, radio, refreshment facilities and tourist information packs.

Llandeloy, Pen-y-cwm, Nr. Solva,
St Davids, Pembrokeshire SA62 6LL
Tel: 01348 837724   Fax: 01348 837622
Email: stay@lochmeyler.co.uk
Website: www.lochmeyler.co.uk

St David's, Pembrokeshire

Lochmeyler Farm Guest House

◆ ◆ ◆ ◆ ◆ ✠

Llandeloy, Pen-y-Cwm, nr Solva, St David's, Pembrokeshire, SA62 6LL
Tel: 01348 837724 Fax: 01348 837622
Email: stay@lockmeyler.co.uk
Web: www.lockmeyler.co.uk
Seasonal closure: 1 November to 28 February
Rooms: 14 all ensuite 🍴 📷 🚭
Pricing: Dbl £40–55 CC: Accepted
Room facilities: 📺 ☎ 🍵 Children: Welcome
Dogs: Welcome Licences: 🍷
Parking: Off-street and monitored
Directions: From Fishguard, follow A487 St David's Road to Mathry, turn left and follow road to Llandeloy. From Haverfordwest, follow A487 to Pen-y-Cwm, turn right to Llandeloy.
See advert on this page

Ramsey House

◆ ◆ ◆ ◆ ◆ 🍷 ✠ 🍸

Lower Moor, St David's, Pembrokeshire, SA62 6RP
Tel: 01437 720321 Fax: 01437 720025
Email: info@ramseyhouse.co.uk
Web: www.ramseyhouse.co.uk
Rooms: 6 all ensuite 🚭
Pricing: Sgl £32–70 Dbl £64–70 Dinner from £16
CC: Accepted Room facilities: 📺 🍵
Dogs: Welcome Licences: 🍷

Parking: Off-street
Directions: From centre of St David's, bear left down hill by HSBC bank, signposted Porthclais, for ½ mile. Ramsey is last house on left.

Y Glennydd Hotel

◆ ◆ ◆ ✠

51 Nun Street, St David's, Pembrokeshire, SA62 6NU
Tel: 01437 720576 Fax: 01437 720184
Seasonal closure: December and January
Rooms: 10 (8 ensuite)
Pricing: Sgl £25–30 Dbl £40–45 Dinner from £16
CC: Accepted Room facilities: 📺 🍵
Children: Welcome Licences: 🍷 Parking: Off-street
Directions: 800 metres from Cross Square, next door to fire station.

Swansea, Glamorgan

Swansea Marriott Hotel

★ ★ ★ ★

Maritime Quarter, Swansea, SA1 3SS
Tel: 01792 642020 Fax: 01792 650345
Web: www.marriotthotels.com/swsdt
Rooms: 117 all ensuite 🍴 🚭
Pricing: Sgl £140 Dbl £150
Dinner from £25 CC: Accepted
Room facilities: 📺 ☎ 🍵 🍵 ❄ Access: 🛗 ♿
Conference: 8 meeting rooms (Thtr 300 max), 24hr-delegate from £135, day-delegate rate from £35
Children: Welcome 🍴 Dogs: Guide dogs only
Licences: 🍸 🍷 Leisure: Indoor pool, Gym
Parking: Off-street and monitored
Directions: Exit J42 M4, then A483 towards the city centre. Follow signs for the Marina where the hotel is situated.

St Anne's Hotel

★ ★ ★

Western Lane, Mumbles, Swansea, SA3 4EY
Tel: 01792 369147 Fax: 01792 360537
Email: info@stanneshotel-mumbles.com
Web: www.stanneshotel-mumbles.com

Overlooked by Oystermouth Castle and with spectacular views over Swansea Bay. Own grounds, large private car park, quiet location in the heart of Mumbles Village.

Rooms: 33 all ensuite
Pricing: Sgl £55 Dbl £69.50
Dinner from £15.50 CC: Accepted
Room facilities: ☐ ☎ ☕ ⚓ Access: ♿
Conference: 2 meeting rooms (Thtr 100 max),
24hr-delegate from £65, day-delegate rate from £25
Children: Welcome ⅋ Dogs: Welcome Licences: ♙♙♙
Leisure: Games room, Snooker/billiards
Parking: Off-street and monitored
Directions: Leave M4 at Junction 42 and take A483 to
Swansea, then A4067 to Mumbles.
See advert on this page

Beaumont Hotel

★★
72–73 Walter Road, Swansea, SA1 4QA
Tel: 01792 643956 Fax: 01792 643044
Email: info@beaumonthotel.co.uk
Web: www.beaumonthotel.co.uk
Rooms: 16 all ensuite
Pricing: Dinner from £10 CC: Accepted
Room facilities: ☐ ☎ ☕ ⚓
Children: Welcome ⅋ Licences: ♙♙♙
Parking: Off-street and monitored
Directions: M4 J42, A483; right at traffic lights at
Tesco, left at roundabout; first right, top of the road,
turn left.
See advert on this page

Fairyhill

Gold Ribbon Winner

★★★ ® ® ®
Reynoldston, Gower, Swansea, SA3 1BS
Tel: 01792 390139 Fax: 01792 391358
Email: postbox@fairyhill.net
Web: www.fairyhill.net
Seasonal closure: 1–18 January

Fairyhill is southwest Wales' only 5-star hotel. With an
award-winning restaurant and wine list. Affordable
luxury set in the heart of the beautiful Gower
Peninsula. Twenty minutes from M4.
Rooms: 8 all ensuite
Pricing: Sgl £120–225 Dbl £140–245 Dinner from £35
CC: Accepted Room facilities: ☐ ☎ ☕ ⚓
Conference: 40 meeting rooms (Thtr 40 max)
Children: Welcome 8yrs min age Dogs: Guide dogs only
Licences: ♙♙♙ Parking: Off-street
Directions: Exit J47 M4; follow signs for Gowerton.
Turn right at traffic lights, follow B4295 for 10½ miles.

Wales

Windsor Lodge

★★

Mount Pleasant, Swansea, SA1 6EG
Tel: 01792 642158 Fax: 01792 648996
Web: www.windsor-lodge.co.uk
Rooms: 19 all ensuite ♨
Pricing: Sgl £60–70 Dbl £70–80 Dinner from £20
CC: Accepted
Room facilities: ▢ ☎ ⬒ ☍
Conference: 1 meeting room (Thtr 30 max)
Children: Welcome ⼑ ☽ Dogs: Welcome
Licences: ♙ Parking: Off-street
Directions: M4 Junction 42, A483 to Sainsbury's. Turn
right at traffic lights beyond Sainsbury's. Turn left at
railway station, then immediately right after second lights.

Grosvenor House

♦♦♦♦ ⤬

Mirador Crescent, Uplands, Swansea, SA2 0QX
Tel: 01792 461522 Fax: 01792 461522
Email: grosvenor@ct6.com
Web: www.ct6.com/grosvenor
Seasonal closure: Christmas and New Year
Rooms: 7 all ensuite ♨ ⊛
Pricing: Sgl £32–34 Dbl £54–58 CC: Accepted
Room facilities: ▢ ⬒ ☍
Children: Welcome 5yrs min age Dogs: Guide dogs only
Parking: Off-street and monitored
Directions: Off A4118, 1 mile from Swansea Railway
Station travelling west, take the third turning on the
right, after St James' Church.

Woodside Guest House

♦♦♦♦ ⤬

Oxwich, Gower, Swansea, SA3 1LS
Tel: 01792 390791
Email: woodside@oxwich.fsnet.co.uk
Web: www.oxwich.fsnet.co.uk
Rooms: 5 (4 ensuite)
Pricing: Sgl £30–39 Dbl £40–62
Room facilities: ▢ ⬒ Children: Welcome Licences: ♙
Parking: Off-street and monitored
Directions: Leave M4 at Junction 42 for Swansea.
Take A4118 Swansea to Porteynon. One mile past
Penmaen, take unmarked road to Oxwich.
See advert on this page

Alexander Hotel

♦♦♦ ⤬

3 Sketty Road, Uplands, Swansea, SA2 0EU
Tel: 01792 470045 Fax: 01792 476012
Email: alexander.hotel@swig-online.co.uk
Web: www.swig-online.co.uk/alexanderhotel
Seasonal closure: Christmas to New Year
Rooms: 7 (6 ensuite) ♨ ⊛
Pricing: Sgl £34–40 Dbl £56–60 CC: Accepted
Room facilities: ▢ ☎ ⬒
Children: Welcome, 4yrs min age ⼑
Dogs: Guide dogs only Licences: ♙
Leisure: Games room
Directions: On A4118, in the Uplands area of Swansea.
On left-hand side at the beginning of Sketty Road, as
you leave the Uplands towards Sketty.

Coast House

♦♦♦

708 Mumbles Road, Mumbles, Swansea, SA3 4EH
Tel: 01792 368702
Email: thecoasthouse@aol.com
Seasonal closure: Christmas
Rooms: 6 all ensuite ♨
Pricing: Sgl £30–35 Dbl £50–60
Room facilities: ▢ ⬒ Children: Welcome
Dogs: Welcome Parking: Off-street
Directions: M4 Junction 42, A483 to Swansea, then
A4067 to Mumbles Village. Coast House is ¹/₂ mile from
shopping area, on right.

Crescent Guest House

♦♦♦ ⤬

132 Eaton Crescent, Uplands, Swansea, SA1 4QR
Tel: 01792 466814 Fax: 01792 466814
Email: conveyatthecrescent@compuserve.com
Web: www.crescentguesthouse.co.uk
Seasonal closure: Christmas to New Year
Rooms: 6 all ensuite ♨ ⊛
Pricing: Sgl £30–35 Dbl £50–55 CC: Accepted
Room facilities: ▢ ⬒
Children: Welcome
Parking: Off-street
Directions: From railway station, take A4118 to St
James' Church, then first left, first right into Eaton
Crescent.

Rock Villa

1 George Bank, Southend, Mumbles,
Swansea, SA3 4EQ
Tel: 01792 366794
Email: rockvilla@tinyworld.co.uk
Web: users.tinyworld.co.uk/rockvilla
Seasonal closure: 21 December to 3 January
Rooms: 6 (4 ensuite)
Pricing: Sgl £22–25 Dbl £22–26 CC: Accepted
Room facilities:
Children: Welcome, 4yrs min age
Dogs: Welcome
Parking: Off-street
Directions: Approximately 4¹/₂ miles from Leisure Centre
down the A483, next to George restaurant and hotel.

Shoreline Hotel

648 Mumbles Road, Mumbles, Swansea, SA3 4QZ
Tel: 01792 366233
Web: www.shorelinehotel.co.uk
Seasonal closure: Christmas
Rooms: 12 all ensuite
Room facilities:
Children: Welcome Licences:
Directions: Leave M4 at Junction 42, follow signs for
Swansea, then to Mumbles. Situated on main Mumbles
seafront, opposite playground.

Hurst Dene

10 Sketty Road, Uplands, Swansea, SA2 0LT
Tel: 01792 280920 Fax: 01792 280920
Email: hurstdeneguesthouse@ntlworld.com
Web: www.hurstdene.co.uk
Rooms: 10 (7 ensuite)
Pricing: Sgl £24–30 Dbl £42.50–48.50
CC: Accepted
Room facilities:
Children: Welcome
Parking: Off-street and monitored
Directions: From M4 junction 42 take A483 towards
Swansea.

Travelodge Swansea (MOTO)

Travel Accommodation
M4 Moto Service Area, Penllergaer,
Nr. Swansea, SA4 1GT
Web: www.travelodge.co.uk
Rooms: 50 all ensuite
Pricing: Sgl £59.40 Dbl £63.85
CC: Accepted
Room facilities: Access:

Tenby, Pembrokeshire

Atlantic Hotel

The Esplanade, Tenby,
Pembrokeshire, SA70 7DU
Tel: 01834 842881
Email: enquiries@atlantic-hotel.uk.com
Web: www.atlantic-hotel.uk.com
Seasonal closure: 20–28 December
Rooms: 42 all ensuite
Pricing: Sgl £66–68 Dbl £90–136 Dinner from £16
CC: Accepted
Room facilities: Access:
Children: Welcome Dogs: Welcome Licences:
Leisure: Indoor pool, Health spa
Parking: Off-street and monitored
Directions: Keep town walls on left, then turn right at
Esplanade. Hotel is halfway along on your right.

Fourcroft Hotel

North Beach, Tenby, Pembrokeshire, SA70 8AP
Tel: 01834 842886 Fax: 01834 842888
Email: bookings@fourcroft-hotel.co.uk
Web: www.fourcroft-hotel.co.uk
Rooms: 43 (42 ensuite)
Pricing: Sgl £40–59 Dbl £80–118 Dinner from £18
CC: Accepted
Room facilities: Access:
Children: Welcome Dogs: Welcome
Licences:
Leisure: Outdoor pool, Health spa,
Games room, Snooker/billiards
Parking: Off-street and monitored
Directions: After 'Welcome to Tenby' signs, fork left
towards North Beach. Down a gentle hill, around a
right-handed sweeping bend, up a hill. At seafront turn
sharp left. Fourcroft is 150 yards along on left.

Heywood Mount Hotel & Spa Leisure Suite

Heywood Lane, Tenby, Pembrokeshire, SA70 8DA
Tel: 01834 842087 Fax: 01834 842113
Email: reception@heywoodmount.co.uk
Web: www.heywoodmount.co.uk
Rooms: 32 all ensuite
Pricing: Sgl £30–48 Dbl £60–96 Dinner from £15
CC: Accepted
Room facilities: Access:
Conference: 1 meeting room
Children: Welcome Dogs: Guide dogs only
Licences:
Leisure: Indoor pool, Gym, Health spa
Parking: Off-street
Directions: Pass 'Welcome to Tenby' sign, look for
brown sign point to right saying Heywood Mount,
follow sign to hotel.

Greenhills Country Hotel

★★

St Florence, Tenby, Pembrokeshire, SA70 8NB
Tel: 01834 871291 Fax: 01834 871948
Email: enquiries@greenhillshotel.co.uk
Web: www.greenhillshotel.co.uk
Seasonal closure: December to March
Rooms: 28 all ensuite
Pricing: Sgl £28–30 Dbl £56–60 Dinner from £12.50
Room facilities: Access:
Children: Welcome Dogs: Guide dogs only
Licences:
Leisure: Outdoor pool, Games room
Parking: Off-street
Directions: In St Florence, pass church on right. Turn
left at hotel signpost. Hotel 250 yards further on.

Kinloch Court Hotel

★★

Queens Parade, Tenby, Pembrokeshire, SA70 7EG
Tel: 01834 842777 Fax: 01834 843097
Rooms: 14 all ensuite
Room facilities:
Children: Welcome Licences:
Leisure: Games room, Snooker/billiards
Parking: Off-street and monitored

Royal Gate House Hotel

★★

North Beach, Tenby,
Pembrokeshire, SA70 7ET
Tel: 01834 842255 Fax: 01834 842441
Email: enquires@royalgatehousehotel.co.uk
Web: www.royalgatehousehotel.co.uk
Rooms: 59 all ensuite
Pricing: Sgl £42–55 Dbl £75–85 Dinner from £17
CC: Accepted
Room facilities: Access:
Conference: 4 meeting rooms (Thtr 140 max)
Children: Welcome Dogs: Welcome Licences:
Leisure: Indoor pool, Games room, Snooker/billiards
Parking: Off-street and monitored
Directions: From M4, take A478 into Tenby.

Broadmead Hotel

Heywood Lane, Tenby,
Pembrokeshire, SA70 8DA
Tel: 01834 842641 Fax: 01834 845757
Web: www.broadmeadhotel.com
Seasonal closure: December to March
Rooms: 20 all ensuite
Pricing: Sgl £27–40 Dbl £54–66 Dinner from £14
CC: Accepted
Room facilities: Access:
Children: Welcome
Licences:
Parking: Off-street and monitored
Directions: On arrival in Tenby, turn right into
Serpentine Road, following signs for Wildlife Park.
Turn right again into Heywood Lane.

Ashby House

24 Victoria Street, Tenby, Pembrokeshire, SA70 7DY
Tel: 01834 842867
Email: ashbyhouse@yahoo.com
Web: www.ashbyhousetenby.co.uk
Rooms: 7 (6 ensuite)
Room facilities: Children: Welcome 3yrs min age
Directions: Driving down South Parade, Town Walls will
be on your left. Turn right up the Esplanade; Victoria
Street is last turning on right.

Pen Mar Hotel

New Hedges, Tenby, Pembrokeshire, SA70 8TL
Tel: 01834 842435 Fax: 01834 842483
Email: info@penmarhotel.co.uk
Web: www.penmarhotel.co.uk
Rooms: 10 (7 ensuite)
Pricing: Sgl £25–30 Dbl £50–60 Dinner from £9
CC: Accepted
Room facilities: Children: Welcome
Licences:
Parking: Off-street and monitored
Directions: Situated on A478 1 mile before Tenby just
outside the village of New Hedges.

Trearddur Bay, Gwynedd

Trearddur Bay Hotel

★★★

Lon Isallt, Trearddur Bay, Anglesey, LL65 2UW
Tel: 01407 860301 Fax: 01407 861181
Email: enquiries@trearddurbayhotel.co.uk
Web: www.trearddurbayhotel.co.uk
Rooms: 42 all ensuite
Pricing: Sgl £82–82 Dbl £90–150 Dinner from £23.50
CC: Accepted Room facilities:
Conference: 4 meeting rooms (Thtr 110 max),
24hr-delegate from £87.50, day-delegate rate from £19.50
Children: Welcome Dogs: Guide dogs only
Licences:
Leisure: Indoor pool, Golf, Riding
Parking: Off-street
Directions: When the A55 terminates turn left onto
B4545 at the roundabout. Continue for 1.7 miles, turn
right at the Power garage.

Moranedd Guest House

◆ ◆ ◆

Trearddur Road, Trearddur Bay, Anglesey,
Gwynedd, LL65 2UE
Tel: 01407 860324 Fax: 01407 861100

Moranedd is a lovely guest house with a sun patio
overlooking three-quarters of an acre of garden in a
quiet cul-de-sac, but only five minutes stroll to the
beach, shops, sailing and golf clubs.
Rooms: 6 (3 ensuite) ⚲ 📺
Pricing: Sgl £20–45 Dbl £40–45 Room facilities: 📺 ☕
Children: Welcome Ħ Dogs: Welcome Licences: ⫼
Parking: Off-street and monitored
Directions: Take A55 to Valley. Turn left at traffic lights
onto B4545 to Trearddur. Continue past Beach Hotel
and turn right at second road through village.
Moranedd is second house on left in Trearddur Road.

Tyn-y-Groes, Gwynedd

The Groes Inn

★ ★ ★ ℞

Tyn-y-Groes, near Conwy, Gwynedd, LL32 8TN
Tel: 01492 650545 Fax: 01492 650545

Tywyn, Gwynedd

Corbett Arms Hotel

★ ★

Tywyn, Gwynedd, LL36 9DG
Tel: 01923 822388 Fax: 01923 824906
Rooms: 41 all ensuite 📺 ⊘
Room facilities: 📺 ☎ ☕ Access: ⫼ ♿
Children: Welcome Ħ Dogs: Welcome Licences: ⫼
Parking: Off-street and monitored
Directions: The Corbett Arms Hotel stands astride the
A493 as it passes north to south from Dolgellau to
Machynlleth.

Greenfield Hotel

★

High Street, Tywyn, Gwynedd, LL36 9AD
Tel: 01654 710354 Fax: 01654 710412
Email: greentywyn@aol.com
Seasonal closure: January Rooms: 8 (6 ensuite) ⚲
Pricing: Sgl £17–19.50 Dbl £34–39 Dinner from £7
CC: AcceptedRoom facilities: 📺 ☕
Children: Welcome Ħ Dogs: Guide dogs only Licences: ⫼
Directions: Situated in High Street opposite Leisure
Centre and Tourist Information Centre.

Usk, Monmouthshire

Glen-yr-Afon House Hotel

★★★

Pontypool Road, Usk, Monmouthshire, NP15 1SY
Tel: 01291 672302 Fax: 01291 672597
Email: enquiries@glen-yr-afon.co.uk
Web: www.glen-yr-afon.co.uk
Rooms: 28 all en-suite
Pricing: Sgl £74–98 Dbl £96–120 Dinner from £15
CC: accepted
Room facilities:
Access:
Conference: meeting rooms (Thtr 140 max)
Children: Welcome
Dogs: Welcome
Licenses:
Parking: Off-street
Directions: Follow A472 through Usk high street over
river bridge follow road around to the right 200 yds
on left.
See advert on previous page

Welshpool, Powys

Lane Farm

◆◆◆◆

Criggion, Welshpool, Powys, SY5 9BG
Tel: 01743 884288 Fax: 01743 885126
Email: lane.farm@ukgateway.net
Web: www.smoothhound.co.uk/hotels/lanefarm
Seasonal closure: 23–26 December
Rooms: 4 all ensuite Pricing: Sgl £23–25 Dbl £36–40
Room facilities: Access: Children: Welcome
Dogs: Welcome Parking: Off-street and monitored
Directions: Situated on B4393 between Crew Green
and Llandrinio, 12 miles from Shrewsbury, 9 miles from
Welshpool.

Wrexham, Clwyd

Llwyn Onn Hall Hotel

★★★★

Cefn Road, Wrexham, Clwyd, LL13 0NY
Tel: 01978 261225 Fax: 01978 363233
Email: llwynonnhall@breathemail.net
Web: www.smoothhound.co.uk/hotel.llwyonn

Surrounded by open countryside this fine 17th century
manor house is set in several acres of mature grounds.
Exposed timbers remain and the original oak staircase
is still in use.
Rooms: 13 all ensuite
Pricing: Sgl £50–64 Dbl £70–84 Dinner from £13
CC: Accepted Room facilities:
Conference: 2 meeting rooms (Thtr 60 max),
24hr-delegate from £105, day-delegate rate from £25
Children: Welcome Dogs: Guide dogs only
Licences: Parking: Off-street
Directions: Between A525 Wrexham–Whitechurch road
and A534 Wrexham–Nantwich road. Near Wrexham
industrial estate, 2m off main Wrexham–Chester A483.

Moreton Park Lodge

★★★

Moreton Park, Gledrid, Chirk, Wrexham,
Clwyd, LL14 5DG
Tel: 01691 776666 Fax: 01691 776655
Email: reservations@moretonpark.com
Web: www.moretonpark.com
Rooms: 46 all ensuite
Pricing: Sgl £44.95–54.95 Dbl £49.90–59.90
Dinner from £8 CC: Accepted
Room facilities: Access:
Conference: 1 meeting room (Thtr 8 max)
Children: Welcome Dogs: Guide dogs only
Licences:
Parking: Off-street and monitored
Directions: At intersection of A5 and B5070, 3 miles
north of Oswestry, 8 miles south of Wrexham.
See advert on previous page

Wynnstay Arms Hotel

★★★

Yorke Street, Wrexham, Clwyd, LL13 8LP
Tel: 01978 291010 Fax: 01978 362138
Rooms: 67 all ensuite Pricing: Sgl £48.95
Dbl £55.90 Dinner from £12.95 CC: Accepted
Room facilities: Access:
Children: Welcome Dogs: Guide dogs only
Licences: Parking: Off-street and monitored
Directions: From A483, off slip road onto A525, follow
for Wrexham, go to T-junction. Take left down hill onto
St Giles Way. Left at T-junction, left Mount Street.

Travelodge Wrexham

Travel Accommodation
A483/A5152, Wrexham By Pass, Rhostyllen, Wrexham,
Clwyd, LL14 4EJ
Web: www.travelodge.co.uk Rooms: 32 all ensuite
Pricing: Sgl £54.40 Dbl £58.85 CC: Accepted
Room facilities: Access:

Relax and Unwind

Take the stress out of finding an hotel with RAC Hotel Reservations

On the move and looking for an hotel or a cosy B&B? Look no further than RAC Hotel Reservations.

With just one phone call, RAC Hotel Reservations gives you unique access to over 3000 quality hotels and B&Bs throughout the UK & Ireland. Each one is inspected, rated and the best ones awarded on your behalf by our team of discerning inspectors for quality and service.

We'll not only source the perfect hotel or B&B to suit your pocket and your needs, we'll also source the latest deals and make the booking for you, completely free of charge*.

So if you are looking for somewhere to relax and unwind, whether on business or leisure, call us now.

Call 0870 603 9109 and quote RAC 05
or visit www.rac.co.uk/hotels

*Calls will be charged at National rates

A to B - we RAC to it

rac

Scotland

Glasgow • • Edinburgh

• Newcastle

Belfast •

Dublin • • Manchester

Birmingham •

Cardiff • London •

Cape Wrath

Butt of Lewis
(Rubha Robhanais)
Port Nis

B801

Nort
Sut

Laxford

Scourie

Eddrachillis
Bay

Càrlabhagh

Stornoway
(Steòrnabhagh)

Port Nan
Giuran

Eye Peninsula
(An Rubha)

Enard
Bay

Lochinver

Inch

**OUTER
HEBRIDES**

ISLE OF LEWIS
(EILEAN LEODHAIS)

Baile Ailein

Assynt-
Coigach

Ledr

Scarp

Loch
Langabhat

T H E   M I N C H

3 hours

Ullapool

*South Lewis, Harris
& North Uist*

Taransay
(Tarasaigh)

Tarbert
(Tairbeart)

Scalpay
(Scalpaigh)

Ardcharnie

Laide

Harris
(Na Hearadh)

Poolewe

Flonn
Loch

Pabbay
(Pabaigh)

Roghadal

Gairloch

Loch Maree

*North Uist
(Uibhist a Tuath)*

Tigh A
Ghearraidh

Lochmaddy
(Loch nam Madadh)

Sound of Monach

T H E   L I T T L E   M I N C H

Loch
Torridon

Loch
Fannich

Kinlochewe

Wester Ross

Achnasheen

Trotternish

Staffin

Loch
Snizort

Uig

Rona

Sound of Raasay

*Benbecula
(Beinn na Faoghla)*

Creag

2 hrs

Edinbane

W E S T E R N   I S L E S

Inner Sound

Shieldaig

HIGHLA

Loch Monar

Loch
Carron

*South Uist
(Uibhist a Deas)*

Dunvegan

Bracadale

Portree

Raasay

**ISLE OF
SKYE**

Drynoch

Kyle of
Lochalsh

Kintail

Glen Affric

Cann

*South Uist
Machair*

Lochboisdale
(Loch Baghasdail)

Sligachan

*Cuillin
Hills*

Broadford

Loch
Mullardoch

Loch

3 hours
(summer)

Soay

Cuanie Inn

R Garry

Shiel Bridge

Castlebay
(Bàgh a'Chaisteil)

Canna

Sound of Canna

Ardvasar

Sound of Sleat

Knoydart

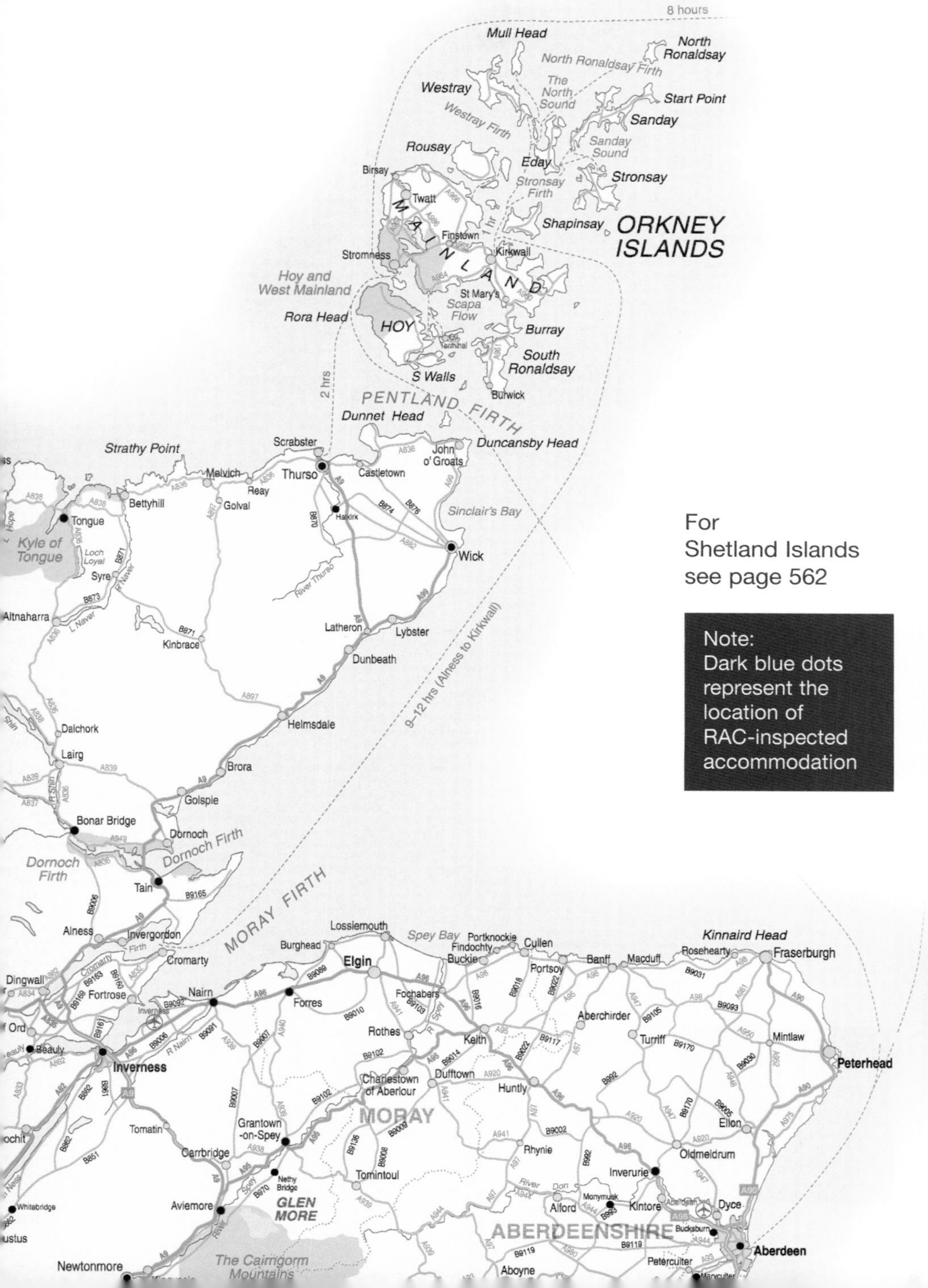

8 hours

Mull Head

North Ronaldsay
North Ronaldsay Firth

Westray
The North Sound
Start Point
Sanday
Sanday Sound

Westray Firth

Rousay
Birsay
Eday
Stronsay
Stronsay Firth

Twatt
Finstown
Shapinsay
ORKNEY ISLANDS

Stromness
Kirkwall

MAINLAND

Hoy and West Mainland
St Mary's
Scapa Flow

Rora Head
HOY
Burray
South Ronaldsay

S Walls
Burwick

PENTLAND FIRTH

Dunnet Head
Duncansby Head

Strathy Point
Scrabster
John o' Groats

Melvich
Thurso
Castletown

Bettyhill
Reay
Golval
Halkirk
Sinclair's Bay

Tongue
Syre
Wick

Kyle of Tongue
Loch Loyal

Altnaharra
Kinbrace
Latheron
Lybster

Dalchork
Dunbeath

Lairg
Helmsdale

Brora

Golspie

Bonar Bridge
Dornoch
Dornoch Firth

Dornoch Firth
Tain

Alness
Invergordon
MORAY FIRTH

Dingwall
Cromarty
Lossiemouth
Spey Bay Portknockie Cullen
Kinnaird Head

Fortrose
Burghead
Findochty
Buckie
Portsoy
Banff Macduff
Rosehearty
Fraserburgh

Beauly
Nairn
Elgin
Fochabers
Aberchirder
Turriff
Mintlaw

Inverness
Forres
Rothes
Keith
Peterhead

Tomatin
Charlestown of Aberlour
Dufftown
Huntly
Ellon

MORAY
Grantown-on-Spey
Rhynie
Oldmeldrum

Carrbridge
Nethy Bridge
Tomintoul
Inverurie
Monymusk
Dyce

Whitebridge
Aviemore
GLEN MORE
Alford
Kintore
Aberdeen

Newtonmore
The Cairngorm Mountains
ABERDEENSHIRE
Aboyne
Peterculter

For Shetland Islands see page 562

Note:
Dark blue dots represent the location of RAC-inspected accommodation

Scotland

Scotland

(Beinn na Faoghla)
Creag
Dunvegan
Bracadale
Portree
Raasay
ISLE OF SKYE
Drynoch
Sligachan
Cuillin Hills
Broadford
Kyle of Lochalsh
Shiel Bridge
Kintail
Glen Affric
Loch Monar
Loch Carron
Loch Mullardoch
Cluanie Inn
R Garry

South Uist (Uibhist a Deas)
South Uist Machair
Lochboisdale (Loch Baghasdail)
Sound of Barra

3 hours (summer)
Soay
Ardvasar
Sound of Sleat
Knoydart
Loch Quoich
Loch Lochy
Loch Arkaig

Castlebay (Bàgh a'Chaisteil)
Barra (Barraigh)
2 hrs
4 hrs (summer)
Canna
Sound of Canna
Rum
6 hours
Mallaig
Morar
Loch Morar
Loch Eil

Mingulay (Miùghlaigh)
The Small Isles
Sound of Rum
Eigg
Arisaig
A830
Glenfinnan
Loch Shiel
Loch Eil
Bonavie
Torlundy
Fort Williar
Corpach

5 hours
Muck
Sound of Arisaig
Morar, Moidart & Ardnamurchan
Acharacle
Strontian
Corran
Onich
Ballachulish
Kinlo
Ben Nevis Glen Co

SEA OF THE HEBRIDES
HEBRIDES
INNER HEBRIDES
Coll
Arinagour
Tobermory
Dervaig
Drumnacroish
Salen
Gruline
Lochaline
Portnacroish
Loch Linnhe
Lynn of Lorr
Connel
Bridge of C

Tiree
Scarinish
1 hr
Loch Tuath
Loch na Keal
ISLE OF MULL
Craignure
Oban
Taynuilt
Loch Awe
Dalmally

Iona
Martyr's Bay
Fionnphort
Bunessan
Kilninver
Firth of Lorn
Kilchrenan
Rockhill
Loch Lom

ARGYLL AND BUTE
Scarba, Lunga & The Garvellachs
Kilmelford
Inveraray
Furnace
ARGYLL

Colonsay
Scalasaig
3 hrs
Ardlussa
JURA
Kilmartin
Crinan
Lochgilphead
Knapdale
Kilmichael
Gareloch head
Coulport
Hele

Jura
Feolin Ferry
Craighouse
Tighnabruaich
Portavadie
Kyles of Bute
Collintraive
Dunoon
Gour
Innellan

Port Askaig
Ballygrant
Bridgend
Tarbert
Rothesay
Ardbeg
Wemyss Bay
Largs

ISLAY
Portnahaven
Laggan Bay
Kennacraig
Clachan
Claonaig
Island of Bute
Millport
West Kilbride

Port Ellen
2 hours
Isle of Gigha
Arminish
Lochranza
North Arran
ISLE OF ARRAN
Brodick
Ardrossan
Saltcoats

2 hrs
Tayinloan
Glenbarr
Port Righ
Kilbrannan Sound
Blackwaterfoot
Lamlash

Campbeltown
Southend
Mull of Kintyre
Turnberry
Girvan
SOU
Ballantrae

ISLAY

Port Askaig
Feolin Ferry
Jura
Port Askaig
Ballygrant
Bridgend
Craighouse
Portnahaven
Laggan Bay
Isle of Gigha
Arminish
Clachan
2 hours
2 hrs
Tarbert
Tighnabruaich
Portavadie
Dunoon
Innellan
Gourock
Wemyss Bay
Rothesay
Largs
Ardbeg
Port Ellen
Tayinloan
Port Righ
Glenbarr
Lochranza
Kennacraig
Claonaig
Island of Bute
Millport
West Kilbride
Brodick
Lamlash
Blackwaterfoot
Firth of Clyde
Kilbrannan Sound
North Arran
ISLE OF ARRAN
Ardrossan
Saltcoats
1 hr
Campbeltown
Southend
Mull of Kintyre
Turnberry
Girvan
Ballantrae
Kirkcolm
Cairnryan
Loch Ryan
Stranraer
Portpatrick
Sandhead
Glenluce
Luce Bay
Drummore
Mull of
SOU

SHETLAND ISLANDS

Herma Ness
Herma Ness
Haroldswick
Unst
Fethaland
North Roe
Yell Sound
YELL
Fetlar
Esha Ness
Esha Ness
St Magnus Bay
Papa Stour
Muckle Roe
Sandness
Walls
MAINLAND
2 hrs
Whalsay
2 hrs
Foula
Foula
5 hrs
5 hrs
(summer only)
Lerwick
Bressay
West Burra
South West Mainland
Sumburgh Head
4 hrs (Lerwick)
4-9 hrs (Sumburgh)
Fair Isle

Milngavie Kirkintilloch Linlithgow WEST Musselburgh Linton
Bishopbriggs M80 Cumbernauld LOTHIAN Corstorphine Haddington
Erskine Clydebank M80 Bathgate Dalmahoy Cramond Tranent EAST St Abb's Head
Paisley Coatbridge Armadale M8 Livingston Dalkeith LOTHIAN Cockburnspath Eyemouth
head Glasgow Airdrie Shotts Whitburn Loanhead Lasswade B6355 Ayton
Glasgow Motherwell Penicuik MIDLOTHIAN Duns Berwick-
East Hamilton Wishaw Rosebank Lauder Greenlaw upon-Tweed
Kilbride Carluke Carnwath Stow Coldstream Holy
warton Strathaven Lanark Peebles Galashiels Cornhill- Island
Kilmarnock Darvel S LANARKSHIRE Quothquan Biggar Innerleithen Melrose on-Tweed Waren Mill
Galston Douglas Broughton Upper St Boswells Kelso Belford
Mauchline Muirkirk Tweeddale Selkirk Eildon & Wooler
Holmhead SCOTTISH Leaderfoot
Cumnock Abington BORDERS Hawick Jedburgh
EAST AYRSHIRE New Sanquhar
Cumnock NORTHUMBERLAND
Dalmellington Moffat Rothbury
Carsphairn Beattock NORTHUMBERLAND
Loch Moniaive Thornhill Otterburn
Doon Langholm Falstone
DUMFRIES AND GALLOWAY Lochmaben Kielder Bellingham
OWAY New Loch Craigadam Dumfries Lockerbie Water
Galloway Ken Crocketford Collin Canonbie
Loch Dee Castle Annan Longtown Upper Denton
Douglas Dalbeattie Nith Gretna Brampton
Fleet Gatehouse Estuary Todhills Carlisle
Valley of Fleet Annan Silloth Abbeytown Dalston
igtown Kirkcudbright Auchencairn Wigton Thursby
Whithorn SOLWAY FIRTH Aspatria
ithorn Solway Maryport Bothel
Burrow Head Coast

Scotland

Gold Ribbon Award

Inverlochy Castle Hotel, Fort William	★★★★	589
Kinnaird, By Dunkeld	★★★	578
Well View Hotel, Moffat	★	608

Blue Ribbon Award

Balbirnie House Hotel, Markinch	★★★★	605
Balmoral Hotel, Edinburgh	★★★★★	579
Banchory Lodge Hotel, Banchory	★★★	571
Cuillin Hills Hotel, Isle of Skye	★★★	601
Darroch Learg Hotel, Ballater	★★★	570
Highland Cottage, Tobermory	★★	600
Ladyburn, Maybole	★★	606
Norton House Hotel, Edinburgh	★★★	582
Pool House, Poolewe	★★★	610
Raemoir House Hotel, Banchory	★★★	571
The Westin Turnberry Resort, Turnberry	★★★★★	615
The Ivy House, Ayr	★★★	568

Little Gem

Browns House, Haddington	♦♦♦♦	595
Craigadam, Castle Douglas	♦♦♦♦♦	574
Dorstan Hotel, Edinburgh	♦♦♦♦	584
Ettrickshaws Country House Hotel, Ettricksbridge	♦♦♦♦♦	611
Gruline Home Farm, Gruline	♦♦♦♦♦	600
Kirkton House, Cardross	♦♦♦♦♦	595
The Pines, Grantown-on-Spey	♦♦♦♦♦	594

Aberdeen

Copthorne Hotel Aberdeen

★★★★ ⌂

122 Huntly Street, Aberdeen, AB10 1SU
Tel: 01224 630404 Fax: 01224 640573
Email: sales.aberdeen@mill-cop.com
Web: www.millenniumhotels.com

Located in the West End of the city centre, this hotel is renowned for its impeccable service. The hotel offers complementary parking. Weekend rates are also available.
Rooms: 89 all ensuite 🛏 ⊗
Pricing: Sgl £60–199 Dbl £76–213 Dinner from £17
CC: Accepted Room facilities: ⬜ ☎ ☕ 📞
Access: ♿ ♿
Conference: 3 meeting rooms (Thtr 200 max), 24hr-delegate from £145, day-delegate rate from £28
Children: Welcome 🍴 Dogs: Welcome
Licences: ◇ ♦ Parking: Off-street and monitored
Directions: Travelling from South, take second left at roundabout, right at next roundabout. Follow Holburn Street for 2 miles. Turn onto Union Street, and take first left, second right.

Maryculter House Hotel

★★★

South Deeside Road, Maryculter, Aberdeen, AB12 5GB
Tel: 01224 732124 Fax: 01224 733510
Email: info@maryculterhousehotel.co.uk
Web: www.maryculterhousehotel.com

This picturesque country house on Royal Deeside dates from 1225. The ideal setting for that tranquil break be it business or pleasure. Old world charm, genuine homely atmosphere and quality Scottish food.
Rooms: 23 all ensuite 🛏 ⊗
Pricing: Sgl £65–115 Dbl £70–120
Dinner from £25
CC: Accepted Room facilities: ⬜ ☎ ☕ 📞
Access: ♿
Conference: 4 meeting rooms (Thtr 200 max), 24hr-delegate from £140, day-delegate rate from £40
Children: Welcome 🍴 🎯 Dogs: Welcome
Licences: ♦♦♦ Parking: Off-street and monitored
Directions: Entering Aberdeen from south (A90), take B9077 for five miles. Hotel located one mile past Mill Inn bridge on the right.

Jays Guest House

♦♦♦♦ ⊗ ⌂

422 King Street, Aberdeen, AB24 3BR
Tel: 01224 638295 Fax: 01224 638295
Email: alice@jaysguesthouse.co.uk
Web: www.jaysguesthouse.co.uk
Rooms: 10 all ensuite ⊗
Pricing: Sgl £35–40 Dbl £60–80 CC: Accepted
Room facilities: ⬜ ☕
Children: Welcome 12yrs min age
Parking: Off-street
Directions: From East End of Union Street, turn left onto King Street and the Jays Guest House is approx ³/₄ mile from this junction.

Arkaig Guest House

♦♦♦ ⊗ ⌂

43 Powis Terrace, Aberdeen, AB25 3PP
Tel: 01224 638872 Fax: 01224 622189
Email: arkaig@netcomuk.co.uk
Web: www.arkaig.co.uk
Rooms: 9 (7 ensuite)
Pricing: Sgl £25–35 Dbl £50–60
Dinner from £10
CC: Accepted Room facilities: ⬜ ☎ ☕
Children: Welcome Dogs: Welcome
Parking: Off-street
Directions: Telephone, fax or email for directions. Easy access from town centre and A96.

Bimini Guest House

♦♦♦

69 Constitution Street, Aberdeen, AB24 5ET
Tel: 01224 646912 Fax: 01224 647006
Email: biminiabz@aol.com
Web: www.bimini.co.uk
Rooms: 8 (6 ensuite) ⊗
Pricing: Sgl £25–37 Dbl £42–55
CC: Accepted
Room facilities: ⬜ ☕
Children: Welcome
Parking: Off-street
Directions: 5 minute walk from town centre, heading towards beachfront.

Scotland

Cedars Private Hotel

 ♦ ♦ ♦

339 Great Western Road, Aberdeen, AB10 6NW
Tel: 01224 583225 Fax: 01224 585050
Email: reservations@cedars-private-
hotel.freeserve.co.uk
Web: www.cedars-private-hotel.freeserve.co.uk
Rooms: 12 all ensuite 🛏 ⊗
Pricing: Sgl £30–45 Dbl £50–54 CC: Accepted
Room facilities: 🖥 ☎ ☕
Children: Welcome Dogs: Welcome
Leisure: Snooker/billiards Parking: Off-street
Directions: Great Western Road crosses Anderson
Drive, which is the city ring road.

Travelodge Aberdeen (SA)

Travel Accommodation
9 Bridge Street, Aberdeen, AB11 6JL
Web: www.travelodge.co.uk
Rooms: 97 all ensuite ⊗
Pricing: Sgl £49.40–57.40 Dbl £53.85–61.85
CC: Accepted Room facilities: 🖥 ☕ Access: ♿

Travelodge Aberdeen West (SA)

Travel Accommodation
A96, Inverurie Road, Bucksburn, Aberdeen, AB21 9BB
Web: www.travelodge.co.uk
Rooms: 48 all ensuite ⊗
Pricing: Sgl £47.40–54.40 Dbl £51.85–58.85
CC: Accepted Room facilities: 🖥 ☕ Access: ♿

Aberfeldy, Perth & Kinross

Moness House hotel & Country Club

★ ★ ★
Crieff Road, Aberfeldy, Perth & Kinross, PH15 2DY
Tel: 01887 820446 Fax: 01887 820062
Rooms: 12 all ensuite 🛏
Pricing: Sgl £42.50 Dbl £60 Dinner from £9
CC: Accepted Room facilities: 🖥 ☎ ☕
Conference: 2 meeting rooms (Thtr 200 max), 24hr-
delegate from £70, day-delegate rate from £25
Children: Welcome ♨ Dogs: Guide dogs only
Licences: ⚓ ♔ Leisure: Indoor pool, Games room,
Snooker/billiards
Parking: Off-street and monitored
Directions: Follow A9 north from Perth towards
Inverness, turn right at Ballinluig A827 to Aberfeldy.
Turn left A826 at traffic lights in Aberfeldy, Moness is
200m on left.

Fortingall Hotel

★ ★
Fortingall, Kenmore, Aberfeldy,
Perth & Kinross, PH15 2NQ
Tel: 01887 830367 Fax: 01887 830367
Email: hotel@fortingall.com
Web: www.fortingall.com
Seasonal closure: January to February
Rooms: 10 all ensuite ⊗ Pricing: Sgl £45 Dbl £70–90

Dinner from £24.50 CC: Accepted
Room facilities: 🖥 ☎ ☕ Conference: 20 meeting
rooms (Thtr 20 max) Dogs: Welcome Licences: ♔
Parking: Off-street
Directions: From Aberfeldy take the road to Tummel
Bridge. At Coshivielle turn left signed to Fortingall. The
hotel is in the village.

Aberfoyle, Perthshire

Inchrie Castle – The Covenanters Inn

♣
The Trossachs, Aberfoyle, Perthshire, KA8 3XD
Tel: 01877 382347 Fax: 01877 382785
Email: enquiries@inchriecastle.co.uk
Web: www.innscotland.com

A former 'Keep' with a long and proud Scottish
tradition. Surrounded by beautiful scenery in the heart
of Scotland's first National Park. Parts of the original
castle remain, including a dungeon where the Stone of
Destiny lay hidden.
Rooms: 50 🛏 Pricing: Sgl £65–100 Dbl £90–160
CC: Accepted Room facilities: 🖥 ☎ ☕
Conference: 5 meeting rooms (Thtr 80 max), 24hr-
delegate from £90, day-delegate rate from £30
Children: Welcome ♨ ☯ Dogs: Welcome
Licences: ⚓ ♔ Parking: Off-street and monitored
Directions: From Glasgow take A81 signposted to
Aberfoyle, continue through village taking left-hand turn
over the hump-back bridge, hotel 400 meters on right.
See advert on facing page

Airdrie, North Lanarkshire

Tudor Hotel

★ ★ ★
39-49 Alexandra Street, Airdrie,
North Lanarkshire, ML6 0BA
Tel: 01236 764144 Fax: 01236 747589
Email: reception@tudor-house.co.uk/
tudorhotel@tinyworld.co.uk
Web: www.tudor-hotel.co.uk
Rooms: 20 all ensuite 🛏 🖼 Pricing: Sgl £39.50–45
Dbl £59.50–65 Dinner from £13.95 CC: Accepted
Room facilities: 🖥 ☎ ☕ ☏
Conference: 3 meeting rooms (Thtr 250 max)
Children: Welcome ♨ Dogs: Guide dogs only
Licences: ⚓ ♔ Leisure: Games room
Parking: Off-street and monitored
Directions: On the main A89 near town centre, Airdrie
train station behind hotel.

A warm Scottish welcome awaits

STONEFIELD CASTLE HOTEL

Breathtaking natural beauty surrounds the Castle standing high on the Kintyre peninsula. The awarded restaurant has one of the finest views on the West Coast, while the garden grounds are renowned for their rare and exotic plants and shrubs.

★★★★

Taste of Scotland Award
2 RAC Dining Awards

Tarbert, Loch Fyne, Argyll PA29 6YJ
Tel: 01880 820836 Fax: 01880 820929

BOWFIELD HOTEL & COUNTRY CLUB

A refreshingly different country hotel offering a wealth of facilities including swimming pool, sauna, jacuzzi, squash courts, gymnasium and health and beauty spa. This perfect country retreat is only 15 minutes from Glasgow Airport.

★★★★

Taste of Scotland Award
2 RAC Dining Awards

Howwood, Renfrewshire PA9 1DB
Tel: 01505 705225 Fax 01505 705230

INCHRIE CASTLE
THE COVENANTERS INN

A former Scottish Keep steeped in the history of Scotland and standing in the beautiful surroundings of The Trossachs. Parts of the original castle remain, including the dungeon where the Stone of Destiny lay hidden.

★★★

Guest access to Buchanan Leisure Club

The Trossachs, Aberfoyle, Perthshire FK8 3XD
Tel: 0187 7382347 Fax: 0187 7382785

THE BUCHANAN ARMS HOTEL
& LEISURE CLUB

In the heart of a conservation village near Loch Lomond, the Buchanan seems to soak up the mood of the beautiful surrounding countryside. Comfort, fine dining and modern leisure facilities.

★★★

Taste of Scotland Award
RAC Dining Award

Drymen, by Loch Lomond, Stirlingshire G63 0BQ
Tel: 01360 660588 Fax 01360 660943

Stonefield Castle Group
HOTELS TOURISM LEISURE

Also Bed & Breakfast accommodation on the beautiful Isle of Iona.
Finlay, Ross, Martyr's Bay, Iona. Tel: 01681 700357 Fax: 01681 700562

Scotland

To view the hotels visit www.innscotland.com

Hotel Seaforth
RAC ★★

An ideal location for golfing, sea angling and shooting, Hotel Seaforth offers splendid accommodation in 19 ensuite bedrooms, most of them overlooking the sea. Relax in the fully equipped leisure centre, or our bar and restaurant.

Dundee Road, Arbroath, Angus DD11 1QF
Tel: 01241 872232
Fax: 01241 877473
Email: hotelseaforth@ukonline.co.uk
www.hotelseaforth.co.uk

Alloway, Ayrshire

The Ivy House
★★★★
Blue Ribbon Winner
2 Alloway, Ayr, Ayrshire, KA7 4NL
Tel: 01292 442336 Fax: 01292 445572
Email: enquiries@theivyhouse.com
Web: www.theivyhouse.uk.com
Rooms: 5 all ensuite
Pricing: Sgl £75–95 Dbl £100–120 Dinner from £28
CC: Accepted Room facilities:
Conference: 3 meeting rooms (Thtr 49 max), 24hr-delegate from £185, day-delegate rate from £35
Children: Welcome
Dogs: Guide dogs only Licences:
Leisure: Golf Parking: Monitored
Directions: From M1 continue on the M74 until Jct 8, take A71 Kilmarnock then follow A77 south towards Ayr. Bypass Ayr, continue on A77 for 2–3 miles, pick up sign for Burns National Heritage Park. Turn right and follow road to T- junction, turn right past Burns Cottage, Ivy House 300m further along road.

Anstruther, Fife

Spindrift
◆◆◆◆
Pittenweem Road, Anstruther, Fife, KY10 3DT
Tel: 01333 310573 Fax: 01333 310573
Email: info@thespindrift.co.uk
Web: www.thespindrift.co.uk

The Spindrift has established a growing reputation for its unique brand of comfort, hospitality, freshly prepared food and service. Convenient for golf, walking, bird watching or exploring the picturesque and historic 'Eastneuk'.
Rooms: 8 all ensuite
Pricing: Dbl £53–62 Dinner from £15 CC: Accepted
Room facilities:
Children: Welcome 10yrs min age Dogs: Welcome
Licences: Parking: Off-street
Directions: Approaching Anstruther from the west, the Spindrift is first on the left. From the east, it is last on the right.

Arbroath, Angus

Hotel Seaforth
★★
Dundee Road, Arbroath, Angus, DD11 1QF
Tel: 01241 872232 Fax: 01241 877473
Email: hotelseaforth@ukonline.co.uk
Web: www.hotelseaforth.co.uk
Rooms: 19 all ensuite
Pricing: Sgl £45–49.50 Dbl £58–63 Dinner from £7.95
CC: Accepted Room facilities:
Conference: 3 meeting rooms (Thtr 120 max), 24hr-delegate from £68, day-delegate rate from £12.50
Children: Welcome Dogs: Welcome Licences:
Leisure: Indoor pool, Gym, Snooker/billiards
Parking: Off-street
Directions: Hotel Seaforth is on the A92, main road from Dundee to Aberdeen, facing the sea.
See advert on this page

Arisaig, Highland

Arisaig Hotel
★★
Arisaig, Highland, PH39 4NH
Tel: 01687 450210 Fax: 01687 450310
Email: arisaighotel@dial.pipex.com
Web: www.arisaighotel.co.uk
Rooms: 13 all ensuite
Pricing: Dinner from £12 CC: Accepted
Room facilities: Children: Welcome
Dogs: Welcome Licences: Leisure: Games room
Parking: Off-street
Directions: Follow A82 through Fort William from south. Turn left onto A830. Arisaig is 35 miles further. Hotel is on right through village.

Auchencairn, Dumfries & Galloway

Balcary Bay Hotel

★★★★ ⟨⟩ ⟨⟩

Auchencairn, Dumfries & Galloway, DG7 1QZ
Tel: 01556 640217 Fax: 01556 640272
Email: reservations@balcary-bay-hotel.co.uk
Web: www.balcary-bay-hotel.co.uk
Seasonal closure: December to February

A magnificent and peaceful setting on the shores of the bay. Ideal base for all leisure facilities or a relaxing holiday. Renowned for good food and wine with warm hospitality.
Rooms: 20 all ensuite
Pricing: Sgl £63 Dbl £112–132 Dinner from £26.50
CC: Accepted Room facilities: ☐ ☎ ⓢ Access: ♿
Children: Welcome ⍭ ✳ Dogs: Welcome
Licences: ⅲ Parking: Off-street
Directions: The hotel is located off the A711 Dumfries-Kirkudbright Road, two miles out of Auchencairn along the Shore Road.

Aviemore, Highland

Ravenscraig Guest House

◆ ◆ ◆

141 Grampian Road, Aviemore, Highland, PH22 1RP
Tel: 01479 810278 Fax: 01479 810210
Email: ravenscrg@aol.com
Web: www.aviemoreonline.com

Victorian villa centrally located providing excellent accommodation for a comfortable and relaxed break. Some rooms have magnificent views over the Cairngorm mountains, also ground floor rooms available.
Rooms: 12 all ensuite ⛲ ⓢ
Pricing: Sgl £20–26 Dbl £40–52 CC: Accepted
Room facilities: ☐ ⓢ Children: Welcome
Dogs: Guide dogs only Parking: Off-street
Directions: Situated towards the quieter north end of Aviemore's main street. Opposite the war memorial, five minutes walk from Railway station.

Ayr, South Ayrshire

Belleisle House

★★★

Doonfoot, Ayr, South Ayrshire, KA7 4DU
Tel: 01292 442331 Fax: 01292 445325
Rooms: 14 all ensuite ⛲ ⏚
Pricing: Dinner from £18.50 (2002 rate) CC: Accepted
Room facilities: ☐ ☎ ⓢ Children: Welcome ⍭
Dogs: Welcome Licences: ⟨⟩ ⅲ
Leisure: Golf Parking: Off-street

Quality Hotel Ayr

★★★

Burns Statue Square, Ayr, South Ayrshire, KA7 3AT
Tel: 01292 263268 Fax: 01292 262293
Email: admin@gb624.u-net.com
Web: www.choicehotels.com
Rooms: 75 all ensuite ⓢ
Pricing: Dinner from £14.50 (2002 rate) CC: Accepted
Room facilities: ☐ ☎ ⓢ ⌕
Access: ⅲ ♿
Children: Welcome ⍭ ✳ Dogs: Welcome
Licences: ⟨⟩ ⅲ
Leisure: Gym, Health spa
Parking: Off-street and monitored
Directions: From A77, take first exit off Holmston roundabout. Follow one-way system round to front of hotel.

Dunduff Farm

◆ ◆ ◆ ◆ ◆ ✺

Dunure, Ayr, Ayrshire, KA7 4LH
Tel: 01292 500225 Fax: 01292 500222
Email: gemmelldunduff@aol.com
Web: www.gemmelldunduff.co.uk

Dunduff Farm is an ideal location for exploring southwest Scotland and its attractions, including Culzean Castle, Robert Burns' Cottage, Burns' Heritage Trail and Ayrshire's finest golf courses. Homely and comfortable accommodation.
Rooms: 3 (2 ensuite) ⓢ
Pricing: Sgl £35–40 Dbl £50–54
CC: Accepted
Room facilities: ☐ ⓢ
Children: Welcome 16yrs min age
Parking: Off-street and monitored
Directions: 6 miles south of Ayr past school on 719.

Horizon Hotel

♦♦♦♦🐕 ✓

Esplanade, Ayr, Ayrshire, KA7 1DT
Tel: 01292 264384 Fax: 01292 264011
Email: mail@horizonhotel.com
Web: www.horizonhotel.com

Ayr's only sea front hotel, five minutes from the vibrant town centre. Dine in our conservatory restaurant, friendly atmosphere. Golfers paradise.
Rooms: 22 (16 ensuite) 🍴 🚭
Pricing: Sgl £38–60 Dbl £50–95 Dinner from £10
CC: Accepted Room facilities: 🖥 🍵 Access: ♿
Conference: 2 meeting rooms (Thtr 180 max)
Children: Welcome ⅓ ⅝ Dogs: Welcome
Licences: ⚖ ⅲ Parking: Off-street and monitored
Directions: Enter Ayr following seafront signs. Hotel at north end of esplanade between pavilion and Citadel Leisure Centre.

Ballachulish, Argyll & Bute

Lyn-Leven Guest House

♦♦♦♦

West Laroch, Ballachulish, Argyll & Bute, PH49 4JP
Tel: 01855 811392 Fax: 01855 811600
Email: lynleven@amserve.net
Web: www.lynleven.co.uk
Seasonal closure: Christmas

A warm Highland welcome awaits you at our award-winning family-run guest house, only one mile from lovely Glencoe. We are situated with attractive gardens overlooking Loch Leven. Private parking.
Rooms: 12 all ensuite 🍴 🚭
Room facilities: 🖥 🍵 Access: ♿
Children: Welcome Dogs: Welcome
Licences: ⅲ Parking: Off-street
Directions: Take A82 to Glencoe and continue for 1 mile. West Laroch sign on left to Ballachulish.

Ballater, Aberdeenshire

Darroch Learg

Blue Ribbon Winner

★★★ ® ® ®

Braemar Road, Ballater, Aberdeenshire, AB35 5UX
Tel: 01339 755443 Fax: 01339 755252
Email: nigel@darrochlearg.co.uk
Web: www.darrochlearg.co.uk
Seasonal closure: January

Darroch Learg offers relaxing country house charm, great views over Royal Deeside and a fine restaurant and wine list. It is close to Ballater and is the ideal centre for enjoying Royal Deeside.
Rooms: 18 all ensuite 📺 🚭
Pricing: Sgl £31.50–63.15 Dinner from £35.50
CC: Accepted Room facilities: 🖥 ☎ 🍵 Access: ♿
Conference: 3 meeting rooms, 24hr-delegate from £99, day-delegate rate from £25
Children: Welcome ⅓ ⅝ Dogs: Welcome
Parking: Off-street and monitored
Directions: Approaching Ballater on A93 from Braemar, turn left into driveway just past 30mph signs.

Monaltrie Hotel

★★

5 Bridge Square, Royal Deeside, Ballater, Aberdeenshire, AB35 5QJ
Tel: 01339 755417 Fax: 01339 755180
Email: monaltrie.hotel@virgin.net
Web: www.monaltriehotel.freeserve.co.uk
Rooms: 24 (22 ensuite) 📺 🚭
Pricing: Dinner from £12.50 (2002 rate) CC: Accepted
Room facilities: 🖥 ☎ 🍵 Children: Welcome ⅓ ⅝
Dogs: Welcome Licences: ⚖ ⅲ Parking: Off-street

Glen Lui Hotel

◆◆◆◆ ❧ ✕ ❦

Invercauld Road, Ballater, Royal Deeside,
Aberdeenshire, AB35 5PP
Tel: 01339 755402 Fax: 01339 755545
Email: infos@glen-lui-hotel.co.uk
Web: www.glen-lui-hotel.co.uk

Small, friendly 4* country house hotel. Spectacular
setting overlooking Lochnagar. Fishing, hill-walking,
shooting. Ensuite bedrooms all non-smoking. Superb
dining with RAC, AA & ToS awards. Private conference
& party facilities.
Rooms: 19 all ensuite ❧ ⊗
Pricing: Sgl £25–45 Dbl £50–90 Dinner from £16.50
CC: Accepted Room facilities: ▢ ☎ ◔ ❧ Access: ♿
Conference: 2 meeting rooms (Thtr 32 max)
Children: Welcome ❧ Dogs: Welcome
Licences: ♦♦♦ Parking: Off-street and monitored
Directions: From Aberdeen turn right into Ballater. Drive
through, over bridge, turn left down Invercauld Road at
auld kirk, drive to end.

Inverdeen House B&B

◆◆◆◆ ✕ ❦

11 Bridge Square, Ballater, Deeside, AB35 5QJ
Tel: 013397 55759 Fax: 013397 55993
Email: info@inverdeen.com
Web: www.inverdeen.com
Rooms: 3 all ensuite ⊗ CC: Accepted
Room facilities: ▢ ◔ Children: Welcome
Dogs: Guide dogs only Parking: Off-street
Directions: At bridge junction coming from Aberdeen,
with village on right, Inverdeen is opposite the junction.

Banchory, Aberdeenshire

Banchory Lodge Hotel

Blue Ribbon Winner

★★★ ❦ ❦ ❦

Dee Street, Banchory, Aberdeenshire, AB31 5HS
Tel: 01330 822625 Fax: 01330 825019
Email: banchorylodgeht@btconnect.com
Web: www.banchorylodge.co.uk
Seasonal closure: 2 weeks in January

Situated five minutes from Banchory town centre, a
Georgian country house hotel in a picturesque and
tranquil riverside setting beside the River Dee.
Rooms: 22 all ensuite ❧ ❒ ⊗
Pricing: Dinner from £25 CC: Accepted
Room facilities: ▢ ☎ ◔ Access: ♿
Conference: 3 meeting rooms (Thtr 50 max), 24hr-
delegate from £105, day-delegate rate from £30
Children: Welcome ⊓ ❧ Dogs: Welcome
Licences: ♦♦♦ Leisure: Fishing, Games room
Parking: Off-street and monitored
Directions: A93 from Aberdeen turn left at traffic lights
in Banchory, from south A957 from Stonehaven to
Banchory.

Raemoir House Hotel

Blue Ribbon Winner

★★★ ❦ ❦ ❦

Banchory, Aberdeenshire, AB31 4ED
Tel: 01330 824884 Fax: 01330 822171
Email: relax@raemoir.com
Web: www.raemoir.com

Rooms: 20 all ensuite ❧ ❒
Pricing: Dinner from £24.50 CC: Accepted
Room facilities: ▢ ☎ ◔ Access: ♿
Children: Welcome ⊓ ❧ Dogs: Welcome
Licences: ◭ ♦♦♦ Leisure: Tennis, Golf
Parking: Off-street and monitored
Directions: 20 miles west of Aberdeen. From A93 to
Banchory, turn right onto A980 Torphins Road. After
1½ miles, hotel is opposite T-junction.

Burnett Arms Hotel

★★

25 High Street, Banchory, Aberdeenshire, AB31 5TD
Tel: 01330 824944 Fax: 01330 825553
Email: theburnett@totalise.co.uk
Web: www.burnettarms.co.uk
Rooms: 16 all ensuite ❧ ⊗
Pricing: Sgl £42–57 Dbl £58–80 Dinner from £16
CC: Accepted Room facilities: ▢ ☎ ◔ ❧
Conference: 2 meeting rooms (Thtr 100 max), 24hr-
delegate from £85, day-delegate rate from £19
Children: Welcome ❧ Dogs: Welcome
Licences: ◭ ♦♦♦ Parking: Off-street and monitored
Directions: On A93 west of Aberdeen in Banchory town
centre. Northern side of street.
See advert on following page

The Burnett Arms Hotel

Historic coaching inn ideally situated for touring Royal Deeside and the northeast of Scotland. 18 miles from Aberdeen and 16 miles from Dyce International Airport (ABZ).

Facilities include two function suites, restaurant, two bars. Surrounding area of Scotland renowned for its breathtaking beauty and golf courses. Golf nearby.

Weekend rates available

25 High Street, Banchory AB31 5TD
Tel: 01330 824944   Fax: 01330 825553
Email: theburnett@totalise.co.uk
Website: www.burnettarms.co.uk

Lovat Arms Hotel

Our Taste of Scotland Kitchen provides an excellent variety of cuisine, much of it produced on our own farm. Our bedrooms are all furnished in clan tartans which adds to the family atmosphere. The Garden and Ceilidh rooms provide excellent areas for small meetings and functions for up to about 60 people.

Beauly, Nr. Inverness IV4 7BS
Tel: 01463 782313   Fax: 01463 782862
Email: lovat.arms@cali.co.uk
Website: www.lovatarms.com

Barrhead, East Renfrewshire

Dalmeny Park Country House Hotel

★★★ ℞

Lochilbo Road, Barrhead, Strathclyde, G78 1LG
Tel: 0141 881 9211 Fax: 0141 881 9214
Email: enquiries@maksu-group.co.uk
Web: www.maksu-group.co.uk
Rooms: 20 all ensuite 🖨 🕸
Pricing: Sgl £65–120 Dbl £85–170 Dinner from £14
CC: Accepted Room facilities: 🖵 ☎ 🍵 📠
Conference: 4 meeting rooms (Thtr 250 max), 24hr-delegate from £98, day-delegate rate from £22
Children: Welcome ⍭ ⍩ Dogs: Welcome Licences: 🜄 ♟
Parking: Off-street and monitored
Directions: Follow A736 through Barrhead towards Irvine. Hotel is on the left as you leave Barrhead.

Beauly, Highland

Lovat Arms Hotel

★★★ ℞

Main Street, Beauly, Highland, IV4 7BS
Tel: 01463 782313 Fax: 01463 782862
Email: info@lovatarms.com
Web: www.lovatarms.com
Rooms: 28 all ensuite Pricing: Sgl £35–45 Dbl £60–90
Dinner from £22 CC: Accepted
Room facilities: 🖵 ☎ 🍵 📠 Conference: 4 meeting rooms (Thtr 60 max) Children: Welcome ⍭ ⍩
Dogs: Welcome Licences: 🜄 ♟
Leisure: Beauty salon, Fishing, Games room
Parking: Off-street and monitored
Directions: Take A9 to Inverness, cross Kessock Bridge, stay on A9 till Tore roundabout. Take first left on A832 to Muiroford, left on A862 to Beauly Hotel which is located at one end off village square.
See advert on this page

Heathmount Guest House

♦♦♦♦ ⍟

Station Road, Beauly, Highland, IV4 7EQ
Tel: 01463 782411
Seasonal closure: Christmas and New Year
Rooms: 5 🕸
Pricing: Sgl £20 Dbl £40 CC: Accepted
Room facilities: 🖵 🍵 Children: Welcome
Dogs: Welcome Parking: Off-street and monitored
Directions: 20m from post office on main road through Beauly Village.

Biggar, South Lanarkshire

Shieldhill Castle

★★★ ℞ ℞ ℞

Quothquan, Biggar, South Lanarkshire, ML12 6NA
Tel: 01899 220035
Fax: 01899 221092
Email: enquiries@shieldhill.co.uk
Web: www.shieldhill.co.uk
Rooms: 16 all ensuite 🍵 🖨 🕸

Pricing: Sgl £95–248 Dbl £67–124 Dinner from £17.50
CC: Accepted Room facilities: ☐ ☎
Conference: 5 meeting rooms (Thtr 400 max)
Children: Welcome ⯑ ⯑ ⯑ Dogs: Welcome
Licences: ⯑ ⯑
Leisure: Beauty salon, Golf, Fishing, Riding
Parking: Off-street and monitored
Directions: From Biggar take B7016 towards Carnwath.
After 3 miles turn left into Shieldhill Road, Castle is 1½
miles on the right.

Blairgowrie, Perth & Kinross

Angus Hotel

★★★
46 Wellmeadow, Blairgowrie,
Perth & Kinross, PH10 6NQ
Tel: 01250 872455 Fax: 01250 875615
Email: reception@theangushotel.com
Web: www.theangushotel.com
Rooms: 81 all ensuite ⯑ Pricing: Dinner from £18.95
(2002 rate) CC: Accepted Room facilities: ☐ ☎ ⯑
Access: ⯑⯑ ⯑ Children: Welcome ⯑ ⯑ Dogs: Welcome
Licences: ⯑ ⯑ Leisure: Indoor pool
Parking: Off-street
Directions: Situated in the centre of Blairgowrie on
the A93.

Bonar Bridge, Highland

Kyle House

◆ ◆ ◆
Dornoch Road, Bonar Bridge, Highland, IV24 3EB
Tel: 01863 766360 Fax: 01863 766360
Email: kylehouse360@msn.com
Seasonal closure: November to January
Rooms: 6 (3 ensuite) ⯑ Room facilities: ☐ ⯑
Children: Welcome 4yrs min age Dogs: Guide dogs only
Licences: ⯑ Parking: Off-street
Directions: On A949, fourth house past newsagents on
left northbound. Fourth house on right entering village
from east side.

Bothwell, South Lanarkshire

Bothwell Bridge Hotel

★★★
89 Main Street, Bothwell, South Lanarkshire, G71 8EU
Tel: 01698 852246 Fax: 01698 854686
Email: bothwell-bridge@hotmail.com
Web: www.bothwellbridge-hotel.com
Rooms: 90 all ensuite ⯑ ⯑ ⯑ Pricing: Sgl £60–65
Dbl £70–75 Dinner from £14.50 CC: Accepted
Room facilities: ☐ ☎ ⯑ ⯑ Access: ⯑⯑ ⯑
Conference: 5 meeting rooms (Thtr 200 max)
Children: Welcome ⯑ ⯑ Dogs: Guide dogs only
Licences: ⯑ ⯑ Parking: Monitored
See advert on this page

Campbeltown, Argyll & Bute

Seafield Hotel

★★
Kilkerran Road, Campbeltown, Argyll, PA28 6JL
Tel: 01586 554385 Fax: 01586 552741
Email: gkennes@aol.com
Web: www.theseafield.co.uk
Rooms: 9 all ensuite Pricing: Sgl £50–60 Dbl £70–90
Dinner from £15 CC: Accepted Room facilities: ☐ ☎ ⯑
Dogs: Welcome Licences: ⯑ ⯑ Parking: Off-street
Directions: From A83 follow signs for Ballycastle ferry
terminal then follow road around loch for about 500m.

Scotland

Dunvalanree

◆◆◆◆◆ 🍴🍴 ✗◎ ☕

Port Righ, Carradale, Campbeltown,
Argyll & Bute, PA28 6SE
Tel: 01583 431226 Fax: 01583 431339
Email: bookin@dunvalanree.com
Web: www.dunvalanree.com

Dunvalanree is between Port Righ and Carradale Bay,
enjoy a "taste of Scotland" menu of local produce and
fall asleep to the sound of the sea.
Rooms: 7 (5 ensuite) ◎
Pricing: Sgl £30–35 Dbl £30–40 Dinner from £20
CC: Accepted Room facilities: 🖵 ☕ Access: ♿
Children: Welcome 🍴 ◎ Dogs: Welcome
Licences: 🍷 ᵼᵼᵼ Parking: Off-street and monitored
Directions: From Tarbert take A83 towards
Campbeltown. Turn left onto B8001 towards Skipness.
After 20 miles in Carradale turn left then right after the
bus stop.

Westbank Guesthouse

◆◆◆ ☕

Dell Road, Campbeltown, Argyll & Bute, PA28 6JG
Tel: 01586 553660 Fax: 01586 553660
Rooms: 7 (5 ensuite) 🍴
Pricing: Sgl £23–27 Dbl £36–46 CC: Accepted
Room facilities: 🖵 ☕ Children: Welcome 🍴
Dogs: Welcome Parking: Monitored
Directions: Follow signs to Heritage Centre. 30m past
centre travelling in Southend direction, turn right into
Dell Road.

Carnoustie, Angus

Letham Grange Hotel

★★★★ 🍴🍴

Colliston, Angus, DD11 4RL
Tel: 01241 890373 Fax: 01241 890725
Email: lethamgrange@sol.co.uk
Web: www.lethamgrange.co.uk
Rooms: 42 all ensuite 🛏 Room facilities: 🖵 ☎ ☕
Access: ♿ Children: Welcome 🍴 ◎
Dogs: Welcome Licences: 🍷 ᵼᵼᵼ
Leisure: Golf Parking: Off-street
Directions: Take A92 to Arbroath, and then the A933
towards Brechin. Take first right after Colliston for
Letham Grange (follow tourist board signs).

Castle Douglas, Dumfries & Galloway

Douglas Arms Hotel

★★★ 🍴🍴

King Street, Castle Douglas,
Dumfries & Galloway, DG7 1DB
Tel: 01556 502231 Fax: 01556 504000
Email: doughot@aol.com
Rooms: 24 all ensuite 🍴 ◎ Room facilities: 🖵 ☎ ☕
Children: Welcome 🍴 Dogs: Welcome
Licences: 🍷 ᵼᵼᵼ Parking: Off-street and monitored
Directions: In centre of town on the main street and
close to the town clock tower.

Kings Arms Hotel

★★

St Andrews Street, Castle Douglas,
Dumfries & Galloway, DG7 1EL
Tel: 01556 502626 Fax: 01556 502097
Email: david@galloway-golf.co.uk
Web: www.galloway-golf.co.uk
Seasonal closure: Dec 25/26 Jan 1/2/3
Rooms: 10 (9 ensuite) 🍴 ◎
Pricing: Sgl £37.50–47.50 Dbl £58–62
Dinner from £12.50 CC: Accepted
Room facilities: 🖵 ☕
Conference: 1 meeting room (Thtr 24 max), 24hr-
delegate from £75 Children: Welcome 🍴 ◎
Dogs: Welcome
Licences: 🍷 ᵼᵼᵼ Parking: Off-street and monitored
Directions: From A75 turn off at sign for Castle
Douglas. Go down main street to town clock, turn left.
Hotel 100 yards on left.

Craigadam   Little Gem

◆◆◆◆◆ 🍴 ✗◎ ☕

Craigadam, Kirkpatrick Durham, Castle Douglas,
Dumfries & Galloway, DG7 3HU
Tel: 01556 650233 Fax: 01556 650233
Email: inquiry@craigadam.com
Web: www.craigadam.com

Craigadam is an elegant country house within a
working farm, individually named and pretty luxurious
suites are each charming and distinctive. Warm
hospitality, log fires, superb Scottish cuisine.
Rooms: 11 all ensuite ◎
Pricing: Sgl £30–40 Dbl £60–70 Dinner from £15
CC: Accepted Room facilities: 🖵 ☕ Access: ♿

Children: Welcome ⋔ ⁏℃ Dogs: Welcome
Licences: ⏀ 𝖎𝖎𝖎 Leisure: Beauty salon, Fishing,
Snooker/billiards Parking: Off-street and monitored
Directions: Leave Dumfries on A75 towards Castle
Douglas. At Crocketford (10 miles) turn onto A712:
property is 2 miles on the right.

Coldstream, Scottish Borders

St Albans
♦ ♦ ♦ ♦

Clouds, Duns, Borders, TD11 3BB
Tel: 01361 883285 Fax: 01361 884534
Email: st_albans@ukf.net
Web: www.scotlandbordersbandb.co.uk
Rooms: 3⊚ Pricing: Sgl £25–28 Dbl £20–27
CC: AcceptedRoom facilities: ▱ ⌁
Children: Welcome 12yrs min age Dogs: Welcome
Directions: Clouds is a lane immediately behind the
police station which is situated in Newtown street.

Collin, Dumfries & Galloway

Travelodge Dumfries
Travel Accommodation
A75, Annan Road, Collin, Dumfries & Galloway, DG1 3SE
Web: www.travelodge.co.uk
Rooms: 40 all ensuite ⊛
Pricing: Sgl £47.40 Dbl £51.85 CC: Accepted
Room facilities: ▱ ⌁ Access: ♿

Crieff, Perth & Kinross

Locke's Acre Hotel
★ ★
7 Comrie Road, Crieff, Perthshire, PH7 4BP
Tel: 01764 652526 Fax: 01764 652526
Email: dickvirow@0800dial.com
Seasonal closure: February Rooms: 6 (4 ensuite)
Pricing: Sgl £30–45 Dbl £56–60 Dinner from £7.50
CC: Accepted Room facilities: ▱ ⌁ Licences: 𝖎𝖎𝖎
Parking: Off-street
Directions: From A9 N, after Dunblane, take A822 to
Crieff. From Perth, A85 to Crieff Hotel on Comrie Road
(A85), opposite McCrosty Park.

Gwydyr House Hotel
♦ ♦ ♦ ♦

Comrie Road, Crieff, Perth & Kinross, PH7 4BP
Tel: 01764 653277 Fax: 01764 653277
Email: george.blackie@iclweb.com
Web: www.smoothhound.co.uk/hotels/gwydyr.html
Rooms: 8 all ensuite ⊛ ⊚
Pricing: Sgl £40–55 Dbl £60–85 Dinner from £17.95
CC: Accepted
Room facilities: ▱ ⌁ Children: Welcome ⋔ ⁏℃
Dogs: Welcome Licences: 𝖎𝖎𝖎
Parking: Off-street and monitored
Directions: Situated on the A85 Comrie Road, going
west from Crieff, opposite MacRosty Park.

Crinan, Argyll & Bute

Crinan Hotel
★ ★ ★ ★
By Lochgilphead, Crinan, Argyll, PA31 8SR
Tel: 01546 830261 Fax: 01546 830292
Email: hryan@crinanhotel.com
Web: www.crinanhotel.com
Rooms: 20 all ensuite ⊛
Pricing: Sgl £75–135 Dbl £150–270 Dinner from £40.50
CC: Accepted Room facilities: ▱ ☎ ⌁ Access: ⱢⱢⱢ
Conference: 2 meeting rooms (Thtr 40 max)
Children: Welcome ⋔ Dogs: Welcome Licences: 𝖎𝖎𝖎
Leisure: Beauty salon, Fishing, Riding
Directions: Airport, M8 westbound, Erskine Bridge,
then A82 to Tarbet, then A83. At Lochgilphead A816,
after 2 miles A841 to Crinan.

Dalmally, Argyll & Bute

Rockhill Farm & Guest House
♦ ♦ ♦
Rockhill, Ardbrecknish, Dalmally,
Argyll & Bute, PA33 1BH
Tel: 01866 833218
Seasonal closure: End October to mid-May
Rooms: 5 (1 ensuite) Room facilities: ▱ ⌁
Children: Welcome 10yrs min age Dogs: Welcome
Parking: Off-street
Directions: From south M74, M73, M18 keep on M8 to
M1898, A82 north.

Denny, Falkirk

Topps Guest House
♦ ♦ ♦
Topps Farm, Fintry Road, Denny, Falkirk, FK6 5JF
Tel: 01324 822471 Fax: 01324 823099
Email: 2lambs@onetel.net.uk
Web: www.thetopps.com
Rooms: 8 all ensuite ⊛ ⊚
Pricing: Dinner from £12 (2002 rate) CC: Accepted
Room facilities: ▱ ☎ ⌁ Access: ♿
Children: Welcome ⋔ Dogs: Welcome
Licences: 𝖎𝖎𝖎 Parking: Off-street
Directions: From Glasgow, A80, A803 to Denny, then
B818, hotel 4 miles on right. From Edinburgh, M9,
M876, off at Denny sign, right at lights, third right onto
B818.

Scotland

Drymen, Stirling

The Buchanan Arms Hotel & Leisure Club

★★★ ♞

Main Street, Drymen, Stirlingshire, G63 0BQ
Tel: 01360 660588 Fax: 01360 660943
Email: enquiries@buchananarms.co.uk
Web: www.innscotland.com

This former droving inn, a short drive from the famous 'bonnie banks' of Loch Lomond, seems to soak up the atmosphere of the beautiful surrounding countryside. A careful blend of character, comfort, fine dining and modern facilities.
Rooms: 52 all ensuite ♨ 🖨 ⊗
Pricing: Sgl £55–100 Dbl £110–100 Dinner from £22.50
CC: Accepted Room facilities: 🖵 ☎ 🍵
Conference: 8 meeting rooms (Thtr 150 max), 24hr-delegate from £105, day-delegate rate from £32
Children: Welcome ♨ ℃
Dogs: Welcome Licences: ◈ ♦♦♦
Leisure: Indoor pool, Gym, Health spa, Beauty salon
Parking: Off-street and monitored
Directions: M8 to Glasgow follow signs to Clyde tunnel, then A81 to Aberfoyle Bearsden Cross roundabout, take A809, follow signs for Drymen.
See advert on page 567

Dumfries, Dumfries & Galloway

Cairndale Hotel and Leisure Club

★★★

English Street, Dumfries, Dumfries & Galloway, DG1 2DF
Tel: 01387 254111 Fax: 01387 250555
Email: sales@cairndale.fsnet.co.uk
Web: www.cairndalehotel.co.uk

"Dinner Dances, Ceilidhs, Cabaret Nights together with excellent leisure facilities add to the enjoyment of a visit to this privately owned hotel close to the centre of Dumfries. Golf breaks also available."
Rooms: 91 all ensuite ♨ 🖨 ⊗
Pricing: Sgl £69–89 Dbl £89–109 Dinner from £20
CC: Accepted Room facilities: 🖵 ☎ 🍵 Access: ⊫ ♿
Conference: meeting rooms (Thtr 300 max)
Children: Welcome ♨ ℃ Dogs: Welcome
Licences: ◈ ♦♦♦ Leisure: Indoor pool, Gym, Health spa, Beauty salon Parking: Off-street
Directions: Following main routes into Dumfries, the hotel is on the northeast edge of the town centre on English Street.

Comlongon Castle Hotel

★★★ ♞

Clarencefield, Dumfries & Galloway, DG1 4NA
Tel: 01387 870283 Fax: 01387 870266
Web: www.comlongon.com
Seasonal closure: January
Rooms: 12 all ensuite ♨ 🖨 ⊗
Pricing: Dinner from £33 (2002 rate) CC: Accepted
Room facilities: 🖵 ☎ 🍵
Children: Welcome ♨ Licences: ◈ ♦♦♦
Parking: Off-street and monitored
Directions: At England/Scotland border, take A75 to Annan, then left onto B724. After 8 miles, at Clarencefield turn left down private drive.

Hetland Hall Hotel

★★★

Carrutherstown, Dumfries & Galloway, DG1 4JX
Tel: 01387 840201 Fax: 01387 840211
Email: hetlandhallhotel@ic24.net
Web: www.hetlandhallhotel.co.uk

Elegant mansion with glorious views over the Solway Firth. Pool and leisure club. Mini pitch-and-putt, satellite TV, superb food, intimate cocktail bar. Log fires. Ideal for weddings and short breaks.
Rooms: 30 all ensuite ♨ 🖨 ⊗
Pricing: Sgl £55–70 Dbl £70–100 Dinner from £19.95
CC: Accepted Room facilities: 🖵 ☎ 🍵 ⚍ Access: ♿
Conference: 4 meeting rooms (Thtr 200 max), 24hr-delegate from £185, day-delegate rate from £18.50
Children: Welcome ♨ ℃ Dogs: Welcome
Licences: ◈ ♦♦♦ Leisure: Indoor pool, Gym
Parking: Off-street and monitored
Directions: On A75 Euroroute, 8 miles east of Dumfries.

Huntingdon House Hotel

 ★★

18 St Mary's Street, Dumfries,
Dumfries & Galloway, DG1 1LZ
Tel: 01387 254893 Fax: 01387 262553
Email: acame4506@aol.com
Web: www.huntingdonhotel.co.uk
Rooms: 8 all ensuite
Pricing: Sgl £40–49 Dbl £58–62 Dinner from £9.95
CC: Accepted Room facilities:
Children: Welcome Dogs: Welcome
Licences:
Parking: Off-street and monitored
Directions: Travel on M74 to Lockerbie; take A709 to
Dumfries; hotel is first on the left on entering Dumfries.

Dunbar, East Lothian

Bayswell Hotel

★★★

Bayswell Park, Dunbar, East Lothian, EH42 1AE
Tel: 01368 862225 Fax: 01368 862225
Email: bayswellhotel@hotmail.com
Web: www.geocities.com/bayswell
Rooms: 18 all ensuite
Pricing: Dinner from £12.50 (2002 rate) CC: Accepted
Room facilities: Access:
Children: Welcome Dogs: Welcome
Parking: Off-street
Directions: Exit the A1 into Dunbar High Street. At the
bottom, turn left (sea on right). Take the first right to hotel.

Dundee, Tayside

Swallow Hotel

 ★★★

Kingsway West, Dundee, DD2 5JT
Tel: 01382 631200 Fax: 01382 631201
Email: swallowrooms@ukonline.co.uk
Web: www.swallowhotels.com

Originally a Scottish mansion house, the Swallow hotel
Dundee is set in its own landscaped grounds close to
the city by-pass, yet surrounded by beautiful
countryside. Catering for both business and leisure
guests, the hotel gives a feeling of space, comfort and
relaxation. The Swallow leisure club includes heated
pool, spa bath, sauna, steam room and solarium as
well as a modern fitness gymnasium.
Rooms: 103 all ensuite
Pricing: Sgl £80–118 Dbl £94–155 Dinner from £22
CC: Accepted Room facilities: Access:
Conference: 9 meeting rooms (Thtr 100 max), 24hr-
delegate from £110, day-delegate rate from £30
Children: Welcome Dogs: Welcome
Licences:
Leisure: Indoor pool, Gym, Health spa
Parking: Monitored
Directions: Off Swallow roundabout of A90 Trunk Road,
3 miles from city centre.

Beach House Hotel

  ◆◆◆◆

22 Esplanade, Broughty Ferry, Dundee, Angus, DD5 2EQ
Tel: 01382 776614 Fax: 01382 420841
Rooms: 5 all ensuite
Pricing: Sgl £35–38 Dbl £45–49 CC: Accepted
Room facilities:
Children: Welcome Licences:
Parking: Monitored
Directions: From Dundee station, 4 miles. 25 minutes
drive from St Andrews, 1 hour drive from Edinburgh, 1
hour 45 minutes from Aberdeen.

Travelodge Dundee

Travel Accommodation
A90, Kingsway, Dundee Ring Road, Dundee,
Tayside, DD2 4TD
Web: www.travelodge.co.uk
Rooms: 32 all ensuite
Pricing: Sgl £49.40 Dbl £53.85 CC: Accepted
Room facilities: Access:

Making a booking?

 Don't forget to mention RAC
Hotels and Bed & Breakfast 2003.

One click does it all

 For the latest special offers and
online booking, plus detailed
information on over 3,000
RAC inspected properties,
visit www.rac.co.uk/hotels

Scotland

Dunfermline, Fife

Pitbauchlie House Hotel

★★★

47 Aberdour Road, Dunfermline, Fife, KY11 4PB
Tel: 01383 722282 Fax: 01383 620738
Email: info@pitbauchlie.com
Web: www.pitbauchlie.com

Situated in landscaped gardens, minutes from M90.
Conference, banqueting, bars and restaurant facilities.
Excellent food with the chef taking advantage of
Scotland's natural larder.
Rooms: 50 all ensuite 🐾 🛋 ⊗
Pricing: Sgl £73–88 Dbl £90–105 Dinner from £22
CC: Accepted
Room facilities: 🖵 ☎ 🛋 🌡 Access: ♿
Conference: 3 meeting rooms (Thtr 150 max)
Children: Welcome ⱺ ⸙ Dogs: Welcome
Licences: ⬦ ♟ Leisure: Gym
Parking: Off-street
Directions: Leave M90 at Junction 2. Continue on A823
towards Dunfermline. Turn right onto B916. Hotel
situated ½ mile on right.

Halfway House Hotel

★★

Main Street, Kingseat, Dunfermline, Fife, KY12 0TJ
Tel: 01383 731661 Fax: 01383 621274
Rooms: 12 all ensuite 🐾 ⊗
Pricing: Sgl £55 Dbl £62 Dinner from £5 CC: Accepted
Room facilities: 🖵 ☎ 🛋
Conference: 4 meeting rooms (Thtr 120 max), 24hr-
delegate from £75, day-delegate rate from £14
Children: Welcome ⱺ
Dogs: Welcome Licences: ⬦ ♟
Leisure: Games room Parking: Off-street
Directions: From M90 take Junction 3, follow signs for
Kingseat, hotel on left of main street.

Dunkeld, Perthshire

Kinnaird   Gold Ribbon Winner

★★★★ ⸙ ⸙ ⸙ ⸙

Kinnaird Estate, by Dunkeld, Perthshire, PH8 0LB
Tel: 01796 482440 Fax: 01796 482289
Email: enquiry@kinnairdestate.com
Web: www.kinnairdestate.com
Rooms: 9 all ensuite 🛋 ⊗
Pricing: Sgl £225–430 Dbl £295–475 Dinner from £45

CC: Accepted Room facilities: 🖵 ☎ 🌡 Access: ♿ ♿
Children: Welcome 12yrs min age Dogs: Welcome
Licences: ⬦ ♟ Leisure: Health spa, Beauty salon,
Tennis, Fishing, Snooker/billiards
Parking: Off-street and monitored
Directions: Travel north on A9 past Perth and Dunkeld.
Turn left onto B893. Hotel is 4 miles along on right.

Dunoon, Argyll & Bute

Esplanade Hotel

★★

West Bay, Dunoon, Argyll, PA23 7HU
Tel: 01369 704070 Fax: 01369 702129
Email: relax@ehd.co.uk
Web: www.ehd.co.uk
Seasonal closure: November to March
Rooms: 63 all ensuite 🐾 🛋 ⊗
Pricing: Sgl £37–47 Dbl £60–90 Dinner from £16
CC: Accepted Room facilities: 🖵 ☎ 🛋 Access: ♿
Conference: 2 meeting rooms (Thtr 70 max)
Children: Welcome ⱺ Dogs: Welcome
Licences: ⬦ ♟ Parking: Off-street
Directions: From Dunoons' main pier turn left, pass
McColls hotel, then turn left down Park Avenue, left
again at foot of avenue.

The Anchorage Hotel & Restaurant

◆ ◆ ◆ ◆ ◆ ⸙ ⸙ ⸙

Shore Road, Sandbank, Dunoon,
Argyll & Bute, PA23 8QG
Tel: 01369 705108 Fax: 01369 705108
Email: long@anchorage.co.uk
Web: www.anchorage.co.uk

Situated on the shores of Holy Loch. Highland
hospitality with homely comfort and individual
attention. Luxurious well-appointed ensuite bedrooms.
Excellent food using local Scottish produce. Non-
smoking throughout.
Rooms: 5 all ensuite 🛋
Pricing: Sgl £35–45 Dbl £55–60 Dinner from £20
CC: Accepted Room facilities: 🛋 Access: ♿
Children: Welcome 12yrs min age
Directions: Turn right out of either ferry terminal,
three miles north of Dunoon on A815 road next to the
loch side.

Ardtully Hotel

297 Marine Parade, Hunters Quay, Dunoon,
Argyll & Bute, PA23 8HN
Tel: 01369 702478

Small friendly hotel set in own grounds with
outstanding views over the Clyde estuary and
surrounding hills, close to amenities.
Rooms: 7 (9 ensuite)
Room facilities: Children: Welcome
Dogs: Welcome Licences:
Parking: Off-street
Directions: On the coast road between Dunoon and
Sandbank, 2 miles from Dunoon overlooking the Firth
of Clyde at Hunters Quay. 200 yards from the Western
Ferry Terminal.

Osborne Hotel

44 Shore Road, Innellan, near Dunoon,
Argyll & Bute, PA23 7TJ
Tel: 01369 830445 Fax: 01369 830445
Email: osbreservations@aol.com
Web: www.osborne-hotel.co.uk
Rooms: 4 all ensuite
Pricing: Sgl £25–30 Dbl £45–50 Dinner from £7.50
CC: Accepted Room facilities:
Children: Welcome Dogs: Welcome
Licences: Leisure: Games room
Directions: Take ferry from Gourock to Dunoon, turn
left, Innellan is 4 miles along the coast; or, via Loch
Lomond onto A815.

East Kilbride, Lanarkshire

Bruce Hotel

★★★
35 Cornwall Street, East Kilbride, Lanarkshire, G74 1AF
Tel: 01355 229771 Fax: 01355 242216
Email: enquiries@maksu-group.co.uk
Web: www.maksu-group.co.uk
Rooms: 65 (94 ensuite)
Pricing: Sgl £60–75 Dbl £80–100 Dinner from £16.50
CC: Accepted Room facilities: Access:
Conference: 8 meeting rooms (Thtr 400 max), 24hr-
delegate from £105, day-delegate rate from £25
Children: Welcome Dogs: Welcome
Licences: Leisure: Beauty salon

Parking: Off-street and monitored
Directions: Leave M74 at Junction 5. Take A725 to East
Kilbride. Follow signs to town centre into Cornwall
Street, hotel is 200m on left.

Edinburgh

The Balmoral

Blue Ribbon Winner

★★★★★★
1 Princes Street, Edinburgh, EH2 2EQ
Tel: 0131 556 2414 Fax: 0131 557 3747
Email: reservations@thebalmoralhotel.com
Web: www.roccofortehotels.com
Rooms: 188 all ensuite
Pricing: Sgl £135–250 Dbl £155–250 Dinner from £25
CC: Accepted Room facilities:
Access:
Conference: 10 meeting rooms (Thtr 350 max), 24hr-
delegate from £270, day-delegate rate from £55
Children: Welcome Dogs: Welcome
Licences:
Leisure: Indoor pool, Gym, Health spa
Parking: Off-street and monitored
Directions: Follow signs to city centre and Waverley rail
station. The Balmoral is adjacent to the station on
Princes street.
See advert on following page

The Scotsman

★★★★★
20 North Bridge, Edinburgh, EH1 1YT
Tel: 0131 556 5565 Fax: 0131 652 3652
Email: reservations@thescotsmanhotel.co.uk
Web: www.thescotsmanhotel.co.uk
Seasonal closure: Christmas Day and Boxing Day
Rooms: 68 all ensuite
Pricing: Sgl £196–281 Dbl £212–297 CC: Accepted
Room facilities: Access:
Conference: 10 meeting rooms (Thtr 70 max)
Children: Welcome Dogs: Welcome
Licences:
Leisure: Indoor pool, Gym, Health spa,
Beauty salon
Parking: Off-street and monitored
Directions: City centre, adjacent to train station and
within a few minutes stroll from the royal mile and
Princes Street.

Scotland

THE BALMORAL
EDINBURGH

The *Balmoral*

SCOTLAND'S MOST PRESTIGIOUS ADDRESS

Historic and charming, modern comforts and facilities, welcoming service and delicious cuisine - a warm welcome awaits you at Rocco Forte's Balmoral in the heart of Edinburgh. Built in 1902, the hotel offers a unique blend of cosmopolitan and traditional Scottish hospitality. All bedrooms have marble bathrooms and are equipped with the latest in-room facilities; many have spectacular views over Edinburgh castle, as do our conference suites. Complete your stay with a visit to our new spa and some mouth-watering cuisine in our restaurants: Hadrian's and Number One.

ROCCO FORTE
HOTELS

The Balmoral 1 Princes Street Edinburgh EH2 2EQ Scotland
Telephone +44 (0)131 556 2414 Facsimile +44 (0)131 557 3747
E-mail reservations@thebalmoralhotel.com Website www.roccofortehotels.com

Carlton Hotel

★★★★

North Bridge, Edinburgh, EH1 1SD
Tel: 0131 472 3000 Fax: 0131 556 2691
Email: carlton@paramount-hotels.co.uk
Web: www.paramount-hotels.co.uk

PARAMOUNT
GROUP OF HOTELS

Rooms: 189 all ensuite 🛏 🚭
Pricing: Sgl £192.50–212.25 Dbl £249.50–299.50
Dinner from £15 CC: Accepted
Room facilities: 📺 ☎ ☕ 📞 Access: ⬆ ♿
Conference: 9 meeting rooms (Thtr 300 max), 24hr-
delegate from £195, day-delegate rate from £55
Children: Welcome ♀ 🐾 Dogs: Welcome
Licences: 🍸 ♟
Leisure: Indoor pool, Gym, Health spa
Parking: Off-street and monitored
Directions: Follow signs for Waverley train station; hotel
is situated above North Bridge.

Marriott Dalmahoy Hotel & Country Club

★★★★★ ℝ ℝ

near Kirknewton, Edinburgh, EH27 8EB
Tel: 0131 333 1845 Fax: 0131 333 1433
Email: reservations.dalmahoy@marriotthotels.co.uk
Web: www.marriott.com/edigs
Rooms: 215 all ensuite 🛏 🚭
Room facilities: 📺 ☎ ☕ 📞 Access: ⬆ ♿
Conference: 10 meeting rooms (Thtr 300 max)
Children: Welcome ♀ Dogs: Guide dogs only
Licences: 🍸 ♟
Leisure: Indoor pool, Gym, Beauty salon,
Tennis, Golf
Parking: Off-street and monitored
Directions: Dalmahoy can be found approximately 7
miles west of Edinburgh on the A71. Edinburgh airport
is 3 miles away.

The Royal Terrace – A Meridien Hotel

★★★★

18 Royal Terrace, Edinburgh, EH7 5AQ
Tel: 0800 028 2840 Fax: 0131 557 5339
Email: reservations.royalterrace@lemeridien.com
Rooms: 108 all ensuite 🛏 🚭 🚭

Pricing: Dinner from £20 CC: Accepted
Room facilities: 📺 ☎ ☕ 📞 Access: ⬆
Conference: 4 meeting rooms (Thtr 100 max), 24hr-
delegate from £175, day-delegate rate from £42
Children: Welcome ♀ Dogs: Guide dogs only
Licences: 🍸 ♟ Leisure: Indoor pool, Gym
Directions: Northeast from Princes Street, located off
Leith Walk, 8 miles from airport, 1/2 mile from Waverley
Station on Royal Terrace.

Braid Hills Hotel

★★★★ ℝ ℝ

134 Braid Road, Edinburgh, Midlothian, EH10 6JD
Tel: 0131 447 8888 Fax: 0131 452 8477
Email: bookings@braidhillshotel.co.uk
Web: www.braidhillshotel.co.uk

Magnificently situated only two miles from the city
centre, yet a world away from the noise and
congestion of the centre itself. An independently
owned hotel.
Rooms: 67 all ensuite 🛏 🚭 🚭
Pricing: Sgl £80–135 Dinner from £21.95 CC: Accepted
Room facilities: 📺 ☎ ☕ 📞
Conference: 2 meeting rooms (Thtr 100 max)
Children: Welcome ♀ Dogs: Guide dogs only
Licences: 🍸 ♟ Parking: Off-street
Directions: From city bypass take A702 Lothianburn
junction to city centre. Hotel is approximately one mile
on right-hand side.

Scotland

Carlton Greens Hotel

★★★

2 Carlton Terrace, Edinburgh, EH7 5DD
Tel: 0131 556 6570 Fax: 0131 557 6680
Email: carltongreens@british-trust-hotels.com
Web: www.british-trust-hotels.com

Elegant yet friendly accommodation. Quiet location. Few minutes' walk from city centre. Magnificent views across Royal Park and Holyrood Palace. Excellent bar and restaurant. All rooms ensuite.
Rooms: 26 all ensuite 🍴 🚭
Pricing: Sgl £45–95 Dbl £80–130 Dinner from £15
CC: Accepted Room facilities: 🖵 ☎ 🗲 Access: ♿
Conference: 1 meeting room (Thtr 12 max), 24hr-delegate from £110, day-delegate rate from £32
Children: Welcome ⼑ Dogs: Welcome Licences: ⼪

Jurys Inn Edinburgh

★★★

43 Jeffrey Street, Edinburgh, EH1 1DG
Tel: +353(0)1 6070000 Fax: +353(0)1 6316999
Email: bookings@jurysdoyle.com
Web: www.jurysdoyle.com

JURYS DOYLE
HOTELS

Rooms: 186 all ensuite 🚭
Pricing: Sgl £95 Dbl £190 Dinner from £18
CC: Accepted Room facilities: 🖵 ☎ 🗲 🖀
Access: |⼁ ♿ Children: Welcome ⼑
Dogs: Guide dogs only Licences: ⼪
Parking: Off-street
Directions: Located 9 miles from airport. Just two minutes walk from Waverley Station.

Norton House Hotel

★★★★ 🍃 🍃

Blue Ribbon Winner

Ingliston, Edinburgh, EH28 8LX
Tel: 0131 333 1275 Fax: 0131 333 5305

Email: nortonhouse@arcadianhotels.co.uk
Web: www.arcadianhotels.co.uk

One of Edinburgh's most stylish country house hotels. Rest assured that a traditional atmosphere without a trace of stuffiness is flawlessly maintained, offering a rare combination of care and comfort.
Rooms: 47 all ensuite 🚭
Pricing: Sgl £150 Dbl £170 Dinner from £28
CC: Accepted Room facilities: 🖵 ☎ 🗲 🖀 Access: ♿
Conference: 10 meeting rooms (Thtr 300 max)
Children: Welcome ⼑ Dogs: Guide dogs only
Licences: ⚓ ⼪ Parking: Off-street
Directions: From Edinburgh, take A8 past the airport. Norton House is $^1/_2$ mile on the left.

Old Waverley Hotel

★★★

43 Princes Street, Edinburgh, EH2 2BY
Tel: 0131 556 4648 Fax: 0131 557 6316
Email: oldwaverleyreservations@paramounthotels.co.uk
Web: www.paramount-hotels.co.uk

PARAMOUNT
GROUP OF HOTELS
Rooms: 66 all ensuite 🍴 🚭
Pricing: Sgl £137 Dbl £184 Dinner from £9.95
CC: Accepted Room facilities: 🖵 ☎ 🗲 Access: |⼁
Conference: 3 meeting rooms (Thtr 100 max), 24hr-delegate from £125, day-delegate rate from £40
Children: Welcome ⼑ Dogs: Guide dogs only
Licences: ⼪ Parking: Monitored
Directions: Follow signs to city centre and Waverley Station. Directly opposite Waverley Station & Scott's Monument.

Quality Hotel Edinburgh

★★★

96 Marine Drive, Crammond Foreshore,
Edinburgh, EH4 5EP
Tel: 0131 336 1700 Fax: 0131 336 4934
Email: admin@gb625.u-net.com
Web: www.choicehotels.com
Rooms: 87 all ensuite
Pricing: Sgl £100.75–110.75 Dbl £120.50–130.50
Dinner from £16.50 CC: Accepted
Room facilities: ☐ ☎ ☕ ⚎ Access: |↕|
Conference: 5 meeting rooms (Thtr 200 max), 24hr-delegate from £90, day-delegate rate from £24
Children: Welcome ⶏ Dogs: Welcome
Licences: ⵝⵝⵝ Leisure: Gym, Health spa
Parking: Off-street

Allison House Hotel

★★★ ⵜ ⵜ

15/17 Mayfield Gardens, Edinburgh, EH9 2AX
Tel: 0131 667 8049 Fax: 0131 667 5001
Email: enquiry@allisonhousehotel.com
Web: www.allisonhousehotel.com
Rooms: 21 (20 ensuite) ⵯ
Pricing: Sgl £38–48 Dbl £55–100 Dinner from £17.50
CC: Accepted Room facilities: ☐ ☎ ☕ ⚎
Children: Welcome ⶏ Dogs: Welcome
Licences: ⵯ ⵝⵝⵝ Parking: Off-street
Directions: Situated on the south side of Edinburgh, 1 mile from city centre on A701.

Royal Ettrick Hotel

★★

13 Ettrick Road, Edinburgh, EH10 5BJ
Tel: 0131 622 6800 Fax: 0131 622 6822
Email: ettrick@festival-inns.co.uk
Web: www.festival-inns.co.uk
Rooms: 12 all ensuite
Room facilities: ☐ ☎ ☕
Children: Welcome Dogs: Guide dogs only
Licences: ⵯ ⵝⵝⵝ Parking: Off-street
Directions: From centre, drive up Lothian Road. Turn right on to Gilmore Place. Continue on to Polwarth Gardens. Hotel is on the left.

Thrums Hotel

★★

14 Minto Street, Edinburgh, EH9 1RQ
Tel: 0131 667 5545/8545 Fax: 0131 667 8707
Seasonal closure: Christmas
Rooms: 14 all ensuite ⵯ
Pricing: Sgl £30–45 Dbl £50–85 Dinner from £11.50
CC: Accepted
Room facilities: ☐ ☎ ☕ Children: Welcome ⶏ
Dogs: Welcome Licences: ⵝⵝⵝ
Parking: Off-street and monitored
Directions: Follow city bypass to Edinburgh South, then take A7/A701 to Newington.

Grosvenor Gardens Hotel

◆◆◆◆◆ ⵝ ⵝ

1 Grosvenor Gardens, Edinburgh, EH12 5JU
Tel: 0131 313 3415 Fax: 0131 346 8732
Email: info@stayinedinburgh.com
Web: www.stayinedinburgh.com
Rooms: 8 all ensuite ⵯ ⵝ
Pricing: Sgl £35–60 Dbl £50–135 CC: Accepted
Room facilities: ☐ ☎ ☕ ⚎ Access: ⵝ
Children: Welcome Parking: Off-street and monitored
Directions: Follow A8 from the airport towards the city centre. Turn left off the A8 (Haymarket Terrace) into Roseberry Crescent. Grosvenor Gardens is the first street on the left.

The Knight Residence

◆◆◆◆◆ ⵝ ⵝ

12 Lauriston, Edinburgh, EH3 9DJ
Tel: 0131 622 8120 Fax: 0131 622 7363
Email: info@theknightresidence.co.uk
Web: www.theknightresidence.co.uk
Rooms: 19 all ensuite ⵯ ⵝ
Pricing: Sgl £99–140 Dbl £99–140 CC: Accepted
Room facilities: ☐ ☎ ☕ ⚎ Access: |↕|
Children: Welcome ⵝ Dogs: Guide dogs only
Parking: Off-street and monitored
Directions: Located close to Edinburgh Castle between the grassmarket and Lothian Road. Call for directions or visit our website.

Acorn Lodge

◆◆◆◆ ⵝ

26 Pilrig Street, Edinburgh, Lothian, EH6 5AJ
Tel: 0131 555 1557 Fax: 0131 555 4475
Email: morag@acornlodge.co.uk
Web: www.acornlodge.co.uk
Rooms: 10 all ensuite ⵯ ⵝ
Room facilities: ☐ ☎ ☕ Children: Welcome ⵝ
Dogs: Guide dogs only
Directions: Follow Queens Street. In city centre go to top of Leith Walk (East End). Take Pilrig Street to left midway down Leith Walk.

Adam Hotel

◆◆◆◆

19 Lansdowne Crescent, Edinburgh, Lothian, EH12 5EH
Tel: 0131 337 1148
Email: welcome@adam-hotel.co.uk
Web: www.adam-hotel.co.uk
Rooms: 13 all ensuite ⵯ ⵝ
Room facilities: ☐ ☎ ☕
Children: Welcome ⵝ Dogs: Guide dogs only
Licences: ⵝⵝⵝ
Directions: Follow signs for city centre then to Haymarket Station. Turn up Roseberry Crescent and fork right into Lansdowne Crescent.

Ashlyn Guest House

◆◆◆◆

42 Inverleith Row, Edinburgh, EH3 5PY
Tel: 0131 552 2954 Fax: 0131 552 2954
Email: reservations@ashlyn-edinburgh.com
Rooms: 8 (5 ensuite) ⚓ ⊗
Pricing: Sgl £25–35 Dbl £55–80
Room facilities: ▯ ☕
Children: Welcome 7yrs min age
Directions: Situated 1 mile north of Princes Street, adjacent to Royal Botanical Gardens, opposite Heriott rugby ground.

Corstorphine Guest House

◆◆◆◆ ☜

188 St Johns Road, Edinburgh, EH12 8SG
Tel: 0131 539 4237 Fax: 0131 539 4945
Email: corsthouse@aol.com
Web: www.corstorphineguesthouse.com
Rooms: 5 all ensuite ⚓ ⊗
Pricing: Sgl £25–59 Dbl £39–99
CC: Accepted
Room facilities: ▯ ☕
Children: Welcome ⼑
Dogs: Guide dogs only
Parking: Off-street and monitored
Directions: From airport: head for city along A8 into Corstorphine. From city, out on A8 towards airport. From M8, head for city by-pass north and city centre.

Corstorphine Lodge Hotel

◆◆◆◆

186 St Johns Road, Corstorphine, Edinburgh, EH12 8SG
Tel: 0131 476 7116 Fax: 0131 476 7117
Email: corstlodge@aol.com
Web: www.corstorphinehotels.co.uk
Corstorphine Lodge hotel is 2 miles from both Edinburgh Airport and the city centre, nearby is Edinburgh Zoo, Murryfield stadium and Edinburgh business park. All bedrooms are equipped with ensuite facilities and colour TV.
Rooms: 12 all ensuite ⚓ 🗂 ⊗
Pricing: Sgl £25–89 Dbl £39–99
CC: Accepted
Room facilities: ▯ ☕
Access: ♿
Children: Welcome ⼑
Dogs: Guide dogs only
Parking: Off-street and monitored
Directions: From city head out along A8 into Corstorphine. From M8 or by-pass, head for bypass north exit, along A8 into Corstorphine. From north, head for A8 into Corstorphine.

Dorstan Hotel   Little Gem

◆◆◆◆

7 Priestfield Road, Edinburgh, EH16 5HJ
Tel: 0131 667 5138 Fax: 0131 668 4644
Email: reservations@dorstan-hotel.demon.co.uk
Web: www.dorstan-hotel.demon.co.uk

Located close to the city centre's many attractions, this tastefully-decorated Victorian house exudes the warm hospitality of its proprietor Mairae Campbell.
Rooms: 14 (12 ensuite) ⊗
Pricing: Sgl £34–50 Dbl £45–90 Dinner from £17
CC: Accepted Room facilities: ▯ ☎ ☕
Children: Welcome Dogs: Guide dogs only
Parking: Off-street and monitored
Directions: A7 Edinburgh, Dalkeith Road, pass through traffic lights, at next traffic lights turn right (Priestfield Road) Dorstan Hotel on left.

Ivy Guest House

◆◆◆◆

7 Mayfield Gardens, Edinburgh, EH9 2AX
Tel: 0131 667 3411 Fax: 0131 620 1422
Email: don@ivyguesthouse.com
Web: www.ivyguesthouse.com
Rooms: 8 (6 ensuite) ⚓ ⊗ Pricing: Sgl £20–70
Dbl £36–75 Room facilities: ▯ ☕ Children: Welcome
Dogs: Welcome Parking: Off-street
Directions: Located on A701 just over 1 mile from Princes Street.

Kew House

◆◆◆◆ ☜

1 Kew Terrace, Murrayfield, Edinburgh, EH12 5JE
Tel: 0131 313 0700 Fax: 0131 313 0747
Email: info@kewhouse.com
Web: www.kewhouse.com

Caring for the more discerning traveller, this immaculate listed building is centrally located with secure parking. Luxurious bedrooms and peaceful residents' bar ensures a memorable stay.
Rooms: 6 all ensuite ⊗
Pricing: Sgl £55–60 Dbl £75–110 Dinner from £10

CC: Accepted Room facilities:
Children: Welcome Dogs: Welcome
Licences: ••• Parking: Off-street and monitored
Directions: Directly on A8 route 1 mile west of Princes Street and on main route from airport.

Kirkland Bed & Breakfast

◆ ◆ ◆ ◆

6 Dean Park Crescent, Edinburgh, EH4 1PN
Tel: 0131 332 5017
Email: m.kirkland@blueyonder.co.uk
Web: www.kirkland.pwp.blueyonder.co.uk

Spacious Victorian family home with character, ten minutes walk from Edinburgh city centre. We offer good information and guidance to help maximise your enjoyment of our home and our wonderful city.
Rooms: 3 (1 ensuite)
Pricing: Dbl £44–60
Room facilities:
Access: Children: Welcome
Directions: From city centre take right turn off Queensferry Road after Dean Bridge. From airport left 5 miles after Stewards Melville College.

The Addison

◆ ◆ ◆ ◆

2 Murrayfield Avenue, Edinburgh, EH12 6AX
Tel: 0131 337 4060 Fax: 0131 337 4080
Email: info@addisonedinburgh.com
Web: www.addisonedinburgh.com
Rooms: 10 all ensuite
Pricing: Dinner from £10 CC: Accepted
Room facilities:
Children: Welcome
Dogs: Guide dogs only
Licences: •••
Directions: From city bypass follow signs for city centre, approximately 4 miles. Take left at Roseburn into Murrayfield Avenue. Hotel just after BMW garage.

The Ben Doran

◆ ◆ ◆ ◆

11 Mayfield Gardens, Edinburgh, EH9 2AX
Tel: 0131 667 8488 Fax: 0131 667 0076
Email: info@bendoran.com
Web: www.bendoran.com

Luxurious Georgian townhouse, beautifully refurbished, central, on bus routes, close to attractions and city centre. Free parking, 4-diamond accommodation, non-smoking, views, family-run with care and utmost pride.
Rooms: 10 (6 ensuite)
Pricing: Sgl £45–95 Dbl £55–175 Dinner from £25
CC: Accepted Room facilities:
Conference: 1 meeting room (Thtr 20 max)
Parking: Off-street
Directions: On A701, 1 mile south of Princes Street, 3 miles north of bypass (A720).

Airport Bed & Breakfast

◆ ◆ ◆

Ingliston Park Lodge, Glasgow Road,
Ingliston, EH28 8NB
Tel: 0131 335 3437 Fax: 0131 335 3437
Rooms: 3 all ensuite Pricing: Sgl £40–45
Dbl £49–60 Room facilities:
Children: Welcome 8yrs min age Dogs: Guide dogs only
Parking: Off-street and monitored
Directions: Comfortable Lodge House 1 mile from Edinburgh airport next to Royal Highlands centre on main A8 route.

Ardleigh Guest House

◆ ◆ ◆

260 Ferry Road, Edinburgh, Lothian, EH5 3AN
Tel: 0131 552 1833 Fax: 0131 552 4951
Email: info@ardleighhouse.com
Web: www.ardleighhouse.com
Rooms: 7 (5 ensuite)
Pricing: Dinner from £10 CC: Accepted
Room facilities: Children: Welcome
Dogs: Guide dogs only Parking: Monitored
Directions: From city bypass follow A90 from Barnton along Queensferry Road into Ferry Road towards Leith, approximately 5 miles.

Boisdale Hotel

◆ ◆ ◆

9 Coates Gardens, Edinburgh, EH12 5LG
Tel: 0131 337 1134 Fax: 0131 313 0048
Rooms: 10 all ensuite
Room facilities: Children: Welcome
Dogs: Welcome

Scotland

Cumberland Hotel

◆ ◆ ◆

1 West Coates, Edinburgh, EH12 5JQ
Tel: 0131 337 1198 Fax: 0131 337 1022
Email: cumblhotel@aol.com
Web: www.cumberlandhotel-edinburgh.com

Located on main tourist route into Edinburgh. Tastefully decorated and furnished to a very high standard. All ensuite bedrooms with tea/coffee-making facilities and cable TV. Attractive cocktail bar and residents' lounge.
Rooms: 10 all ensuite ⚭ ⊗ Pricing: Sgl £29–89
Dbl £49–109 CC: Accepted Room facilities: ▢ ☕
Conference: 1 meeting room (Thtr 20 max)
Children: Welcome ᚼ Dogs: Guide dogs only
Licences: ⫟ Parking: Off-street and monitored
Directions: From airport take A8 towards Haymarket. From city centre head for West End past the Haymarket Station. We are 200 yards on the right.

Galloway Guest House

◆ ◆ ◆

22 Dean Park Crescent, Edinburgh, EH4 1PH
Tel: 0131 332 3672 Fax: 0131 332 3672
Rooms: 10 (6 ensuite) ⚭ Pricing: Sgl £30–45
Dbl £40–60 CC: Accepted Room facilities: ▢ ☕
Children: Welcome ᚼ Dogs: Welcome
Directions: 1km from Princes Street west end on A9.

Maple Leaf

◆ ◆ ◆

23 Pilrig Street, Edinburgh, Lothian, EH6 5AN
Tel: 0131 554 7692 Fax: 0131 554 9919
Email: info@themapleleaf.com
Web: www.themapleleaf.com
Rooms: 11 all ensuite ⚭ ⊡ ⊗
Pricing: Dinner from £10 CC: Accepted
Room facilities: ▢ ☕ Children: Welcome
Dogs: Guide dogs only
Directions: Follow Queen Street in city centre to Eastend by John Lewis at Leith Walk. Pilrig Street to left midway down Leith Walk.

Newington Guest House

◆ ◆ ◆

18 Newington Road, Edinburgh, EH9 1QS
Tel: 0131 667 3356 Fax: 0131 667 8307
Email: newington.guesthouse@dial.pipex.com
Web: www.newington-gh.co.uk
Rooms: 9 all ensuite ⊡ ⊗ Room facilities: ▢ ☎ ☕
Children: Welcome 9yrs min age

Dogs: Welcome Licences: ⫟ Parking: Off-street
Directions: Centrally situated in south side of city, on A68/A7, main bus route.

Thistle Court Hotel

◆ ◆ ◆

5 Hampton Terrace, Edinburgh, Lothian, EH12 5JD
Tel: 0131 313 5500 Fax: 0131 313 5511
Email: info@thistlecourt.co.uk
Web: www.thistlecourt.co.uk
Rooms: 16 all ensuite ⚭ ⊗ Pricing: Dinner from £11
CC: Accepted Room facilities: ▢ ☎ ☕ Access: ⌊⫟
Children: Welcome ᚼ ⫰ Dogs: Guide dogs only
Licences: ⟁ ⫟ Parking: Off-street and monitored
Directions: From city bypass follow for city centre through Corstorphine past zoo to Murrayfield under bridge at Roseburn 250 metres on right.

Averon City Centre Guest House

◆ ◆

44 Gilmore Place, Edinburgh, EH3 9NQ
Tel: 0131 229 9932
Email: info@averon.co.uk
Web: www.averon.co.uk Rooms: 12 (8 ensuite) ⚭
Room facilities: ▢ ☕ Access: ⌁ Children: Welcome
Parking: Off-street and monitored
Directions: From Princes Street go up Lothian Road and turn right at the Kings Theatre.

Park Hotel

◆ ◆

4–6 Alvanley Terrace, Whitehouse Loan,
Edinburgh, EH9 1DU
Tel: 0131 622 6800 Fax: 0131 622 6822
Email: park@festival-inns.co.uk
Web: www.festival-inns.co.uk
Rooms: 19 all ensuite ⚭ Room facilities: ▢ ☎ ☕
Children: Welcome Dogs: Guide dogs only Licences: ⫟
Leisure: Games room
Directions: From city centre, walk up Lothian Road, continue on to Home Street, then Leven Street. Turn left on to Whitehouse Loan.

Travelodge Edinburgh Central (SA)

Travel Accommodation
33 St Marys Street, Edinburgh, EH1 1TA
Web: www.travelodge.co.uk
Rooms: 193 all ensuite ⊗ Pricing: Sgl £74.40
Dbl £78.85 CC: Accepted Room facilities: ▢ ☕
Access: ⌁

Travelodge Edinburgh South

Travel Accommodation
A720, 46 Dreghorn Link, A720 City by-pass,
Edinburgh, EH13 9QR
Web: www.travelodge.co.uk
Rooms: 72 all ensuite ⊗ Pricing: Sgl £57.40
Dbl £61.85 CC: Accepted Room facilities: ▢ ☕
Access: ⌁

Edzell, Angus

Glenesk Hotel

★★★

High Street, Edzell, Angus, DD9 7TF
Tel: 01356 648319 Fax: 01356 647333
Email: gleneskhotel@btconnect.com
Web: www.gleneskhotel.co.uk
Rooms: 24 all ensuite 🐾 Pricing: Dinner from £20
CC: Accepted Room facilities: 🖥 ☎ 🍵
Children: Welcome ♨ Dogs: Welcome
Licences: 🔺 ᴪ Leisure: Indoor pool, Gym, Golf,
Games room, Snooker/billiards
Parking: Off-street

Erskine, Renfrewshire

The Erskine Bridge Hotel

★★★

Riverside, Erskine, Renfrewshire, PA8 6AN
Tel: 0141 812 0123 Fax: 0141 812 7642
Email: erskineres@cosmopolitan-hotels.com
Web: www.cosmopolitan-hotels.com
Rooms: 177 all ensuite 🐾 ⊗
Pricing: Sgl £60–70 Dbl £66–76 Dinner from £15.95
CC: Accepted Room facilities: 🖥 ☎ 🍵 📞 Access: ⊔ ♿
Conference: 18 meeting rooms (Thtr 500 max), 24hr-
delegate from £110, day-delegate rate from £25
Children: Welcome ♨ Dogs: Welcome
Licences: 🔺 ᴪ Leisure: Indoor pool, Gym, Health
spa, Beauty salon, Games room
Directions: M8 Junction 30, M898 to first junction. Turn
right at first roundabout, straight over second, turn left
at third, right at fourth.

Falkirk

Comfort Inn

★★

Manor Street, Falkirk, FK1 1NT
Tel: 01324 624066 Fax: 01324 611785
Email: admin@gb626.u-net.com
Web: www.choicehotels.com
Rooms: 33 all ensuite ⊗ Pricing: Sgl £40–55
Dbl £60–72 CC: Accepted Room facilities: 🖥 ☎ 🍵
Conference: 4 meeting rooms (Thtr 160 max), 24hr-
delegate from £45.50, day-delegate rate from £25.50
Children: Welcome ♨ ⫶℃ Licences: ᴪ
Leisure: Gym Parking: Off-street
Directions: From M876 motorway follow signs for
Falkirk town centre, the hotel is situated adjacent, next
to Callender square shopping centre.

Falkland, Fife

Covenanter Hotel

◆◆◆

The Square, Falkland, Fife, KY15 7BU
Tel: 01337 857224 Fax: 01337 857163
Web: www.covenanterhotel.com

Historic coaching inn, located at the centre of the
beautiful village of Falkland. Relaxing atmosphere
combined with excellent cuisine. Perfectly located for
Falkland Palace, surfing, walking and other outdoor
pursuits.
Rooms: 5 all ensuite 🐾 ⊗
Pricing: Sgl £45 Dbl £55 Dinner from £12
CC: Accepted Room facilities: 🖥 ☎ 🍵
Children: Welcome ♨ Dogs: Guide dogs only
Licences: ᴪ Parking: Off-street

Fintry, Stirlingshire

Culcreuch Castle Hotel

Culcreuch Castle & Country Park, Fintry,
Stirling, G63 0LW
Tel: 01360 860555 Fax: 01360 860556
Email: info@culcreuch.com
Web: www.culcreuch.com
Rooms: 13 all ensuite 🐾 ⚲ ⊗
Pricing: Sgl £85–95 Dbl £140–160 Dinner from £25
CC: Accepted Room facilities: 🖥 ☎ 🍵 📞 Access: ♿
Conference: 4 meeting rooms (Thtr 150 max), 24hr-
delegate from £97.50, day-delegate rate from £27.50
Children: Welcome ♨ ⫶℃ Dogs: Welcome
Licences: 🔺 ᴪ Leisure: Fishing, Games room
Parking: Off-street and monitored
Directions: From Stirling take A811 west to Kippen,
then B822 south-west to Fintry. From Glasgow take
A81 north to Killearn, then B818 east to Fintry.
See advert on previous page

Forres, Moray

Ramnee Hotel

★★★★

Victoria Road, Forres, Moray, IV36 3BN
Tel: 01309 672410 Fax: 01309 673392
Email: ramneehotel@btconnect.com
Rooms: 20 all ensuite 🐾 ⚲ ⊗
Pricing: Dinner from £22.50 (2002 rate) CC: Accepted
Room facilities: 🖥 ☎ 🍵
Children: Welcome ♨ Dogs: Welcome
Licences: 🔺 ᴪ Parking: Off-street
Directions: From A96 Inverness-Aberdeen Road at
Forres, turn left onto Forres by-pass east of town.
Hotel is 500m on right.

Park Hotel
★★
Victoria Road, Forres, Moray, IV36 3BN
Tel: 01309 672611 Fax: 01309 672328
Rooms: 12 all ensuite ⊗
Pricing: Sgl £42.50–55 Dbl £55–60 Dinner from £16
CC: Accepted Room facilities: ▢ ☎ ⬭
Access: ♿ Children: Welcome
Dogs: Guide dogs only Licences: ◁ ⅲ
Parking: Off-street
Directions: Leave A96 by-pass at the east end of
Forres; we are the first hotel on the right.

Fort William, Highland

Inverlochy Castle Hotel   Gold Ribbon Winner
★★★★★ 🏵🏵🏵
Torlundy, Fort William, Highland, PH33 6SN
Tel: 01397 702177 Fax: 01397 702953
Email: info@inverlochycastlehotel.com
Web: www.inverlochycastlehotel.com
Seasonal closure: January to March

Inverlochy Castle was built in 1863 near the site of the
original 13th century fortress, and nestles in the
foothills of Ben Nevis, sitting amid some of Scotland's
finest scenery, once enjoyed by Queen Victoria herself.
The beauty and tranquility of the castle's setting is
remarkable, and in keeping with the grandeur of its
surroundings.
Rooms: 17 all ensuite ♨ 📶 ⊗
Pricing: Sgl £205–290 Dbl £290–435
Dinner from £52.50 CC: Accepted
Room facilities: ▢ ☎ ⬱
Conference: 1 meeting room (Thtr 24 max)
Children: Welcome ⅌ 🐎 ⅈ Dogs: Welcome
Licences: ◁ ⅲ
Leisure: Tennis, Fishing, Games room, Snooker/billiards
Parking: Off-street and monitored
Directions: Accessible from the A82 Trunk Road from
Glasgow to Fort William.

Moorings Hotel
★★★ 🏵🏵🏵
Banavie, Fort William, Invernesshire, PH33 7LY
Tel: 01397 772797 Fax: 01397 772441
Email: reservations@moorings-fortwilliam.co.uk
Web: www.moorings-fortwilliam.co.uk

Sitting in the shadow of Ben Nevis, this award-winning
hotel offers its guests a truly warm welcome, with good
food, cosy bedrooms and friendly service. 10 superior
rooms also available.
Rooms: 28 all ensuite 📶 ⊗
Pricing: Sgl £46 Dinner from £23 CC: Accepted
Room facilities: ▢ ☎ ⬭
Conference: 1 meeting room (Thtr 120 max), 24hr-
delegate from £86, day-delegate rate from £11
Children: Welcome 14yrs min age ⅌
Dogs: Welcome Licences: ⅲ
Parking: Off-street
Directions: 2 miles north of Fort William, take A830 to
Banavie, turn right, hotel 200 metres on 8004.

Grand Hotel
★★ 🏵🏵
Gordon Square, Fort William, Highland, PH33 6DX
Tel: 01397 702928 Fax: 01397 702928
Email: enquiries@grandhotel.scotland.co.uk
Web: www.grandhotel-scotland.co.uk
Seasonal closure: January Rooms: 30 all ensuite ♨ ⊗
Pricing: Sgl £30–45 Dbl £50–70 Dinner from £20
CC: Accepted Room facilities: ▢ ☎ ⬭
Children: Welcome ⅌ ⅈ Dogs: Guide dogs only
Licences: ◁ ⅲ Parking: Off-street
Directions: Located in the town centre at the west end
of the pedestrianised high street. Parking is to front
and rear of hotel.

Factor's House
◆◆◆◆◆ 🏵 ⨯ ⌣
Torlundy, Fort William, Highland, PH33 6SN
Tel: 01397 702177 Fax: 01397 702953
Email: info@inverlochy.co.uk
Web: www.inverlochy.co.uk
Seasonal closure: November to March
Rooms: 5 all ensuite ♨ Pricing: Dinner from £15.50
(2002 rate) CC: Accepted Room facilities: ▢ ☎ ⬭
Children: Welcome ⅌ 🐎 ⅈ Licences: ⅲ
Leisure: Tennis, Fishing Parking: Off-street and monitored
Directions: Accessible by the A82 Trunk Road from
Glasgow to Fort William.

Scotland

Distillery House

◆ ◆ ◆ ◆

North Road, Nevis Bridge, Fort William,
Invernesshire, PH33 6LH
Tel: 01397 700103 Fax: 01397 702980
Email: disthouse@aol.com
Web: www.fort-william.net/distillery-house
Seasonal closure: Dec to Jan
Rooms: 7 all ensuite ⊛ Pricing: Sgl £20–35
Dbl £20–35 CC: Accepted Room facilities: ▢ ☕
Children: Welcome Dogs: Welcome
Parking: Off-street and monitored
Directions: From north, turn right at second set of
traffic lights. From south, the hotel is on the left after
Glen Nevis roundabout.

Galashiels, Borders

Kingsknowes Hotel

★ ★ ★ ★ ☜

1 Selkirk Road, Galashiels, Borders, TD1 3HY
Tel: 01896 758375 Fax: 01896 750377
Email: enquiries@kingsknowes.co.uk
Web: www.kingsknowes.co.uk
Rooms: 11 all ensuite ⚲ ⊛ Pricing: Sgl £54 Dbl £80
Dinner from £15 CC: Accepted
Room facilities: ▢ ☎ ☕ ⚲ Conference: 3 meeting
rooms (Thtr 60 max) Children: Welcome 廾 🐎
Dogs: Welcome Licences: ◁ ᴪᴪᴪ
Leisure: Riding Parking: Off-street and monitored
Directions: From Edinburgh, or Junc. 40 of M6, follow A7
to Glashiels. From Newcastle, follow A68 to Galashiels.

Millennium Hotel Glasgow

In an historic city centre location, this
refurbished town house offers a relaxed
environment with contemporary interiors,
complemented by fashionable
conservatories overlooking George Square.

George Square, Glasgow, G2 1DS
Tel: 0141 332 6711 Fax: 0141 332 4264

sales.glasgow@mill-cop.com
www.millenniumhotels.com

Gatehouse of Fleet, Dumfries & Galloway

Bank Of Fleet Hotel

◆ ◆ ◆

47 High Street, Gatehouse of Fleet,
Dumfries & Galloway, DG7 2HR
Tel: 01557 814302 Fax: 01557 814302

Resting in the heart of Galloway this small family-run
hotel has earned a good reputation for excellent
cuisine and is ideally placed for golfing, hillwalking or
fishing pursuits. Three day dinner bed and breakfast
packages available.
Rooms: 6 (5 ensuite) Room facilities: ▢ ☕
Children: Welcome 廾 Dogs: Welcome
Licences: ᴪᴪᴪ Leisure: Indoor pool

Glasgow

Millennium Hotel Glasgow

★ ★ ★ ★ ☜

George Square, Glasgow, G2 1DS
Tel: 0141 332 6711 Fax: 0141 332 4264
Email: sales.glasgow@mill-cop.com
Web: www.millenniumhotels.com

In an historic city centre location, this refurbished town
house offers a relaxed environment with contemporary
interiors, complemented by fashionable conservatories
overlooking George Square.
Rooms: 117 all ensuite ⊛ Pricing: Sgl £104–200
Dbl £104–200 Dinner from £20 CC: Accepted
Room facilities: ▢ ☎ ☕ ⚲ ❄ Access: ♿ ⚲
Conference: 6 meeting rooms (Thtr 30 max), 24hr-
delegate from £170, day-delegate rate from £55
Children: Welcome 廾 Dogs: Guide dogs only
Licences: ᴪᴪᴪ
Directions: M8 motorway junction 15, straight through the
first six sets of traffic lights, turning left at the seventh.
See advert on this page

Jurys Glasgow Hotel

★★★

Great Western Road, Glasgow, G12 0XP
Tel: +353(0)1 6070000 Fax: +353(0)1 6136999
Email: bookings@jurysdoyle.com
Web: www.jurysdoyle.com

JURYS DOYLE
HOTELS

Rooms: 137 all ensuite ⊛
Pricing: Sgl £84.50–131.50 Dbl £96–143
Dinner from £18.50 CC: Accepted
Room facilities: ▢ ☎ ⬛ ⬛ Access: ⫯ ⚲
Children: Welcome ⴱ Dogs: Guide dogs only
Licences: ⬥ ⵜⵜⵜ
Leisure: Indoor pool, Gym, Health spa,
Beauty salon
Parking: Off-street and monitored
Directions: Located 7 miles from Glasgow Int'l Airport.
Central Station 3 miles, just 10 mins from bustling city
centre.

Kings Park Hotel

★★★★ ⬤ ⬤ ⬤

Mill Street, Rutherglen, Glasgow, G73 2AR
Tel: 0141 647 5491 Fax: 0141 613 3022
Email: enquiries@maksu-group.co.uk
Web: www.maksu-group.co.uk
Rooms: 26 all ensuite ⊛
Pricing: Sgl £70–100 Dbl £80–120 Dinner from £19.50
CC: Accepted Room facilities: ▢ ☎ ⬛ ⵏ
Conference: 3 meeting rooms (Thtr 220 max), 24hr-
delegate from £95, day-delegate rate from £20
Children: Welcome ⴱ ⵖ Dogs: Welcome
Licences: ⬥ ⵜⵜⵜ
Parking: Off-street and monitored
Directions: Follow A730 from Glasgow towards East
Kilbride. Hotel is situated on the left in the suburb on
Rutherglen.

Quality Hotel Glasgow

★★★

99 Gordon Street, Glasgow, G1 3SF
Tel: 0141 221 9680 Fax: 0141 226 3948
Email: admin@gb627.u-net.com
Web: www.choicehotels.com
Rooms: 222 all ensuite ⬥ ⬛ ⊛
Pricing: Sgl £110–127.50 Dbl £140–161.50
Dinner from £14.50 CC: Accepted
Room facilities: ▢ ☎ ⬛ Access: ⫯ ⚲
Conference: 21 meeting rooms (Thtr 600 max)
Children: Welcome ⴱ ⵖ Dogs: Welcome
Licences: ⬥ ⵜⵜⵜ
Leisure: Indoor pool, Gym, Health spa, Beauty salon
Parking: Off-street and monitored
Directions: From M8 Westbound take Junction 19 onto
Argyle Street and left onto Oswald Street. NCP car
park on right.

Sherbrooke Castle Hotel

★★★★ ⬤ ⬤

11 Sherbrooke Avenue, Pollockshields,
Glasgow, G41 4PG
Tel: 0141 427 4227 Fax: 0141 427 5685
Email: mail@sherbrooke.co.uk
Web: www.sherbrooke.co.uk
Rooms: 21 all ensuite ⬥ ⬛ ⊛ Pricing: Sgl £65–75
Dbl £106–125 Dinner from £22 CC: Accepted
Room facilities: ▢ ☎ ⬛ Access: ⚲
Conference: 4 meeting rooms (Thtr 200 max), 24hr-
delegate from £140, day-delegate rate from £26
Children: Welcome ⴱ
Dogs: Welcome Licences: ⬥ ⵜⵜⵜ
Parking: Off-street and monitored
Directions: Close to Junction 1 M77. Close to
Junctions 22 and 23 from City M8. Close to Junction
27 from Glasgow Aiport.

Swallow Hotel

★★★★ ⬤ ⬤

517 Paisley Road West, Glasgow, G51 1RW
Tel: 0141 427 3146 Fax: 0141 427 4059
Email: glasgow.swallow@whitbread.com
Web: www.swallowhotels.com

SWALLOW
HOTELS

Rooms: 117 all ensuite ⊛
Pricing: Sgl £79–99 Dbl £95–115 Dinner from £18.50
CC: Accepted Room facilities: ▢ ☎ ⬛ ⵏ
Access: ⫯ ⚲
Conference: 6 meeting rooms (Thtr 300 max), 24hr-
delegate from £110, day-delegate rate from £30
Children: Welcome 15yrs min age ⴱ Dogs: Welcome
Licences: ⬥ ⵜⵜⵜ Leisure: Indoor pool, Gym
Parking: Monitored
Directions: At Junction 23 of M8, turn right into Paisley
Road West. Hotel located 400 yards on right-hand side.

Scotland

The Glynhill Hotel & Leisure Club

★★★

169 Paisley Road, Renfrew, Nr. Glasgow Airport,
Glasgow, PA4 8XB
Tel: 0141 886 5555 Fax: 0141 885 2838
Email: glynhillleisurehotel@msn.com
Web: www.glynhill.com

Ideal, convenient base for business executives and
tourists alike. Set in a quiet location with two excellent
restaurants, superb leisure club, major conference
centre and friendly, efficient staff.
Rooms: 125 all ensuite ♨ ⊛
Pricing: Sgl £64–94 Dbl £74–104 Dinner from £19.50
CC: Accepted Room facilities: ▢ ☎ ☕
Children: Welcome ⪫ ≷℃ Dogs: Guide dogs only
Licences: ⟁ ⅲ Leisure: Indoor pool, Gym
Parking: Off-street and monitored
Directions: On M8 towards Glasgow Airport, turn off at
Junction 27. Take A741 towards Renfrew Cross. Hotel
on right.

Kelvingrove Hotel

Situated in the heart of Glasgow's West
End, the newly refurbished Kelvingrove
Hotel is minutes from Glasgow City Centre
and offers 25 edrooms, 23 of which have
ensuite facilities

944 Saunchiehall Street,
Glasgow G3 7TH
Tel: 0141 339 5011   Fax: 0141 339 6566
Email:kelvingrove.hotel@business,ntl.com
Website:www.kelvingrove-hotel.co.uk

Argyll Hotel

★★

973 Sauchiehall Street, Glasgow, G3 7TQ
Tel: 0141 337 3313 Fax: 0141 337 3283
Email: info@argyllhotelglasgow.co.uk
Web: www.argyllhotelglasgow.co.uk

Ideal location half a mile west of city centre. Minutes'
walk to SECC, Kelvingrove art galleries/museum and
Glasgow University. Traditional bar/restaurant. Good
value with warm Scottish hospitality.
Rooms: 38 all ensuite ♨ ⊠ ⊛
Pricing: Sgl £48–58 Dbl £62–72 Dinner from £15
CC: Accepted Room facilities: ▢ ☎ ☕ ☏ Access: ⅼⅼ
Conference: 1 meeting room (Thtr 30 max)
Children: Welcome ⪫ Dogs: Guide dogs only
Licences: ⟁ ⅲ Parking: Off-street and monitored
Directions: Leave M8 at junction 18, go straight ahead to
second set of traffic lights. Turn right into Berkeley Street,
right into Elderslie Street, then first left into Sauchiehall
Street and the Argyll Hotel is 3 blocks on the left.

Dunkeld Hotel

★

10/12 Queen's Drive, Glasgow, G42 8BS
Tel: 0141 424 0160 Fax: 0141 423 4437
Email: dunkeldhotel@aol.com
Web: www.dunkeld-hotel.co.uk
Rooms: 21 all ensuite ♨ ⊠ ⊛
Pricing: Dinner from £12 (2002 rate) CC: Accepted
Room facilities: ▢ ☎ ☕ ☏ Children: Welcome ⪫ ≷℃
Dogs: Welcome Licences: ⟁ ⅲ
Parking: Off-street and monitored
Directions: From end of M74 follow signs for Rutherglen,
then Mount Florida: through lights at Asda, turn right at
lights into Cathcart Road. First left is Queen's Drive.

Angus Hotel

♦♦♦

970 Sauchiehall Street, Glasgow, G3 7TQ
Tel: 0141 357 5155 Fax: 0141 339 9469
Email: info@angushotelglasgow.co.uk
Web: www.angushotelglasgow.co.uk
Rooms: 18 all ensuite ♨ ⊛
Pricing: Sgl £38–44 Dbl £58 CC: Accepted
Room facilities: ▢ ☎ ☕
Children: Welcome Dogs: Guide dogs only
Directions: Leave M8 at Junction 18. At second set of

traffic lights, turn right into Berkeley Street. At end turn right, then first left into Sauchiehall Street. The Angus hotel is 400 metres on the right.

Kelvingrove Hotel

 ◆ ◆ ◆

944 Sauchiehall Street, Glasgow, G3 7TH
Tel: 0141 339 5011 Fax: 0141 339 6566
Email: kelvingrove.hotel@business.ntl.com
Web: www.kelvingrove-hotel.co.uk
Rooms: 25 (23 ensuite) 🛏 ⊗
Room facilities: 📺 ☎ ☕ 🗝
Children: Welcome Dogs: Welcome
Directions: M8 Junction 18 follow signs to Kelvingrove Museum for $1/2$ mile west.
See advert on this page

McLays Guest House

 ◆ ◆

264–276 Renfrew Street, Charing Cross, Glasgow, G3 6TT
Tel: 0141 332 4796 Fax: 0141 353 0422
Email: info@mclays.com
Web: www.mclaysgh.co.uk
Rooms: 62 (39 ensuite) 🛏 ⊗
Pricing: Sgl £24–29 Dbl £40–48 CC: Accepted
Room facilities: 📺 ☎ ☕ 🗝 Access: |↟|
Children: Welcome Dogs: Guide dogs only
Directions: Directly behind Sauchiehall Street, at the western end of Renfrew Steet. Exit J18 off the M8

Smith's Hotel

 ◆ ◆

963 Sauchiehall Street, Glasgow, G3 7TQ
Tel: 0141 339 6363 Fax: 0141 334 1892
Web: www.smiths-hotel.com
Rooms: 33 (9 ensuite)
Pricing: Sgl £21–36 Dbl £38–52 CC: Accepted
Room facilities: 📺 ☕ Children: Welcome
Dogs: Guide dogs only Parking: Off-street
Directions: $3/4$ km from city centre. Next to the West End (University). Taxi from city centre approx £4.

Charing Cross Guest House

 ◆

310 Renfrew Street, Glasgow, G3 6UW
Tel: 0141 332 2503 Fax: 0141 353 3047
Email: enquiries@charing-x.com
Web: www.charing-x.com
Rooms: 25 (10 ensuite)
Pricing: Sgl £24–29 Dbl £38–44 CC: Accepted
Room facilities: 📺 ☎ ☕ 🗝
Children: Welcome Parking: Off-street
Directions: Exit J18 M8, Charing Cross, take first left for Sauchiehall Street and then two first lefts onto Renfrew Street.

Georgian House

 ◆

29 Buckingham Terrace, Great Western Road, Kelvinside, Botanic Gardens, Glasgow, Lanarkshire, G12 8ED
Tel: 0141 339 0008
Email: thegeorgianhouse@yahoo.com
Web: www.thegeorgianhousehotel.com

This restored Georgian town house residence retains many original features to create stylish comfort in the midst of the vibrant West End. Overlooking the Botanic Garden, close to restaurants, theatres and major sights.
Rooms: 12 (8 ensuite) 🛏 🚭 ⊗
Pricing: Sgl £25–40 Dbl £48–80 CC: Accepted
Room facilities: 📺 ☕ 🗝 Children: Welcome 🛏 🍵
Parking: Off-street
Directions: Exit Jct 17, M8, onto Great Western Road. After $1 1/2$ miles, turn right at Botanic Gardens, 360° at roundabout, 2nd left Buckingham Terrace.

Travelodge Dumbarton

Travel Accommodation
A82, Milton, Dumbarton, Glasgow, G82 2TZ
Web: www.travelodge.co.uk
Rooms: 32 all ensuite ⊗
Pricing: Sgl £49.40 Dbl £53.85 CC: Accepted
Room facilities: 📺 ☕ Access: ♿

Travelodge Glasgow Airport (SA)

Travel Accommodation
A761, Glasgow Airport Business Park,
Off Sandering Road, PA3 2AR
Web: www.travelodge.co.uk
Room facilities: 📺 ☕

Scotland

Travelodge Glasgow Central (SA)

Travel Accommodation
5-11 Hill Street, Glasgow, G3 6PR
Web: www.travelodge.co.uk
Rooms: 95 all ensuite 🚭
Pricing: Sgl £54.40 Dbl £58.85 CC: Accepted
Room facilities: 🖵 ♨ Access: ♿

Travelodge Glasgow Paisley Road (SA)

Travel Accommodation
M8, 251 Paisley road, Glasgow, G5 8RA
Web: www.travelodge.co.uk
Rooms: 75 all ensuite 🚭
Pricing: Sgl £54.40 Dbl £58.85 CC: Accepted
Room facilities: 🖵 ♨ Access: ♿

Glenmoriston, Highland

Cluanie Inn

★★

Glenmoriston, Highland, IV63 7YW
Tel: 01320 340238 Fax: 01320 340293
Email: cluanie@ecosse.net
Web: www.cluanie.co.uk
Rooms: 14 (12 ensuite) 🍴 🚗
Room facilities: 🖵 Children: Welcome ☕
Dogs: Welcome
Licences: ♟♟♟
Parking: Off-street and monitored
Directions: The Cluanie Inn lies on the A87 halfway
between Loch Ness and the Isle of Skye.

Grantown-on-Spey, Moray

Culdearn House Hotel

★★ ☕ ☕ ☕

Woodlands Terrace, Grantown-on-Spey,
Moray, PH26 3JU
Tel: 01479 872106 Fax: 01479 873641
Email: culdearn@globalnet.co.uk
Web: www.culdearn.com
Seasonal closure: November to February
Rooms: 9 all ensuite 🚭
Pricing: Sgl £50 Dbl £100 Dinner from £25
CC: Accepted Room facilities: 🖵 ♨ Access: ♿
Dogs: Guide dogs only Licences: ♟♟♟
Parking: Off-street and monitored
Directions: Enter Grantown from southwest on A95.
Turn left at 30mph sign.

Navigation with a difference

 Smartnav-In-Car satellite navigation
with live traffic information and much
more at a fraction of the cost of
traditional satellite navigation.
Call 0800 096 1740

Ardconnel House

◆◆◆◆◆ 🛎 ✳ ☕

Woodlands Terrace, Grantown-on-Spey,
Moray, PH26 3JU
Tel: 01479 872104 Fax: 01479 872104
Email: enquiry@ardconnel.co.uk
Web: www.ardconnel.co.uk
Rooms: 6 all ensuite 🚗 🚭
Pricing: Sgl £30–35 Dbl £60–70 Dinner from £20
CC: Accepted Room facilities: 🖵 ♨
Children: Welcome 8yrs min age
Dogs: Guide dogs only Licences: ♟♟♟
Parking: Off-street
Directions: On the A95 south-west entry to town.

Ravenscourt House Hotel

◆◆◆◆◆ ✳ ☕

Seafield Avenue, Grantown-on-Spey, Moray, PH26 3JG
Tel: 01479 872286 Fax: 01479 873260
Rooms: 8 all ensuite 🍴 🚭
Pricing: Sgl £30–35 Dbl £60–70 Dinner from £16.50
Room facilities: 🖵 ♨ Access: ♿
Children: Welcome 🍴 Dogs: Welcome
Licences: ♟♟♟
Parking: Off-street and monitored
Directions: Turn left at Bank of Scotland. Ravenscourt
is 200m on right-hand side.

The Pines

Little Gem

◆◆◆◆◆ 🛎 ✳ ☕

Woodside Avenue, Grantown-on-Spey,
Moray, PH26 3JR
Tel: 01479 872092
Email: info@thepinesgrantown.co.uk
Web: www.thepinesgrantown.co.uk
Seasonal closure: November to February

In its beautiful quiet woodland setting, experience the
comforts of a small hotel in this historic ancestral
Highland home. Two spacious lounges, two intimate
dining rooms, and a small library.
Rooms: 8 all ensuite 🚭
Pricing: Sgl £38–48 Dbl £66–90 Dinner from £25
CC: Accepted Room facilities: 🖵 ♨
Children: Welcome 12yrs min age Dogs: Welcome
Licences: ♟♟♟ Parking: Off-street
Directions: On entering the town from the south take
A939 to Tomintoul, then turn first right.

Garden Park Guest House

◆ ◆ ◆ ◆ ◇

Woodside Avenue, Grantown-on-Spey, Moray, PH26 3JN
Tel: 01479 873235 Fax: 01479 873235
Email: gardenpark@tiscali.co.uk
Web: visitscotland.co.uk
Seasonal closure: November to February
Rooms: 5 all ensuite Pricing: Sgl £20–25 Dbl £40–50
Dinner from £12 Room facilities: ▢ ☕
Children: Welcome 12yrs min age Licences: ♦♦♦
Parking: Off-street
Directions: Turn off High Street into Forest Road.
Garden Park is at corner of Forest Road and Woodside
Avenue.

Gretna, Dumfries & Galloway

Gretna Chase Hotel

★ ★ ★ ◇

Gretna, Dumfries & Galloway, DG16 5JB
Tel: 01461 337517 Fax: 01461 337766
Email: enquiries@gretnachase.co.uk
Web: www.gretnachase.co.uk
Rooms: 20 all ensuite ◇ ◇ ◇
Pricing: Sgl £55–75 Dbl £79–159 CC: Accepted
Room facilities: ▢ ☎ ☕ ♦ Access: ♿
Children: Welcome ♦ Licences: ♦♦♦
Directions: 6 miles north of Jct 44, take slip road for
Gretna. Turn left at junction; hotel is 600 yards on right.

Solway Lodge Hotel

★ ★

Annan Road, Gretna, Dumfries & Galloway, DG16 5DN
Tel: 01461 338266 Fax: 01461 337791
Web: www.solwaylodge.co.uk
Rooms: 10 all ensuite ◇ Room facilities: ▢ ☎ ☕
Children: Welcome Dogs: Welcome
Licences: ♦♦♦ Parking: Off-street
Directions: From south, take second exit at roundabout
('Town Centre'). Lodge 200m on right.

Surrone House Hotel

◆ ◆ ◆

Annan Road, Gretna, Dumfries & Galloway, DG16 5DL
Tel: 01461 338341 Fax: 01461 338341
Email: enquires@surronehouse.co.uk
Web: www.surronehouse.co.uk
Rooms: 7 (6 ensuite) ◇ ◇ Pricing: Sgl £40 Dbl £50
Dinner from £10.50 CC: Accepted Room facilities: ▢ ☕
Children: Welcome Licences: ♦♦♦ Parking: Off-street
Directions: On main road through Gretna (not the by-
pass).

Haddington, East Lothian

Brown's Hotel   Little Gem

◆ ◆ ◆ ◆ ◇ ◇ ◇

1 West Road, Haddington, East Lothian, EH41 3RD
Tel: 01620 822254 Fax: 01620 822254
Email: info@browns-hotel.com

Web: www.browns-hotel.com
Rooms: 5 all ensuite Pricing: Sgl £65–74 Dbl £95–108
Dinner from £31.50 CC: Accepted
Room facilities: ▢ ☎ ☕ Children: Welcome ♦
Dogs: Guide dogs only Licences:
Parking: Off-street
Directions: Take main road into Haddington, B6471 off
route A1, from Edinburgh.

Halkirk, Caithness

Ulbster Arms Hotel

★ ★ ◇

Bridge Street, Halkirk, Caithness, KW12 6XY
Tel: 01847 831641 Fax: 01847 831206
Email: ulbster-arms@ecosse.net
Web: www.ulbsterarms.co.uk
Rooms: 10 all ensuite
Pricing: Sgl £37–43 Dbl £61–76 Dinner from £12.50
CC: Accepted Room facilities: ▢ ☎ ☕ ♦
Conference: 1 meeting room (Thtr 14 max), day-
delegate rate from £20
Children: Welcome ♦ Dogs: Welcome
Licences: ♦♦♦ Parking: Off-street and monitored
Directions: Halkirk is 109 miles north of Inverness.
Follow A9, then turn left onto A895.

Helensburgh, Argyll & Bute

Kirkton House   Little Gem

◆ ◆ ◆ ◆ ◆ ◇ ◇ ◇

Darleith Road, Cardross, Argyll & Bute, G82 5EZ
Tel: 01389 841951 Fax: 01389 841868
Email: rac@kirktonhouse.co.uk
Web: www.kirktonhouse.co.uk
Seasonal closure: December to January

Converted 18th century farmstead, in tranquil country
setting with panoramic views of the Clyde. Wine and
dine by oil lamplight. In best guides yet informal and
unpretentious.
Rooms: 6 all ensuite ◇
Pricing: Sgl £40–48.50 Dbl £60–77 Dinner from £17.50
CC: Accepted Room facilities: ▢ ☎ ☕ ♦
Access: ♿ Children: Welcome ♦ ◇
Dogs: Welcome Licences: ♦♦♦ Parking: Off-street
Directions: Turn north off A814 at the west end of
Cardross Village, up Darleith Road. Kirkton is 1/2 mile
on right.

Howwood, Renfrewshire

Bowfield Hotel & Country Club

★★★

Howwood, Renfrewshire, PA9 1DB
Tel: 01505 705225 Fax: 01505 705230
Email: enquires@bowfieldhotel.co.uk
Web: www.innscotland.com

A refreshingly different hotel combining traditional
character and award-winning dining with a superb leisure
club. Facilities at this former 19th century mill include
swimming pool, sauna, squash courts, gymnasium and
beauty spa. A perfect retreat in the country.
Rooms: 23 all ensuite ✪
Pricing: Sgl £75 Dbl £110–120 Dinner from £20
CC: Accepted Room facilities: ☐ ☎ 🖫
Conference: 4 meeting rooms (Thtr 80 max), 24hr-
delegate from £100, day-delegate rate from £30
Children: Welcome ♑ ℀
Dogs: Guide dogs only Licences: ◈ ♦♦♦
Leisure: Indoor pool, Gym, Health spa, Beauty salon,
Games room, Snooker/billiards
Parking: Off-street and monitored
Directions: M8 to Glasgow airport: take A737 Irvine
road, Howwood exit on left, follow hotel signs through
the village.
See advert on page 567

Innerleithen, Borders

Corner House Hotel

♦♦♦

1 Chapel Street, Innerleithen, Tweedale,
Borders, EH44 6HN
Tel: 01896 831181 Fax: 01896 831182
Email: cornerhousehotel@talk21.com
Seasonal closure: one week in October
Rooms: 6 all ensuite ✪ 🖼
Pricing: Dinner from £9.50 CC: Accepted
Room facilities: ☐ 🖫 Children: Welcome
Dogs: Welcome Licences: ◈ ♦♦♦
Parking: Off-street and monitored
Directions: Follow A703 from Edinburgh to Peebles,
then take the A72 to Innerleithen, approximately 25
miles.

Inveraray, Argyll & Bute

Loch Fyne Hotel

★★★

Shore Street, Inveraray, Argyll, PA32 8XT
Tel: 01499 302 148 Fax: 01499 302 348
Email: lochfyne@british-trust-hotels.com
Web: www.british-trust-hotels.com

Quiet location. Close to town. Magnificent views
across Loch Fyne. Original building over 100 years old.
All rooms ensuite. Excellent bar, bistro and restaurant.
15 metre pool with sauna and steam rooms.
Rooms: 80 all ensuite ✪
Pricing: Sgl £75–78 Dbl £125–130 Dinner from £18
CC: Accepted Room facilities: ☐ ☎ 🖫 Access: ⬆ ♿
Conference: 2 meeting rooms (Thtr 50 max), 24hr-
delegate from £74, day-delegate rate from £18
Children: Welcome ♑ ℀ Dogs: Welcome
Licences: ◈ ♦♦♦ Leisure: Indoor pool, Health spa
Parking: Off-street

Invergarry, Highland

Glengarry Castle Hotel

★★★

Invergarry, Highland, PH35 4HW
Tel: 01809 501254 Fax: 01809 501207
Email: castle@glengarry.net
Web: www.glengarry.net
Seasonal closure: mid-November to mid-March

Fine Victorian mansion in extensive wooded grounds on
the shores of Loch Oich. Privately owned and personally
managed by the MacCallum family for over 40 years.
Rooms: 26 (25 ensuite) 🖼 ✪
Pricing: Sgl £57–77 Dbl £92–146 Dinner from £26
CC: Accepted Room facilities: ☐ ☎ 🖫 🖍
Children: Welcome ♑ ℀ Dogs: Welcome
Licences: ♦♦♦ Leisure: Tennis, Fishing
Parking: Off-street and monitored
Directions: Located on the A82, overlooking Loch Oich,
1 mile from Invergarry.

Inverness, Highland

Loch Ness House Hotel

★★★

Glenurquhart Road, Inverness, Highland, IV3 8JL
Tel: 01463 231248 Fax: 01463 239327
Email: lnhhchris@aol.com
Web: www.smoothhound.co.uk/hotels/lochness.html
Rooms: 22 all ensuite
Pricing: Dinner from £18.50 CC: Accepted
Room facilities: Access:
Children: Welcome Dogs: Welcome
Licences: Parking: Off-street
Directions: Situated on A82 (Fort William). From A9, turn left at Longman roundabout, follow A82 signs for 2½ miles. Beside Torvean golf course and Caledonian Canal.

Lochardil House Hotel

★★★★

Stratherrick Road, Inverness, Highland, IV2 4LF
Tel: 01463 235995 Fax: 01463 713394
Email: lochardil@ukonline.co.uk
Rooms: 12 all ensuite
Pricing: Dinner from £18 CC: Accepted
Room facilities:
Children: Welcome Dogs: Guide dogs only
Licences: Parking: Off-street
Directions: From A9 Police HQ take Walter Scott Drive through five roundabouts then right into Stratherrick Road, hotel 500 yards on right.

Priory Hotel

★★★

The Square, Beauly, IV4 7BX
Tel: 01463 782309 Fax: 01463 782531
Email: reservations@priory-hotel.com
Web: www.priory-hotel,com
Rooms: 34 all ensuite
Pricing: Dinner from £12.50 CC: Accepted
Room facilities: Access:
Children: Welcome Dogs: Welcome
Leisure: Games room, Snooker/billiards
Parking: Off-street and monitored
Directions: A9 by-pass Inverness approx. 5 miles to Tore roundabout. Exit first left, follow sign for Beauly. Hotel is in village square.

Royal Highland Hotel

★★★

Station Square, Inverness, Highland, IV1 1LG
Tel: 01463 231926 Fax: 01463 710705
Email: info@royalhighlandhotel.co.uk
Web: www.royalhighlandhotel.com
Rooms: 70 all ensuite
Pricing: Sgl £69–85 Dbl £110–132
Dinner from £20
CC: Accepted Room facilities:
Access:
Conference: 3 meeting rooms (Thtr 200 max), 24hr-

delegate from £75, day-delegate rate from £27
Children: Welcome Dogs: Welcome
Licences: Parking: Off-street
Directions: Follow signs for city centre, hotel is adjacent to railway station.

Alban House

◆◆◆◆

Bruce Gardens, Inverness, Highland, IV3 5EN
Tel: 01463 714301 Fax: 01463 714236
Email: enquires@alban-house.freeserve.co.uk

Family-run guesthouse where hospitality counts. All rooms ensuite, free off street parking, large garden with fish pond. Come as a guest, leave as a friend, all bedrooms finished to a high standard and have tea/coffee, complimentary biscuits, colour TV in all rooms, outstanding breakfast enjoyed by all our guests.
Rooms: 6 all ensuite
Pricing: Sgl £30–45 Dbl £56–60
Dinner from £15
CC: Accepted Room facilities:
Access:
Children: Welcome
Dogs: Welcome
Parking: Off-street and monitored
Directions: On the West side of Inverness just off where Tomnahurich Street and Glenur & Uhart Road join (A82). 7 min walk from railway station.

Scotland

Culduthel Lodge

◆◆◆◆ 🍷 🌮 ❦

14 Culduthel Road, Inverness, Highland, IV2 4AG
Tel: 01463 240089 Fax: 01463 240089
Email: rac@culduthel.com
Web: www.culduthel.com

In quiet location near city centre, elegant rooms for the discerning traveller, four-posters and suites available, imaginative cooking with fine wines, car parking in landscaped grounds.
Rooms: 12 all ensuite 🖨 ⊗
Pricing: Sgl £45 Dbl £90–110 Dinner from £20
CC: Accepted Room facilities: 🖵 ☎ 🍷 📞
Children: Welcome Dogs: Welcome
Licences: 🔱 👪 Parking: Off-street
Directions: Take Castle Street from Inverness centre. This leads straight into Culduthel Road – lodge is on right.

Westbourne Guest House

◆◆◆◆ 🌮

50 Huntly Street, Inverness, Highland, IV3 5HS
Tel: 01463 220700 Fax: 01463 220700
Email: richard@westbourne.org.uk
Web: www.westbourne.org.uk

Situated on the west bank overlooking the River Ness, five minutes' walk from the city centre, restaurants, pubs, train and bus stations. Hotel accommodation at a guesthouse price. Built 1998.
Rooms: 10 all ensuite 🐾 ⊗
Pricing: Sgl £25–40 Dbl £50–80 CC: Accepted

Room facilities: 🖵 🍷 Access: ♿
Children: Welcome Dogs: Welcome
Parking: Off-street and monitored
Directions: Leave A9 at A82. Proceed straight over 3 roundabouts, cross Friars Bridge. Take 1st left into Wells Street, then into Huntly Street.

Clisham House

◆◆◆

43 Fairfield Road, Inverness, Highland, IV3 5QP
Tel: 01463 239965 Fax: 01463 239854
Email: clisham@dircon.co.uk
Web: www.clisham.dircon.co.uk

A non-smoking guesthouse within walking distance of the town centre, with a reputation for good food, warm welcome and Highland hospitality. All rooms are furnished to a high standard with guests' comfort a priority.
Rooms: 5 all ensuite Pricing: Sgl £26 Dbl £52
Room facilities: 🖵 🍷 Parking: Off-street

Sunnyholm

◆◆◆

12 Mayfield Road, Inverness, Highland, IV2 4AE
Tel: 01463 231336
Email: ago7195587@aol.com
Web: www.invernessguesthouse.com
Rooms: 4 all ensuite ⊗
Room facilities: 🖵 🍷 Access: ♿
Children: Welcome 2yrs min age �🍴
Parking: Off-street and monitored
Directions: From town centre, travel up Castle Street onto Culduthel Road. At first set of traffic lights turn left onto Mayfield Road. Sunnyholm is halfway up on right.

Travelodge Inverness

Travel Accommodation
A9/A96, Stoneyfield, A96 Inverness Road, Inverness, IV2 7PA
Web: www.travelodge.co.uk
Pricing: Sgl £47.40 Dbl £51.85 CC: Accepted
Room facilities: 🖵 🍷

Inverurie, Aberdeenshire

Strathburn Hotel

★ ★ ★

Burghmuir Drive, Inverurie, Aberdeenshire, AB51 4GY
Tel: 01467 624422 Fax: 01467 625133
Email: strathburn@btconnect.com
Web: www.strathburn-hotel.co.uk
Rooms: 25 all ensuite
Pricing: Sgl £55–90 Dbl £40–110
Dinner from £18.75 CC: Accepted
Room facilities: ☐ ☎ ☕ ✆ Access: ☈
Conference: 1 meeting room (Thtr 30 max),
24hr-delegate from £105, day-delegate rate from £18
Children: Welcome ⟊ Dogs: Welcome
Licences: ⅲ Parking: Off-street
Directions: From Aberdeen Airport head north on A96
for 10 miles. At Blackhall roundabout (Safeway) turn
right then left at next roundabout.

Isle of Arran

Kinloch Hotel

★ ★ ★

Blackwaterfoot, Brodick, Isle of Arran,
Ayrshire, KA27 8ET
Tel: 01770 860444 Fax: 01770 860447
Email: kinloch@cqm.co.uk
Web: www.kinloch-arran.com

Comfortable surroundings, first class food and
spectacular scenery. With 43 bedrooms, 7 luxury suites
and a full range of leisure facilities, offering superb
accommodation and exemplary service on every level.
Rooms: 43 all ensuite 🐾 🖾
Pricing: Sgl £24.50–49 Dbl £49–98
Dinner from £22 CC: Accepted
Room facilities: ☐ ☎ ☕ Access: ⅲ ☈
Conference: 3 meeting rooms (Thtr 150 max)
Children: Welcome ⟊ ⅉ Dogs: Welcome
Licences: ⚓ ⅲ
Leisure: Indoor pool, Gym, Health spa, Beauty salon,
Games room, Snooker/billiards Parking: Off-street
Directions: Ferry from Ardrossan; take B880 and
follow signs for Blackwaterfoot. Hotel is in centre
of village.

Isle of Bute, Argyll & Bute

Palmyra

◆ ◆ ◆ ◆ ⅋ ⌇

12 Ardbeg Road, Rothesay, Isle of Bute, PA20 0NJ
Tel: 01700 502929 Fax: 01700 505712
Web: www.isle-of-bute.com/palmyra
Rooms: 5 all ensuite ⊛
Pricing: Sgl £30–43 Dbl £58–69
Room facilities: ☐ ☕
Children: Welcome ⟊
Parking: Off-street
Directions: Ferry terminal; turn right at main road; drive
³/₄ of a mile until you see Palmyra sign.

Isle of Iona

Finlay Ross

◆ ◆

Martyr's Bay, Isle of Iona, Argyll, PA76 6SP
Tel: 01681 700357 Fax: 01681 700562
Email: enquires@finlayrossiona.co.uk
Web: www.innscotland.com

Comfortable bed and breakfast accommodation on the
beautiful Isle of Iona. With stunning views and the
peacefulness of island life, it is the perfect retreat.
Silver beaches, scenic walks and the magnificent 13th
century Abbey make it unique.
Rooms: 13 (4 ensuite)
Pricing: Sgl £27–30 Dbl £46–52 Room facilities: ☐ ☕
Children: Welcome
Directions: Calmac ferry from Oban to Craignure, Mull,
then by road to Fionnphort, then short ferry crossing to
the Isle of Iona.
See advert on page 567

Scotland

Isle of Islay, Argyll & Bute

Port Askaig Hotel

★★

Port Askaig, Isle of Islay, Argyll & Bute, PA46 7RD
Tel: 01496 840 245 Fax: 01496 840 295
Email: hotel@portaskaig.co.uk
Web: www.portaskaig.co.uk

This 400-year-old inn overlooks the Sound-of-Islay, the picturesque harbour and lifeboat station. Situated in own gardens. The best of home-cooked food. Bars open all day.
Rooms: 8 (6 ensuite) ⊛
Pricing: Sgl £26–32 Dbl £60–78 Dinner from £25
CC: Accepted Room facilities: 🖵 🖨
Conference: 25 meeting rooms, 24hr-delegate from £60, day-delegate rate from £20
Children: Welcome 5yrs min age 🍴 Dogs: Welcome
Licences: ♦♦♦ Leisure: Snooker/billiards
Parking: Off-street and monitored
Directions: Harbourside at Port Askaig ferry terminal. From Port Ellen terminal or from Islay airport follow straight route through Bowmore and Bridgend.

Isle Of Mull, Argyll & Bute

Highland Cottage   Blue Ribbon Winner

★★★ 🍴🍴

Breadalbane Street, Tobermory, Isle of Mull,
Argyll & Bute, PA75 6PD
Tel: 01688 302030
Email: davidandjo@highlandcottage.co.uk
Web: www.highlandcottage.co.uk
Seasonal closure: restricted opening in winter

Cosy family-run hotel in quiet setting in upper Tobermory conservation area. Four-poster beds and elegant lounges. Unrivalled hospitality from resident owners. Wildlife, walking, superb scenery or just relax!
Rooms: 6 all ensuite 🖼 ⊛

Pricing: Sgl £72–90 Dbl £95–115 Dinner from £28.50
CC: Accepted Room facilities: 🖵 ☎ 🖨 Access: ♿
Children: Welcome 9yrs min age 🍴 🅲
Dogs: Welcome Licences: ♦♦♦ Parking: Off-street
Directions: From roundabout at top of town go straight across stone bridge. Immediately turn right. Hotel is on right opposite fire station.

Gruline Home Farm   Little Gem

◆◆◆◆◆ 🍴🍴 🌸 🍃

Gruline, Isle of Mull, Argyll & Bute, PA71 6HR
Tel: 01680 300581 Fax: 01680 300573
Email: boo@gruline.com
Web: www.gruline.com

Centrally situated Georgian/ Victorian farmhouse (non-working), and Mull's finest B&B offering outstanding levels of hospitality and superb cuisine, prepared by our chef/proprietor. Enjoy total luxury and relaxation with us.
Rooms: 2 all ensuite ⊛
Pricing: Sgl £57 Dbl £64 Dinner from £25
CC: Accepted Room facilities: 🖵 🖨
Children: Welcome 16yrs min age Parking: Off-street
Directions: North on A849 to Salen; take B8035, drive 2 miles to fork, go left, past church, farm is next left.

Druimnacroish

◆◆◆◆ 🍃

Druimnacroish, Dervaig, Isle of Mull, Argyll & Bute,
PA75 6QW
Tel: 01688 400274 Fax: 01688 400274
Email: rac@druimnacroish.co.uk
Web: www.druimnacroish.co.uk
Seasonal closure: Closed Nov-Feb
Rooms: 6 all ensuite ⊛
Pricing: Sgl £42–60 Dbl £64–84 CC: Accepted
Room facilities: 🖨 Children: Welcome 6yrs min age
Dogs: Welcome Licences: ♦♦♦ Parking: Off-street
Directions: Two miles south of Dervaig, on road to Salen

Ask the experts

To book a Hotel or Guest Accommodation, or for help and advice, call RAC Hotel Reservations on 0870 603 9109 and quote 'Guide 2003'

Bellachroy Hotel

♦ ♦ ♦

Main Street, Dervaig, Isle of Mull,
Argyll & Bute, PA75 6QW
Tel: 01688 400314 Fax: 01688 400447
Email: rac@bellachroy.co.uk
Web: www.bellachroy.co.uk
Rooms: 7 (4 ensuite) ⬤ Pricing: Sgl £18–28
Dbl £36–56 Dinner from £10 CC: Accepted
Room facilities: ⬤ Children: Welcome ⥀ Dogs: Welcome
Licences: ⫿⫿⫿ Leisure: Games room Parking: Off-street
Directions: From Craignure follow Tobermory Road
until junction for Dervaig. Take Dervaig Road to end,
then turn right. Hotel is after 100 metres.

Isle of Skye, Highland

Cuillin Hills Hotel

★ ★ ★ ★ ⥀ ⥀ ⥀

Portree, Isle of Skye, Highland, IV51 9QU
Tel: 01478 612003 Fax: 01478 613092
Email: office@cuillinhills.demon.co.uk
Web: www.cuillinhills.demon.co.uk

Spectacularly located with breathtaking views over
Portree Bay to the Cuillin mountains. Award-winning
restaurant; high standards of service and an informal
and relaxing atmosphere.
Rooms: 28 all ensuite ⬤ ⬤
Pricing: Sgl £45–100 Dbl £90–200 Dinner from £29.50
CC: Accepted Room facilities: ⬜ ☎ ⬤ Access: ⬤
Conference: 2 meeting rooms (Thtr 140 max), 24hr-
delegate from £160, day-delegate rate from £18
Children: Welcome ⥀ Dogs: Guide dogs only
Licences: ⬤ ⫿⫿⫿ Parking: Off-street and monitored
Directions: Turn right ¼ mile north of Portree off the
A855 and follow signs for the hotel.

Hotel Eilean Iarmain

★ ★ ⥀ ⥀ ⥀

Isleornsay, Sleat, Isle of Skye, Highland, IV43 8QR
Tel: 01471 833332 Fax: 01471 833275
Email: bookings@eilean-iarmain.co.uk
Web: www.eileaniarmain.co.uk
Rooms: 16 all ensuite ⬤ ⬤ ⬤
Room facilities: ☎ ⬤ Access: ⬤
Children: Welcome ⥀ ⬤ Dogs: Welcome
Licences: ⫿⫿⫿ Parking: Off-street
Directions: Arriving by car, cross the Skye Bridge.
Follow A850 for 7 miles, turn left onto A851 for 8 miles.
Turn left at Isleornsay Road sign and drive to the hotel
on the harbour front (½ mile).

Royal Hotel

★ ★

Bank Street, Portree, Isle of Skye, Highland, IV51 9BU
Tel: 01478 612525 Fax: 01478 613198
Email: info@royal-hotel.demon.co.uk
Web: www.royal-hotel.demon.co.uk
Rooms: 21 ⬤
Pricing: Sgl £52–59 Dbl £78–88 Dinner from £19.50
CC: Accepted Room facilities: ⬜ ☎ ⬤
Conference: 20 meeting rooms (Thtr 60 max)
Children: Welcome ⥀ Dogs: Welcome
Leisure: Gym, Beauty salon, Snooker/billiards
Parking: Off-street
Directions: Follow A87 from Kyle of Lochalsh across
Skye bridge to Portree, follow road right A855, Hotel
approx 3 miles on left overlooking harbour.

Shorefield House

♦ ♦ ♦ ♦ ⬤ ⬤

Edinbane, Isle of Skye, Highland, IV51 9PW
Tel: 01470 582444 Fax: 01470 582414
Email: shorefieldhouse@aol.com
Web: www.shorefield.com
Rooms: 5 all ensuite ⬤ ⬤
Pricing: Sgl £24–32 Dbl £23–28 CC: Accepted
Room facilities: ⬤ Access: ⬤
Children: Welcome ⥀ Parking: Off-street
Directions: From Portree take A87 (U16). After 5 miles
take A850 (Dunvegan). Travel 9 miles to Lower
Edinbane.

Jedburgh, Borders

Ferniehirst Mill Lodge

♦ ♦ ♦

Jedburgh, Borders, TD8 6PQ
Tel: 01835 863279 Fax: 01835 863279
Email: ferniehirstmill@aol.com
Rooms: 9 all ensuite
Pricing: Sgl £23 Dbl £46 Dinner from £14
CC: Accepted Room facilities: ☎ ⬤
Children: Welcome Dogs: Welcome
Licences: ⫿⫿⫿ Leisure: Fishing, Riding
Parking: Off-street and monitored
Directions: 2½ miles south of Jedburgh, 8 miles north
of Scottish border, ⅓ mile off A68 on east side.

Kelso, Borders

Cross Keys Hotel

★ ★ ★ ⥀

36–37 The Square, Kelso, Borders, TD5 7HL
Tel: 01573 223303 Fax: 01573 225792
Email: cross-keys-hotel@easynet.co.uk
Web: www.cross-keys-hotel.co.uk
Rooms: 27 all ensuite ⬤ ⬤ Pricing: Sgl £49.90–65
Dbl £58–80 Dinner from £10 CC: Accepted
Room facilities: ⬜ ☎ ⬤ Access: ⫿⫿⫿ ⬤
Children: Welcome ⥀ ⬤ Dogs: Welcome
Licences: ⬤ ⫿⫿⫿ Parking: Off-street and monitored

Ednam House Hotel

★★★★ ⓡⓡ

Bridge Street, Kelso, Borders, TD5 7HT
Tel: 01573 224168 Fax: 01573 226319
Email: contact@ednamhouse.com
Web: www.ednamhouse.com
Seasonal closure: 24 Dec – 6 Jan

32 bedroom Georgian Mansion on the banks of the
river Tweed and in the heart of the picturesque town of
Kelso. Renowned for its comfort, atmosphere and
delicious food.
Rooms: 32 all ensuite 🛏 ⓢ
Pricing: Sgl £61–67 Dbl £89–124 CC: Accepted
Room facilities: 🖥 ☎ 🍵 🍸
Conference: 2 meeting rooms (Thtr 200 max)
Children: Welcome 🏄 🐾 Dogs: Welcome
Licences: 🍷 Leisure: Games room
Parking: Off-street
Directions: Off the town square on Bridge street
leading to the Abbey.

Kilchrenan, Argyll & Bute

Taychreggan Hotel

★★★★ ⓡⓡⓡ

Taynuilt, Kilchrenan, Argyll & Bute, PA35 1HQ
Tel: 01866 833211/366 Fax: 01866 833244
Email: info@taychregganhotel.co.uk
Web: www.tachregganhotel.co.uk
Rooms: 19 all ensuite 🛏 ⓢ
Pricing: Sgl £90–117 Dbl £100–127 Dinner from £37.50
CC: Accepted Room facilities: ☎ 🍵
Children: Welcome 14yrs min age Dogs: Welcome
Licences: 🍷 Leisure: Fishing, Snooker/billiards
Parking: Off-street and monitored
Directions: From Glasgow follow M8 to Erskine Bridge,
then A82 to Tyndrum. Take A85 to Taynuilt, then B845
to Kilchrenan.

Kilmarnock, Ayreshire

Travelodge Kilmarnock

Travel Accommodation
A71/A76/A77, Kilmarnock by-pass, Kilmarnock,
Ayreshire, KA1 5LQ
Web: www.travelodge.co.uk
Rooms: 40 all ensuite ⓢ
Pricing: Sgl £47.40 Dbl £51.85 CC: Accepted
Room facilities: 🖥 🍵 Access: ♿

Kinross, Perthshire

Travelodge Kinross (MOTO)

Travel Accommodation
M90 Moto Service Area, Turfhills Tourist Centre,
Kinross, Perthshire, KY13 7NQ
Web: www.travelodge.co.uk
Rooms: 35 all ensuite ⓢ
Pricing: Sgl £54.40 Dbl £58.85 CC: Accepted
Room facilities: 🖥 🍵 Access: ♿

Kirkcaldy, Fife

Dean Park Hotel

★★★★ ⓡ

Chapel Level, Kirkcaldy, Fife, KY2 6QW
Tel: 01592 261635 Fax: 01592 261371
Email: info@deanparkhotel.co.uk
Web: www.deanparkhotel.co.uk

Beautifully-appointed and professionally-run hotel with
custom-built conference facilities. Well situated for
leisure activities (golf, fishing etc). Excellent table (RAC
Dining Award) and cellar.
Rooms: 34 all ensuite 🍴🛏 ⓢ
Pricing: Sgl £59 Dbl £69 Dinner from £18.50
CC: Accepted Room facilities: 🖥 ☎ 🍵 🍸
Access: ♿ ♿
Conference: 6 meeting rooms (Thtr 300 max)
Children: Welcome 🏄 Dogs: Guide dogs only
Licences: 🍷 🏋 Parking: Off-street
Directions: Take A92 Edinburgh-Dunfermline road to
Kirkcaldy. Take A910 to first roundabout.

Belvedere Hotel

★ ★

Coxstool, West Wmyss, Kirkcaldy, Fife, KY1 4SL
Tel: 01592 654167 Fax: 01592 655279
Email: info@thebelvederehotel.com
Web: www.thebelvederehotel.com

Located in the picturesque village of West Wemyss the Belvedere hotel, 18 miles from St Andrews, offers excellent food and warm hospitality with magnificent views across the Firth of Forth.
Rooms: 20 all ensuite
Pricing: Sgl £40–57.50 Dbl £50–70 Dinner from £10
CC: Accepted Room facilities: Access:
Conference: 2 meeting rooms (Thtr 30 max)
Children: Welcome Dogs: Welcome
Licences: Parking: Off-street and monitored
Directions: At J2A of M90 follow A92 to 'Kirkcaldy east'. Follow A915 'Leven', take sign to 'coal town of Wemyss' hotel 1 mile.

Kyle, Highland

Lochalsh Hotel

★ ★ ★

Ferry Road, Kyle of Lochalsh, Highland, IV40 8AF
Tel: 01599 534202 Fax: 01599 534881
Email: mdmacrae@lochalsh-hotel.demon.co.uk

A family-owned hotel overlooking the Isle of Skye. An oasis of comfort and good living in the Scottish highlands, with 38 bedrooms – all ensuite.
Rooms: 38 all ensuite
Pricing: Dinner from £22 CC: Accepted
Room facilities: Access:
Conference: 1 meeting room (Thtr 50 max)
Children: Welcome Dogs: Welcome
Licences: Parking: Off-street and monitored
Directions: From south, turn left at Kyle traffic lights. Hotel 75m from lights.

Laide, Highland

The Sheiling

◆ ◆ ◆ ◆

Achgarve, Laide, Ross-shire, IV22 2NS
Tel: 01445 731487 Fax: 01445 731487
Email: maciver@thesheilingholidays.com
Web: www.thesheilingholidays.com
Seasonal closure: Christmas & New Year
Rooms: 2 all ensuite   Pricing: Dbl £46–52
Room facilities: Parking: Off-street
Directions: To reach us from Inverness take A9 to Tore roundabout and then A835 Ullapool Road to Braemore junction. Turn left on to the A8321 Gairloch Road to Laide. At Laide post office take the road behind the shop and post office, drive on the Mellon Udricle Road for 1¹⁄₂ miles along the road, on the right is the Sheiling.

Langbank, Renfrewshire

Gleddoch House Hotel

★ ★ ★ ★ ★

Old Greenock Road, Langbank, Renfrewshire, PA14 6YE
Tel: 01475 540711 Fax: 01475 540201

Largs, Ayrshire

Brisbane House Hotel

★ ★ ★ ★

14 Greenock Road, Esplanade, Largs,
Ayrshire, KA30 8NF
Tel: 01475 687200 Fax: 01475 676295
Email: enquiries@maksu-group.co.uk
Web: www.maksu-group.co.uk
Rooms: 23 all ensuite   Pricing: Sgl £70–100
Dbl £85–130 Dinner from £9.50 CC: Accepted
Room facilities: Conference: 2 meeting rooms (Thtr 140 max), 24hr-delegate from £105, day-delegate rate from £22 Children: Welcome
Dogs: Welcome
Licences: Parking: Off-street and monitored
Directions: From Glasgow, follow the Irvine Road and at Loch Winnoch start following signs for Largs. Hotel is on right past main town.

Priory House Hotel

★ ★ ★

Broomfields, Largs, Ayrshire, KA30 8DR
Tel: 01475 686460 Fax: 01475 689070
Email: enquiries@maksu-group.co.uk
Web: www.maksu-group.co.uk
Rooms: 21 all ensuite   Pricing: Sgl £70–100
Dbl £85–130 Dinner from £11.50 CC: Accepted
Room facilities: Access:
Conference: 3 meeting rooms (Thtr 140 max), 24hr-delegate from £105, day-delegate rate from £22
Children: Welcome Dogs: Welcome
Licences: Parking: Off-street and monitored
Directions: Entering Largs on A78, take turning into John Street near BP service station. Hotel is at end of road on seafront.

Queens Hotel

★★

North Promenade, Largs, Ayrshire, KA30 8QW
Tel: 01475 675311 Fax: 01475 675313

Lerwick, Shetland Isles

Glen Orchy House

◆◆◆◆ ✦ ⚲

20 Knab Road, Lerwick, Shetland Isles, ZE1 0AX
Tel: 01595 692031 Fax: 01595 692031
Email: glenorchy.house@virgin.net
Web: www.guesthouselerwick.com
Rooms: 24 all ensuite ⊗
Pricing: Sgl £41.50–42.50 Dbl £68–69 Dinner from £15
CC: Accepted Room facilities: ▯ ☎ ⚱ ❄ Access: ⚹
Children: Welcome ⼍ Dogs: Welcome
Licences: ⼮ Parking: Off-street
Directions: Follow main route until Church/Knab
Road/Annsbrae/Greenfield junction. Turn right from
south, straight ahead from north, onto Knab Road.
See advert on next page

Lochgilphead, Argyll & Bute

Stag Hotel and Restaurant

★★

Argyll Street, Lochgilphead, Argyll & Bute, PA31 8NE
Tel: 01546 602496 Fax: 01546 603549
Email: staghotel@ukhotels.com
Web: www.staghotel.com

Clean comfortable serviced accommodation at an
attractive and affordable price, all rooms ensuite, bar,
restaurant, meeting rooms available, ideal base for
walking, fishing, touring the west coast of Scotland.
Rooms: 18 all ensuite ⚱ Pricing: Dinner from £4.95
CC: Accepted Room facilities: ▯ ☎ ⚱ Children:
Welcome ⼍ ⚶ Dogs: Guide dogs only Licences: ⼮
Leisure: Games room
Directions: Follow A82/83 Glasgow, Campbeltown,
Lochgilphead, town centre, at mini-roundabout turn
right into Argyll Street, hotel at junction of Lorne street
and Argyll Street.

Lochinver, Sutherland

Inver Lodge Hotel

★★★★ ⚲ ⚲ ⚲

Lochinver, Sutherland, IV27 4LU

Tel: 01571 844496 Fax: 01571 844395
Email: stay@inverlodge.com
Web: www.inverlodge.com
Seasonal closure: November to March

Our foreground is Lochinver Bay and The Minch; our
backdrop, the great peaks of Sutherland: Canisp and
Suilven. The hotel combines modern facilities and
comforts with the traditional ambience of a Highland
lodge.
Rooms: 20 all ensuite
Pricing: Sgl £80–90 Dbl £140–150 Dinner from £35
CC: Accepted Room facilities: ▯ ☎ ⚱
Children: Welcome 10yrs min age ⼍
Dogs: Welcome Licences: ⼮
Leisure: Fishing, Snooker/billiards Parking: Off-street
Directions: On entering Lochinver, head towards
pier/harbour. Take first left after tourist information
centre for private road to hotel.

Lochmaben, Dumfries & Galloway

Magdalene House

◆◆◆◆ ⚲ ✦ ⚲

Bruce Street, Lochmaben,
Dumfries & Galloway, DG11 1PD
Tel: 01387 810439 Fax: 01387 810439
Email: mckerrellofhillhouse@ukonline.co.uk
Rooms: 3 all ensuite ⚱ ⚱ ⊗
Pricing: Dinner from £15
Room facilities: ▯ ⚱ Children: Welcome ⼍ ⚶
Dogs: Welcome Parking: Off-street and monitored
Directions: Take M74 to Lockerbie and A709 to
Lochmaben. Past High Street Road turns left.
Magdalene House is first left.

Lockerbie, Dumfries & Galloway

Lockerbie Manor Hotel

★★★

Boreland Road, Lockerbie,
Dumfries & Galloway, DG11 2RG
Tel: 01576 202610 Fax: 01576 203046
Email: info@lockerbiemanorhotel.co.uk
Web: www.lockerbiemanorhotel.co.uk
Rooms: 32 all ensuite ⚱ ⚱ ⊗
Pricing: Sgl £55–85 Dbl £69–105 Dinner from £20.95
CC: Accepted Room facilities: ▯ ☎ ⚱ Access: ⚹

Conference: 4 meeting rooms (Thtr 150 max), 24hr-
delegate from £88, day-delegate rate from £15.50
Children: Welcome Ħ ⅋Ⅽ Dogs: Welcome
Licences: ◬ ⅲ
Leisure: Games room, Snooker/billiards
Parking: Off-street and monitored
Directions: Located half a mile from M74 Junction 17.
See advert on this page

Mallaig, Highland

Morar Hotel

★★

Morar, Mallaig, Highland, PH40 4PA
Tel: 01687 462346 Fax: 01687 462212
Email: enquiries@morarhotel.co.uk
Web: www.morarhotel.co.uk
Seasonal closure: April–Oct
Rooms: 28 all ensuite ⅌ Pricing: Sgl £25–40
Dbl £50–80 CC: Accepted Room facilities: ▫ ⅌
Conference: 1 meeting room (Thtr 100 max)
Children: Welcome 14yrs min age Ħ
Dogs: Welcome Licences: ◬ ⅲ Parking: Off-street
Directions: In the village of Morar on the A830 Fort
William/Mallaig road, 3 miles from Mallaig.

West Highland Hotel

★★

Mallaig, Highland, PH41 4QZ
Tel: 01687 462210 Fax: 01687 462130
Email: westhighland.hotel@virgin.net
Web: www.westhighlandhotel.co.uk
Rooms: 39 all ensuite ⅌ ⊗
Pricing: Dinner from £16 (2002 rate) CC: Accepted
Room facilities: ▫ ⅌ Children: Welcome Ħ
Dogs: Welcome Licences: ◬ ⅲ
Parking: Off-street and monitored
Directions: From Fort William, turn right at roundabout,
then first right up hill. From Skye ferry, turn left at
roundabout, then first right uphill.

Markinch, Fife

Balbirnie House

★★★★★ ⅌ ⅌ ⅌

Balbirnie Park, Markinch, by Glenrothes, Fife, KY7 6NE
Tel: 01592 610066 Fax: 01592 610529
Email: info@balbirnie.co.uk
Web: www.balbirnie.co.uk
Rooms: 30 all ensuite ⅌ ⅌
Pricing: Sgl £130–160 Dbl £190–250
Dinner from £31.50 CC: Accepted
Room facilities: ▫ ☎ ⅌ ⅌ Access: ♿
Conference: 8 meeting rooms (Thtr 250 max), 24hr-
delegate from £160, day-delegate rate from £42
Children: Welcome Ħ Dogs: Welcome
Licences: ◬ ⅲ Leisure: Golf Parking: Off-street
Directions: From Edinburgh, follow signs for Forth
Road Bridge (M90). Leave at Junction 2a and take
A92. Follow signs to Glenrothes. Across third
roundabout, turn right at signs for Balbirnie Park.

Scotland

Maybole, Ayrshire

Ladyburn

Blue Ribbon Winner

★★★ ℝ ℝ ℝ

Ladyburn, Maybole, Ayrshire, KA19 7SG
Tel: 01655 740585 Fax: 01655 740580
Email: jh@ladyburn.demon.co.uk
Web: www.ladyburn.co.uk
Rooms: 5 all ensuite 🖨 🚭 Pricing: Sgl £90–110
Dbl £160–200 Dinner from £30 CC: Accepted
Room facilities: 📺 🕾 ☕ 🌢 Dogs: Guide dogs only
Licences: 🜲 ♦♦♦ Parking: Off-street
Directions: A77, B7024 to Crosshill. Right at war
memorial, left after 2 miles. After a further ¾ mile,
Ladyburn is on the right.

Melrose, Borders

Dryburgh Abbey Hotel

★★★

St Boswells, Melrose, Borders, TD6 0RQ
Tel: 01835 822261 Fax: 01835 823945
Email: enquiries@dryburgh.co.uk
Web: www.dryburgh.co.uk

Breathtakingly set on the banks of the Tweed, in acres
of grounds and gardens. A family-owned hotel where
food excellence, first class professional and friendly
service come guaranteed.
Rooms: 38 all ensuite 🍴 🖨
Pricing: Sgl £45–89 Dbl £90–178 Dinner from £26
CC: Accepted Room facilities: 📺 🕾 ☕ Access: ♦♦ &
Children: Welcome ♯ ⁖℃ Dogs: Welcome
Licences: 🜲 ♦♦♦ Leisure: Indoor pool, Fishing
Parking: Off-street and monitored
Directions: Take A68 to St Boswells. Turn onto B6404
and head through village. After 2 miles turn left on to
B6356. Continue for 2 miles to hotel entrance.

George & Abbotsford Hotel

★★

High Street, Melrose, Borders, TD6 9PD
Tel: 01896 822308 Fax: 01896 823363
Email: enquiries@georgeandabbotsford.co.uk
Web: www.georgeandabbotsford.co.uk
Rooms: 30 all ensuite 🍴 🖨
Room facilities: 📺 🕾 ☕ Children: Welcome ♯
Dogs: Welcome Licences: 🜲 ♦♦♦
Parking: Off-street
Directions: Use the A7 or A68 Trunk Road, joined by
the A6091 bypass. Hotel is midway up High Street.

Braidwood B&B

♦♦♦♦ 🗶

Buccleuh, Melrose, Roxburghshire, TD6 9LD
Tel: 01896 822488
Email: braidwood.melrose@virgin.net
Web: http:/homepge.virgin.net/braidwood.melrose
Rooms: 4 (2 ensuite)
Pricing: Sgl £25–28 Dbl £40–46
Room facilities: 📺 ☕ Children: Welcome ♯ ⁖℃
Dogs: Welcome
Directions: Centrally situated next to Post Office and
close to Abbey.

Clint Lodge

♦♦♦♦ ℝ 🍴

Clint Hill, St Boswells, near Melrose,
Roxburghshire, TD6 0DZ
Tel: 01835 822027 Fax: 01835 822656
Email: clintlodge@aol.om
Web: www.clintlodge.co.uk

Clint Lodge is a beautiful country house in the heart of
the Scottish borders offering top class accommodation
for tourists and sporting parties-golf, fishing, shooting.
Family-run with outstanding cuisine.
Rooms: 5 (4 ensuite)
Pricing: Sgl £45 Dbl £80–95 Dinner from £25
CC: Accepted Room facilities: 📺 🕾 ☕
Dogs: Welcome Parking: Off-street
Directions: At St Boswells take the B6404. Continue on
this road for two miles, turning left onto the B6356
(signposted Clint Lodge, Scott's View and Earlston).
Drive through Clint Mains village, veering left and
follow this road to Clint Lodge (1 mile on the right hand
side).

The Old Abbey School

♦♦♦♦

Waverley Road, Melrose, Roxburghshire, TD6 9SH
Tel: 01896 823432
Email: oneill@abbeyschool.fsnet.co.uk
Seasonal closure: December to February
Rooms: 3 (1 ensuite) 🍴 🚭 Room facilities: ☕
Children: Welcome ♯ Dogs: Guide dogs only
Parking: Off-street and monitored
Directions: From Melrose High Street take the main
road to Galashiels. The house is the second on the left
on Waverley Road.

Moffat, Dumfries & Galloway

Auchen Castle Hotel

★★★

Beattock, near Moffat, Dumfries & Galloway, DG10 9SH
Tel: 01683 300407 Fax: 01683 300667
Email: reservations@auchen-castle-hotel.co.uk
Web: www.auchen-castle-hotel.co.uk
Rooms: 25 all ensuite Pricing: Sgl £58.50–75
Dbl £76–140 Dinner from £25 CC: Accepted
Room facilities: ☐ ☎ ☕ ☏ Conference: 3 meeting
rooms (Thtr 50 max), 24hr-delegate from £125, day-
delegate rate from £25 Children: Welcome ♬ 🐎
Dogs: Welcome Licences: ♙♙♙ Leisure: Tennis, Fishing
Parking: Off-street and monitored
Directions: 1 mile north on B7076 from A/M74 Junction
15 (Moffat turn-off).
See advert on next page

Mobile traffic information

Just dial 1740* from any mobile
phone to get up-to-the-minute
RAC traffic information on
motorways and major A roads.
Try it now! *Calls to 1740 cost up to 59p
per minute. Check with your network.

Moffat House Hotel

★★★★

High Street, Moffat, Dumfries & Galloway, DG10 9HL
Tel: 01683 220039 Fax: 01683 221288
Email: moffat@talk21.com
Web: www.moffathouse.co.uk
Rooms: 21 all ensuite 🐕 ⛳ 🚭
Pricing: Sgl £55–60 Dbl £76–94 Dinner from £7
CC: Accepted Room facilities: ☐ ☎ ☕ ☏ Access: ♿
Conference: 2 meeting rooms (Thtr 80 max), 24hr-
delegate from £94, day-delegate rate from £28
Children: Welcome 12yrs min age ♬ ☕
Dogs: Welcome Licences: ☕ ♙♙♙
Parking: Off-street and monitored
Directions: One mile east off M74 at J15. Set in Moffat
Square.

Star Hotel

★★

44 High Street, Moffat, Dumfries & Galloway, DG10 9EF
Tel: 01683 220156 Fax: 01683 221524
Email: tim@famousstarhotel.com
Web: www.famousstarhotel.com
Rooms: 8 all ensuite 🐕 🚭
Pricing: Dinner from £5 (2002 rate) CC: Accepted
Room facilities: ☐ ☎ ☕ Children: Welcome ♬
Licences: ♙♙♙ Leisure: Games room
Directions: Situated 1 mile off M74 Junction 15. The
hotel is on the right-hand side in the town centre.

Scotland

Well View Hotel

★ ℝ ℝ ℝ

Ballplay Road, Moffat, Dumfries & Galloway, DG10 9JU
Tel: 01683 220184 Fax: 01683 220088
Email: info@wellview.co.uk
Web: www.wellview.co.uk

Mid-Victorian villa set in half an acre of garden and overlooking the town, with superb views of surrounding hills.
Rooms: 6 all ensuite 🖨 ⊗
Pricing: Sgl £58–70 Dbl £78–110 Dinner from £30
CC: Accepted Room facilities: 🖵 ☕
Conference: 2 meeting rooms (Thtr 16 max)
Children: Welcome 🍴 Dogs: Welcome
Licences: ♦♦♦ Parking: Off-street
Directions: From Moffat, A708 for Selkirk. Half mile left into Ballplay Road. then 300 yards on right.

Monymusk, Aberdeenshire

Grant Arms Hotel

◆ ◆

Monymusk, Aberdeenshire, AB51 7HJ
Tel: 01467 651226 Fax: 01467 651494

Musselburgh, East Lothian

Travelodge Edinburgh East (MOTO)

Travel Accommodation
A1, Old Craighall, Musselburgh, EH21 8RE
Web: www.travelodge.co.uk
Rooms: 45 all ensuite ⊗
Pricing: Sgl £57.40 Dbl £61.85 CC: Accepted
Room facilities: 🖵 ☕ Access: ♿

Nairn, Highland

Alton Burn Hotel

★ ★

Alton Burn Road, Nairn, Highland, IV12 5ND
Tel: 01667 452051

Nethy Bridge, Highland

Nethybridge Hotel

★ ★

Nethy Bridge, Highland, PH25 3DP
Tel: 01479 821203 Fax: 01479 821686
Email: salesnethybridge@strathmorehotels.com

Web: www.strathmorehotels.com
Rooms: 69 all ensuite ♣ 🖨 Pricing: Dinner from £15
CC: Accepted Room facilities: 🖵 ☎ ☕ Access: ⬆ ♿
Children: Welcome 🍴 ☕ Dogs: Welcome
Licences: ◭ ♦♦♦ Leisure: Games room
Parking: Off-street

Newton Stewart, Dumfries & Galloway

Galloway Arms Hotel

★ ★ ℝ

54–58 Victoria Street, Newton Stewart,
Dumfries & Galloway, DG8 6DB
Tel: 01671 402653 Fax: 01671 401202
Email: information@gallowayarms.fs.net
Web: www.gallowayarmshotel.net

Newton Stewart's oldest hotel established 1750. Now completely refurbished and enlarged by the purchase of building next door. Comfortable hotel specialising in fresh Galloway produce. New bar, lounge and restaurant.
Rooms: 19 all ensuite ♣ ⊗
Pricing: Sgl £29.50–35 Dbl £55–65 Dinner from £12.95
CC: Accepted Room facilities: 🖵 ☎ ☕ Access: ♿
Conference: 3 meeting rooms (Thtr 75 max)
Children: Welcome 🍴 Dogs: Welcome
Licences: ◭ ♦♦♦ Parking: Off-street and monitored
Directions: In centre of Newton Stewart, opposite Town Hall clock. Private parking down lane beside hotel.

Newtonmore, Invernesshire

Glen Hotel

★ ★

Main Street, Newtonmore, Invernesshire, PH20 1DD
Tel: 01540 673203
Rooms: 10 all ensuite ♣
Pricing: Sgl £20–25 Dbl £40 Dinner from £5
CC: Accepted Room facilities: 🖵 ☕
Children: Welcome 🍴 Dogs: Welcome
Licences: ♦♦♦ Leisure: Games room Parking: Off-street
Directions: Half way between Perth and Inverness, just off the A9.

North Berwick, East Lothian

The Marine

★ ★ ★

Cromwell Road, North Berwick, East Lothian, EH39 4LZ
Tel: 0870 400 8129 Fax: 01620 894480
Email: marine@heritage-hotels.co.uk

Web: www.macdonald-hotels.co.uk
Rooms: 83 all ensuite
Pricing: Sgl £75 Dbl £150 Dinner from £24
CC: Accepted Room facilities: 🖵 ☎ 🍵 📠 Access: ⟂ ♿
Conference: 5 meeting rooms Children: Welcome ⼍
Dogs: Welcome Licences: ⼪
Leisure: Outdoor pool, Beauty salon, Tennis,
Games room, Snooker/billiards
Parking: Off-street and monitored
Directions: From A1 City bypass, take A198 signposted
North Berwick. From A198 turn at traffic lights into
Hamilton Road, North Berwick. Hotel is second on right.

Oban, Argyll & Bute

Royal Hotel
★★★
Argyll Square, Oban, Argyll & Bute, PA34 4BE
Tel: 01631 563021 Fax: 01631 562811
Rooms: 91 (103 ensuite) ⊗
Pricing: Dinner from £15 (2002 rate) CC: Accepted
Room facilities: 🖵 ☎ 🍵 Access: ⟂ ♿
Children: Welcome ⼍ ☕ Dogs: Welcome
Licences: ⟁ ⼪ Parking: Off-street
Directions: In town centre, five minutes from
ferry/rail/bus terminals.

Falls of Lora Hotel
★★
Connel Ferry, by Oban, Oban, Argyll & Bute, PA37 1PB
Tel: 01631 710483 Fax: 01631 710694
Seasonal closure: mid-December to January

Overlooking Loch Etive, this owner-run hotel has
inexpensive family rooms for complete luxury! The
cocktail bar has an open log fire and over 100 brands
of whisky; there is an extensive Bistro menu.
Rooms: 30 all ensuite
Pricing: Sgl £30–53 Dbl £39–111 Dinner from £17.50
CC: Accepted Room facilities: 🖵 ☎ 🍵 Access: ♿
Conference: 1 meeting room (Thtr 45 max)
Children: Welcome ⼍ ☕ Dogs: Welcome
Licences: ⼪ Parking: Off-street
Directions: A82, A85. Hotel is half a mile past Connel
signpost, 5 miles before Oban.

King's Knoll Hotel
★★
Dunollie Road, Oban, Argyll & Bute, PA34 5JH
Tel: 01631 562536 Fax: 01631 566101

Email: info@kingsknollhotel.co.uk
Web: www.kingsknollhotel.co.uk
Seasonal closure: January to mid-February
Rooms: 15 (13 ensuite) 📠 ⊗ Pricing: Sgl £24–56
Dbl £48–64 Dinner from £12 CC: Accepted
Room facilities: 🖵 🍵 Children: Welcome ⼍
Dogs: Welcome Licences: ⼪ Parking: Off-street
Directions: First hotel on left as you enter Oban from
North/East on A85 main road.

Glenbervie Guest House
♦♦♦♦ ✎ ☕
Dalriach Road, Oban, Argyll & Bute, PA34 5JD
Tel: 01631 564770 Fax: 01631 566723
Rooms: 8 (6 ensuite) ⊗ Pricing: Sgl £22–30
Dbl £22–30 Dinner from £12 CC: Accepted
Room facilities: 🖵 🍵 Children: Welcome 5yrs min age
Licences: ⼪ Parking: Off-street

Loch Etive House
♦♦♦♦ ✎
Connel, Oban, Argyll & Bute, PA37 1PH
Tel: 01631 710400 Fax: 01631 710680
Email: frankwop@btinternet.com
Web: www.frankwopbtinternet.co.uk
Rooms: 5 (3 ensuite) ⊗
Pricing: Sgl £21.50–35 Dbl £37–55 Dinner from £13.50
CC: Accepted Room facilities: 🖵 🍵
Children: Welcome Dogs: Welcome
Licences: ⼪ Parking: Off-street
Directions: From A85 in Connel turn left St Oran's
Church, we are 100 yards on the left.

Ronebhal Guest House
♦♦♦♦ ✎ ☕
Connel, by Oban, Argyll & Bute, PA37 1PJ
Tel: 01631 710310/813 Fax: 01631 710310
Email: ronebhal@btinternet.com
Web: www.ronebhal.co.uk
Seasonal closure: December to January
Rooms: 5 (4 ensuite) ⊗ Room facilities: 🖵 🍵
Children: Welcome 7yrs min age Parking: Off-street
Directions: Off A85 in Connel village, 4th house past
the Connel Bridge junction, overlooking the bay.

Onich, Highland

Onich Hotel
★★★★ ☂ ☂
Onich, Highland, PH33 6RY
Tel: 01855 821214 Fax: 01855 821484
Email: enquiries@onich-fortwilliam.co.uk
Web: www.onich-fortwilliam.co.uk
Rooms: 25 all ensuite ✎ Pricing: Dinner from £23
(2002 rate) CC: Accepted Room facilities: 🖵 ☎ 🍵
Children: Welcome ⼍ ☕ Dogs: Welcome Licences: ⼪
Leisure: Games room, Snooker/billiards Parking: Off-street
Directions: The Onich hotel is situated on the A82 in
the village of Onich, overlooking Loch Linnhe, 12 miles
south of Fort William.

Peebles, Borders

Lindores Bed & Breakfast

◆ ◆ ◆ ✕

60 Old Town, Peebles, Borders, EH45 8JE
Tel: 01721 720441
Email: lane.lindores@virgin.net
Web: www.aboutscotland.co.uk/peebles/lindores.html
Seasonal closure: November
Rooms: 4 (2 ensuite) ⊛
Pricing: Dinner from £9 Room facilities: ▢ ▣
Access: ⏦ Children: Welcome ⊓
Dogs: Welcome
Parking: Off-street and monitored
Directions: Property is to the west of Peebles, on the A72 next to Millers Farm Shop.

Perth, Perth & Kinross

Murrayshall House Hotel and Golf Course

★ ★ ★ ⍨ ⍨ ⍨

Scone, Perth, Perth & Kinross, PH2 7PH
Tel: 01738 551171 Fax: 01738 552595
Email: info@murrayshall.co.uk
Web: www.murrayshall.co.uk
Rooms: 41 all ensuite ⍤
Pricing: Dinner from £25.25 (2002 rate) CC: Accepted
Room facilities: ▢ ☎ ▣ ⌕
Access: ⏦ Children: Welcome ⊓ ⍱
Dogs: Welcome Licences: ⬠ ⵜⵜⵜ
Leisure: Gym, Tennis, Golf
Parking: Off-street and monitored
Directions: From Perth take A94 to Coupar Angus. Turn right off A94 just before the village of Scone.

Quality Hotel Perth

★ ★ ★

Leonard Street, Perth, PH2 8HE
Tel: 01738 624141 Fax: 01738 639912
Email: admin@gb628.u-net.com
Web: www.choicehotels.com
Rooms: 70 all ensuite ⍤ ⌨ ⊛
Pricing: Sgl £30–89.75 Dbl £30–99.75
Dinner from £14.50 CC: Accepted
Room facilities: ▢ ☎ ▣ ⌕ Access: ⍙ ⏦
Conference: 7 meeting rooms (Thtr 45 max), 24hr-delegate from £95, day-delegate rate from £28
Children: Welcome ⊓ ⍱ Dogs: Welcome
Licences: ⬠ ⵜⵜⵜ
Parking: Off-street and monitored
Directions: From M90/A90, turn left into Marshall Place, which runs into Kings Place, then Leonard Street. Adjacent to railway station.

Salutation Hotel

★ ★ ★

South Street, Perth, Perth & Kinross, PH2 8PH
Tel: 01738 630066 Fax: 01738 633598
Email: salutation@perth.fsnet.co.uk
Web: www.strathmorehotels.com
Rooms: 84 all ensuite ⍤ ⌨ ⊛

Pricing: Sgl £45–65 Dbl £80–90 Dinner from £15.50
CC: Accepted Room facilities: ▢ ☎ ▣ ⌕ Access: ⍙
Conference: 1 meeting room (Thtr 250 max), 24hr-delegate from £68, day-delegate rate from £20
Children: Welcome ⊓ ⍱ Dogs: Welcome Licences: ⬠ ⵜⵜⵜ
Directions: Situated in the centre of Perth, M85 from Dundee, A9 from Inverness, A9 from Stirling/Glasgow, M90 from Edinburgh.

Clunie Guest House

◆ ◆ ◆ ✕ ⍥

12 Pitcullen Crescent, Perth, Perth & Kinross, PH2 7HT
Tel: 01738 623625 Fax: 01738 623238
Email: ann@clunieperth.freeserve.co.uk
Web: www.clunieguesthouse.co.uk
Rooms: 7 all ensuite ⍤ ⊛ Pricing: Sgl £19–25
Dbl £38–46 CC: AcceptedRoom facilities: ▢ ▣
Children: Welcome Dogs: Welcome Parking: Off-street
Directions: Situated on A94 Perth/Couper Angus Road. Leave M90 at Junction 11 and follow signs for A94.

Pitlochry, Perth & Kinross

Balrobin Hotel

★ ★

Higher Oakfield, Pitlochry, Perth & Kinross, PH16 5HT
Tel: 01796 472901 Fax: 01796 474200
Email: info@balrobin.co.uk
Web: www.balrobin.co.uk
Seasonal closure: November to February
Rooms: 15 (14 ensuite) ⊛
Pricing: Sgl £29–42 Dbl £60–80 Dinner from £18
CC: Accepted Room facilities: ▢ ▣
Children: Welcome 5yrs min age
Dogs: Welcome Licences: ⵜⵜⵜ Parking: Off-street
Directions: From town centre, follow brown tourist signs.

Knockendarroch House Hotel

★ ★ ⍨ ⍨

Higher Oakfield, Pitlochry, Perth & Kinross, PH16 5HT
Tel: 01796 473473 Fax: 01796 474068
Email: info@knockendarroch.co.uk
Web: www.knockendarroch.co.uk
Seasonal closure: November to February
Rooms: 12 all ensuite ⌨ ⊛ Pricing: Dbl £70–90
Dinner from £23 CC: Accepted Room facilities: ▢ ☎ ▣
Access: ⏦ Children: Welcome 10yrs min age
Licences: ⵜⵜⵜ Parking: Off-street
Directions: Enter Pitlochry from A9 on main street (Atholl Road), take Bonnethill Road, Toberargan Road, then Higher Oakfield; three minutes walk from town centre.

Poolewe, Highland

Pool House

Blue Ribbon Winner

★ ★ ★ ⍨ ⍨ ⍨

By Inverewe Garden, Poolewe, Highland, IV22 2LD
Tel: 01445 781272 Fax: 01445 781403
Email: enquiries@poolhousehotel.com
Web: www.poolhousehotel.com
Rooms: 5 all ensuite ⌨ ⊛

Pricing: Sgl £95–120 Dbl £190–330 Dinner from £38.50
CC: Accepted Room facilities: ☐ ☎ ◻
Children: Welcome 10yrs min age
Dogs: Guide dogs only Licences: ◭ ♦♦♦
Leisure: Snooker/billiards Parking: Off-street
Directions: 6 miles north of Gairloch on the A382, situated by the bridge in Poolewe, by the River Ewe.

Rosebank, Lanarkshire

Popinjay Hotel

★★★ ⌇

Lanark Road, Rosebank, Lanarkshire, ML8 5QB
Tel: 01555 860441 Fax: 01555 860204
Email: popinjayhotel@attglobal.net
Web: www.popinjayhotel.co.uk
Rooms: 38 all ensuite ⌇ ⌇
Pricing: Dinner from £18.50 (2002 rate)
CC: Accepted Room facilities: ☐ ☎ ◻ Access: ↟↟ ♿
Children: Welcome ⍭ ⌇ Dogs: Welcome
Licences: ◭ ♦♦♦ Parking: Off-street
Directions: 4 miles from M74, on the A72 between Hamilton and Lanark.

Rosyth, Fife

Gladyer Inn

★★

10 Heath Road, Ridley Drive, Rosyth, Fife, KY11 2BT
Tel: 01383 419977 Fax: 01383 411728
Email: gladyer@aol.com
Web: www.gladyerinn.co.uk
Rooms: 21 all ensuite ⌇ Pricing: Sgl £39.50 Dbl £55
CC: Accepted Room facilities: ☐ ☎ ◻
Conference: 2 meeting rooms (Thtr 80 max), 24hr-delegate from £60, day-delegate rate from £15
Children: Welcome ⍭ Dogs: Guide dogs only
Licences: ♦♦♦ Parking: Off-street
Directions: Leave M90 at Junction 1. Follow signs into Rosyth. Go straight on at roundabout. Take first left.

Saltcoats, Ayrshire

Lochwood Farm Steading

♦♦♦♦ ⌇ ⌇

Saltcoats, Ayrshire, KA21 6NG
Tel: 01294 552529 Fax: 02194 553315
Email: elaine@lochwoodfarm.fsbusiness.co.uk
Rooms: 4 all ensuite ⌇ ⌇ Pricing: Sgl £26–30
Dbl £42–50 Dinner from £17.50 CC: Accepted
Room facilities: ☐ ◻ Access: ♿ Children: Welcome
Dogs: Guide dogs only Parking: Off-street and monitored

Selkirk, Borders

Ettrickshaws Country House Hotel

Little Gem

♦♦♦♦♦ ⌇ ⌇ ⌇ ⌇

Ettrickbridge, Selkirk, Borders, TD7 5HW
Tel: 01750 52229 Fax: 01750 52229

Email: jenny@ettrickshaws.co.uk
Web: www.ettrickshaws.co.uk

In the heart of the beautiful Scottish Borders, Ettrickshaws offers a warm friendly welcome. Salmon fishing, walking and field sports complemented by good food, fine wines and spacious comfortable accommodation.
Rooms: 5 all ensuite ⌇
Pricing: Sgl £55–70 Dbl £90–110 Dinner from £22.50
CC: Accepted Room facilities: ☐ ☎ ◻
Children: Welcome 12yrs min age
Dogs: Welcome Licences: ♦♦♦
Parking: Off-street and monitored
Directions: From Selkirk town square take A708 Moffat Road. After ½ mile turn left onto B7009 to Ettrickbridge. Ettrickshaws 1 mile past village on left hand side (7 miles from Selkirk).

Shetland Isles

Busta House Hotel

★★★ ⌇

Brae, Shetland Isles, ZE2 9QN
Tel: 01806 522506 Fax: 01806 522588
Email: reservations@bustahouse.com
Web: www.bustahouse.com
Rooms: 20 all ensuite ⌇ ⌇
Pricing: Dinner from £27.50 (2002 rate) CC: Accepted
Room facilities: ☐ ☎ ◻ ⌇
Children: Welcome Dogs: Welcome
Parking: Off-street
Directions: Travel north on A970; turn left at Brae onto well-signposted road for approximately half a mile.

Shetland Hotel

★★★ ⌇

Holmsgarth Road, Lerwick, Shetland Isles, ZE1 0PW
Tel: 01595 695515 Fax: 01595 695828
Email: reception@shetlandhotel.co.uk
Web: www.shetlandhotels.com
Rooms: 65 all ensuite ⌇ ⌇
Pricing: £69–89.90 Dinner from £9.50 CC: Accepted
Room facilities: ☐ ☎ ◻ ⌇ Access: ↟↟ ♿
Conference: 5 meeting rooms (Thtr 200 max)
Children: Welcome ⍭ Licences: ♦♦♦
Leisure: Games room
Parking: Off-street and monitored
Directions: Conveniently located opposite main ferry terminal for Lerwick, and on main route north out of town.

Scotland

Shieldaig, Highland

Tigh an Eilean Hotel

★ ⓡ ⓡ ⓡ

On Loch Torridon, Shieldaig, Wester Ross, IV54 8XN
Tel: 01520 755251 Fax: 01520 755321
Email: tighaneileanhotel@shieldaig.fsnet.co.uk
Seasonal closure: November to March

Family-run hotel in unspoilt old fishing village, amid
Torridon mountains. Glorious views. Restaurant serves
fine local produce, including seafood delivered daily
from jetty to kitchen door.
Rooms: 11 all ensuite Pricing: Sgl £40–55 Dbl £46–58
Dinner from £28 CC: Accepted Room facilities: 🍵
Children: Welcome �ⱨ Dogs: Welcome
Licences: ⅲ Parking: Off-street
Directions: At centre of quiet village off A896. Parking
opposite. Train: Strathcarron; bus connects with
lunchtime train, or hotel happy to meet.

Spean Bridge, Highland

Letterfinlay Lodge Hotel

★ ★ ⓡ

Lochlochy, Spean Bridge, Highland, PH34 4DZ
Tel: 01397 712622
Email: letterfinlay@ecossetel.com
Seasonal closure: November to mid-March
Rooms: 13 (9 ensuite) 🍴 Pricing: Sgl £32–40
Dbl £64–80 Dinner from £12 CC: Accepted
Room facilities: 📺 ☎ 🍵 Children: Welcome ⱨ 🐾
Dogs: Welcome Licences: ⚖ ⅲ
Leisure: Games room, Snooker/billiards Parking: Off-street
Directions: 7 miles north of Spean Bridge, on shore of
Lochlochy on the A82.

St Andrews, Fife

The Rusacks

★ ★ ★ ★ ⓡ ⓡ

Pilmour Links, St Andrews, Fife, KY16 9JQ
Tel: 0870 400 8128 Fax: 01334 477896
Email: rusacks@heritage-hotels.co.uk
Web: www.macdonald-hotels.co.uk
Rooms: 68 all ensuite 🍴 Pricing: Sgl £124 Dbl £248
Dinner from £35 CC: Accepted Room facilities: 📺 ☎ 🍵 🍹
Access: ⅼⅼ ♿ Conference: 3 meeting rooms (Thtr 90
max) Children: Welcome ⱨ Dogs: Welcome
Licences: ⚖ ⅲ Leisure: Golf
Parking: Off-street and monitored

Directions: Enter St Andrews on the A91. Rusacks is
500 yards into town on the left-hand side.

Scores Hotel

★ ★ ★

76 The Scores, St Andrews, Fife, KY16 9BB
Tel: 01334 472451 Fax: 01334 473947
Email: office@scoreshotel.co.uk
Rooms: 30 all ensuite 🍴 Ⓢ Pricing: Sgl £73–97
Dbl £103–157 Dinner from £17.95 CC: Accepted
Room facilities: 📺 ☎ 🍵 Access: ⅼⅼ
Conference: 2 meeting rooms (Thtr 200 max)
Children: Welcome ⱨ 🐾 Dogs: Guide dogs only
Licences: ⚖ ⅲ Parking: Off-street
Directions: M90 J2A, follow A91 to St Andrews. Over
first small roundabout, then second. First left and then
first right.

St Fillans, Perth & Kinross

The Four Seasons Hotel

★ ★ ★ ⓡ ⓡ ⓡ

St Fillans, Perth & Kinross, PH6 2NF
Tel: 01764 685333 Fax: 01764 685444
Email: info@thefourseasonshotel.co.uk
Web: www.thefourseasonshotel.co.uk
Seasonal closure: February

The finest lochside location in the southern Highlands.
Contemporary cuisine using the best ingredients
available from Scotland's natural larder, catering for the
imaginative to more traditional diner.
Rooms: 12 all ensuite 🍴 Ⓢ
Pricing: Sgl £44–74 Dbl £82–98 Dinner from £18
CC: Accepted Room facilities: 📺 ☎ 🍵
Children: Welcome ⱨ 🐾 Dogs: Welcome
Licences: ⚖ ⅲ Parking: Off-street
Directions: On the A85 at the west end of St Fillans, at
the east end of Loch Earn.

Stirling, Stirlingshire

Stirling Highland Hotel

★ ★ ★ ★ ⓡ ⓡ

Spittal Street, Stirling, Stirlingshire, FK8 1DU
Tel: 01786 272727 Fax: 01786 272829
Email: stirling@paramount-hotels.co.uk
Web: www.paramount-hotels.co.uk

PARAMOUNT
GROUP OF HOTELS

Rooms: 96 all ensuite 🐾 ⊗
Pricing: Dinner from £22.50 CC: Accepted
Room facilities: ▢ ☎ ☕ ⁀ Access: ⊥⊥ ♿
Conference: 6 meeting rooms (Thtr 100 max),
24hr-delegate from £150, day-delegate rate from £43
Children: Welcome ☍ Dogs: Welcome Licences: ◭ ♟♟♟
Leisure: Indoor pool, Gym, Health spa, Beauty salon,
Snooker/billiards Parking: Off-street and monitored
Directions: Exit J10 M9; follow ring road and signs to
Stirling Castle. Hotel is on left.

Royal Hotel

★★★★ ⓡ ⓡ
55 Henderson Street, Bridge of Allan,
Stirlingshire, FK9 4HG
Tel: 01786 832284 Fax: 01786 834377
Email: stay@royal-stirling.co.uk
Web: www.royal-stirling.co.uk
Rooms: 32 all ensuite ⊗ Pricing: Sgl £65–85
Dbl £70–120 Dinner from £23.50 CC: Accepted
Room facilities: ▢ ☎ ☕ Access: ⊥⊥ Conference: 4
meeting rooms (Thtr 150 max), 24hr-delegate from
£130, day-delegate rate from £34
Children: Welcome ☍ ⁣ Dogs: Welcome
Licences: ◭ ♟♟♟ Parking: Off-street and monitored
Directions: Leave M9 at Junction 11. At large
roundabout, take fourth turning signposted Bridge of
Allan. Follow road (A9) into village centre. Hotel is on left.

Travelodge Stirling (MOTO)

Travel Accommodation
M9/M80 Moto Service Area, Pirnhall, Stirling, FK7 8EU
Web: www.travelodge.co.uk
Rooms: 37 all ensuite ⊗ Pricing: Sgl £54.40
Dbl £58.85 CC: AcceptedRoom facilities: ▢ ☕
Access: ♿

Strontian, Argyll & Bute

Strontian Hotel

★★ ⓡ
Acharacle, Strontian, Argyll & Bute, PH36 4HZ
Tel: 01967 402029 Fax: 01967 402314
Email: strontianhotel@supanet.com

Web: www.strontianhotel.supanet.com
Rooms: 6 all ensuite 🐾 ⊗
Pricing: Sgl £30–35 Dbl £50–65 Dinner from £12
CC: Accepted Room facilities: ▢ ☎ ☕
Conference: 1 meeting room (Thtr 50 max)
Children: Welcome ☍ Dogs: Welcome
Licences: ♟♟♟ Leisure: Games room Parking: Off-street
Directions: From A82 take Corran ferry to Ardgour. Turn
left off ferry on A861. Hotel on right as you enter Strontian.

Tain, Highland

Morangie House Hotel

★★★ ⓡ
Morangie Road, Tain, Ross-shire, IV19 1PY
Tel: 01862 892281 Fax: 01862 892872
Email: wynne@morangiehotel.com
Web: www.morangiehotel.com
Rooms: 26 all ensuite 🐾 ⌗ ⊗
Pricing: Sgl £65–75 Dbl £100–120 Dinner from £10
CC: Accepted Room facilities: ▢ ☎ ☕ Access: ♿
Conference: 3 meeting rooms (Thtr 60 max), 24hr-
delegate from £65, day-delegate rate from £10
Children: Welcome ☍ ⁣ Dogs: Welcome
Licences: ◭ ♟♟♟ Parking: Off-street
Directions: Turn right off A9 at northern entrance to
Tain. Hotel is first building on the right.

Tarbert, Argyll & Bute

Stonefield Castle Hotel

★★★★ ⓡ ⓡ
Loch Fyne, Tarbert, Argyll & Bute, PA29 6YJ
Tel: 01880 820836 Fax: 01880 820929
Email: enquiries@stonefieldcastle.co.uk
Web: www.innscotland.com

Breathtaking natural beauty surrounds the Castle
which stands high on the Kintyre peninsula and
commands views over Loch Fyne. The restaurant has
one of the finest views on the West Coast, while
woodland grounds are renowned for exotic plants.
Rooms: 33 all ensuite 🐾 ⊗
Pricing: Sgl £85–135 Dbl £170–220 Dinner from £25
CC: Accepted Room facilities: ▢ ☎ ☕ Access: ⊥⊥
Conference: 4 meeting rooms (Thtr 150 max), 24hr-
delegate from £115, day-delegate rate from £36
Children: Welcome ☍ ⁣ Dogs: Welcome
Licences: ◭ ♟♟♟ Leisure: Fishing, Snooker/billiards
Parking: Off-street and monitored
Directions: From Glasgow, A82 then A83 from Loch
Lomond. Entrance is on the left-hand side, two miles
north of the village of Tarbert.
See advert on page 567

Scotland

Columba Hotel

East Pier Road, Tarbert, Loch Fyne,
Argyll & Bute, PA29 6UF
Tel: 01880 820808 Fax: 01880 820808
Email: info@columbahotel.com
Web: www.columbahotel.com
Seasonal closure: Christmas
Rooms: 10 all ensuite
Pricing: Sgl £37.75 Dbl £75.90–91.90
Dinner from £22.50 CC: Accepted
Room facilities:
Conference: 1 meeting room (Thtr 30 max)
Children: Welcome Dogs: Welcome
Licences: Leisure: Games room
Parking: Off-street
Directions: As you enter Tarbert on A83, turn left
around the harbour. Columba Hotel is 1/2 mile from
junction.

Victoria Hotel

Barmore Road, By Loch Fyne, Tarbert,
Argyll, PA29 6TW
Tel: 01880 820236 Fax: 01880 820638
Email: www.victoriahotel.net
Web: www.victoriahoteltarbert.co.uk
Rooms: 5 all ensuite
Pricing: Sgl £32–42 Dbl £58–64 Dinner from £8
CC: Accepted Room facilities:
Children: Welcome Dogs: Welcome
Licences:
Leisure: Games room, Snooker/billiards
Directions: Follow signs to Tarbert. Enter Tarbert from
Lochgilphead, hotel is 200 metres on right-hand side
facing harbour.

Thurso, Highland

St Clair Hotel

Sinclair Street, Thurso, Highland, KW14 7AJ
Tel: 01847 896481 Fax: 01847 896481
Web: www.stclairhotel.co.uk
Rooms: 32 all ensuite
Pricing: Dinner from £13 (2002 rate) CC: Accepted
Room facilities:
Children: Welcome Dogs: Welcome Licences:
Directions: At first set of traffic lights go straight on; at
second set of traffic lights turn sharp left. Directions
from A9 north.

Tobermory

The Western Isles Hotel

Tobermory, Isle of Mull, Argyllshire, PA75 6PR
Tel: 01688 302012 Fax: 01688 302297
Email: wihotel@aol.com
Web: www.mullhotel.com
Seasonal closure: 18th – 28th Dec 2002

This 28 bedroomed Victorian hotel, built in 1883,
stands majestically against the skyline overlooking the
colourful town, Tobermory bay and the Sound of Mull.
Outstanding views, a haven of tranquillity.
Rooms: 28 all ensuite
Pricing: Sgl £35–92 Dbl £65–202 Dinner from £26
CC: Accepted Room facilities:
Conference: 2 meeting rooms (Thtr 60 max)
Children: Welcome Dogs: Welcome
Licences: Parking: Off-street

Tongue, Highland

Ben Loyal Hotel

Main Street, Tongue, Highland, IV27 4XE
Tel: 01847 611216 Fax: 01847 611336
Email: benloyalhotel@btinternet.com
Web: www.benloyal.co.uk
Rooms: 10 all ensuite
Pricing: Sgl £25–32 Dbl £50–64 Dinner from £24
CC: Accepted Room facilities:
Conference: 2 meeting rooms (Thtr 30 max)
Children: Welcome Dogs: Welcome
Licences: Leisure: Fishing, Games room
Parking: Off-street and monitored
Directions: From A9, take road to Bonar Bridge. Follow
A836 north to junction with A838. Turn left at junction
into village.

Troon, South Ayrshire

Marine Hotel

★★★★

Crosbie Road, Troon, South Ayrshire, KA10 6HE
Tel: 01292 314444 Fax: 01292 316922
Email: marine@paramount-hotels.co.uk
Web: www.paramount-hotels.co.uk

PARAMOUNT
GROUP OF HOTELS

Rooms: 74 all ensuite 🛏 📺 ⊗
Pricing: Sgl £117.25 Dbl £174.50 Dinner from £18
CC: Accepted Room facilities: 🖵 ☎ 🍵 Access: |↓↑
Conference: 6 meeting rooms (Thtr 200 max), 24hr-
delegate from £170, day-delegate rate from £48
Children: Welcome � ⅜€ Dogs: Welcome
Licences: ⟁ ♦♦♦ Leisure: Indoor pool, Gym,
Health spa, Beauty salon Parking: Off-street
Directions: Take M77/A77 to Prestwick Airport. Turn right at
B749 to Troon. Hotel is on left by Royal Troon Golf Club.

South Beach Hotel

★★★

73 South Beach, Troon, South Ayrshire, KA10 6EG
Tel: 01292 312033 Fax: 01292 318348
Email: info@southbeach.co.uk
Web: www.southbeach.co.uk
Rooms: 34 all ensuite 🛏 ⊗ Pricing: Sgl £30–85
Dbl £60–110 CC: Accepted Room facilities: 🖵 ☎ 🍵
Access: 🚹 Conference: 2 meeting rooms (Thtr 110 max)
Children: Welcome � ⅜€ Dogs: Welcome
Licences: ⟁ ♦♦♦ Parking: Off-street
Directions: Situated on the main road into Troon from
Prestwick, facing the sea.

Turnberry, South Ayrshire

The Westin-Turnberry Resort

Blue Ribbon Winner

★★★★★★
Turnberry, South Ayrshire, KA26 9LT
Tel: 01655 331000 Fax: 01655 331706
Email: turnberry@westin.com
Web: www.turnberry.co.uk
Seasonal closure: Christmas

The world renowned 5 star Westin Turnberry Resort is
located in spectacular coastal surroundings with
unrivalled facilities. Including world class golf on the
famous links courses, the Colin Montgomerie Links
Golf Academy. With an award-winning Spa, excellent
conference facilities, an exclusive development of
luxury lodges and cottages, and a variety of outdoor
pursuits without peer.
Rooms: 221 all ensuite 📺 ⊗
Pricing: Sgl £150–320 Dbl £155–375 Dinner from £25
CC: Accepted Room facilities: 🖵 ☎ 🍵 Access: |↓↑ 🚹
Conference: 14 meeting rooms (Thtr 275 max), 24hr-
delegate from £195, day-delegate rate from £40
Children: Welcome � ⅜€ Dogs: Welcome
Licences: ⟁ ♦♦♦ Leisure: Indoor pool, Gym,
Health spa, Beauty salon, Tennis, Golf, Fishing, Riding,
Snooker/billiards Parking: Off-street and monitored
Directions: Turnberry is located just off the A77
Glasgow to Stranraer Road, 15 miles south of Ayr.

Malin Court Hotel

★★★ 🅡 🅡 🅡

Girvan, Turnberry, South Ayrshire, KA26 9PB
Tel: 01655 331457 Fax: 01655 331072
Email: info@malincourt.co.uk
Web: www.malincourt.co.uk
Rooms: 18 all ensuite 🛏 ⊗ Pricing: Sgl £72–82
Dbl £104–124 Dinner from £12 CC: Accepted
Room facilities: 🖵 ☎ 🍵 Access: |↓↑ 🚹
Conference: 3 meeting rooms (Thtr 200 max), 24hr-
delegate from £65.50, day-delegate rate from £21.95
Children: Welcome � Dogs: Welcome
Licences: ⟁ ♦♦♦ Parking: Off-street and monitored
Directions: On A74 take Ayr exit. From Ayr, take the
A719 to Turnberry and Maidens.

Whitebridge, Highland

Whitebridge Hotel

★★ 🅡

Whitebridge, Highland, IV2 6UN
Tel: 01456 486226 Fax: 01456 486413
Email: info@whitebridgehotel.co.uk
Web: www.whitebridgehotel.co.uk
Rooms: 12 (11 ensuite) 🛏
Pricing: Sgl £28–35 Dbl £50–56 Dinner from £15
CC: Accepted Room facilities: 🖵 🍵
Children: Welcome Dogs: Welcome Licences: ♦♦♦
Leisure: Fishing, Games room Parking: Off-street
Directions: From A82 at Fort Augustus follow B862 for
9 miles. From Inverness, follow B862 for 24 miles.

Wick, Highland

Mackay's Hotel

★★

Union Street, Wick, Highland, KW1 5ED
Tel: 01955 602323 Fax: 01955 605930
Web: www.mackayshotel.co.uk
Rooms: 30 all ensuite 🛏 📺 Pricing: Dinner from
£19.50 (2002 rate) CC: Accepted
Room facilities: 🖵 ☎ 🍵 Access: |↓↑
Children: Welcome � Dogs: Guide dogs only
Licences: ⟁ ♦♦♦

Scotland

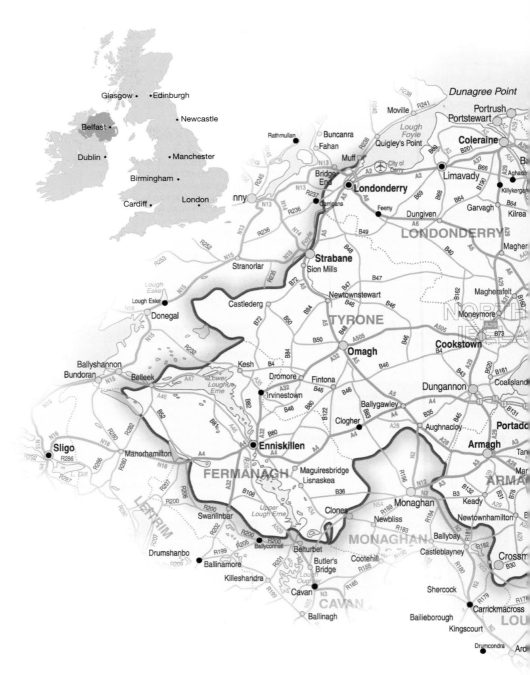

Note:
Dark blue dots
represent the
location of
RAC-inspected
accommodation

Republic of Ireland

Republic of Ireland

Republic of Ireland

Gold Ribbon Award

Aghadoe Heights Hotel, Killarney	★★★★	665
Caragh Lodge, Caragh Lake	★★	633
Cashel House Hotel, Connemara	★★★	635
Hayfield Manor, Cork	★★★★	638
The K Club, Straffan	★★★★★	679
Longueville House & Presidents Restaurant, Mallow	★★★	673
Marlfield House Hotel, Gorey	★★★	661
Mount Juliet Hotel, Thomastown	★★★★	663
Park Hotel, Kenmare	★★★★	666
Sheen Falls Hotel, Kenmare	★★★★	662
The Merrion Hotel, Dublin	★★★★★	645
Tinakilly Country House Hotel, Wicklow	★★★	684

Blue Ribbon Award

Dunbrody Country House, Arthurstown	★★★	629
Glenlo Abbey, Galway	★★★★	659
Glin Castle, Glin	★★★	661
Gregans Castle Hotel, Ballyvaughan	★★★	631
Harveys Point Country House, Donegal Town	★★★	644
Herbert Park Hotel, Dublin	★★★★	646
Killarney Park Hotel, Killarney	★★★★	666
Moyglare Manor Hotel, Maynooth	★★★	674
The Lodge & Spa at Inchydoney Island, Clonakilty	★★★★	640

Little Gem

Ahernes Seafood Restaurant & Accommodation, Yougal	♦♦♦♦♦	684
Ballywarren Country House, Cong	♦♦♦♦♦	637
Byrne's Mal Dua House, Clifden	♦♦♦♦♦	636
Churchtown House, Rosslare	♦♦♦♦♦	678
Coursetown Country House, Athy	♦♦♦♦♦	628
Earls Court Guest House, Killarney	♦♦♦♦♦	668
Emlagh House, Dingle	♦♦♦♦♦	643
Flemingstown House, Killmallock	♦♦♦♦♦	669
Glasha Accommodation, Via Clonmel	♦♦♦♦♦	630
Greenmount House, Dingle	♦♦♦♦♦	643
Ivyleigh House, Portlaoise	♦♦♦♦♦	676
Kilmokea Country Manor & Gardens, Campile	♦♦♦♦♦	633
Mount Royd Country House, Nr. Derry	♦♦♦♦	634
Rathcoursey House, Nr. Midleton	♦♦♦♦♦	675
The Castle Country House, Dungarvan	♦♦♦♦♦	658
Trinity Lodge, Dublin	♦♦♦♦	656

Northern Ireland

Bangor, Co. Down

Marine Court Hotel
★★★ ℞

The Marina, 18-20 Quay Street, Bangor,
Co. Down, BT20 5ED
Tel: 028 9145 1100 Fax: 028 9145 1200
Email: admin@marinecourt.fsnet.co.uk
Web: www.marinecourthotel.net
Rooms: 52 all ensuite ⊗
Pricing: Sgl £65–80 Dbl £75–90 Dinner from £8.95
CC: Accepted Room facilities: ▢ ☎ ⬙ Access: ⊞ ♿
Conference: 4 meeting rooms (Thtr 250 max), 24hr-
delegate from £110, day-delegate rate from £23.50
Children: Welcome ℍ ℃ Licences: ◁ ⦀
Leisure: Indoor pool, Gym
Parking: Off-street and monitored
Directions: Located on Quay Street near central pier on
marina.

Belfast, Co. Antrim

Culloden
★★★★★ ℞

Bangor Road, Holywood, Belfast, Co. Antrim, BT18 0EX
Tel: 028 9042 5223 Fax: 028 9042 6777
Email: res@cull.hastingshotels.com
Web: www.hastingshotels.com
Rooms: 79 all ensuite ⬙ ⊗
Pricing: Sgl £160–180 Dbl £200–220 Dinner from £30
CC: Accepted Room facilities: ▢ ☎ ⬙ ☏
Access: ⊞ Conference: 8 meeting rooms (Thtr 500 max)
Children: Welcome ℍ ℃
Dogs: Guide dogs only Licences: ◁ ⦀
Leisure: Indoor pool, Gym, Health spa,
Beauty salon, Tennis, Snooker/billiards
Parking: Off-street and monitored
Directions: 6 miles from Belfast city centre via A2,
signposted Bangor.

Dunadry Hotel and Country Club
★★★★ ℞

2 Islandreagh Drive, Dunadry, Co. Antrim, BT41 2HA
Tel: 028 9038 5050 Fax: 028 9038 5055
Email: mooneyhotelgroup@talk21.com
Web: www.mooneyhotelgroup.com
Rooms: 83 all ensuite ⬙ ⊗
Pricing: Dinner from £10 CC: Accepted
Room facilities: ▢ ☎ ⬙ ☏
Access: ⊞ ♿ Children: Welcome ℍ ℃
Dogs: Guide dogs only Licences: ◁
Leisure: Indoor pool, Gym, Health spa,
Beauty salon Parking: Off-street and monitored

Directions: From Belfast take M2, follow signs to
Templepatrick and Belfast airport. Take A57 and turn
left to Templepatrick. At roundabout go straight
through Templepatrick village. Take 2nd turn at next
roundabout. The Dunadry is 1 mile, on the left.

Hastings Europa Hotel
★★★★ ℞

Great Victoria Street, Belfast, Co. Antrim, BT2 7AP
Tel: 028 9032 7000 Fax: 028 9032 7800
Email: res@eur.hastingshotels.com
Web: www.hastingshotels.com
Seasonal closure: 24–25 December
Rooms: 240 all ensuite ⊗
Pricing: Sgl £110–160 Dbl £160–180 Dinner from £15
CC: Accepted Room facilities: ▢ ☎ ⬙ ☏
Access: ⊞
Conference: 16 meeting rooms (Thtr 750 max)
Children: Welcome ℍ ℃ Dogs: Welcome
Licences: ◁ ⦀ Leisure: Beauty salon
Parking: Off-street and monitored

Hastings Stormont Hotel
★★★★★ ℞ ℞

Upper Newtownards Road, Belfast,
Co. Antrim, BT4 3LP
Tel: 028 9065 1066 Fax: 028 9048 0240
Email: res@stor.hastingshotels.com
Web: www.hastingshotels.com
Rooms: 109 all ensuite ⬙ ⊗
Pricing: Sgl £110 Dbl £145 Dinner from £18
CC: Accepted Room facilities: ▢ ☎ ⬙ ☏
Access: ⊞
Conference: 16 meeting rooms (Thtr 500 max)
Children: Welcome ℍ ℃ Dogs: Guide dogs only
Licences: ◁ ⦀
Parking: Off-street
Directions: From Belfast city centre, follow A2 to
Newtownards. Turn right at Stormont Parliament
Buildings.

McCausland Hotel
★★★★ ℞

34-38 Victoria Street, Belfast, Co. Antrim, BT1 3GH
Tel: 028 9022 0200 Fax: 028 9022 0220
Email: info@mccauslandhotel.com
Web: www.mccauslandhotel.com
Seasonal closure: 24–27 December
Rooms: 60 all ensuite ⊗ Room facilities: ▢ ☎ ⬙ ☏
Access: ⊞
Conference: 3 meeting rooms (Thtr 64 max)
Children: Welcome ℍ ℃ Dogs: Guide dogs only
Licences: ⦀ Parking: Off-street and monitored
Directions: The hotel is located on Victoria street
between Anne street and the Albert clock tower.

Dukes Hotel
★★★

65 University Street, Belfast, Co. Antrim, BT7 1HL
Tel: 028 9023 6666 Fax: 028 9023 7177

Northern Ireland

Jurys Inn Belfast

★★★

Fisherwick Place, Great Victoria Street, Belfast, BT2 7AP
Tel: +353(0)1 6070000 Fax: +353(0)1 6316999
Email: bookings@jurysdoyle.com
Web: www.jurysdoyle.com

Rooms: 190 all ensuite 🍴 🚭
Pricing: Sgl £71–73 Dbl £71–73 Dinner from £17.50
CC: Accepted Room facilities: 🖥 ☎ 🍵 ☕
Access: |↕| 🚹 Children: Welcome, 12yrs min age 🍴
Dogs: Guide dogs only Licences: ♦♦♦
Parking: Off-street
Directions: Located 2 miles from Belfast City Airport.
Great Victoria Station 2 mins walk. Inn is adjacent to
Opera House and City Hall.

Old Inn

★★★★ R R

Main Street, Crawfordsburn, Co. Down, BT19 1JH
Tel: 028 9185 3255 Fax: 028 9185 2775
Email: info@theoldinn.com
Web: www.theoldinn.com
Rooms: 32 all ensuite 🍴 🗐
Pricing: Dinner from £16 (2002 rate) CC: Accepted
Room facilities: 🖥 ☎ 🍵 ☕ Access: 🚹
Children: Welcome 🍴 Licences: ◁ ♦♦♦
Parking: Off-street
Directions: Drive along A2 from Belfast towards
Bangor. Three miles past Holywood, take the B20 to
Crawfordsburn. The hotel is on the main street.

Ramada Belfast

117 Milltown Road, Shaws Bridge, Belfast,
Co. Down, BT8 7XP
Tel: 028 9092 3500
Email: mail@ramadabelfast.com
Web: www.ramada-hotels.com
Rooms: 120 all ensuite 🚭
Pricing: Sgl £110–130 Dbl £110–130 Dinner from £20
CC: Accepted
Room facilities: 🖥 ☎ 🍵 ☕ ❄ Access: |↕| 🚹
Conference: 12 meeting rooms (Thtr 900 max), 24hr-
delegate from £135.50, day-delegate rate from £38.50
Children: Welcome 🍴 Dogs: Guide dogs only
Licences: ◁ ♦♦♦ Leisure: Indoor pool, Gym,
Beauty salon Parking: Off-street and monitored
Directions: Ramada Belfast is 10 minutes from the city
centre and airport in a leafy south Belfast suburb.

Travelodge Belfast

Travel Accommodation
15 Brunswick Street, Belfast, BT2 7GE
Web: www.travelodge.co.uk
Rooms: 90 all ensuite 🚭
Pricing: Sgl £47.40–64.40 Dbl £51.85–68.85
CC: Accepted Room facilities: 🖥 🍵 Access: 🚹

Bushmills, Co. Antrim

Bushmills Inn

★★★★ R R

9 Dunluce Street, Bushmills,
Co. Antrim, BT57 8QG
Tel: 028 2073 2339 Fax: 028 2073 2048
Email: rac@bushmillsinn.com
Web: www.bushmillsinn.com

"A living museum of Ulster hospitality." Turf fires, gas
lights and aged timbers set the tone for this legendary
coaching inn & mill house at the gateway to the Giant's
Causeway.
Rooms: 32 all ensuite 🍴 🗐 🚭
Pricing: Sgl £58–138 Dbl £88–188 Dinner from £28
CC: Accepted Room facilities: 🖥 ☎ 🍵 ☕ Access: 🚹
Conference: 3 meeting rooms (Thtr 40 max),
24hr-delegate from £98, day-delegate rate from £25
Children: Welcome 🍴 ☕ Dogs: Guide dogs only
Licences: ♦♦♦ Parking: Off-street and monitored
Directions: On the A2 Antrim coast road in Bushmills
village with main entrance as you cross the River Bush.

Carrickfergus, Co. Antrim

Dobbins Inn Hotel

★★

6-8 High Street, Carrickfergus, Co. Antrim, BT38 7AF
Tel: 028 9335 1905 Fax: 028 9335 1905
Email: info@dobbinsinnhotel.co.uk
Web: www.dobbinsinnhotel.co.uk
Rooms: 15 all ensuite 🍴 🚭
Pricing: Sgl £44–48 Dbl £64–70 Dinner from £12
CC: Accepted Room facilities: 🖥 ☎ 🍵
Children: Welcome 🍴 Dogs: Welcome
Licences: ◁ ♦♦♦ Parking: Monitored
Directions: Situated approximately 10 miles from
Belfast City Airport, 15 miles from Belfast International
Airport, 14 miles from port of Larne, 10 miles from port
of Belfast.

Clogher, Co. Tyrone

Corick Country House

20 Corick Road, Clogher, Co Tyrone, BT76 0BZ
Tel: 028 8554 8216 Fax: 028 8554 9531
Email: corickhousehotel@netscapeonline.co.uk
Web: www.corickhousehotel.com
Rooms: 10 all ensuite
Pricing: Sgl £30–40 Dbl £25–40 Dinner from £19.95
CC: Accepted Room facilities: Access:
Conference: 3 meeting rooms (Thtr 200 max),
24hr-delegate from £50, day-delegate rate from £20
Children: Welcome Dogs: Welcome
Licences: Parking: Off-street and monitored

Coleraine, Co. Londonderry

Brown Trout Golf & Country Inn

Agivey Road, Aghadowey, Co. Londonderry, BT51 4AD
Tel: 028 7086 8209 Fax: 028 7086 8878
Email: bill@browntroutinn.com
Web: www.browntroutinn.com
Rooms: 15 all ensuite
Pricing: Sgl £50–60 Dbl £65–85 Dinner from £15
CC: Accepted Room facilities:
Access:
Conference: 2 meeting rooms (Thtr 40 max),
24hr-delegate from £65, day-delegate rate from £15
Children: Welcome Dogs: Welcome
Licences: Leisure: Gym, Golf, Fishing
Parking: Off-street
Directions: On intersection of A54 B66 7 miles south of
Coleraine.

Heathfield Farm

31 Drumcroone Road, Killykergan, Coleraine,
Co. Londonderry, BT51 4EB
Tel: 028 295 58245 Fax: 028 295 58245
Email: relax@heathfield.com
Web: www.heathfieldfarm.com
Rooms: 3 all ensuite
Pricing: Sgl £25–30 Dbl £45–50 Dinner from £15
CC: Accepted Room facilities:
Children: Welcome Dogs: Welcome
Parking: Off-street and monitored
Directions: On A29 Garvagh/Coleraine road. Two miles
north of Garvagh, 7 miles south of Coleraine.

Comber, Co. Down

The Old Schoolhouse Inn

Castle Espie, Ballydrain Road, Comber,
Co. Down, BT23 6EA
Tel: 028 97541182 Fax: 028 97541583
Rooms: 10 all ensuite
Pricing: Sgl £45 Dbl £65 Dinner from £17.95
CC: Accepted Room facilities: Access:

Conference: 2 meeting rooms (Thtr 60 max)
Children: Welcome Dogs: Guide dogs only
Licences: Parking: Off-street and monitored
Directions: A22 to Comber from Belfast, follow signs
for Castle Espie N.W.T 500 yards past it on left.

Enniskillen, Co. Fermanagh

Killyhevlin Hotel

Killyhevlin, Enniskillen, Co. Fermanagh, BT74 6RW
Tel: 028 6632 3481 Fax: 028 6632 4726
Email: info@killyhevlin.com
Web: www.killyhevlin.com
Seasonal closure: 24–25 December
Rooms: 43 all ensuite
Pricing: Sgl £65–77.50 Dbl £90–115
Dinner from £22.50 CC: Accepted
Room facilities: Access:
Conference: 7 meeting rooms (Thtr 600 max),
24hr-delegate from £105, day-delegate rate from £21
Children: Welcome
Dogs: Welcome
Licences: Parking: Off-street and monitored
Directions: Situated on A4, due east of Enniskillen, on
main Dublin/Belfast road.

Feeny, Co. Londonderry

Drumcovitt House and Barn

704 Feeny Road, Feeny, Co. Londonderry, BT47 4SU
Tel: 028 7778 1224 Fax: 028 7778 1224
Email: drumcovitt.feeny@btinternet.com
Web: www.drumcovitt.com

Listed Georgian house. Centrally heated. Log fires,
glorious setting. Stroll lanes, hill walk, fish, golf.
Approximately 1 hour ferries, airports, Giant's
Causeway. 30 minutes Donegal Sperrins, Derry City.
Relax. Enjoy.
Rooms: 9 (3 ensuite)
Pricing: Sgl £21–25 Dbl £48–50
Dinner from £15
CC: Accepted Room facilities:
Access:
Children: Welcome Dogs: Welcome
Leisure: Games room Parking: Off-street
Directions: From A6 Belfast-Derry road, a quarter-mile
west of Dungiven take the B74 to Feeny. After 3 miles,
Drumcovitt is on right.

Northern Ireland

Irvinestown, Co. Fermanagh

Mahon's Hotel

★★

Enniskillen Road, Irvinestown,
Co. Fermanagh, BT94 1GS
Tel: 028 6862 1656 Fax: 028 6862 8344
Email: info@mahonshotel.co.uk
Web: www.mahonshotel.co.uk
Rooms: 18 ✿ 🖉
Pricing: Sgl £27.50–32.50 Dbl £55–60
Dinner from £14 CC: Accepted Room facilities:
🖵 ☎ 🍵
Children: Welcome ⊬ ⅀℃ Dogs: Welcome
Licences: ◈ ⅲ Leisure: Tennis, Riding, Games room
Parking: Off-street and monitored

Larne, Co. Antrim

Hastings Ballygally Castle

★★★

274 Coast Road, Ballygally, Co. Antrim, BT40 2QZ
Tel: 028 2858 3212 Fax: 028 2858 3681
Email: res@bgc.hastingshotels.com
Web: www.hastingshotels.com
Rooms: 44 all ensuite ✿ ⊗
Pricing: Sgl £75–95 Dbl £105–125 Dinner from £15
CC: Accepted Room facilities: 🖵 ☎ 🍵 ✆
Access: ⅼⅼ⅃ ⅁
Conference: 4 meeting rooms (Thtr 200 max)
Children: Welcome ⊬ ⅀℃ Dogs: Guide dogs only
Licences: ◈ ⅲ Parking: Off-street
Directions: 20 miles north of Belfast on the Antrim
coast road (M2 From Belfast, then A8 to Larne). 4
miles north of Larne on Antrim coast.

Derrin Guest House

◆◆◆

2 Princes Gardens, Larne, Co. Antrim, BT40 1RQ
Tel: 028 2827 3269 Fax: 028 2827 3269
Email: info@derrinhouse.co.uk
Web: www.derrinhouse.co.uk
Seasonal closure: 25–26 December
Rooms: 6 (4 ensuite) ✿ ⊗
Room facilities: 🖵 🍵 Children: Welcome ⅀℃
Dogs: Welcome Parking: Off-street
Directions: Turn off Harbour highway (A8) for A2
coastal route. After traffic lights at main street take first
road on left.

Limavady, Co. Londonderry

Radisson Roe Park Hotel & Golf Resort

★★★★ ⅀ ⅀

Roe Park, Limavady, Co. Londonderry, BT49 9LB
Tel: 028 7772 2222 Fax: 028 7772 2313
Email: reservations@radissonroepark.com
Web: www.radissonroepark.com
Rooms: 64 all ensuite ✿ 🖉 ⊗
Pricing: Sgl £74 Dbl £98 CC: Accepted
Room facilities: 🖵 ☎ 🍵 ✆ Access: ⅼⅼ⅃ ⅁

Conference: 7 meeting rooms (Thtr 400 max),
24hr-delegate from £85, day-delegate rate from £20
Children: Welcome ⊬ ⅀℃
Dogs: Guide dogs only Licences: ⅲ
Leisure: Indoor pool, Gym, Beauty salon, Golf,
Games room, Snooker/billiards
Parking: Off-street and monitored
Directions: Situated on A2 Londonderry-Limavady
Road, 16 miles from Londonderry, 1 mile from
Limavady. Resort is 10 miles from city of Derry and 45
miles from Belfast airport.

Londonderry, Co. Londonderry

Hastings Everglades

★★★★ ⅀

Prehen Road, Waterside, Londonderry,
Co. Londonderry, BT47 2NH
Tel: 028 7134 6722 Fax: 028 7134 9200
Email: res@egh.hastingshotels.com
Web: www.hastingshotels.com
Rooms: 64 all ensuite ✿ ⊗
Pricing: Sgl £90–105 Dbl £115–130 Dinner from £18
CC: Accepted Room facilities: 🖵 ☎ 🍵 Access: ⅼⅼ⅃
Conference: 5 meeting rooms (Thtr 400 max)
Children: Welcome ⊬ ⅀℃ Dogs: Guide dogs only
Licences: ⅲ Parking: Off-street
Directions: Follow main A6 route to Londonderry.
Follow signs for Strabane/Omagh. Go ahead at traffic
lights at bridge. Hotel second left.

Tower Hotel Derry

★★★★

The Diamond, Derry, BT48 6HL
Tel: 028 7137 1000 Fax: 028 7137 1234
Web: www.towerhotelgroup.ie
Seasonal closure: 24–27 December inclusive
Rooms: 95 all ensuite Room facilities: 🖵 ☎ 🍵 ✆
Access: ⅼⅼ⅃ Children: Welcome ⊬
Dogs: Guide dogs only Licences: ◈ ⅲ
Leisure: Gym Parking: Off-street and monitored

Quality Hotel Da Vincis

★★★ ⅀

15 Culmore Road, Derry, BT48 9EN
Tel: 028 7127 9111
Email: info@davincishotel.com
Web: www.davincishotel.com
Seasonal closure: 24–26 December
Rooms: 70 all ensuite ✿ ⊗
Pricing: Sgl £69–86 Dbl £75–92
Dinner from £10.50 CC: Accepted
Room facilities: 🖵 ☎ 🍵 ✆
Access: ⅼⅼ⅃ ⅁
Conference: 2 meeting rooms (Thtr 30 max)
Children: Welcome ⊬ Dogs: Guide dogs only
Licences: ◈ ⅲ Parking: Off-street and monitored
Directions: Entering City from Belfast or Coleraine
follow signs for Foyle Bridge. Turn left at end of the
bridge onto the Culmore Road. Quality hotel Da Vincis
located 1/2 mile on the left.

Travelodge City of Derry

22-24 Strand Road, BT47 2AB
Web: www.travelodge.co.uk
Rooms: 39 all ensuite ⊗
Pricing: Sgl £47.40–54.40 Dbl £51.85–58.85
CC: Accepted Room facilities: ☐ ☕ Access: ♿

Travelodge Derry (Belfast) (SA)

Travel Accommodation
22-24 Strand Road, Derry City, BT47 2AB
Web: www.travelodge.co.uk
Rooms: 40 all ensuite ⊗
Pricing: Sgl £47.40–54.40 Dbl £51.85–58.85
CC: Accepted Room facilities: ☐ ☕ Access: ♿

Newcastle, Co. Down

Hastings Slieve Donard Hotel

★★★★ ®
Downs Road, Newcastle, Co. Down, BT33 0AH
Tel: 028 4372 3681 Fax: 028 4372 4830
Email: res@sdh.hastingshotels.com
Web: www.hastingshotels.com
Rooms: 124 all ensuite ⊗ ⊗
Pricing: Sgl £110–130 Dbl £170–190 Dinner from £23
CC: Accepted Room facilities: ☐ ☎ ☕ Access: ⥮ ♿
Conference: 16 meeting rooms (Thtr 825 max)
Children: Welcome � ⊰℄ Dogs: Guide dogs only
Licences: ⟁ ▥
Leisure: Indoor pool, Gym, Health spa,
Beauty salon, Games room
Parking: Off-street and monitored
Directions: From Belfast, take A24 and follow signs to
Newcastle. From Dublin, take R174 to Newry then A2
and follow signs to Newcastle.

Burrendale Hotel & Country Club

★★★ ® ®
51 Castlewellan Road, Newcastle, Co. Down, BT33 0JY
Tel: 028 4372 2599 Fax: 028 4372 2328
Email: reservations@burrendale.com
Web: www.burrendale.com
Rooms: 69 all ensuite ⊗ ⊗
Pricing: Dinner from £16 (2002 rate) CC: Accepted
Room facilities: ☐ ☎ ☕ ☏ Access: ⥮
Children: Welcome ⌐ ⊰℄ Dogs: Guide dogs only
Licences: ⟁ ▥
Leisure: Indoor pool, Gym, Health spa,
Beauty salon, Games room
Parking: Off-street
Directions: From Belfast, take A24 to Newcastle, then
A50 Castlewellan Road.

Plan your route

Visit www.rac.co.uk for RAC's
interactive route planner, including
up to the minute traffic reports.

Republic of Ireland

Achill Island, Co. Mayo

Achill Cliff House Hotel

★★★

Keel, Achill Island, Co. Mayo
Tel: +353(0)98 43400 Fax: +353(0)98 43007
Email: info@achillcliff.com
Web: www.achillcliff.com
Rooms: 10 all ensuite ☺
Pricing: Sgl €40–80
Dbl €60–140 Dinner from €22 CC: Accepted
Room facilities: 🖵 ☎ ☕ 📞
Access: ♿ Children: Welcome ♀
Licences: 🍴
Parking: Off-street and monitored
Directions: Coming from Achill Sound, hotel is on right-hand side of road in village of Keel.

One click does it all

Book RAC inspected hotels and
B&Bs at www.rac.co.uk/hotels

Coatesland Guesthouse (Hogans)

Your hosts Florence and Donal welcome you
to our award-winning guesthouse.
All our rooms are ensuite with direct dial
telephone/on-line service, tea/coffee-making
facilities and many other little extras.
Generous Guest Lounge with Satellite TV,
Supervised car park. Only two minute's drive
to the town centre.

Kilarney/Tralee Road, N21, Adare, Co. Limerick
Tel: (00353) 61-396372   Fax: (00353) 61-396833
email: coatesfd@indigo.ie
website: http://indigo.ie/~coatesfd/

Lavelles Sea Side House

◆◆◆

Achill Island, Dooega, Co. Mayo
Tel: +353(0)98 45116
Email: seasidehouse@eircom.net
Seasonal closure: November to March
Rooms: 14 all ensuite ☕ ☺
Pricing: Sgl €35–45 Dbl €60–70 Dinner from €20
CC: Accepted Room facilities: ☕
Children: Welcome ♀ ☕

Adare, Co. Limerick

Adare Manor Hotel & Golf Resort

★★★★ ☕ ☕

Adare, Co. Limerick
Tel: +353(0)61 396566 Fax: +353(0)61 396124
Email: reservations@adaremanor.com
Web: www.adaremanor.com
Rooms: 63 all ensuite 📠
Room facilities: 🖵 ☎ Access: ⛰ ♿
Conference: 3 meeting rooms (Thtr 200 max)
Children: Welcome ♀ ☕
Licences: ⬧ 🍴
Leisure: Indoor pool, Gym, Health spa,
Beauty salon, Golf, Fishing, Riding
Parking: Off-street and monitored
Directions: 30 km from Shannon Airport, 10 km from
Limerick City in the south-west of Ireland.

Berkeley Lodge

◆◆◆◆ ☒

Station Road, Adare, Co. Limerick
Tel: +353(0)61 396857 Fax: +353(0)61 396857
Email: berlodge@iol.ie
Web: www.adare.org
Rooms: 6 all ensuite ☕ ☺
Pricing: Sgl €50–58 Dbl €65
CC: Accepted
Room facilities: 🖵 ☕
Children: Welcome, 2yrs min age ♀
Parking: Off-street
Directions: Take route N21 (Limerick) via Killarney to
Adare. Turn right at roundabout. Hotel is fifth house on
the right after petrol station.

Coatesland House Bed & Breakfast (Hogans)

◆◆◆◆ ☒ ☕

Tralee/Killarney Road (N21), Adare, Co. Limerick
Tel: +353(0)61 396372 Fax: +353(0)61 396833
Email: coatesfd@indigo.ie
Web: indigo.ie/~coatesfd/
Seasonal closure: 25 December
Rooms: 6 all ensuite ☕ ☺
Pricing: Sgl €38–42 Dbl €63.50–68 CC: Accepted
Room facilities: 🖵 ☎ ☕
Children: Welcome ♀ ☕
Dogs: Welcome Parking: Off-street and monitored
Directions: 1 km from village centre.
See advert on this page

Arthurstown

Dunbrody Country House *Blue Ribbon Winner*

★★★★ ⓇⓇⓇ

Arthurstown, near Waterford,
Co. Wexford
Tel: +353(0)51 389600 Fax: +353(0)51 389601
Email: dunbrody@indigo.ie
Web: www.dunbrodyhouse.com
Seasonal closure: 22–27 December

Dunbrody cookery school now offering 4 & 2 day
residential courses.
Rooms: 22 all ensuite ❧ ⊗
Pricing: Sgl €117.50 Dbl €195–285 Dinner from €50
CC: Accepted Room facilities: ▢ ☎ ♨ Access: ♿
Conference: 1 meeting room (Thtr 70 max)
Children: Welcome ℃ Dogs: Guide dogs only
Licences: ⬥ ♙ Leisure: Riding
Parking: Off-street and monitored
Directions: From Dublin via M11/N11 to Wexford and
R733 to Arthurstown. From Cork N25 via Waterford
and passage east car ferry Ballyhack.

Athy, Co. Kildare

Coursetown Country House *Little Gem*

◆◆◆◆◆ ❀ ❧

Stradbally Road, Athy, Co. Kildare
Tel: +353(0)507 31101 Fax: +353(0)507 32740
Seasonal closure: Christmas

Large country house in 260-acre farm. Bedrooms
designed for maximum guest comfort. Tastefully
appointed fully accessible wheelchair-friendly suite.
Excellent breakfast with homemade bread and
preserves. Lovely secluded garden.

Rooms: 4 all ensuite ⊗
Pricing: Sgl €60 Dbl €100 CC: Accepted
Room facilities: ▢ ☎ ♨ Access: ♿
Children: Welcome, 8yrs min age Dogs: Welcome
Parking: Off-street
Directions: Turn off N78 at Athy or N80 at Stradbally
onto R428. House is 3km from Athy and 9km from
Stradbally.

Ballinamore, Co. Leitrim

Riversdale Farm Guesthouse

◆◆◆◆

Ballinamore, Co. Leitrim
Tel: +353(0)78 44122 Fax: +353(0)78 44813
Email: riversdaleguesthouse@eircom.net
Web: www.riversdalefarmguesthouse.com
Seasonal closure: 30 November to 31 January
Rooms: 13 all ensuite ❧
Pricing: Sgl €38–45 Dbl €76–90
Dinner from €18
CC: Accepted Room facilities: ☎ ♨
Children: Welcome, 5yrs min age ♨ ℃
Dogs: Guide dogs only
Licences: ♙
Leisure: Indoor pool, Gym, Fishing, Games room
Parking: Off-street
Directions: From centre Ballinamore on R202 follow
signpost Riversdale or Carrigallen. Riversdale is 1½
miles on left, sign at entrance.

Ballinasloe, Co. Galway

Haydens Gateway Business & Leisure Hotel

★★★

Dunlo Street, Ballinasloe, Co. Galway
Tel: +353(0)6568 23000 Fax: +353(0)6568 23759
Email: reservations@lynchotels.com
Web: www.lynchotels.com
Rooms: 48 all ensuite
Pricing: Sgl €62–176 Dbl €87–288
Dinner from €25 CC: Accepted Room facilities:
▢ ☎ ♨ ♨
Access: ⬆ ♿
Conference: 4 meeting rooms (Thtr 300 max),
24hr-delegate from €105, day-delegate rate from €32
Children: Welcome ♨ Dogs: Guide dogs only
Licences: ⬥ ♙
Parking: Off-street and monitored
Directions: Located in the heart of Ballinasloe, just 30
minutes from Galway Airport (N6 road).

Republic of Ireland

Ballingeary, Co. Cork

Gougane Barra Hotel

★ ★

Gougane Barra, Ballingeary, Co. Cork
Tel: +353(0)26 47069 Fax: +353(0)26 47226
Email: gouganebarrahotel@eircom.net
Web: www.gouganebarrahotel.com

Rooms: 27 all ensuite Pricing: Sgl €82–93
Dbl €114–136 Dinner from €30 CC: Accepted
Room facilities: ☐ ☎ ☺ Children: Welcome ♌
Dogs: Guide dogs only Licences: ♦♦♦

Ballyconnell, Co. Cavan

Slieve Russell Hotel Golf & Country Club

★ ★ ★ ★ ☜

Ballyconnell, Co. Cavan
Tel: +353(0)49 9526444 Fax: +353(0)49 9526046
Email: slieve-russell@quinn-hotels.com
Web: www.quinnhotels.com
Rooms: 159 all ensuite ☺☺ 🎏 Pricing: Sgl €130–185
Dbl €220–300 Dinner from €40 CC: Accepted
Room facilities: ☐ ☎ ☺ ☏ Access: ⏅ ⅓
Conference: 7 meeting rooms (Thtr 800 max),
24hr-delegate from €146, day-delegate rate from €38
Children: Welcome ♌ 🐎 Dogs: Guide dogs only
Licences: ♦♦♦ Leisure: Indoor pool, Gym, Beauty salon,
Tennis, Golf, Games room, Snooker/billiards
Parking: Off-street and monitored
Directions: N3 to Cavan; take Emiskillen road through
Belturbet to Ballyconnell.

Ballycotton, Co. Cork

Bayview Hotel

★ ★ ★ ★ ☜ ☜

Ballycotton, Co. Cork,
Tel: +353(0)21 4646746 Fax: +353(0)21 4646075
Email: info@bayviewhotel.net
Web: www.bayviewhotel.net
Seasonal closure: November to March
Rooms: 35 all ensuite ☺☺ ☺ Pricing: Sgl €121–139
Dbl €178–214 Dinner from €45 CC: Accepted
Room facilities: ☐ ☎ ☺ ☏ Access: ⅓⅓
Conference: 2 meeting rooms (Thtr 40 max)
Children: Welcome ♌ ☽ Dogs: Guide dogs only
Licences: ♦♦♦ Parking: Off-street and monitored
Directions: At Castlemantyr on the N25, turn onto the
R632. Follow the signs for Ballycotton.

Ballyheigue, Co. Kerry

White Sands Hotel

★ ★ ★

Ballyheigue, Co. Kerry
Tel: +353(0)66 33357

Ballylickey, Co. Galway

Sea View House Hotel

★ ★ ★

Ballylickey, Bantry, Co. Galway
Tel: +353(0)27 50462 Fax: +353(0)27 51555
Email: seaviewhousehotel@eircom.net
Seasonal closure: Mid November to mid March
Rooms: 17 all ensuite ☺☺
Room facilities: ☐ ☎ ☺
Access: ⅓
Children: Welcome ♌ ⅛ Dogs: Welcome
Licences: ♦♦♦ Parking: Monitored
Directions: On main route N71, 3 miles from Bantry, 7
miles from Glengariff.

Ballymacarbry, Co. Waterford

Glasha   Little Gem

♦ ♦ ♦ ♦ ♦ ☜ ☜

Glasha, Ballymacarbry, via Clonmel, Co. Waterford,
Ballymacarbry, via Clonmel, Waterford,
Tel: +353(0)52 36108 Fax: +353(0)52 36108
Email: glasha@eircom.net
Web: www.glashafarmhouse.com
Seasonal closure: 1 December to 1 February

Multiple award-winning RAC 5 diamond and AA 5
diamond family farmhouse in the beautiful nine valley.
Ideal for an activity based holiday or just for a relaxing
break. Superb accommodation winners of the RAC
Warm Welcome award,
Rooms: 8 all ensuite ☺
Pricing: Sgl €45–50 Dbl €90–100
Dinner from €35
CC: Accepted Room facilities: ☐ ☺
Access: ⅓
Dogs: Guide dogs only
Parking: Off-street and monitored
Directions: Take the 671 between Clonmel and
Duwgarwaw, we have 3 signs for Glasha on the 671.

Hanoras Cottage, Country House & Restaurant

◆◆◆◆◆

Nire Valley, Ballymacarbry, Co. Waterford
Tel: +353(0)52 36134 Fax: +353(0)52 36540
Email: hanorascottage@eircom.net
Web: www.hanorascottage.com
Rooms: 10 all ensuite ⊛
Pricing: Dbl €85–135 Dinner from €42
CC: Accepted
Room facilities: ☐ ☎ ⊙ Licences: ♦♦♦
Leisure: Health spa
Parking: Off-street and monitored
Directions: From Clonmel or Dungarvan take R672 to Ballymacarbry. Turn off at Melody's Pub. We are signposted from there, directly beside the Nire Church.
See advert on this page

Ballyvaughan, Co. Clare

Gregans Castle Hotel

★★★★ ♦♦ *Blue Ribbon Winner*

Ballyvaughan, Co. Clare
Tel: +353(0)65 7077005 Fax: +353(0)65 7077111
Email: res@gregans.ie
Web: www.gregans.ie
Seasonal closure: 1 December to 13 February

Antique furnishings and turf fires decorate this country house, a family-operated hotel, with views of garden, valley, Burren mountains and Galway Bay. Winner of awards for food, hospitality and service.
Rooms: 22 all ensuite ⬚ ⊛
Pricing: Sgl €110–260 Dbl €160–280
Dinner from €23 CC: Accepted
Room facilities: ☎
Access: ♿ Conference: 1 meeting room (Thtr 30 max)
Children: Welcome ♯ ⊰ Licences: ♦♦♦
Parking: Off-street and monitored
Directions: 3½ miles south of Ballyvaughan village on road N67, approx 1 hour from Shannon International Airport.
See advert on this page

Traffic news

Sign up now for one month's free trial of RAC Route Minder for personalised traffic information. Visit www.rac.co.uk/routeminder

Republic of Ireland

Rusheen Lodge

◆◆◆◆ ⚹

Knocknagrough, Ballyvaughan, Co. Clare
Tel: +353(0)65 7077092 Fax: +353(0)65 7077152
Email: rusheen@iol.ie
Web: www.rusheenlodge.com
Seasonal closure: December to January
Rooms: 9 all ensuite ⊛
Pricing: Sgl €50–65 Dbl €76–90 CC: Accepted
Room facilities: ▢ ☎ ⊜
Access: ♿ Children: Welcome ⅋ℂ
Dogs: Guide dogs only Parking: Off-street
Directions: From Ballyvaughan village, take N67 south
for ³/₄ km. Rusheen Lodge is on the left-hand side of
the road.

Baltimore, Co. Cork

Baltimore Harbour Hotel

★★★ ℞

Baltimore, Co. Cork
Tel: +353(0)28 20361 Fax: +353(0)28 20466
Email: info@bhrhotel.ie
Web: www.bhrhotel.ie
Seasonal closure: Sun/Thur, Nov to 17 March

The hotel is situated in the picturesque village of
Baltimore overlooking the harbour and islands, award
winning restaurant, full leisure facilities, lounge with
open fire, friendly relaxed atmosphere.
Rooms: 70 all ensuite ⊛ ⊛
Pricing: Sgl €80–115 Dbl €120–180 CC: Accepted
Room facilities: ▢ ☎ ⊜ Access: ⅃↑ ♿
Conference: 100 meeting rooms (Thtr 140 max),
24hr-delegate from €150, day-delegate rate from €70
Children: Welcome ⅋ ℂ Dogs: Guide dogs only
Licences: ⟁ ⅏
Leisure: Indoor pool, Gym, Riding, Games room
Parking: Off-street and monitored
Directions: From Cork take the N71 to Skibbereen,
then the R595 to Baltimore. Before entering the village
turn right for the hotel.

Casey's of Baltimore Hotel

★★★★ ℞

Baltimore, Co. Cork
Tel: +353(0)28 20197 Fax: +353(0)28 20509
Email: caseys@eircom.net
Web: www.caseysofbaltimore.com

Rooms: 14 all ensuite
Pricing: Sgl €82–93 Dbl €114–136 Dinner from €32
CC: Accepted Room facilities: ▢ ☎ ⊜ ⚲
Children: Welcome ⅋ ℂ Licences: ⟁ ⅏
Parking: Off-street
Directions: From Cork city take the N71 road to
Skibbereen. From Skibbereen take the R595 road to
Baltimore. Hotel is on the R595 near Baltimore.

Bantry, Co. Cork

Westlodge Hotel

★★★

Bantry, Co. Cork
Tel: +353(0)27 50360 Fax: +353(0)27 50438
Email: reservations@westlodgehotel.ie
Web: www.westlodgehotel.ie
Rooms: 90 all ensuite ⊛ ⊛
Pricing: Sgl €70–80 Dbl €140–200 Dinner from €22
CC: Accepted Room facilities: ▢ ☎ ⊜
Access: ⅃↑ ♿
Conference: 3 meeting rooms (Thtr 300 max)
Children: Welcome ⅋ ⊁ ℂ Dogs: Guide dogs only
Licences: ⟁ ⅏
Leisure: Indoor pool, Gym, Health spa, Tennis,
Snooker/billiards Parking: Monitored
Directions: Situated on Bantry Bay.

Blarney, Co. Cork

Ashlee Lodge

✚

Tower, Blarney, Co. Cork
Tel: +353(0)21 4385346 Fax: +353(0)21 4385726
Email: info@ashleelodge.com
Web: www.ashleelodge.com

We provide the best international standards of
accommodation, luxury rooms with air conditioning,
widescreen TV and hi-fi, king-size beds. Free use of
sauna and hot tub, gourmet breakfasts.
Rooms: 10 all ensuite ⊛
Pricing: Sgl €80–150 Dbl €80–160 CC: Accepted
Room facilities: ▢ ☎ ⊜ ⚲ ❄
Access: ♿ Children: Welcome
Dogs: Guide dogs only Leisure: Health spa
Parking: Off-street and monitored
Directions: Located on Blarney-Killarney road R617, in
the village of Tower, just outside Blarney village.

Blessington, Co. Wicklow

Downshire House Hotel

★★★★ ☕

Blessington, Co. Wicklow
Tel: +353(0)45 865199 Fax: +353(0)45 865335
Email: info@downshirehouse.com
Web: www.downshirehouse.com
Seasonal closure: 23 December to 5 January
Rooms: 25 all ensuite
Pricing: Sgl €45–84.50 Dbl €52–152 Dinner from €43
Room facilities: ☐ ☎ Children: Welcome � ☕
Dogs: Guide dogs only Licences: ⟐ ♦♦♦
Parking: Off-street
Directions: On N81 25 km south of Dublin, on main
street, Blessington.

Bray, Co. Wicklow

Esplanade Hotel

★★★

Bray, Co. Wicklow
Tel: +353(0)1 286 2056 Fax: +353(0)1 286 6496
Email: esplan@regencyhotels.com
Web: www.regencyhotels.com
Rooms: 40 all ensuite ♧ ⊟ ⊗
Pricing: Dinner from €18 CC: Accepted
Room facilities: ☐ ☎ ⊗
Children: Welcome � Dogs: Guide dogs only
Licences: ⟐ ♦♦♦ Leisure: Gym, Health spa
Parking: Off-street
Directions: Bray is 19km south of Dublin, off the M11.

Royal Hotel & Leisure Centre

★★★

Main Street, Bray, Co. Wicklow
Tel: +353(0)1 2862935 Fax: +353(0)1 2867373
Email: royal@regencyhotels.com
Web: www.regencyhotels.com
Rooms: 91 all ensuite ⊟ ⊗
Pricing: Dinner from €16.95 CC: Accepted
Room facilities: ☐ ☎ ⊗ ♦ Access: ⌁
Children: Welcome ♂ ⤵ ☕ Dogs: Welcome
Licences: ⟐ ♦♦♦
Leisure: Indoor pool, Gym, Beauty salon
Parking: Off-street and monitored
Directions: As you enter Bray, the hotel is on the top of
the hill on the left-hand side.

Campile, Co. Wexford

Kilmokea Country Manor & Gardens

Little Gem

♦♦♦♦♦ ⋇ ⤸

Kilmokea, Great Island, Campile, Co. Wexford
Tel: +353(0)51 388109 Fax: +353(0)51 388776

Caragh Lake, Co. Kerry

Caragh Lodge

Gold Ribbon Winner

★★ ☕ ☕ ☕

Caragh Lake, Co. Kerry
Tel: +353(0)66 9769115 Fax: +353(0)66 9769316
Email: caraghl@iol.ie
Web: www.caraghlodge.com
Seasonal closure: Mid October to end April

Victorian fishing lodge in 7 acres, award-winning
gardens on shore of Caragh lake, one mile from
famous Ring of Kerry. Comfortable lounges with open
log fires and antiques, renowned for excellent food.
Rooms: 15 all ensuite
Pricing: Sgl €130–130 Dbl €180–325 Dinner from €35
CC: Accepted Room facilities: ☎
Children: Welcome, 12yrs min age Licences: ♦♦♦
Parking: Off-street and monitored
Directions: From Killorglin, take N70 towards Glenbeigh.
Turn left after 3 miles at signpost 'Caragh Lodge'. Turn
left at end of road. Caragh Lodge is on right.

Carlow Town, Co. Carlow

Barrowville Town House

♦♦♦♦♦ ⋇ ⤸

Kilkenny Road, Carlow Town, Co. Carlow
Tel: +353(0)59 9143324 Fax: +353(0)59 9141953
Web: www.barrowvillehouse.com

Five-diamond Georgian listed town house. Well
appointed bedrooms. Traditional or buffet breakfast
served in conservatory overlooking gardens. Excellent
location for golf or touring Southeast/Midlands.
Rooms: 7 all ensuite ⊗
Pricing: Sgl €45–55 Dbl €70–75 CC: Accepted
Room facilities: ☐ ☎ ⊗ Parking: Off-street
Directions: On N9 south side of Carlow Town at fifth
traffic light on right. Travelling north, 50 metres before
first right, on left.

Celtic Guest Accommodation

34 Hillview Drive, Rathnapish, Carlow Town,
Co. Carlow
Tel: +353(0)503 35762
Seasonal closure: Christmas to New Year
Rooms: 6 (5 ensuite) ⊗
Pricing: Sgl €18–25 Dbl €40–50
Room facilities: ▢ ☕ Children: Welcome
Dogs: Guide dogs only
Parking: Off-street and monitored
Directions: Main Dublin to Carlow road, pass through roundabout to town centre, 1st B&B on left-hand side, 10 minute walk from city centre.

Carrick-on-Shannon, Co. Leitrim

The Landmark Hotel

★★★★ ⓡ
Carrick-on-Shannon, Co. Leitrim
Tel: +353(0)78 22222 Fax: +353(0)78 22233
Email: landmarkhotel@eircom.net
Web: www.thelandmarkhotel.com
Rooms: 50 all ensuite ⊗
Pricing: Sgl €121–136 Dbl €190–220 Dinner from €40
CC: Accepted Room facilities: ▢ ☎ ☕ Access: ↥ ♿
Conference: 4 meeting rooms (Thtr 575 max)
Children: Welcome Ħ Dogs: Guide dogs only
Licences: ♦ ♦♦♦ Leisure: Gym
Parking: Off-street
Directions: Located on the N4 Sligo-Dublin road. Approaching Carrick from Dublin, take the first exit off the roundabout and we are on the right-hand side.

Carrickmacross, Co. Monaghan

Nuremore Hotel & Country Club

★★★★ ⓡ
Carrickmacross, Co. Monaghan
Tel: +353(0)42 9661438 Fax: +353(0)42 9661853
Email: nuremore@eircom.net
Web: nuremore-hotel.ie
Rooms: 72 all ensuite ⊗ ⊡ ⊗
Pricing: Sgl €150–200 Dbl €220–300 Dinner from €45
CC: Accepted Room facilities: ▢ ☎ ☕ ☏
Access: ↥ ♿
Conference: 10 meeting rooms (Thtr 250 max)
Children: Welcome Ħ ⅍ Dogs: Guide dogs only
Licences: ♦♦♦
Leisure: Indoor pool, Gym, Health spa,
Beauty salon, Tennis, Golf, Snooker/billiards
Parking: Off-street and monitored
Directions: Situated 80km north of Dublin on N2, 2km south of town of Carrickmacross from Belfast. Take A1 south to Dundalk then follow signs for Carrickmacross.

Carrigaline, Co. Cork

Carrigaline Court Hotel & Leisure Centre

★★★★ ⓡ
Main Street, Carrigaline, Co. Cork
Tel: +353(0)21 4852100 Fax: +353(0)21 4371103
Email: carrigcourt@eircom.net
Web: www.carrigcourt.com
Pricing: Sgl €120–180 Dbl €180–220 Dinner from €35
CC: Accepted Room facilities: ▢ ☎ ☕ ☏ Access: ↥
Conference: 3 meeting rooms (Thtr 350 max)
Children: Welcome Ħ Dogs: Guide dogs only
Licences: ♦ ♦♦♦ Leisure: Indoor pool, Gym
Parking: Off-street and monitored
Directions: Follow the south ring road until the Shannonpark roundabout, then follow prominent signs for Carrigaline, located 15 mins drive from city centre.

Carrigans, Co. Donegal

Mount Royd Country Home   Little Gem

♦ ♦ ♦ ♦ ⓡ
Carrigans, near Derry, Co. Donegal
Tel: +353(0)74 40163 Fax: +353(0)74 40400
Email: jmartin@mountroyd.com
Web: www.mountroyd.com
Seasonal closure: Christmas

A warm welcome awaits our guests at our award-winning family home where every comfort is assured. Ideal for touring Inishowen, Giants' Causeway and Grianan of Aileach. AA and RAC winner 2000.
Rooms: 4 all ensuite ⊗
Pricing: Sgl €38.50 Dbl €55–60
Room facilities: ▢ ☕
Children: Welcome, 10yrs min age Ħ ⅍
Parking: Off-street and monitored
Directions: Carrigans signposted off N13 and N14 on R236. From Londonderry take A40. Mount Royd in Carrigans village.

Cashel, Co. Galway

Cashel House Hotel

★★★★ 🍲 🍲 🍲

Cashel, Connemara, Co. Galway
Tel: +353(0)95 31001 Fax: +353(0)95 31077
Email: info@cashel-house-hotel.com
Web: www.cashel-house-hotel.com
Seasonal closure: 5 January to 5 February

An oasis of elegance, charm and good food surrounded by 10 acres of one of Ireland's best gardens and 1,500 square miles of unspoilt Connemara's mountains and boglands.
Rooms: 32 all ensuite 🎴 🚫
Pricing: Sgl €75–270 Dbl €150 Dinner from €45
CC: Accepted Room facilities: 🖵 ☎ 🍵 📞
Access: ♿
Children: Welcome, 8yrs min age 🍴
Dogs: Welcome Licences: 🍸
Leisure: Tennis, Riding
Parking: Off-street and monitored
Directions: Take N59 from Galway, 1 mile after Recess take left turn. Hotel is signposted from there.

Castlebar, Co. Mayo

Breaffy House Hotel

★★★

Castlebar, Co. Mayo
Tel: +353(0)65 6823000 Fax: +353(0)65 6823759
Email: reservations@lynchotels.com
Web: www.lynchotels.com
Rooms: 59 all ensuite 🍲 🚫
Pricing: Sgl €89–270 Dbl €121–414
Dinner from €25 CC: Accepted
Room facilities: 🖵 ☎ 🍵
Access: 🛗 ♿
Conference: 7 meeting rooms (Thtr 300 max),
24hr-delegate from €108, day-delegate rate from €33
Children: Welcome 🍴 🍼
Dogs: Guide dogs only
Licences: 🔔 🍸 Leisure: Gym
Parking: Off-street and monitored
Directions: Breaffy House Hotel is situated 4km outside Castlebar on the N60 going towards Tuam and Galway.

Cavan, Co. Cavan

Hotel Kilmore

★★★

Dublin Road, Cavan, Co. Cavan
Tel: +353(0)49 4332288 Fax: +353(0)49 4332458
Email: kilmore@quinn-hotels.com
Web: www.quinnhotels.com
Seasonal closure: 24–26 December
Rooms: 39 all ensuite
Pricing: Sgl €75–85 Dbl €130–160 Dinner from €37.50
CC: Accepted
Room facilities: 🖵 ☎ 🍵 📞 Access: ♿
Conference: 4 meeting rooms (Thtr 550 max)
Children: Welcome, 12yrs min age 🍴 🍼
Licences: 🍸 Parking: Off-street and monitored
Directions: From Belfast, take A3 to Lisburn. Go to Portadown, Armagh and Monaghan. Take N54 to Clones and Cavan (via bypass). Follow road towards Dublin. Hotel on left.

Clifden, Co. Galway

Alcock & Brown Hotel

★★★★ 🍲 🍲

The Square, Clifden, Co. Galway
Tel: +353(0)95 21206 Fax: +353(0)95 21842
Email: alcockandbrown@eircom.net
Web: www.alcockandbrown-hotel.com
Seasonal closure: 22–26 December
Rooms: 19 all ensuite 🚫
Pricing: Sgl €70–94 Dbl €100–130 Dinner from €33
CC: Accepted Room facilities: 🖵 ☎ 🍵
Children: Welcome 🍴 Dogs: Welcome
Licences: 🔔 🍸
Directions: From Dublin take N6 to Galway, then N59 to Clifden. Hotel is in centre of village.

Ardagh Hotel & Restaurant

★★★★ 🍲 🍲 🍲

Ballyconneely Road, Clifden, Co. Galway
Tel: +353(0)95 21384 Fax: +353(0)95 21314
Email: ardaghhotel@eircom.net
Web: www.commerce.ie/ardaghhotel
Seasonal closure: November to March
Rooms: 21 all ensuite 🍲
Pricing: Sgl €96.65–109.35 Dbl €143.30–168.60
Dinner from €25 CC: Accepted
Room facilities: 🖵 ☎ 🍵 Children: Welcome 🍴
Dogs: Welcome Licences: 🍸
Leisure: Games room, Snooker/billiards
Parking: Off-street
Directions: From Clifden Town follow signs to Ballyconneely. Ardagh Hotel is 2 miles out of Clifden.

Making a booking?

Don't forget to mention RAC Hotels and Bed & Breakfast 2003.

Renvyle House Hotel

★★★★ ℛ ℛ

Renvyle, Connemara, Co. Galway
Tel: +353(0)95 43511 Fax: +353(0)95 43515
Email: renvyle@iol.ie
Web: www.renvyle.com
Seasonal closure: January to February
Rooms: 69 all ensuite
Pricing: Sgl £55–140 Dbl £96–198 Dinner from £30
CC: Accepted Room facilities: 💻 ☎ 🍵 📠 Access: ♿
Conference: 2 meeting rooms (Thtr 120 max)
Children: Welcome 🍴 🧸 ℃ Dogs: Welcome
Licences: ◇ ⅲ
Leisure: Outdoor pool, Tennis, Golf, Fishing,
Riding, Snooker/billiards
Parking: Off-street and monitored
Directions: Take N59 west from Galway. At recess turn
right, at Kylemore turn left. At Letterfrack turn right.
Continue for 5 miles.
See advert on next page

Station House Hotel

★★★

Clifden, Connemara, Co. Galway
Tel: +353(0)95 21699 Fax: +353(0)95 21667
Email: reservations@stationhousehotel.com
Web: www.stationhousehotel.com
Seasonal closure: Christmas

Set on the former site of Clifden railway station this
unique hotel is a must, only 1 hour from Galway city.
Ideal base for touring Keylemore Abbey, Connermara
National Park, Aran Islands and more.
Rooms: 78 all ensuite
Pricing: Sgl €100–190 Dbl €160–200 Dinner from €30
CC: Accepted Room facilities: 💻 ☎ 🍵 📠
Access: ♿ ♿
Conference: 3 meeting rooms (Thtr 300 max)
Children: Welcome 🍴 Dogs: Guide dogs only
Licences: ◇ ⅲ
Leisure: Indoor pool, Gym, Beauty salon,
Games room
Parking: Off-street
Directions: N59 from Galway city.

Buttermilk Lodge Guest House

♦ ♦ ♦ ♦ ⚡ ℃

Westport Road, Clifden, Co. Galway
Tel: +353(0)95 21951
Fax: +353(0)95 21953
Email: buttermilk@anu.ie
Web: www.buttermilklodge.com
Seasonal closure: January
Rooms: 11 all ensuite 🅂
Room facilities: 💻 ☎ 📠
Children: Welcome, 5yrs min age
Dogs: Guide dogs only Parking: Off-street
Directions: From Galway, turn right at Esso station; we
are 400 metres on left. From Westport, we are on right
100 metres after 'Clifden' sign.

Byrnes' Mal Dua House   Little Gem

♦ ♦ ♦ ♦ ⚡ ℃

Galway Road, Clifden, Co. Galway
Tel: +353(0)95 21171 Fax: +353(0)95 21739
Email: info@maldua.com
Web: www.maldua.com
Rooms: 14 all ensuite 🅂
Pricing: Sgl €44–70 Dbl €88–140
Dinner from €15 CC: Accepted
Room facilities: 💻 ☎ 🍵 📠 Access: ♿
Conference: 3 meeting rooms (Thtr 30 max)
Children: Welcome 🍴 🧸 ℃ Dogs: Guide dogs only
Licences: ⅲ
Parking: Off-street and monitored
Directions: Entering Clifden on N59 from Galway we
are located on right-hand side as you approach town.

Dún Rí Guest House

♦ ♦ ♦ ♦ ⚡

Hulk Street, Clifden, Co. Galway
Tel: +353(0)95 21625
Fax: +353(0)95 21635
Email: dunri@anu.ie
Web: www.connemara.net/dun-ri
Seasonal closure: November to February
Rooms: 10 all ensuite 🅂
Room facilities: 💻 ☎ 🍵 📠
Children: Welcome, 4yrs min age 🍴 ℃
Parking: Off-street
Directions: Entering Clifden on N59, take left before
Statoil Station. Road will bring you directly to Dún Rí
Guest House.

Benview House

◆ ◆ ◆

Bridge Street, Clifden, Co. Galway
Tel: +353(0)95 21256 Fax: +353(0)95 21226
Email: benviewhouse@ireland.com
Web: www.connemara-tourism.org

Charming mid-19th century town of immense character.
Our family has been extending traditional family
hospitality to our guests continuously since 1926.
Recommended by Frommer and Le Petit Fute guides.
Rooms: 9 all ensuite ✪
Pricing: Sgl €30–45 Dbl €27–32 CC: Accepted
Room facilities: ▢ ☎ ☺
Children: Welcome ⊓ ☼
Dogs: Welcome

Kingstown House

◆ ◆ ◆

Bridge Street, Clifden, Co. Galway
Tel: +353(0)95 21470 Fax: +353 95 21530
Seasonal closure: 23 – 28 December
Rooms: 8 (7 ensuite) ✪ ⊘
Room facilities: ▢ ☺
Children: Welcome ☼
Directions: Enter Clifden on N59; second B&B on the
right at beginning of one-way system.

Renvyle House Hotel

Renvyle House Hotel is spectacularly
located on the west coast of Ireland, nestled
between the Twelve Bens and the Atlantic
Ocean. It is a place full of old world charm
and history, fine food, an extensive wine list
and comfortable rooms.
The hotel is situated on 200 acres
and offers extensive on-site facilities
including golf, trout fishing, claypigeon
shooting, archery, tennis and snooker.

Renvyle, Connemara, Co. Galway
Tel: +353(0)95 43511   Fax: +353(0)95 43515
renvyle@iol.ie
www.renvyle.com

Cong, Co. Mayo

Ballywarren Country House   Little Gem

◆ ◆ ◆ ◆ ◆ ☂ ☒ ☙

Cross, Cong, Co. Mayo
Tel: +353 (0)92 46989 Fax: +353 (0)92 46989
Email: ballywarrenhouse@iercom.net
Web: www.ballywarrenhouse.com

Ballywarren is a charming country home with beautiful
rooms, large bathrooms, four-poster and hand-carved
beds, peat and log fires, and excellent food and wine.
Magnificent scenery, plenty of fishing and music.
Rooms: 3 all ensuite ▤ ⊘
Pricing: Sgl €92–98 Dbl €124–140 Dinner from €35
CC: Accepted Room facilities: ▢ ☎ ⚒ ☍
Children: Welcome, 12yrs min age Dogs: Welcome
Licences: ●●● Parking: Off-street
Directions: ³/₄ mile from Cross towards Cong on the
right-hand side.

Connemara, Co. Galway

The Anglers Return

◆ ◆ ◆

Toombeola, Roundstone, Connemara, Co. Galway
Tel: +353(0)95 31091 Fax: +353(0)95 31091
Email: lynnhill@eircom.net
Web: www.anglersreturn.itgo.com
Seasonal closure: December to February

Charming and peaceful 18th century house in beautiful
setting overlooking Salmon river near the 12 Bens.
Warm welcome, turf fires, woodland gardens,
wonderful walk, sea fishing, golf, golden beaches,
excellent restaurants nearby.
Rooms: 5 (1 ensuite) ⛱ ⊗
Pricing: Sgl €50–55 Dbl €71–76 Room facilities: ◲
Children: Welcome 8yrs min age ⟨ Parking: Off-street
Directions: From Galway, N59 Galway/Clifden Road,
turn left on R341, Roundstone Road, for 4 miles. The
Anglers Return on left.

Cork City, Co. Cork

Hayfield Manor   Gold Ribbon Winner

★ ★ ★ ★ ★ ⧫ ⧫ ⧫
Perrott Avenue, College Road, Cork City, Co. Cork
Tel: +353(0)21 484 5900 Fax: +353(0)21 431 6839
Email: enquiries@hayfieldmanor.ie
Web: www.hayfieldmanor.ie
Rooms: 88 all ensuite ⊗
Pricing: Sgl €250–280 Dbl €343–535 Dinner from €58
CC: Accepted Room facilities: ▢ ☎ ➚ ❄
Access: ⼁ ⅊
Conference: 6 meeting rooms (Thtr 100 max),
24hr-delegate from €315, day-delegate rate from €65
Children: Welcome ⟨ Dogs: Guide dogs only
Licences: ﹟
Leisure: Indoor pool, Gym, Health spa,
Beauty salon
Parking: Off-street and monitored
Directions: Travelling west from city centre, take N70
for Killarney. Turn left at university gates off Western
Road. At top of road turn right and immediately left;
hotel at top of avenue.
See advert on next page

Jurys Cork Hotel

★ ★ ★ ★ ★ ⧫ ⧫
Western Road, Cork, Co. Cork
Tel: +353(0)1 6070000 Fax: +353(0)1 6316999
Email: bookings@jurysdoyle.com
Web: www.jurysdoyle.com

🐉JURYSDOYLE
HOTELS

Rooms: 185 all ensuite
Pricing: Sgl €169–211 Dbl €209–254 Dinner from €25
CC: Accepted Room facilities: ▢ ☎ ➚ ☍
Access: ⼁ ⅊ Children: Welcome 12yrs min age ⟨ ⟨
Dogs: Guide dogs only Licences: ⬨ ﹟
Leisure: Indoor pool, Outdoor pool, Gym
Parking: Off-street and monitored
Directions: Follow signpost for Kerry route. Junction of
N22 follow signs city centre. Hotel well signposted
from this.

Kingsley Hotel

★ ★ ★ ★ ⧫
Victoria Cross, Cork, Co. Cork
Tel: +353(0)21 4800 500 Fax: +353(0)21 4800 527
Web: www.kingsleyhotel.com

Set majestically along the banks of the river Lee —
sheer luxury and contentment.
Rooms: 69 all ensuite ⛱ 🖥 ⊗
Pricing: Dinner from €45 CC: Accepted
Room facilities: ▢ ☎ ➚ ☍ ❄ Access: ⼁ ⅊
Conference: 11 meeting rooms (Thtr 3 max)
Children: Welcome ⟨ Dogs: Guide dogs only
Licences: ⬨ ﹟
Leisure: Indoor pool, Gym, Health spa, Beauty salon
Parking: Monitored
Directions: Located on the N22 from Cork, 7km from
Cork Airport. Private Helipad.

Hayfield Manor Hotel

Located beside the University College and set in two acres of mature gardens, Cork's premier 5star hotel retains the serene and unhurried tranquillity of a true country house hotel, combining the elegance and dignity of an earlier age with all the comfort and luxury the modern traveller could wish for.

As a family owned hotel the proprietors Joe and Margaret Scally have brought warm and homely touches to guest rooms, which, while offering the most modern in-room technology, retain the traditional feel of an elegant private residence. Luxuriously spacious rooms offer marble bathrooms and garden views, with individually controlled air conditioning, fine terry cloth bathrobes and baskets brimming with toiletries. From their room guests have direct access to an exclusive private health club where even the pool has views across a formal garden. Whether you wish to work out in the fitness suite, enjoy the steam room or simply relax in the outdoor Jacuzzi, it's the complete health facility.

No stay at Hayfield Manor Hotel is complete without sampling the award winning cuisine and friendly but discreet service at the Manor Room Restaurant, acclaimed by local society and hotel guests alike.

Hayfield Manor offers the perfect location for off site meetings with a dedicated executive board room, syndicate rooms, and a conference that can cater for up to 100 persons theatre style.

The famous Old Head Golf Links is one of many in the locality, and just one of the attractions to be found amid the superb scenery of Ireland's southwest. Hayfield Manor Hotel is only a 5-minute drive from Cork International Airport.

Perrott Avenue, College Road, Cork
Tel: +353 (0)21 484 5900 Fax: +353 (0)21 431 6839
Email: enquiries@hayfieldmanor.ie Web:www.hayfieldmanor.ie

Lodge & Spa at Inchydoney Island

Blue Ribbon Winner

★★★★★ ♖ ♖ ♖

Inchydoney Island, Clonakilty, West Cork
Tel: +353(0)23 33143/21107 Fax: +353(0)23 35229
Email: reservations@inchydoneyisland.com
Web: www.inchydoneyisland.com
Seasonal closure: 25–26 December
Rooms: 63 (6 ensuite) ♒ ⚏ ☻
Pricing: Sgl €169.40–187 Dbl €286–302.50
Dinner from €50 CC: Accepted
Room facilities: ▢ ☎ ☺ ☙ Access: ⌊↑⌋ ♿
Conference: 6 meeting rooms (Thtr 300 max),
24hr-delegate from €193, day-delegate rate from €50
Children: Welcome ♔ ⅌ Licences: ⚘ ♙♙♙
Leisure: Indoor pool, Gym, Health spa,
Beauty salon, Games room, Snooker/billiards
Parking: Off-street and monitored
Directions: Take N71 from Cork to Clonakilty.

Silver Springs Moran Hotel

★★★★ ♖

Tivoli, Cork, Co. Cork
Tel: +353(0)21 4507533 Fax: +353(0)21 4507641
Email: silversprings@morangroup.ie
Web: www.morangroup.ie

Situated on the upper reaches of the river Lee, 4-star hotel is only a five minutes drive from the city centre. 15 minutes from Cork airport. 109 luxury ensuite bedrooms, choice of bars and restaurants. Excellent cuisine. Full leisure centre.
Rooms: 109 all ensuite ☻
Pricing: Sgl €95–115 Dbl €115–145
Dinner from €28.50 CC: Accepted
Room facilities: ▢ ☎ ☺ Access: ⌊↑⌋ ♿
Conference: 15 meeting rooms
Children: Welcome ♔ ⚒ ⅌ Dogs: Guide dogs only
Licences: ⚘ ♙♙♙
Leisure: Indoor pool, Gym, Health spa,
Beauty salon, Tennis
Parking: Off-street and complimentary
Directions: From airport, follow signs to N25, through tunnel. Take first left and head for Cork centre. Turn left onto flyover, right at top; hotel is on left.

Jurys Inn Cork

★★★

Anderson's Quay, Cork, Co. Cork
Tel: +353(0)1 6070000 Fax: +353(0)1 6316999
Email: bookings@jurysdoyle.com
Web: www.jurysdoyle.com

⚜ JURYS DOYLE
HOTELS

Seasonal closure: Christmas
Rooms: 133 all ensuite ♒ ☻ Pricing: Sgl €78–88
Dbl €78–88 Dinner from €20
CC: Accepted
Room facilities: ▢ ☎ ☺ ☙
Access: ⌊↑⌋ ♿
Children: Welcome ♔ Dogs: Guide dogs only
Licences: ♙♙♙
Directions: Located 4 miles/6 km from airport. Follow signs for City Centre.

The Gresham Metropole

★★★

MacCurtain Street, Cork, Co. Cork
Tel: +353(0)21 4508122 Fax: +353(0)21 4506450
Email: info@gresham-metropolehotel.com
Web: www.gresham-hotels.com

GRESHAM HOTELS

Newly refurbished, features state of the art swimming pool and gym.
Rooms: 113 all ensuite ♒ ☻
Pricing: Sgl €145-350 Dbl €190-350 Dinner from €25
CC: Accepted Room facilities: ▢ ☎ ☺ Access: ⌊↑⌋ ♿
Children: Welcome Dogs: Guide dogs only
Licences: ♙♙♙ Leisure: Indoor pool, Gym, Health spa
Parking: Off-street and monitored
Directions: The back of the hotel is facing onto Patricks Quay overlooking the river Lee. The entrance to the hotel is on Mac Curtain Street, in the centre of Cork City.

Ambassador Hotel Best Western

St Lukes, Cork City, Co. Cork
Tel: 021 4551996 Fax:
reservations@ambassadorhotel.ie
Email: www.ambassadorhotel.ie
Seasonal closure: 24 & 26 December
Rooms: 60 all ensuite 🛏 🚭 Pricing: Sgl €90–110
Dbl €115–140 Dinner from €35 CC: Accepted
Room facilities: 🖵 ☎ 🍵 📞 Access: ⅲ ♿
Conference: 4 meeting rooms (Thtr 80 max)
Children: Welcome ♀ Dogs: Guide dogs only
Licences: ♀♀ Parking: Off-street and monitored
Directions: Take a left turn at end of Maclurtoun Street
at lights, proceed up Summerhill and take left turn at
St Lukes cross.

Crawford House

Western Road, Cork, Co. Cork
Tel: +353(0)21 4279000 Fax: +353(0)21 4279927
Email: crawford@indigo.ie
Web: www.crawfordguesthouse.com

This superior guesthouse offers bed and breakfast in a
contemporary setting. All rooms furnished with oak
wood furniture and king-sized beds. Jacuzzi ensuites
with power showers. Enjoy breakfast in the light-filled
conservatory.
Rooms: 12 all ensuite 🚭
Pricing: Sgl €60–110 Dbl €90–115 CC: Accepted
Room facilities: 🖵 ☎ 🍵 📞 Children: Welcome ♀
Parking: Off-street and monitored
Directions: Ten-minute walk from city centre. Located
directly across from University College, Cork. N8 from
Dublin, N22 from Kerry.

Fairy Lawn Guesthouse

Western Road, Cork, Co. Cork
Tel: +353(0)21 4543444 Fax: +353(0)21 4544337
Email: fairylawn@holidayhound.com
Web: www.holidayhound.com/fairylawn.htm

Rooms: 14 all ensuite 🚭
Pricing: Sgl €55–69 Dbl €70–98 CC: Accepted
Room facilities: 🖵 ☎ 🍵 Children: Welcome
Parking: Off-street
Directions: From city centre (Patrick Street) proceed
to Capitol cineplex, turn right at lights onto
Washington Street. Straight on past gates of UCC
and guesthouse is on right before next traffic lights.

Garnish House

Western Road, Cork City, Co. Cork
Tel: +353(0)21 4275111 Fax: +353(0)21 4273872
Email: garnish@iol.ie
Web: www.garnish.ie

A stay in Garnish House is a memorable one. Tastefully
appointed rooms, with optional ensuite jacuzzi and our
extensive gourmet breakfast is certain to please, 24
hrs reception for enquiries. Convenient to ferry, airport
& bus terminal and 5 minutes walk to city centre. Ideal
base to visit Southern Ireland. Suites and Studios also
available.
Rooms: 14 (20 ensuite) 🛏 🚭
Pricing: Sgl €44–90 Dbl €80–160
CC: Accepted Room facilities: 🖵 ☎ 🍵
Access: ♿ Children: Welcome ♀ 🐎 🍼
Dogs: Welcome
Parking: Off-street and monitored
Directions: N8 from Dublin, N22 from Kerry. Close to
bus and rail stations, opposite Cork University, 20 min
drive from Cork airport.

Killarney Guest House

Western Road, Cork, Co. Cork
Tel: +353(0)21 270290 Fax: +353(0)21 271010
Email: killarneyhouse@iol.ie
Web: killarneyguesthouse.com
Rooms: 19 all ensuite 🚭
Room facilities: 🖵 ☎ 🍵 Children: Welcome ♀
Parking: Off-street and monitored
Directions: 10 minutes' walk from city centre and
across from Cork University. N8 from Dublin and N22
from Kerry.

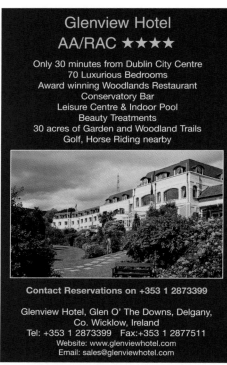
Lancaster Lodge

◆ ◆ ◆ ◆

Lancaster Quay, Western Road, Cork, Co. Cork
Tel: +353(0)21 4251125 Fax: +353(0)21 4251126
Email: info@lancasterlodge.com
Web: www.lancasterlodge.com
Seasonal closure: 23-25 December
Rooms: 39 all ensuite
Pricing: Sgl €70–130 Dbl €100–160
CC: Accepted
Room facilities: ▢ ☎ ☐ ⅃
Access: ⅃⅃ ⅃ Children: Welcome
Dogs: Guide dogs only
Parking: Off-street and monitored
Directions: Located alongside Jurys Hotel on the
Western road in Cork. 5-minute walk to city centre.

Antoine House

◆ ◆ ◆

Western Road, Cork City, Co. Cork
Tel: +353(0)21 273494 Fax: +353(0)21 273092
Web: antoinehouse.com
Rooms: 10 all ensuite ⅃⅃ ⊗
Pricing: Sgl €40–60 Dbl €60–100
CC: Accepted
Children: Welcome ⅃ Dogs: Guide dogs only
Parking: Off-street and monitored
Directions: Situated on the Western road,
opposite UCC.

Roserie Villa

◆ ◆ ◆

Mardyke Walk, off Western Road, Cork, Co. Cork
Tel: +353(0)21 272958 Fax: +353(0)21 274087
Rooms: 16 all ensuite ⊗
Pricing: Sgl €38–60 Dbl €70–90 CC: Accepted
Room facilities: ▢ ☎ ⊿
Access: ♿ Children: Welcome ⧖ Parking: Monitored
Directions: Take Washington Street, onto Western Rd,
take right at university college, first house on right.

Travelodge Cork

Travel Accommodation
R600, Black Ash, Kinsale Road Roundabout,
Frankfield Road, Cork, Co. Cork
Web: www.travelodge.co.uk
Rooms: 40 all ensuite ⊗
Pricing: Sgl €53.45–53.45 Dbl €57.90–57.90
CC: Accepted Room facilities: ▢ ⊿ Access: ♿

Delgany, Co. Wicklow

Glenview Hotel

★ ★ ★ ★ ★ ℞ ℞

Glen O' The Downs, Delgany, Co. Wicklow,
Tel: +353(0)1 2873399 Fax: +353(0)1 2877511
Email: glenview@iol.ie
Web: www.glenview.com
Rooms: 70 all ensuite ❤ ⊗
Room facilities: ▢ ☎ ⊿ ℄
Access: |�??| Conference: 5 meeting rooms (Thtr 200 max)
Children: Welcome, 12yrs min age ⧖
Dogs: Guide dogs only Licences: ◁
Leisure: Indoor pool, Gym, Beauty salon,
Games room, Snooker/billiards
Parking: Off-street and monitored
Directions: Take N11 southbound towards Wexford.
After village of Kilmacanogue, continue southbound for
approximately 2 miles where you will see signs for the
Glenview Hotel.
See advert on previous page

Dingle, Co. Kerry

Dingle Skellig Hotel

★ ★ ★ ℞

Dingle, Co. Kerry
Tel: +353(0)66 9150200 Fax: +353(0)66 9151501
Email: reservations@dingleskellig.com
Web: www.dingleskellig.com
Rooms: 112 all ensuite ⊗
Pricing: Sgl €78–145 Dbl €118–240
Dinner from €45 CC: Accepted
Room facilities: ▢ ☎ Access: |�??| ♿
Conference: 4 meeting rooms (Thtr 250 max)
Children: Welcome ⧖ ⛶
Dogs: Guide dogs only Licences: ◁ ♦♦♦
Leisure: Indoor pool, Gym, Health spa, Games room
Parking: Off-street
Directions: Hotel on the shores of Dingle Harbour as
you enter the town from the main Killarney/Tralee road.

Emlagh House
Little Gem

◆ ◆ ◆ ◆ ◆ ⌘ ℞

Dingle, Co. Kerry
Tel: +353(0)66 9152345 Fax: +353(0)66 9152369
Email: info@emlaghhouse.com
Web: www.emlaghhouse.com
Seasonal closure: 15–28 Dec, 5 January to 1 March
Rooms: 10 all ensuite ⊗
Pricing: Sgl €120 Dbl €200 CC: Accepted
Room facilities: ▢ ☎ ℄ ❄
Access: |�??| ♿ Children: Welcome, 8yrs min age
Dogs: Guide dogs only Licences: ♦♦♦
Parking: Off-street and monitored
Directions: As you approach Dingle you will pass a
Shell station and Emlagh is on the first left.
See advert on previous page

Greenmount House
Little Gem

◆ ◆ ◆ ◆ ◆ ⌘ ℞

Upper John Street, Dingle, Co. Kerry
Tel: +353(0)66 9151414 Fax: +353(0)66 9157974
Email: mary@greenmounthouse.com
Web: www.greenmounthouse.com
Seasonal closure: 10-27 December
Rooms: 12 all ensuite ❤ ⊗
Pricing: Sgl €60–110 Dbl €90–145 CC: Accepted
Room facilities: ▢ ☎ ⊿ Access: ♿
Children: Welcome, 8yrs min age Parking: Off-street
Directions: On entering Dingle take right turn at
roundabout, right at next junction. The hotel is situated
up hill, 350 metres on left.

Alpine House Guest House

◆ ◆ ◆ ◆ ⌘

Mail Road, Dingle, Co. Kerry
Tel: +353(0)66 9151250 Fax: +353(0)66 9151966
Email: alpinedingle@eircom.net
Web: www.alpineguesthouse.com

Newly renovated guest house. Beautifully furnished
bedrooms, all with spacious bathrooms. Non-smoking.
Private car park. Town centre is a 2-minute walk away.
Rooms: 10 all ensuite ⊗
Pricing: Sgl €35–60 Dbl €50–90
CC: Accepted Room facilities: ▢ ☎ ⊿
Children: Welcome, 5yrs min age
Dogs: Guide dogs only Parking: Off-street
Directions: On route N86 at entrance to Dingle town. 2
minutes' walk from town centre.

Bambury's Guesthouse

◆◆◆◆

Mail Road, Dingle, Co. Kerry
Tel: +353(0)66 9151244 Fax: +353(0)66 9151786
Email: bamburysguesthouse@eircom.net
Web: www.bamburysguesthouse.com

Overlooking Dingle town this beautiful appointed property is just a stroll from the town, luxurious accommodation with style and comfort. 12 ensuite bedrooms, a warm welcome awaits you at our family run guest house.
Rooms: 12 all ensuite ⚫ ⊗
Pricing: Sgl €35–60 Dbl €70–100 CC: Accepted
Room facilities: 🖵 ☎ 🗗 Access: ♿
Children: Welcome, 4yrs min age
Dogs: Guide dogs only Parking: Off-street
Directions: On the N86 into Dingle. Hotel is situated after the Shell station as you enter Dingle.

Cleevaun

◆◆◆◆ ※ ☕

Milltown, Dingle, Co. Kerry
Tel: +353(0)66 9151108 Fax: +353(0)66 9152228
Web: www.cleevaun.com
Seasonal closure: Mid-November to mid-March
Rooms: 9 all ensuite ⊗
Pricing: Sgl €55–85 Dbl €40–48 CC: Accepted
Room facilities: 🖵 ☎ 🗗
Directions: Route 559. Take first left off first roundabout. Follow signs for Sleahead. With water on left, pass marina. Turn left at next roundabout. Cross bridge. Cleevaun 500 metres on left.

Doyle's Town House

◆◆◆◆ ※ ☕

John Street, Dingle, Co. Kerry
Tel: +353(0)66 9151174 Fax: +353(0)66 9151816
Email: cdoyles@iol.ie
Web: www.doylesofdingle.com
Seasonal closure: Mid-November to mid-February
Rooms: 8 all ensuite ⊗
Pricing: Sgl €107–115 Dbl €45–67 CC: Accepted
Room facilities: 🖵 ☎ 🗗 Access: ♿
Children: Welcome, 8yrs min age Licences: 👤

Milltown House

◆◆◆◆ ※ ☕

Dingle, Co. Kerry
Tel: +353(0)66 9151372 Fax: +353(0)66 9151095
Email: milltown@indigo.ie
Web: indigo.ie/~milltown

Seasonal closure: 30 November to 1 February
Rooms: 10 all ensuite ⊗ Pricing: Sgl €65–140
Dbl €100–155 CC: Accepted Room facilities: 🖵 ☎ 🗗
Access: ♿ Children: Welcome, 12yrs min age
Dogs: Guide dogs only Parking: Off-street and monitored
Directions: Leave Dingle on Sleahead Drive Road. Take next two left turns. House less than 1 mile west of Dingle town.

Donegal, Co. Donegal

Harvey's Point Country Hotel

Blue Ribbon Winner

★★★★ ☕ ☕
Lough Eske, Donegal, Co. Donegal
Tel: +353(0)73 22208 Fax: +353(0)73 22352
Email: info@harveyspoint.com
Web: www.harveyspoint.com
Rooms: 20 all ensuite 🖼 Pricing: Sgl €108–118
Dbl €178–198 Dinner from €45 CC: Accepted
Room facilities: 🖵 ☎ 🗗 Conference: 3 meeting rooms (Thtr 250 max), 24hr-delegate from €150, day-delegate rate from €25 Dogs: Welcome Licences: ⚓ 👤
Leisure: Tennis, Fishing Parking: Off-street
Directions: 6km outside Donegal town.

Ardeevin

◆◆◆◆ ※ ☕

Lough Eske, Barnesmore, Donegal, Co. Donegal,
Tel: +353(0)73 21790 Fax: +353(0)73 21790
Email: seanmcginty@eircom.net
Web: www.members.tripod.com/~Ardeevin

Charming country residence, overlooking Lough Eake and Donegal Bay. Surrounded by Bluestack mountains with Sligo mountains close by. All bedrooms have a pamoramic view of Lough Eake with its salmon, sea trout, brown trout and char. There are many forest walks and serveral small lakes in the mountains within walking distance convenient to beaches, golf course, horse riding within 8km.
Rooms: 6 all ensuite 🖼 ⊗ Pricing: Sgl €35–40
Dbl €55–65 Room facilities: 🖵 🗗
Children: Welcome,10yrs min age
Parking: Off-street and monitored
Directions: Take N15 from Donegal Town, Derry/Letterkenny road for 4km. Turn left at sign for Ardeevin (past garage).

Dromoland, Co. Clare

Clare Inn Golf and Leisure Hotel

★★★

Dromoland, Co. Clare
Tel: +353(0)6568 23000 Fax: +353(0)6568 23759
Email: reservations@lynchotels.com
Web: www.lynchotels.com
Rooms: 183 all ensuite
Pricing: Sgl €70–176 Dbl €95–288 Dinner from €25
CC: Accepted Room facilities:
Access:
Conference: 5 meeting rooms (Thtr 400 max),
24hr-delegate from €112, day-delegate rate from €32
Children: Welcome
Dogs: Guide dogs only Licences:
Leisure: Indoor pool, Gym, Health spa, Tennis,
Golf, Riding, Games room
Parking: Off-street and monitored
Directions: Located just 10 minutes drive from
Shannon International Airport on the main Galway
Road (N18) on the Dromoland Estate.

Dublin

Conrad Dublin

★★★★★★

Earlsfort Trarrace, Dublin 2
Tel: +353(0)602 8900 Fax: +353(0)676 5424
Email: dubhc-salesadm@hilton.com
Web: www.conraddublin.com
Rooms: 191 all ensuite
Pricing: Sgl €380–380 Dbl €380–380 Dinner from €34
CC: Accepted Room facilities:
Access:
Children: Welcome Licences:
Leisure: Gym
Parking: Off-street and monitored
Directions: Located in the city centre, on the south side
of St Stephen's Green, at the end of Leeson Street.

Le Méridien Shelbourne

★★★★★★

27 St Stephens Green, Dublin 2,
Tel: 0800 028 2840 Fax: +353(0)1 6616006
Email: shelbourneinfo@lemeridien.com
Web: www.shelbourne.ie
Rooms: 190 all ensuite
Room facilities: Access:
Conference: 11 meeting rooms (Thtr 400 max),
24hr-delegate from €245, day-delegate rate from €68
Children: Welcome Dogs: Welcome
Licences: Leisure: Indoor pool, Gym,
Health spa, Beauty salon
Parking: Off-street and monitored
Directions: In the heart of Dublin city centre, close to
Trinity College.

Merrion Hotel

Gold Ribbon Winner

★★★★★★

Upper Merrion Street, Dublin 2
Tel: +353(0)1 603 0600 Fax: +353(0)1 603 0700
Email: info@merrionhotel.com
Web: www.merrionhotel.com

The Merrion Dublin's most luxurious 5-star hotel is
created from four 18th century townhouses and a
contemporary garden wing. Facilities include 145
bedrooms and suites, 2 bars, 2 restaurants, private
gardens and health club.
Rooms: 145 all ensuite
Pricing: Sgl €325–405 Dbl €375–465
Dinner from €24.75 CC: Accepted
Room facilities: Access:
Conference: 6 meeting rooms (Thtr 50 max)
Children: Welcome Dogs: Guide dogs only
Licences:
Leisure: Indoor pool, Gym, Health spa, Beauty salon
Parking: Off-street and monitored
Directions: Situated at the top of Upper Merrion Street
on left, opposite government buildings, in the heart of
Dublin city.

The Berkeley Court

★★★★★★

Lansdowne Road, Dublin 4
Tel: +353(0)1 6090000 Fax: +353(0)1 6316999
Email: bookings@jurysdoyle.com
Web: www.jurysdoyle.com

JURYS DOYLE
HOTELS

Rooms: 188 all ensuite
Pricing: Sgl €296–387 Dbl €321–412 Dinner from €42
CC: Accepted Room facilities:
Access:
Children: Welcome, 12yrs min age
Dogs: Guide dogs only Licences:
Leisure: Beauty salon
Parking: Off-street and monitored
Directions: Follow signs to city centre. East Link toll,
over bridge. Follow signs for RDS. Turn right at Jurys
Hotel. Berkeley is on right.

The Westbury Hotel

★★★★★ ℞ ℞

Grafton Street, Dublin 4
Tel: +353(0)1 6070000 Fax: +353(0)1 6316999
Email: bookings@jurysdoyle.com
Web: www.jurysdoyle.com

Pricing: Sgl €313–405 Dbl €338–476 Dinner from €50

Alexander Hotel at Merrion Square

★★★★ ℞

Fenian Street, Dublin 2
Tel: +353 (0)1 607 3700 Fax: +353 (0)1 661 5663
Email: alexanderres@ocallaghanhotels.ie
Web: www.ocallaghanhotels.ie
Rooms: 102 all ensuite ⊛
Pricing: Dinner from €21.35 (2002 rate) CC: Accepted
Room facilities: ▢ ☎ ☺ ☏ ❋ Access: ♿
Licences: ⚔
Directions: The Alexander is located at the corner of
Fenian Street and South Cumberland Street, just off
Merrion Square.

Fitzpatrick Castle

★★★★

Killiney, Co. Dublin
Tel: +353(0)1 2305 556/400
Fax: +353(0)1 2305 466/430
Email: reservations@fitzpatricks.com
Web: www.fitzpatrickhotels.com
Seasonal closure: 24–27 December
Rooms: 113 all ensuite ⚐ ⊛
Pricing: Sgl €147–187 Dbl €170–270
Dinner from €45 CC: Accepted
Room facilities: ▢ ☎ ☺ ☏ Access: ♿
Conference: 9 meeting rooms (Thtr 500 max)
Children: Welcome ♏ ⚘
Dogs: Guide dogs only Licences: ⚜ ⚔
Leisure: Indoor pool, Gym, Health spa, Beauty salon
Parking: Off-street and monitored
Directions: Coast road to Dalkey village then turn
inland to top of Killiney hill.

Fitzwilliam Hotel

★★★★ ℞ ℞ ℞

St Stephens Green, Dublin 2
Tel: +353(0)1 4787000 Fax: +353(0)1 4787878

Herbert Park Hotel

★★★★ ℞   *Blue Ribbon Winner*

Ballsbridge, Dublin 4
Tel: +353(0)1 6672200 Fax: +353(0)1 6672595
Email: reservations@herbertparkhotel.ie
Web: www.herbertparkhotel.ie

This award-winning, contemporary-style hotel is five
minutes from the city centre, with spectacular views
over 48-acre Herbert park. Adjacent to the RDS.
Facilities include gym and meeting rooms.
Rooms: 153 all ensuite ⊛
Pricing: Sgl €130–265 Dbl €160–330
Dinner from €45 CC: Accepted
Room facilities: ▢ ☎ ☏ ❋
Access: ♿ ♿
Conference: 4 meeting rooms (Thtr 100 max)
Children: Welcome ♏ ⚘ Dogs: Guide dogs only
Licences: ⚔ Leisure: Gym, Tennis
Parking: Off-street and monitored
Directions: From Nassau Street go straight out of
Mount Street and Northumberland Road into
Ballsbridge; first turn right after the bridge, next right.

Jurys Ballsbridge Hotel

★★★★ ℞

Ballsbridge, Dublin 4
Tel: +353(0)1 6070000 Fax: +353(0)1 6316999
Email: bookings@jurysdoyle.com
Web: www.jurysdoyle.com

Rooms: 303 all ensuite
Pricing: Sgl €222–300 Dbl €241–319 Dinner from €22
CC: Accepted Room facilities: ▢ ☎ ☺ ☏
Access: ♿ ♿ Children: Welcome, 12yrs min age ♏ ⚘
Dogs: Guide dogs only Licences: ⚜ ⚔
Leisure: Indoor pool, Outdoor pool, Gym,
Health spa, Beauty salon
Parking: Off-street and monitored
Directions: Follow signs to city centre, then East Link
Toll Bridge, go over bridge, follow signs for RDS. Hotel
is on left.

Red Cow Moran Hotel

★★★★

Naas Road, Dublin 22
Tel: +353(0)1 4593650 Fax: +353(0)1 4591588
Email: sales@morangroup.ie
Web: www.redcowhotel.com
Seasonal closure: Christmas

Red Cow Moran Hotel combines classic elegance with modern design. Each of the hotel's 123 deluxe bedrooms are fully air-conditioned. Guests have a choice of 3 restaurants and 4 bars and a nightclub in the complex. Free parking.
Rooms: 123 all ensuite ⊛
Pricing: Sgl €120–145 Dbl €185–215
Dinner from €26.50 CC: Accepted
Room facilities: ▯ ☎ ▨ ☏ ❄ Access: ⏏ ♿
Conference: 14 meeting rooms (Thtr 500 max)
Children: Welcome ⋔ Dogs: Guide dogs only
Licences: ♔
Parking: Off-street and monitored
Directions: From Dublin airport – drive towards city on M1; take first exit to M50 southbound and cross toll bridge; take exit 9, N7/The South. Hotel at top of slipway.

The Burlington Hotel

★★★★

Upper Leeson Street, Dublin 4
Tel: +353(0)1 6070055 Fax: +353(0)1 6609625
Email: bookings@jurysdoyle.com
Web: www.jurysdoyle.com

JURYS DOYLE
HOTELS

Rooms: 504 all ensuite
Pricing: Sgl €220–274 Dbl €240–324 Dinner from €30
CC: Accepted Room facilities: ▯ ☎ ☏
Access: ⏏ ♿ Children: Welcome ⋔ ⁌
Parking: Off-street and monitored
Directions: Take N7 out of town. Go up Naas Road until you come to Newlands Cross, go right. At second set of lights turn left. Go up that road for ¼ mile and turn left.

The Davenport Hotel at Merrion Square

★★★★

Lower Merrion Street, Dublin 2,
Tel: +353(0)1 6073900 Fax: +353(0)1 6615663
Email: davenportres@ocallaghanhotels.ie
Web: www.ocallaghanhotels.ie
Rooms: 115 all ensuite ⊛
Pricing: Dinner from €21.35 (2002 rate) CC: Accepted
Room facilities: ▯ ☎ ▨ ☏ ❄ Access: ♿ Licences: ♔
Directions: On Lower Merrion Street, just off Merrion Square.

The Gresham

★★★★

23 Upper O'Connell Street, Dublin 1
Tel: +353 (0)1 8746881 Fax: +353 (0)1 8787175
Email: reservations@thegresham.com
Web: www.gresham-hotels.com

GRESHAM HOTELS

Behind the elegant façade lie luxury bedrooms, an award-winning restaurant and comfortable bars.
Rooms: 288 all ensuite ⚗ ⊛
Pricing: Sgl €122.50–305 Dbl €165–325
Dinner from €29.95 CC: Accepted
Room facilities: ▯ ☎ ☏ Access: ⏏ ♿
Conference: 26 meeting rooms (Thtr 350 max)
Children: Welcome ⋔ Dogs: Guide dogs only
Licences: ⚘ ♔ Leisure: Gym
Parking: Off-street and monitored
Directions: Situated on Dublin's main thoroughfare, O'Connell Street.

Deer Park Hotel & Golf Courses

RAC ★★★

Just 9 miles from Dublin city and airport, Deer Park is an elegant 3-star hotel, set in the tranquil surroundings of Howth Castle Estate. Set in 400 acres of parkland, the hotel features Ireland's largest golf complex (4 courses), 78 ensuite bedrooms, luxury indoor pool, sauna and steam room.

Howth, Co. Dublin

Tel: +335 1 8322624   Fax: +335 1 8392405
Email: sales@deerpark.iol.ie
Website: www.deerpark-hotel.ie

Browne's Brasserie & Townhouse

★★★★ Townhouse 🐦 🐦 🐦
22 St Stephens Green, Dublin 2
Tel: +353(0)1 6383939 Fax: +353(0)1 6383900
Email: info@brownesdublin.com
Web: www.brownesdublin.com
Seasonal closure: 24 December to 4 January
Rooms: 12 all ensuite 🚗 ⊛ Pricing: Sgl €170–180
Dbl €205–425 Dinner from €47 CC: Accepted
Room facilities: 🖵 ☎ 🍵 ⚲ ❋ Access: ᰮ ♿
Conference: 1 meeting room (Thtr 40 max),
24hr-delegate from €300, day-delegate rate from €50
Children: Welcome ᵮ 🐾 Dogs: Guide dogs only
Licences: ᴭᴭᴭ
Directions: Brownes is on the north side of St Stephens Green in the heart of Dublin.

Ashling Hotel — Best Western

★★★
Parkgate Street, Dublin 8
Tel: +353(0)1 6772324 Fax: +353(0)1 6793783
Email: info@ashlinghotel.ie
Web: www.ashlinghotel.ie
Seasonal closure: 22–27 December
Rooms: 150 all ensuite ❧ Pricing: Sgl €99–150
Dbl €116–198 Dinner from €25 CC: Accepted
Room facilities: 🖵 ☎ 🍵 Access: ᰮ ♿
Conference: 11 meeting rooms (Thtr 200 max)
Children: Welcome ᵮ Dogs: Guide dogs only
Licences: ⟁ ᴭᴭᴭ Parking: Off-street and monitored
Directions: Easily-found location by car/rail/bus. By car, take city centre route and briefly follow River Liffey westward. Take taxi or 'Airlink' public bus from airport.

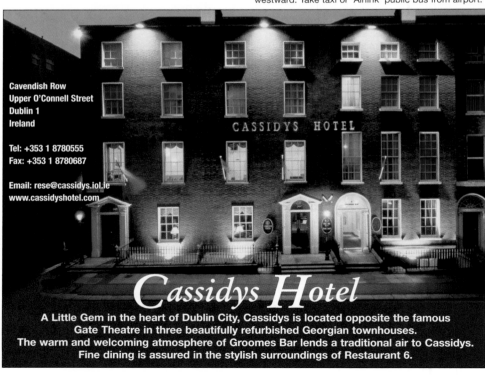

Cassidys Hotel

★★★

Cavendish Row, Upper O'Connell Street, Dublin 1
Tel: +353(0)1 8780555 Fax: +353(0)1 8780687
Email: rese@cassidys.iol.ie
Web: www.cassidyshotel.com
Seasonal closure: 24–27 December
Rooms: 88 all ensuite
Pricing: Sgl €80–200 Dbl €80–200
Dinner from €20 CC: Accepted
Room facilities: Access:
Conference: 4 meeting rooms (Thtr 80 max)
Children: Welcome
Dogs: Guide dogs only
Licences:
Parking: Off-street and monitored
Directions: Continue up O'Connell Street away from
the river. Cassidy's is located opposite the famous
Gate Theatre on Cavendish Row.
See advert on previous page

Deer Park Hotel & Golf Courses

★★★

Howth, Co. Dublin
Tel: +353(0)1 8322624 Fax: +353(0)1 8392405
Email: sales@deerpark.iol.ie
Web: www.deerpark-hotel.ie
Rooms: 80 all ensuite
Pricing: Sgl €103–114 Dbl €154–178 Dinner from €32
CC: Accepted Room facilities: Access:
Conference: 3 meeting rooms (Thtr 100 max)
Children: Welcome Dogs: Guide dogs only
Licences: Leisure: Indoor pool, Tennis, Golf
Parking: Off-street and monitored
Directions: Follow coast road via Clontarf. Through
Sutton Cross and Deer Park is on your right before
Howth Harbour.
See advert on previous page

Finnstown Country House Hotel

★★★★

Newcastle Road, Lucan, Dublin
Tel: +353(0)1 601 0700 Fax: +353(0)1 628 1088
Email: manager@finnstown-hotel.ie
Web: www.finnstown-hotel.ie
Rooms: 53 all ensuite
Pricing: Sgl €121–150 Dbl €178–300 Dinner from €34
CC: Accepted Room facilities: Access:
Conference: 7 meeting rooms (Thtr 300 max),
24hr-delegate from €220, day-delegate rate from €80
Children: Welcome Dogs: Welcome
Licences:
Leisure: Indoor pool, Gym, Tennis,
Games room, Snooker/billiards
Parking: Off-street and monitored
Directions: From Dublin, travel along South Quays,
passing Heuston Station. Continue on N4. At traffic
lights after Texaco garage, turn left. Hotel on right after
two roundabouts.

Hibernian Hotel

★★★★

Eastmoreland Place, Ballsbridge, Dublin 4
Tel: +353(0)1 6687666 Fax: +353(0)1 6602655
Email: info@hibernianhotel.com
Web: www.hibernianhotel.com
Seasonal closure: Christmas
Rooms: 40 all ensuite
Room facilities: Access:
Conference: 1 meeting room (Thtr 40 max)
Children: Welcome
Dogs: Guide dogs only
Licences: Parking: Off-street and monitored
Directions: Turn right from Mespil Road into Baggot
Street Upper, then left into Eastmoreland Place. The
Hibernian is at the end on the left.

Jurys Green Isle Hotel

★★★

Naas Road, Dublin 22
Tel: +353(0)1 6070000 Fax: +353(0)1 6316999
Email: bookings@jurysdoyle.com
Web: www.jurysdoyle.com

JURYS DOYLE
HOTELS

Rooms: 90 all ensuite
Pricing: Sgl €137–196 Dbl €150–209 Dinner from €20
CC: Accepted Room facilities:
Access:
Children: Welcome, 12yrs min age
Dogs: Guide dogs only
Licences:
Parking: Off-street and monitored
Directions: M50 southbound. Exit 9 on to N7
southbound. Right at two lights. 2nd left past garage.
Hotel 600 yards on left.

Jurys Inn Christchurch

★★★

Christchurch Place, Dublin 8
Tel: +353(0)1 6070000 Fax: +353(0)1 6316999
Email: bookings@jurysdoyle.com
Web: www.jurysdoyle.com

JURYS DOYLE
HOTELS

Seasonal closure: Christmas
Rooms: 182 all ensuite
Pricing: Sgl €96–110 Dbl €96–110 Dinner from €18
CC: Accepted Room facilities:
Access: Children: Welcome
Dogs: Guide dogs only Licences:
Parking: Off-street and monitored
Directions: Located 7 miles/10 km from airport. Follow
signs to city centre. Inn located opposite Christchurch
Cathedral at the top of Dame Street.

Jurys Inn Custom House

★★★

Custom House Quay, Dublin 1
Tel: +353(0)1 6070000 Fax: +353(0)1 6316999
Email: bookings@jurysdoyle.com
Web: www.jurysdoyle.com

Seasonal closure: Christmas
Rooms: 239 all ensuite 🛏 🚭
Pricing: Sgl €96–110 Dbl €96–110 Dinner from €18
CC: Accepted Room facilities: 🖥 ☎ 🍵 📞
Access: ⬆ 🚹 Children: Welcome 🍴
Dogs: Guide dogs only Licences: 🍸
Directions: Located 6 miles/10 km from Dublin airport.
Follow signs for city centre. Take left at bridge. Inn is
on the left.

Jurys Montrose Hotel

★★★

Stillorgan Road, Dublin 4
Tel: +353(0)1 6070000 Fax: +353(0)1 6316999
Email: bookings@jurysdoyle.com
Web: www.jurysdoyle.com

Rooms: 179 all ensuite 🚭
Pricing: Sgl €137–196 Dbl €150–209 Dinner from €20
CC: Accepted Room facilities: 🖥 ☎ 🍵 📞
Access: ⬆ 🚹 Children: Welcome 12yrs min age 🍴 ☕
Dogs: Guide dogs only Licences: 🍸
Parking: Off-street and monitored
Directions: M50 follow signs for N11, cross toll bridge,
pass Jurys Tara, take right at lights. Follow road to
Woodbine. At the top, take left.

Jurys Skylon Hotel

★★★

Upper Drumcondra Road, Dublin 9
Tel: +353(0)1 6070000 Fax: +353(0)1 6316999
Email: bookings@jurysdoyle.com
Web: www.jurysdoyle.com

Rooms: 88 all ensuite 🚭
Pricing: Sgl €137–196 Dbl €150–209 Dinner from €20
CC: Accepted Room facilities: 🖥 ☎ 🍵 📞
Access: ⬆ 🚹
Children: Welcome, 12yrs min age 🍴
Dogs: Guide dogs only Licences: 🍸
Parking: Off-street and monitored
Directions: From airport, M1 to city centre. 3 miles on
the right.

Jurys Tara Hotel

★★★

Merrion Road, Dublin 4
Tel: +353(0)1 6070000 Fax: +353(0)1 6316999
Email: bookings@jurysdoyle.com
Web: www.jurysdoyle.com

Seasonal closure: Christmas
Rooms: 113 all ensuite 🚭
Pricing: Sgl €137–196 Dbl €150–209 Dinner from €20
CC: Accepted Room facilities: 🖥 ☎ 🍵 📞
Access: ⬆ 🚹
Children: Welcome, 12yrs min age 🍴
Dogs: Guide dogs only Licences: 🍸 🍸
Parking: Off-street and monitored
Directions: M50 City Centre. Follow N11 and Ferry
signs. Cross toll bridge. Follow Strand Road. Cross
Railtrack. Hotel is on the left.

Longfields Hotel

★★★★ 🇷 🇷

10 Lower Fitzwilliam Street, Dublin 2
Tel: +353(0)1 6761367 Fax: +353(0)1 6761542
Email: info@longfields.ie
Web: www.longfields.ie

A centrally located, charming, intimate hotel with
period furnishings and an excellent restaurant.
Rooms: 26 all ensuite 🚭
Pricing: Sgl €130 Dbl €130 Dinner from €23.50
CC: Accepted Room facilities: 🖥 ☎ 🍵 📞
Access: ⬆
Conference: 1 meeting room (Thtr 20 max),
24hr-delegate from €175
Children: Welcome
Dogs: Guide dogs only
Licences: 🍸
Directions: From airport, follow signs for city centre
then O'Connell Street. Around front of Trinity College to
left, pass Shelbourne Hotel onto Baggot Street. At
main junction of Lower and Upper Baggot streets,
hotel first on left of Fitzwilliam Street.

Marine Hotel

★★★

Sutton Cross, Sutton, Dublin 13
Tel: +353(0)1 8390000 Fax: +353(0)1 8390442
Email: info@marinehotel.com
Web: www.marinehotel.com
Seasonal closure: Christmas
Rooms: 48 all ensuite 🚭 Room facilities: 📺 ☎ 🍵
Access: ↕ ♿
Conference: 7 meeting rooms (Thtr 75 max)
Children: Welcome, 12yrs min age 🍴 Licences: ◁ ♟
Leisure: Indoor pool, Tennis Parking: Monitored

Mount Herbert Hotel

★★★

Herbert Road, Lansdowne Road, Dublin 4
Tel: +353(0)1 668 4321 Fax: +353(0)1 660 7077
Email: info@mountherberthotel.ie
Web: www.mountherberthotel.ie

Stately Victorian residence 5 minutes from city centre
in Dublin's exclusive embassy belt. Facilities include
180 modern bedrooms, restaurant, licensed bar, coffee
bar, sauna, gift shop, conference centre, private car
park and picturesque gardens.
Rooms: 180 all ensuite 🚭
Pricing: Sgl €89.90–198 Dbl €127–198
Dinner from €28.50 CC: Accepted
Room facilities: 📺 ☎ 🍵 Access: ↕ ♿
Children: Welcome 🍴 ♟ Dogs: Guide dogs only
Licences: ♟ Parking: Off-street and monitored
Directions: From city centre, Nassau Street at Trinity
College along Merrion Square, Mount Street,
Northumberland Rd. At Lansdowne Rd turn left. Cross
DART line, pass rugby stadium, cross bridge to hotel.

Parliament Hotel

★★★

Temple Bar, Dublin 2
Tel: +353(0)1 6708777 Fax: +353(0)1 6708787
Email: parl@regencyhotels.com
Web: www.regencyhotels.com
Rooms: 63 all ensuite 🚭 🚭
Pricing: Dinner from €18 CC: Accepted
Room facilities: 📺 ☎ 🍵 📞
Access: ↕ ♿ Children: Welcome 🍴
Dogs: Guide dogs only
Directions: Located in Temple Bar opposite Dublin
Castle, 2 minutes from Trinity College.

Regency Airport Hotel

★★★

Swords Road, Whitehall, Dublin 9
Tel: +353(0)1 8373544 Fax: +353(0)1 8373174
Email: regency@regencyhotels.com
Web: www.regencyhotels.com
Rooms: 210 all ensuite 🚭 🚭
Pricing: Dinner from €21 CC: Accepted
Room facilities: 📺 ☎ 🍵 📞
Access: ↕ ♿
Children: Welcome 🍴 ♟
Dogs: Guide dogs only
Licences: ◁ ♟
Parking: Off-street and monitored
Directions: Travelling from Belfast, pass Dublin airport,
travel down Airport road towards city centre. At
motorway end, go through lights, hotel is on left.

Royal Dublin Hotel

★★★

O'Connell Street, Dublin 1
Tel: +353(0)1 8733666 Fax: +353(0)1 8733120
Email: enq@royaldublin.com
Web: www.royaldublin.com
Rooms: 117 all ensuite 🚭 🚭
Pricing: Dinner from €19.50 (2002 rate)
CC: Accepted
Room facilities: 📺 ☎ 🍵 📞 Access: ↕
Children: Welcome
Licences: ◁ ♟
Parking: Off-street and monitored
Directions: In city centre, from O'Connell Bridge go north
up O'Connell Street. Hotel is at end of street on left.

Temple Bar Hotel

★★★

Fleet Street, Dublin 2,
Tel: +353(0)1 6773333 Fax: +353(0)1 6773088
Web: www.templebarhotel.com
Seasonal closure: 23–25 December
Rooms: 129 all ensuite 🚭
Pricing: Sgl €145 Dbl €190 Dinner from €22
CC: Accepted Room facilities: 📺 ☎ 🍵 📞
Access: ↕ ♿ Children: Welcome 🍴
Dogs: Guide dogs only Licences: ◁ ♟

The North Star Hotel

★★★

Amien Street, Dublin 1
Tel: +353(0)1 8881600 Fax: +353(0)1 8881604
Email: groupsales@regencyhotels.com
Web: www.regencyhotels.com
Rooms: 121 all ensuite 🚭 🚭 🚭
Pricing: Dinner from €19 CC: Accepted
Room facilities: 📺 ☎ 🍵 📞 ✳
Access: ↕ ♿ Children: Welcome 🍴 ♟
Licences: ◁ ♟ Leisure: Gym, Health spa,
Beauty salon Parking: Off-street and monitored
Directions: The hotel is located in Dublin city centre
opposite the International Financial Services Centre,
ten minutes from Temple Bar.

Uppercross House

★★★

26/30 Upper Rathmines Road 1, Dublin 6
Tel: +353(0)1 4975486 Fax: +353(0)1 4975361
Email: uppercrosshotel@ireland.com
Web: www.uppercrosshousehotel.com
Rooms: 49 all ensuite 🛏 ⊗
Pricing: Sgl £63–89 Dbl £50–79 Dinner from £20
CC: Accepted Room facilities: 🖵 ☎ 🍵 📞
Access: ⬆ ♿ Conference: 1 meeting room (Thtr 24
max)Children: Welcome 🍴 ☽ Dogs: Welcome
Licences: ⬧ ♟ Parking: Off-street and monitored
Directions: From Dublin Airport/the north: M50
southbound, exit junction 11 towards city centre for
approximately 5 miles to Rathmines.

White Sands Hotel

★★★

Coast Road, Portmarnock, Co. Dublin
Tel: +353(0)1 8460003 Fax: +353(0)1 8460420
Email: sandshotel@eircom.net
Web: www.whitesandshotel.ie
Seasonal closure: 24-25 December
Rooms: 32 all ensuite 🛏 🖼 ⊗
Room facilities: 🖵 ☎ 🍵 📞 Access: ⬆ ♿
Conference: 1 meeting room (Thtr 100 max)
Children: Welcome 🍴 Dogs: Guide dogs only
Licences: ⬧ ♟
Parking: Off-street and monitored
Directions: Take Belfast road from Dublin Airport. Turn
right at sign for Malahide at 3rd roundabout. Turn left
at T-junction and follow through to Portmarnock.
See advert on this page

Wynn's Hotel

★★★

35-39 Lower Abbey Street, Dublin 1
Tel: +353(0)1 8745131 Fax: +353(0)1 8741556
Email: info@wynnshotel.ie
Web: www.wynnshotel.ie
Rooms: 70 all ensuite ⊗
Pricing: Sgl €83–108 Dbl €121–165 Dinner from €22
CC: Accepted Room facilities: 🖵 ☎ 🍵 Access: ⬆
Conference: 5 meeting rooms (Thtr 150 max)
Children: Welcome 🍴 Licences: ⬧ ♟
Parking: Off-street and monitored
See advert on following page

Aberdeen Lodge

◆◆◆◆◆ ☽ ☕ ☂

53 Park Avenue, Ballsbridge, Dublin 4
Tel: +353(0)1 2838155 Fax: +353(0)1 2837877
Email: aberdeen@iol.ie
Web: www.halpinsprivatehotels.com
Rooms: 18 all ensuite 🛏 🖼 ⊗
Pricing: Sgl €99–124 Dbl €119–150 CC: Accepted
Room facilities: 🖵 ☎ 🍵 📞 Access: ♿
Children: Welcome 🍴 Licences: ♟
Parking: Off-street and monitored
Directions: Minutes from city centre by DART or car.
Take Merrion Road towards Sydney Parade DART
station, then first left onto Park Avenue.
See advert on next page

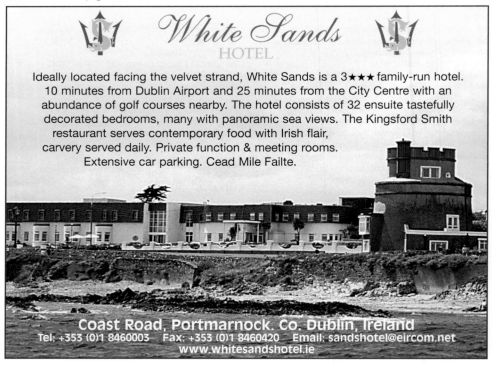

Halpin's Private Hotels

ABERDEEN LODGE, BLAKES TOWNHOUSE & MERRION HALL
Ballsbridge, Dublin 4
Ph: 00 353 1 2838155   Fax: 00 353 1 2837877
Email: halpins@iol.ie   www.halpinsprivatehotels.com

Aberdeen Lodge ★★★★ ITB   *Merrion Hall* ★★★★ ITB   *Blakes Townhouse* ★★★★ ITB

Luxury Edwardian properties

Set among the embassies in the exclusive Ballsbridge area of Dublin city.
Elegant, spacious rooms and suites overlooking gardens and cricket grounds,
fine food and modern comforts, all one expects of a private hotel.
Each with grand drawing rooms, Library, air-conditioned suites,
Jacuzzis, four-poster beds. Private car park.

Within minutes of Stephens Green, beside DART, Landsdowne Road
& RDS Convention centre. Direct Luxury Coach Link to and from
Dublin Airport (20 mins €6). Sealink & Irish Ferries Terminals (10 mins)

*Halpin's Privatehotels are the perfect base
for exploring the sights of the city.*
Accolades – AAA ♦♦♦♦♦ RƎC ITB ★★★★, Times, Green Book,
Johansens, Best Loved Hotels, Charming Hotels, RAC and Galtee dining awards

Sister property of **Halpins Townhouse Hotel** Kilkee, which is located close to
Shannon Airport, Cliffs of Moher and the Burren region.

Wynn's Hotel

Ideal city centre location.
Wynn's is a 3-Star family-run hotel close to
fashionable shops, theatres, galleries and
places of interest.
Conference, banqueting and wedding
facilities for small or large groups.
Peacock Restaurant serves contemporary
and reasonably priced food prepared
on the premises.
A welcoming atmosphere is provided
in the Saints and Scholars Bar.

35-39 Lower Abbey Street, Dublin 1, Eire
Tel: +353(0)1 8745131 Fax: +353(0)1 8741556
Email: info@wynnshotel.ie
Web: www.wynnshotel.ie

Butlers Town House

◆◆◆◆◆

44 Lansdowne Road, Ballsbridge, Dublin
Tel: +353(0)1 6674022 Fax: +353(0)1 6673960
Email: info@butlers-hotel.com
Web: www.butlers-hotel.com
Rooms: 19 all ensuite
Room facilities: 🖵 ☎ 🔌 ❄ Access: ♿
Children: Welcome Dogs: Guide dogs only
Licences: ♦♦♦
Parking: Off-street and monitored
Directions: Hotel is located on the corner of
Shelbourne Road and Lansdowne Road in the area of
Ballsbridge, just south of the city centre.

Glenogra

◆◆◆◆◆ ✗

64 Merrion Road, Ballsbridge, Dublin 4
Tel: +353(0)1 6683661 Fax: +353(0)1 6683698
Email: glenogra@indigo.ie
Web: www.glenogra.com
Seasonal closure: Christmas to New Year
Rooms: 12 all ensuite 🟤
Pricing: Sgl € 75–85 Dbl € 105–125 CC: Accepted
Room facilities: 🖵 ☎ 🔌
Children: Welcome Parking: Off-street
Directions: Situated opposite Four Seasons Hotel in
Ballsbridge on main route from Dun Laoghaire car ferry.

Harrington Hall Ltd

◆◆◆◆◆ ✗

70 Harcourt Street, Dublin 2
Tel: +353(0)1 4753497 Fax: +353(0)1 4754544
Email: harringtonhall@eircom.net
Web: www.harringtonhall.com
Rooms: 28 all ensuite 🟤 🟤
Pricing: Sgl € 127–165 Dbl € 165–220 CC: Accepted
Room facilities: 🖵 ☎ 🔌 🔌
Access: ♦♦♦ ♿ Conference: 2 meeting rooms
Children: Welcome 🟤 Dogs: Guide dogs only
Licences: ♦♦♦
Parking: Off-street and monitored
Directions: Follow signs to city centre, Harrington Hall
is on Harcourt street, which enters south west corner
of St Stephen's Green. Attention: one-way.

Merrion Hall

◆◆◆◆◆ ✗

54 Merrion Road, Ballsbridge, Dublin 4
Tel: +353(0)1 6681426 Fax: +353(0)1 6684280
Email: merrionhall@iol.ie
Web: www.halpinsprivatehotels.com
Rooms: 24 all ensuite 🟤 🟤 🟤
Pricing: Sgl € 99–124 Dbl € 119–150 CC: Accepted
Room facilities: 🖵 ☎ 🔌 🔌
Access: ♿ Children: Welcome 🍴
Licences: ♦♦♦ Leisure: Health spa
Parking: Off-street and monitored
Directions: Located in Ballsbridge, close to city centre on
Merrion Road. Minutes from city centre by DART or bus.
See advert on previous page

66 Townhouse

◆◆◆◆ ✗

66 Northumberland Road, Ballsbridge, Dublin 4
Tel: +353(0)1 6600471 Fax: +353(0)1 6601051
Seasonal closure: 22 December to 6 January
Rooms: 9 (8 ensuite)
Pricing: Sgl € 80–140 Dbl € 120–200 CC: Accepted
Room facilities: 🖵 ☎ 🔌 Children: Welcome 🍴 🟤
Parking: Off-street and monitored
Directions: 66 Townhouse is 1 mile southbound from
Trinity College/city centre — in diplomatic/hotels/
banking area.

Baggot Court

◆◆◆◆ ✗

92 Lower Baggot Street, Dublin 2
Tel: +353(0)66 12819 Fax: +353(0)66 10253
Email: baggot@indigo.ie
Seasonal closure: Christmas and New Year
Rooms: 11 all ensuite 🟤
Pricing: Sgl £55–80 Dbl £65–110 CC: Accepted
Room facilities: 🖵 ☎ 🔌
Children: Welcome, 8yrs min age
Dogs: Guide dogs only
Parking: Off-street and monitored
Directions: Located in the city centre, south of St
Stephens Green on no.10 bus route from O'Connell
street.

Charleville Lodge

268-272 North Circular Road, Phisborough, Dublin 7
Tel: +353(0)1 8386633 Fax: +353(0)1 8385854
Email: charleville@indigo.ie
Web: www.charlevillelodge.ie

Charleville Lodge (former home to Lord Charleville) is a beautifully-restored terrace of Edwardian houses, offering all the luxury expected from a large hotel, whilst retaining the old-world charm.
Rooms: 30 all ensuite
Pricing: Sgl €55–85 Dbl €70–140
CC: Accepted
Room facilities: ☐ ☎ Access: ♿
Children: Welcome
Parking: Off-street and monitored
Directions: North from city centre (O'Connell Street) to Phisborough, then take left fork at St Peter's Church. 200 metres on the left; or, take no.60 bus.

Eliza Lodge

23/24 Wellington Quay, Temple Bar, Dublin 2
Tel: +353(0)1 671 8044 Fax: +353(0)1 671 8362
Email: info@dublinlodge.com
Web: www.dublinlodge.com
Seasonal closure: Christmas
Rooms: 18 all ensuite
Pricing: Sgl €76–95 Dbl €90–190
CC: Accepted
Room facilities: ☐ ☎
Access: Children: Welcome
Dogs: Guide dogs only
Directions: Located at foot of Millennium Bridge, second bridge after O'Connell Bridge. 25 minutes' drive from Dublin Airport.

Glenveagh Town House

31 Northumerland Road, Ballsbridge, Dublin
Tel: +353(0)1 6684612 Fax: +353(0)1 6684559

Kilronan House

70 Adelaide Road, Dublin 2
Tel: +353(0)1 4755266 Fax: +353(0)1 4782841
Email: info@dublinn.com
Web: www.dublinn.com

Exclusive Georgian house within walking distance of St Stephen's Green, Trinity College and most of Dublin's historic landmarks. Under the personal supervision of owner Terry Masterson.
Rooms: 12 all ensuite
Pricing: Sgl €76–76 Dbl €100–152 CC: Accepted
Room facilities: ☐ ☎ Children: Welcome
Dogs: Welcome Parking: Off-street and monitored
Directions: Drive down St Stephen's Green east onto Earlsfort Terrace. Proceed onto Adelaide Road. House is on right-hand side.

Kingswood Country House

Kingswood, Naas Road, Clondalkin
Tel: +353(0)1 4592428 Fax: +353(0)1 4592207
Email: kingswoodcountryhse@eircom.net
Rooms: 7 all ensuite Pricing: Sgl €80 Dbl €115
CC: Accepted Room facilities: ☐ ☎
Children: Welcome Dogs: Welcome
Licences: Parking: Off-street and monitored
Directions: From M50 Dublin ring road take N7 exit. Hotel is 3 miles on N7 heading south, clearly signposted.

Republic of Ireland

Trinity Lodge

◆ ◆ ◆ ◆ ※ ⚐   Little Gem

12 South Frederick Street, Dublin 2,
Tel: +353(0)1 6795044 Fax: +353(0)1 6795223
Email: trinitylodge@eircom.net
Seasonal closure: 22–27 December

Trinity Lodge offers elegant Georgian ensuite
accommodation in the heart of Dublin. Grafton street,
Temple Bar and all of Dublin's historic and business
districts are only minutes away.
Rooms: 13 all ensuite Pricing: Sgl €90–220
Dbl €200–360 CC: Accepted
Room facilities: ▢ ☎ ⬧ ⬧ ❄ Children: Welcome
Parking: Off-street and monitored
Directions: Lodge is situated in city centre, beside
Trinity College, off Nassau Street.

Harcourt Inn

◆ ◆ ◆

27 Harcourt Street, Dublin 2
Tel: +353(0)1 478 3927 Fax: +353(0)1 478 2550
Email: harcourt@indigo.ie
Seasonal closure: Christmas to New Year
Rooms: 15 all ensuite Ⓢ Pricing: Sgl €55–80
Dbl €65–110 CC: Accepted Room facilities: ▢ ☎ ⬧
Children: Welcome, 8yrs min age Dogs: Guide dogs only
Directions: Located in the city centre, on the west side
of St Stephen's Green.

Redbank Guesthouse & Restaurant

◆ ◆ ◆ ⚐ ⚐

6-7 Church Street, Skerries, Co. Dublin
Tel: +353(0)1 8490439 Fax: +353(0)1 8491598
Email: redbank@eircom.net
Web: www.redbank.ie
Seasonal closure: Restaurant 24–27 December

Building now listed for protection, confirming the
McCoy's sense of style, having converted this old bank
into one of Ireland's finest restaurants and guest
houses, featuring the catch of the day at Skerries Pier.
Rooms: 12 all ensuite
Pricing: Sgl €50–70 Dbl €95–110 Dinner from €42
CC: Accepted Room facilities: ▢ ☎ ⬧ ⬧ Access: ♿
Conference: 2 meeting rooms (Thtr 30 max)
Children: Welcome Licences: ⬧ ♣
Parking: Off-street and monitored
Directions: 20 minutes off the N1 Dublin to Belfast
road. From the south, through village of Lusk. From the
north, turn to left at Balbriggan and follow coast road.

Saint Andrews

◆ ◆ ◆

1&3 Lambay Road, Drumcondra
Tel: +353(0)1 8374684 Fax: +353(0)1 8570446
Email: andrew@dublinn.com
Rooms: 16 all ensuite Ⓢ
Pricing: Sgl €45–50 Dbl €86–96 CC: Accepted
Room facilities: ▢ ☎ Children: Welcome
Parking: Off-street and monitored

Blakes Townhouse

❖

50 Merrion Road, Ballsbridge, Dublin 4
Tel: +353(0)1 6688324 Fax: +353(0)1 6684280
Email: blakestownhouse@iol.ie
Web: www.halpinsprivatehotels.com
Rooms: 13 all ensuite ⬧ Ⓢ
Pricing: Sgl €99–124 Dbl €119–150 CC: Accepted
Room facilities: ▢ ☎ ⬧
Access: ♿ Children: Welcome ♨
Licences: ♣ Parking: Off-street and monitored
Directions: Located in Ballsbridge, close to city centre
on the Merrion Road. Minutes from city centre by
DART or bus.
See advert on page 653

Travelodge Dublin Navan Road

Travel Accommodation
N3 Little Chef, Auburn Avenue Roundabout, Navan
Road, Castleknock, Dublin 151
Web: www.travelodge.co.uk
Rooms: 100 all ensuite Ⓢ
Pricing: Sgl €101.92–101.92 Dbl €106.37–106.37
CC: Accepted Room facilities: ▢ ⬧ Access: ♿

Ask the experts

ⓘ To book a Hotel or Guest
Accommodation, or for help
and advice, call RAC Hotel
Reservations on 0870 603 9109
and quote 'Guide 2003'

Dun Laoghaire, Co. Dublin

The Gresham Royal Marine

★★★

Marine Road, Dun Laoghaire, Co. Dublin
Tel: +353(0)1 280 1911 Fax: +353(0)1 280 1089
Email: info@gresham-royalmarinehotel.com
Web: www.gresham-hotels.com

GRESHAM HOTELS

Victorian façade, 103 ensuite bedrooms, many with
magnificent views over Dublin Bay.
Rooms: 103 all ensuite
Pricing: Sgl €222–260 Dbl €230–300 Dinner from €35
CC: Accepted Room facilities: Access:
Conference: 11 meeting rooms (Thtr 450 max)
Children: Welcome Dogs: Guide dogs only
Licences: Parking: Off-street and monitored
Directions: Directly opposite Holyhead to Dun
Laoghaire car ferry.

Tara Hall

♦ ♦ ♦

24 Sandycove Road, Dun Laoghaire, Co. Dublin
Tel: +353(0)1 2805120 Fax: +353(0)1 2805120
Email: tarahall@indigo.ie
Rooms: 8 (7 ensuite) Pricing: Sgl €22–30
Dbl €60–80 Dinner from €11 CC: Accepted
Room facilities: Children: Welcome
Dogs: Welcome Parking: Off-street

Dundalk, Co. Louth

Ballymascanlon House Hotel

★★★

Ballymascanlon, Dundalk, Co. Louth
Tel: +353(0)42 9371124 Fax: +353(0)42 9371598
Email: info@ballymascanlon.com
Web: www.globalgolf.com/ballymascanlon
Rooms: 90 all ensuite Pricing: Sgl €102
Dbl €145 Dinner from €36 CC: Accepted
Room facilities: Access:
Conference: 6 meeting rooms (Thtr 300 max)
Children: Welcome Dogs: Guide dogs only
Licences: Leisure: Indoor pool, Gym, Health
spa, Tennis, Golf Parking: Off-street
Directions: We are situated 2 miles north of Dundalk,
off main Belfast Road (on Carlingford Road).

Fairways Hotel

★★★

Dublin Road, Dundalk, Co. Louth
Tel: +353(0)42 9321500 Fax: +353(0)42 9321511
Email: info@fairways.ie
Web: www.fairways.ie
Rooms: 101 all ensuite Pricing: Sgl €80–110
Dbl €125–160 Dinner from €35 CC: Accepted
Room facilities: Access:
Conference: 10 meeting rooms (Thtr 1000 max)
Children: Welcome Dogs: Guide dogs only
Licences: Leisure: Beauty salon Parking: Off-street
Directions: Three miles south of Dundalk and
approximately 1 hour 15 mins from Dublin or Belfast.

Dunfanaghy, Co. Donegal

Arnolds Hotel

★★★★

Dunfanaghy, Co. Donegal
Tel: +353(0)74 36208 Fax: +353(0)74 36352
Email: arnoldshotel@eircom.net
Web: www.arnoldshotel.com
Seasonal closure: November to March
Rooms: 30 all ensuite Pricing: Sgl €90–100
Dbl €120–150 Dinner from €23.20 CC: Accepted
Room facilities: Children: Welcome
Dogs: Guide dogs only Licences: Leisure: Riding
Parking: Off-street and monitored
Directions: Take N56 northwest from Letterkenny. After
23 miles, hotel is on left as you enter village.
See advert on this page

Dungarvan, Co. Waterford

The Castle Country House   Little Gem

◆ ◆ ◆ ◆ ◆ ✹ ❦

Mill Street, Dungarvan, Co. Waterford
Tel: +353(0)58 68049 Fax: +353(0)58 68099
Email: castlefm@iol.ie
Web: www.castlecountryhouse.com
Seasonal closure: November to February

Award-winning restored wing of 15th century castle on large dairy farm. Excellent cuisine and elegant decor. Breakfast menu.
Rooms: 5 all ensuite ⊗
Pricing: Sgl €60–70 Dbl €80–90 CC: Accepted
Room facilities: ▢ ☕ Children: Welcome ⅄
Dogs: Welcome Licences: ♦♦♦
Parking: Off-street
Directions: Located 15km off N25.

Ennis, Co. Clare

Woodstock Hotel

★ ★ ★ ★ ♟

Shanaway Road, Ennis, Co. Clare
Tel: +353(0)65 6846600 Fax: +353(0)65 6846611
Email: info@woodstockhotel.com
Web: www.woodstockhotel.com
Seasonal closure: 24–26 December
Rooms: 67 all ensuite ⊗
Pricing: Dinner from €34.50 CC: Accepted
Room facilities: ▢ ☎ ☕ ✆ Access: ⇞ ♿
Conference: 3 meeting rooms (Thtr 200 max)
Children: Welcome ⅄ ☀ Dogs: Guide dogs only
Licences: ♦♦♦ Leisure: Indoor pool, Gym, Health spa, Beauty salon, GolfParking: Off-street and monitored
Directions: From Limerick follow N18 to Ennis, take exit for Lahinch (N85). After 1km make left turn, continue 1km to Hotel.

West Country Conference and Leisure

★ ★ ★

Clare Road, Ennis, Co. Clare
Tel: +353(0)6568 23000 Fax: +353(0)6568 23759
Email: reservations@lynchotels.com
Web: www.lynchotels.com
Rooms: 152 all ensuite ⊛ ⊗
Pricing: Sgl €70–176 Dbl €95–288 Dinner from €25
CC: Accepted Room facilities: ▢ ☎ ☕ ✆

Access: ⇞ ♿ Conference: 10 meeting rooms (Thtr 650 max), 24hr-delegate from €112, day-delegate rate from €32 Children: Welcome ⅄ ☀ ☀
Dogs: Guide dogs only Licences: ⟁ ♦♦♦
Leisure: Indoor pool, Gym, Health spa, Beauty salon, Snooker/billiards
Parking: Off-street and monitored
Directions: Located on the main Limerick/Galway road (N18). Just 20 mins drive from Shannon Airport and 10 mins walk from Ennis town.

Ennistymon, Co. Clare

Grovemount House

◆ ◆ ◆ ◆ ✹

Lahinch Road, Ennistymon, Co. Clare
Tel: +353(0)65 7071431 Fax: +353(0)65 7071823
Email: grovemnt@gofree.indigo.ie
Seasonal closure: November to April
Rooms: 8 all ensuite ⊛ ⊗
Pricing: Sgl €38–45 Dbl €58–76 CC: Accepted
Room facilities: ▢ ☎ ☕
Access: ♿ Children: Welcome ⅄
Parking: Off-street and monitored
Directions: Take N85 from Ennis to Ennistymon, N67 from Ennistymon to Lahinch. Grovemount House is situated on outskirts of Ennistymon on right-hand side.

Faithlegg, Co. Waterford

Faithlegg House Hotel

★ ★ ★ ★ ♟ ♟

Faithlegg, Co. Waterford,
Tel: +353(0)51 382000 Fax: +353(0)51 380010
Web: www.faithlegg.com
Seasonal closure: 22–26 December
Rooms: 82 all ensuite ⊞ ⊗ Pricing: Sgl €190–245
Dbl €250–335 Dinner from €42 CC: Accepted
Room facilities: ▢ ☎ ☕ ✆ Access: ⇞ ♿
Children: Welcome Licences: ⟁ ♦♦♦ Leisure: Indoor pool, Gym, Beauty salon, Golf, Snooker/billiards
Parking: Off-street and monitored

Fermoy, Co. Cork

Ballyvolane House

◆ ◆ ◆ ◆ ♟ ✹

Castlelyons, near Fermoy, Co. Cork
Tel: +353(0)25 36349 Fax: +353(0)25 36781
Email: ballyvol@iol.ie
Web: www.ballyvolanehouse.ie

Originally built in 1728, Ballyvolane was remodelled in Italianate style. Bluebell woodland gardens, also formal walled garden. Three small trout lakes and private salmon fishing.
Rooms: 6 all ensuite
Pricing: Sgl €85–100 Dbl €65–80 Dinner from €37
CC: Accepted Room facilities: ▢ ⊟
Children: Welcome ⊬ Licences: ♦♦♦ Parking: Off-street
Directions: From Cork, right off N8 at the River Bride, just before Rath Cormac (R628). Follow House signs.

Galway, Co. Galway

Ardilaun House Hotel Conference Centre and Leisure Club
★★★★ ☜
Taylors Hill, Galway, Co. Galway
Tel: +353(0)91 521433 Fax: +353(0)91 521546
Email: ardilaun@iol.ie Web: www.ardilaunhousehotel.ie
Seasonal closure: 22–28 December
Rooms: 90 all ensuite ☜ ⊛
Pricing: Sgl €130–160 Dbl €200–260 Dinner from €30
CC: Accepted Room facilities: ▢ ☎ ⊟ ☍
Access: ↥ ♿
Conference: 8 meeting rooms (Thtr 400 max), 24hr-delegate from €120, day-delegate rate from €35
Children: Welcome ⊬ ☃ ⊱ Dogs: Welcome
Licences: ⬨ ♦♦♦
Leisure: Indoor pool, Gym, Health spa, Beauty salon, Snooker/billiards
Parking: Off-street and monitored
Directions: Approaching Galway take N6 to Galway City West. Then follow signs for N59 Clifden and then the N6 for Salthill. Taylor's Hill is enroute.

Galway Bay Golf and Country Club Hotel
★★★★ ☜
Oranmore, Co. Galway
Tel: +353(0)65 6823000 Fax: +353(0)65 6823759
Email: reservations@lynchotels.com
Web: www.lynchotels.com
Rooms: 92 all ensuite ☜ ⊛
Pricing: Sgl €89–270 Dbl €121–414 Dinner from €25
CC: Accepted Room facilities: ▢ ☎ ⊟ ☍
Access: ↥ ♿
Conference: 4 meeting rooms (Thtr 275 max), 24hr-delegate from €125, day-delegate rate from €35
Children: Welcome ⊬ Dogs: Guide dogs only
Licences: ⬨ ♦♦♦ Leisure: Gym, Golf
Parking: Off-street and monitored
Directions: In Oranmore village follow signs for Maree. At the new church take the first exit to the right. Hotel is 5–10 minutes down this road.

Glenlo Abbey Hotel
★★★★★ ☜☜ Blue Ribbon Winner
Busheypark, Co. Galway
Tel: +353(0)91 526666 Fax: +353(0)91 527800
Email: info@glenloabbey.ie Web: www.glenlo.com
Rooms: 46 all ensuite ☶ ⊛
Pricing: Dinner from €40 CC: Accepted

Room facilities: ▢ ☎ ☍ Access: ↥ ♿
Children: Welcome ⊬ ⊱ Dogs: Guide dogs only
Licences: ♦♦♦ Leisure: Golf, Fishing, Riding
Parking: Off-street and monitored
Directions: Situated 4 km from Galway city centre on the N59 to Clifden.
See advert on this page

Park House Hotel
★★★★ ☜
Forster Street, Eyre Square, Galway, Co. Galway
Tel: +353(0)91 564924 Fax: +353(0)91 569219
Email: parkhousehotel@eircom.net
Web: www.parkhousehotel.ie
Rooms: 57 all ensuite
Pricing: Sgl €95 Dbl €155 Dinner from €37.95
CC: Accepted Room facilities: ▢ ☎ ⊟ ☍
Access: ↥ ♿ Children: Welcome ⊬ Licences: ♦♦♦
Parking: Off-street and monitored
Directions: Follow all signs for city centre. Hotel is situated on Forster Street, off Eyre Square. Car park is at rear of hotel.
See advert on following page

It's easier online

For all your motoring and travel needs, www.rac.co.uk

Park House Hotel

An oasis of luxury and calm situated in the city centre of Galway. Award-winning hotel and restaurant – "Hotel of the Year Ireland 2000 – Les Routiers". Park Room Restaurant – Bord Failte Awards of Excellence over many years. Les Routiers Plat d'Or 2000. Private, secure residents' car park.

Forster Street, Eyre Square, Galway
Tel: 353 91 564924   Fax: 353 91 569219
Email: parkhousehotel@eircom.net
www.parkhousehotel.ie

Brennans Yard Hotel
★★★
Lower Merchants Road, Galway, Co. Galway
Tel: +353(0)91 568166 Fax: +353(0)91 568262
Email: info@brennansyardhotel.com
Web: www.brennansyardhotel.com
Rooms: 45 all ensuite
Pricing: Sgl €80–87 Dbl €99–139 CC: Accepted
Room facilities:
Access: ⏐⏐↑ ⅄ Children: Welcome ♀ ⅀⅃
Dogs: Guide dogs only Licences: ⅄⅄⅄
Parking: Off-street and monitored
Directions: From Eyre Square, in Salway city centre, turn left after Great Southern, right and right again to Brennans Yard Hotel.
See advert on this page

Imperial Hotel
★★★
Eyre Square, Galway, Co. Galway
Tel: +353(0)91 63033

Jurys Inn Galway
★★★
Quay Street, Galway, Co. Galway
Tel: +353(0)1 6070000 Fax: +353(0)1 6316999
Email: bookings@jurysdoyle.com
Web: www.jurysdoyle.com

JURYS DOYLE
H O T E L S

Seasonal closure: Christmas
Rooms: 128 all ensuite
Pricing: Sgl €94–170 Dbl €94–170 Dinner from €20
CC: Accepted Room facilities:
Access: ⏐⏐↑ ⅄ Children: Welcome ♀
Dogs: Guide dogs only Licences: ⅄⅄⅄
Directions: Located 5 miles/8 km from Galway airport. Train station 5 mins walk. Centrally located beside Spanish Arch and overlooking Galway Bay.

Menlo Park Hotel
★★★
Terryland, Headford Road, Galway,
Tel: +353(0)91 761122 Fax: +353(0)91 761222
Email: menlopkh@iol.ie
Web: www.menloparkhotel.com
Rooms: 66 all ensuite
Pricing: Sgl €75–160 Dbl €115–190 Dinner from €25
CC: Accepted Room facilities: Access: ⏐⏐↑ ⅄
Conference: 5 meeting rooms (Thtr 400 max)
Children: Welcome ♀ ⅀⅃ Dogs: Guide dogs only
Licences: ⅄⅄⅄ Parking: Off-street and monitored
Directions: Junction N84 and N6 at Headford Road. Follow signs Castlebar eastern approach, follow signs Castlebar Clifden.

The Galway Ryan

★★★

Dublin Road, Galway City East, Galway, Co. Galway
Tel: +353(0)91 753181 Fax: +353(0)91 753187
Email: info@galwayryan.com
Web: www.ryan-hotels.com

A modern hotel, with recently refurnished bedrooms,
close to Galway city.
Rooms: 96 all ensuite 🐾 ⊗
Pricing: Sgl €171.40–211.40 Dbl €182.80–222.80
Dinner from €24 CC: Accepted
Room facilities: 🖵 ☎ 🍵 Access: ↕↑ ৬
Conference: 2 meeting rooms (Thtr 30 max)
Children: Welcome Dogs: Guide dogs only
Licences: ⬦ ♦♦♦ Leisure: Indoor pool, Gym, Tennis
Parking: Off-street and monitored
Directions: Follow the signs for Galway East when
approaching Galway from Dublin.

Almara House

◆◆◆◆ 🗶 🍸

2 Merlin Gate, Merlin Park, Dublin Road, Galway,
Co. Galway
Tel: +353(0)91 755345 Fax: +353(0)91 771585
Email: matthewkiernan@eircom.net
Web: www.almarahouse.com
Seasonal closure: 1 week at Christmas
Rooms: 4 all ensuite Pricing: Sgl €40–50 Dbl €60–90
CC: Accepted Room facilities: 🖵 🍵
Children: Welcome 🍴 Dogs: Guide dogs only
Parking: Off-street and monitored
Directions: Located beside Dublin(N6)/Shannon(N18)
junction, beside Corrib Great Southern hotel and
Gallway Crystal factory, follow signs for Merlin Park.

Glin, Co. Limerick

Glin Castle

★★★ 🍸 Blue Ribbon Winner

Glin, Co. Limerick
Tel: +353(0)68 34173 Fax: +353(0)68 34364
Email: knight@iol.ie
Web: www.glincastle.com
Seasonal closure: 1 November to 15 March
Rooms: 15 all ensuite 🗹 ⊗

Pricing: Sgl €280–440 Dbl €280–440 Dinner from €47
CC: Accepted Room facilities: 🖵 ☎ 🔌
Conference: 1 meeting room (Thtr 20 max)
Children: Welcome, 10yrs min age 🍴 🌢
Dogs: Welcome Licences: ♦♦♦ Leisure: Tennis
Parking: Off-street and monitored
Directions: 32 miles west of Limerick city on N69, 4
miles east of Tarbert/Killimar car ferry.

See advert on following page

Gorey, Co. Wexford

Marlfield House

Gold Ribbon Winner

★★★★ 🍸 🍸 🍸

Courtown Road, Gorey, Co. Wexford,
Tel: +353(0)55 21124 Fax: +353(0)55 21572
Email: info@marlfieldhouse.ie
Web: www.marlfieldhouse.com
Seasonal closure: Mid December to January

Set in 36 acres of magnificent gardens and filled with
numerous antiques, Marlfield's true Irish hospitality and
cuisine have gained it world acclaim.
Rooms: 20 all ensuite 🗹 ⊗
Pricing: Sgl €135 Dbl €260–700 Dinner from €56
CC: Accepted Room facilities: 🖵 ☎ Access: ৬
Conference: 2 meeting rooms (Thtr 20 max),
24hr-delegate from €295
Children: Welcome 🍴 🌢 Dogs: Welcome
Licences: ♦♦♦ Leisure: Tennis
Parking: Off-street and monitored
Directions: Marlfield House is 1 mile outside Gorey on
the Courtown Road R742.

Ashdown Park Hotel

Coach Road, Gorey, Co. Wexford
Tel: +353(0)55 80500 Fax: +353(0)55 80777
Email: info@ashdownparkhotel.com
Web: www.ashdownparkhotel.com
Seasonal closure: 24–26 December
Rooms: 60 all ensuite Pricing: Sgl €108 Dbl €150
Dinner from €31 CC: Accepted
Room facilities: 🖵 ☎ 🍵 Access: ↕↑ ৬
Conference: 6 meeting rooms (Thtr 800 max),
24hr-delegate from €150, day-delegate rate from €40
Children: Welcome 🍴 Dogs: Guide dogs only
Licences: ♦♦♦ Leisure: Indoor pool, Gym
Parking: Off-street
Directions: Take M11/N11 southbound from Dublin,
pass Ashford Rathnew. Bypass Arklow, Gorey. Before
railway bridge turn left. Hotel on left.

Glin Castle

Glin Castle, home of the 29th Knight of Glin, has been in the FitzGerald family for 700 years. Neo-classical halls, elaborate plasterwork, flying staircase and mahogany library with hidden door all surveyed by ancestral portraits.

Pleasure park, walled kitchen garden and spectacular spring garden with rare species. The castle is guarded by three fort lodges, one of which is is a craft shop and tea-rooms.

Glin Castle is a member of Ireland's Blue Book.

Glin, Co. Limerick, Ireland
Tel: 068 34173/34112   Fax: 068 34364
Email: knight@iol.ie
Website: www.glincastle.com

Woodlands Country House

♦ ♦ ♦ ♦ ♦ ⚬ ☙

Killinierin, Gorey, Co. Wexford
Tel: +353(0)402 37125 Fax: +353(0)402 37133
Email: info@woodlandscountryhouse.com
Web: www.woodlandsconryhouse.com
Seasonal closure: October to March
Rooms: 6 all ensuite ⚭ ⊗
Pricing: Sgl €55–60 Dbl €80–90 CC: Accepted
Room facilities: ▢ ⚘ Children: Welcome ⅏
Dogs: Guide dogs only
Licences: ⅲ
Leisure: Tennis, Riding, Games room, Snooker/billiards
Parking: Off-street and monitored
Directions: Located 1 mile off N11, 3 miles north of Gorey, one hour from Dublin or Rosslare Harbour.

Kenmare, Co. Kerry

Park Hotel Kenmare   Gold Ribbon Winner
★★★★★ ❀ ❀ ❀ ❀
Kenmare, Co. Kerry,
Tel: +353(0)64 41200 Fax: +353(0)64 41402
Email: info@parkkenmare.com
Web: www.parkkenmare.com
Seasonal closure: 29 Oct to 23 Dec, 2 Jan to 19 April

Rooms: 46 all ensuite ⚭ ⊠ ⊗
Pricing: Sgl €206–233 Dbl €366–518
Dinner from €64 CC: Accepted
Room facilities: ▢ ☎ ⚘ Access: ⅱ ♿
Children: Welcome ⅏ ⚬ Dogs: Welcome
Licences: ⚑ ⅲ
Leisure: Gym, Tennis, Golf, Snooker/billiards
Parking: Off-street and monitored
Directions: Located at the top of Kenmare.

Sheen Falls Lodge   Gold Ribbon Winner
★★★★★ ❀ ❀ ❀
Kenmare, Co. Kerry
Tel: +353(0)64 41600 Fax: +353(0)64 41386
Email: info@sheenfallslodge.ie
Web: www.sheenfallslodge.ie
Seasonal closure: January

A haven set within 300 acres of magical woodlands and crystal cascading waterfalls. With its luxurious rooms and sumptuous cuisine, the Lodge retains the warm, welcoming atmosphere of a country manor house.
Rooms: 61 all ensuite ⚭ ⊗
Pricing: Dinner from €65 CC: Accepted
Room facilities: ▢ ☎ ⚘
Access: ⅱ ♿
Conference: 5 meeting rooms (Thtr 120 max)
Children: Welcome ⅏ Licences: ⅲ
Leisure: Indoor pool, Gym, Health spa, Beauty salon, Tennis, Fishing, Riding, Games room, Snooker/billiards
Parking: Off-street and monitored
Directions: From Kenmare, take N71 towards Glengarriff. Turn left after suspension bridge. Sheen Falls Lodge is on the left-hand side.

Kilkee, Co. Clare

Ocean Cove Business and Leisure Hotel

★★★

Kilkee Bay, Kilkee, Co. Clare
Tel: +353(0)6568 23000 Fax: +353(0)6568 23759
Email: reservations@lynchotels.com
Web: www.lynchotels.com
Rooms: 50 all ensuite
Pricing: Sgl €62–176 Dbl €87–288 Dinner from €25
CC: Accepted Room facilities: Access:
Conference: 2 meeting rooms (Thtr 100 max), 24hr-delegate from €105, day-delegate rate from €32
Children: Welcome Dogs: Guide dogs only
Licences:
Leisure: Gym, Games room, Snooker/billiards
Parking: Off-street and monitored
Directions: Located on the main N67/N68 road, the Ocean Cove Hotel overlooks the Atlantic Ocean and offers commanding views of the bay.

Halpins Town House Hotel

♦♦♦♦

Erin Street, Kilkee, Co. Clare
Tel: +353(0)65 9056032 Fax: +353(0)65 9056317
Email: halpinstownhouse@iol.ie
Web: www.halpinsprivatehotels.com
Seasonal closure: December to February
Rooms: 12 all ensuite
Pricing: Sgl €57–76 Dbl €89–114 Dinner from €25
CC: Accepted Room facilities:
Children: Welcome Licences:
Parking: Off-street and monitored
Directions: Hotel is in the centre of Kilkee. Shannon Airport 50-minute drive away on N67, Killimer Car Ferry 10 miles away.
See advert on page 653

Kilkenny, Co. Kilkenny

Kilkenny Ormonde Hotel

★★★★

Ormonde Street, Kilkenny, Co. Kilkenny
Tel: +353(0)56 23900 Fax: +353(0)56 23977
Email: info@kilkennyormonde.com
Web: www.kilkennyormonde.com
Rooms: 118 all ensuite
Room facilities: Access:
Children: Welcome
Dogs: Guide dogs only Licences:
Leisure: Indoor pool, Gym, Health spa
Parking: Off-street and monitored
Directions: City centre. Just off High Street, five minutes walk to train station.

Kilkenny River Court Hotel

★★★★

The Bridge, John Street, Kilkenny, Co. Kilkenny
Tel: +353(0)56 23388 Fax: +353(0)56 23389
Email: reservations@kilrivercourt.com
Web: www.kilrivercourt.com
Seasonal closure: 25–26 December
Rooms: 90 all ensuite
Pricing: Dinner from €20 (2002 rate) CC: Accepted
Room facilities: Access:
Children: Welcome Licences:
Leisure: Indoor pool, Gym, Beauty salon
Parking: Off-street
Directions: Kilkenny Castle is a landmark: the hotel is situated directly opposite across river. Entrance under archways at bridge in city centre.

Mount Juliet Conrad

Gold Ribbon Winner

★★★★

Thomastown, Co. Kilkenny
Tel: +353(0)56 73000 Fax: +353(0)56 73019
Email: mountjulietinfo@conradhotels.com
Web: www.ConradHotels.com

Mount Juliet, Ireland's premier sporting estate with lush gardens, championship golf course, hosts of WGC American Express championship in September 2002, new spa and health club, award-winning fine-dining and luxurious accommodation... a haven of peace so rarely found in today's busy world.
Rooms: 58 all ensuite Pricing: Dinner from €45
CC: Accepted Room facilities: Access:
Conference: 4 meeting rooms (Thtr 75 max)
Children: Welcome Licences:
Leisure: Indoor pool, Gym, Tennis, Golf, Fishing, Riding, Snooker/billiards
Parking: Off-street and monitored
Directions: Situated in the south-east of Ireland 75 miles from Dublin, 55 from Rosslare. Train services to Thomastown; helipad on site.

Hotel Kilkenny

★★★

College Road, Kilkenny, Co. Kilkenny
Tel: +353(0)56 62000 Fax: +353(0)56 65984
Web: www.griffingroup.ie
Rooms: 103 all ensuite
Pricing: Sgl €80–159 Dbl €120–300 Dinner from €35
CC: Accepted Room facilities: Access:
Conference: 7 meeting rooms (Thtr 400 max)
Children: Welcome Licences:
Leisure: Indoor pool, Gym, Health spa, Beauty salon Parking: Off-street
Directions: From city centre, turn onto Patrick Street, then take first right onto Ormonde Road. Hotel is through traffic lights on the left.

Hibernian Hotel

1 Ormonde Street, Kilkenny, Co. Kilkenny
Tel: +353 (0)56 71888 Fax: +353 (0)56 71877
Email: info@hibernian.iol.ie
Web: www.kilkennyhibernianhotel.com
Seasonal closure: Christmas
Rooms: 42 all ensuite 🖥 ⊛ Pricing: Dinner from €14
(2002 rate) Room facilities: ▢ ☎ Access: ⌊↑
Children: Welcome ⍚ Dogs: Guide dogs only
Licences: ⬙ ⭍⭍⭍
Parking: Off-street and monitored
Directions: The hotel is in the city centre.

Belmore Country Home

Jerpoint Church, Thomastown, Co. Kilkenny
Tel: +353(0)56 24228
Email: belmorehouse@eircom.net
Web: www.belmorehouse.com
Seasonal closure: Christmas
Rooms: 3 all ensuite
Pricing: Sgl €35–40 Dbl €30–35 CC: Accepted
Children: Welcome Dogs: Welcome
Leisure: Fishing, Games room
Parking: Off-street and monitored
Directions: Turn off main N9 road near Jerpoint Abbey,
towards Stoney Ford/Mount Juliet. House signposted
to right — second entrance.

Chaplins

Castlecomer Road, Kilkenny, Co. Kilkenny
Tel: +353(0)56 52236
Email: chaplins@eircom.net
Seasonal closure: Christmas
Rooms: 6 all ensuite ⊛ Pricing: Dbl €64–80
CC: Accepted Room facilities: ▢ ⊛
Children: Welcome Parking: Off-street
Directions: Chaplins is situated in Kilkenny city on the
N77 Alhy-Dublin road.

Killarney, Co. Kerry

Aghadoe Heights Hotel   Gold Ribbon Winner
★★★★★ 🐾 🐾 🐾
Lakes of Killarney, Killarney, Co. Kerry,
Tel: +353(0)64 31766 Fax: +353(0)64 31345
Email: info@aghadoeheights.com
Web: www.aghadoeheights.com

Quietly located, 5 minutes from Killarney with
breathtaking views of the ever-changing lakes and
mountains. This exceptional hotel is internationally
renowned for outstanding standards of service,
comfort and cuisine.
Rooms: 63 all ensuite 🖥 ⊛
Pricing: Sgl €250–334 Dbl €310–786 Dinner from €54
CC: Accepted Room facilities: ▢ ☎ 🌡 ❄ Access: ⌊↑ ⪦
Conference: 3 meeting rooms (Thtr 150 max)
Children: Welcome, 12yrs min age ⍚ ⅀℃ Licences: ⭍⭍⭍
Leisure: Indoor pool, Gym, Beauty salon, Tennis
Parking: Off-street and monitored
Directions: North exit Killarney Town 2 miles off N22,
signposted from junction.

Dunloe Castle Hotel
★★★★ 🐾 🐾
Beaufort, Killarney, Co. Kerry
Tel: +353(0)64 44111 Fax: +353(0)64 44583
Email: reception.dunloe@kih.liebherr.com
Web: www.iol.ie/khl
Seasonal closure: October to April
Rooms: 110 all ensuite 🐾 ⊛
Pricing: Sgl €207–275 Dbl €207–275 CC: Accepted
Room facilities: ▢ ☎ 🌡 Access: ⌊↑ ⪦
Conference: 6 meeting rooms (Thtr 250 max)
Children: Welcome ⍚ Dogs: Guide dogs only
Licences: ⭍⭍⭍
Leisure: Indoor pool, Gym, Tennis, Fishing, Riding,
Games room
Parking: Off-street and monitored
Directions: Located 6 miles outside of Killarney, facing
the Gap of Dunloe. Follow signs for Killorglin on
entering Killarney.
See advert on previous page

Hotel Europe
★★★★★ 🐾 🐾
Fossa, Killarney, Co. Kerry
Tel: +353 (0)64 31900 Fax: +353 (0)64 37900
Email: sales@kih.liebherr.com
Web: www.iol.ie/khl
Seasonal closure: 1 November to 1 March
Rooms: 205 all ensuite 🐾 ⊛
Pricing: Sgl €180 Dbl €200 Dinner from €45
CC: Accepted Room facilities: ▢ ☎ 🌡 Access: ⌊↑
Conference: 10 meeting rooms (Thtr 415 max)
Children: Welcome ⍚ Dogs: Guide dogs only
Licences: ⬙ ⭍⭍⭍ Leisure: Indoor pool, Gym,
Beauty salon, Tennis, Fishing, Riding, Games room,
Snooker/billiards Parking: Off-street and monitored
Directions: From Killarney take N72 direction Killorglin.
Hotel Europe on left approx 2 miles from town.
See advert on previous page

Making a booking?

Don't forget to mention RAC
Hotels and Bed & Breakfast 2003.

Cahernane House Hotel

★★★★ ⚐

Muckross Road, Killarney, Co. Kerry
Tel: +353(0)64 31895 Fax: +353(0)64 34340
Email: cahernane@eircom.net
Web: www.cahernane.ie
Rooms: 38 all ensuite 🛁 ⓢ
Pricing: Dinner from €45 CC: Accepted
Room facilities: 🖥 ☎ ⓢ 📞 Access: ᴵᴵ � &
Conference: 1 meeting room (Thtr 30 max)
Children: Welcome ⴱ ⅌ⓒ Dogs: Guide dogs only
Licences: ⅲ Leisure: Tennis, Fishing, Snooker/billiards
Parking: Off-street and monitored
Directions: Outside Killarney town on the Kenmare road — N71.

Killarney Park Hotel

★★★★ ⚐ ⚐ ⚐

Blue Ribbon Winner

Kenmare Place, Killarney, Co. Kerry
Tel: +353(0)64 35555 Fax: +353(0)64 35266
Email: info@killarneyparkhotel.ie
Web: www.killarneyparkhotel.ie
Seasonal closure: December
Rooms: 75 all ensuite ⓢ
Pricing: Sgl €230–368.50 Dbl €230–368.50
Dinner from €45 CC: Accepted
Room facilities: 🖥 ☎ ⓢ 📞 ❋ Access: ᴵᴵ &
Conference: 3 meeting rooms (Thtr 150 max)
Children: Welcome ⴱ ⅌ⓒ Licences: ⅲ
Leisure: Indoor pool, Gym, Games room,
Snooker/billiards Parking: Off-street and monitored

Directions: Take N22 from Cork to Killarney, at first roundabout, take first exit, second roundabout, take second exit. At third roundabout take first exist, Killarney Park is second entrance on left.

Killarney Royal

★★★★★ ⚐ ⚐

College Street, Killarney, Co. Kerry
Tel: +353(0)64 31853
Email: royalhot@iol.ie
Web: www.killarneyroyal.ie
Seasonal closure: 22–28 December
Rooms: 29 all ensuite ⓢ
Pricing: Dinner from €35 (2002 rate) CC: Accepted
Room facilities: 🖥 ☎ 📞 Access: ᴵᴵ &
Children: Welcome ⴱ ⅌ⓒ Dogs: Guide dogs only
Licences: ⅲ Parking: Off-street
Directions: Centre of Killarney across from the railway station.

Randles Court Hotel

★★★★ ⓡ

Muckross Road, Killarney, Co. Kerry
Tel: +353(0)64 35333 Fax: +353(0)64 35206
Email: info@randlescourt.com
Web: www.randlescourt.com
Seasonal closure: One week at Christmas

Truly one of Killarney's gems. This deluxe hotel offers
the elegance and charm of a country house with
excellent service and facilities. Only walking distance
from Killarney town, yet pleasantly secluded.
Rooms: 50 all ensuite ⓣ ⓢ
Pricing: Sgl €90–150 Dbl €140–230 Dinner from €40
CC: Accepted Room facilities: ▢ ☎ Access: |↓↑
Conference: 1 meeting room (Thtr 80 max),
24hr-delegate from €199, day-delegate rate from €59
Children: Welcome ☒ ☕ Dogs: Welcome Licences: ⚏
Leisure: Indoor pool, Gym, Health spa, Beauty salon
Parking: Off-street and monitored
Directions: Located on the Muckross Road towards
Muckross House. As you leave Killarney, we are on the
left-hand side, ¼ mile.

Riverside Hotel

★★★★ ⓡ

Muckross Road, Killarney, Co. Kerry
Tel: +353(0)64 39200 Fax: +353(0)64 39202
Email: stay@riversidehotelkillarney.com
Web: www.riversidehotelkillarney.com
Rooms: 69 all ensuite ⓢ Pricing: Sgl €80–120
Dbl €140–200 Dinner from €35 CC: Accepted
Room facilities: ▢ ☎ ☏ Access: |↓↑ ♿
Children: Welcome Licences: ⚏
Parking: Off-street and monitored
Directions: Follow signs for Killarney town centre and
then for Muckross Road Hotel is on the right, 1km from
town centre.
See advert on previous page

Castlerosse Hotel

★★★

Killarney, Co. Kerry
Tel: +353 (0)64 31144 Fax: +353 (0)64 31031
Email: info@crnk.ie
Web: www.castlerossehotelkillarney.com
Seasonal closure: 3 November to 14 March
Rooms: 121 all ensuite ⓣ Pricing: Sgl €95–108
Dbl €128–166 Dinner from €36 CC: Accepted

Room facilities: ▢ ☎ ☏ Access: |↓↑ ♿
Children: Welcome ☒ ☕ Dogs: Guide dogs only
Licences: ⚏ ⚏ Leisure: Indoor pool, Gym, Tennis,
Golf Parking: Off-street and monitored

Holiday Inn Killarney

★★★

Muckross Road, Killarney, Co. Kerry
Tel: +353(0)64 33000 Fax: +353(0)64 33001
Email: reservations@holidayinnkillarney.com
Web: www.holidayinnkillarney.com
Seasonal closure: Christmas
Rooms: 101 all ensuite ⓣ ⓢ
Pricing: Sgl €175 Dbl €198 Dinner from €24
CC: Accepted Room facilities: ▢ ☎ ☏ ☏ Access: |↓↑ ♿
Conference: 3 meeting rooms (Thtr 80 max)
Children: Welcome ☒ ☕ Dogs: Guide dogs only
Licences: ⚏ Leisure: Indoor pool, Gym
Parking: Off-street
Directions: Follow signs for Killarney town centre, and
then for Muckross Road; hotel is on the right 2
minutes' drive from the centre.

The Killarney Ryan

★★★

Cork Road, Killarney, Co. Kerry
Tel: +353(0)64 31555 Fax: +353(0)64 32438
Email: info@killarneyryan.com
Web: www.ryan-hotels.com

A modern hotel set within extensive grounds, featuring
a leisure centre, sports hall, tennis courts, crazy golf
and play areas. An ideal location from which to explore
the delights of Kerry.
Rooms: 168 all ensuite ⓣ
Pricing: Sgl €168 Dbl €181 Dinner from €25
CC: Accepted Room facilities: ▢ ☎ Access: |↓↑
Children: Welcome ☒ ☕ Dogs: Guide dogs only
Licences: ⚏ ⚏ Leisure: Indoor pool, Tennis,
Games room Parking: Off-street and monitored
Directions: 2km from Killarney town centre on N22.

Republic of Ireland

White Gates Hotel

★ ★ ★

Muckross Road, Killarney, Co. Kerry
Tel: +353(0)64 31164 Fax: +353(0)64 34850
Email: whitegates@iol.ie
Rooms: 27 all ensuite
Room facilities: Access:
Conference: 1 meeting room (Thtr 40 max)
Children: Welcome Dogs: Guide dogs only
Licences: Parking: Off-street and monitored
Directions: Outside Killarney Town on Muckross Road
to Kenmare.

Earls Court House

Little Gem

♦ ♦ ♦ ♦ ♦

Woodlawn Junction, Muckross Road, Killarney,
Co. Kerry
Tel: +353(0)64 34009 Fax: +353(0)64 34366
Email: info@killarney-earlscourt.ie
Web: www.killarney-earlscourt.ie
Seasonal closure: December to February

Family run 4-star hideaway, 5 minutes walk to town
centre. Country house ambience — antiques,
paintings, open fires, home baking & Irish hospitality.
Spacious bedrooms, king beds, suites with four poster
beds, private parking.
Rooms: 18 all ensuite
Pricing: Sgl €60–90 Dbl €104–130 CC: Accepted
Room facilities: Children: Welcome
Dogs: Welcome Licences:
Parking: Off-street
Directions: Take Muckross Road from Killarney. At the
traffic light, take a left and Earls Court House is third
house on your left.

Foley's Townhouse

♦ ♦ ♦ ♦ ♦

23 High Street, Killarney, Co. Kerry
Tel: +353(0)64 31217 Fax: +353(0)64 34683
Rooms: 28 all ensuite
Pricing: Dinner from €20 (2002 rate) CC: Accepted
Room facilities:
Children: Welcome
Licences:
Parking: Off-street and monitored
Directions: Town centre location on right-hand side of
High Street (when travelling north, direction Tralee).

Fuchsia House

♦ ♦ ♦ ♦ ♦

Muckross Road, Killarney, Co. Kerry
Tel: +353(0)64 33743 Fax: +353(0)64 36588
Email: fuchsiahouse@eircom.net
Web: www.fuchsiahouse.com
Seasonal closure: November to end February
Rooms: 10 all ensuite
Pricing: Sgl €60–90 Dbl €80–112 CC: Accepted
Room facilities: Access:
Children: Welcome Leisure: Games room
Parking: Off-street and monitored
Directions: Take Muckross road N71 south from
Killarney. After the traffic lights 3rd house on the right.

Ashville Guest House

♦ ♦ ♦ ♦

Rock Road, Killarney, Co. Kerry
Tel: +353(0)64 36405 Fax: +353(0)64 36778
Email: ashvillehouse@eircom.net
Web: www.ashvillekillarney.com

Spacious, family-run guest house, two minutes' walk
from the town centre, situated on the main Tralee road
(N22). Private car park. Comfortably furnished ensuite
bedrooms. Your ideal touring base.
Rooms: 12 all ensuite
Pricing: Sgl €40–65 Dbl €56–78 CC: Accepted
Room facilities: Children: Welcome
Parking: Off-street and monitored
Directions: On main Tralee road (N22), two minutes
walk from town centre.

Killarney Villa

◆◆◆◆

Cork/Mallow Road (N72), Killarney, Co. Kerry
Tel: +353(0)64 31878 Fax: +353(0)64 31878
Email: killarneyvilla@eircom.net
Web: www.killarneyvilla.com
Seasonal closure: November to April
Rooms: 6 all ensuite
Pricing: Sgl €30–40 Dbl €56–68 CC: Accepted
Room facilities:
Children: Welcome, 6yrs min age
Dogs: Welcome Parking: Off-street and monitored
Directions: Take N22 out of Killarney. Travel through
two roundabouts on the Cork Mallow road for 1.3
miles. Take left at the Mallow N72 junction for 200
metres, to Killarney Villa on left.

Ross Castle Lodge

◆◆◆◆

Ross Road, Killarney, Co. Kerry
Tel: +353(0)64 36942 Fax: +353(0)64 36942
Email: rosscastlelodge@killarneyb-and-b.com
Web: www.killarneyb-and-b.com

Rooms: 4 all ensuite
Pricing: Dbl €26–35 CC: Accepted
Room facilities:
Parking: Off-street and monitored
Directions: 100 yards past Cineplex Cinema, turn right
at Texaco garage. House is on left immediately after
Ross Golf Club.

Killorglin, Co. Kerry

Grove Lodge

◆◆◆◆

Killarney Road, Killorglin, Co. Kerry
Tel: +353(0)66 9761157 Fax: +353(0)66 9762330
Rooms: 10 all ensuite
Room facilities:
Access:
Children: Welcome
Parking: Off-street
Directions: Located on N72, 300 metres from Killorglin
Bridge, on the Killarney exit from Killorglin.

Kilmallock, Co. Limerick

Flemingstown House
Little Gem

◆◆◆◆◆

Kilmallock, Co. Limerick
Tel: +353(0)63 98093 Fax: +353(0)63 98546
Email: flemingstown@keltec.ie
Web: www.ils.ie/flemingstown
Seasonal closure: December to February

Approached by a long avenue, this 18th-century
farmhouse is the ideal location for relaxation and
gourmet food combined. Ideal base for touring the
south of Ireland.
Rooms: 5 all ensuite
Pricing: Dbl €80–100 Dinner from €40 CC: Accepted
Room facilities: Children: Welcome
Parking: Off-street and monitored
Directions: On the road from Kilmallock to Kilfinane 2
miles sign at entrance.

Kilmessan, Co. Meath

The Station House Hotel

★★★

Kilmessan, Co. Meath
Tel: +353(0)46 25239 Fax: +353(0)46 25588
Email: info@thestationhousehotel.com
Web: www.thestationhousehotel.com

In the countryside of Meath, the Station House Hotel &
Signal Restaurant, reputed for excellence in customer
service and hospitality, is home away from home. Set
on 5 acres of gardens, it offers amenities we appreciate
today along with much of yesterday's charm.
Rooms: 20 all ensuite
Pricing: Sgl €76–85 Dbl €114–152 Dinner from €12.95
CC: Accepted Room facilities: Access:
Conference: 3 meeting rooms (Thtr 400 max),
24hr-delegate from €150, day-delegate rate from €75
Children: Welcome Dogs: Guide dogs only
Licences: Parking: Off-street and monitored
Directions: From Dublin N3 to Dunsmaughlin, left at
end of village Y junction, turn right to Dunsany, right
and left in Dunsany to Filmessan.

Republic of Ireland

Kinsale, Co. Cork

Trident Hotel

★★★★ ⍩ ⍩

World's End, Kinsale, Co. Cork
Tel: +353(0)21 4772301 Fax: +353(0)21 4774173
Email: info@tridenthotel.com
Web: www.tridenthotel.com
Seasonal closure: Christmas

On the water's edge in historic Kinsale, the Trident offers unrivalled panoramic views over marina and harbour, with award-winning cuisine and service. Golf, walking tours, scenic cruise, sailing nearby.
Rooms: 58 all ensuite
Pricing: Sgl €75–150 Dbl €100–190
Dinner from €20 CC: Accepted
Room facilities: ☐ ☎ ⍟ Access: |⍐| ⍩
Children: Welcome ⍑ ⍟ Licences: ⍡⍡⍡ Leisure: Gym
Parking: Off-street and monitored
Directions: Take the R600 to Kinsale from Cork City. The Trident is located at the end of Pier Road on the waterfront.

Long Quay House

◆ ◆ ◆ ◆

Long Quay, Kinsale, Co. Cork
Tel: +353(0)21 4774563 Fax: +353(0)21 4773201
Email: longquayhouse@eircom.net
Seasonal closure: December
Rooms: 7 all ensuite ⍟
Pricing: Sgl £50–70 Dbl £76–100 CC: Accepted
Room facilities: ☐ ☎ ⍟ Children: Welcome ⍑ ⍟
Dogs: Guide dogs only
Directions: Take R600 from Cork to Kinsale. Hotel on right as you enter Kinsale, just before supermarket and post office.

Old Bank House

◆ ◆ ◆ ◆ ⍟ ⍟

11 Pearse Street, next to Post office, Kinsale, Co. Cork
Tel: +353(0)21 4774075 Fax: +353(0)21 4774296
Email: oldbank@indigo.ie
Web: www.oldbankhousekinsale.com
Seasonal closure: 4 days over Christmas.

The Old Bank House is a Georgian residence of great character and charm, which has been consistently voted one of the "Top 100 Places to Stay in Ireland" every year since 1990. Gourmet Irish breakfast cooked to order each morning by Master Chef Michael Riese. A warm welcome awaits you from Michael, Marie and Katy Riese.
Rooms: 17 all ensuite
Pricing: Sgl €170–270 Dbl €170–270 CC: Accepted
Room facilities: ☐ ☎ Access: |⍐|
Children: Welcome, 10yrs min age Licences: ⍡⍡⍡
Directions: At start of Kinsale town, next door to Post Office, 11km on R600 from Cork airport.

Knock, Co. Mayo

Belmont Hotel

★★★ ⍩

Knock, Co. Mayo
Tel: +353(0)94 88122 Fax: +353(0)94 88532
Email: belmonthotel@eircom.net
Web: www.belmonthotel.ie
Rooms: 63 all ensuite ⍟ ⍟ ⍟
Pricing: Sgl €55–72 Dbl €84–112 Dinner from €30
CC: Accepted Room facilities: ☐ ☎ ⍟ ⍟ Access: |⍐| ⍩
Conference: 4 meeting rooms (Thtr 300 max)
Children: Welcome ⍑ ⍟ Dogs: Welcome
Licences: ⍟ ⍡⍡⍡ Leisure: Gym, Health spa
Parking: Off-street and monitored
Directions: Leaving Knock in the direction of Galway, take a left turn and go 200 metres.

Lakes of Killarney, Co. Kerry

Muckross Park Hotel

★★★★★ ⍩ ⍩

Muckross Village, Killarney, Co. Kerry
Tel: +353(0)64 31938 Fax: +353(0)64 31938
Email: muckrossparkhotel@eircom.net
Web: www.muckrosspark.com

The hotel is set in the heart of Killarney's National Park and boasts a proud tradition dating from 1975. Molly Darcy is our award-winning, traditional Irish pub and restaurant, and is an experience not to be missed.
Rooms: 27 all ensuite
Pricing: Sgl € 110–135 Dbl € 77–105 CC: Accepted
Room facilities:
Conference: 2 meeting rooms (Thtr 200 max)
Children: Welcome ⫪ Dogs: Guide dogs only
Licences: Parking: Off-street
Directions: Situated 4 km outside Killarney on the Main Kenmare Road N71, adjacent to Killarney's World Famous National Park, Muckross House and Gardens.

Kathleens Country House

Madams Height, Tralee Road (N22), Lakes of Killarney, Killarney, Co. Kerry
Tel: +353(0)64 32810 Fax: +353(0)64 32340
Email: info@kathleens.net
Web: www.kathleens.net
Seasonal closure: November to February

Kathleens is an award-winning family-run charming oasis of tranquillity. Traditional welcome. Ideal golf and touring base. Non-smoking.
Rooms: 17 all ensuite
Pricing: Sgl € 50–120 Dbl € 100–140 CC: Accepted
Room facilities: Access:
Children: Welcome, 4yrs min age Licences: ⫪
Parking: Off-street
Directions: 1 mile north of Killarney Town in scenic rural surrounds, accessible through N22.

Limerick, Co. Limerick

Castletroy Park Hotel

★★★★
Dublin Road, Limerick, Co. Limerick
Tel: +353(0)61 335566 Fax: +353(0)61 331117
Email: sales@castletroy-park.ie
Web: www.castletroy-park.ie
Rooms: 107 all ensuite
Pricing: Sgl £195–560 Dbl £220–610 Dinner from £38
CC: Accepted Room facilities: Access:
Conference: 9 meeting rooms (Thtr 450 max)
Children: Welcome ⫪ Licences: ⫪
Leisure: Indoor pool, Gym
Parking: Off-street and monitored
Directions: Situated on main Dublin road (N7), 3 miles from Limerick city and 25 minutes from Shannon International Airport.

Jurys Limerick Hotel

★★★★ 𝆕 𝆕 𝆕
Ennis Road, Limerick, Co. Limerick
Tel: +353(0)1 6070000 Fax: +353(0)1 6316999
Email: bookings@jurysdoyle.com
Web: www.jurysdoyle.com

JURYS DOYLE
HOTELS

Rooms: 95 all ensuite
Pricing: Sgl € 147–188 Dbl € 162–244 Dinner from € 19
CC: Accepted Room facilities: Access:
Children: Welcome, 12yrs min age ⫪
Dogs: Guide dogs only Licences: ⫪
Leisure: Indoor pool, Gym, Health spa, Tennis,
Parking: Off-street and monitored
Directions: Follow signs for Limerick city, along O'Connell Street take right over Sarsfield bridge onto Ennis Road, hotel is on left.

Radisson SAS Hotel

★★★★
Ennis Road, Limerick, Co. Limerick
Tel: +353(0)61 326666 Fax: +353(0)61 326281
Email: sales.limerick@raddissonsas.com
Web: www.radissonsas.com
Seasonal closure: Christmas
Rooms: 154 all ensuite
Pricing: Sgl € 165–210 Dbl € 158 Dinner from € 22
CC: Accepted Room facilities: Access:
Conference: 6 meeting rooms (Thtr 560 max), 24hr-delegate from € 171, day-delegate rate from € 45
Children: Welcome ⫪
Dogs: Guide dogs only Licences: ⫪
Leisure: Indoor pool, Gym, Tennis
Parking: Off-street
Directions: From Dublin to Limerick follow N7 and then N18 towards Shannon, hotel 6km from city centre. From Shannon follow N18, hotel is 16km on the left.

South Court Business and Leisure Hotel

★★★★ 𝆕 𝆕 𝆕
Adare Road, Raheen, Limerick, Co. Limerick
Tel: +353(0)6 5682 3000 Fax: +353(0)6 5682 3759
Email: reservations@lynchotels.com
Web: www.lynchotels.com
Rooms: 124 all ensuite
Pricing: Sgl € 115–270 Dbl € 147–414 Dinner from € 25
CC: Accepted Room facilities: Access:
Conference: 10 meeting rooms (Thtr 1250 max), 24hr-delegate from € 145, day-delegate rate from € 40
Children: Welcome ⫪
Dogs: Guide dogs only Licences: ⫪
Leisure: Indoor pool, Gym, Health spa
Parking: Off-street and monitored
Directions: Located on the main Cork/Killarney road (N20), the South Court Hotel offers an ideal base for touring the Shannon region.

The Gresham Ardhu

★ ★ ★ ★

Ennis Road, Limerick, Co. Limerick
Tel: +353(0)61 453922 Fax: +353(0)61 326333
Email: info@gresham-ardhuhotel.com
Web: www.gresham-hotels.com

GRESHAM HOTELS

A Georgian building dating back to 1780 which has been recently restored to its former elegance.
Rooms: 181 all ensuite 🛏 🚭
Pricing: Sgl €120–120 Dbl €158–158
Dinner from €24.50 CC: Accepted
Room facilities: 📺 ☎ 🍵 Access: ⬆ ♿
Conference: 10 meeting rooms
Children: Welcome 🍴 🍼 Licences: ⚜ 👪
Leisure: Gym Parking: Off-street and monitored
Directions: The Hotel is situated on the N18 on the Ennis Road.

Jurys Inn Limerick

★ ★ ★

Lower Mallow Street, Limerick, Co. Limerick
Tel: +353(0)1 6070000 Fax: +353(0)1 6316999
Email: bookings@jurysdoyle.com
Web: www.jurysdoyle.com

JURYS DOYLE
HOTELS

Seasonal closure: Christmas
Rooms: 151 all ensuite 🛏 🚭
Pricing: Sgl €75–79 Dbl €75–79
Dinner from €17
CC: Accepted Room facilities: 📺 ☎ 🍵 ⬆
Access: ⬆ ♿
Children: Welcome 🍴
Dogs: Guide dogs only
Licences: 👪
Parking: Off-street and monitored
Directions: Located 15 miles/24 km from Shannon International airport. Colbert train station 1 mile/2km. Heart of the city on the banks of Shannon.

Woodfield House Hotel

★ ★ ★

Ennis Road, Limerick, Co. Limerick
Tel: +353(0)61 453022 Fax: +353(0)61 326755
Email: woodfield@eircom.net
Web: www.woodfieldhousehotel.com
Seasonal closure: December 24-25
Rooms: 26 all ensuite 🛏 🚭
Pricing: Sgl €75–88 Dbl €126–142
CC: Accepted
Room facilities: 📺 ☎ ⬆
Access: ♿
Children: Welcome 🍴
Licences: ⚜ 👪
Parking: Off-street and monitored
Directions: Situated 1 mile outside the city centre on the north side of Limerick city, on the main Shannon road.

Travelodge Limerick

Travel Accommodation
N18, Ennis Road Roundabout, Co. Limerick,
Web: www.travelodge.co.uk
Rooms: 40 all ensuite 🚭
Pricing: Sgl €85.92 Dbl €92.84
CC: Accepted Room facilities: 📺 🍵 Access: ♿

Lisdoonvarna, Co. Clare

Kincora Country House Inn & Restaurant

◆ ◆ ◆ ◆ 🍴 ☕ 🍷

Lisdoonvarna, Co. Clare
Tel: +353(0)65 7074300 Fax: +353(0)65 7074490
Email: kincorahotel@eircom.net
Web: www.kincora-hotel.com
Seasonal closure: November to February

Relax in peace and tranquility at our award-winning family-run hotel. Enjoy excellent cuisine in our restaurant/art gallery, set in feature gardens. Nearby are Cliff's of Moher and Burren and 2 local golf courses.
Rooms: 14 all ensuite 🚭
Pricing: Sgl €60–100 Dbl €75–120 Dinner from €40
CC: Accepted Room facilities: 📺 ☎ ⬆ Access: ♿
Conference: 1 meeting room (Thtr 40 max)
Children: Welcome, 12yrs min age Licences: ⚜ 👪
Parking: Off-street and monitored
Directions: From Lisdoonvarna town centre, take the Doolin Road. Hotel is on the first junction ¼km from town centre.

Macroom, Co. Cork

Castle Hotel and Leisure Centre

Main Street, Macroom, Co. Cork
Tel: +353(0)26 41074 Fax: +353(0)26 41505
Email: castlehotel@eircom.net
Web: www.castlehotel.ie
Seasonal closure: 25–27 December
Rooms: 60 all ensuite
Pricing: Sgl €82–103 Dbl €114–155 Dinner from €30
CC: Accepted Room facilities: □ ☎ ⬚ ❄
Access: ⬚ ⬚ Conference: 3 meeting rooms (Thtr 80
max) Children: Welcome ⍗ ⬚ Licences: ⬚ ⬚
Leisure: Indoor pool, Gym, Health spa
Parking: Off-street and monitored
Directions: On the N22, 25 miles from Cork and 30
miles from Killarney.

The Mills Inn

Ballyvourney, Macroom, Co. Cork
Tel: +353(0)26 45237 Fax: +353(0)26 45454
Email: millinn@eircom.net
Web: www.millsinn.ie
Rooms: 12 all ensuite
Pricing: Sgl €30–45 Dbl €60–90 CC: Accepted
Room facilities: □ ☎ ⬚ Access: ⬚
Conference: 1 meeting room (Thtr 60 max)
Children: Welcome ⍗ Dogs: Welcome
Licences: ⬚ ⬚ Parking: Off-street and monitored
Directions: N22 — an hour from Cork, 20 minutes from
Kilarrey, close to Gougae Barra and Bantry Bay.

Malahide, Co. Dublin

Grand Hotel

★★★★

Malahide, Co. Dublin
Tel: +353(0)1 8450000 Fax: +353(0)1 81450987
Email: info@thegrand.ie
Web: www.thegrand.ie
Seasonal closure: Christmas

Rooms: 150 all ensuite ⬚ ⬚ Pricing: Sgl €135–135
Dbl €175–175.50 Dinner from €32 CC: Accepted
Room facilities: □ ☎ ⬚ ⬚ Access: ⬚ ⬚
Children: Welcome ⍗ Licences: ⬚ ⬚
Leisure: Indoor pool, Gym, Health spa,
Beauty salon, Tennis Parking: Off-street and monitored
Directions: From Dublin airport, go northwards on
Belfast road; turn right for Malahide at appropriate
roundabout.

Mallow, Co. Cork

Longueville House Hotel — Gold Ribbon Winner

★★★★ ⬚ ⬚ ⬚

Mallow, Co. Cork
Tel: +353(0)22 47156 Fax: +353(0)22 47459
Email: info@longuevillehouse.ie
Web: www.longuevillehouse.ie
Seasonal closure: Mid-November to mid-March

Longueville House is situated in the heart of 500 acres
of wooded estate overlooking the Blackwater river
valley. The house is a listed Georgian Manor (1720) and
is owned by the O'Callagham family, your hosts.
Rooms: 20 all ensuite ⬚ ⬚ ⬚
Pricing: Sgl €90–320 Dbl €170–340 Dinner from €50
CC: Accepted Room facilities: □ ☎ ⬚
Conference: 3 meeting rooms (Thtr 45 max)
Children: Welcome ⍗ ⬚ Dogs: Welcome
Licences: ⬚ Parking: Monitored
Directions: 3 miles west of Mallow, via the N72 to
Killarney. Turn right at Ballyclough junction.

Springfort Hall Country House

★★★

Mallow, Co. Cork
Tel: +353(0)22 21278 Fax: +353(0)22 21557
Email: stay@springfort-hall.com
Web: www.springfort-hall.com
Seasonal closure: 23–28 December
Rooms: 49 all ensuite ⬚ ⬚
Pricing: Sgl €75–90 Dbl €120–135
Dinner from €30 CC: Accepted
Room facilities: □ ☎ ⬚ Access: ⬚
Conference: 3 meeting rooms (Thtr 360 max),
24hr-delegate from €127, day-delegate rate from €36
Children: Welcome ⍗
Licences: ⬚ ⬚ Parking: Off-street and monitored
Directions: From Cork take N20 to Newtwopothouse.
Turn right towards Doneraile, hotel on right approx ½
mile. From Limerick take N20 through Charleville and
Buttevant and on to Newtwopothouse, turn left towards
Doneraile, hotel on the right approx ½ mile. From Dublin
N8 to Mallow. Take N20 to Newtwopothouse. Turn right
towards Doneraile, hotel on the right.

Maynooth, Co. Kildare

Moyglare Manor Hotel
Blue Ribbon Winner

★★★ 🍽🍽🍽

Maynooth, Co. Kildare
Tel: +353(0)1 6286351 Fax: +353(0)1 6285405
Email: info@moyglaremanor.ie
Web: www.moyglaremanor.ie
Seasonal closure: 24–26 December

Beautiful countryside just 18 miles from Dublin.
Opulent grade-A family-run hotel and restaurant, highly
acclaimed for excellent cuisine and fine wines.
Embracing elegance and charm of country living.
Rooms: 16 all ensuite 🛏 🖨
Pricing: Sgl €160 Dbl €260–315
Dinner from €30 CC: Accepted
Room facilities: 🖥 ☎ 🔌 Access: ♿

Conference: 3 meeting rooms (Thtr 30 max),
24hr-delegate from €200
Children: Welcome, 12yrs min age
Dogs: Guide dogs only Licences: ♟
Parking: Off-street and monitored
Directions: Travelling west on N4/M4, take slip road for
Maynooth. Keep right at Catholic church to Moyglare
Road. Hotel is after 2km.

Midleton, Co. Cork

Ballymaloe House

★★★ 🍽🍽

Shangarry, Midleton, Co. Cork
Tel: +353(0)21 4652531 Fax: +353(0)21 4652021
Email: res@ballymaloe.ie
Web: www.ballymaloe.ie
Seasonal closure: 23–26 December
Rooms: 33 all ensuite Pricing: Sgl €110–165
Dbl €190–270 Dinner from €57 CC: Accepted
Room facilities: ☎ 🔌 Access: ♿ Conference: 3 meeting
rooms (Thtr 30 max) Children: Welcome ♟ 🐾
Dogs: Guide dogs only Licences: ♟
Leisure: Outdoor pool, Tennis, Golf Parking: Off-street
Directions: From Cork, take N25 to Midleton, then the
Ballycotton Road via Cloyne (signposted from Midleton).

Rathcoursey House

♦♦♦♦♦ ✕ ☝

Ballinacurra, near Midleton, Co. Cork,
Tel: +353(0)21 4613418 Fax: +353(0)21 4613393
Email: beth@rathcoursey.com
Web: www.rathcoursey.com
Rooms: 6 (5 ensuite) Access: &
Children: Welcome ♁ ⅋ Dogs: Welcome
Parking: Off-street and monitored
Directions: At roundabout for Midleton on N25 take
Whitegate exit. Turn right after 1¹/₂ miles at crossroads
("East Ferry Scenic Route"). After another 1¹/₂ miles
look for arrow on left. Entrance is around next bend.
Follow the arrows.

Monasterevin, Co. Kildare

Hazel Hotel
★★

Dublin Road, Monasterevin, Co. Kildare,
Tel: +353 (0)45 525373 Fax: +353 (0)45 525810
Email: sales@hazelhotel.com
Web: www.hazelhotel.com
Seasonal closure: 24–25 December
Rooms: 24 all ensuite
Pricing: Sgl €60–80 Dbl €100–120 CC: Accepted
Room facilities: ▢ ☎ ☕ ☍ Access: &
Conference: 4 meeting rooms
Children: Welcome ♁ Parking: Off-street and monitored
Directions: The hotel is situated on the N7
Cork/Limerick road to the west of Monasterevin.
See advert on previous page

Mountshannon, Co. Clare

Mountshannon Hotel
★★

Main Street, Mountshannon, Co. Clare
Tel: +353(0)61 927162

Naas, Co. Kildare

Killashee House Hotel and Spa
★★★★★ ☝☝

Killcullen Road, Naas, Co. Kildare
Tel: +353(0)45 879277 Fax: +353(0)45 879266
Email: reservations@killasheehouse.com
Web: www.killasheehouse.com
Seasonal closure: 25–26 December

Originally a Victorian hunting lodge in 1861 Killashee
House has 84 luxurious rooms including suites.
Excellent conference and leisure facilities. Enjoy
mouthwatering food in Turners Restaurant.
Rooms: 84 all ensuite
Pricing: Sgl €144–419 Dbl €198–419 Dinner from €40
CC: Accepted Room facilities: ▢ ☎ ☍ Access: ⅃↑ &
Conference: 24 meeting rooms (Thtr 1200 max)
Children: Welcome ♁ Dogs: Guide dogs only
Licences: ♦♦♦
Leisure: Indoor pool, Gym, Health spa,
Beauty salon
Parking: Off-street and monitored
Directions: 30 mins from Dublin on N7 to Naas then 1
mile along R448 Killcullen Road.

Harbour Hotel & Restaurant
★★

Limerick Road, Naas, Co. Kildare
Tel: +353(0)45 879145 Fax: +353(0)45 874002
Seasonal closure: Christmas to New Year
Rooms: 10 all ensuite
Pricing: Sgl €57–65 Dbl €89–95 Dinner from €25
CC: Accepted Room facilities: ▢ ☎ ☕
Licences: ◭ ♦♦♦
Parking: Off-street and monitored

Ballinagappa Country House
♦♦♦♦♦ ✕ ☝

Clane, near Naas, Co. Kildare
Tel: +353(0)45 892087 Fax: +353(0)45 892087
Email: ballinagappahouse@eircom.net
Web: www.ballinagappa.com
Rooms: 3 (2 ensuite) ☒ Room facilities: ▢ ☕ ☍
Children: Welcome ♁ ⅋ Dogs: Welcome
Parking: Off-street and monitored
Directions: From the N4, go towards Naas; Clane is 6¹/₂
miles. Take second right, and Ballinagappa is 1¹/₂ miles
on the left.

Nenagh, Co. Tipperary

Abbey Court Hotel & Trinity Leisure Club
★★★

Dublin Road, Nenagh, Co. Tipperary
Tel: +353(0)67 41111 Fax: +353(0)67 41022
Email: abycourt@indigo.ie
Web: www.abbeycourt.ie
Rooms: 82 all ensuite ☒
Pricing: Dinner from €16.31 (2002 rate) CC: Accepted
Room facilities: ▢ ☎ ☕ ☍ Access: ⅃↑ &
Children: Welcome ♁ Dogs: Guide dogs only
Licences: ◭ ♦♦♦
Leisure: Indoor pool, Gym, Health spa,
Beauty salon
Parking: Off-street and monitored
Directions: The Abbey Court Hotel located off the main
Dublin to Limerick (N7) road within easy access to
Shannon, Cork and Dublin airports.

New Ross, Co. Wexford

Creacon Lodge Hotel

◆◆◆◆

New Ross, Co. Wexford,
Tel: +353(0)51 421897 Fax: +353(0)51 422560
Email: info@creaconlodge.com
Web: www.creaconlodge.com
Seasonal closure: 23–28 December
Rooms: 10 all ensuite 🛏 ⊗
Pricing: Sgl €57–77 Dbl €98–148 Dinner from €17.50
CC: Accepted Room facilities: ☐ ☎ Access: ♿
Children: Welcome 🍴 Dogs: Guide dogs only
Licences: 🍷 ♟ Parking: Off-street and monitored
Directions: From Wexford take N25 to New Ross. Just
before reaching New Ross turn left on R733. After
5km, turn left for Creacon Lodge.

Oranmore, Co. Galway

Moorings Restaurant & Guest House

◆◆◆ ®

Oranmore, Co. Galway
Tel: +353(0)91 790462 Fax: +353(0)91 790462
Email: themoorings@eircom.net
Web: www.galway.net/moorings
Rooms: 6 all ensuite 🛏
Pricing: Dinner from €35 CC: Accepted
Room facilities: ☐ ☎ ⊙
Children: Welcome 🍴 Licences: ♟
Parking: Off-street and monitored
Directions: From roundabout on approach road from
Dublin/Cork/Limerick into Oranmore village. At T-junction
turn right; Moorings is on the right on main street.

Portlaoise, Co. Laois

Ivyleigh House   Little Gem

◆◆◆◆◆ ❀ ℱ

Bank Place, Church Street, Portlaoise, Co. Laois
Tel: +353(0)502 22081 Fax: +353(0)502 63343
Email: dinah@ivyleigh.com
Web: www.ivyleigh.com
Seasonal closure: 22 December to 2 January

Luxurious listed Georgian accommodation, excellent
service and breakfast award-winner, two minutes walk
from town centre, antique furnishings, log fires and
home baking, superior rooms with individual themes
and private parking.

Rooms: 4 all ensuite ⊗
Pricing: Sgl €75 Dbl €110 CC: Accepted
Room facilities: ☐ ☎ ⊙ 🔌
Children: Welcome, 8yrs min age
Parking: Off-street and monitored
Directions: 40 meters from Church Street multi storey
car park.

Portmagee, Co. Kerry

Moorings

◆◆◆◆

Portmagee Village, Co. Kerry,
Tel: +353(0)66 9477108 Fax: +353(0)66 9477220
Email: moorings@iol.ie
Web: www.moorings.ie
Seasonal closure: November to February
Rooms: 14 all ensuite ⊗ Room facilities: ☐ ☎ ⊙ 🔌
Access: ♿ Children: Welcome 🍴 Licences: ♟
Parking: Off-street
Directions: Follow the Ring of Kerry road – Killarney to
Caherciveen. Three miles outside Caherciveen, turn
right for Portmagee. Moorings is in centre of village.

Portumna, Co. Galway

Shannon Oaks Hotel and Country Club

★★★★★

St Joseph's Road, Portumna, Co. Galway
Tel: +353(0)509 41777 Fax: +353(0)509 41357
Email: sales@shannonoaks.ie
Web: www.shannonoaks.ie
Rooms: 63 all ensuite 🛏 📶 ⊗
Pricing: Dinner from €22.50 CC: Accepted
Room facilities: ☐ ☎ ⊙ 🔌 ❄ Access: ⬆ ♿
Children: Welcome 🍴 🦮 Dogs: Guide dogs only
Licences: 🍷 ♟
Leisure: Indoor pool, Gym, Health spa,
Beauty salon, Tennis, Golf, Fishing, Riding
Parking: Off-street and monitored
Directions: Shannon Oaks Hotel & Country Club is
located on St Joseph's Road in the village of
Portumna.

See advert on next page

Rathmullan, Co. Donegal

Rathmullan House

★★★★ 🛏 🛏 🛏

Rathmullan, Letterkenny, Co. Donegal
Tel: +353(0)74 58188 Fax: +353(0)74 58200
Email: info@rathmullanhouse.com
Web: www.rathmullanhouse.com
Seasonal closure: January to mid-February

This gracious Georgian house stands in lovely tranquil gardens that run down to the shores of Lough Swilly. Superb food and wines served in award-winning Bedouin-style resturant.
Rooms: 24 all ensuite 🐾 🚗
Pricing: Sgl €95–107 Dbl €166–236
Dinner from €30 CC: Accepted
Room facilities: 📺 ☎ 🛢 Access: ♿
Children: Welcome 🍴 ☕
Dogs: Guide dogs only
Licences: 🍾
Leisure: Indoor pool, Beauty salon, Tennis
Parking: Off-street and monitored
Directions: From Belfast airport, follow A6 to Derry. Follow N13 to Letterkenny, and on arrival turn right into Ramelton. After bridge turn right to Rathmullan. Hotel is situated 500m north of village.

Roscommon, Co. Roscommon

Abbey Hotel

★★★

Roscommon, Co. Roscommon
Tel: +353(0)903 26505 Fax: +353(0)903 26021
Email: sales@abbeyhotel.ie

The Abbey Hotel, set in its own private grounds, is ideally situated for the touring holidaymaker. Excellent restaurant and spacious comfortable accommodation that compare favourably with the best international standards.
Rooms: 49 all ensuite 🚗 🚭
Pricing: Sgl €85–95 Dbl €62.50–75 Dinner from €35
CC: Accepted Room facilities: 📺 ☎ 🛢 Access: 🏃 ♿
Children: Welcome 🍴 ☕ Licences: 🍷 🍾
Leisure: Indoor pool, Gym, Tennis
Parking: Off-street
Directions: The hotel is on the Galway Road (N63), southern side of Roscommon town in town itself.

Plan your route

Visit www.rac.co.uk for RAC's interactive route planner, including up to the minute traffic reports.

Are you covered?

For competitively priced travel insurance, buy online at www.rac.co.uk or call RAC Travel Sales on 0800 55 00 55. Quote GUI3

Gleesons Townhouse

◆◆◆◆◆�

Market Square, Roscomon, Roscomon
Tel: +353(0)903 26954 Fax: +353(0)903 27425
Email: info@gleesonstownhouse.com
Web: www.gleesontownhouse.com

Magnificent guest house/restaurant situated in a
tastefully resorted listed 19th Century Town House with
an attractive finish of cut limestone and blue bangor
quarry slates. Located in the town centre next door to
Tourist Office/Museum. We offer superb
accommodation with all 19 rooms appointed to a 4-
star standard. Private car parking. Experience "The
Manse" restaurant where all the old values of guest
satisfaction, comfort and value for money prevail. Fully
licensed for beers/spirits/wine. We also offer luxurious
air-conditioned private conference/party room for all
guests. Angler's/golf facility centre on site. Highly
recommended in international guide books.
Rooms: 19 all ensuite ⌂ ⊗
Pricing: Sgl €45–55 Dbl €40–50 Dinner from €20
CC: Accepted Room facilities: ▢ ☎ ⊿ ☏
Conference: 2 meeting rooms (Thtr 80 max)
Children: Welcome �🍴 ⁑ Dogs: Welcome
Licences: ♦♦♦ Parking: Off-street and monitored

Rooms: 99 all ensuite
Pricing: Sgl €90–120 Dbl €160–220 Dinner from €35
CC: Accepted Room facilities: ▢ ☎ ☏ Access: ⌂⌂ ♿
Children: Welcome ⌂ 🏇 ⁑ Licences: ♦♦♦
Leisure: Indoor pool, Gym, Health spa,
Beauty salon, Tennis, Snooker/billiards
Parking: Off-street and monitored
Directions: From Dublin airport, take N11 to Rosslare,
signposted South-East (Gorey, Enniscorthy, Wexford,
Rosslare). The hotel is situated in Rosslare Strand.

Churchtown House   Little Gem

◆◆◆◆◆☁ ⌇ ⚘ ☙

Tagoat, Rosslare, Co. Wexford
Tel: +353(0)53 32555 Fax: +353(0)52 32577
Email: info@churchtownhouse.com
Web: www.churchtownhouse.com

Set in the Irish countryside between Wexford and
Rosslare, Churchtown offers an elegant retreat for
short or long visits, special inclusive rates for extended
stays, beaches, golf and gardens to visit.
Rooms: 12 all ensuite ⊗
Pricing: Sgl €75 Dbl €120 Dinner from €35
CC: Accepted Room facilities: ▢ ☎ Access: ♿
Children: Welcome Dogs: Guide dogs only
Licences: ♦♦♦ Parking: Off-street
Directions: Half a mile from the N25 at Tagoat. Turn
between pub and church onto R736 at Tagoat village.

Rosslare, Co. Wexford

Kelly's Resort Hotel

★★★★★ ☁ ☁

Rosslare, Co. Wexford
Tel: +353(0)53 32114 Fax: +353(0)53 32222
Email: kellyhot@iol.ie
Web: www.kellys.ie
Seasonal closure: 8 December to 22 February

Renowned resort hotel. Fine food and wine,
indoor/outdoor amenities. Extensive leisure and beauty
complex. Special spring–autumn activity midweeks, 2-
day weekends and 5-day midweeks.

Roundstone, Co. Galway

Roundstone House Hotel

★★★ ☁ ☁

Roundstone, Connemara, Co. Galway
Tel: +353(0)95 35864 Fax: +353(0)95 35944
Email: diar@eircom.net
Seasonal closure: November to 1 April

Rooms: 12 all ensuite ⌂
Pricing: Sgl €48.50–55 Dbl €82–96 Dinner from €38

CC: Accepted Room facilities: 💻 ☎ 🍵
Children: Welcome ☂ Licences: ⚓ ⋔
Directions: Take the N59 from Galway and then R341 at Ballynahinch.

Heatherglen House

◆ ◆ ◆ 🦢

Roundstone, Co. Galway,
Tel: +353(0)95 35837 Fax: +353(0)95 35837
Web: spkeane@eircone.net
Seasonal closure: November to February
Rooms: 4 all ensuite
Pricing: Sgl €50 Dbl €60
Parking: Off-street
Directions: Take N59 from Galway to Roundstone.

Sligo, Co. Sligo

Tower Hotel

★ ★ ★

Quay Street, Sligo, Co. Sligo
Tel: +353(0)71 44000 Fax: +353(0)71 46888
Email: towersl@iol.ie
Web: www.towerhotelsligo.com
Seasonal closure: 23-29 December
Rooms: 58 all ensuite 🍴
Pricing: Sgl €85 Dbl €135 D
inner from €27
CC: Accepted Room facilities: 💻 ☎ 🍵 Access: 🛗
Children: Welcome ☂ Dogs: Guide dogs only
Licences: ⚓ ⋔
Parking: Off-street and monitored

Spiddal, Co. Galway

Suan na Mara

◆ ◆ ◆ ◆ ◆ 🦢 ✂ 🦢

Stripe, Furbo, Spiddal, Co. Galway
Tel: +353(0)91 591512 Fax: +353(0)91 591632
Email: adm@suannamara.com
Web: www.suannamara.com

Premier national winner country homes award. Chef owned. Laundry, Internet, hairdryer, trousers press. Complementary fresh fruit. Imaginative breakfast menu. Evening meal. Discover the difference for yourself. Your comfort is guaranteed.
Rooms: 4 all ensuite 🍴
Pricing: Sgl €50 Dbl €75 Dinner from €25

CC: Accepted Room facilities: 💻 🍵
Children: Welcome ☂ ☕
Directions: Furbo is 14km west Galway, city route 336, after Connenara Coast hotel on your left, take first right at church.

Straffan, Co. Kildare

The K Club   Gold Ribbon Winner

★ ★ ★ ★ ★ 🔴 🔴 🔴

Straffan, Co. Kildare,
Tel: +353(0)1 6017200 Fax: +353(0)1 6017297
Email: resortsales@kclub.ie
Web: www.kclub.ie
Rooms: 95 all ensuite 🍴 🎞 🚭
Pricing: Sgl £295 Dbl £358
Dinner from £75 CC: Accepted
Room facilities: 💻 ☎ 🧹 Access: 🛗 ♿
Conference: 5 meeting rooms (Thtr 120 max)
Children: Welcome ☂ ☕ Dogs: Welcome
Licences: ⋔
Leisure: Indoor pool, Gym, Health spa, Beauty salon, Tennis, Golf, Fishing, Riding, Games room, Snooker/billiards
Parking: Off-street and monitored
Directions: Take N7 south as far as the Kill crossing, turn right at traffic lights. Resort is 5 miles, and is well-signposted from that point.
See advert on next page

Barberstown Castle

★ ★ ★ ★ 🔴 🔴

Straffan, Co. Kildare
Tel: +353(0)1 6288157 Fax: +353(0)1 6277027
Email: castleir@iol.ie
Web: www.barberstowncastle.com
Seasonal closure: 24-27 December, 10-20 January
Rooms: 22 all ensuite 🎞 🚭
Pricing: Sgl €137.50 Dbl €110 Dinner from €39.50
CC: Accepted Room facilities: 💻 ☎ 🧹 Access: ♿
Conference: 2 meeting rooms (Thtr 30 max)
Children: Welcome, 12yrs min age Licences: ⋔
Parking: Off-street and monitored
Directions: N4 west from Dublin – exit at Maynooth/Straffan. M50 south from Dublin – exit at "Kill" junction.

Swords, Co. Dublin

Travelodge Dublin Airport

Travel Accommodation
N1 Little Chef, Pinnock Hill Roundabout, Swords, Co. Dublin
Web: www.travelodge.co.uk
Rooms: 100 all ensuite 🚭
Pricing: Sgl €101.92 Dbl €108.84
CC: Accepted Room facilities: 💻 🍵 Access: ♿

Tahilla, Co. Kerry

Tahilla Cove Country House

◆ ◆ ◆ ◆

Tahilla, near Sneem, Co. Kerry
Tel: +353(0)64 45204 Fax: +353(0)64 45104
Email: tahillacove@eircom.net
Web: www.tahillacove.com
Seasonal closure: October to April
Rooms: 9 all ensuite Pricing: Sgl €80 Dbl €120
CC: Accepted Room facilities: ▢ ☎ ☕
Children: Welcome Dogs: Welcome
Directions: Located just off N70 ring of Kerry road, 5 miles east of Sneem, 11 miles west of Kenmare.

Tallaght, Co. Dublin

Plaza Hotel

★ ★ ★ ★

Belgard Road, Tallaght, Dublin 24
Tel: +353(0)1 4624200 Fax: +353(0)1 4624600
Email: sales@plazahotel.ie
Web: www.plazahotel.ie
Seasonal closure: 23–31 December
Rooms: 122 all ensuite ⊛ Room facilities: ▢ ☎ ⌕
Access: ⇞ ♿
Conference: 11 meeting rooms (Thtr 220 max)
Children: Welcome Ħ Dogs: Guide dogs only
Licences: ⬥ Parking: Off-street and monitored

Tralee, Co. Kerry

Ballyseede Castle

★ ★ ★ ♞ ♞ ♞

Ballyseede, Tralee, Co. Kerry
Tel: +353(0)66 7125799 Fax: +353(0)66 7125287
Email: ballyseede@eircom.net
Web: www.ballyseedecastle.com
Rooms: 12 all ensuite ▱ ⊛
Pricing: Sgl €90–120 Dbl €150–210
Dinner from €36 CC: Accepted
Room facilities: ▢ ☎
Licences: ⬥ ♟ Parking: Off-street and monitored
Directions: Located off the N21 from Limerick and the N22 from Cork.

Barnagh Bridge Guesthouse

◆ ◆ ◆ ◆ ⚐

Cappaclogh, Camp, Tralee, Co. Kerry
Tel: +353(0)66 7130145 Fax: +353(0)66 7130299
Email: bbguest@eircom.net
Seasonal closure: November to March
Rooms: 5 all ensuite ⊛
Room facilities: ▢ ☎ ☕
Children: Welcome, 10yrs min age Ħ
Parking: Off-street and monitored
Directions: Leave N86 at Camp. Follow Conor Pass Road, R560, for 1 mile.

Glenduff House

◆ ◆ ◆ ◆ ✳

Tralee, Co. Kerry
Tel: +353(0)66 7137105 Fax: +353(0)66 7137099
Email: glenduffhouse@eircom.net
Web: www.tralee-insight.com/glenduff
Seasonal closure: November to mid-March
Rooms: 5 all ensuite
Room facilities: ▢ ☎ Children: Welcome ⱨ ℀
Licences: ⅲ
Parking: Off-street and monitored
Directions: From Tralee take route to race course off
N21 at Clash roundabout and continue for 4½ miles.

Waterford, Co. Waterford

Granville Hotel

★ ★ ★ ★ ☕ ☕

Meagher Quay, Waterford, Co. Waterford
Tel: +353(0)51 305555 Fax: +353(0)51 305566
Email: stay@granville-hotel.ie
Web: www.granville-hotel.ie
Seasonal closure: 25–26 December
Rooms: 100 all ensuite ❧ ⊗
Pricing: Dinner from €25 (2002 rate) CC: Accepted
Room facilities: ▢ ☎ ⬍
Access: ⅼⅼ Children: Welcome ⱨ
Licences: ⟁ ⅲ Parking: Off-street and monitored
Directions: City centre, on the quay opposite
clocktower.

Dooley's Hotel

★ ★ ★

The Quay, Waterford, Co. Waterford
Tel: +353(0)51 873531 Fax: +353(0)51 870262
Email: hotel@dooleys-hotel.ie
Web: www.dooleys-hotel.ie
Rooms: 113 all ensuite ❧ ▦ ⊗
Pricing: Dinner from €24 (2002 rate) CC: Accepted
Room facilities: ▢ ☎ ☕ ⬍ Access: ⅼⅼ ⅊
Children: Welcome ⱨ Licences: ⟁ ⅲ
Directions: Located in Waterford City on the quayside.
Follow N25 route to the city centre.

Jurys Waterford Hotel

★ ★ ★

Ferrybank, Waterford, Co. Waterford
Tel: +353(0)1 6070000 Fax: +353(0)1 6316999
Email: bookings@jurysdoyle.com
Web: www.jurysdoyle.com
Seasonal closure: Christmas

⁂JURYS DOYLE
HOTELS

Rooms: 98 all ensuite ⊗
Pricing: Sgl €120–158 Dbl €133–202 Dinner from €19
CC: Accepted Room facilities: ▢ ☎ ☕ ☕
Access: ⅼⅼ Children: Welcome ⱨ
Dogs: Guide dogs only Licences: ⟁ ⅲ
Leisure: Indoor pool, Gym, Health spa,

Beauty salon, Tennis
Parking: Off-street and monitored
Directions: Follow sign city centre, drive along Quay,
over bridge take 3rd exit off roundabout. Hotel is left
side of dual carriageway.

Tower Hotel

★ ★ ★

The Mall, Waterford, Co. Waterford
Tel: +353(0) 51 875801 Fax: +353(0) 51 870129
Web: www.towerhotelwaterford.com
Seasonal closure: 23–27 December
Rooms: 140 all ensuite ❧
Pricing: Sgl €115 Dbl €150 Dinner from €24
CC: Accepted Room facilities: ▢ ☎ ☕ Access: ⅼⅼ ⅊
Children: Welcome ⱨ ⅏ Dogs: Guide dogs only
Licences: ⟁ ⅲ
Leisure: Indoor pool, Gym, Health spa
Parking: Off-street and monitored

Belmont House

◆ ◆ ◆ ✳ ⚘

Belmont Road/Rosslare Road, Ferrybank,
Waterford, Co. Waterford
Tel: +353(0)51 832174
Email: belmonthouse@eircom.net
Seasonal closure: November to April
Rooms: 4 all ensuite ❧ ⊗
Pricing: Dbl £56–64 Children: Welcome, 7yrs min age
Parking: Off-street
Directions: 2km from Waterford Bridge on Rosslare
Road (N25) – 4th house on right, after Ferrybank
Church.

Travelodge Waterford

Travel Accommodation
N25, N25 Little Chef, Cork Road, Waterford,
Co. Waterford
Web: www.travelodge.co.uk
Rooms: 32 all ensuite ⊗
Pricing: Sgl €85.92 Dbl €92.84
CC: Accepted Room facilities: ▢ ☕ Access: ⅊

Waterville, Co. Kerry

Brookhaven

◆ ◆ ◆ ◆ ✳

New Line Road, Waterville, Co. Kerry
Tel: +353(0)66 9474431 Fax: +353(0)66 9474724
Email: brookhaven@esatclear.ie
Web: www.euroka.com/brookhaven
Seasonal closure: December to February
Rooms: 5 all ensuite ❧ ⊗
Pricing: Sgl €50–88 Dbl €70–115 CC: Accepted
Room facilities: ▢ ☎ ☕ ⬍ Children: Welcome ⱨ ℀
Parking: Off-street
Directions: Located on the N70 route (Ring of Kerry
road), 1km to the north side of the village of Waterville.

Westmeath, Co. Westmeath

Hodson Bay Hotel

★★★ ♖

Athlone, Co. Westmeath
Tel: +353(0)902 80500 Fax: +353(0)902 80520
Email: info@hodsonbayhotel.com
Web: www.hodsonbayhotel.com
Rooms: 133 all ensuite ♨ 🖘
Pricing: Dinner from €32 CC: Accepted
Room facilities: 🖵 ☎ 🖘 📞 Access: ⏐↥ ⅋
Conference: 10 meeting rooms (Thtr 1000 max)
Children: Welcome ♀ Dogs: Guide dogs only
Licences: ⟁ ⅰⅰⅰ Leisure: Indoor pool, Gym, Health
spa, Beauty salon, Golf
Parking: Off-street and monitored
Directions: The hotel is located off the N61
Roscommon road just 5 minutes from Athlone Town,
90 minutes from Dublin International Airport.

Westport, Co. Mayo

Hotel Westport

★★★★ ♖

Newport Road, Westport, Co. Mayo
Tel: +353(0)98 25122 Fax: +353(0)98 26739
Email: reservations@hotelwestport.ie
Web: www.hotelwestport.ie
Rooms: 129 all ensuite 🖘
Pricing: Sgl €115–140 Dbl €95–115 Dinner from €35
CC: Accepted Room facilities: 🖵 ☎ 🖘 📞
Access: ⏐↥ ⅋

Talbot Hotel

This superior three-star hotel, established in
1905, has been completely refurbished with
all the modern amenities. The hotel, which
has 98 ensuite bedrooms, enjoys a central
location, offers private parking, and business
and leisure facilities.

Trinity Street, Wexford, Co. Wexford
Tel: +353(0)53 22566   Fax: +353(0)53 23377
sales@talbothotel.ie   www.talbothotel.ie

Conference: 6 meeting rooms (Thtr 450 max)
Children: Welcome ♀ ⅈ℮ Dogs: Guide dogs only
Licences: ⅰⅰⅰ Leisure: Indoor pool, Gym
Parking: Off-street
Directions: Take N5 to Castlebar, N60 to Westport. At
end of Castlebar Street turn right before the bridge.
Turn right at lights and take immediate left at hotel
signpost. Follow to end of road.

The Atlantic Coast Hotel

★★★★ ♖ ♖

The Quay, Westport, Mayo,
Tel: +353(0)98 29000 Fax: +353(0)98 29111
Email: reservations@atlanticcoasthotel.com
Web: www.atlanticcoasthotel.com
Seasonal closure: 23–27 December
Rooms: 85 all ensuite ♨
Pricing: Sgl €114–134 Dbl €185–227 CC: Accepted
Room facilities: 🖵 ☎ 🖘 📞 Access: ⏐↥ ⅋
Conference: 4 meeting rooms (Thtr 140 max)
Children: Welcome ♀ ⅈ℮ Dogs: Guide dogs only
Licences: ⟁ ⅰⅰⅰ Leisure: Indoor pool, Gym
Parking: Off-street and monitored

Castlecourt Hotel

★★★

Castlebar Street, Westport, Co. Mayo
Tel: +353(0)98 25444 Fax: +353(0)98 28622
Email: info@castlecourt.ie
Web: www.castlecourthotel.ie
Seasonal closure: Christmas
Rooms: 140 all ensuite ♨ 🖘
Pricing: Sgl €115–175 Dbl €120–240 Dinner from €30
CC: Accepted Room facilities: 🖵 ☎ 🖘 Access: ⏐↥ ⅋
Children: Welcome ♀ 🐎 ⅈ℮ Dogs: Guide dogs only
Licences: ⟁ ⅰⅰⅰ
Leisure: Indoor pool, Gym, Health spa, Beauty salon
Parking: Off-street and monitored
Directions: Approaching from the main Castlebar Road
(N5), the Castlecourt Hotel is located at the first set of
traffic lights.

Wexford, Co. Wexford

Ferrycarrig Hotel

★★★★ ♖ ♖

Ferrycarrig Bridge, Wexford, Co. Wexford
Tel: +353(0)53 20999 Fax: +353(0)53 20982
Web: www.griffingroup.ie
Rooms: 103 all ensuite ♨
Pricing: Sgl €100–120 Dbl €150–190 Dinner from €42
CC: Accepted Room facilities: 🖵 ☎ 🖘 📞
Access: ⏐↥ ⅋ Children: Welcome ♀ Licences: ⅰⅰⅰ
Leisure: Indoor pool, Gym, Health spa, Beauty salon
Parking: Off-street
Directions: Travelling on N11 from Enniscorthy to
Wexford town, hotel is 2 miles from Wexford on the
Enniscorthy Road, overlooking River Slavey estuary.

Cedar Lodge Hotel

★★★ ⓡ

Carrigbyrne, Newbawn, New Ross, Co. Wexford
Tel: +353(0)51 428386 Fax: +353(0)51 428222
Email: cedarlodge@tinet.ie
Web: www.prideofeirehotels.com
Seasonal closure: January
Rooms: 28 all ensuite Pricing: Sgl €80–140
Dbl €170–200 Dinner from €40 CC: Accepted
Room facilities: ▢ ☎ ☐ ❋ Access: ⓒ
Children: Welcome ☍ Dogs: Guide dogs only
Licences: ◈ ♦♦♦ Parking: Off-street and monitored
Directions: We are on the N25 road between Wexford
and New Ross.

Talbot Hotel

★★★ ⓡ

Trinity Street, Wexford, Co. Wexford
Tel: +353(0)53 22566 Fax: +353(0)53 23377
Email: sales@talbothotel.ie Web: www.talbothotel.ie

Everything you need is here, superbly appointed
bedrooms, an excellent restaurant, a great bar, state-
of-the-art conference facilities and a fully equipped
health & fitness centre.
Rooms: 98 all ensuite ⊗ Pricing: Sgl €80–90
Dbl €150–160 Dinner from €38 CC: Accepted
Room facilities: ▢ ☎ ☐ ➷ Access: ⌊⌋ ⓒ
Conference: 6 meeting rooms (Thtr 500 max)
Children: Welcome ☍ ☷ Dogs: Guide dogs only
Licences: ♦♦♦ Leisure: Indoor pool, Gym, Beauty salon
Parking: Off-street and monitored
Directions: From Dublin and Rosslare, take N11,
following signs for Wexford. The hotel is in the town
centre, on the quay.
See advert on this page

Whitford House Hotel

★★★ ⓡ

New Line Road, Wexford, Co. Wexford
Tel: +353(0)53 43444 Fax: +353(0)53 46399
Email: whitford@indigo.ie
Web: www.whitford.ie
Seasonal closure: 23 December to 3 January
Rooms: 36 all ensuite ⧢
Pricing: Sgl €80–101 Dbl €120–152 Dinner from €35
CC: Accepted Room facilities: ▢ ☎ ☐ Access: ⓒ
Children: Welcome ☍ ⓒ Licences: ♦♦♦
Leisure: Indoor pool Parking: Off-street
Directions: Situated 2 miles from Wexford Town, 10
miles from Rosslare Port, easy access to N11 and N25.
See advert on this page

Ballinkeele House

◆ ◆ ◆ ◆ ◆ ✹ ♈

Ballymurn, Enniscorthy, Co. Wexford
Tel: +353(0)53 38105 Fax: +353(0)53 38468
Email: info@ballinkeele.com
Web: www.ballinkeele.com
Seasonal closure: 12 November to 28 February

Ballinkeele is an historic house, built in 1840,
surrounded by woodland, ponds and farmland. A place
to unwind with good food, wine and a tranquil
atmosphere. Bicycles and croquet.
Rooms: 5 all ensuite 📷 ⑨
Pricing: Sgl €65–75 Dbl €70–85 Dinner from €55
CC: Accepted Children: Welcome, 3yrs min age
Licences: ⚗ Parking: Off-street
Directions: From Wexford take N11 north to Oilgate
village and turn right at signpost. From Enniscorthy,
take N11 south to Oilgate village and turn left at
signpost.

Wicklow, Co. Wicklow

The Brooklodge Hotel

★ ★ ★ ★ ★ ♈ ♈ ♈

Macreddin Village, Co. Wicklow
Tel: +353(0) 40236444 Fax: +353(0) 40236580
Email: brooklodge@macreddin.ie
Web: www.brooklodge.com

The perfect country house hotel, warm, friendly and
relaxed, deep in spectacular countryside yet only an
hour from South Dublin. Featuring the sublime
Strawberry Tree Restaurant.
Rooms: 40 all ensuite 📷 Pricing: Sgl €127.50–190
Dbl €175–270 Dinner from €48 CC: Accepted
Room facilities: 📺 ☎ ☕ 🔌 Access: ⊔ 🦽
Conference: 4 meeting rooms (Thtr 275 max)
Children: Welcome Dogs: Welcome Licences: ⚘ ⚗
Leisure: Riding, Games room, Snooker/billiards

Parking: Off-street and monitored
Directions: South from Dublin Ciry, N11 to Rathnew (29
miles), R752 to Rathdrum (8 miles), R753 to Aughrim (7
miles), follow signs to Macreddin Village (2 miles).

Tinakilly House Hotel
Gold Ribbon Winner

★ ★ ★ ★ ♈ ♈ ♈

Rathnew, Wicklow, Co. Wicklow
Tel: +353(0)404 69274 Fax: +353(0)404 67806
Email: reservations@tinakilly.ie
Web: www.tinakilly.ie
Rooms: 51 all ensuite 📷
Pricing: Sgl €163–186 Dbl €204–250 Dinner from €46
CC: Accepted Room facilities: 📺 ☎ ☕
Access: ⊔ 🦽
Conference: 4 meeting rooms (Thtr 65 max)
Children: Welcome Dogs: Guide dogs only
Licences: ⚗ Leisure: Beauty salon, Tennis
Parking: Off-street and monitored
Directions: Take N11/M11 (Dublin-Wicklow-Wexford
road) to Rathnew village. At roundabout, follow R750 to
Wicklow Town. Entrance to hotel is 500m from village.

Youghal, Co. Cork

Ahernes Seafood Restaurant &
Accommodation
Little Gem

◆ ◆ ◆ ◆ ◆ ♈ ♈ ✹ ♈

163 North Main Street, Youghal, Co. Cork
Tel: +353(0)24 92424 Fax: +353(0)24 93633
Email: ahernes@eircom.net
Web: www.ahernes.com

'Rooms with a seafood view' gourmet hotel in a
perfect location to tour the south-east — beautiful
beach, numerous golf courses. Fota ¹/₂ hour, Old Head
of Kinsale 1 hour, Cork airport 40 minutes.
Rooms: 12 all ensuite 🍴 ⑨
Pricing: Sgl £110–115 Dinner from £30 CC: Accepted
Room facilities: 📺 ☎ Access: 🦽
Conference: 1 meeting room (Thtr 15 max)
Children: Welcome ♨ ❄ Dogs: Guide dogs only
Licences: ⚗ Parking: Off-street and monitored
Directions: On N25 between Cork and Waterford.
From Waterford, take the sign for town centre —
Ahernes on left.

Relax and Unwind

Take the stress out of finding an hotel with RAC Hotel Reservations

On the move and looking for an hotel or a cosy B&B? Look no further than RAC Hotel Reservations.

With just one phone call, RAC Hotel Reservations gives you unique access to over 3000 quality hotels and B&Bs throughout the UK & Ireland. Each one is inspected, rated and the best ones awarded on your behalf by our team of discerning inspectors for quality and service.

We'll not only source the perfect hotel or B&B to suit your pocket and your needs, we'll also source the latest deals and make the booking for you, completely free of charge*.

So if you are looking for somewhere to relax and unwind, whether on business or leisure, call us now.

Call 0870 603 9109 and quote RAC 05
or visit www.rac.co.uk/hotels

*Calls will be charged at National rates

A to B – we RAC to it

RAC

Channel Islands & Isle of Man

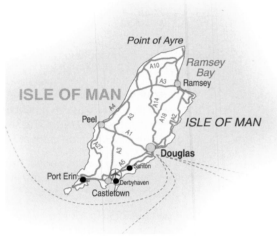

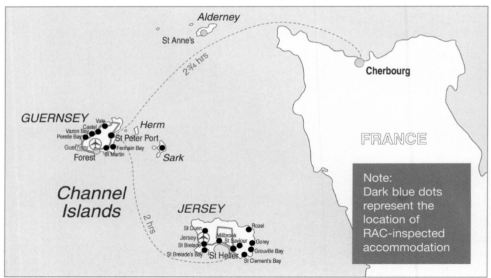

Note:
Dark blue dots represent the location of RAC-inspected accommodation

Gold Ribbon Award

Blue Ribbon Award

Chateau la Chaire Hotel, St Martin	★★★	692	The Atlantic Hotel, St Brelade ★★★★ 690
Longueville Manor House, St Saviour's	★★★★	691	

Guernsey

St Pierre Park Hotel

★★★★

Rohais, St Peter Port, Guernsey, GY1 1FD
Tel: 01481 728282 Fax: 01481 712041
Email: info@stpierreparkhotel.com
Web: www.stpierreparkhotel.com

Set in 45 acres, this superb hotel boasts a 9-hole golf course, superb leisure facilities including indoor pool, beauty salons and tennis courts, plus two award winning restaurants.
Rooms: 131 all ensuite
Pricing: Sgl £130–140 Dbl £170–180
Dinner from £21.50 CC: Accepted
Room facilities: Access:
Conference: 5 meeting rooms (Thtr 130 max), 24hr-delegate from £170, day-delegate rate from £40
Children: Welcome Dogs: Guide dogs only
Licences:
Leisure: Indoor pool, Gym, Health spa, Beauty salon, Tennis, Golf, Snooker/billiards Parking: Off-street
Directions: 10 minutes' drive from airport and harbour front. Hire cars provide free maps.

Best Western Hotel de Havelet

★★★

Havelet, St Peter Port, Guernsey, GY1 1BA
Tel: 01481 722199 Fax: 01481 714057
Email: havelet@sarniahotels.com
Web: www.havelet.sarniahotels.com

This Georgian house enjoys a superb location on the outskirts of St Peter Port. With its choice of restaurants, attractive health suite and gardens, De Havelet makes an excellent holiday base.
Rooms: 34 all ensuite
Pricing: Sgl £50–100 Dbl £80–130 Dinner from £16.50
CC: Accepted Room facilities:
Conference: 1 meeting room (Thtr 40 max), 24hr-delegate from £120, day-delegate rate from £35
Children: Welcome Dogs: Guide dogs only
Licences: Leisure: Indoor pool
Parking: Off-street
Directions: From the airport, turn left and follow signs for St Peter Port. At bottom of Val de Terres Hill, turn left up Havelet Hill (signposted). Hotel on right of hill.

Green Acres Hotel

★★★

Les Hubits, St Martins, Guernsey, GY4 6LS
Tel: 01481 235711 Fax: 01481 235971
Email: greenacres@guernsey.net
Web: www.greenacreshotel.guernsey.net
Rooms: 43 all ensuite
Pricing: Sgl £33–53 Dbl £35–45 Dinner from £15
CC: Accepted Room facilities: Access:
Conference: 1 meeting room (Thtr 40 max), 24hr-delegate from £52.50, day-delegate rate from £20.50
Children: Welcome Dogs: Guide dogs only
Licences: Leisure: Outdoor pool
Parking: Off-street
Directions: Follow hotel signs from the three main roads that surround Les Hubits area in the south-east corner of Guernsey.

Hotel Bon Port

★★★

Moulin Huet Bay, St Martins, Guernsey, GY4 6EW
Tel: 01481 239249 Fax: 01481 239596
Email: mail@bonport.com
Web: www.bonport.com
Rooms: 18 all ensuite
Pricing: Dbl £40–150 Dinner from £18.50
CC: Accepted Room facilities: Access:
Conference: 1 meeting room (Thtr 60 max), 24hr-delegate from £100, day-delegate rate from £60
Children: Welcome Dogs: Welcome
Licences: Leisure: Outdoor pool, Gym
Parking: Off-street
Directions: From airport follow road to St Martins village. Follow road signs to Bon Port – blue signs mainly fixed to lamp posts.

Hotel Hougue du Pommier

★★★★ ℞ ℞

Hougue du Pommier Road, Castel, Guernsey, GY5 7FQ
Tel: 01481 256531 Fax: 01481 256260
Email: hotel@houguedupommier.guernsey.net
Web: www.hotelhouguedupommier.com

Standing in 10 acres, this 18th century farmhouse has been carefully developed into a charming country house hotel. Situated on the west of the island and 5 kilometres from the capital of St Peter Port.
Rooms: 43 all ensuite ⬤ ✉ ⬤
Pricing: Sgl £35–64 Dbl £70–108 Dinner from £17.25
CC: Accepted Room facilities: ☐ ☎ ⬤
Children: Welcome ♭ ⅝℃ Dogs: Welcome
Licences: ⅰⅰⅰ Leisure: Outdoor pool
Parking: Off-street and monitored
Directions: From Cobo Bay, take the road inland to Route de Hougue du Pommier. Ten minutes' drive from St Peter Port and 20 minutes from the airport.

L'Atlantique Hotel

★★★★ ℞ ℞ ℞

Perelle Bay, St Saviours, Guernsey, GY7 9NA
Tel: 01481 264056 Fax: 01481 263800
Email: enquiries@perellebay.com
Web: www.perellebay.com
Seasonal closure: November to March
Rooms: 23 all ensuite ⬤
Pricing: Sgl £42.50–55 Dbl £72–97 Dinner from £19.50
CC: Accepted Room facilities: ☐ ☎ ⬤
Children: Welcome ♭ ⅝℃ Dogs: Guide dogs only
Licences: ⅰⅰⅰ Leisure: Outdoor pool
Parking: Off-street
Directions: Situated on the west coast. Turn right out of airport. Continue until you reach the west coast. Turn right and follow the coast for 1½ miles.

La Favorita Hotel

★★★★ ℞

Fermain Bay, Guernsey, GY4 6SD
Tel: 01481 235666 Fax: 01481 235413
Email: info@favorita.com
Web: www.favorita.com
Seasonal closure: January to February
Rooms: 33 all ensuite ⬤ ⬤
Pricing: Dbl £75–100 Dinner from £15 CC: Accepted

Room facilities: ☐ ☎ ⬤ ✆ Access: ⅼⅼⅰ ♿
Conference: 1 meeting room (Thtr 60 max)
Children: Welcome ♭ ⅝℃ Dogs: Guide dogs only
Licences: ⅰⅰⅰ Leisure: Indoor pool
Parking: Off-street and monitored
Directions: Follow signs for Fermain Bay at junction of Sausmarez/Fort roads.

La Trelade Country House Hotel

★★★

Forest Road, St Martins, Guernsey, GY4 6UB
Tel: 01481 235454 Fax: 01481 237855
Email: latrelade@guernsey.net
Web: www.latrelade.co.uk
Rooms: 45 all ensuite ⬤ ✉
Pricing: Dinner from £17 CC: Accepted
Room facilities: ☐ ☎ ⬤ Access: ⅼⅼⅰ
Conference: 3 meeting rooms (Thtr 100 max), 24hr-delegate from £75, day-delegate rate from £25
Children: Welcome ♭ ⅝℃ Dogs: Guide dogs only
Licences: ⅰⅰⅰ Leisure: Indoor pool, Gym
Parking: Off-street
Directions: From airport turn left, hotel 1 mile. From harbour, follow signs to airport through St Martins; 3 miles on left.

Le Chalet Hotel

★★★★ ℞

Fermain Bay, St Martins, Guernsey, GY4 6SD
Tel: 01481 235716 Fax: 01481 235718
Email: chalet@sarniahotels.com
Web: www.chalet.sarniahotels.com
Seasonal closure: mid-October to mid-April

Idyllically nestling in wooded Fermain valley, Le Chalet is perfectly situated close to the picturesque bay and coastal cliff walks. A courtesy bus operates into St Peter Port.
Rooms: 41 all ensuite
Pricing: Sgl £44–45 Dbl £65–110 Dinner from £16.50
CC: Accepted Room facilities: ☐ ☎ ⬤
Children: Welcome ♭ Dogs: Guide dogs only
Licences: ⅰⅰⅰ Parking: Off-street
Directions: From Guernsey airport, turn left and follow signs for St Martins and St Peter Port. After Sausmarez Manor, follow signs for Fermain Bay and Le Chalet.

Les Rocquettes Hotel

★★★ ℞

Les Gravees, St Peter Port, Guernsey, GY1 1RN
Tel: 01481 722146 Fax: 01481 714543
Email: rocquettes@sarniahotels.com
Web: www.rocquettes.sarniahotels.com

Conveniently located in St Peter Port, Les Rocquettes offers excellent leisure facilities, comfortable, well-equipped bedrooms and good food and service.
Rooms: 51 all ensuite ⊛
Pricing: Sgl £42–85 Dbl £68–110 Dinner from £16
CC: Accepted Room facilities: 🖵 ☎ ⛾ 🖑
Access: ⍑ ⅊
Conference: 2 meeting rooms (Thtr 110 max), 24hr-delegate from £100, day-delegate rate from £25
Children: Welcome ⼍ Dogs: Guide dogs only
Licences: ▮▮▮
Leisure: Indoor pool, Gym, Beauty salon
Parking: Off-street
Directions: From airport turn left. At 2nd traffic lights turn left. Continue straight on at next traffic lights and over roundabout. At 4th lights turn right. At filter turn left. At next filter turn left into Les Gravees. Hotel on right.

Moores Hotel

★★★ ℞

Le Pollet, St Peter Port, Guernsey, GY1 1WH
Tel: 01481 724452 Fax: 01481 714037
Email: moores@sarniahotels.com
Web: www.moores.sarniahotels.com

Ideally located for business or leisure, Moores Hotel is in the heart of St Peter Port. The marinas and ferries to the smaller islands are just a stroll away.
Rooms: 49 all ensuite ⛌ ⊛
Pricing: Sgl £55–90 Dbl £76–120 Dinner from £17.50
CC: Accepted Room facilities: 🖵 ☎ ⛾ 🖑 Access: ⍑
Conference: 2 meeting rooms (Thtr 50 max), 24hr-delegate from £120, day-delegate rate from £35

Children: Welcome ⼍ Dogs: Guide dogs only
Licences: ▮▮▮ Leisure: Gym
Directions: From airport follow signs to St Peter Port along sea front. On North Esplanade take left turn into Lower Pollet and continue to hotel on right.

Peninsula Hotel

★★★

Les Dicqs, Vale, Guernsey, GY6 8JP
Tel: 01481 48400 Fax: 01481 48706

Saints Bay Hotel & Restaurant

★★★

Icart Point, St Martins, Guernsey, GY4 6JG
Tel: 01481 238888 Fax: 01481 235558
Email: info@saintsbayhotel.com
Web: www.saintsbayhotel.com
Rooms: 36 all ensuite
Pricing: Sgl £35–70 Dbl £44–100
Dinner from £18.50 CC: Accepted
Room facilities: 🖵 ☎ ⛾
Children: Welcome ⼍ ⅏ Dogs: Guide dogs only
Licences: ▮▮▮
Leisure: Outdoor pool
Parking: Off-street and monitored
Directions: The Saints Bay Hotel and Clifftop Restaurant are located at Icart point on the island's most southerly tip.
See advert on this page

Channel Islands

The Duke of Richmond Hotel

★★★

Cambridge Park, St Peter Port, Guernsey,
Channel Islands, GY1 1UY
Tel: 01481 726221 Fax: 01481 728945
Email: duke@guernsey.net
Web: www.dukeofrichmond.co.uk

Conveniently situated and enjoying picturesque views
overlooking St Peter Port and the neighbouring islands.
This combined with traditional hospitality and
comfortable rooms make this hotel your perfect choice
when staying in Guernsey.
Rooms: 75 all ensuite
Pricing: Sgl £47.50–67.50 Dbl £70–150
Dinner from £16.50 CC: Accepted
Room facilities: Access:
Children: Welcome Dogs: Welcome
Licences: Leisure: Outdoor pool
Directions: Located adjacent to Candie Gardens and
the Island's Beau Sejour conference and leisure centre.

Grange Lodge Hotel

★★

The Grange, St Peter Port, Guernsey, GY1 1RQ
Tel: 01481 725161 Fax: 01481 724211
Email: receptionist@grange-lodge.hotel.freeserve.co.uk
Web: www.grange-lodge.hotel.freeserve.co.uk
Rooms: 30 all ensuite
Pricing: Sgl £34–42 Dbl £68–92 Dinner from £14
CC: Accepted Room facilities:
Children: Welcome Dogs: Guide dogs only
Licences:
Leisure: Outdoor pool, Snooker/billiards
Parking: Off-street

Sunnycroft Hotel

★★

5 Constitution Steps, St Peter Port, Guernsey, GY1 2PN
Tel: 01481 723008 Fax: 01481 712225
Email: sunnycroft@accom.guernseyci.com
Web: www.guernseytourism.com/sunnycroft
Seasonal closure: November to March
Rooms: 14 all ensuite
Pricing: Sgl £30–45 Dbl £60–90 Dinner from £13.50
CC: Accepted Room facilities:
Licences: Parking: Off-street

La Grande Mare Hotel Golf & Country Club

Vazon Bay, Castel, Guernsey, GY5 7LL
Tel: 01481 256576 Fax: 01481 256532
Email: hotellagrandemare@gtonline.net
Web: www.lgm.guernsey.net
Rooms: 14 (11 ensuite)
Pricing: Sgl £84–94 Dbl £148–168 Dinner from £19.95
CC: Accepted Room facilities: Access:
Conference: 1 meeting room (Thtr 40 max)
Children: Welcome Dogs: Guide dogs only
Licences: Leisure: Indoor pool, Outdoor pool, Gym,
Health spa, Beauty salon, Tennis, Golf, Fishing
Parking: Off-street and monitored
Directions: Drive through roundabout to Julians Ave and
Grange road, straight at filter, down Rohais, left into
Rohais de Havt until lights, follow road to coast, turn left.

Marine Hotel

◆ ◆ ◆

Well Road, St Peter Port, Guernsey, GY1 1WS
Tel: 01481 724978 Fax: 01481 711729
Rooms: 11 all ensuite
Pricing: Sgl £18.50–29.75 Dbl £37–55.50
CC: Accepted Room facilities:
Children: Welcome Dogs: Guide dogs only
Directions: Well Road is situated just off Glatengy
Esplanade, opposite Queen Elizabeth II Marina. Just 5
minutes walk from ferry and town.

Atlantic Hotel

★★★★   Blue Ribbon Winner

Le Mont de la Pulente, St Brelade, Jersey, JE3 8HE
Tel: 01534 744101 Fax: 01534 744102
Email: info@theatlantichotel.com
Web: www.theatlantichotel.com
Seasonal closure: 5 January to 6 February

In private local ownership since 1970, this four-star
luxury hotel is the sole Channel Islands member of
Small Luxury Hotels of the World.
Rooms: 50 all ensuite
Pricing: Sgl £140–170 Dbl £180–265 Dinner from £30
CC: Accepted Room facilities: Access:
Conference: 2 meeting rooms (Thtr 60 max)
Children: Welcome Dogs: Guide dogs only
Licences:
Leisure: Indoor pool, Outdoor pool, Gym, Tennis
Parking: Off-street and monitored
Directions: From the A13 take the B35 to Le Mont de la
Pulente. Hotel sign is on the right.

Hotel La Place

★★★★ ⓡ ⓡ

Route Du Coin, La Haule, St Brelade, Jersey, JE3 8BT
Tel: 01534 744261 Fax: 01534 745164
Email: hotlaplace@aol.com
Web: www.jersey.co.uk/hotels/laplace
Rooms: 42 all ensuite
Pricing: Sgl £65–116 Dbl £70–228 Dinner from £24.95
CC: Accepted Room facilities:
Conference: 2 meeting rooms (Thtr 100 max), 24hr-
delegate from £130, day-delegate rate from £42
Children: Welcome Dogs: Welcome Licences:
Leisure: Outdoor pool
Parking: Off-street and monitored
Directions: Approaching St Aubin from St Helier, at La
Haule Manor turn right. Take second left then first right.
200 yards on right.

L'Horizon

★★★★ ⓡ ⓡ ⓡ

St Brelade's Bay, St Brelade, Jersey, JE3 8EF
Tel: 01534 743101 Fax: 01534 746269
Email: hotellhorizon@jerseymail.co.uk
Web: www.hotelhorizon.com
Rooms: 107 all ensuite
Pricing: Sgl £110 (2002 rate) Dbl £210 (2002 rate)
Dinner from £29 (2002 rate) CC: Accepted
Room facilities:
Access: Children: Welcome
Dogs: Guide dogs only Licences:
Leisure: Indoor pool, Gym
Parking: Off-street and monitored
Directions: Three miles from airport, six miles from
harbour.

Longueville Manor

 Gold Ribbon Winner

★★★★ ⓡ ⓡ ⓡ ⓡ

St Saviours, Jersey, JE2 7WF
Tel: 01534 725501 Fax: 01534 731613
Email: longman@itl.net
Web: www.longuevillemanor.com

Stunning 18th Century Norman manor, set in a 16-acre
wooded valley. Luxurious bedrooms, award-winning
restaurant and beautiful gardens. Member of Relais &
Châteaux.
Rooms: 30 all ensuite
Pricing: Sgl £170–285 Dbl £200–450
Dinner from £37.50 CC: Accepted
Room facilities: Access:

Conference: 3 meeting rooms (Thtr 40 max), 24hr-
delegate from £247.50, day-delegate rate from £55
Children: Welcome Dogs: Welcome
Licences: Leisure: Outdoor pool, Tennis
Parking: Off-street
Directions: From Jersey airport, take A1 to St Helier
and then A3 towards Gorey. Longueville Manor is
situated approximately 1 mile on left.

St Brelade's Bay Hotel

★★★★ ⓡ ⓡ

St Brelade's Bay, Jersey, JE3 8EF
Tel: 01534 746141 Fax: 01534 747278
Email: info@stbreladesbayhotel.com
Web: www.stbreladesbayhotel.com
Seasonal closure: October to April
Rooms: 72 all ensuite
Pricing: Dinner from £30 CC: Accepted
Room facilities: Access:
Conference: 1 meeting room (Thtr 20 max), 24hr-
delegate from £125, day-delegate rate from £35
Children: Welcome Licences:
Leisure: Outdoor pool, Gym, Tennis, Games room,
Snooker/billiards Parking: Off-street
Directions: Located in the southwest of the island.

Beau Couperon Hotel and Appartments

★★★★ ⓡ ⓡ

Rozel Bay, St Martin, Jersey, JE3 6AN
Tel: 01534 865522 Fax: 01534 865332
Email: beaucouperon@southernhotels.com
Web: www.jerseyhols.com/beaucouperon
Seasonal closure: 15 January to 11 April
Rooms: 36 all ensuite
Pricing: Sgl £36.70–72.10 Dbl £73.40–144.20
Dinner from £13.50 CC: Accepted
Room facilities: Children: Welcome
Dogs: Guide dogs only Licences:
Leisure: Outdoor pool
Parking: Off-street and monitored
Directions: From St Helier, follow signs for St Martin. At
St Martin's church turn right, directly followed by a left
turn. Follow signs towards Rozel Bay.

Beausite Hotel

★★★

Grouville Bay, Grouville, Jersey, JE3 9DJ
Tel: 01543 857577 Fax: 01543 857211
Email: beausite@jerseymail.co.uk
Web: www.southernhotels.co.uk
Seasonal closure: November to February
Rooms: 76 all ensuite
Pricing: Dinner from 12.95 CC: Accepted
Room facilities: Access:
Children: Welcome Dogs: Welcome
Licences:
Leisure: Indoor pool, Gym, Games room,
Snooker/billiards Parking: Off-street
Directions: Follow A1 east to the A17. At Georgetown
take the A3 towards Gorey. The hotel is on the left at
Grouville.

Bergerac Hotel

★★★

La Rue Voisin, Portelet Bay, St Brelade, Jersey, JE3 8AT
Tel: 01534 745991 Fax: 01534 743010
Email: southern@itl.net
Web: www.southernhotels.com
Seasonal closure: November to early March
Rooms: 50 all ensuite
Pricing: Sgl £35.50–70 Dbl £71–93 Dinner from £12
CC: Accepted Room facilities: 🖵 ☎ 🛁 Access: ♿
Children: Welcome ⋔ Dogs: Welcome
Licences: 🍷 ⅲ
Leisure: Indoor pool, Outdoor pool, Gym, Health spa,
Beauty salon, Games room, Snooker/billiards
Parking: Off-street and monitored
Directions: From the airport, head towards St Brelades
then St Aubin. Turn right at Woodbine Corner and
follow signs to Portelet and Bergerac hotels.

Chateau La Chaire   Gold Ribbon Winner

★★★★ 🎗 🎗

Rozel, St Martin, Jersey, JE3 6AJ
Tel: 01534 863354 Fax: 01534 865137
Email: res@chateau-la-chaire.co.uk
Web: www.chateau-la-chaire.co.uk

A charming Victorian house, beautifully decorated and
furnished. Set in terraced, wooded gardens. 14
bedrooms, all ensuite.
Rooms: 14 all ensuite 🗐
Pricing: Dbl £132–182 Dinner from £29.50
CC: Accepted Room facilities: 🖵 ☎
Children: Welcome 7yrs min age ⋔
Dogs: Guide dogs only Licences: ⅲ
Parking: Off-street and monitored

Chateau Valeuse Hotel

★★★★ 🎗 🎗 🎗

St Brelade's Bay, Jersey, JE3 8EE
Tel: 01534 746281 Fax: 01534 747110
Email: chatval@itl.net
Web: www.user.super.net.uk/~chatval
Seasonal closure: Mid October to mid April

Set in the heart of beautiful St Brelade's Bay this family
run hotel offers traditional courtesy and service
together with modern amenities, excellent restaurant
and award-winning garden, guests return year by year.
Rooms: 34 all ensuite
Pricing: Sgl £36–53 Dbl £72–106 Dinner from £20
CC: Accepted Room facilities: 🖵 ☎ 🛁
Children: Welcome 5yrs min age ⋔ ⅃🎇
Dogs: Guide dogs only Licences: ⅲ
Leisure: Outdoor pool Parking: Off-street
Directions: From airport south from harbour west to St
Brelades Bay. Hotel up lane to Churchill Memorial Park.

Moorings Hotel

★★★★ 🎗 🎗

Gorey Pier, Gorey, Jersey, JE3 6EW
Tel: 01534 853633 Fax: 01534 857618
Rooms: 5 Pricing: Sgl £42.50 (2002 rate)
Dbl £85 (2002 rate) Dinner from £20.50 (2002 rate)
CC: Accepted Room facilities: 🖵 ☎ 🛁
Children: Welcome ⋔ ⅃🎇 Licences: ⅲ
Directions: Situated on the east coast of the island,
near to golf club. Four miles from town centre and
eight miles from airport.

Pomme d'Or Hotel

★★★★ 🎗 🎗

Liberation Square, St Helier, Jersey, JE1 3UF
Tel: 01534 880110 Fax: 01534 737781
Email: enquiries@pommedorhotel.com
Web: www.pommedorhotel.com
Rooms: 142 all ensuite 🕸 🅢
Pricing: Sgl £100–161 Dbl £160–222
Dinner from £17.95 CC: Accepted
Room facilities: 🖵 ☎ 🛁 ☏ Access: ⅃↥ ♿
Conference: 11 meeting rooms (Thtr 220 max), 24hr-
delegate from £111.50, day-delegate rate from £37
Children: Welcome ⋔ ⅃🎇 Dogs: Guide dogs only
Licences: ⅲ
Directions: A one-way system operates around the
hotel and access to the square is available eastbound
from La Route de la Liberation.

Pontac House Hotel

★★★

St Clement's Bay, St Clements, Jersey, JE2 6SE
Tel: 01534 857771 Fax: 01534 857031
Email: pontac@jerseyhols.com
Web: www.jerseyhols.com/pontachouse
Seasonal closure: December to February
Rooms: 27 all ensuite 🛴 Room facilities: ☐ ☎ 🖨
Children: Welcome ♒ ♨ Dogs: Guide dogs only
Licences: ⚗ ⛄ Leisure: Outdoor pool,
Games room Parking: Off-street and monitored
Directions: From St Helier follow the A4 coast road to
Gorey, approx. 2¹/₂ miles. Entrance to hotel car park is
at the rear.
See advert on this page

Revere Hotel

★★★

Kensington Place, St Helier, Jersey, JE2 3PA
Tel: 01534 611111 Fax: 01534 611116
Email: reservations@revere.co.uk
Web: www.revere.co.uk
Rooms: 58 (57 ensuite) 🛴 🖨 ⑤
Pricing: Sgl £35–60 Dbl £70–120 Dinner from £15.50
CC: Accepted Room facilities: ☐ ☎ 🖨 ⛄
Conference: 1 meeting room (Thtr 16 max)
Children: Welcome ♒ ♨ Dogs: Guide dogs only
Licences: ⛄ Leisure: Outdoor pool
Directions: 20 minutes from the airport and five
minutes from the ferry terminal.

Royal Hotel

★★★

David Place, St Helier, Jersey, JE2 4TD
Tel: 01534 726521 Fax: 01534 811046
Email: royalhotel@itl.net
Web: www.royalhoteljersey.com
Rooms: 88 all ensuite 🖨
Pricing: Sgl £72–81.50 Dbl £117–137
Dinner from £16.95 CC: Accepted
Room facilities: ☐ ☎ 🖨 Access: ⛄
Conference: 6 meeting rooms (Thtr 400 max), 24hr-
delegate from £125, day-delegate rate from £35
Children: Welcome ♒ Dogs: Welcome Licences: ⛄
Directions: Follow signs for the ring road, then Rouge
Bouillon A14. Turn right at roundabout and right at
traffic lights into Midvale Road. Past two lights, hotel is
on left corner at lights.

Royal Yacht

★★★

Weighbridge, St Helier, Jersey, JE2 3NF
Tel: 01534 720511 Fax: 01534 767729
Email: theroyalyacht@mail.com
Rooms: 43 all ensuite 🛴 ⑤
Pricing: Sgl £46.50 (2002 rate) Dbl £93 (2002 rate)
Dinner from £15.50 (2002 rate) CC: Accepted
Room facilities: ☐ ☎ 🖨 Access: ⛄
Children: Welcome ♒ ♨ Dogs: Welcome Licences: ⛄
Directions: Located in the heart of St Helier, walking
distance to all business houses. Four miles from airport.

Windmills Hotel

★★★

Mont Gras d'Eau, St Brelade, Jersey, JE3 8ED
Tel: 01534 744201 Fax: 01534 744202
Email: info@windmillshotel.com
Web: www.windmillshotel.com
Seasonal closure: 18th October

This family-run hotel's tranquil setting enjoys
breathtaking views over St Brelade's bay. Modern
facilities complement its established reputation for
personal service and delicious food, making an ideal
choice for your Jersey experience.
Rooms: 38 all ensuite
Pricing: Sgl £45–63 Dbl £70–106 Dinner from £15
CC: Accepted Room facilities: ☐ ☎ 🖨 Access: ⛄
Children: Welcome ♒ ♨ Licences: ⛄
Leisure: Outdoor pool, Gym, Health spa,
Games room Parking: Off-street and monitored
Directions: Head to St Brelades along A13. Turn down
Mont Gras d'Eau, turn right next to Hotel Mirimar.

Beau Rivage Hotel

★★

St Brelade's Bay, St Brelade, Jersey, JE3 8EF
Tel: 01534 745983 Fax: 01534 747127
Email: beau@jerseyweb.demon.co.uk
Web: www.jersey.co.uk/hotels/beau
Seasonal closure: November to March inc.
Rooms: 27 all ensuite 🛏 🚭 🚳
Pricing: Sgl £47–73 Dbl £64–116 Dinner from £15
CC: Accepted Room facilities: 📺 ☎ 🍵 Access: ♿
Children: Welcome 🍴 🎦 Licences: 🎎
Leisure: Games room Parking: Off-street
Directions: The hotel is located on the seaward side of
the coast road, in the centre of St Brelade's Bay

Dolphin Hotel

★★★ 🏵 🏵

Gorey Pier, Gorey, Jersey, JE3 6EW
Tel: 01534 853370 Fax: 01534 855343
Email: cavin@itl.net
Rooms: 15 all ensuite 🛏
Pricing: Sgl £29 (2002 rate) Dbl £38 (2002 rate)
Dinner from £17.50 (2002 rate) CC: Accepted
Room facilities: 📺 ☎ 🍵 Children: Welcome 🍴 🎦
Directions: Situated underneath Mont Orgueil Castle,
facing the harbour of Gorey Pier, four miles from town
centre and eight from the airport.

Hotel Savoy

★★

Rouge Bouillon, St Helier, Jersey, JE2 3ZA
Tel: 01534 619916 Fax: 01534 506969
Email: enquiries@hotelsavoyjersey.com
Web: www.hotelsavoyjersey.com
Seasonal closure: December to January

Standing in it's own grounds only a short walk from St
Helier's town centre, close to beach and harbour,
offering fresh food, fine wines and superb service.

Rooms: 61 all ensuite 🛏 🚳
Room facilities: 📺 ☎ 🍵 Access: ♿ 🚻
Children: Welcome 🍴 🎦 Licences: 🔱 🎎
Leisure: Outdoor pool, Games room Snooker/billiards
Parking: Off-street
Directions: Located opposite St Helier police station.

Sarum Hotel

★★★ 🏵

19-21 New St John's Road, St Helier, Jersey, JE2 3LD
Tel: 01534 758163 Fax: 01534 731340
Email: sarum@jerseyweb.demon.co.uk
Web: www.jersey.co.uk/hotels/sarum
Seasonal closure: November to March incl.
Rooms: 47 all ensuite 🚭 Pricing: Sgl £39.50–58.50
Dbl £64–102 CC: Accepted Room facilities: 📺 ☎ 🍵
Access: ♿ 🚻 Dogs: Guide dogs only Licences: 🎎
Leisure: Outdoor pool Parking: Off-street
Directions: The hotel is located to the western side of
St Helier, less than ½ a mile from the town centre.

White Heather Hotel

★★

Rue de Haut, Millbrook, St Lawrence, Jersey, JE3 1JZ
Tel: 01534 720978 Fax: 01534 720968
Seasonal closure: November to April
Rooms: 33 all ensuite 🛏
Pricing: Dinner from £8.25 CC: Accepted
Room facilities: 📺 ☎ 🍵
Children: Welcome 3yrs min age 🍴 Licences: 🎎
Leisure: Indoor pool Parking: Off-street
Directions: On A1 between St Helier and St Aubin, take
the A11 and turn right at the school.

Millbrook House Hotel

◆◆◆◆ 🚳

Rue de Trachy, Millbrook, St Helier, Jersey, JE2 3JN
Tel: 01534 733036 Fax: 01534 724317
Email: millbrook.house@jerseymail.co.uk
Web: www.millbrookhousehotel.com
Seasonal closure: 7 October to 3 May

Peace, quiet and character, where the air is clear and
traditional values are maintained. 10 acres of grounds,
car park, 27 ensuite rooms, memorable food and wines.
Rooms: 27 all ensuite
Pricing: Sgl £35–40 Dbl £70–80 Dinner from £10
CC: Accepted Room facilities: 📺 ☎ 🍵 Access: ♿
Children: Welcome Licences: 🎎 Leisure: Golf
Parking: Off-street
Directions: 1½ miles west from St Helier off A1.

Hotel des Pierres

◆ ◆ ◆

Greve de Lecq Bay, St Ouen, Jersey, JE3 2DT
Tel: 01534 481858 Fax: 01534 485273
Email: despierres@jerseyhols.com
Web: www.jerseyhols.com
Seasonal closure: 15 December to 11 January
Rooms: 16 all ensuite 🛏 ⊘ Pricing: Sgl £25.50–35.50
Dbl £48–71 Dinner from £10.85 CC: Accepted
Room facilities: 💻 ☕ Children: Welcome ☕
Licences: 🚻 Leisure: Gym
Parking: Off-street and monitored

Sark

Aval Du Creux Hotel

★ ★ ★ 🍴 🍴

Harbour Hill, Sark, Via Guernsey, GY9 0SB
Tel: 01481 832036 Fax: 01481 832368
Email: avalducreux@freeuk.com
Web: www.avalducreux.com
Rooms: 20 all ensuite 🛏 Pricing: Dinner from £18.95
CC: Accepted Room facilities: 💻 ☎ ☕ 🍽 Access: ♿
Children: Welcome 🍴 ☕ Dogs: Welcome
Licences: 🚻 Leisure: Outdoor pool, Fishing Riding
Parking: Off-street and monitored
Directions: Hotel is situated on the right at the top of
Harbour Hill.
See advert on this page

Dixcart Bay Hotel

★ ★

Isle of Sark, Channel Islands, GY9 0SD
Tel: 01481 832015 Fax: 01481 832164
Email: dixcart@itl.net
Web: www.dixcart.guernseyci.com
Seasonal closure: Mid October to Easter
Rooms: 15 all ensuite 🛏
Pricing: Sgl £37.50–57.50 Dbl £75–115
Dinner from £16 CC: Accepted Room facilities: 💻 ☎ ☕
Conference: 1 meeting room (Thtr 20 max)
Children: Welcome 🍴 ☕ Dogs: Welcome Licences: 🚻
Directions: From top of Harbour Hill take avenue
through centre of village. Turn left, following signs to
Dixcart Hotel.
See advert on this page

Hotel Petit Champ

◆ ◆ ◆ ◆ 🍴 🍴 ☕

Sark, Guernsey, GY9 0SF
Tel: 01481 832046 Fax: 01481 832469
Email: hpc@island-of-sark.co.uk
Web: www.island-of-sark.co.uk
Seasonal closure: October to Easter
Rooms: 13 all ensuite
Pricing: Sgl £39–47.50 Dbl £74–91 Dinner from £19.25
CC: Accepted Children: Welcome 6yrs min age 🍴
Dogs: Guide dogs only Licences: 🚻
Leisure: Outdoor pool
Directions: Follow the signposted lane towards the sea
from the Methodist chapel.

Isle of Man

Mount Murray Hotel and Country Club

★★★★

Santon, Isle of Man, IM4 2HT
Tel: 01624 661111 Fax: 01624 611116
Email: hotel@mountmurray.com
Web: www.mountmurray.com
Rooms: 90 all ensuite
Pricing: Sgl £55–87.50 Dbl £75–125
Dinner from £18.95 CC: Accepted
Room facilities:
Access:
Conference: 6 meeting rooms (Thtr 300 max)
Children: Welcome
Dogs: Guide dogs only
Licences:
Leisure: Indoor pool, Gym, Health spa, Beauty salon, Tennis, Golf
Parking: Off-street
Directions: From airport take main road to Douglas. Turn left at Santon, hotel is signposted.

Port Erin Royal Hotel

★★★

Promenade, Port Erin, Isle of Man, IM9 6LH
Tel: 01624 833116 Fax: 01624 835402
Email: rac@porterinhotels.com
Web: www.porterinhotels.com
Seasonal closure: Dec to Jan
Rooms: 79 all ensuite
Pricing: Sgl £28–49 Dbl £56–98 Dinner from £14.95
CC: Accepted Room facilities: Access:
Children: Welcome
Dogs: Guide dogs only
Licences:
Leisure: Indoor pool, Games room, Snooker/billiards
Parking: Off-street and monitored
Directions: Take road signs from either the sea terminal or airport marked 'Port Erin and the South'. Hotel on the upper promenade facing the sea.
See advert on this page

Port Erin Imperial Hotel

★★

Promenade, Port Erin, Isle of Man, IM9 6LH
Tel: 01624 832122 Fax: 01624 835402
Email: rac@porterinhotels.com
Web: www.porterinhotels.com
Seasonal closure: November to February
Rooms: 51 all ensuite
Pricing: Sgl £26–45 Dbl £52–90 Dinner from £11.95
CC: Accepted Room facilities:
Access: Children: Welcome
Dogs: Guide dogs only Licences:
Parking: Off-street and monitored
Directions: Follow directions from either the sea terminal or airport marked 'Port Erin and the South'. Hotel on the upper promenade facing the sea.
See advert on this page

Castletown Golf Links Hotel

Fort Island, Derbyhaven, Isle of Man, IM9 1UA
Tel: 01624 822201 Fax: 01624 824633

Relax and Unwind

Take the stress out of finding an hotel with RAC Hotel Reservations

On the move and looking for an hotel or a cosy B&B? Look no further than RAC Hotel Reservations.

With just one phone call, RAC Hotel Reservations gives you unique access to over 3000 quality hotels and B&Bs throughout the UK & Ireland. Each one is inspected, rated and the best ones awarded on your behalf by our team of discerning inspectors for quality and service.

We'll not only source the perfect hotel or B&B to suit your pocket and your needs, we'll also source the latest deals and make the booking for you, completely free of charge*.

So if you are looking for somewhere to relax and unwind, whether on business or leisure, call us now.

Call 0870 603 9109 and quote RAC 05
or visit www.rac.co.uk/hotels

*Calls will be charged at National rates

A to B - we RAC to it

RAC

Distance Chart

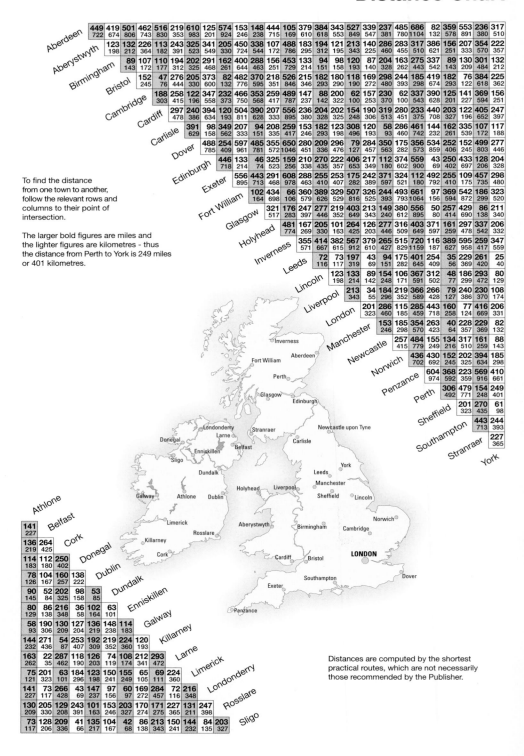

To find the distance from one town to another, follow the relevant rows and columns to their point of intersection.

The larger bold figures are miles and the lighter figures are kilometres - thus the distance from Perth to York is 249 miles or 401 kilometres.

Distances are computed by the shortest practical routes, which are not necessarily those recommended by the Publisher.

Key to Maps

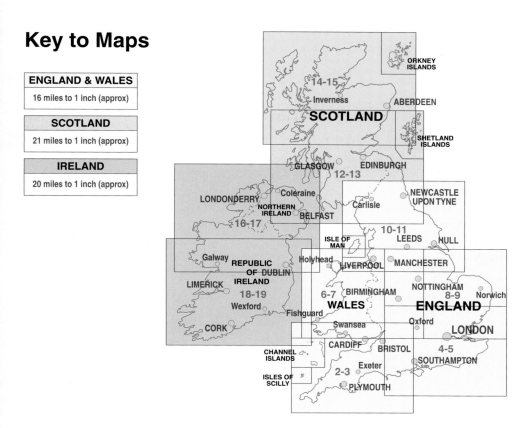

ENGLAND & WALES
16 miles to 1 inch (approx)

SCOTLAND
21 miles to 1 inch (approx)

IRELAND
20 miles to 1 inch (approx)

ORKNEY ISLANDS

14-15
Inverness
ABERDEEN
SCOTLAND
SHETLAND ISLANDS
GLASGOW EDINBURGH
12-13
Coleraine NEWCASTLE UPON TYNE
LONDONDERRY Carlisle
NORTHERN IRELAND BELFAST
16-17 10-11
ISLE OF MAN LEEDS HULL
Galway REPUBLIC
OF DUBLIN Holyhead LIVERPOOL MANCHESTER
LIMERICK OF IRELAND
18-19 6-7 BIRMINGHAM NOTTINGHAM
Wexford 8-9 Norwich
Fishguard WALES ENGLAND
CORK Swansea Oxford
LONDON
CHANNEL ISLANDS CARDIFF BRISTOL 4-5
SOUTHAMPTON
ISLES OF SCILLY 2-3 Exeter
PLYMOUTH

Legend

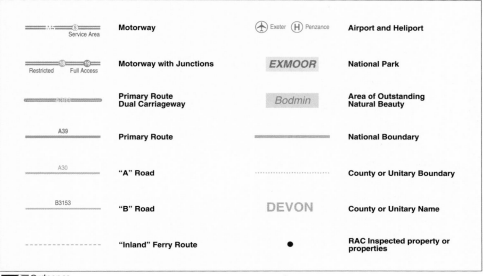

═══S═══ Service Area	Motorway	✈ Exeter Ⓗ Penzance	**Airport and Heliport**
═══18═══19═══ Restricted Full Access	**Motorway with Junctions**	*EXMOOR*	**National Park**
═══════	**Primary Route Dual Carriageway**	*Bodmin*	**Area of Outstanding Natural Beauty**
A39	**Primary Route**	━━━━━━━	**National Boundary**
A30	**"A" Road**	··············	**County or Unitary Boundary**
B3153	**"B" Road**	DEVON	**County or Unitary Name**
-----------	**"Inland" Ferry Route**	●	**RAC Inspected property or properties**

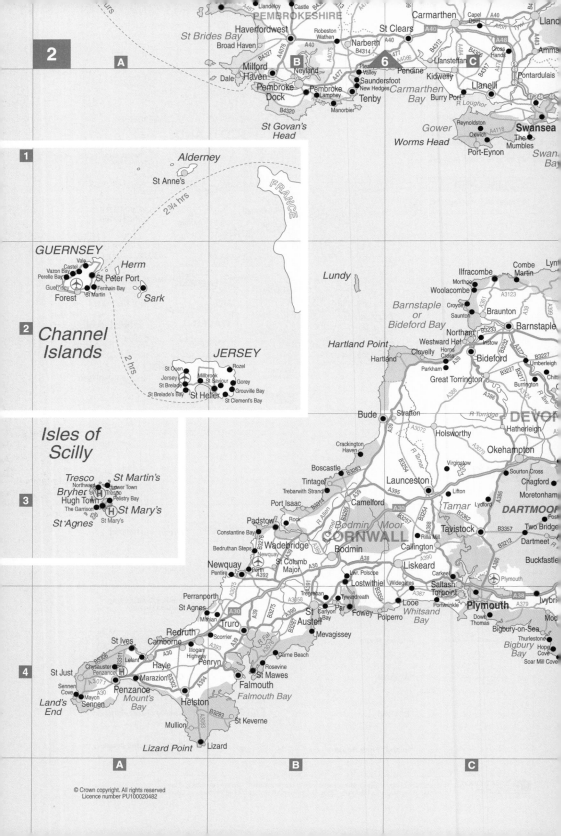

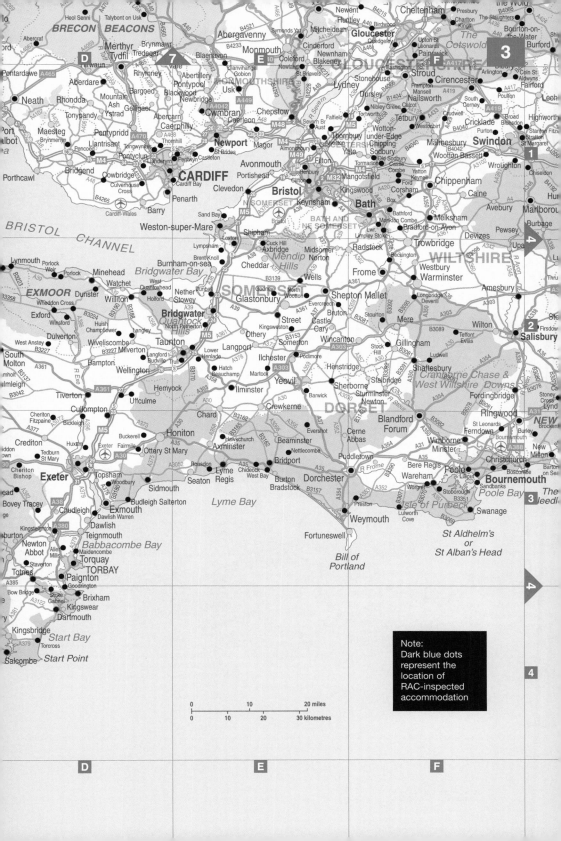

Note:
Dark blue dots represent the location of RAC-inspected accommodation

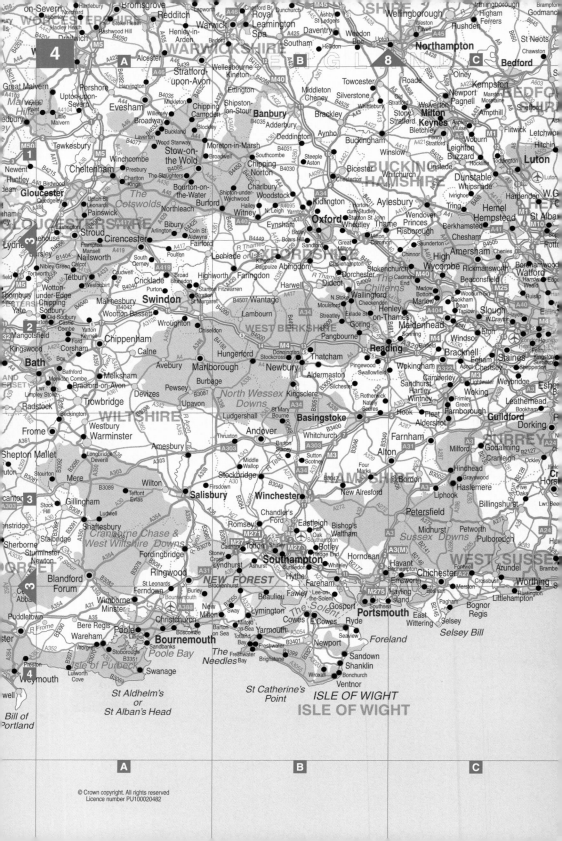

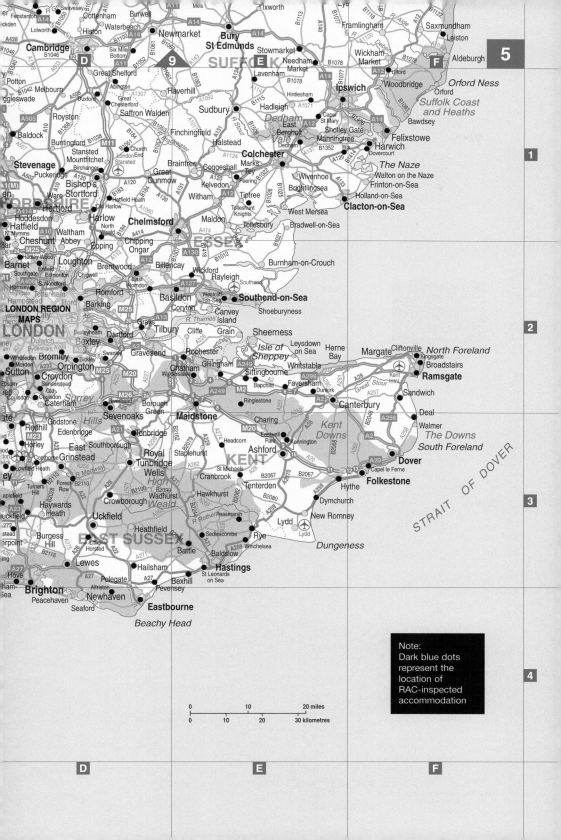

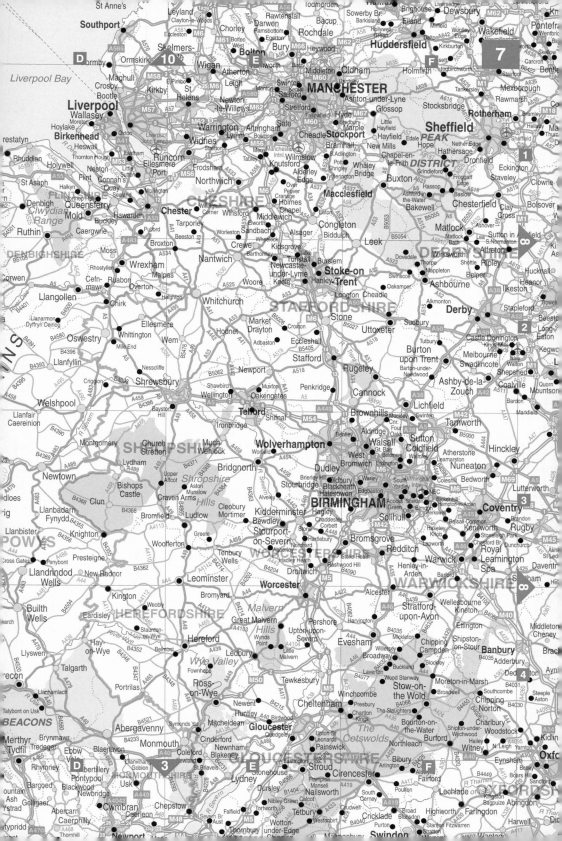

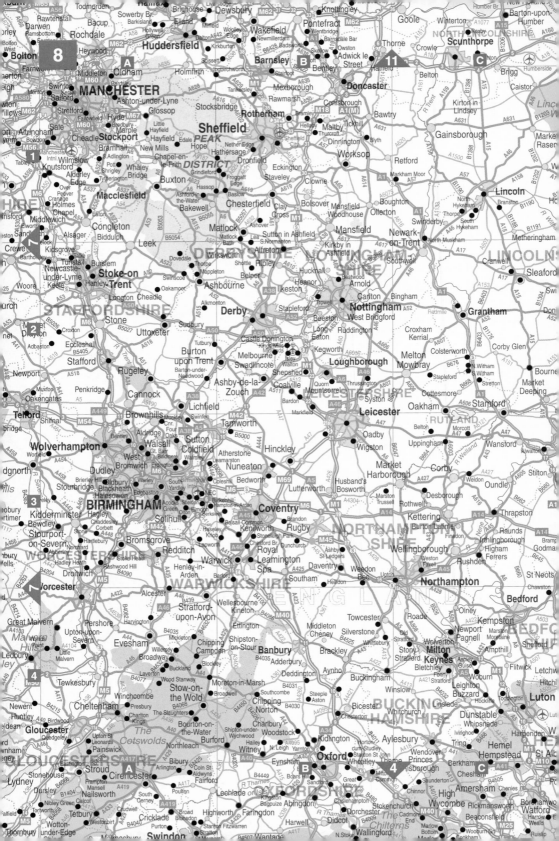

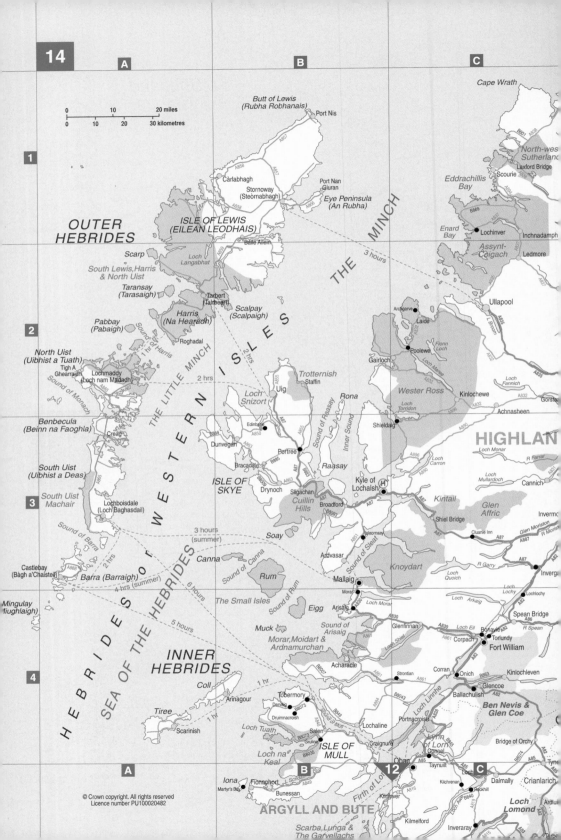

Index to maps of Great Britain

Index to maps of Great Britain

Index to maps of Ireland

Index to maps of Ireland

Notes

Notes

Find us at over 130 locations throughout the UK!

Aberdeen: Tel. 01224 626955

Aberdeen Airport: Tel. 01224 770955

Barking: Tel. 0208 472 4617

Basildon: Tel.01268 530707

Basingstoke: Tel.01256 477777

Bath: Tel.01225 481898

Bedford: Tel. 01234 269565

Belfast City: Tel. 028 9032 5520

Belfast City Airport: Tel. 028 9073 9400

Belfast Int'l Airport: Tel. 028 9442 2285

Birmingham Airport: Tel. 0121 782 5481

Birmingham City: Tel. 0121 622 6131

Birmingham North: Tel. 0121 500 6050

Birmingham South: Tel. 0121 778 2525

Birmingham (Vans only): Tel. 0121 633 3686

Bolton: Tel. 01204 365373

Bournemouth/Poole: Tel.01202 667300

Bracknell: Tel. 01344 481188

Bradford: Tel. 01274 722155

Brighton: Tel. 01273 202426

Bristol: Tel. 01179 525414

Bristol Airport: Tel. 01275 474821

Bury St. Edmunds: Tel. 01284 747164

Cambridge: Tel. 01223 365438

Cardiff: Tel. 029 2049 6256

Carlisle: Tel. 01228 542707

Carmarthen: Tel. 01267 222504

Chelmsford: Tel. 01245 450660

Chester: Tel. 01244 390008

Coleraine: Tel. 0287 032 0409

Coventry: Tel. 024 7667 7042

Crawley: Tel. 01293 513031

Croydon: Tel. 0208 680 4800

Darlington: Tel. 01325 353659

Dartford: Tel. 01322 277808

Derby: Tel. 01332 382251

Doncaster: Tel. 01302 310061

Dover: Tel. 01304 201421

Dundee: Tel. 01382 224037

East Midlands Airport: Tel. 01332 853551

Eastbourne: Tel. 01323 725153

Edenbridge: Tel. 01732 862483

Edinburgh Airport: Tel. 0131 333 1922

Edinburgh City: Tel. 0131 337 8686

Enfield: Tel. 0208 805 7676

Exeter: Tel. 01392 250858

Finchley: Tel. 0208 446 0194

Fulham: Tel. 0207 384 2444

Gatwick Airport: Tel. 01293 567790

Glasgow Airport: Tel. 0141 887 7915

Glasgow City: Tel. 0141 204 1051

Gloucester: Tel. 01452 421133

Guernsey: Tel. 01481 236902

Guildford: Tel. 01483 302283

Hamilton: Tel. 01698 828281

Harlington: Tel. 0208 897 6536

Harlow: Tel. 01279 417408

Heathrow Airport: Tel. 0870 191 0600

High Wycombe: Tel. 01494 527853

Hull: Tel. 01482 343223

Inverness: Tel. 01463 238084

Ipswich: Tel. 01473 724665

Isle of Man: Tel. 01624 825855

Jersey: Tel. 01534 495000

Kennington: Tel. 0207 820 0202

Kings Cross: Tel. 0207 278 2273

Kingston Upon Thames: Tel. 0208 549 8791

Lancing: Tel. 01903 752086

Leeds: (Vans Only) Tel. 0113 282 7004

Leeds: 0113 277 7997

Leigh: Tel. 01942 683134

Leicester: Tel. 0116 251 0455

Lewisham: Tel. 0208 297 2424

Lincoln: Tel. 01522 512233

Liverpool: Tel. 0151 259 1316

Luton: Tel. 01582 417723

Luton Airport: Tel. 01582 486414

Maidstone: Tel. 01622 671941

Manchester Airport: Tel. 0161 499 3320

Manchester City: Tel. 0161 834 3020

Manchester (Vans Only): Tel. 01942 888876

Marble Arch: Tel. 0207 408 1255

Middlesbrough: Tel. 01642 218941

Milton Keynes: Tel. 01908 271077

Newbury: Tel. 01635 582525

Newcastle Airport: Tel. 0191 214 5222

Newcastle Upon Tyne: Tel. 0191 477 2202

Newport: 01633 246979

Newquay: Tel. 01637 850750

North Cheam: Tel. 0208 641 1431

Northampton: Tel. 01604 259101

Norwich: Tel. 01603 631912

Nottingham: Tel. 0115 986 0308

Orpington: Tel. 01689 898128

Oxford: Tel. 01865 240471

Park Royal: Tel. 0208 961 0110

Pembroke: Tel. 01646 686661

Peterborough: Tel. 01733 310283

Plymouth: Tel. 01752 220877

Portsmouth Harbour: Tel. 0239 2870701

Portsmouth: Tel. 0239 266 0811

Preston: Tel. 01772 723434

Prestwick Airport: Tel. 01292 671222

Rochester: Tel. 01634 813056

Reading: Tel. 01189 757388

Salisbury: Tel. 01722 413878

Sheffield: Tel. 0114 275 4111

Slough: Tel. 01753 534442

Southampton: Tel. 023 8022 7373

Southampton Airport: Tel. 023 8065 2059

Southend on Sea: Tel. 01702 616574

St Albans: Tel. 01727 873893

Stansted Airport: Tel. 01279 506534

Stevenage: Tel. 01438 748847

Stirling: Tel. 01786 812828

Stockport: Tel. 0161 476 6001

Stoke-on-Trent: Tel. 01782 747473

Streatham: Tel. 0208 679 9867

Sunderland: Tel. 0191 564 0960

Swansea: Tel. 01792 643336

Swindon: Tel. 01793 831160

Taunton: 01823 283517

Tamworth: Tel. 01827 265906

Telford: Tel. 01952 291925

Warrington: Tel. 01925 573501

Watford: Tel. 01923 233340

Wellingborough: Tel. 0870 2403015

Wigan: Tel. 01942 498010

Wolverhampton: Tel. 01902 452227

Worcester: Tel. 01905 420699

Yeovil: Tel. 01935 427961

York: Tel. 01904 612141

CENTRAL RESERVATIONS 0870 400 4582

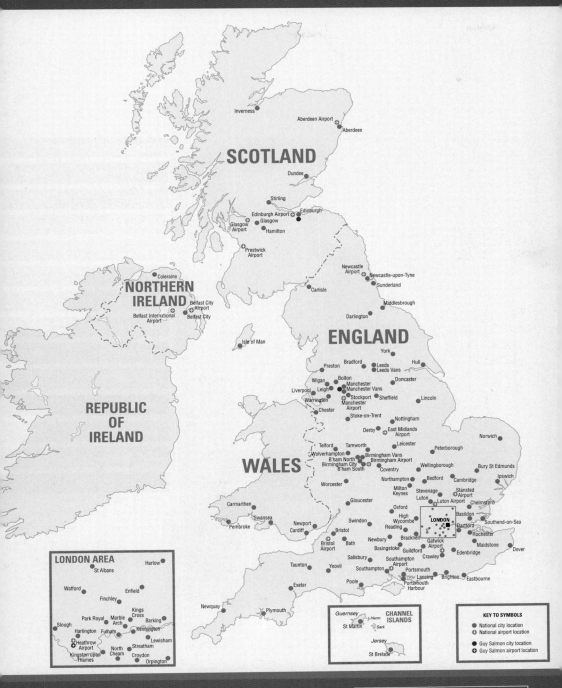

SCOTLAND

Inverness
Aberdeen Airport
Aberdeen
Dundee
Stirling
Edinburgh Airport — Edinburgh
Glasgow Airport — Glasgow
Hamilton
Prestwick Airport

NORTHERN IRELAND

Coleraine
Belfast City Airport
Belfast International Airport
Belfast City

REPUBLIC OF IRELAND

Newcastle Airport — Newcastle-upon-Tyne
Sunderland
Carlisle
Middlesbrough
Darlington
Isle of Man

ENGLAND

York
Bradford — Leeds / Leeds Vans — Hull
Preston
Wigan — Bolton — Doncaster
Liverpool — Leigh / Manchester / Manchester Vans
Warmington — Stockport / Sheffield — Lincoln
Chester — Manchester Airport
Stoke-on-Trent
Nottingham
Derby — East Midlands Airport
Telford — Tamworth — Leicester — Peterborough — Norwich
Wolverhampton
B'ham North — Birmingham Vans
Birmingham City — Birmingham Airport — Wellingborough — Bury St Edmunds
B'ham South — Coventry — Bedford — Cambridge — Ipswich
Worcester — Northampton — Milton Keynes — Stevenage — Stansted Airport — Chelmsford
Gloucester — Oxford — Luton / Luton Airport — Basildon
High Wycombe — LONDON — Dartford — Southend-on-Sea
Reading — Rochester
Swindon — Bracknell — Gatwick Airport — Maidstone
Newport — Bristol — Newbury — Crawley — Edenbridge — Dover
Cardiff — Bristol Airport — Bath — Basingstoke — Guildford — Eastbourne
Salisbury — Southampton Airport — Brighton
Carmarthen — Swansea — Taunton — Yeovil — Southampton — Portsmouth — Lancing
Pembroke — Poole — Portsmouth Harbour
Newquay — Exeter
Plymouth

WALES

LONDON AREA

Harlow
St Albans
Watford — Enfield
Finchley
Kings Cross — Barking
Park Royal — Marble Arch — Kennington — Lewisham
Slough — Fulham
Harlington — Streatham
Heathrow Airport — North Cheam — Croydon
Kingston upon Thames — Orpington

CHANNEL ISLANDS

Guernsey — Herm
St Martin — Sark
Jersey
St Brelade

KEY TO SYMBOLS

- National city location
- National airport location
- Guy Salmon city location
- Guy Salmon airport location

www.nationalcar.co.uk   ≋National Car Rental

Key of Regions

Region	Value
Republic of Ireland	618
Northern Ireland	616
Scotland	558
Isle of Man	686
Wales	518
Southwest	180
Northwest	454
West Midlands	344
Southeast	66
Northeast	392
London	26
East Midlands	316
East Anglia	290
Channel Islands	686